D1088187

NUCLEI
AND PARTICLES

INSTITUT INTERNATIONAL DE PHYSIQUE SOLVAY

SEPTIÈME CONSEIL DE PHYSIQUE -- BRUXELLES. 22-29 OCTOBRE 1933

H. A. KRAMERS N. F. MOTT G. GAMOW P. BLACKETT M. COSYNS Aug. PICCARD

E. STAHEL P. A. M. DIRAC J. ERRERA C. D. ELLIS E. O. LAWRENCE

E. HENRIOT F. JOLIOT W. HEISENBERG E. T. S. WALTON P. DEBYE B. CABRERA W. BOTHE Ed. BAUER J. E. VERSCHAFFELT J. D. COCKROFT L. ROSENFELD

F. PERRIN E. FERMI M. S. ROSENBLUM W. PAULI E. HERZEN R. PEIERLS

E. SCHRODINGER Mme I. JOLIOT N. BOHR A. JOFFÉ Mme CURIE O. W. RICHARDSON Lord RUTHERFORD M. de BROGLIE Mlle L. MEITNER J. CHADWICK

P. LANGEVIN Th. DE DONDER L. de BROGLIE

Absents : A. EINSTEIN et Ch.-Eug. GUYE

NUCLEI AND PARTICLES

An Introduction to Nuclear and Subnuclear Physics

EMILIO SEGRE
Professor of Physics
University of California, Berkeley

W. A. BENJAMIN, INC.
New York 1965 *Amsterdam*

NUCLEI AND PARTICLES
An Introduction to Nuclear and Subnuclear Physics

Copyright © 1964 by W. A. Benjamin, Inc.
All rights reserved

Library of Congress Catalog Card Number 64-21231
Manufactured in the United States of America

The manuscript was put into production on June 13, 1963; *this volume was published on September* 20, 1964; *second printing with corrections December* 10, 1965

The publisher is pleased to acknowledge the assistance of Cecilia Duray-Bito, who produced the illustrations, and William Prokos, who designed the cover and dust jacket

W. A. BENJAMIN, INC.
New York, New York 10016

3456K098

Preface

THIS BOOK is addressed to physics students, chemists, and engineers who want to acquire enough knowledge of nuclear and subnuclear physics to be able to work in this field. The book is definitely an introduction. The coverage is rather broad, but the treatment has been kept as simple as possible, compatible with a professional understanding of the subject.

While I have tried to convey as much as possible an intuitive understanding of the phenomena encountered, it is nonetheless impossible to discuss nuclear physics without a moderate use of quantum mechanics; and it is assumed that the person who wishes to become acquainted with nuclear physics is also willing to acquire the background in physics necessary to an understanding of this specialized subject. In my opinion, the presentation of nuclear physics at the introductory level should be the same for both the future theoretical physicist and the future experimental physicist. This account should be useful to a beginner regardless of his intended specialization.

The book aims at the same level as Rasetti's *Elements of Nuclear Physics* and Fermi's notes collected by Orear, Rosenfeld, and Schluter. I have drawn liberally from the latter. In the selection of materials I have followed my personal preferences. This may have resulted in an emphasis on some parts of nuclear physics better known to me, at the expense of others equally important. Furthermore most of my own work has been experimental, and this necessarily affects my outlook. The permissible length of such a book and my own knowledge of the subject are some of the limiting factors. However, I hope that some loose ends will provide food for thought to interested students and stimulate them to further reading.

The bibliography appended to every chapter lists for the most part review articles and monographs suited to more detailed study. Little of the original literature is included. Although many important and exciting papers are thus omitted, the references selected are probably the most profitable for a beginner. The Selected Bibliography gives the catalog of a small, basic, personal library for a research worker in the area covered by this book.

Problems vary considerably in difficulty. Some are simple numerical applications, and others contain interesting supplements to a discussion in the text.

In teaching an undergraduate course in nuclear physics, I have found it possible to cover in two semesters a large portion of the material in this book. For a shorter course one might omit completely Part I (which is of interest mainly to prospective experimental nuclear physicists and which contains fewer fundamentals) and reduce drastically the content of some of the other chapters. In general, I have tried to make the individual chapters relatively independent of each other, even at the risk of repetition. Sections beginning and ending with a heavy black dot may be omitted in the first reading; these often require a deeper knowledge of quantum mechanics on the part of the student than does the rest of the book.

I want to acknowledge gratefully the help of numerous colleagues who have read sections of this book and often have given me valuable advice. In particular, I want to thank Drs. Chamberlain, Fano, Frauenfelder, Goldberger, Judd, Rasmussen, Rosenfeld, Shafer, Steiner, Telegdi, Trilling, and Wu. The responsibility for any errors in this text is, of course, entirely mine. My thanks also go to Mrs. Patricia Brown, who patiently typed the manuscript, and to my wife Elfriede Segrè, who compiled the indexes.

E. SEGRÈ

Berkeley, California
July 1964

Contents

Selected Bibliography

THE FOLLOWING selected bibliography lists books covering a wider range of subjects than the works cited at chapter ends. In referring to this bibliography we shall use an abbreviated form of the last name(s) of the author(s) and the year of publication of the book. For example, (**Ra 56**) means Ramsey, N. F., *Molecular Beams*, Oxford University Press, New York, 1956.

Introductory

Bethe, H. A., and Philip Morrison, *Elementary Nuclear Theory*, 2nd ed., Wiley, New York, 1956 (**BM 56**).

Elton, L. R. B., *Introductory Nuclear Theory*, Wiley-Interscience, New York, 1959 (**El 59**).

Evans, R. D., *The Atomic Nucleus*, McGraw-Hill, New York, 1955 (**Ev 55**).

Fermi, Enrico, *Nuclear Physics*, University of Chicago Press, Chicago, 1950 (**Fe 50**).

Friedlander, Gerhart, and J. W. Kennedy, *Nuclear and Radiochemistry*, Wiley, New York, 1955 (**FK 55**).

Green, A. E. S., *Nuclear Physics*, McGraw-Hill, New York, 1955 (**Gr 55**).

Halliday, David, *Introductory Nuclear Physics*, 2nd ed., Wiley, New York, 1953 (**Ha 55**).

More Advanced Texts

Blatt, J. M., and V. F. Weisskopf, *Theoretical Nuclear Physics*, Wiley, New York, 1952 (**BW 52**).

Condon, E. U., and Hugh Odishaw, *Handbook of Physics*, McGraw-Hill, New York, 1958 (**CO 58**).

De Benedetti, S., *Nuclear Interactions*, Wiley, New York, 1964.

Flügge, S., *Encyclopedia of Physics*, Vols. 38–45, Springer, Berlin, 1955– (**Fl E**).

Preston, M. A., *Physics of the Nucleus*, Addison-Wesley, Reading, Mass., 1962 (**P 62**).

Segrè, Emilio, *Experimental Nuclear Physics*, Wiley, New York, 1953–1959 (**Se 59**).

Important Monographs

Ajzenberg-Selove, Fay, *Nuclear Spectroscopy*, Parts A and B, Academic Press, New York, 1960 (**AS 60**).

Bethe, H. A., and F. de Hoffmann, *Mesons and Fields*, Row, Peterston, Evanston, Ill., 1955 (**BH 55**).

Endt, P. M., and P. B. Smith (eds.), *Nuclear Reactions*, North-Holland, Amsterdam, 1962 (**En 62**).

Fermi, Enrico, *Elementary Particles*, Yale University Press, New Haven, Conn., 1951 (**Fe 51**).

Fretter, W. B., *Introduction to Experimental Physics*, Prentice-Hall, New York, 1954 (**Fr 54**).

Glasstone, Samuel, and M. C. Edlund, *The Elements of Nuclear Reactor Theory*, Van Nostrand, Princeton, N.J., 1952 (**GE 52**).

Goldberger, M. L., and K. W. Watson, *Collision Theory*, Wiley, New York, 1964.

Haïssinsky, M., *Nuclear Chemistry and Its Applications*, Addison-Wesley, Reading, Mass., 1964.

Heitler, W., *The Quantum Theory of Radiation*, 3rd ed., Oxford University Press, New York, 1954 (**He 54**).

Hevesy, G., *Radioactive Indicators*, Wiley-Interscience, New York, 1948 (**Hev 48**).

Hughes, D. J., *Pile Neutron Research*, Addison-Wesley, Reading, Mass., 1953 (**Hu 53**).

Jackson, J. D., *The Physics of Elementary Particles*, Princeton University Press, Princeton, N.J., 1958 (**Ja 58**).

Kopfermann, Hans, *Nuclear Moments*, Academic Press, New York, 1958 (**Ko 58**).

Livingston, M. S., and J. P. Blewett, *Particle Accelerators*, McGraw-Hill, New York, 1962.

Lock, W. O., *High Energy Nuclear Physics*, Methuen, London, 1960 (**Lo 60**).

Marshak, R. E., and E. C. G. Sudarshan, *Introduction to Elementary Particle Physics*, Wiley-Interscience, New York, 1961 (**Ma 61**).

Mayer, M. G., and J. H. D. Jensen, *Elementary Theory of Nuclear Shell Structure*, Wiley, New York, 1955 (**MJ 55**).

Mott, N. E., and H. B. W. Massey, *The Theory of Atomic Collisions*, 2nd ed., Oxford University Press, New York, 1949 (**MM 49**).

Ramsey, N. F., *Molecular Beams*, Oxford University Press, New York, 1956 (**Ra 56**).

Rossi, Bruno, *High Energy Particles*, Prentice-Hall, New York, 1952 (**Ro 53**).

Siegbahn, Kai, *Beta- and Gamma-Ray Spectroscopy*, North-Holland, Amsterdam, 1955 (**Si 55**); Second Edition, 1965 (**Si 65**).

Smyth, H. D., *Atomic Energy for Military Purposes*, Princeton University Press, Princeton, N.J., 1946 (**Sm 46**).

Wahl, A. C., and N. A. Bonner, *Radioactivity Applied to Chemistry*, Wiley, New York, 1951 (**Wa 51**).

Weinberg, A. M., and E. Wigner, *The Physical Theory of Neutron Chain Reactors*, University of Chicago Press, Chicago, 1959 (**WW 59**).

Williams, W. S. C., *An Introduction to Elementary Particles*, Academic Press, New York, 1961 (**W 61**).

Atlases

General Electric Co., *Nuclear Chart, Schenectady*, N.Y., 1964.

W. Gentner, H. Maier-Leibnitiz, and W. Bothe, *An Atlas of Typical Expansion Chamber Photographs*, Pergamon Press, London, 1954 (**GMLB 54**).

C. F. Powell, P. H. Fowler, and D. H. Perkins, *The Study of Elementary Particles by the Photographic Method*, Pergamon Press, London, 1959 (**PFP 59**).

Rochester, G. D., and J. G. Wilson, *Cloud Chamber Photographs of the Cosmic Radiation*, Pergamon Press, London, 1952 (**RW 52**).

Sullivan, W. H., *Trilinear Chart of Nuclear Species*, U.S. Government Printing Office, Washington D.C., 1957–

In addition to these books, there are excellent review articles in

Annual International Conference on High Energy Physics (RoC).

Annual Reviews of Nuclear Science (*Ann. Rev. Nucl. Sci.*).

Progress in Elementary Particle and Cosmic Ray Physics (*Progr. Elem. Particle Cosmic Ray Phys.*).

Progress in Nuclear Physics (*Progr. Nucl. Phys.*).

Reviews of Modern Physics (*Rev. Mod. Phys.*).

Supplemento al Nuovo Cimento (in English) (*Nuovo Cimento, Suppl.*).

Almost none of the publications listed above are completely up to date, and the year of publication must always be kept in mind in consulting them. The list is by no means complete but should be sufficient as a starting point for finding more detailed bibliographical data. All literature is abstracted in *Nuclear Science Abstracts*.

A set of notes on quantum mechanics to be used for reference is

Fermi, Enrico, *Notes on Quantum Mechanics*, University of Chicago Press, Chicago, 1961 (**Fe 61**).

Standard books on quantum mechanics are, e.g.,

Mandl, F., *Quantum Mechanics*, Butterworth, London, 1957 (**Ma 57**).

Messiah, Albert, *Quantum Mechanics*, 2 vols., Wiley, New York, 1961–1962 (**Me 61**).

Schiff, L. I., *Quantum Mechanics*, McGraw-Hill, New York, 1954 (**Sc 54**).

As a reference for electromagnetism, we suggest

Jackson, J. D., *Classical Electrodynamics*, Wiley, New York, 1962 (**Ja 62**).

The "constants" of physics, including masses of particles, etc., are in a continuous process of revision, as measurement precision improves. A recent list of physical constants is given in *Physics Today*, **17**, 48 (1964).

CHAPTER I

History and Introduction

ALTHOUGH SPECULATION on the nature of matter appears at the very dawn of Greek philosophy, a scientific study of this subject, in the modern sense, was not initiated until in the sixteenth century, when experiment and mathematical analysis, which together constitute what we today call the "scientific method," were first used in conjunction with each other. However, simpler and easier problems had to be solved before the structure of matter could be investigated scientifically. It is true that the original steps in the kinetic theory of gases, employing strictly atomic models, were taken by Daniel Bernoulli in the eighteenth century (1738). But the branch of science in which atomic concepts first assumed a fundamental importance was chemistry. The tremendous success of the atomic hypothesis (Dalton, 1803), in explaining both qualitatively and quantitatively the innumerable facts of chemistry, the construction of tables of atomic weights, the discovery of Avogadro's law (1811) and of Faraday's laws of electrolysis (1833) all are major achievements of the first part of the nineteenth century. They made the atomic hypothesis highly plausible, and it is surprising, perhaps, that the very existence of atoms should have remained the subject of a deep skepticism lasting into the early years of the twentieth century.

It must be pointed out, however, that an explanation of all the facts of chemistry then known required only a very general hypothesis, one almost completely lacking any details of the specific properties of atoms, such as their mass, size, and shape. Detailed knowledge of atomic structure was acquired only after 1910. In the early history of this last development, chemistry, kinetic theory, and the study of electrical discharges in gases played a very important role. With the advent of quantum theory, spectroscopy became the main tool for the exploration of the "outer layers" of the atom. In recent years, the nucleus has come under intense study, and the burgeoning of a subnuclear physics is already apparent.

The first experimental discoveries that made possible an attack on the structure of the atom followed each other in rapid succession. In 1895 Röntgen discovered X rays, early in 1896 Becquerel discovered radioactivity, and a little later Sir J. J. Thomson, Wiechert, and Kaufmann gave proof of the independent existence of the negative electron. These were soon followed by the introduction into physics of the idea of quanta of energy, a concept that developed in a rather roundabout way (Planck, 1900). Quantum concepts, which originated in thermodynamics, were destined to dominate the entire field of the physics of small objects. Together with Einstein's special theory of relativity (1905), they form the foundation on which modern physics rests. While it is impossible to recount here the fascinating history of the interrelations of all these lines of inquiry, a single example will not be out of place.

Becquerel discovered radioactivity while at the suggestion of Poincaré, investigating in uranium salts a hypothetical relation between optical fluorescence and the then recently discovered X rays. This relation proved to be illusory, but the pertinent studies opened the gate to momentous developments. Marie Curie observed that, although the radioactivity of uranium compounds taken from pure chemicals was proportional to the uranium content, the ores from which they were extracted showed much more radioactivity than could be accounted for by the uranium content alone. She then performed chemical analyses of the ores and measured the radioactivity of the different fractions she had isolated (Fig. 1-1). This method, which was, and still is, fundamental to radiochemistry, led to the discovery of polonium and radium (1898). Surprise followed surprise when it was found that the radioactive atoms changed their chemical identity with time. Intense study of the phenomenon led to the theory of radioactive decay (Rutherford and Soddy, 1903; von Schweidler, 1905). According to this theory, radioactive atoms of a certain species will disintegrate spontaneously, the number that disintegrate per unit time being, on the average, proportional to the total number present but showing fluctuations characteristic of random phenomena. The law is expressed by the differential equation for the average number of atoms or nuclei, N,

$$-\,dN = \lambda N\,dt$$

or by its integral

$$N(t) = N(0)e^{-\lambda t}$$

where the "decay constant" λ is a characteristic of the nucleus. Investigation of the rays emitted during disintegration led to their classification into three types (Fig. 1-2).

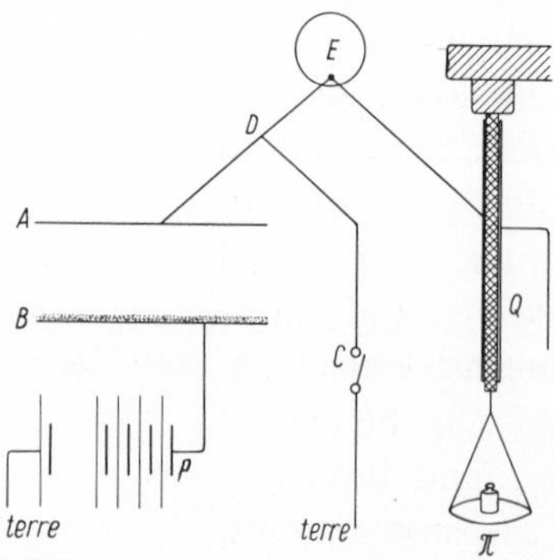

Figure 1-1 Apparatus used by Mme M. Curie to measure the conductivity of air under the influence of radioactive radiations. AB, plate capacitor; the radioactive substance is in B; CD, ground connection; E, electrometer; P, battery; Q, piezoelectric quartz; π, weight. [Mme Curie, 1899.]

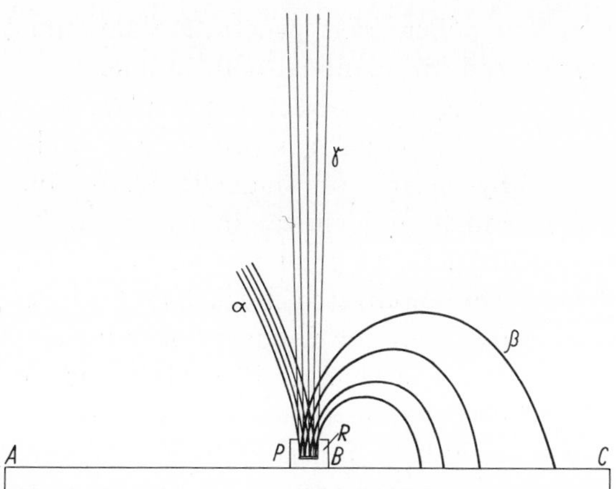

Figure 1-2 Deflection of alpha, beta, and gamma rays in a magnetic field. The nomenclature is due to Rutherford (1899). [Mme Curie, Thesis, 1904.]

Alpha rays are strongly ionizing particles and are absorbed by a few centimeters of air. The deflection of alpha particles in electric and magnetic fields identified them as helium atoms with a double positive charge, or He^{++}. This conclusion was confirmed by a direct experiment in which alpha particles were introduced into an evacuated glass tube. After a sufficient number had accumulated, an electric discharge in the tube showed the helium spectral lines (Rutherford and Royds, 1908) (see Fig. 1-3).

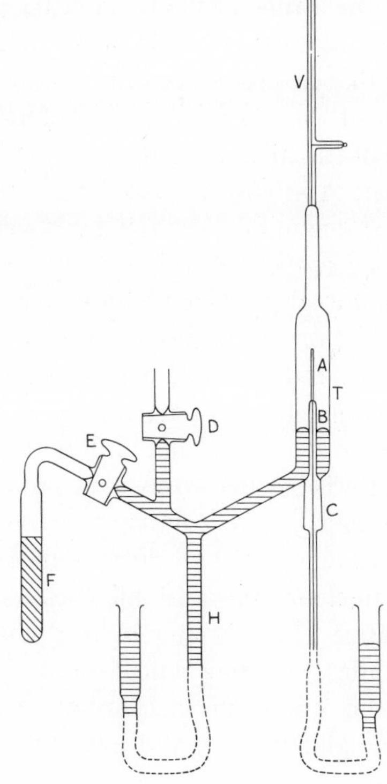

Figure 1-3 Radon contained in the thin-walled capillary tube *AB* expels alpha particles through the walls. Helium accumulates in the evacuated space *T* and when compressed in the capillary *V* shows, in an electric discharge, the characteristic spectrum. [Rutherford and Royds, 1908.]

Beta rays penetrate aluminum a few tenths of a millimeter thick and are identical with atomic electrons. They were identified by their deflection in electric and magnetic fields.

Gamma rays penetrate several centimeters of lead, are undeflected by electric or magnetic fields, and are high-energy electromagnetic radiation identical in nature to X rays. Other types of radiation or particles of great importance to nuclear physics, such as the neutron, were discovered much later and were not considered in the early days following the discovery of radioactivity.

The changes in chemical identity resulting from the emission of particles by radioactive substances were summarized in the displacement law enunciated by Russell, Soddy, and Fajans (1913): A substance is transformed (1) by emission of an alpha particle, into the substance that precedes it by two places in the periodic system; (2) by emission of a beta particle, into the substance that follows it by one place in the periodic system. The atomic weight diminishes by four units in the first case, and remains unchanged in the second. An alpha disintegration followed by two beta disintegrations should, therefore, result in a substance having a different atomic weight but "occupying the same place" (isotope) in the periodic table as the "parent" substance. The concept of isotope thus developed for radioactive elements was extended by J. J. Thomson and Aston to the ordinary stable elements (1913–1919).

The discovery by von Laue (1912) of the diffraction of X rays opened up a new field of spectroscopy. In the hands of Moseley it led to the concept of atomic number Z and to the clarification of the concept of a chemical element. All atoms having the same atomic number belong to the same element. A little earlier, in 1911, Rutherford in studying the scattering of alpha particles by foils of different materials had found that he could account for the experimental results by a planetary model of the atom. The atomic number Z was then interpreted as the charge of the nucleus in units of the same magnitude as the charge of the electron. Applying to this simple model the idea of the quantum, Bohr (1913) accounted for the hydrogen spectrum with admirable precision. This discovery was the starting point for the tumultuous development of atomic physics that culminated in the late 1920s in the establishment of quantum mechanics (Heisenberg, Born, de Broglie, Schrödinger, Pauli, Dirac, and others). The application of quantum mechanics to atomic phenomena was particularly fertile because, although the frame of the theory was new and different, the Coulomb law of electricity was all that was needed to explain innumerable phenomena of spectroscopy, chemistry, and solid-state physics and, in general, to give a complete account of the atomic and molecular properties as distinguished from the nuclear ones. In all these studies it was usually sufficient to schematize the nucleus as a point charge with a certain mass. For a while the theoretical study of the nucleus profited only slightly from quantum mechanics, for the interaction law governing the nuclear constituents, and even their identity, was unknown. Indeed present knowledge of the interaction law is still far from complete.

In 1919 Rutherford succeeded in breaking up nitrogen nuclei, by alpha-particle bombardment and in showing that hydrogen nuclei were emitted (Fig. 1-4). For these the word *proton* (πρῶτον = first) was coined, because it was thought that they were a sort of primordial universal substance, reviving an old hypothesis of Prout (1815).

Because protons often appeared in nuclear disintegrations, and some nuclei were known to emit electrons, the most natural hypothesis about the nuclear construction of a complex nucleus was that it consisted of A protons and $A-Z$ electrons, where A is an integer called the *mass number*. This accounted for the fact that single isotopes have atomic masses approximately equal to integral multiples of the atomic mass of hydrogen. Departures from the exact integral numbers were taken to represent the binding energy of the nuclei according to Einstein's relation (1905)

$$E = \Delta mc^2$$

where E is the binding energy and Δm the mass defect, or difference between, the sum of the masses of the constituents and the mass of the complex nucleus.

However, the hypothesis of a nucleus composed of electrons and protons proved untenable, for reasons that will be discussed later, and was replaced by a model now universally accepted, according to which the nucleus comprises Z protons and $A-Z$ neutrons. The neutron, discovered in a dramatic succession of events in which Bothe, Joliot, and Chadwick played a vital part, is neutral and has a mass approximately equal to that of the proton (1932).

In 1934 I. Curie and F. Joliot discovered that many stable elements under the bombardment of alpha particles became radioactive isotopes

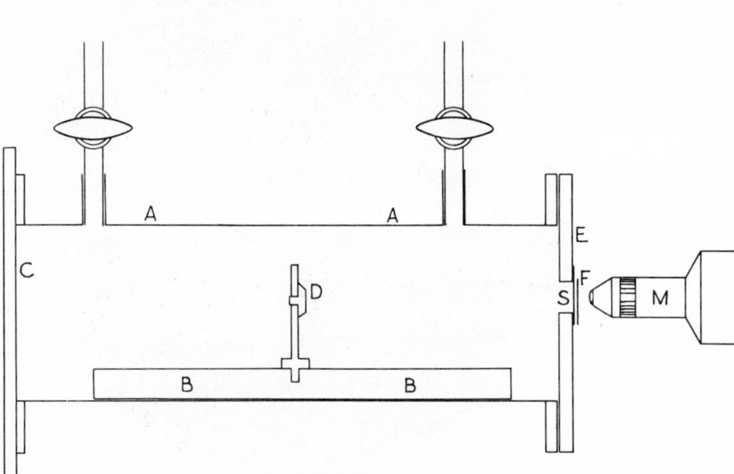

Figure 1-4 Apparatus used by Rutherford for disintegrating the nitrogen nucleus. The alpha particles emitted by the source D were absorbed in the gas used to fill the box. When the gas through which the particles passed was nitrogen, scintillations were observed on the screen F even when the absorbing matter between the source and the screen was sufficient to stop the primary alpha particles. Rutherford concluded that the scintillations were due to protons ejected with great speed from the nitrogen nucleus by the impact of an alpha particle. [Rutherford, 1919.]

of other commonly stable elements (artificial radioactivity). Soon thereafter Fermi, Amaldi, Pontecorvo, Rasetti, and Segrè showed that neutrons could be slowed down to thermal energies and that at low velocities they were particularly effective in disintegrating other nuclei. This discovery was followed by the fission of uranium (Hahn and Strassmann, 1938), a particular reaction in which neutrons split the uranium nucleus into two large fragments, with the emission of several additional neutrons. This opened the way to the liberation of nuclear energy on a large scale (Fermi, 1942) and to its practical application.

Quantum mechanics in the hands of Dirac had predicted the existence of a positive electron. The positive electron, or positron, was discovered by C. D. Anderson in 1932 (Fig. 1-5), and the similar antiparticle on the nuclear level, the antiproton, was discovered by Chamberlain, Segrè, Wiegand, and Ypsilantis in 1955.

In the early 1930s the first particle accelerators (Cockcroft and Walton, 1931; Lawrence, 1931) were invented and built.

The phenomenology of beta decay presented great puzzles, which were in part overcome by Fermi (1933) with the help of the neutrino hypothesis of Pauli (1930). This proved to be a step of great theoretical importance. It furnished the model that inspired Yukawa's theory of nuclear forces (1935). In his theory H. Yukawa postulated the existence of a particle (the meson or pion) having a mass intermediate between the mass of the electron and that of the proton.

Particles of intermediate mass between that of the proton and of the electron were detected in the thirties by several investigators, including Rossi, Anderson, Neddermeyer, Stevenson, and Street. However they proved to be, not the expected ones (Conversi, Pancini, and Piccioni, 1947), but another unsuspected type. Nevertheless, the Yukawa

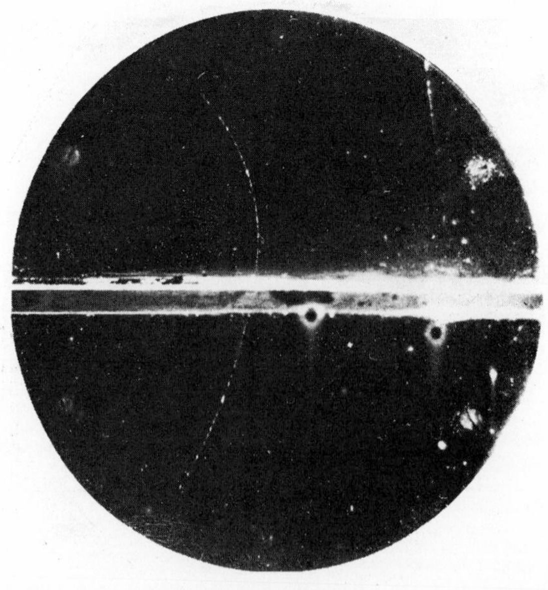

Figure 1-5 Positron. A particle travels from the lower to the upper part of a cloud chamber, as indicated by the fact that it loses energy in crossing the central lead plate. Its charge is positive, as indicated by the curvature in the magnetic field applied to the chamber. The curvature and specific ionization indicate that it has electronic mass. [C. D. Anderson, 1932.]

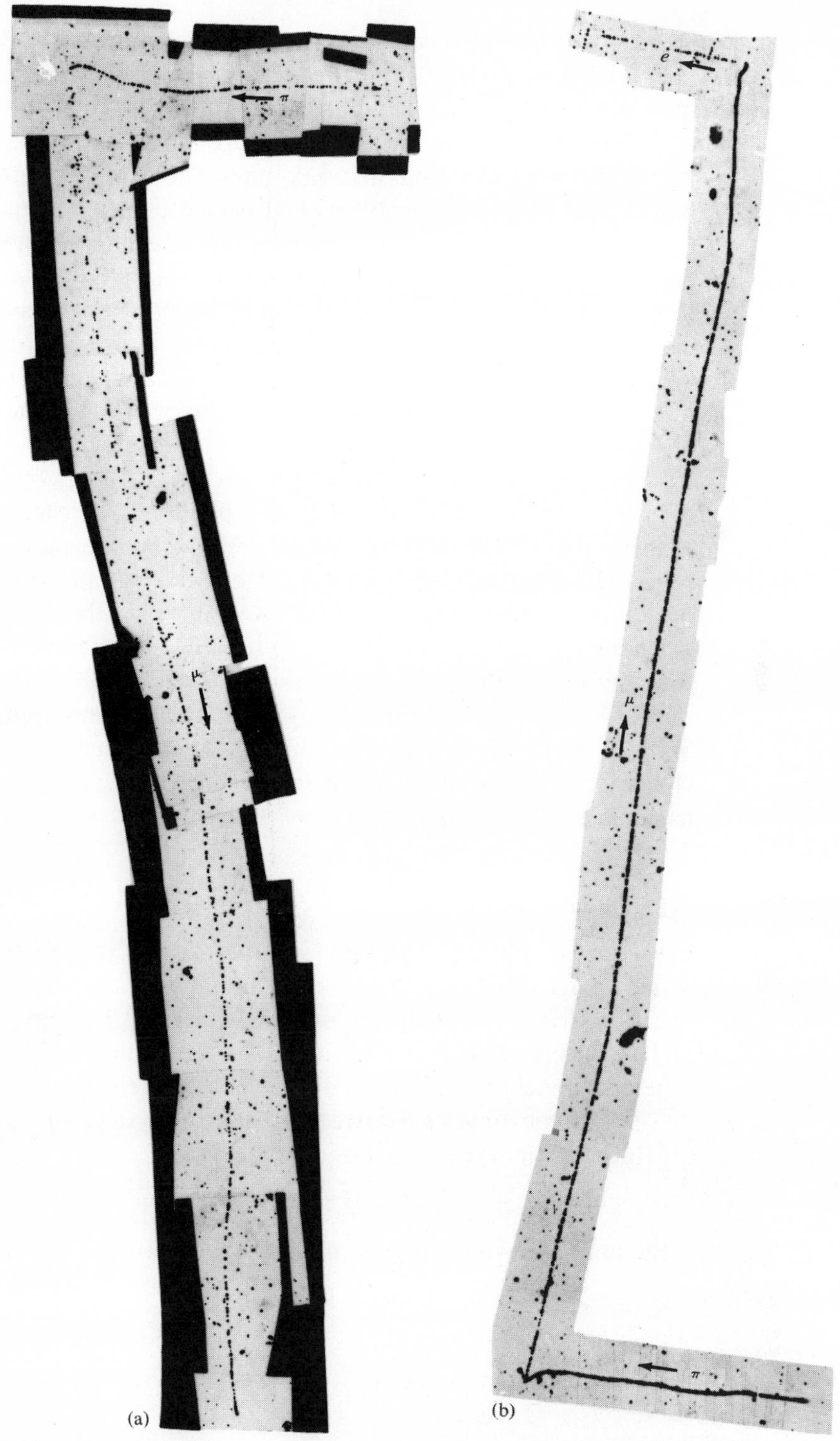

Figure 1-6 A pion from cosmic rays seen in .. photograph emulsion. (a) First observation of the decay of a pion. [Lattes, Muirhead, Occhialini, and Powell, 1947.] (b) An early observation of the π-μ-e decay. The particles travel in the direction of increasing ionization. The range of the μ is 600 microns. [Courtesy Professor C. F. Powell.]

meson was ultimately found (Lattes, Occhialini, and Powell, 1947; Fig. 1-6). There promptly followed the discovery of several other particles that are still only slightly understood.

In recent years an unforeseen failure of the invariance with respect to parity transformation in weak interactions (Lee and Yang, 1957) has created many new problems and perspectives for future work.

This extremely sketchy historical outline has touched upon only the milestones in the development of nuclear physics, without regard to applications or techniques. It cannot be emphasized enough that the whole development bears a resemblence to the evolution of a living being. All parts are deeply and vitally interrelated, and the development of highly abstract theories is as necessary to progress as the construction of gigantic accelerating machines.

The influence exerted on other branches of science by the unfolding of nuclear physics has been deep and powerful: In chemistry artificial elements have been created (Segrè, 1937), and the periodic table has been extended considerably (McMillan, Seaborg, and others). The use of isotopes (Hevesy and Paneth, 1913) as tracers in chemistry and biology has added a tool to these sciences probably comparable in importance with the use of the balance and the microscope. Similarly the medical sciences have benefited greatly, and even geology and archaeology have felt the effect of nuclear methods. And, of course, the tremendous technological possibilities, both in peace and war, that nuclear physics has opened up are obvious.

1-1 Units

Nuclear physics employs several systems of units particularly suited to its problems. In order to be able to use them freely as the occasion arises, we shall mention them briefly. The cgs system comes and is widely used first, but as it is often numerically inconvenient, different branches of physics have developed their own systems.

In atomic physics Hartree provided a system of "atomic units" in which the charge of the electron,

$$e = 4.8030 \times 10^{-10} \text{ esu} \tag{1-1.1}$$

is the unit of charge; the rest mass of the electron,

$$m = 9.1091 \times 10^{-28} \text{ g} \tag{1-1.2}$$

is the unit of mass; and Planck's constant divided by 2π,

$$\hbar = \frac{h}{2\pi} = 1.0545 \times 10^{-27} \text{ erg sec} \tag{1-1.3}$$

is the unit of angular momentum or action. In this system the unit of length is the radius of the first Bohr orbit, in hydrogen,

$$a_0 = \frac{\hbar^2}{me^2} = 0.52917 \times 10^{-8} \text{ cm} \tag{1-1.4}$$

the unit of velocity is the electron velocity in this orbit,

$$v_0 = \frac{e^2}{\hbar} \tag{1-1.5}$$

and the unit of energy is twice the ionization potential of hydrogen,

$$\frac{me^4}{\hbar^2} = 4.359 \times 10^{-11} \text{ erg} \tag{1-1.6}$$

In practical nuclear physics lengths are sometimes expressed in fermis (F), 10^{-13} cm, and nuclear cross sections are generally measured in barns, 10^{-24} cm^2. Energies are expressed in eV or MeV (electron volts, million electron volts),

$$1 \text{ eV} = 1.6021 \times 10^{-12} \text{ erg} \tag{1-1.7}$$

Masses may also be measured in MeV by using mc^2 in place of m. For instance, the rest mass m of the electron is 0.51101 MeV, because numerically mc^2 expressed in MeV takes that value. Similarly, momenta may be measured in MeV/c. To do this, multiply the momentum by the velocity of light. The result has the dimensions of energy and can be expressed in MeV. This number then gives the measure of the momentum in MeV/c.

The relativistic relation between total energy W (including rest energy) and momentum p is

$$c^2p^2 + m^2c^4 = W^2 \tag{1-1.8}$$

With the two limiting cases

$$W = mc^2 + \frac{p^2}{2m} \qquad \text{nonrelativistic, or n.r.} \tag{1-1.9}$$

$$W = cp \qquad \text{extreme relativistic, or e.r.} \tag{1-1.10}$$

In the e.r. case, the energy in MeV is numerically equal to the momentum in MeV/c. In the n.r. case, calling E the kinetic energy,

$$p = (2mE)^{1/2} \tag{1-1.11}$$

and the momentum in MeV/c is given numerically by this relation if the energy and the mass are expressed in MeV, as indicated above.

Velocities are often measured by taking the velocity of light as the unit. They are then indicated by the dimensionless quantity

$$\beta = \frac{v}{c} \tag{1-1.12}$$

The quantity

$$\gamma = \frac{1}{(1 - \beta^2)^{1/2}} = \frac{W}{m} \tag{1-1.13}$$

is also important.

In theoretical work a system of units in which

$$\hbar = c = 1 \tag{1-1.14}$$

is frequently used. It is then possible to assume as a unit of length the quantity $\hbar/mc$, where m is the mass of a specific particle (e.g., the electron). The rest energy of the particle in question is then taken to be the unit of energy. In such a system many universal constants disappear from the formulas.

The lengths $\lambda\!\!\!^{-}_c = \hbar/mc$ are called the *Compton wavelengths* of the particles. The Compton wavelength of the electron is 3.8615×10^{-11} cm, of the charged pi meson (pion) 1.413×10^{-13} cm, and of the proton 2.1031×10^{-14} cm.

Another unit of length often used is the classical radius of the electron,

$$\frac{e^2}{mc^2} = r_0 = 2.8178 \times 10^{-13}\text{ cm} \tag{1-1.15}$$

The classical radius of the electron, its Compton wavelength, and the first Bohr radius are related according to the equations,

$$a_0 = \frac{\lambda\!\!\!^{-}_c}{\alpha} = \frac{r_0}{\alpha^2} \tag{1-1.16}$$

where

$$\alpha = \frac{e^2}{\hbar c} = 1/137.039 \tag{1-1.17}$$

is the dimensionless Sommerfeld fine-structure constant.

In mass-spectrographic work the unit of mass was one-sixteenth the mass of O^{16}. In 1961 it was changed to one-twelfth the mass of C^{12}, (see Chap. 5).

We shall use these different units according to convenience and, when necessary, shall specify them in detail.

1-2 Terminology and Definitions

A few terms that may not be familiar from elementary physics are defined briefly below.

A *nucleon* is a neutron or a proton. A *nuclide* is a certain species of nucleus characterized by the atomic number Z and the mass number A. The terms nucleus and nuclide can often be interchanged without confusion. All nuclides with the same Z are *isotopes;* all nuclides with the same A are *isobars;* all nuclides with the same A-Z are *isotones*. Nuclides that have the same A and Z but different states of excitation are called *isomers*.

One of the most important concepts in nuclear physics is that of cross section. Consider a beam of intensity I, a beam of protons, for example, for which I protons cm^{-2} sec^{-1}, cross a region containing target nuclei. The target contains N nuclei cm^{-3} of material. A thickness dx of target will contain $N\,dx$ nuclei per square centimeter, and the beam crossing it will be attenuated by collisions. If dI is the change in the intensity, we expect dI to be proportional to I and to $N\,dx$.

$$dI = -I\sigma N\,dx \tag{1-2.1}$$

The proportionality factor σ, which has the dimensions of area, is called the *nuclear cross section*, of the target for the particles of the beam. The reason for this name is that, if we think of the target as extremely magnified and look at it from the direction of the impinging beam, we see a picture like that in Fig. 1-7. The irregularly disposed spots represent the nuclei of the target. Their number is $N\,dx$ per square centimeter. The area they occupy is $\sigma N\,dx$, and if the particles hitting them are removed from the beam, the variation of the intensity is indeed given by Eq. (1-2.1).

Integration of Eq. (1-2.1) gives, for σ constant,

$$I(x) = I(0)e^{-N\sigma x} \tag{1-2.2}$$

where $I(0)$ is the incident intensity and x is the thickness traversed. The quantity

$$N\sigma = \mu \tag{1-2.3}$$

is sometimes used and is called the *absorption coefficient*; its reciprocal is the mean free path λ. The number

$$\frac{I(x)}{I(0)} = e^{-N\sigma x} \tag{1-2.4}$$

is often called *attenuation*.

Not all radiation is attenuated according to Eq. (1-2.2), because when the beam changes its properties (e.g., energy) in crossing the target, σ may depend on x. In such cases we cannot speak of an absorption coefficient.

We may also make finer distinctions in the cross section. For instance, we may consider whether the collision is elastic or inelastic, designating the corresponding cross sections σ_{el} and σ_{inel}. By *elastic collision* is meant a collision in which projectile and target before and after the collision are the same and have the same energy in the center-of-mass (c.m.) system. To illustrate, a proton and an aluminum nucleus upon collision are deflected from their trajectories in the c.m. system without change of energy and spin orientation; the collision is then elastic. If the proton produces a transmutation or leaves the aluminum in an excited state, the collision is inelastic.

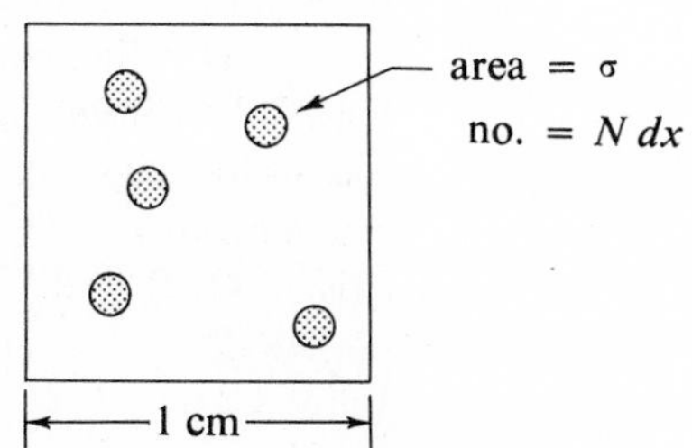

Figure 1-7 Five nuclei, each of cross section σ, are shown in a target of unit area. The probability that a particle crossing the unit area will hit a nucleus is $N^*\sigma$, where N^* is the number of nuclei per unit area and σ is the nuclear cross section; N^* = (number of nuclei per unit volume) × (thickness of the target).

The number of particles per unit area per unit time scattered elastically is given by

$$- dI_{\text{el}} = I\sigma_{\text{el}} N\, dx \qquad \textbf{(1-2.5)}$$

The corresponding number undergoing inelastic processes is given by

$$- dI_{\text{inel}} = I\sigma_{\text{inel}} N\, dx \qquad \textbf{(1-2.6)}$$

The total attentuation will be

$$- dI = - dI_{\text{el}} - dI_{\text{inel}} = I(\sigma_{\text{el}} + \sigma_{\text{inel}})N\, dx \qquad \textbf{(1-2.7)}$$

and we write

$$\sigma_{\text{tot}} = \sigma_{\text{inel}} + \sigma_{\text{el}} \qquad \textbf{(1-2.8)}$$

We may also consider in which direction the particles are scattered and may define a differential scattering cross section in the direction (θ,φ) by considering the number of particles scattered in the infinitesimal solid angle $d\omega$ in the direction (θ,φ),

$$dI_{\text{sc}} \text{ into } d\omega \text{ in direction } (\theta,\varphi) = \frac{d\sigma(\theta,\varphi)}{d\omega} IN\, dx\, d\omega \qquad \textbf{(1-2.9)}$$

In the case of inelastic scattering, we may consider the energy of the scattered particle and may define a differential scattering cross section in the energy interval between E and $E + dE$,

$$dI_{\text{sc}} \text{ in energy interval } dE = \frac{d\sigma}{dE} IN\, dx\, dE \qquad \textbf{(1-2.10)}$$

From these examples it is clear how to define $d^2\sigma/dE\, d\omega$ for particles scattered in a certain direction and at a certain energy. It must be pointed out that occasionally differential cross sections are written, not as $d\sigma/d\omega$, but simply as $\sigma(\theta,\varphi)$.

Cross sections are often measured in barns (10^{-24} cm^2) and differential cross sections correspondingly in barns per steradian.

Bibliography

Beyer, R. T. (ed.), *Foundations of Nuclear Physics*, Dover, New York, 1949.

Birks, J. B., *Rutherford at Manchester*, Benjamin, New York, 1963.

Curie, Ève, *Madame Curie*, Doubleday, New York, 1937.

Curie, Marie, *Oeuvres de Marie Skłodowska Curie*, Pańˊstwowe Wydawnictwo Naukowe, Warsaw, 1954.

Eve, A. S., *Rutherford*, Macmillan, London, 1939.

Fermi, E., *Collected Papers of Enrico Fermi, Vol. I*, University of Chicago Press, Chicago, 1962.

Fermi, L., *Atoms in the Family*, University of Chicago Press, Chicago, 1954.

Fierz, M., and V. Weisskopf (eds.), *Theoretical Physics in the Twentieth Century*, Wiley-Interscience, New York, 1960.

Frisch, O. R. (ed.), *Trends in Atomic Physics*, Wiley-Interscience, New York, 1959.

Joliot-Curie, Fréderic et Irène, *Oeuvres scientifiques complètes*, Presses Universitaires de France, 1961.

Les Prix Nobel, Imprimerie Royale, P. A. Norstedt and Söner Publishers, Stockholm, 1902-present.

Millikan, R. A., *The Autobiography of R. A. Millikan*, Prentice-Hall, Englewood Cliffs, N. J., 1950.

Planck, M., *Physikalische Abhandlungen und Vorträge*, F. Vieweg, Braunschweig, 1958.

Rutherford, E., *The Collected Papers of Lord Rutherford of Nelson*, Vol. I, II, Wiley-Interscience, New York, 1962.

Thomson, J. J., *Recollections and Reflections*, G. Bell, London, 1936.

Whittaker, E. T., *A History of Theories of Aether and Electricity*, 2 vols., Harper Torchbooks, New York, 1960.

Yukawa, H., and K. Chihiro, "Birth of the Meson Theory," *Am. J. Phys.*, **18,** 154 (1950).

Problems

1-1 In the system of units $\hbar = c = 1$ we may further assume an arbitrary unit of mass. For instance, the mass of the electron is often taken as a unit. Other derived units are then given by

Notation	Meaning	Customary notation	Value
m	Mass of electron	m	
m	Energy	mc^2	
m	Momentum	mc	
m	Frequency	$mc^2/\hbar$	
$1/m$	Time	$\hbar^2/mc$	
$1/m$	Length	$\hbar/mc$	
e^2	Fine-structure constant	$e^2/\hbar c$	1/137.04
e^2/m	Classical radius of electron	e^2/mc^2	
$1/me^2$	Bohr radius	$a_0 = \hbar^2/me^2$	

Fill the last column, using the units you prefer. For instance, you may use for energy MeV, for momentum Mev/c, for length fermis, etc.

1-2 Make universal curves of p/m, E/mc^2, and E_{kin}/mc^2, using a table of hyperbolic functions with $\beta = v/c$ as the independent variable.

1-3 Calculate the mean free path corresponding to the cross section of 1 barn per nucleon in liquid hydrogen, air at STP, Al, Cu, and Pb.

1-4 Plot a graph of energy in MeV versus momentum in MeV/c for electrons, pions, protons from $E = 10^{-3}$ to 10^3 MeV.

1-5 A nucleus of mass 200 has a scattering cross section $d\sigma/d\omega = 0.01$ barn at 45° in the laboratory system for protons. A beam of protons of 3 cm diameter containing 10^7 protons cm^{-2} sec^{-1} falls on a foil of 1 mg cm^{-2} thickness. How many protons per second fall on a 10-cm^2 surface that is perpendicular to a line at 45° from the axis of the incident-beam area and that is located at a distance of 1 m from the scatterer?

1-6 A beam of neutrons has a momentum equal to 10 BeV/c. How far do the neutrons have to travel before 50 per cent have decayed? (Mean life of the neutron, 1,013 sec.)

PART I

Tools

CHAPTER II

The Passage of Radiations through Matter

ALTHOUGH THIS SUBJECT is really a part of atomic physics rather than of nuclear physics, the effects of the passage of radiations through matter are of paramount importance to all nuclear experiments; in fact, a thorough knowledge of these effects is absolutely indispensable to the experimental nuclear physicist. Many arguments treated in this chapter are primarily applications of electromagnetism; for these (Ja 62) is an excellent reference.

2-1 Introduction

There are three main types of radiation: charged heavy particles of mass comparable with the nuclear mass, electrons, and electromagnetic radiation. For all of them the interactions to be considered are electromagnetic. (Neutrons behave quite differently and will be treated in Chap. 12.) The behavior of mesons and other particles is intermediate between that of electrons and of nuclei, as will be seen from what follows.

A striking difference in the absorption of the three types of radiation is that only heavy charged particles have a range. That is, a monoenergetic beam of heavy charged particles, in traversing a certain amount of matter, will lose energy without changing the number of particles in the beam. Ultimately they will all be stopped after having crossed practically the same thickness of absorber. This minimum amount of absorber that stops a particle is its range: e.g., the range of polonium alpha particles, of energy 5.30 MeV, is 3.84 cm of air at STP (15°C and 760 mm pressure). For electromagnetic radiation, on the other hand, the absorption is exponential. Energy is removed from the beam and degraded; i.e., the intensity decreases in such a way that

$$-\frac{dI}{I} = \mu\, dx \tag{2-1.1}$$

where I is the intensity of the primary radiation, μ is the absorption coefficient, and dx is the thickness traversed. Electrons exhibit a more complicated behavior. They radiate electromagnetic energy easily because they have a large value of e/m and hence are subject to violent accelerations under the action of electric forces. Moreover, they undergo scattering to such an extent that they follow irregular trajectories.

We shall now define a few terms which recur frequently in this chapter. Consider a parallel beam of monoenergetic particles (e.g., protons) moving through an absorber. As they travel, they lose energy. The energy lost per unit path length is the *specific energy loss* and its average value is the *stopping power* of the absorbing substance. The *specific ionization* is the number of ion pairs produced per unit path length. The specific energy loss and the specific ionization are subject to fluctuations; hence we define a mean specific energy loss, a mean specific ionization, etc. The fluctuations in energy loss also produce fluctuations in range (*straggling*). A plot of the number of particles in the beam penetrating to a certain depth gives the curve of Fig. 2-1. The abscissa R_0 of the point passed by half the particles is called the *mean range*. The abscissa R_1, the intersection of the x axis with the tangent at the point of steepest descent, is called the extrapolated range. The difference between the extrapolated and mean range is sometimes called the *straggling parameter*.

The curve showing the specific ionization as a function of the residual range is known as a *Bragg curve*. It is necessary to distinguish between the Bragg curve of an individual particle (Fig. 2-2) and the average Bragg curve for a beam of particles (Fig. 2-3).

Often the thickness is measured in g cm^{-2} of absorber. One then speaks of a mass absorption coefficient, mass stopping power, etc. The relation between the absorption coefficient μ and the mass absorption coefficient μ' is found by noting that the thickness x (in cm) is related to the thickness t (in g cm^{-2}) by

$$\rho x = t \tag{2-1.2}$$

where ρ is the density of the medium. Consequently,

$$\mu x = \frac{\mu t}{\rho} = \mu' t \tag{2-1.3}$$

and hence the mass absorption coefficient is

$$\mu' = \frac{\mu}{\rho} \tag{2-1.4}$$

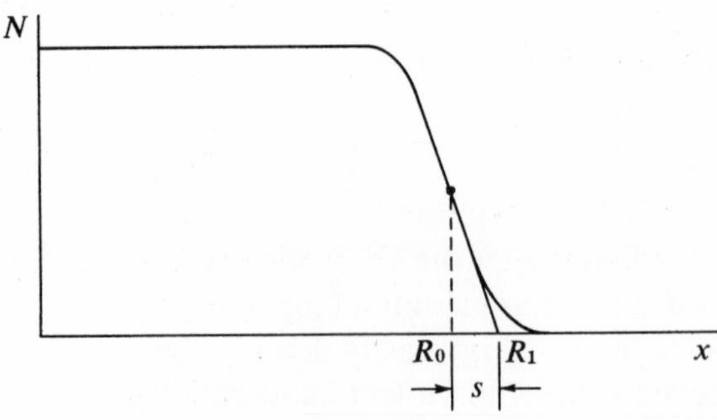

Figure 2-1 Range curve showing the number of particles in a beam penetrating to a given depth.

Figure 2-2 Bragg curve of an individual alpha particle. Ionization of an alpha particle, in ion pairs per millimeter, as a function of its residual range, according to experiments by Holloway and Livingston. [*Phys. Rev.*, **54,** 29 (1938).] In experiment $\rho_{air} = 1.184$ mg cm^{-3} (15°C, 760 mm Hg).

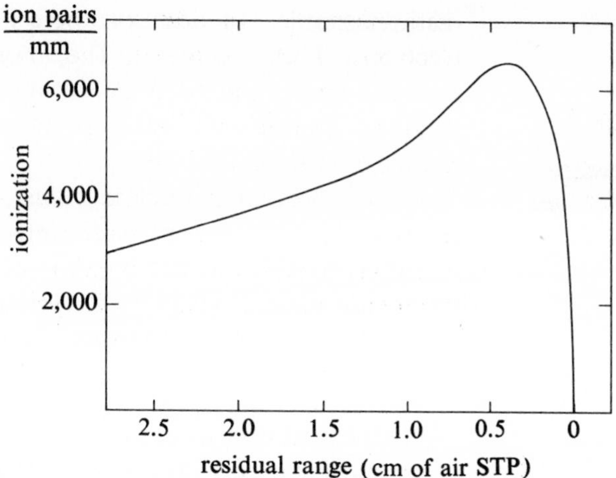

The atomic absorption coefficient μ_a is sometimes employed when thicknesses are measured in atoms per square centimeter; we have then, by an argument similar to the previous one,

$$\mu_a = \frac{\mu}{N} \qquad \textbf{(2-1.5)}$$

where N is the number of atoms per cubic centimeter.

2-2 Rutherford Scattering

Consider a particle of charge ze traversing matter of atomic number Z, for instance, a proton traversing a piece of aluminum. Occasionally the proton will collide elastically with an aluminum nucleus and will undergo "Rutherford scattering"; i.e., the electrostatic repulsion from the nucleus will deflect it.

Elastic nuclear collisions give rise to large changes in the direction of the impinging particle but not, on the average, to significant energy losses. In a cloud-chamber picture (Fig. 2-4) a nuclear collision is easily

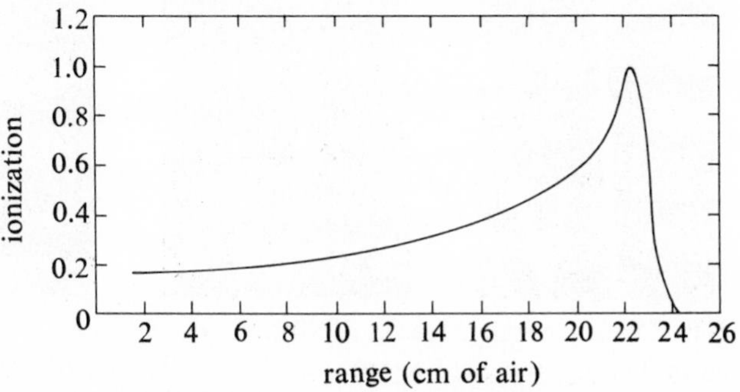

Figure 2-3 Bragg curve for a beam of protons. In experiment $\rho_{air} = 1.166$ mg cm^{-3}. Ordinate scale arbitrary. [R. R. Wilson, Cornell University.]

distinguishable. In addition there are collisions with the extranuclear electrons. These constitute the main cause of energy loss at energies below several hundred MeV, although they produce only an extremely small scattering of heavy particles. Inelastic nuclear collisions are treated in Chap. 11.

The effect of a nuclear collision can be calculated classically as follows: Assume that the scattering center has an infinite mass (in other words, is fixed) and that it exerts a repulsive electrostatic force on the impinging proton, given by Ze^2/r^2. This force, which has a potential

$$V(r) = +\frac{Ze^2}{r} \tag{2-2.1}$$

produces a motion whose orbit lies in the plane of the fixed center and the initial velocity vector. If $\mathbf{r}$ is the radius vector from the force center (located at the origin) to the proton and $\mathbf{p} = m\dot{\mathbf{r}}$, the proton's momentum, Newton's second law of motion gives

$$\dot{\mathbf{p}} = \frac{Ze^2\mathbf{r}}{r^3} \tag{2-2.2}$$

Multiplying both sides vectorially by $\mathbf{r}$, we have

$$\mathbf{r} \times \dot{\mathbf{p}} = 0 \tag{2-2.3}$$

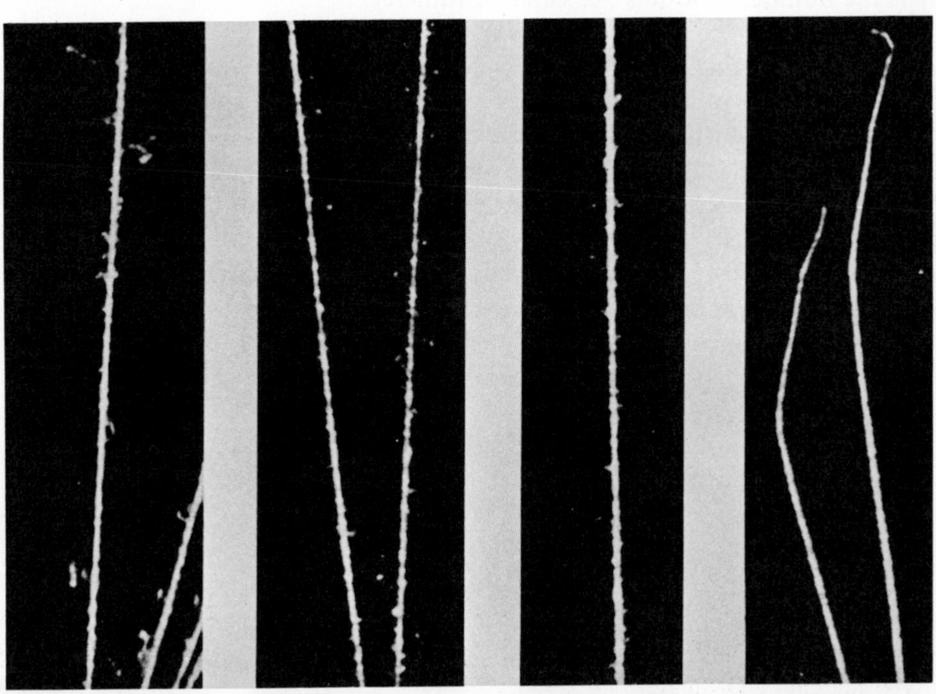

Figure 2-4 Cloud-chamber tracks of alpha rays showing delta rays. The first picture is in air, the last three in helium; the gas pressure in the chamber is such that the tracks cross about 10^{-5} g cm^{-2} of air equivalent. Note nuclear collisions in the section on the right. [T. Alper, *Z. Physik*, **67,** 172 (1932).]

Thus angular momentum

$$\mathbf{L} = \mathbf{r} \times \mathbf{p} \tag{2-2.4}$$

is a constant of the motion, since its time derivative is zero.

The total energy

$$\frac{p^2}{2m} + \frac{Ze^2}{r} = E \tag{2-2.5}$$

is another constant of the motion.

The vector

$$\boldsymbol{\epsilon} = \frac{-1}{Ze^2m}\mathbf{L} \times \mathbf{p} + \frac{\mathbf{r}}{r} \tag{2-2.6}$$

which in the plane of the motion, is also constant in time, as can be verified by calculating $\dot{\boldsymbol{\epsilon}}$ according to Eqs. (2-2.1), (2-2.2), and the formula for the vector triple product.

Scalar multiplication of Eq. (2-2.6) on both sides by $\mathbf{r}$, by using the formula for the mixed triple product, gives

$$\boldsymbol{\epsilon} \cdot \mathbf{r} = \frac{L^2}{me^2Z} + r \tag{2-2.7}$$

This equation can be interpreted easily by using polar coordinates with polar axis in the direction of $\boldsymbol{\epsilon}$. Equation (2-2.7) then reads

$$\epsilon r \cos\varphi = \frac{+L^2}{me^2Z} + r \tag{2-2.8}$$

or

$$r = \frac{-L^2/me^2Z}{1 - \epsilon\cos\varphi}$$

which for $\epsilon > 1$ is the equation of a hyperbola of eccentricity ϵ.

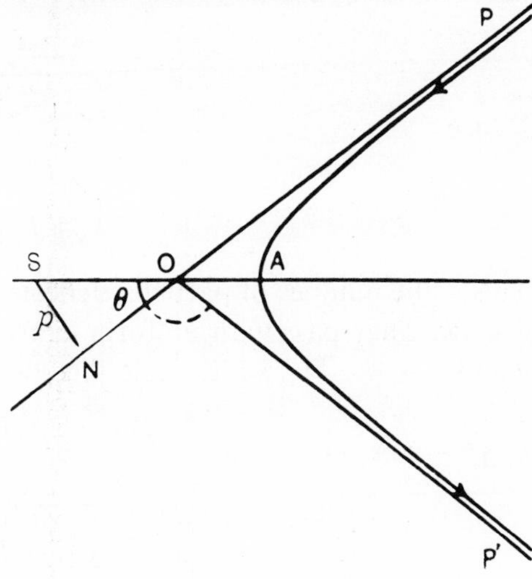

Figure 2-5 Orbit of a particle undergoing Rutherford scattering. [Original from Rutherford, *Phil. Mag.*, **21**, 672 (1911).] The notation used here is somewhat different.

The angle between the asymptotes not containing the hyperbola (Fig. 2-5) defines the deflection of the particle θ. It is found by determining the difference between the values of $\varphi = \pm\varphi_1$ for which the denominator is zero and taking the supplementary angle to this difference. One finds

$$\cos\varphi_1 = \frac{1}{\epsilon} = \sin\frac{\theta}{2} \tag{2-2.9}$$

or

$$\frac{Ze^2}{2Eb} = \tan\frac{\theta}{2} \tag{2-2.10}$$

where $b = L/(2mE)^{1/2}$ is the impact parameter, defined as the distance between the center of force and the limiting line of flight of the particle, for large values of r.

We can now calculate the probability of a deflection θ for protons crossing a foil of a substance of atomic number Z. We assume that the deflection is the consequence of a single nuclear collision. This is the case for large deflections. Small deflections are generally the result of the combined action of many collisions as will be seen later. We shall thus evaluate the nuclear-scattering cross section $d\sigma/d\omega$ and the probability of scattering through an angle between θ and $\theta + d\theta$ in crossing a foil of thickness x of a material containing N nuclei per unit volume. The probability $P(\theta)\,d\omega$ for scattering through angle θ into an element of solid angle $d\omega$ is given by

$$P(\theta)\,d\omega = \frac{d\sigma}{d\omega}Nx\,d\omega \tag{2-2.11}$$

Consider one nucleus of the scatterer and an incident beam containing one proton per unit surface area. If a proton has an impact parameter b with respect to the scatterer, the deflection is given by (2-2.10).

The number of protons dn having an impact parameter between b and $b + db$ is $2\pi b\,db = dn$, where, from Eq. (2-2.10),

$$db = -\frac{Ze^2}{4E}\frac{d\theta}{\sin^2(\theta/2)} \tag{2-2.12}$$

Hence

$$|dn| = \pi\left(\frac{Ze^2}{2E}\right)^2\frac{\cos(\theta/2)}{\sin^3(\theta/2)}|d\theta| \tag{2-2.13}$$

This is the number of particles deflected through an angle between θ and $\theta + d\theta$. They pass with uniform density between two cones of aperture θ and $\theta + d\theta$. The solid angle included between these cones is

$$d\omega = 2\pi\sin\theta\,d\theta \tag{2-2.14}$$

and

$$\frac{dn}{d\omega} = \frac{1}{4}\left(\frac{Ze^2}{2E}\right)^2\frac{1}{\sin^4(\theta/2)} \tag{2-2.15}$$

The quantity $dn/d\omega$ is dimensionally an area, and comparison with Eq. (2-2.11) shows that the differential-scattering cross section is

$$\frac{d\sigma}{d\omega} = \frac{1}{4}\left(\frac{e^2Z}{mv^2}\right)^2 \frac{1}{\sin^4(\theta/2)} \tag{2-2.16}$$

This is the famous Rutherford scattering formula (Rutherford, 1912). Put in convenient numerical form it is

$$\frac{d\sigma}{d\theta} = 2\pi \sin\theta \frac{d\sigma}{d\omega} = \frac{0.8139Z^2}{E^2\,(\text{MeV})} \frac{\sin\theta}{\sin^4(\theta/2)} \times 10^{-26}\ \text{cm}^2 \text{ per nucleus} \tag{2-2.17}$$

The experimental verification was carried out in detail by Rutherford, Geiger, Marsden, and others and led to the formulation of the planetary model of the atom.

Formula (2-2.16) can be extended to other particles besides the proton by replacing Z with Zz, where z is the atomic number of the projectile. Equation (2-2.16) is not relativistic and refers to a fixed center. Moreover, it considers only Coulomb forces, neglects both the finite size of the nucleus and specific nuclear forces, and is calculated classically without regard to quantum mechanics. In spite of all these approximations, the equation gives excellent results in many practical cases, notably for the scattering of particles having a computed minimum distance of approach to a target larger than approximately $1.2 \times 10^{-13}A^{1/3}$ cm, where A is the mass number of the target. The failure of Eq. (2-2.16) for cases where this distance becomes smaller is evidence that specific nuclear forces become operative. In fact, it was just such failure that provided the first indication of the "nuclear radius."

It is possible to generalize Eq. (2-2.16) to take into account the finite mass of the target. One obtains

$$\frac{d\sigma}{d\omega} = \left(\frac{e^2zZ}{mv^2}\right)^2 \frac{1}{\sin^4\theta} \frac{\{\cos\theta \pm [1-(m/M)^2\sin^2\theta]^{1/2}\}^2}{[1-(m/M)^2\sin^2\theta]^{1/2}} \tag{2-2.18}$$

where M is the mass of the target and m is the mass of the projectile. For $m < M$ the positive sign only should be used before the square root. For $m > M$ the expression should be calculated for positive and negative signs and the results added to obtain $d\sigma/d\omega$. The angle θ is the laboratory angle. If the colliding particles are identical, important quantum-mechanical corrections are necessary, and Eq. (2-2.18) is no longer applicable (Mott, 1930) (see Chap. 10).

An important limiting case of Eq. (2-2.16), also valid relativistically, is obtained when the deflection angle θ is small compared with 1 rad,

$$\frac{d\sigma}{d\omega} = \left(\frac{2Zze^2}{p\beta c}\right)^2 \frac{1}{\theta^4} \qquad \beta = \frac{v}{c} \tag{2-2.19}$$

For extremely small angles, which correspond to large impact parameters, the nuclear charge is screened by the atomic electrons, and Eq. (2-2.19) is invalid. It is this screening effect that prevents the equation from diverging for $\theta \to 0$. An important practical application of

Eq. (2-2.19), to the problem of multiple scattering, will be discussed later.

The Rutherford scattering formula can be obtained also by means of quantum mechanics; in this case Born's approximation (see Appendix B) happens to give the correct result. The simple derivation is given here as an example of the application of Born's approximation. The fundamental formula (see Appendix B) is

$$\frac{d\sigma}{d\omega} = \frac{1}{4\pi^2\hbar^4}\frac{p^2}{v^2}|U_{\mathbf{p}-\mathbf{p}'}|^2 \tag{2-2.20}$$

Use of Eq. (2-2.20) requires the calculation of the matrix element $U_{\mathbf{p}-\mathbf{p}'}$ for the potential Ze^2/r. We have

$$U_{\mathrm{pp}'} = Ze^2 \int \frac{\exp(i/\hbar)(\mathbf{p} - \mathbf{p}')\cdot\mathbf{r}}{r}\, d\tau \tag{2-2.21}$$

This integral is best calculated by transforming it to polar coordinates with a polar axis in the direction **p**–**p**′. Designate by θ the scattering angle and by μ the cosine of the angle between **r** and **p**–**p**′, and observe that $|\mathbf{p}| = |\mathbf{p}'|$ and $|\mathbf{p}-\mathbf{p}'| = 2p\sin(\theta/2) \equiv k\hbar$. In the integral (2-2.21) the volume element becomes $2\pi\, d\mu r^2\, dr$, and we have

$$U_{\mathrm{pp}'} = Ze^2 \int_{-1}^{1}\int_{0}^{\infty} \frac{e^{ik\mu r}}{r}\, 2\pi\, d\mu\, r^2\, dr \tag{2-2.22}$$

Integrating with respect to μ gives

$$U_{\mathrm{pp}'} = Ze^2 4\pi \int_0^\infty \frac{\sin kr}{kr^2}\, r^2\, dr \tag{2-2.23}$$

This last integral oscillates in value when the upper limit is considered, but it is easy to prove, for instance, by replacing Ze^2/r by $(Ze^2/r)e^{-\alpha r}$ and after integration going to the limit $\alpha \to 0$ that we must take 0 as the value at the upper limit. We thus obtain

$$U_{\mathrm{pp}'} = \frac{4\pi Ze^2}{k^2} = \frac{\pi\hbar^2 Ze^2}{p^2\sin^2(\theta/2)} \tag{2-2.24}$$

and by using Eq. (2-2.20) we find

$$\frac{d\sigma}{d\omega} = \frac{1}{4\pi^2\hbar^4}\frac{p^2}{v^2}\frac{\pi^2\hbar^4 Z^2e^4}{p^4\sin^4(\theta/2)} = \frac{Z^2e^4}{4p^2v^2}\frac{1}{\sin^4(\theta/2)} \tag{2-2.25}$$

which is identical to Eq. (2-2.16).

2-3 Energy Loss Due to Ionization

In addition to the nuclear collisions mentioned above, a heavy charged particle moving through matter collides also with atomic electrons. The greatest part of the energy loss occurs in these collisions. Sometimes the atomic electrons receive so much energy that they become free and are clearly visible in cloud-chamber pictures (Fig. 2-4, delta rays). Sometimes the atom is excited but not ionized. In any case, the energy for these processes comes from the kinetic energy of the incident particle, which is thereby slowed down. Figure 2-3 gives a plot of specific ionization versus range. Since the energy spent in forming an ion pair in a gas happens to be approximately independent of the energy of the particle forming the ions, this curve approximates the curve of specific energy loss.

To calculate the rate of energy loss by a particle of charge ze as it progresses through a medium containing $\mathcal{N}$ electrons cm^{-3}, we first consider the electrons as free and at rest. The force between the heavy particle and the electron is ze^2/r^2, where r is the distance between them. The trajectory of the heavy particle is not appreciably affected by the light electron, and we can consider the collision as lasting such a short time that the electron acquires an impulse without changing its position during the collision. By this hypothesis the impulse acquired by the electron must be perpendicular to the trajectory of the heavy particle and can be calculated by

$$\Delta p_{\perp} = \int_{-\infty}^{\infty} e\mathcal{E}_{\perp}\, dt = \int e\mathcal{E}_{\perp} \frac{dx}{v} = ze^2 \int_{-\infty}^{\infty} \frac{1}{r^2} \cos\theta \frac{dx}{v} \qquad \textbf{(2-3.1)}$$

where $\mathcal{E}_{\perp}$ is the component of the electric field at the position of the electron normal to the trajectory of the particle (Fig. 2-6) and v is the velocity of the heavy particle, which is taken to be constant during the collision. The integral is easily evaluated by applying Gauss's theorem to a cylinder of radius b having the trajectory as its axis. Note that the flux of $\mathcal{E}$ through this cylinder is given by

$$\phi = \int \mathcal{E}_{\perp}\, 2\pi b\, dx = 4\pi ze \qquad \textbf{(2-3.2)}$$

Replacing the second integral of Eq. (2-3.1) by its value obtained from Eq. (2-3.2),

$$\Delta p = \frac{2ze^2}{bv} \qquad \textbf{(2-3.3)}$$

The energy transferred to the electron is then

$$\frac{(\Delta p)^2}{2m} = \frac{2}{m}\left(\frac{ze^2}{bv}\right)^2 \qquad \textbf{(2-3.4)}$$

and since there are $2\pi\mathcal{N} b\, db\, dx$ electrons per length dx that have a

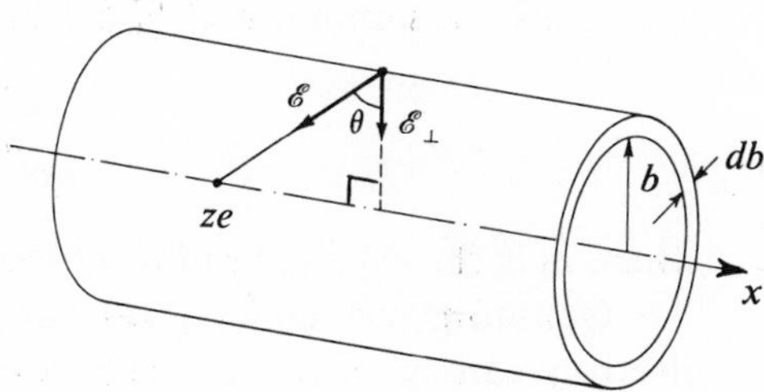

Figure 2-6 Transfer of momentum to an electron by a moving heavy charge.

distance between b and $b + db$ from the heavy ion, the energy loss per path length dx is

$$-\frac{dE}{dx} = 2\pi\mathcal{N}\int b\,db\,\frac{(\Delta p)^2}{2m} = 4\pi\mathcal{N}\frac{z^2e^4}{mv^2}\int_{b_{\min}}^{b_{\max}}\frac{db}{b}$$

$$= 4\pi\mathcal{N}\frac{z^2e^4}{mv^2}\log\frac{b_{\max}}{b_{\min}} \tag{2-3.5}$$

This is the stopping power of the absorbing medium. At first, one might be tempted to extend the integral from zero to infinity, obtaining a divergent result. To do so, however, would be incompatible with the hypotheses under which Eq. (2-3.4) was derived; for instance, distant collisions last a long time, and the corresponding energy transfer is not given by this equation.

Equation (2-3.5) also shows that the energy loss due to collisions with nuclei is negligible compared with the energy loss to electrons. In considering nuclear collisions we would find a factor Z^2 in the numerator and also the nuclear mass instead of the electron mass in the denominator. The increase in the denominator is the dominating factor.

We shall now discuss the values of $b_{\max}$ and $b_{\min}$ which are suitable to the problem. For $b_{\max}$ we consider that the electrons are not free but are bound in atomic orbits. The adiabatic principle of quantum mechanics states that one cannot induce transitions from one quantum state to another by a time-dependent perturbation if the variation of the perturbation is small during the periods τ of the system. In our case it can be assumed that the duration of the perturbation is the time b/v during which the heavy particle is near the electron and that in order to produce transitions the condition $b/v < \tau = 1/\nu$ must be fulfilled. This determines $b_{\max}$ as $< v/\langle\nu\rangle$, where $\langle\nu\rangle$ is an appropriate average of the frequencies of the atom. Taking relativistic corrections into account, the duration of the perturbation is shortened by a factor $(1 - \beta^2)^{-1/2}$. The limit for $b_{\max}$ given by the adiabatic condition then becomes

$$b_{\max} = \frac{v}{\langle\nu\rangle(1 - \beta^2)^{1/2}} \tag{2-3.6}$$

The limits for $b_{\min}$ are several: first, in an elastic collision it is impossible to change the momentum of an electron by an amount greater than $2mv$ as can be easily seen if we consider the heavy particle at rest and the electron impinging on it. This implies, according to Eq. (2-3.3), a minimum classical impact parameter

$$b_{\min\text{ cl}} = \frac{ze^2}{mv^2} > \frac{ze^2}{mc^2} = zr_0 \tag{2-3.7}$$

where r_0 is the classical radius of the electron, 2.8×10^{-13}cm.

Quantum mechanics gives another limit to $b_{\min}$ inasmuch as the electron can be localized with respect to the heavy ion only to the

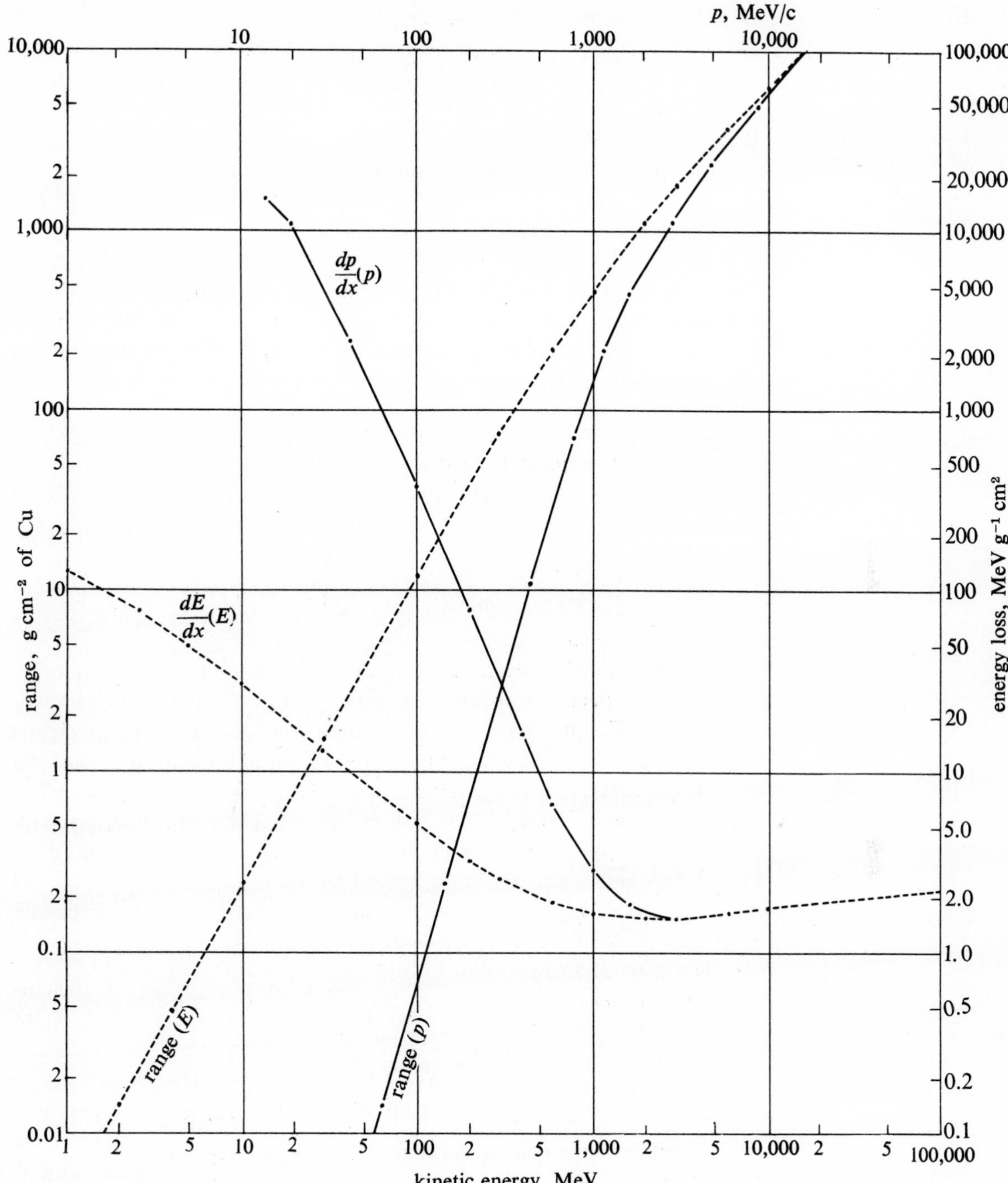

Figure 2-7 Graph of stopping power vs. energy and of specific momentum loss versus momentum for heavy particles in copper. In the same figure range-energy and range-momentum relations for protons in copper. All scales are logarithmic. The figure may be used for other particles. Remember $-dE/dx = z^2\lambda(v)$ and the scaling laws of Sec. 2-3.

accuracy of its de Broglie wavelength; that is,

$$b_{\min\,\mathrm{qm}} > \frac{\hbar}{p} = \frac{\hbar(1 - \beta^2)^{1/2}}{mv} \tag{2-3.8}$$

We must now introduce in Eq. (2-3.5) the smallest value of $b_{\max}$ and the largest value of $b_{\min}$. Over a large velocity interval this gives

$$-\frac{dE}{dx} = \frac{4\pi z^2 e^4}{mv^2}\mathcal{N}\log\frac{mv^2}{\hbar\langle\nu\rangle(1 - \beta^2)} \tag{2-3.9}$$

The quantity $2\pi\hbar\langle\nu\rangle$ is a special average of the excitation and ionization potentials in the atom of the stopping material. It can be calculated by using the Thomas–Fermi model of the atom. Bloch (1933) found that it is approximately proportional to Z,

$$2\pi\hbar\langle\nu\rangle = I = BZ \tag{2-3.10}$$

A better semiempirical formula is $I/Z = 9.1(1 + 1.9Z^{-2/3})$ eV for $B \geq 4$. A more precise calculation of the stopping power, performed by Bethe, gives

$$-\frac{dE}{dx} = \frac{4\pi z^2 e^4}{mv^2}\mathcal{N}\left[\log\frac{2mv^2}{I(1 - \beta^2)} - \beta^2\right] \tag{2-3.11}$$

A sample of the stopping-power curve is given in Fig. 2-7.

At very low velocities, i.e., when v is comparable with the velocity of the atomic electrons around the heavy particle (in the case of hydrogen, $v = c/137$), the heavy ion neutralizes itself by capturing electrons for part of the time. This result is a rapid falloff of ionization at the very end of the range. On the other hand, at extremely high energies, with $v \sim c$, ionization increases, for several reasons. The relativistic contraction of the Coulomb field of the ion increases $b_{\max}$ according to Eq. (2-3.6) and decreases $b_{\min}$ according to Eq. (2-3.8). Part of the energy is carried away as light (Cerenkov radiation). This last effect will be discussed in Sec. 2-5.

The general form of Eq. (2-3.11) allows us to draw some conclusions of considerable practical importance. We can write Eq. (2-3.11) as

$$-\frac{dE}{dx} = z^2\lambda(v)$$

or remembering that the kinetic energy of a particle of mass M is $E = M\epsilon(v)$, where ϵ is a function of the velocity only, we have, using E as a variable,

$$-\frac{dE}{dx}(E) = z^2\lambda_E(E/M) \tag{2-3.12}$$

or, using v as a variable,

$$-\frac{dv}{dx}(v) = \frac{z^2}{M}\lambda_v(v) \tag{2-3.13}$$

Relations (2-3.12) and (2-3.13) allow us to write the energy loss as a function of energy for any particle, once the energy loss as a function of energy is known for protons. In particular, protons, deuterons, and tritons of the same velocity have the same specific energy loss.

Similar scaling relations obtain for the range. Using the velocity as a variable, one has

$$R_v(v) = \int_0^v \left(\frac{dv}{dx}\right)^{-1} dv = \frac{M}{z^2}\int_0^v [\lambda_v(v)]^{-1}\, dv = \frac{M}{z^2}\,\rho_v(v) \qquad \textbf{(2-3.14)}$$

or, using energy as a variable,

$$R_E\,(E/M) = \frac{M}{z^2}\,\rho_E\,(E/M) \qquad \textbf{(2-3.15)}$$

For clarity we have indicated explicitly the independent variable to be used in the functions.

Equation (2-3.14) is not exact, for the neutralization phenomena occurring at the end of the range and other corrections are neglected; but it is sufficiently accurate for most cases, excluding very low energies. As an example of the application of Eq. (2-3.15) we can verify that a deuteron of energy E has twice the range of a proton of energy $E/2$.

A semiempirical power law valid from a few MeV to 200 MeV for the proton range-energy relations is

$$R(E) = \left(\frac{E}{9.3}\right)^{1.8}$$

where E is in MeV and R is in meters of air.

Sample numerical data on range-energy relations are provided in Fig. 2-7 and in Fig. 2-8, which presents a nomogram useful for approximate estimates.

The mass stopping power is more often used than $-dE/dx$, the (linear) stopping power. The mass stopping power depends on the factors $\mathcal{N}/\rho$ and I of the stopping substances. The number of electrons per cubic centimeter, $\mathcal{N}$, is roughly proportional to the density ρ. If this proportionality were exact, only the dependence of I on Z would influence the mass stopping power. Actually, $\mathcal{N}/\rho$, and hence the mass stopping power, decreases with Z.

Heavier ions, such as C^{12}, O^{16}, and A^{40}, are slowed down by ionization loss in much the same way as alpha particles. The part of the range where the effective charge on the ion changes is emphasized, and the maximum stopping power is reached at velocities increasing with Z. For example, for C^{12} and A^{40} the maximum specific ionization occurs at approximately $v/c = 0.037$ and 0.059, which correspond to energies of 8 and 65 MeV, respectively. At lower energies the decrease of the effective nuclear charge overcompensates the effect of the diminishing velocity and the stopping-power decrease with energy. In other words, the behavior is the same, on an exaggerated scale, as that observed at the end of the Bragg curve for protons and alpha particles (Fig. 2-2).

The extreme case is furnished by fission fragments. Their effective charge is large, reaching about 20e at the beginning of the range; and nuclear collisions are an important source of energy loss. If a fragment of atomic number Z_1 crosses a medium of atomic number Z_2 and nuclear mass M_2, the specific energy loss to nuclei is proportional to

$$Z_1^2 \frac{Z_2^2}{M_2} \qquad \textbf{(2-3.16)}$$

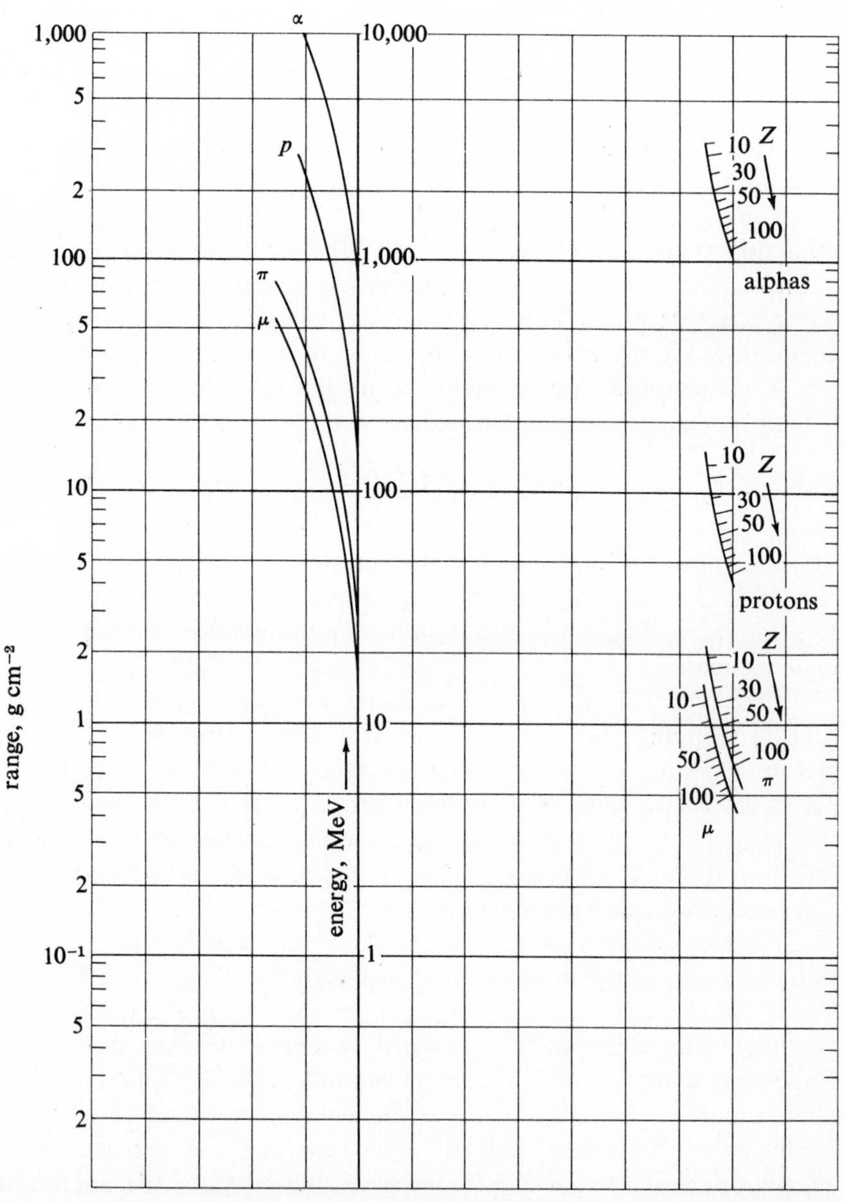

Figure 2-8 Nomogram by R. R. Wilson for range-energy relation. Left scales range in grams per square centimeter. Middle scale, kinetic energy in MeV. Right-hand scale, atomic number Z of stopping material and mass of particle. To use, connect range, energy, and Z by a straight line. [(Se 59).]

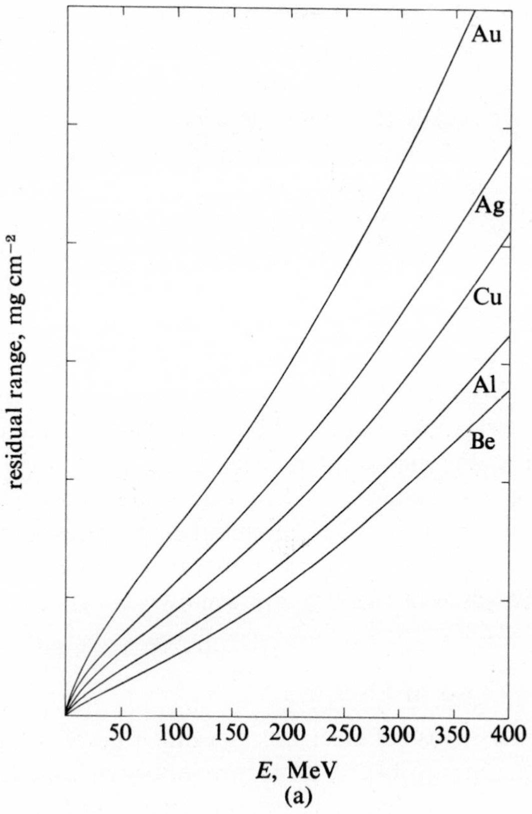

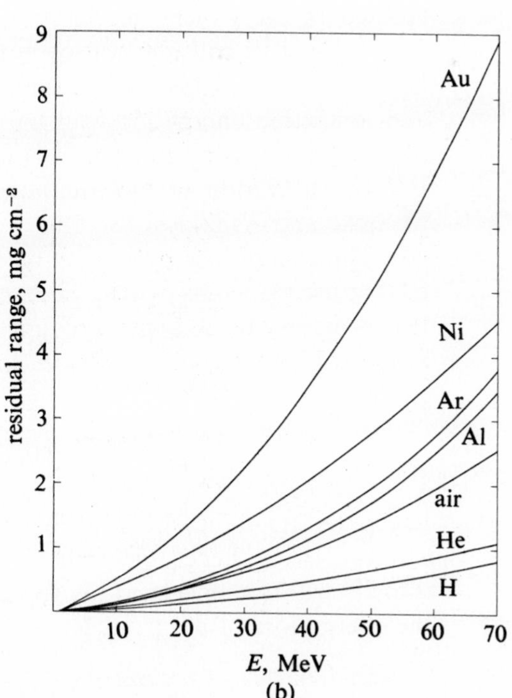

Figure 2-9 Range-energy relation for (a) Ar^{40} [E. L. Hubbard, UCRL 9053] and (b) median-mass heavy fission fragments ($A \simeq 140$). [C. B. Fulmer, *Phys. Rev.*, **108,** 1113 (1957).]

whereas the loss to electrons is proportional to

$$Z_{1}{}^{2}{}_{\text{eff}}\frac{Z_2}{m} \tag{2-3.17}$$

The first equation, (2-3.16), applies to close nuclear collisions where the entire charges of the fragment and the target are effective. In the case of electronic collisions only the net charge $Z_{1\text{eff}}$ of the fission fragment, with whatever electrons it carries along, is effective, and the target electrons have unit charge. The factor Z_2 of Eq. (2-3.17) arises from the presence of Z_2 electrons per nucleus. The approximate value of $Z_{1\text{eff}}$ is obtained by assuming that the fragment will lose all the electrons whose orbital velocity in the atom is smaller than the velocity of the fragment itself (see Fig. 2-9).

The two causes of energy loss considered above may be comparable, but the energy loss due to nuclear collisions is concentrated in few events, while the electronic collisions are much more uniformly distributed along the range. The nuclear collisions originate the peculiar branches observable in cloud-chamber pictures of fission fragments. The concentration of the nuclear energy loss in a few events is the cause of the great value of the straggling shown by fission fragments.

2-4 Energy Loss of Electrons

The energy loss of electrons is a much more complicated phenomenon than the energy loss by ionization of heavy ions, for in addition there is an energy loss due to electromagnetic radiation (*bremsstrahlung*) emitted in the violent accelerations that occur during collisions (Fig. 2-10). We shall consider the two effects separately, confining ourselves here to the energy loss due to ionization. The combination of radiation and ionization energy loss will be treated in Sec. 2-11. At low energies ($\ll 2mc^2$) the loss by ionization is much greater than that by radiation. For the derivation of the equations and a bibliography see the article of Bethe and Ashkin in (Se 59).

The energy loss by ionization may be treated in a manner similar to that used for heavy ions, but there are several important differences. It is necessary to take into account the identity of the particles involved in the collision and their reduced mass. The formula for nonrelativistic electrons is

$$-\frac{dE}{dx} = \frac{4\pi e^4 \mathcal{N}}{mv^2}\left(\log\frac{mv^2}{2I} - \tfrac{1}{2}\log 2 + \tfrac{1}{2}\right) \tag{2-4.1}$$

Except for small factors in the logarithmic term, this formula is the same as Eq. (2-3.11); hence, electrons and protons of the same nonrelativistic velocity will lose energy at the same rate. For high relativistic velocities the energy loss of electrons is

$$-\frac{dE}{dx} = \frac{4\pi e^4}{mc^2}\mathcal{N}\left[\log\frac{2mc^2}{I} - \tfrac{3}{2}\log(1-\beta^2)^{1/2} - \tfrac{1}{2}\log 8 + \tfrac{1}{16}\right] \tag{2-4.2}$$

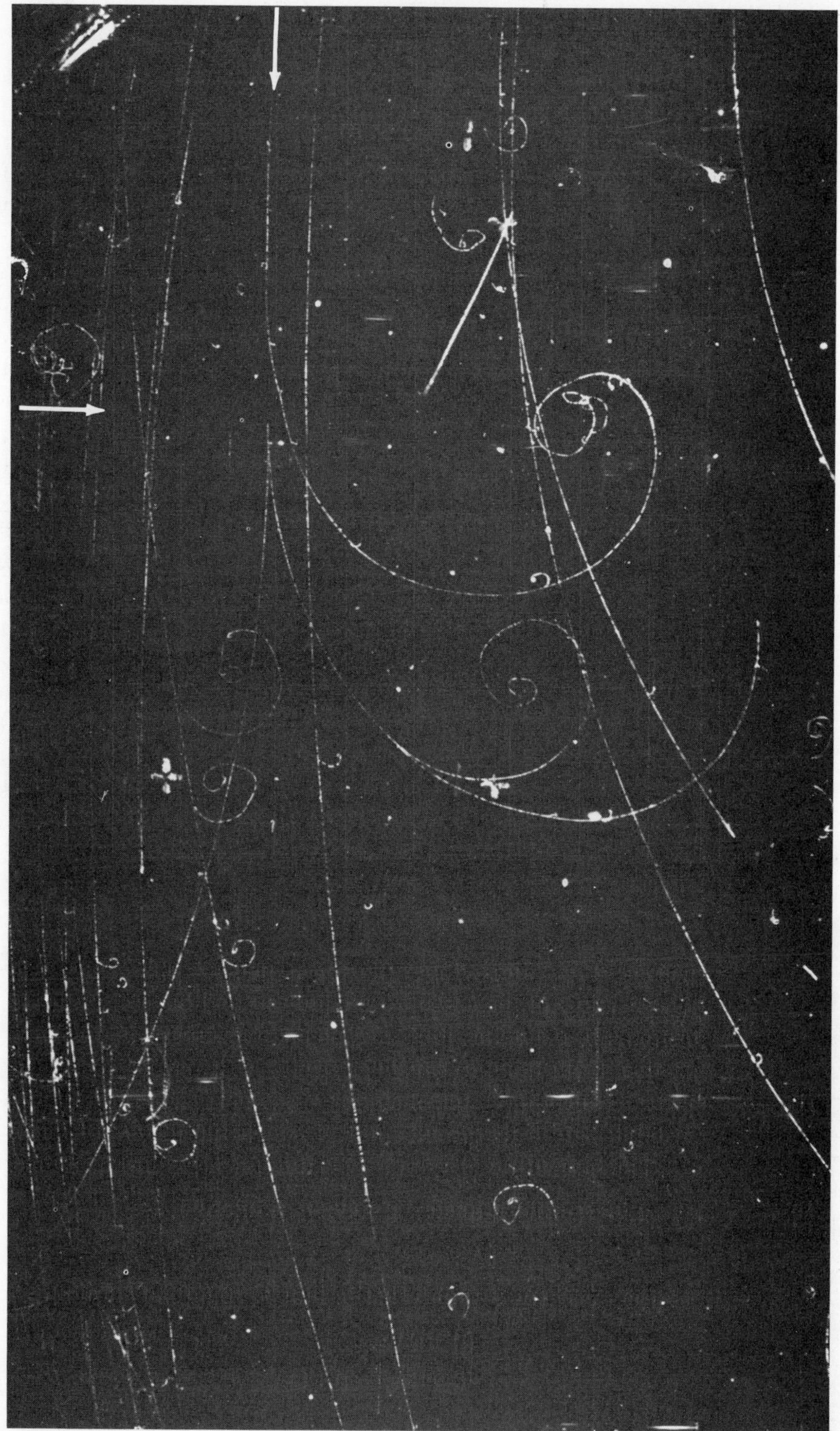

Figure 2-10 An electron loses energy by radiation as shown by the sudden increase in curvature of its trajectory. The emitted quantum makes an electron-positron pair. [Propane bubble chamber, courtesy Lawrence Radiation Laboratory.]

whereas for protons it is

$$-\frac{dE}{dx} = \frac{4\pi e^4}{mc^2}\mathcal{N}\left[\log\frac{2mc^2}{I} + 2\log\frac{1}{(1-\beta^2)^{1/2}} - 1\right] \quad \textbf{(2-4.3)}$$

At equal values of β, the two expressions differ by less than 10 per cent up to proton energies of 10^{10} eV. The difference between the average energy loss of electrons and positrons is even smaller.

An important practical difference between the behavior of heavy particles and electrons arises from the fact that the trajectories of electrons in matter are not straight lines, especially at low energies ($E \ll mc^2$). For this reason the actual path length of an electron passing through two points may be appreciably longer than the distance between these points measured on a straight line, as can be seen in Fig. 2-11. Thus, electrons of the same energy are not all stopped by the same thickness of material, and the concept of range has a limited validity.

For practical measurements of electron energy we can use the extrapolated range. It is important to note, however, that the geometry of the apparatus influences the result. Thus, in order to use the data found in the literature, one must reproduce the experimental arrangement used to obtain them (Fig. 2-12).

In the case of beta rays the electrons have a continuous energy spectrum, but it is still possible to find a relation between the upper limit of the energy of the spectrum E and the maximum range R (in g cm^{-2} of aluminum) of the electrons (Feather, 1938). A relation frequently used for a rapid determination of E (MeV) is

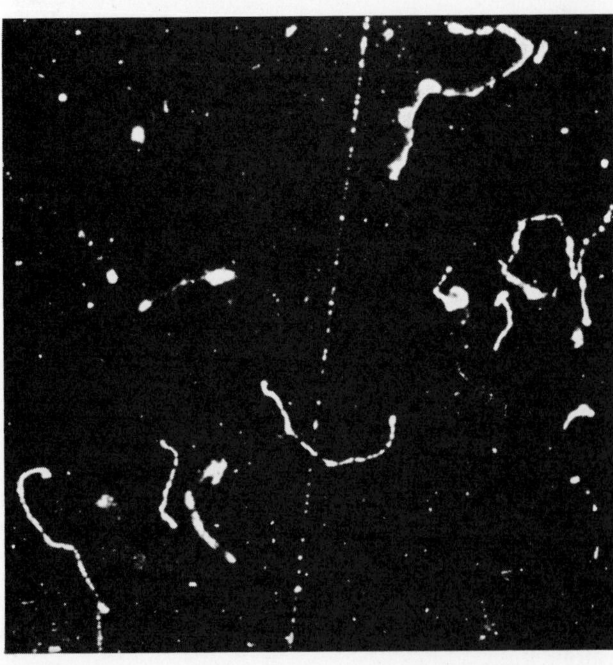

Figure 2-11 Slow electrons showing a curved path due to scattering. A fast electron goes straight. [Original from C. T. R. Wilson, 1923.]

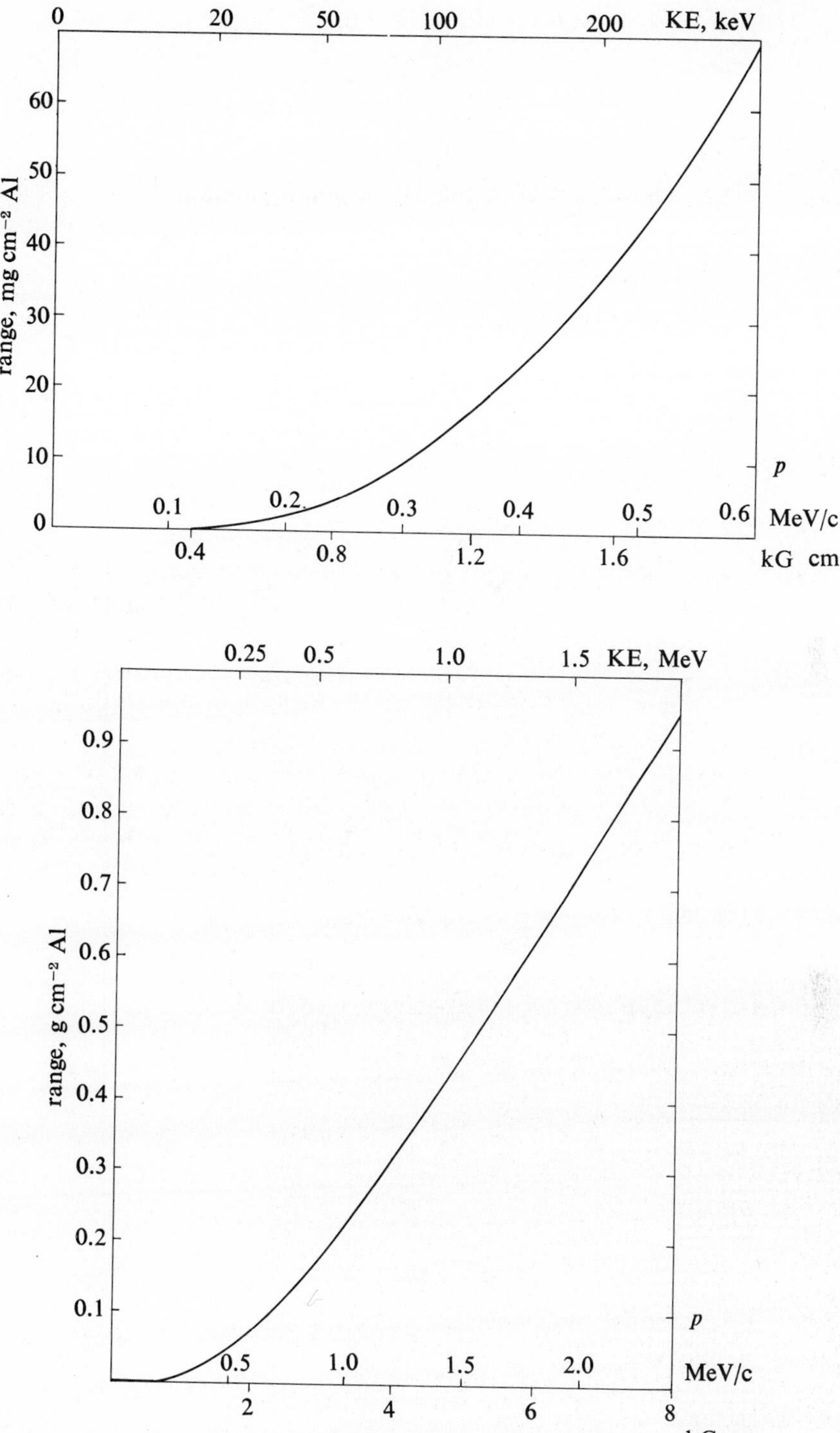

Figure 2-12 Range of electrons in aluminum. Abscissa on lower scale, momentum in MeV/c and in $Br = cp/e$ (3,327 G·cm = 1 MeV/c). Abscissa on upper scale, KE in MeV. [(Se 59).]

$$R = \begin{cases} 0.542E - 0.133 & 0.8 < E < 3 \\ 0.407E^{1.38} & 0.15 < E < 0.8 \end{cases} \qquad \textbf{(2-4.4)}$$

See Fig. 2-13 for a range-energy plot usable for beta emitters.

2-5 Polarization Effects—Cerenkov Radiation

The derivation of Eq. (2-3.11) did not take into account the electrical polarization of the medium in which the heavy ion moves. The dielectric constant of the medium weakens the electric field acting at a distance from the ion, causing a decrease of the energy transfer to atoms located far from the ion, and hence a decrease in the mass stopping power. Thus, in the case of a medium in two phases of different density, such as water and vapor, the lower density phase has a higher mass

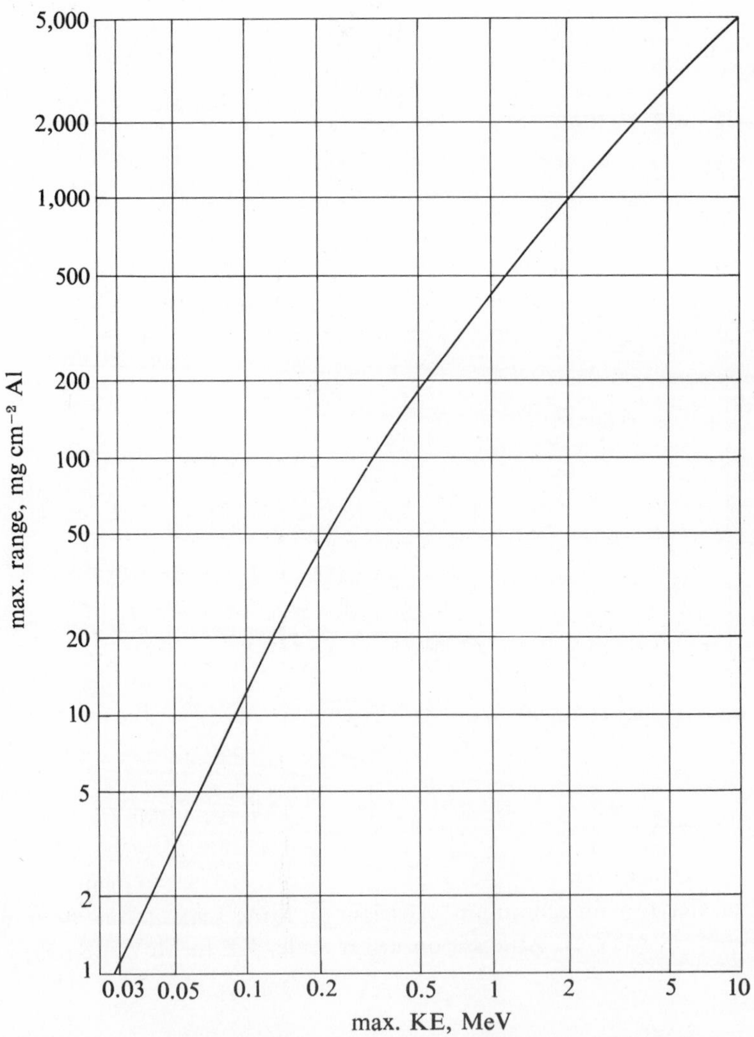

Figure 2-13 Range-energy plot of some common beta emitters (logarithmic scales). [(Si 55).]

stopping power. This effect is appreciable, however, only for relativistic velocities and seldom amounts to more than a few per cent.

Another important effect of the dielectric constant is the production of Cerenkov radiation (Cerenkov; Frank and Tamm, 1937). If a charge moves with a velocity βc in a medium of refractive index n, its electric field propagates with velocity c/n; and if $\beta c > c/n$, a phenomenon similar to the production of a bow wave results. Figure 2-14 gives the Huyghens' construction for the electromagnetic waves emitted by the particle along its path. At time $t = 0$, the particle is at O. One second later it is at P after traveling a distance $OP = \beta c$. The front of the electromagnetic wave is on the surface of the cone of aperture $\sin^{-1}(1/n\beta)$, which means that the rays of the corresponding light make an angle $\theta = \cos^{-1}(1/n\beta)$ with the trajectory of the particle. The intensity of the Cerenkov light can be calculated semiclassically [see for instance (Ja 62)]: for the number of quantum radiated per unit length with frequency between ν and $\nu + d\nu$ one has

$$dn = \frac{2\pi e^2}{\hbar c}\left(1 - \frac{1}{n^2\beta^2}\right)\frac{d\nu}{c} = \frac{2\pi e^2}{\hbar c}\sin^2\theta\,\frac{d\nu}{c} \qquad \textbf{(2-5.1)}$$

In the spectral region between 3,000 and 6,000 Å Eq. (2-5.1) thus gives approximately 750 $\sin^2\theta$ photons per centimeter. The spectrum is a continuum.

The light is polarized, with its electric vector pointing in the PQ direction. The measure of the angle θ of Cerenkov light may be used to determine the value of β for the particle. The density effect and the Cerenkov light are interrelated, both being functions of the dielectric constant of the medium.

2-6 Ionization in Gases and Semiconductors

A charged particle passing through a gas ionizes it. However, only part of the energy goes into ionizing the gas and into imparting kinetic energy to the electrons. A sizable fraction is spent in exciting the atoms below the ionization limit, and some of it is then transformed into detectable scintillation light. The average amount of energy required per ion formed, is remarkably independent of the charge, mass, and velocity of the particle producing the ionization, but depends on the gas in which the ions are formed. There is no simple physical explanation

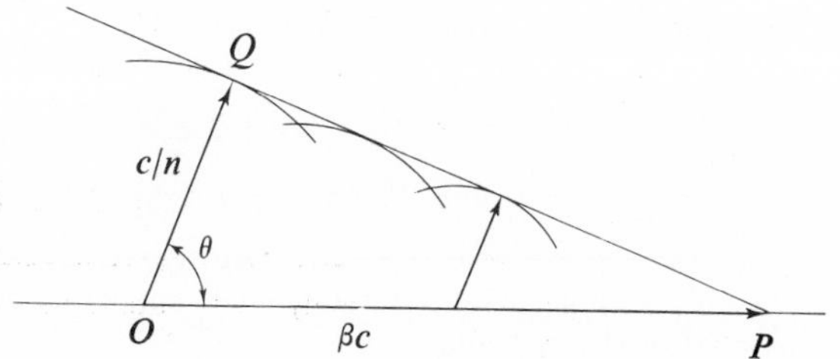

Figure 2-14 Huyghens' construction for electromagnetic waves emitted by a moving charged particle. Origin of Cerenkov radiation.

of this fact, which is the consequence of the relative importance of a series of processes. Table 2-1 gives the average energy spent per ion pair formed in some of the most important gases.

The primary act of ionization results in electrons, some of which (delta rays) have sufficient energy to produce secondary ions.

If the ions are formed in a gas subject to an electric field, they move under the action of the field. The average velocity w in the direction of the field, called the *drift velocity*, is proportional to the field. The constant of proportionality μ is called the *mobility*. We can see the essential factors involved in the drift velocity if we assume that the ions have a certain mean free path λ in the gas and that their average random velocity is u. The velocity u may be equal to the velocity of thermal agitation, but it is not necessarily so. If we think of an electron bouncing between heavy atoms, we see that it will not transfer much of its energy to the atoms unless it can excite them by inelastic collision. In the case of noble gases the required energies are of the order of 10 eV. Under the action of the field the electron will acquire a large velocity u, which is randomized in direction by the collisions until an inelastic collision causes a considerable decrease in velocity. If the electric field $\mathscr{E}$ lies in the z direction, an electron will drift in time τ between collisions by an amount

$$\frac{1}{2}\frac{e}{m}\mathscr{E}\tau^2 = \frac{1}{2}\frac{e\mathscr{E}}{m}\left(\frac{\lambda}{u}\right)^2 \tag{2-6.1}$$

in the z direction, because it is subject to the force $e\mathscr{E}$. The number of collisions per second is u/λ; hence the drift velocity is

$$w = \frac{1}{2}\frac{e\mathscr{E}}{m}\frac{\lambda}{u} = \mu\mathscr{E} \tag{2-6.2}$$

Clearly a low value of the random velocity u increases the mobility μ. For heavy ions the mobility is of the order of 1 cm sec^{-1} per volt cm^{-1} at STP; for electrons it is about 1,000 times larger. In very pure noble gases the mobility of electrons may be increased by as much as a factor of 10 by adding a small amount of a polyatomic impurity. The electrons then lose their energy by exciting rotational or vibrational states of the impurity molecules. This keeps u low and increases λ, for the Ramsauer effect produces an increase in λ on decreasing u, and both effects tend to increase w.

Table 2-1 w = eV per Ion Pair for Different Gases[a]

He	Ne	Ar	Xe	H_2	O_2	N_2	CO_2	Air	
42.7	36.8	26.4	21.9	36.3	32.5	36.5	34.3	35.0	Polonium α particle
42.3	36.6	26.4	22.0	36.3	30.9	34.9	32.9	33.8	Tritium β rays

[a] Note that extremely small amounts of impurities can effect w noticeably, especially in helium.

If, between collisions, the electron acquires enough kinetic energy to ionize the gas, the conditions for a multiplicative discharge are satisfied. Multiplicative processes and discharges are of fundamental importance in gas counters, proportional counters, and Geiger–Müller counters. For discharge mechanisms in counters, see Korff in (Fl E).

The energy spent per ion pair formed in solid semiconductors is about ten times smaller (3 eV) than in gases. A typical mobility is 10^3 cm sec^{-1} per volt cm^{-1}. The application of semiconductors to particle detection is briefly treated in Chap. 3.

2-7 Multiple Scattering

Section 2-2 treated the scattering due to the Coulomb force of a single nucleus acting on a charged particle. In addition to this single scattering, we must consider the cumulative effect of many small nuclear deflections that produce a deviation θ from the original direction of a particle. Consider a particle impinging normally on a foil and emerging with a given deviation θ. This deviation may result from a single scattering event or from an accumulation of many small scatterings. One criterion for deciding whether a particular deflection is most likely to be the result of one collision or of multiple scattering is obtained by considering an angle θ_1 such that the particle in crossing the foil is likely to have only one scatter as large as θ_1. Then deflections larger than θ_1 are very likely to be the result of a single scattering; deflections smaller than θ_1, the result of multiple scattering.

Clearly the distinction between deflections due to single scattering or to the multiple scattering cannot be made solely on the basis of the deflection angle θ. Large deflections may be caused by a few relatively wide-angle scatterings (plural scattering). The complete theory (Molière, 1948; Snyder and Scott, 1949; Nigam, Sundaresan, and Wu, 1959), however, is beyond the scope of this book. Figure 2-15 illustrates the relation between single, plural, and multiple scattering.

● In order to give an elementary theory of multiple scattering, we shall neglect the effects of plural scattering and limit the discussion to deflections $\theta \ll \theta_1$ due to many collisions.

Using an argument similar to the one preceding Eq. (2-3.3), we consider the collision of a rapidly moving incident particle of charge ze against a nucleus of charge Ze and find for the transverse impulse given to the incident particle

$$\frac{\Delta p}{p} = \frac{2zZe^2}{bvp} \tag{2-7.1}$$

This expression remains correct for relativistic momenta p. Furthermore for small deflections we have in a single collision

$$\frac{\Delta p}{p} = \theta \tag{2-7.2}$$

If a particle traverses a foil, there will be many collisions, each deflecting the particle by a small angle θ_i, and the resulting deviation will be the sum of all the θ_i. In this sum naturally one must take into account the fact that the θ_i occur in different directions, incoherently. We shall designate by Θ the total angular deviation of each particle and by Θ_x, Θ_y its projections on two fixed directions perpendicular to each other and to the direction of motion.

Designating φ_i by the azimuth of the plane of any single collision giving rise to the single deflection θ_i, we have, summing over single collisions,

$$\Theta_x = \sum_i \theta_i \cos \varphi_i \tag{2-7.3}$$

$$\Theta_y = \sum_i \theta_i \sin \varphi_i \tag{2-7.4}$$

from which we derive

$$\Theta^2 = \Theta_x{}^2 + \Theta_y{}^2 = (\sum_i \theta_i \cos \varphi_i)^2 + (\sum_i \theta_i \sin \varphi_i)^2 \tag{2-7.5}$$

Taking into account that the individual scatterings are incoherent and hence that

$$\overline{\cos \varphi_i \cos \varphi_j} = \tfrac{1}{2}\delta_{ij} \tag{2-7.6}$$

(indicating by the bar the average over collisions), we have

$$\langle \Theta^2 \rangle = \langle \sum_i \theta_i{}^2 \rangle = \sum_i \overline{\theta_i{}^2} \tag{2-7.7}$$

(indicating by $\langle\ \rangle$ the average over particles). Note that the most probable value of Θ and of Θ_x or Θ_y is zero but that $\langle \Theta \rangle$ and $\langle \Theta^2 \rangle$ are necessarily positive, whereas $\langle \Theta_x \rangle$ is zero. There are also the relations

$$\langle \Theta^2 \rangle = 2\langle \Theta_x{}^2 \rangle = 2\langle \Theta_y{}^2 \rangle \tag{2-7.8}$$

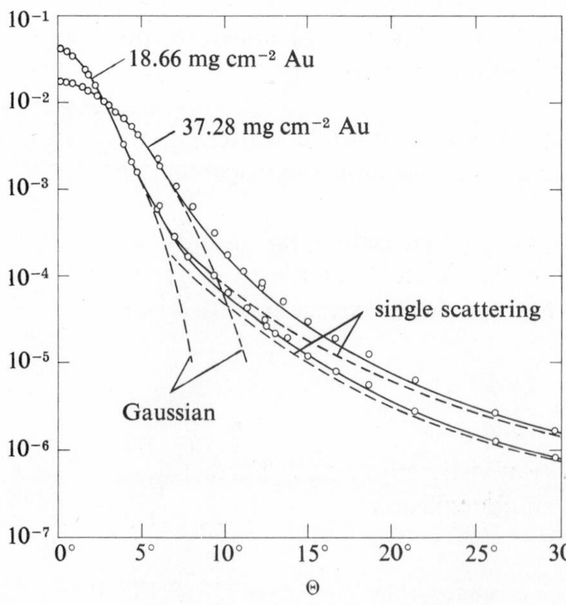

Figure 2-15 Angular distribution of electrons scattered from Au at 15.7 MeV. Solid lines indicate the distribution expected from the Molière theory for small and large-angle multiple scattering, with an extrapolation in the transition region; dashed lines, the distributions according to the gaussian and single-scattering theories. The ordinate scale gives the logarithm of the fraction of the beam scattered within 9.696 $\times 10^{-3}$ sr. [R. D. Birkhoff in (Fl E).]

The study of the distribution of Θ_x for many particles passing the foil gives a distribution which for small Θ_x is approximately gaussian. This approximation will not suffice for the wings of the distribution. Here a very few large deflections are much more likely to cause large deviations than an accumulation of many small deflections. Confining ourselves to the gaussian region, we shall assume that the probability of finding a deviation between Θ_x and $\Theta_x + d\Theta_x$ is

$$P(\Theta_x)\, d\Theta_x = \frac{e^{-\Theta_x^2/\langle\Theta^2\rangle}}{(\pi\langle\Theta^2\rangle)^{1/2}}\, d\Theta_x \tag{2-7.9}$$

To evaluate $\langle\Theta^2\rangle$, start from Eq. (2-7.7) and replace $\overline{\theta_i^2}$ by the value obtained from squaring Eq. (2-7.2), taking into account Eq. (2-7.1). By integrating over the range of permissible values of the impact parameter b, we obtain

$$\langle\Theta^2\rangle = 2\pi Nx \int_{b_{\min}}^{b_{\max}} \left(\frac{2zZe^2}{bvp}\right)^2 b\, db \tag{2-7.10}$$

where N is the number of nuclei per cubic centimeter and x the thickness of the absorber. It is implicitly assumed that the thickness x is practically equal to the path length of the particle in the absorber. Because of the screening of the nucleus by the atomic electrons, the effective Z depends on b, but we shall take Z out of the integral and shall take into account the screening effect by a proper choice of $b_{\max}$. Then, neglecting the change in v and p, in passing through the foil we have

$$\langle\Theta^2\rangle = \frac{8\pi NxZ^2z^2e^4}{v^2p^2} \log \frac{b_{\max}}{b_{\min}} \tag{2-7.11}$$

As pointed out previously, the effective charge in this formula is a function of b. At $b_{\max}$ the charge should be completely screened. In a crude way this can be approximated by choosing

$$b_{\max} = \frac{a_0}{Z^{1/3}} \tag{2-7.12}$$

where a_0 is the Bohr radius. This value may be justified by the Fermi–Thomas statistical model of the atom. On the other hand, we require that $b_{\min}$ give a deflection angle (in a single collision) small compared with 1 rad. This gives

$$b_{\min} = \frac{2zZe^2}{vp} \tag{2-7.13}$$

Other considerations may govern the choice of $b_{\min}$, such as the nuclear radius or the de Broglie wavelength of the particle. The result is not very sensitive to the choice of $b_{\min}$ and $b_{\max}$, which appear only logarithmically in Eq. (2-7.11). ●

As a very crude approximation of Eq. (2-7.11) pv is, passing from the nonrelativistic to the extreme-relativistic case, always between twice the kinetic energy and the kinetic energy of the particle. Neglecting all other functions of the velocity in Eq. (2-7.11), we can write, remembering Eq. (2-7.7),

$$\langle \Theta^2 \rangle \sim \frac{Z^2}{(KE)^2} \tag{2-7.14}$$

and as a numerical example for electrons

$$\begin{aligned} &\frac{6 \times 10^8 x}{[E(\text{keV})]^2} \qquad x = \text{cm of lead} \\ &\frac{7000x}{[E(\text{keV})]^2} \qquad x = \text{cm of air} \end{aligned} \tag{2-7.15}$$

Another formula for $\langle \Theta^2 \rangle$ that is practically useful is due to Rossi and Greisen. They measured the thickness t' in radiation lengths (see Sec. 2-11) and found

$$\langle \Theta^2 \rangle = z^2 \left(\frac{E_s}{pv} \right)^2 t' \tag{2-7.16}$$

where $E_s = (4\pi \times 137)^{1/2} \times mc^2 = 21.2$ MeV. See also Fig. 2-16.

A very important and elegant application of multiple scattering is its use in measuring the pv of a particle traversing a photographic emulsion. Indicating by α the average projected angle of deflection in degrees for a track length t in microns, the approximate formula is

$$\langle \alpha \rangle = \frac{kzt^{1/2}}{pv} \tag{2-7.17}$$

where $k = 26.0 \text{ MeV} \times \text{degree}/(100\mu)^{1/2}$ for singly charged particles.

2-8 Straggling

The energy loss calculated in Sec. 2-3 is an average value. For each particle the actual value fluctuates around the average value, with two consequences. For a given path length the energy loss and ionization fluctuate. For a given energy loss the path length fluctuates. The latter phenomenon is called *straggling*.

● Assume that in crossing a thickness x the average energy loss is E_0 and that in a specific case the energy loss is E. We want to calculate $\langle (E - E_0)^2 \rangle$. Remembering that $\langle E \rangle = E_0$ by definition and developing the square, we have immediately

$$\langle (E - E_0)^2 \rangle = \langle E^2 \rangle - \langle 2E_0 E \rangle + \langle E_0{}^2 \rangle = \langle E^2 \rangle - E_0{}^2 \tag{2-8.1}$$

Now suppose that many particles, all of the same initial energy, are sent through the absorber. In crossing the thickness x there will be collisions for which the energy loss is E_r. Their number is ν_r for a specific particle; averaged over all the particles it is $\langle \nu_r \rangle$. The numbers ν_r and $\langle \nu_r \rangle$ are related by (see Chap. 5)

$$\langle (\nu_r - \langle \nu_r \rangle)^2 \rangle = \langle \nu_r \rangle \tag{2-8.2}$$

which is valid if the numbers ν_r, found in many trials, are statistically independent. Considering a large number P of particles, we then have

$$\langle E^2 \rangle - E_0{}^2 = \frac{1}{P} \sum_{i=1}^{P} \sum_{r} (\nu_r{}^{(i)} E_r - \langle \nu_r \rangle E_r)^2 = \sum_r \langle \nu_r \rangle E_r{}^2 \tag{2-8.3}$$

Now

$$\langle \nu_r \rangle = N \int \sigma_r \, dx \tag{2-8.4}$$

where σ_r is the differential cross section for energy loss E_r and N is the number of atoms per cubic centimeter in the absorber. Replacing ν_r in Eq. (2-8.3) gives

$$\langle E^2 \rangle - E_0{}^2 = N \sum_r \int \sigma_r E_r{}^2 \, dx \tag{2-8.5}$$

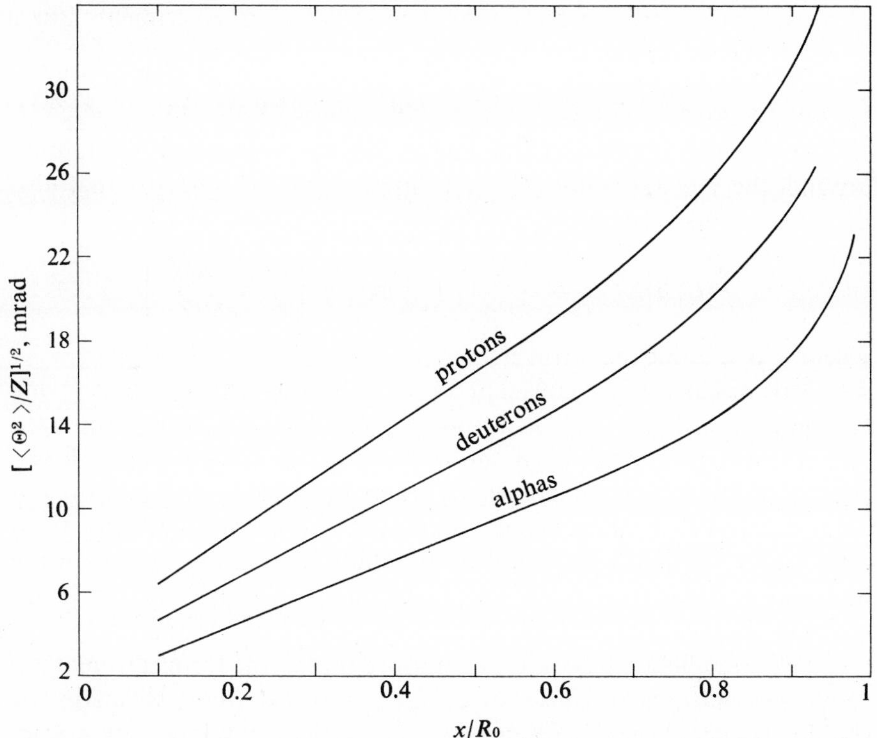

Figure 2-16 Multiple-scattering angle (unprojected) vs. fraction of range traversed by protons, deuterons, and alpha particles. [Milburn and Schecter, UCRL 2234 (rev. ed.).]

Using the results of Sec. 2-3, we can evaluate the sum over r by observing that

$$-\frac{dE}{dx} = N \sum_r \sigma_r E_r = \frac{4\pi z^2 e^4}{mv^2} NZ \int \frac{db}{b} \tag{2-8.6}$$

Now E_r and b are related by

$$E_r = \frac{2z^2 e^4}{mv^2 b^2} \tag{2-8.7}$$

which on logarithmic differentiation gives

$$\frac{dE_r}{E_r} = -\frac{2\,db}{b} \tag{2-8.8}$$

Using Eq. (2-8.7), we have approximately

$$N \sum_r \sigma_r E_r^2 = \frac{2\pi z^2 e^4 NZ}{mv^2} \int_{E_{min}}^{E_{max}} dE = \frac{2\pi z^2 e^4 NZ}{mv^2}(E_{max} - E_{min}) \tag{2-8.9}$$

In this formula we can take $E_{max} = 2mv^2$, which is the classical limit for heavy particles and for E_{min} zero. We thus obtain from Eqs. (2-8.9) and (2-8.5)

$$\frac{d}{dx}(\langle E^2 \rangle - E_0^2) = 4\pi z^2 e^4 NZ \tag{2-8.10}$$

This formula was given by Bohr in 1915. Although only approximate, it gives results in reasonable agreement with experiment. For a finite thickness Δx Eq. (2-8.10) gives

$$\langle E^2 \rangle - E_0^2 = \langle (E - E_0)^2 \rangle = 4\pi z^2 e^4 NZ\,\Delta x \tag{2-8.11}$$

If it is assumed that the actual energy loss has a gaussian distribution around the average value E_0, it follows from Eq. (2-8.10) that this distribution takes the form

$$P(E)\,dE = \frac{dE}{(8\pi^2 z^2 e^2 NZx)^{1/2}} \exp - \left[\frac{(E - E_0)^2}{8\pi z^2 e^4 NZx}\right] \tag{2-8.12}$$

where x is the thickness traversed.

This discussion has considered only collisions with electrons giving an energy transfer very small compared with the total energy and even with the energy straggling of the heavy particle. Larger energy losses such as occur in nuclear collisions are in most cases rare and do not contribute much to the average loss, but they influence the fluctuations appreciably, giving to the gaussian distribution a tail on the side of the high energy losses (Fig. 2-17). This fact sometimes makes the distinction between average and most probable energy loss important.

The straggling effects are much more important for electrons than for heavy particles, because an electron may lose half its energy by simple elastic collision, whereas a heavy particle may lose only a fraction of its energy (of order m/M). Radiation losses add further to electron straggling. Thus electron straggling reaches values of the order of

0.20 of the total energy loss. Moreover, the most probable energy loss for an electron is much less than the average energy loss (Fig. 2-18). For example, for high-energy electrons ($E \gg mc^2$), Goldwasser, Mills, and Hanson (1953) have found the semiempirical formula for the most probable energy loss,

$$\Delta E_p = 2\pi Ne^4 \frac{Zx}{mc^2}\left(\log \frac{x}{a_0} - 0.37\right)$$

where x is the thickness of the material traversed and a_0 is the Bohr radius; $\hbar^2/me^2 = 0.53\ 10^{-8}$ cm. The average energy loss according to Eq. (2-4.2) is

$$\Delta E_{\text{av}} = 2\pi e^4 \frac{NZx}{mc^2}\left(\log \frac{E^3}{2mc^2I^2} + \frac{1}{8}\right)$$

(compare Fig. 2-18).

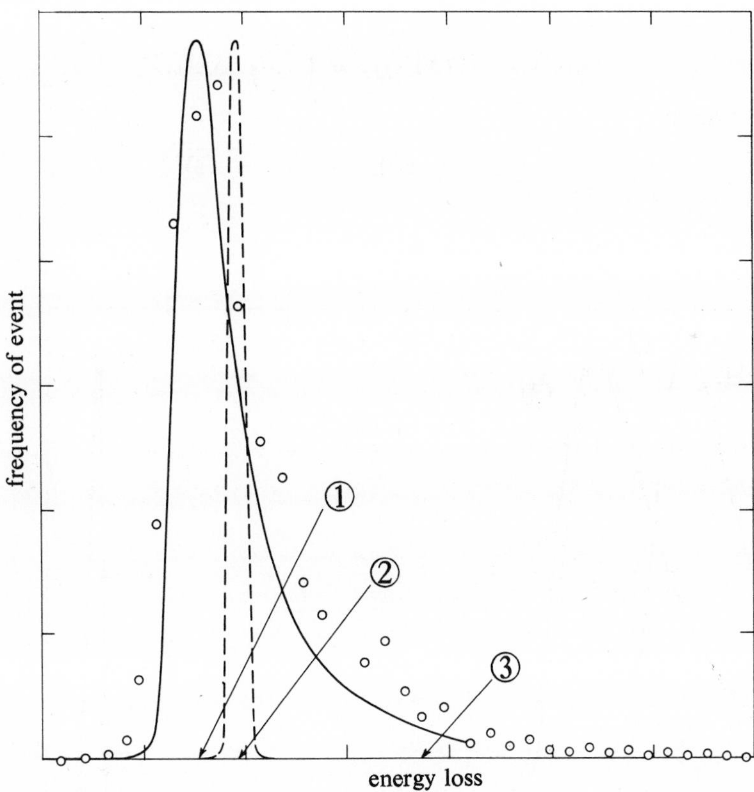

Figure 2-17 Frequency distribution of energy losses of 31.5 MeV protons in a proportional counter. Dashed curve, simple theory (Gaussian); solid curve, Landau–Symon theory; circles indicate experimental points. The energy scale of the experimental points has been adjusted arbitrarily to give the best average fit with the theoretical curve. (1) Most probable total energy loss; (2) average total energy loss; (3) maximum possible energy loss in a single collision. [Igo, Clark, and Eisberg, *Phys. Rev.*, **89**, 879 (1953).]

Turning now to the second problem, that of the fluctuations in range for a given initial energy, we also postulate here an approximate gaussian distribution of ranges around the average range R_0,

$$P(R)\,dR = \frac{1}{2s}\exp - \left[\frac{\pi}{4s^2}(R - R_0)^2\right] dR \tag{2-8.13}$$

The parameter s^2 has the value

$$s^2 = \frac{\pi}{2}\langle(R - R_0)^2\rangle \tag{2-8.14}$$

as can be seen by calculating $\langle(R-R_0)^2\rangle$ from Eq. (2-8.13). The quantity s, called straggling (Fig. 2-19), is the difference between the average range R_0 and the extrapolated range R_1 in the case of a gaussian distribution of ranges (see Fig. 2–1).

The fluctuation in range and in energy loss are related. For a small thickness dx and a small energy loss dE, the fluctuations in residual range and the fluctuations in energy loss are related by

$$(\Delta E^2)_{dx} = \left(\frac{dE}{dx}\right)^2 (\Delta x^2)_{dE} \tag{2-8.15}$$

where

$$(\Delta E^2)_{dx} = \langle(E - E_0)^2\rangle \tag{2-8.16}$$

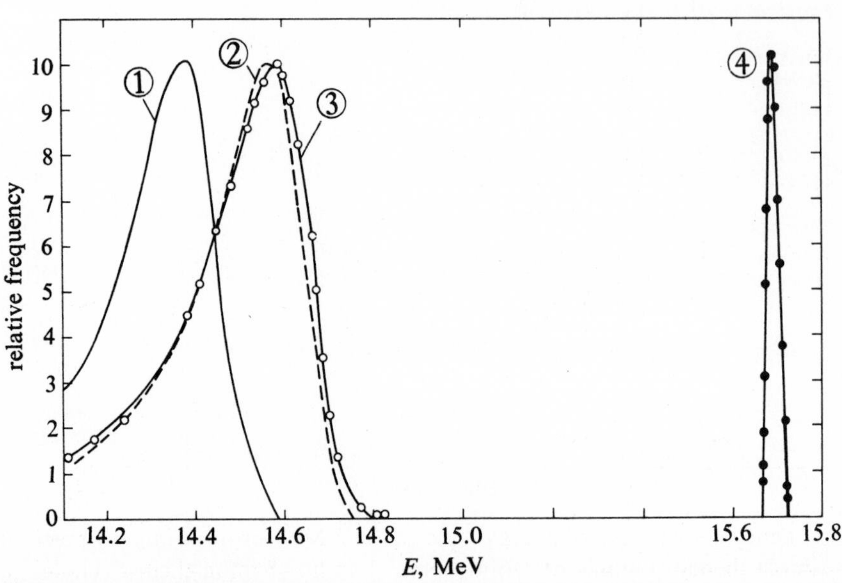

Figure 2-18 Energy distribution of an "unobstructed" electron beam and the calculated and experimental distributions of electrons that have passed through 0.86 g cm^{-2} of aluminum. (1) Landau theory without density correction; (2) Landau theory with Fermi density correction; (3) experiment; (4) incident beam. [Goldwasser, Mills, and Hanson, *Phys. Rev.*, **88,** 1137 (1952).]

is relative to the traversal of thickness dx and

$$(\Delta x^2)_{dE} = \langle (x - x_0)^2 \rangle \tag{2-8.17}$$

is the standard deviation squared for the residual range after an energy loss dE. For a finite thickness we have, summing the $(\Delta x^2)_{dE}$, and recalling Eq. (2-8.11), which shows that $(\Delta E^2)_{dx}$ is proportional to dx,

$$\begin{aligned} \langle (x - x_0)^2 \rangle &= \int_0^{x_0} \frac{(\Delta E^2)_{dx}}{dx} \left(\frac{dE}{dx}\right)^{-2} dx \\ &= \int_0^{E_0} \frac{(\Delta E^2)_{dx}}{dx} \left(\frac{dE}{dx}\right)^{-3} dE \\ &= 4\pi z^2 e^4 NZ \int_0^{E_0} \left(\frac{dE}{dx}\right)^{-3} dE \end{aligned} \tag{2-8.18}$$

This relation is also only approximate. For numerical values, see Fig. 2-18. The effects of straggling are much greater for electrons than for heavy ions, but they cannot be treated in a simple fashion. In the passage, through matter of very heavy ions, fission fragments, for example, the phenomena of scattering and straggling acquire great importance, because there are occasional single collisions of anomalous importance as discussed in Sec. 2-3. ●

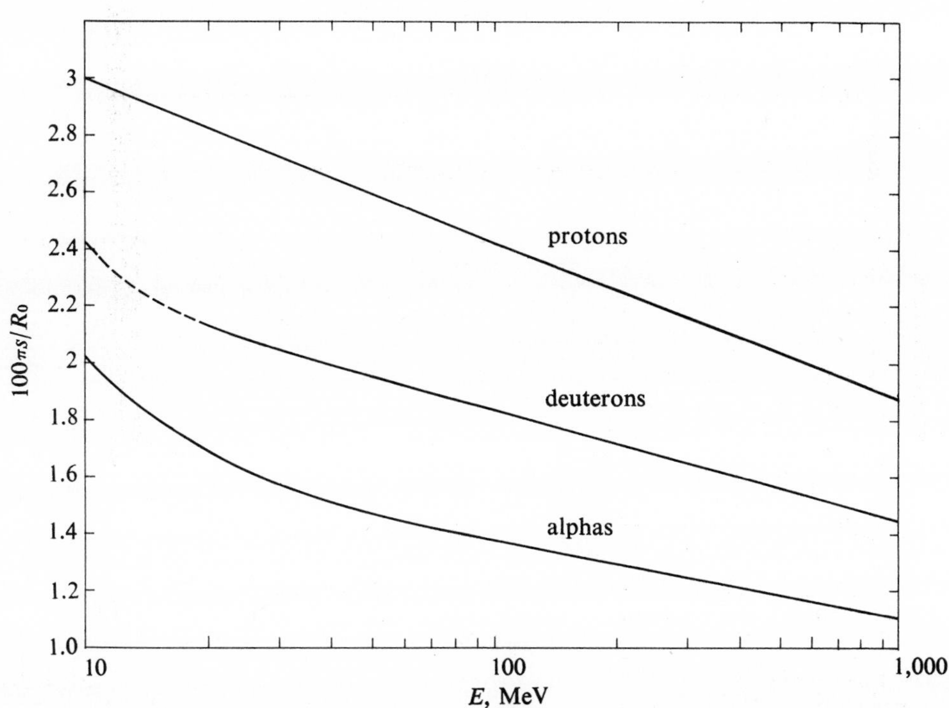

Figure 2-19 Range straggling as a function of energy. Abscissa logarithmic scale MeV. Ordinate $100\pi s/R_0 = 100\pi^{3/2}\, 2^{-1/2} \langle (R - R_0)^2 \rangle^{1/2} R_0^{-1}$. [Milburn and Schecter, UCRL 2234 (rev. ed.).]

2-9 Passage of Gamma Rays through Matter

The interaction of electromagnetic radiation with matter produces three main types of phenomena:

1. Photoelectric effect
2. Scattering on free electrons (Thomson, Rayleigh, and Compton)
3. Electron-positron pair production

Each of these processes is itself fairly complex, being accompanied by secondary effects such as the emission of Auger electrons and fluorescent radiation in (1), the emission of recoil electrons in (2), and the subsequent annihilation of positrons in (3). The three processes have different relative importance in different spectral regions, depending on the atomic number of the absorber, as shown in Fig. 2-20.

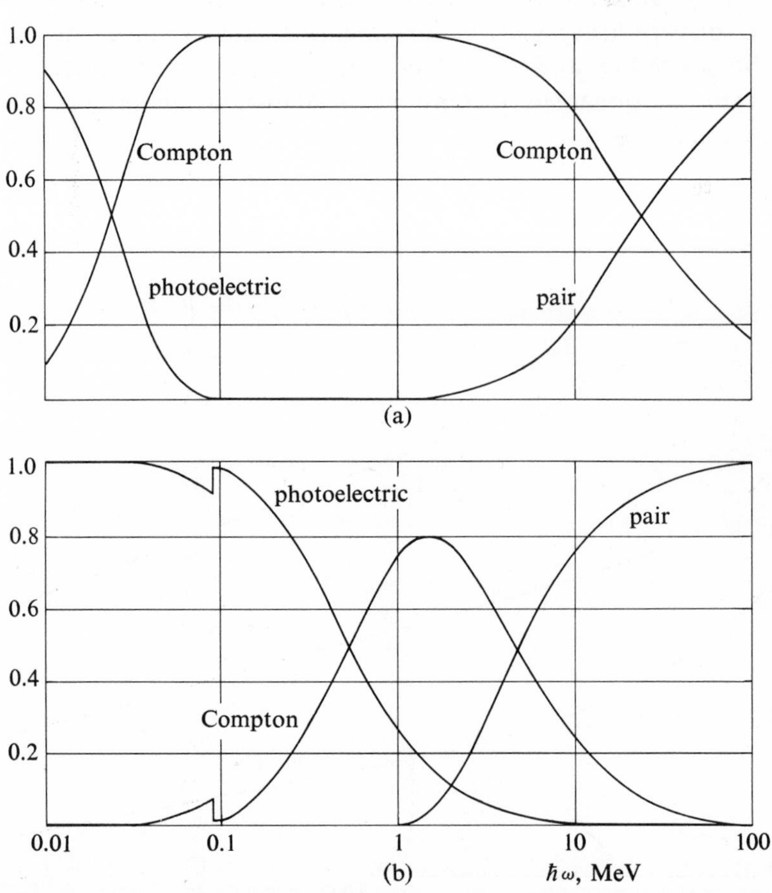

Figure 2-20 Relative contributions of various photon interactions to the total attenuation coefficient for (a) carbon and (b) lead. Abscissa logarithmic scale in MeV. Ordinate fraction of total attenuation due to phenomena indicated on curve. [White, private communication.] [(Fl E).]

In photoelectric absorption the energy of one photon is used to remove one of the electrons from an inner shell of an atom of the absorber element. Clearly this process can occur only if the incoming gamma ray has an energy higher than the binding energy of the electron to be removed. We have thus a series of jumps in the curve of the absorption coefficient, corresponding to the binding energy of the different orbits (see Fig. 2-21). These energies are given approximately by Moseley's law,

$$E = Rhc \frac{(Z - \sigma)^2}{n^2} \tag{2-9.1}$$

where $Rhc = 13.605$ eV, Z is the atomic number, σ the screening constant, and n the principal quantum number of the different electronic orbits. In the K series $n = 1$, in the L series $n = 2$, etc. The screening constant σ has the approximate value 3 for the K shell and 5 for the L shell, but for precise values one must consider the different screening for the S, P, and other orbits and the spin-orbit interaction. Tables of X-ray levels are found in (Se 59), Vol. III, p. 270. Figure 2-21 shows the mass-absorption coefficient for platinum, separating the contributions of different levels. Figure 2-22 shows the atomic-absorption coefficient of substances with different Z for X rays of 1 Å wavelength ($\hbar\omega = 12{,}398$ eV). There are several semiempirical expressions and extensive tables for the mass-absorption coefficient. The order of magnitude of the photoelectric atomic-absorption cross section is $r_0^2 Z^5/137^4$.

The jumps in absorption coefficients provide a method for bracketing X-ray wavelengths in small intervals by measuring the absorption

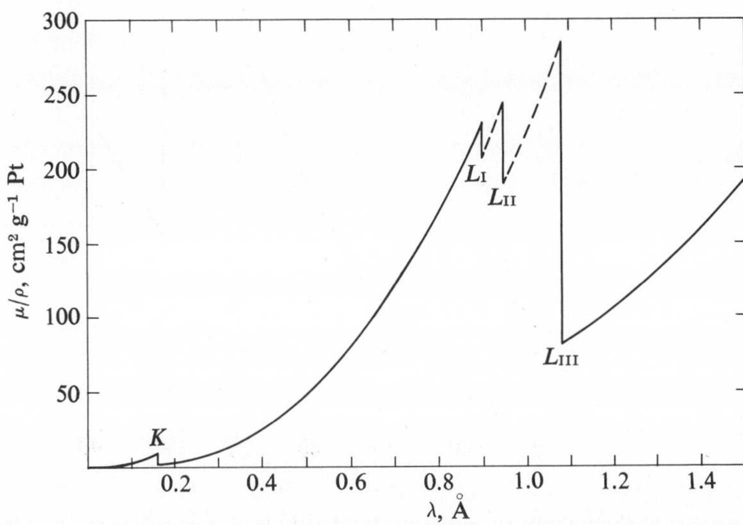

Figure 2-21 Mass-absorption coefficient of platinum as a function of the wavelength of the incident X rays. [W. Bothe, in Geiger Scheel, *Handbuch der Physik*, Springer, Berlin, 1933.]

in elements with adjacent values of Z, one having the K or L absorption edge above and one having it below the wavelength to be measured.

The vacancy created by the ejection of an electron from the inner shells is filled by outer electrons falling into it, and this process may be accompanied by the emission of *fluorescent radiation*. Alternatively it is possible that no fluorescent radiation is emitted but that an electron from an outer shell is ejected. For instance, a vacancy in a K shell may be filled by an L electron and another L electron emitted with energy $E_K - 2E_L$. Similarly, if the K vacancy is filled by an L electron and an M electron is emitted, the ejected electron will have the kinetic energy $E_K - E_L - E_M$. Here E_K and E_L are the binding energies of the K and L electrons. These and similar processes are called *Auger processes*, after their discoverer.

The emission of fluorescent radiation and the emission of Auger electrons are competing processes. The number of X rays emitted per vacancy in a given shell is called its *fluorescent yield*, indicated by β. One can analyze the phenomenon in more detail and distinguish the fluorescent yields for the different upper and lower levels. One has obviously

$$\beta_K = \beta_{KL} + \beta_{KM} \cdots \tag{2-9.2}$$

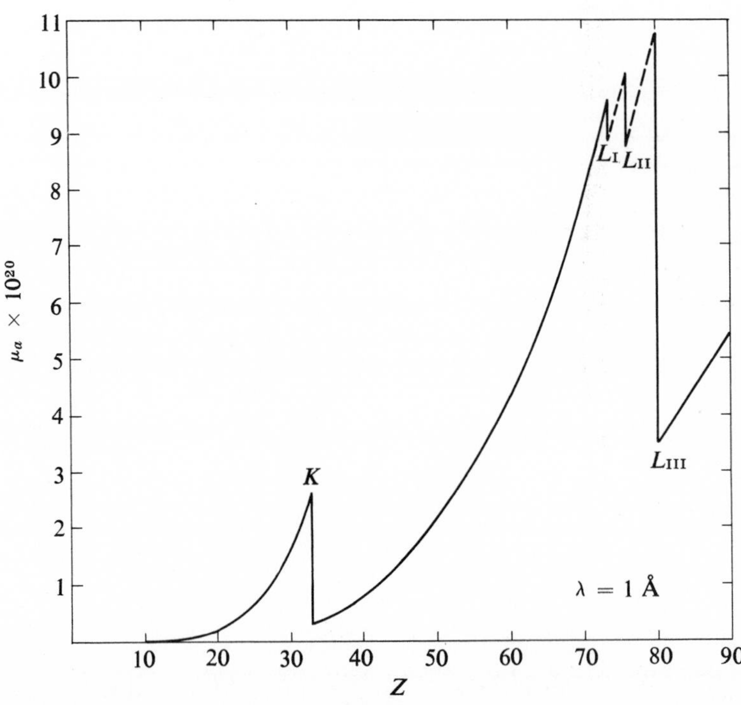

Figure 2-22 Atomic-absorption coefficient of substances of different Z for X rays having $\lambda = 1$ Å. The atomic-absorption coefficient $\mu_a = \mu A/\rho N_0$, where A is the atomic weight of the absorber and N_0 is Avogadro's number. [W. Bothe, in Geiger Scheel, *Handbuch der Physik*, Springer, Berlin, 1933.]

where β_{KL} indicates the partial fluorescent yields for filling the K level from the other levels. Figure 2-23 shows the fluorescent yield for the K level as a function of Z. Fluorescent yields are important in the study of orbital electron-capture processes.

Thomson and Compton Scatterings

In the photoelectric effect it is essential that the electron be bound. However, even a free electron in the variable electromagnetic field of a beam of X rays is set in oscillatory motion and radiates as an oscillator. The radiation appears as scattered X rays. A classical theory on this effect was given by J. J. Thomson as follows: Consider a plane sine wave traveling in the x direction, with the electric vector polarized in the z direction and having intensity I_0 (Fig. 2-24). From electromagnetic theory we have the following relations:

$$I_0 = \frac{\langle \mathbf{E}^2 \rangle}{4\pi} c = \frac{\langle \mathbf{H}^2 \rangle}{4\pi} c \tag{2-9.3}$$

where **E** and **H** are the instantaneous amplitudes of the electric and magnetic fields. Now an electron in this field will be subject to the force

$$e\mathbf{E} = e\mathbf{E}_0 \sin \omega t \tag{2-9.4}$$

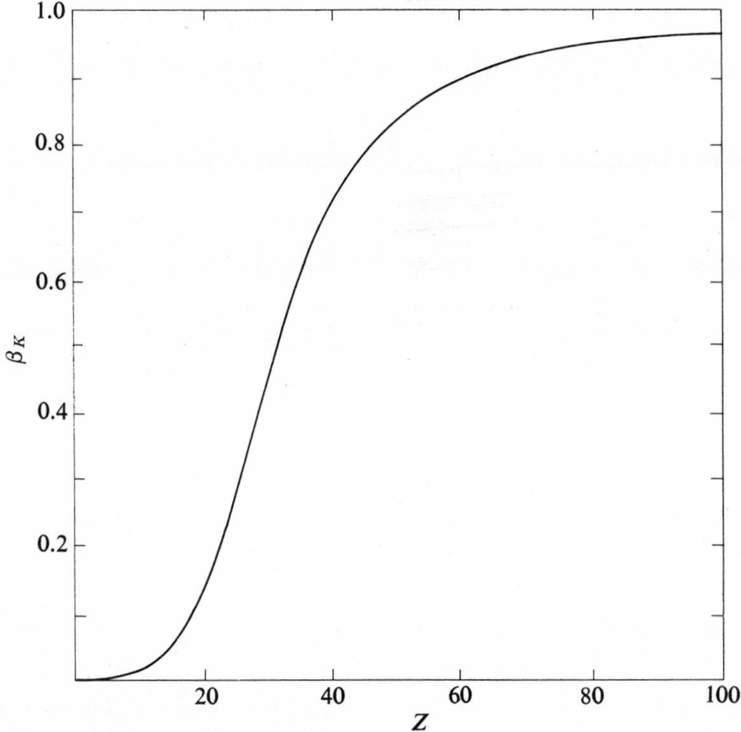

Figure 2-23 Fluorescent yield for K level as a function of Z.

where ω is the frequency of the wave, and it acquires the acceleration

$$\mathbf{a} = \frac{e\mathbf{E}_0}{m} \sin \omega t \tag{2-9.5}$$

Electromagnetic theory shows that a charge e subject to an acceleration **a** radiates energy at the average rate

$$\langle W \rangle = \frac{2}{3} \frac{e^2}{c^3} \langle a^2 \rangle \tag{2-9.6}$$

and in our case the average power radiated, if we recall that $\langle \sin^2 \omega t \rangle = \frac{1}{2}$ is

$$\langle W \rangle = \frac{1}{2} \frac{2}{3} \frac{e^4}{c^3} \frac{E_0^2}{m^2} = \frac{8\pi}{3} \left(\frac{e^2}{mc^2} \right)^2 I_0 \tag{2-9.7}$$

This power is subtracted from the primary beam, and we can equate it to the intensity falling on the scattering cross section of the electron σ_T. There results from Eq. (2-9.7)

$$\sigma_T = \frac{8\pi}{3} \left(\frac{e^2}{mc^2} \right)^2 = \frac{8\pi}{3} r_0^2 \tag{2-9.8}$$

where

$$r_0 = \frac{e^2}{mc^2} = 2.82 \times 10^{-13} \text{ cm} \tag{2-9.9}$$

and is called the *classical radius* of the electron.

The radiation emitted in the case of polarized incident radiation has the same polarization and angular distribution as that emitted by a dipole oriented in the direction of the incident field. The intensity must obviously be axially symmetric around the direction of the field (z axis); and if φ is the angle between **E** and the direction of observation **r**, we know from the classical theory of electricity that the intensity at distance r decreases as r^2 and has an angular distribution

$$I = \frac{I_0}{r^2} \left(\frac{e^2}{mc^2} \right)^2 \sin^2 \varphi \tag{2-9.10}$$

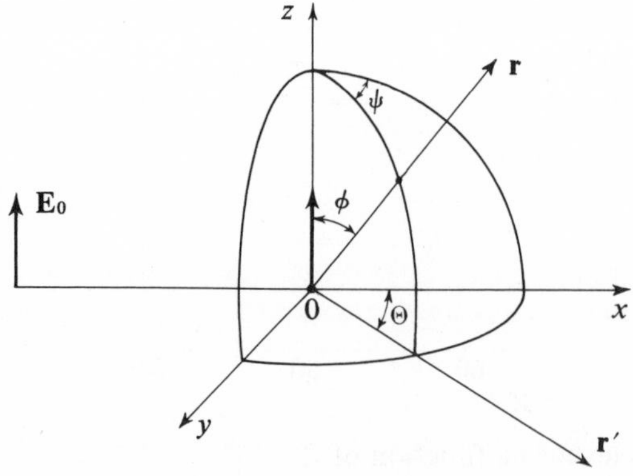

Figure 2-24 Thomson scattering of an electromagnetic wave. Notations.

The scattered rays are polarized with the electric vector in the rz plane. If the primary light is unpolarized, the intensity of scattered light must be axially symmetric around the direction of propagation x. The intensity can be calculated by superimposing incoherently the effects of primary light polarized in the z and y directions each of intensity $I_0/2$. Because of axial symmetry around x, let us consider only the xy plane and in it the direction $\mathbf{r}'$ making an angle Θ with x. The beam polarized in the z direction gives an intensity

$$I_z = \frac{I_0}{2r^2} r_0^2 \tag{2-9.11}$$

because for this beam $\varphi = 90°$. The beam polarized in the y direction gives an intensity

$$I_y = \frac{I_0}{2r^2} r_0^2 \cos^2 \Theta \tag{2-9.12}$$

because the angle between E_y and $\mathbf{r}'$ is $(\pi/2) - \Theta$. The sum of the intensities is thus

$$I = \frac{I_0}{2r^2} r_0^2 (1 + \cos^2 \Theta) \tag{2-9.13}$$

The polarization of this radiation is

$$\frac{I_z - I_y}{I_z + I_y} = \frac{1 - \cos^2 \Theta}{1 + \cos^2 \Theta} \tag{2-9.14}$$

It will be noted that Eq. (2-9.13) for angular dependence does not contain the frequency of the radiation.

Thomson's theory gives an atomic-scattering cross section proportional to Z; in fact, even before the present atomic model was developed, the atomic number of the lightest elements was measured by Barkla and others while observing the scattering of X rays. However, if the momentum transferred by the photon is small compared with the momentum of the electron in the atom, one must sum the amplitudes of the X rays scattered by all electrons in an atom. This scattering is called *Rayleigh scattering*, and the corresponding atomic-scattering cross section is of the order

$$r_0^2 Z^2$$

Thomson's scattering does not take into account the quantum aspects of light and for energies comparable with mc^2 or larger gives results in disagreement with experiment. For one thing, it has been found experimentally that the frequency of the scattered light differs from that of the incident light. That this must be the case follows from conservation of energy and momentum if we interpret scattering as the elastic collision of light quanta with electrons. Assume that the quanta have an energy $\hbar\omega$ and a momentum $\hbar\omega/c$ directed in the direction of propagation of light. Conservation of energy and of momentum give the following relation between the wavelength of the incident and scattered light (λ and λ', respectively) and the direction of scattering:

$$\lambda' - \lambda = \frac{2\pi\hbar}{mc}(1 - \cos\Theta) \qquad \frac{2\pi\hbar}{mc} = 24.262 \times 10^{-11}\ \text{cm} = \lambda_c \tag{2-9.15}$$

The change of wavelength or of frequency on scattering is the Compton effect, named for its discoverer, A. H. Compton (1922).

The recoil electron goes in a direction Φ such that

$$\tan\Phi = \frac{\cot(\Theta/2)}{1 + \alpha} \qquad \alpha = \frac{\hbar\omega}{mc^2} = \frac{\lambda_c}{\lambda} \tag{2-9.16}$$

and its kinetic energy is

$$E_{\text{kin}} = \hbar\omega \frac{2\alpha\cos^2\Phi}{(1 + \alpha^2)^2 - \alpha^2\cos^2\Phi} \tag{2-9.17}$$

as shown in Fig. 2-25. The problems of intensity and polarization cannot be treated by elementary means. We must confine ourselves to stating the result for the Compton scattering cross section for an electron (formula of Klein and Nishina).

$$\sigma_c = 2\pi r_0^2 \left\{\frac{1 + \alpha}{\alpha^2}\left[\frac{2(1 + \alpha)}{1 + 2\alpha} - \frac{1}{\alpha}\log(1 + 2\alpha)\right] + \frac{1}{2\alpha}\log(1 + 2\alpha) - \frac{1 + 3\alpha}{(1 + 2\alpha)^2}\right\} \tag{2-9.18}$$

Figures 2-26 and 2-27 show a diagram of the angular distribution of Compton-scattered X rays for different values of α.

Pair Production

The last mechanism of absorption to be considered is the transformation of a gamma ray into an electron–positron pair, also called *materialization*. The principle of conservation of energy and momentum prevents this from occurring in free space. There must be a nucleus or an electron in order to balance energy and momentum in the transformation. The threshold energy in the c.m. system for the materialization process is $2mc^2 = 1.022$ MeV.

This energy is very close to the threshold in the laboratory system

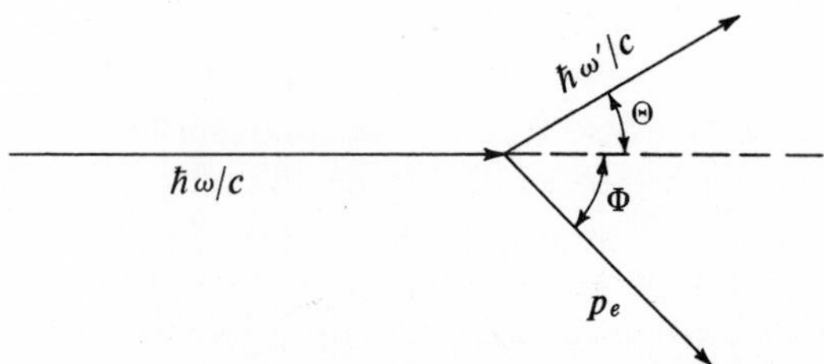

Figure 2-25 Compton scattering. Notations and diagram showing the conservation of energy and momentum.

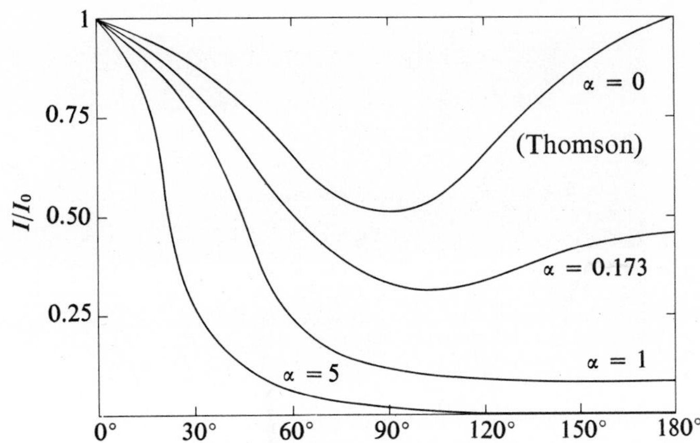

Figure 2-26 Angular distribution of Compton-scattered X rays as a function of energy ($\alpha = \hbar\omega/mc^2$).

for materialization near a nucleus, which by its recoil ensures the conservation of momentum. When the recoil is absorbed by an electron, the threshold required by the conservation of energy and momentum in the laboratory system is $4mc^2$, and there are two electrons and a positron acquiring appreciable momentum. In a cloud or bubble chamber they form a *triplet* (Fig. 2-28). Pairs can also be produced by heavy-particle collision, by electron-electron collisions, in mesonic decay, and by internal conversion in some gamma transitions. Some of these phenomena will be described later.

The atomic-pair-production cross section is of the order $r_0{}^2Z^2/137$, for relativistic energies.

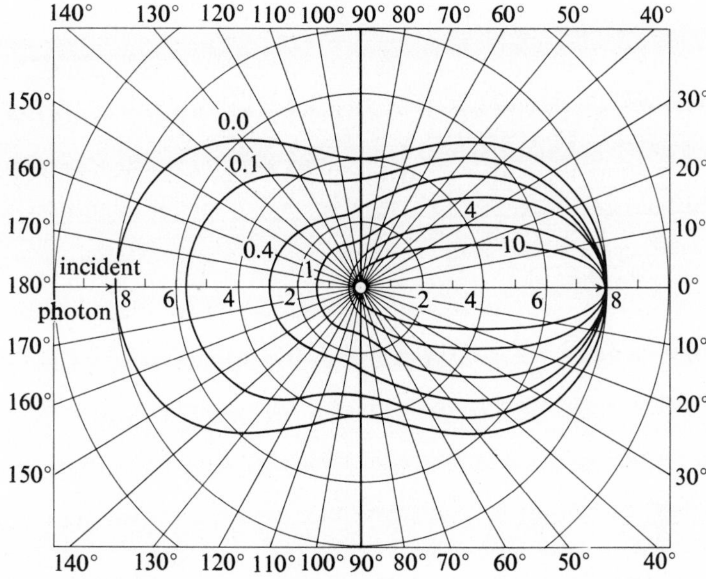

Figure 2-27 Polar diagram of the differential cross section per electron for Compton scattering. Curves labeled according to $\alpha = \hbar\omega/mc^2$ of incident photon. Unit of $d\sigma/d\omega = 10^{-26}\ \mathrm{cm}^{-2}\ \mathrm{sr}^{-1}$.

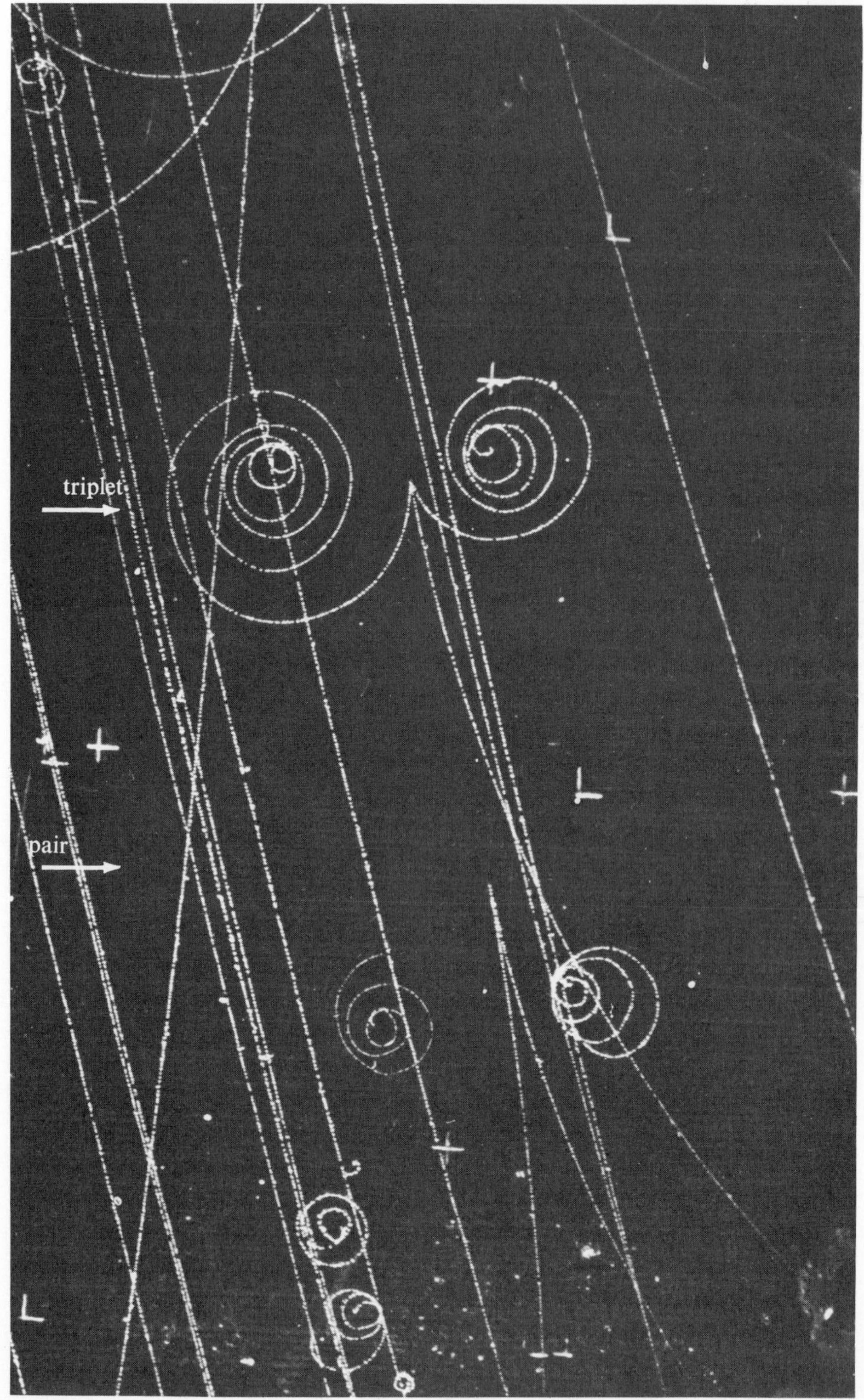

Figure 2-28 Formation of an electron-positron pair in the field of an electron (triplet). Formation of a pair in the field of a proton (pair). (Hydrogen bubble chamber.) [Courtesy Lawrence Radiation Laboratory.]

Figure 2-29 summarizes the main results on the absorption of gamma rays and gives the absorption coefficient as a function of energy and Z in typical examples.

2-10 Radiation Loss by Fast Electrons

As mentioned before, the main cause of energy loss for a very fast electron ($E \gg mc^2$) traversing matter is the electromagnetic radiation it emits because of the accelerations to which it is subject (see Fig. 2-10). At low energy ($E \ll mc^2$) this radiation loss is unimportant compared with the ionization loss, but at high energy it becomes preponderant. The energy loss by radiation is proportional to Z^2 of the material and increases linearly with the electron's energy. The energy loss from ionization and excitation is proportional to Z and increases only logarithmically with energy. Thus, radiation loss predominates at the higher energies. More quantitatively, the approximate ratio of the two losses is (E in MeV)

$$\frac{(dE/dx)_{\mathrm{rad}}}{(dE/dx)_{\mathrm{ion}}} = \frac{EZ}{1{,}600\, mc^2} = \frac{EZ}{800} \qquad \textbf{(2-10.1)}$$

It is clear that there is an energy E_c for which the two energy losses are equal (see Table 2-2).

The radiated energy appears as X rays and forms the bremsstrahlung, or continuous X-ray spectrum observed in ordinary X-ray tubes. At high energy the phenomena accompanying the bremsstrahlung are quite complicated, and they reach colossal proportions in the formation of showers containing millions of particles in the case of high-energy cosmic rays. For the theory of bremsstrahlung, we shall confine our-

Table 2-2 Radiation Length X_0 and Critical Energy E_c for Various Substances

Substance	Z	At. wt.	X_0, g cm^{-2}	E_c, MeV
H	1	1	58	340
He	2	4	85	220
C	6	12	42.5	103
N	7	14	38	87
O	8	16	34.2	77
Al	13	27	23.9	47
A	18	39.9	19.4	34.5
Fe	26	55.8	13.8	24
Cu	29	63.6	12.8	21.5
Pb	82	207.2	5.8	6.9
Air			36.5	83
Water			35.9	93

selves to a semiquantitative treatment of a special case, following Fermi. We shall also, however, give the results for cases where Fermi's hypotheses do not apply.

The main idea of Fermi's treatment (Fermi, 1924; Weizsäcker, 1937; Williams, 1933) is to consider the electromagnetic field produced by a charge in motion, to Fourier-analyze it, and to calculate the effect on other charges of the single Fourier components. This is simple if the cross section for the electromagnetic interaction of X rays on the charges is known.

To take a specific example, we shall consider an electron of velocity $v \simeq c$ passing by a nucleus of charge Ze. However, we shall first use a system of reference in which the electron is at rest, the nucleus passing by it, and shall calculate the effect of the nuclear electromagnetic field by performing a Fourier analysis and treating the single components according to Thomson's formula (Sec. 2-9). The result will be the energy radiated by the electron in its rest system, which ultimately we shall transform back to the laboratory system.

In the rest system of the electron the nucleus moves with velocity $-v$. The electric field of the nucleus, **E**, is contracted in the direction of motion, and a magnetic field **H** appears perpendicular to **E** and to the direction of motion. Its magnitude is almost equal to **E**. These two fields

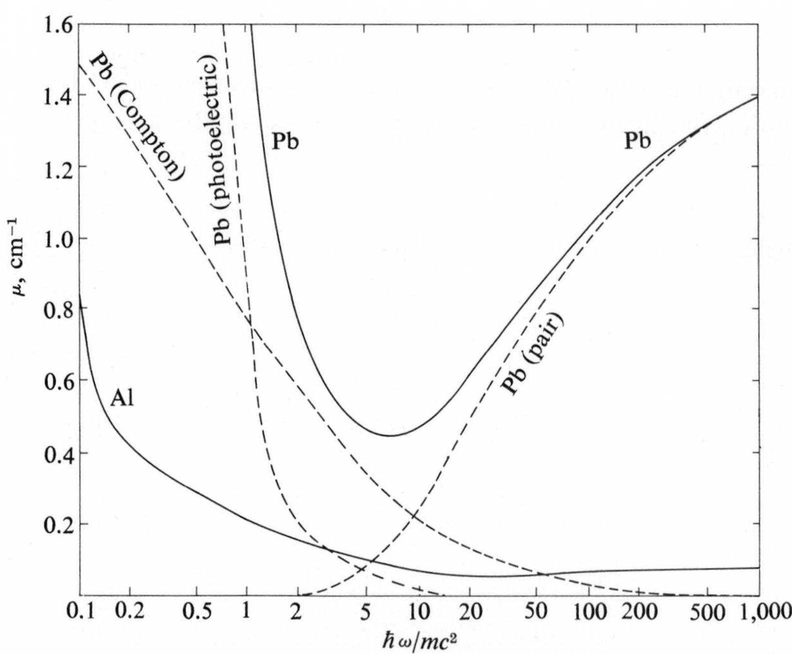

Figure 2-29 Total absorption coefficients of X rays by lead and aluminum as a function of energy (solid lines). Photoelectric absorption of aluminum is negligible at the energies here considered. Dashed lines show separately the contributions of photoelectric effect, Compton scattering, and pair production for Pb. Abscissa, logarithmic energy scale; $\hbar\omega/mc^2 = 1$ corresponds to 511 keV.

are indistinguishable from a plane electromagnetic wave when seen from the electron. This wave undergoes scattering on the electron, and the scattered quanta, when viewed from the laboratory system, appears as the bremsstrahlung.

● The calculation consists of the following steps:

1. Transform by Lorentz transformation the electric field of the nucleus to the rest system of the electron.

2. Fourier-analyze the resulting electromagnetic pulse in the electron rest system.

3. Find the density of photons corresponding to the pulse of electromagnetic radiation.

4. Calculate the probability of scattering of these photons, using the Thomson scattering cross section σ_T.

5. Transform back to the laboratory frame of reference.

For the sake of simplicity we shall omit most numerical factors, inserting the correct one in the end result.

Asterisks, indicate quantities in the laboratory frame; symbols without asterisks, quantities in the electron frame. For the electron $v^*/c = \beta^* \simeq 1$, and its energy W^* is

$$W^* = \frac{mc^2}{(1 - \beta^{*2})^{1/2}} = \gamma mc^2 \gg mc^2 \tag{2-10.2}$$

1. *The electric field* produced by the nucleus at the electron in the laboratory frame is

$$E_\perp^* = \frac{Ze}{b^2} \tag{2-10.3}$$

where b is the impact parameter. The symbol $\perp$ or $\parallel$ means perpendicular or parallel to $\mathbf{v}$. Lorentz transformation of $\mathbf{E}$ gives, in the electron frame,

$$E_\perp = E_\perp^* \gamma, \qquad H_\varphi = E_\perp^* \beta\gamma \tag{2-10.4}$$

where H_φ means the magnetic field in the direction perpendicular to $\mathbf{v}$ and $\mathbf{E}$. If

$$\beta \simeq 1, \gamma \gg 1 \text{ and } E_\perp = H_\varphi \gamma \tag{2-10.5}$$

as in a plane electromagnetic wave.

2. *In the electron frame* the region of strong electromagnetic field extends for a distance of order of magnitude b/γ on either side of the electron in the direction of $\mathbf{v}$. The exact expressions are

$$\mathbf{E} = eZ \frac{\gamma(\mathbf{b} + \mathbf{v}t)}{(b^2 + \gamma^2 v^2 t^2)^{3/2}} \tag{2-10.6}$$

$$\mathbf{H} = \frac{eZ}{c} \frac{\gamma \mathbf{b} \times \mathbf{v}}{(b^2 + \gamma^2 v^2 t^2)^{3/2}} \tag{2-10.7}$$

and they can be Fourier-analyzed, leading to formulas containing Bessel functions (Fermi, 1924).

We shall simply approximate the time dependence of E and H by a gaussian curve of proper width, a procedure which will simplify the calculation without affecting its essential point (Fig. 2-31). We thus assume

$$E = H = \frac{\gamma Ze}{b^2} e^{-c^2\gamma^2 t^2/2b^2} \tag{2-10.8}$$

The Fourier transform of this expression is

$$E = H = \frac{Ze}{bc}\sqrt{\frac{2}{\pi}}\int_0^\infty e^{-b^2\omega^2/2\gamma^2 c^2}\cos\omega t\, d\omega \tag{2-10.9}$$

as can be seen, it being recalled that

$$\sqrt{\frac{2}{\pi}}\int_0^\infty e^{-x^2/2}\cos ux\, dx = e^{-u^2/2} \tag{2-10.10}$$

Hence the spectral analysis of the pulse gives again a gaussian of width $\gamma c/b$ (Fig. 2-31). The region occupied by the electromagnetic pulse has the shape of a disk, and we want to find the energy per unit area of the disk. This is a function of the distance b from the axis of the disk and is evaluated as follows: At distance b the fields have the value

$$E = H = \frac{Ze\gamma}{b^2} \tag{2-10.11}$$

the energy density is

$$\frac{E^2 + H^2}{8\pi} \simeq \frac{Z^2e^2\gamma^2}{b^4} \tag{2-10.12}$$

and the thickness of the disk is b/γ [Eqs. (2-10.6) and (2-10.7)]. Hence, the energy per square centimeter of disk surface is

$$\frac{Z^2e^2\gamma^2}{b^4}\frac{b}{\gamma} \simeq \frac{Z^2e^2\gamma}{b^3} \tag{2-10.13}$$

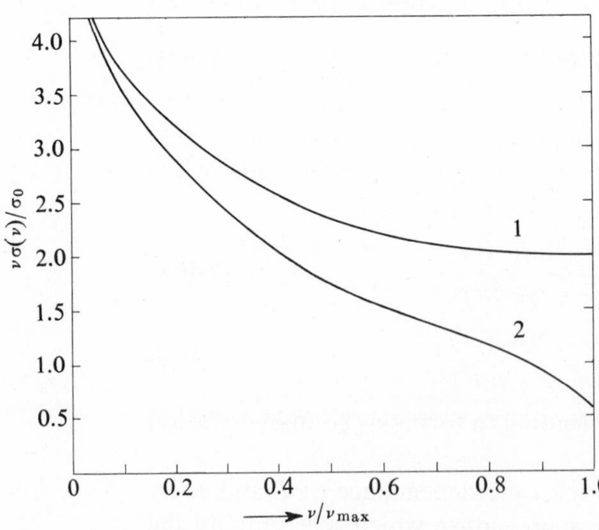

Figure 2-30 Integrated bremsstrahlung cross section vs. frequency. Curve 1 refers to an energy of about $27Z^2$ eV, curve 2 to an energy of $4{,}300Z^2$ eV. Frequency is in units of the upper frequency limit; $\sigma_0 = \frac{16}{3}Z^2\alpha^3 a_0^2\,(\mathrm{Ry}/E_0) = (Z^2\ \mathrm{Ry}/E_0) \times 5.8 \times 10^{-23}\ \mathrm{cm}^2$. [(Fl E).]

3. We approximate the gaussian equation of the spectral analysis by a rectangle of width $\gamma c/b$. This is justifiable, because the frequencies of interest are only those for which $\nu \ll mc^2/h$ in the laboratory system; these are contained within a relatively flat portion of the gaussian. This rectangular spectral distribution has as a consequence the relation

$$\frac{\Delta\nu^*}{\nu^*_{\max}} = \Delta\nu^* \frac{b}{\gamma c} \tag{2-10.14}$$

Now, if we consider the section of the discoidal electromagnetic disturbance at distance b, the energy per unit area is given by Eq. (2-10.13), which has to be distributed over the rectangular frequency spectrum having an upper limit $\gamma c/b$. The number of quanta with a frequency in the interval $\Delta\nu^*$ is thus

$$\begin{aligned} &\frac{Z^2e^2\gamma}{b^3}\frac{b}{\gamma c}\frac{\Delta\nu^*}{h\nu^*} \qquad \text{for } \nu^* < \frac{\gamma c}{b} \\ &0 \qquad \text{for } \nu^* > \frac{\gamma c}{b} \end{aligned} \tag{2-10.15}$$

4. The mean number of scattering processes for photons of frequency ν^* occurring at distance b is

$$\sigma_T \times (\text{surface density of photons of frequency } \nu^*)$$

$$= \frac{Z^2e^2}{b^2\hbar c}\frac{\Delta\nu^*}{\nu^*}\sigma_T \tag{2-10.16}$$

The total cross section per nucleus $\Sigma(\nu^*)\,\Delta\nu^*$ will be the integral of the preceding expression multiplied by $2\pi b\,db$,

$$\Sigma\Delta\nu^* = \frac{Z^2e^2}{\hbar c}\frac{\Delta\nu^*}{\nu^*}\sigma_T \int_{b_{\min}}^{b_{\max}} 2\pi\frac{db}{b} \tag{2-10.17}$$

and

$$\Sigma\Delta\nu^* = 2\pi\frac{Z^2e^2}{\hbar c}\sigma_T\frac{\Delta\nu^*}{\nu^*}\log\frac{b_{\max}}{b_{\min}} \tag{2-10.18}$$

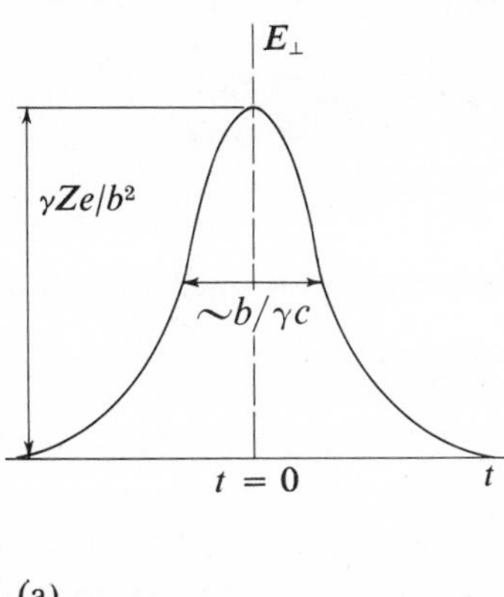

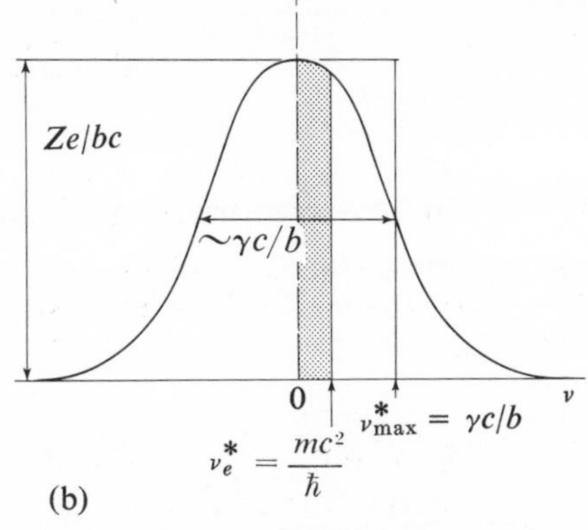

Figure 2-31 Electromagnetic pulse seen by an electron and its Fourier transform: (a) pulse, (b) spectral distribution.

We must now discuss the limits b_{max} and b_{min}. For b_{max} there are at least two limitations, the first being that the atomic electrons screen the nucleus. It is possible to estimate an atomic radius beyond which the electrostatic action of the nucleus is completely screened by the electrons by using the Thomas-Fermi statistical method for calculating the density of the electron cloud. One finds that

$$b'_{max} = \frac{a_0}{Z^{1/3}} \tag{2-10.19}$$

A second limitation arises from the fact that for a given ν^* the maximum impact parameter cannot exceed the limit

$$b''_{max} = \frac{c\gamma}{\nu^*} \tag{2-10.20}$$

since for $b > b_{max}$ the frequency ν^* is not present in the pulse; at high energy $b'_{max} < b''_{max}$, and hence b'_{max} is the governing parameter. One estimate of the lower limit b_{min} is the Compton wavelength of the electron h/mc.

Using the values of b'_{max} and b_{min} and inserting some numerical factors from more precise calculations, one obtains

$$\Sigma(\nu^*)\,\Delta\nu^* = Z^2\left(\frac{e^2}{\hbar c}\right)\frac{\Delta\nu^*}{\nu^*}\,\sigma_T \log\frac{183}{Z^{1/3}} = Z^2\left(\frac{e^2}{\hbar c}\right) r_0{}^2\,\frac{\Delta\nu^*}{\nu^*}\log\frac{183}{Z^{1/3}} \tag{2-10.21}$$

5. This must now be transformed to the laboratory system using the relation

$$\frac{\Delta\nu^*}{\nu^*} = \frac{\Delta\nu}{\nu} \tag{2-10.22}$$

which derives immediately from the relation between ν^* and ν. ●

Introducing this value in Eq. (2-10.21), we obtain, after taking into account neglected numerical factors,

$$\Sigma(\nu)\,\Delta\nu = \frac{4}{137}\,Z^2\,\frac{\Delta\nu}{\nu}\,r_0{}^2 \log\frac{183}{Z^{1/3}} \tag{2-10.23}$$

Before integrating to find the total energy loss, we shall examine the limits of validity of the result. First of all, an electron cannot radiate more energy than its kinetic energy; thus an upper limit is set on the frequencies in the bremsstrahlung spectrum,

$$h\nu_{max} = mc^2(\gamma - 1) \tag{2-10.24}$$

Also, the cross-section expression diverges at low frequencies, but the energy carried away does not diverge. The total energy loss to photons of frequency ν per path length dx is equal to (energy per photon) × (number of nuclei cm^{-3}) × $[\Sigma(\nu)\,d\nu]$ × dx. On integration of the frequency range, even on the assumption of a lower limit equal to zero, the total average energy loss is given by

$$-\left\langle\frac{dE}{dx}\right\rangle_{\text{rad}} = \int_0^{\nu_{\max}} h\nu N\ \Sigma(\nu)\, d\nu$$
$$= 4Z^2 \frac{N}{137} r_0^2 h\nu_{\max} \log \frac{183}{Z^{1/3}} \quad \textbf{(2-10.25)}$$

This expression is approximate and is valid for $E_0 \gg 137mc^2Z^{-1/3}$. The formulas valid under different hypotheses differ only in having included in the logarithm a function of energy.

Further, since an electron may lose an appreciable fraction of its energy to a single photon, the actual energy loss fluctuates widely from the average value. The energy distribution in the bremsstrahlung spectrum is shown in Fig. 2-30.

There are many detailed questions of great theoretical and practical importance concerning the bremsstrahlung. We shall mention only the polarization and angular distribution of the radiation. At low energy ($E \ll mc^2$) as in ordinary X-ray tubes, most of the X rays near the upper frequency limit are polarized with their electric vector parallel to the direction of motion of the electron, and the intensity has a maximum in the direction perpendicular to the direction of motion. At very high energy ($E \gg mc^2$) the average angle of emission of a quantum is

$$\theta = \frac{mc^2}{E} \quad \textbf{(2-10.26)}$$

independent of the energy of the emitted quantum. This distribution gives the characteristic narrow pencils of electromagnetic radiation beams observed in electron accelerators.

The electric vector of high-energy bremsstrahlung is prevalently normal to the plane of the incident electron and the X ray.

If the electron beam generating the bremsstrahlung is polarized, the polarization of the bremsstrahlung itself is affected. Notably, if the electron spin is in the direction of motion, the radiation tends to be circularly polarized with the angular momentum parallel to the spin of the electron.

Pair production is closely related to the bremsstrahlung. If we consider pair production as the absorption of a gamma quantum (in the presence of a nucleus) by an electron in a negative energy state, which is thereby excited to a positive energy state, and the bremsstrahlung as the transition of an ordinary electron from one positive energy state to another in the presence of a nucleus (accompanied by the emission of a gamma ray), it is clear that the processes are similar.

Calculation of the pair-production cross section gives for the case $h\nu \gg mc^2$

$$\sigma_{\text{pair}} = \frac{e^2}{\hbar c} Z^2 r_0^2 \left(\frac{28}{9} \log \frac{183}{Z^{1/3}} - \frac{2}{27}\right) \quad \textbf{(2-10.27)}$$

which is similar to Eq. (2-10.23).

The energy of the gamma ray is apportioned between the electron and positron as shown in Fig. 2-32, and both particles travel in approximately the same direction as the gamma ray for $E \gg mc^2$. The average angle between the direction of motion of the created electron and the gamma ray is

$$\theta = \frac{mc^2}{E} \tag{2-10.28}$$

in striking analogy to Eq. (2-10.26).

2-11 Radiation Length, Showers

Bremsstrahlung and pair production combine to produce the spectacular phenomenon of showers. Starting with a single high-energy electron or gamma quantum, a multiplicative process (see Fig. 2-33)

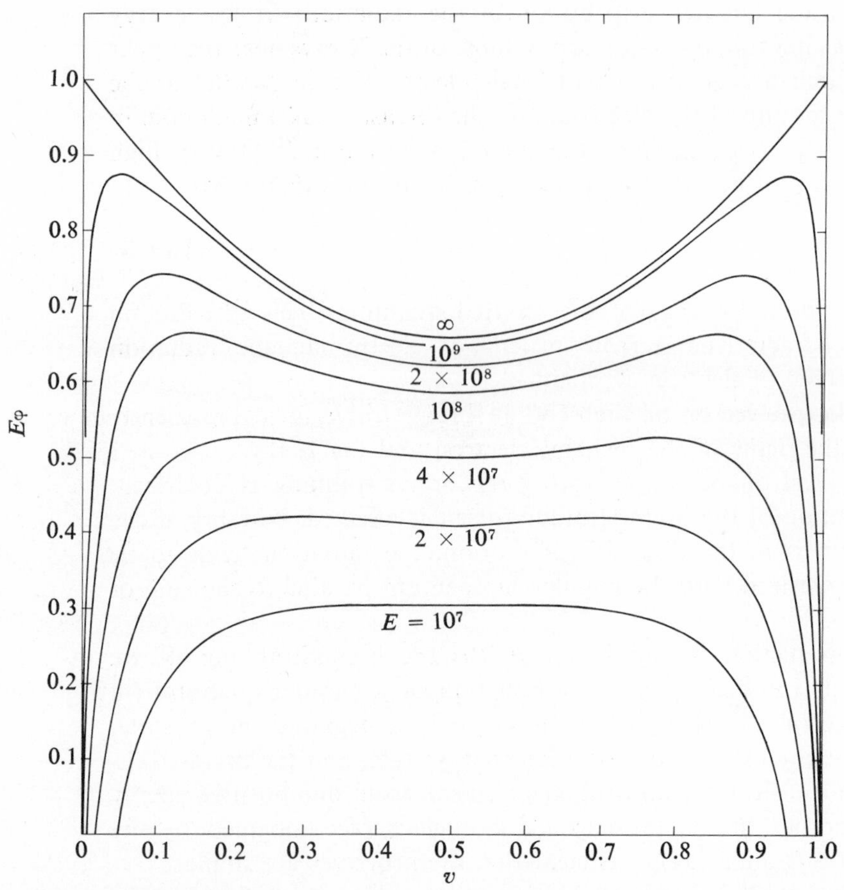

Figure 2-32 Division of energy between electron and positron in pair production. Differential probability of pair production per radiation length of lead for photons of various energies. Abscissa v = (total energy of one electron divided by energy of primary photon) = E'/E. Ordinate: $E \times$ (probability per radiation length of producing electron in a unit of energy interval at E). The curves are labeled according to E in eV. [Rossi and Greisen, *Rev. Mod. Phys.*, **13**, 259 (1941).]

produces a number of electrons and gamma rays and forms the *shower*. A precise mathematical theory of showers is very complicated, even when restricted to average behavior; furthermore the fluctuations from the average are usually large. Monte Carlo calculations of showers have been made and are very useful in practical cases. However, some basic concepts, such as radiation length, are of great importance in shower theory as well as in other phenomena. We shall now develop them very briefly, together with an extremely simplified shower model.

Equation (2-10.25) shows that, on the average, an electron loses its energy by radiation according to

$$-\frac{dE}{E} = \frac{dx}{X_0} \tag{2-11.1}$$

with

$$\frac{1}{X_0} = \frac{4Z^2N}{137} r_0^2 \log \frac{183}{Z^{1/3}}$$

Equation (2-11.1) gives on immediate integration,

$$\langle E \rangle = E_0 e^{-x/X_0} \tag{2-11.2}$$

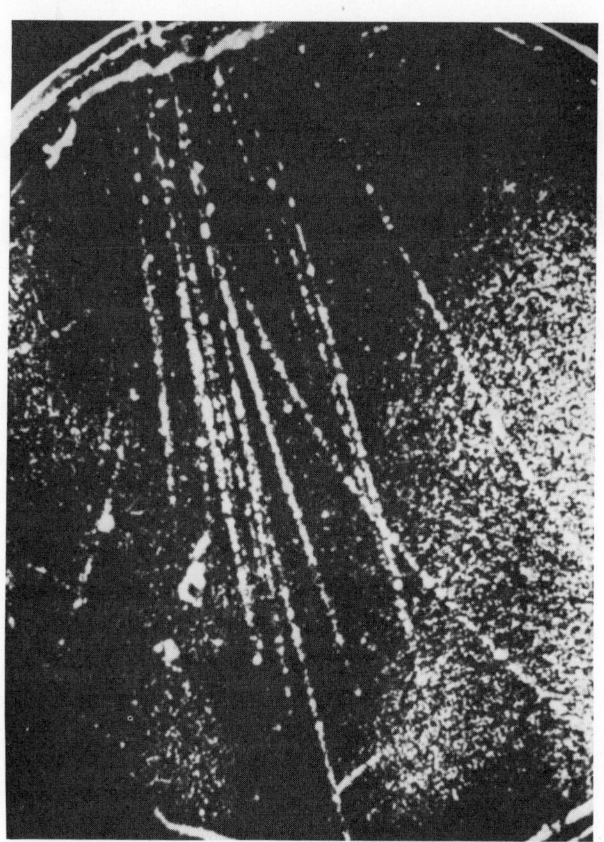

Figure 2-33 First shower observed by Blackett and Occhialini in a cloud chamber triggered by counters in coincidence above and below the chamber. [*Proc. Roy. Soc.* (*London*), **139,** 699 (1933).]

This relation is valid when the radiation loss predominates over ionization loss, as is the case for energies larger than a certain critical energy E_c. The quantity X_0 is called *radiation length* and depends on Z and ρ the density of the medium; it is roughly proportional to $1/Z\rho$. The critical energy E_c is crudely represented according to Eq. (2-10.1) by

$$E_c(\text{MeV}) = \frac{800}{Z} \tag{2-11.3}$$

(See also Table 2–2.)

Similarly, gamma rays have a mean free path for pair production X_p, which is obtained from Eq. (2-10.28) and is found to be

$$X_p = \frac{9}{7} X_0 \tag{2-11.4}$$

Let us now consider the oversimplified shower model. The conservation of momentum gives to the whole shower, an axis in the direction of the momentum of the first electron. The shower spreads laterally much less than it propagates longitudinally, as is clear from Eqs. (2-10.26) and (2-10.28). Thus the following discussion will be limited to the shower propagation in the direction of the initial particle.

An electron of energy E gives rise in one radiation length to about three gamma rays, which, in turn, give rise in a mean free path to about three pairs. The number of particles in the shower, N, starts to grow exponentially with the progress of the shower,

$$N(x) = e^{\gamma x} \tag{2-11.5}$$

Gamma is such that for

$$x_1 = X_0 + X_p \qquad N = e^{\gamma x_1} = 6 \tag{2-11.6}$$

but

$$X_0 + X_p = \frac{16}{7} X_0 \tag{2-11.7}$$

and hence

$$\gamma = \frac{\log 6}{(16/7)X_0} = \frac{0.78}{X_0} \tag{2-11.8}$$

In an actual shower, electrons, positrons, and photons are simultaneously present. Furthermore, the number of photons, especially of low energy, ends by being approximately twice as large as the number of particles. The number of particles in the shower increases until energy starts to dissipate, primarily by ionization and the Compton effect rather than radiation and pair production. At this point the particles have reached the energy E_c, and if we assume that the average energy of electrons, positrons, and gamma rays is the same, namely, E_c, their number is $E_0/3E_c$. This occurs at a distance

$$X_c = \frac{X_0}{0.78} \log \frac{E_0}{3E_c} \tag{2-11.9}$$

from the origin; and

$$N_{\max} = \frac{E_0}{3E_c} = e^{0.78X_c/X_0} \quad \textbf{(2-11.10)}$$

This estimate neglects energy losses by ionization, the energy going into the rest mass of the pairs and other important factors that depress $N_{\max}$ to a value nearer $\frac{1}{6}(E_0/E_c)$. More detailed expressions for high energy and low Z are

$$N_{\max} = 0.31 \frac{E_0}{E_c}\left(\log \frac{E_0}{E_c} - 0.37\right)^{-1/2} \quad \textbf{(2-11.11)}$$

and

$$X_c = 1.01 X_0\left(\log \frac{E_0}{E_c} - 1\right) \quad \textbf{(2-11.12)}$$

The results of more precise evaluations are shown in Fig. 2-34. At low energy, 300 MeV for example, the general treatment becomes very complicated, in part because the cross sections depend on the energies. Useful results are obtainable, however, by the Monte Carlo method (Fig. 2-35). The lateral distribution of a shower has also been studied, but we must refer for more details to (Ro 53).

2-12 Positron Annihilation

The annihilation process of the positron and electron is of great theoretical and practical importance. It is impossible to conserve energy and momentum if only one gamma quantum is emitted in the annihilation of a pair. The simplest possible process, starting from a pair *with*

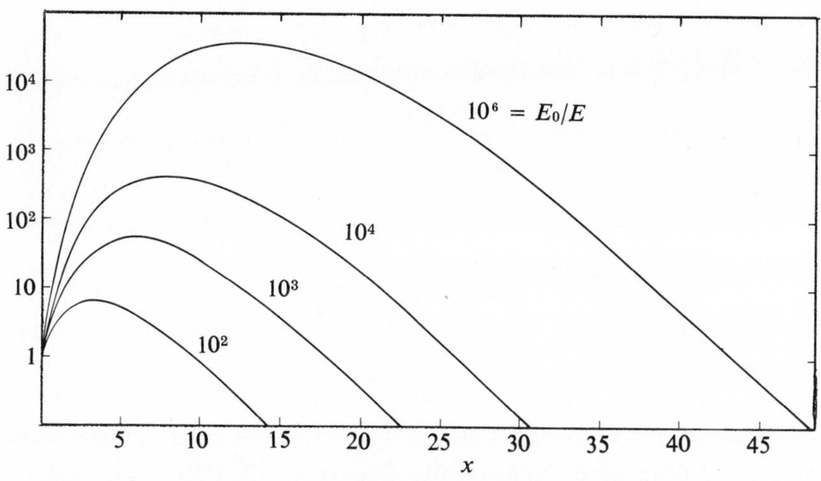

Figure 2-34 The average number of electrons of energy greater than E in a shower initiated by an electron of energy E_0 as a function of depth x (in radiation lengths). Ordinates in logarithmic scale. Each curve is labeled according to a value of E_0/E. [(Ro 53).]

small relative velocity v, is then the annihilation into two gamma rays, each with an energy $\hbar\omega = mc^2$ and traveling in opposite directions. This is the most important mode of annihilation; only when this mode is forbidden by some special selection rule do more complicated processes occur, for example, three-gamma annihilation. The cross section for the annihilation process can be presumed to be proportional to r_0^2. Moreover, the cross section should be proportional to v^{-1}. This important result is supported by the following argument: A positron crossing a foil of electron density $\mathcal{N}$ and thickness x, with velocity v, has a probability of annihilation of

$$\sigma(v)\mathcal{N}x = P \tag{2-12.1}$$

Now, as long as the velocity of the positron is small compared with the atomic velocities of the electrons, the probability of annihilation will be proportional to the time $t = x/v$ spent by the positron in the foil, because the relative velocity of the positron and the electrons is little affected by the small velocity of the positron. On changing velocity the only way in which P in Eq. (2-12.1) can become proportional to t is to make $\sigma = \alpha/v$, with α constant. Then

$$P = \frac{\alpha}{v}\mathcal{N}x = \alpha\mathcal{N}t \tag{2-12.2}$$

as required. Indeed, a detailed (and advanced) calculation gives

$$\langle\sigma\rangle = \pi r_0^2 \frac{c}{v} \tag{2-12.3}$$

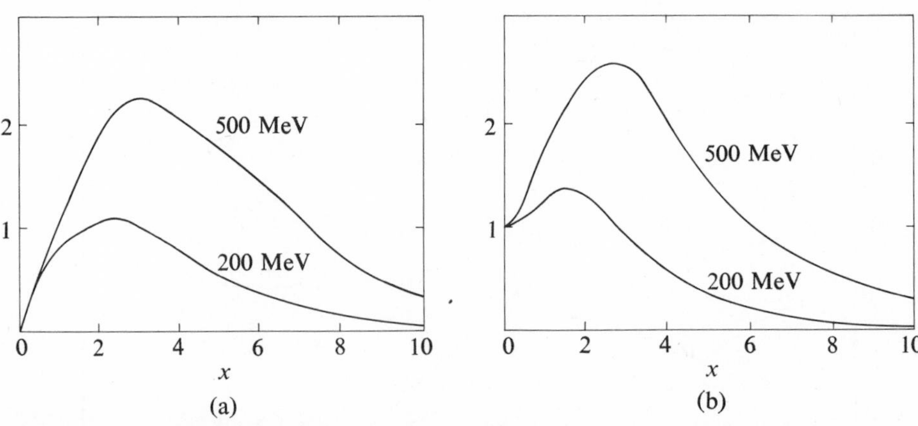

Figure 2-35 (a) The expected number of electrons with energy ⩾ 10 MeV in a shower plotted against depth x (in radiation lengths = 0.51 cm Pb). The shower is initiated by a photon and the absorber is lead. The curves are labeled according to the energy of the primary in MeV. (b) Same as (a) except that the shower is initiated by an electron. [D. F. Crawford and H. Messel, *Phys. Rev.*, **128**, 2352 (1962).]

where the average is over the two possible mutual directions of the spin; this is valid if

$$\frac{e^2}{\hbar c}\, mc^2 \ll T \ll mc^2 \tag{2-12.4}$$

where T is the relative kinetic energy of the positrons.

● A positron-electron system bound together as a sort of hydrogen atom is called *positronium*. Positronium is unstable because of the electron-positron pair annihilation giving rise to gamma rays. The annihilation rate depends on the overlapping of the electron-positron clouds; annihilation thus occurs mainly in the ground state of the system. This state has no orbital angular momentum; the spins of the two particles can be parallel ($^3S_1$) or antiparallel ($^1S_0$). It is possible to prove by considering the "parity" of a two-gamma-quanta system and that of positronium in $^1S_0$ and $^3S_1$ states that only the singlet state can annihilate into two quanta. These are correlated as follows: The gamma rays, in order to conserve momentum, must be collinear; moreover, if a gamma ray is analyzed with an apparatus which detects linear polarization and is found to be linearly polarized in a given direction, its conjugate will be polarized in a direction perpendicular to the first. Similarly, if one is analyzed with an apparatus which detects circular polarization and is found to be, e.g., left circular, its conjugate will be found to be right circular. Compare the similar situation in the decay of the neutral pion (Chap. 14), and for the theory see Bethe and de Hoffmann (BH 55).

For an unbound S state, Eq. (2-12.3) is made more specific by considering separate annihilation cross sections for singlet or triplet states. The cross sections for two-quanta annihilation, are

$$^3\sigma_{2\gamma} = 0 \qquad {}^1\sigma_{2\gamma} = 4\pi r_0{}^2 \frac{c}{v} \tag{2-12.5}$$

The probability of annihilation per unit time, or the reciprocal of the mean life, can be written as

$$\frac{1}{\tau} = \sigma_{2\gamma} \mathcal{N} v \tag{2-12.6}$$

where $\mathcal{N}$ is the density of the electrons and v the relative velocity of the positron and electron. In the bound case $\mathcal{N}$ is the density of the electron at the positron position, which is given by the absolute square of the wave function ψ at the origin. For the singlet state

$$\begin{aligned} \frac{1}{\tau_{2\gamma}} &= {}^1\sigma_{2\gamma} v |\psi(0)|^2 = 4\pi r_0{}^2 \frac{c}{v} v \frac{1}{\pi}\left(\frac{1}{2Zna_0}\right)^3 \\ &= \frac{1}{2}\left(\frac{e^2}{\hbar c}\right)^5 \frac{mc^2}{\hbar}\frac{1}{n^3} = \frac{1}{1.25 \times 10^{-10} n^3}\ \text{sec}^{-1} \end{aligned} \tag{2-12.7}$$

where a_0 is the Bohr radius and n is the total quantum number of the orbit.

For triplet states the mean life is about 1,115 $\approx 8\hbar c/e^2$ times longer, and in the case of free collisions the ratio between three and two quanta annihilation is

$$\frac{\frac{3}{4}\,{}^3\sigma_{3\gamma}}{\frac{1}{4}\,{}^1\sigma_{2\gamma}} = \frac{3}{1{,}115} = \frac{1}{372} \tag{2-12.8}$$

The positronium atom itself was detected by Deutsch (1949) by slowing down positrons in freon (CCl_2F_2) and measuring the mean life of the triplet state that is formed in three-fourths of the captures. Starting observation 10^{-7} sec after the arrival of a positron in the gas, singlet positronium, which is formed in one-fourth of the captures, has already decayed by the time observation begins and is thus not found. What is seen is only the decay of triplet positronium, provided that this is not converted by collisions to the singlet state. When the conversion does not occur, the mean life of positronium is independent of the pressure of the gas in which the positrons are stopped.

When capture occurs in the presence of molecules with a finite magnetic moment, such as O_2, the triplet states are converted to singlet states by collision and the singlet states decay in about 10^{-10} sec. The apparent mean life is thus the mean life for conversion from triplet to singlet states and is proportional to the pressure of the paramagnetic gas. The apparatus used and the dependence on pressure of the decay constant of positrons in freon and in O_2 are shown in Figs. 2-36 and 2-37. The interpretation is confirmed by the observation of three gamma rays in coincidence, corresponding to the annihilation of orthopositronium (triplet states), and of the two gamma rays, corresponding to the annihilation of parapositronium (singlet states), and of free positrons. ●

2-13 Polarization Phenomena

The study of polarization phenomena in electron and X-ray beams has become of great importance in recent years. As a consequence

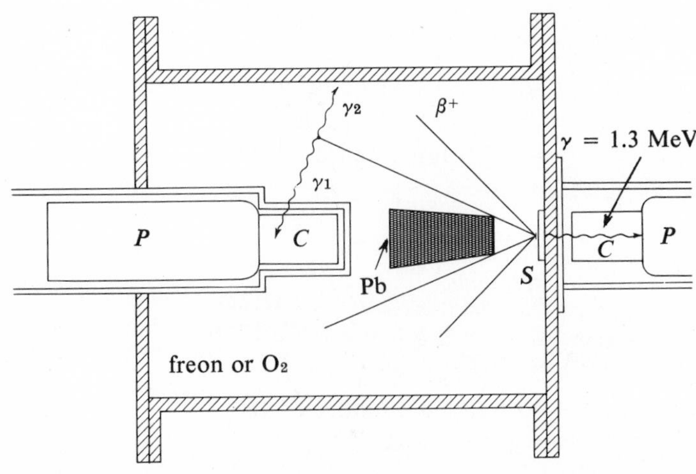

Figure 2-36 Apparatus used by Deutsch to measure the lifetime of positrons in gases. *P*, photomultipliers; *C*, sensitive crystals of NaI (Tl activated); *S*, source of Na^{22}; γ_1, γ_2, 0.51 annihilation gamma rays. [Deutsch, *Phys. Rev.*, **83,** 866 (1951).]

experimental techniques for polarization and analysis have been developed.

The electron has spin $\frac{1}{2}$ and presents the simplest polarization phenomena. The polarization of a beam is defined as a vector **P** in the direction of the expectation vector of the spin and of length $2\langle \mathbf{s} \rangle$. Operationally **P** is measured by observing the number of electrons in the beam that have a spin parallel (N_+) or antiparallel (N_-) to a given direction, giving the quantity

$$|P| = \frac{N_+ - N_-}{N_+ + N_-} \qquad \text{(2-13.1)}$$

The direction in which P is maximum is the direction of **P**, and $|P|$ is given by Eq. (2-13.1). Clearly $|\mathbf{P}|$ varies between 0 and 1, the former case corresponding to an unpolarized beam, the latter to that of a beam completely polarized. The electrons of a beam have a momentum **k**. If **P** and **k** are parallel, the beam is longitudinally polarized; if **k** and **P** are perpendicular, the beam is transversally polarized. The quantity

$$\mathscr{H} = \frac{\mathbf{P} \cdot \mathbf{k}}{|P|\,|k|} \qquad \text{(2-13.2)}$$

is often called the *helicity* of the electron. If the spin points in the direction of **k**, the helicity is $+1$; if it points in the opposite direction, the helicity is -1. An ordinary right-handed screw has positive helicity; i.e., in turning, the relation between the linear momentum with which it advances and its angular momentum corresponds to a positive helicity (see Chap. 9).

Beta decay often gives rise to electrons longitudinally polarized,

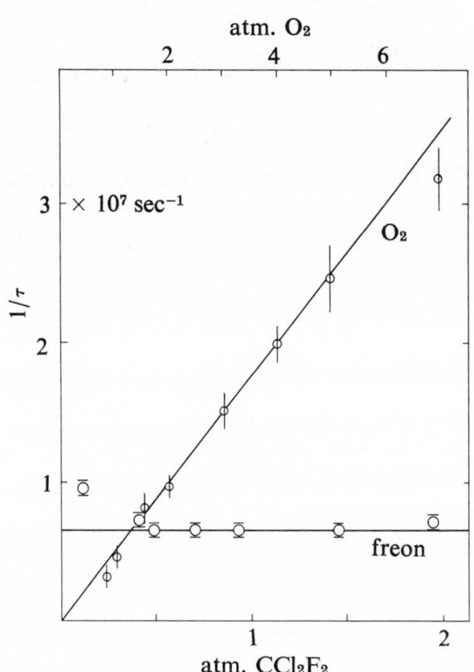

Figure 2-37 Pressure dependence of the decay rates of positrons in O_2 and in freon. [Deutsch, *Phys. Rev.*, **83,** 866 (1951).]

with P near 1; however, for practical reasons it is generally desirable to have beams transversely polarized. The rotation of the spin can be accomplished by deflecting the beam in an electric field. In the nonrelativistic case (assuming the value $g = 2$ for the ratio of the magnetic moment in Bohr magnetons and the spin), the spin remains parallel to itself, while the vector $\mathbf{k}$ may rotate (Fig. 2-38). Note that in a magnetic field the angle between $\mathbf{P}$ and $\mathbf{k}$ does not vary; therefore if the polarization is initially longitudinal, it remains longitudinal. For these simple conclusions the hypothesis $g = 2$, and the nonrelativistic approximation are essential.

Electrons can be polarized by several methods and correspondingly analyzed for polarization. We shall mention only the methods that have found practical application. The oldest is coulomb scattering by nuclei which was originally proposed by Mott and is known as *Mott scattering*. This method may be used for both polarization and analysis. Figure 2-39 shows schematically a typical double-scattering experiment. Figure 2-40 gives the asymmetry to be expected.

In Mott scattering we obtain transverse polarization and observe only transverse polarization.

Scattering of electrons or positrons on electrons depends on the relative spin orientation (Møller and Bhabha scattering). In practice it is possible to partially polarize the spins of the scatterer by using a magnetized ferromagnetic target. The change in scattering cross section is observed as a variation of intensity of the scattered electrons. Measurements are always made on a differential basis, i.e., by magnetizing the target first in one direction and then in the opposite direction. This is especially necessary because the best electron polarization obtainable in iron involves only 2 out of 26 electrons, and the resulting effects are very small.

The annihilation cross section for an electron-positron pair depends also on the relative spin orientation (see Sec. 2-12). Consequently, the polarization of a slow positron beam can be detected by passing it through a magnetized ferromagnetic foil.

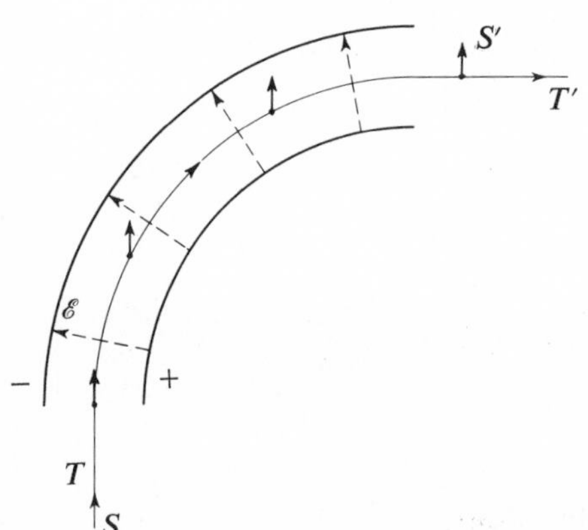

Figure 2-38 Spin rotation. Deflection of an electron beam in an electric field; nonrelativistic approximation. Dashed lines, electric-field lines; short arrows, spin orientation (S and S' are initial and final orientation); T, T', trajectory of electron; the polarization changes from longitudinal to transverse.

X rays also show polarization phenomena. For their description we may use the conventional optical nomenclature and distinguish between linear and circular polarization. Compton and Thomson scattering depend on the polarization of the incident beam. Thus for plane-polarized X rays the Klein–Nishina formula gives for scattering in the θ direction contained in a plane making the angle ψ with the direction of polarization (Fig. 2-24),

$$\frac{d\sigma}{d\Omega} = \frac{r_0^2}{2}\alpha^2\left(\frac{1}{\alpha} + \alpha - 2\sin^2\theta\cos^2\psi\right) \tag{2-13.3}$$

where $\alpha = \hbar\omega/mc^2$. The variation of the scattered intensity as a function of ψ indicates the direction of polarization of the incident beam.

In order to analyze circularly polarized X rays, we need a scatterer with polarized electrons, such as a magnetized ferromagnet. The scattering cross section, analogous to Møller scattering, is different for X rays circularly polarized, with their direction of rotation parallel or antiparallel to that of the electron spin. Therefore circularly polarized X rays are attenuated differently according to whether they cross a ferromagnet magnetized parallel or antiparallel to their direction of propagation.

The photodisintegration of the deuteron affords another method of detecting the linear polarization of X rays, because the proton is ordinarily ejected in the direction of polarization of the incident beam.

The polarization of electrons and X rays also gives rise to very interesting and important second-order phenomena in which they are

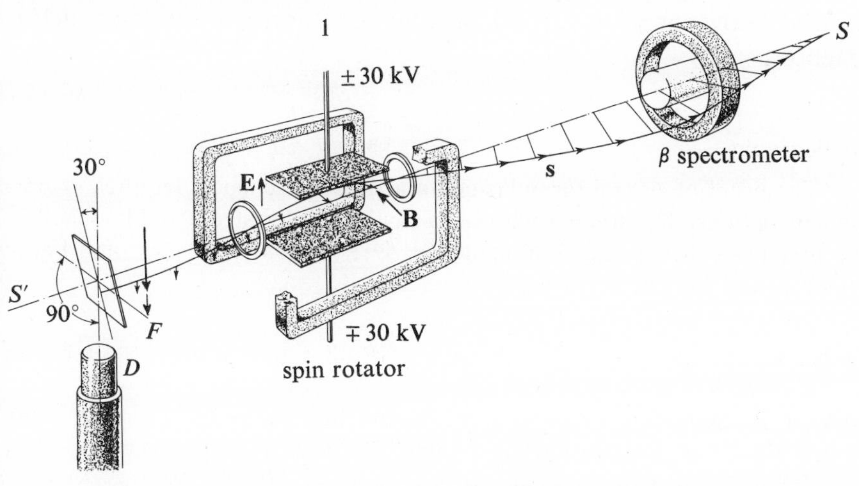

Figure 2-39 Crossed electric and magnetic fields to change electron polarization from longitudinal to transverse. A beta spectrometer is used to select the energy of the electrons from source S. The spin rotator changes the spin orientation indicated by **s**, but has no action on the trajectory ($E = Bv/c$). The gold foil F scatters by 90° the electrons which are detected by D. The detector and foil assembly can rotate around SS' to determine asymmetry. [Cavanagh et al., *Phil. Mag.*, **2,** 1105 (1957).]

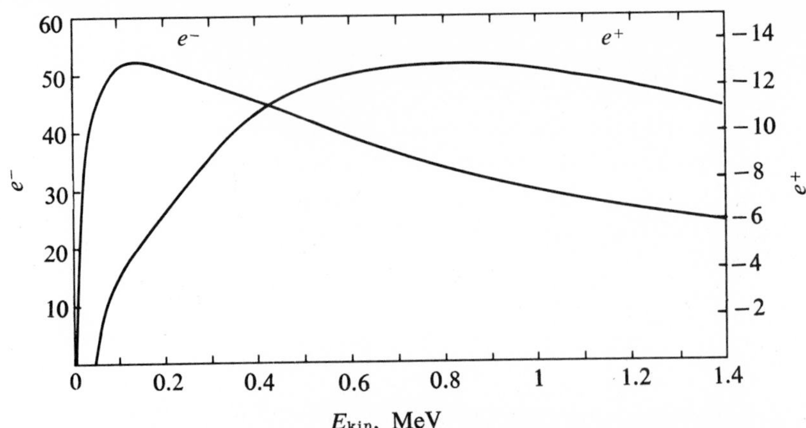

Figure 2-40 Polarization in Mott scattering. The asymmetry percentage 200 $|a|$ in a single scattering experiment of a totally polarized beam as a function of the energy for electrons and positrons ($Z = 80$). Scattering angle 90°. [H. A. Tolhoek, *Rev. Mod. Phys.*, **28,** 277 (1956).]

mutually interrelated. For example, the bremsstrahlung produced by a longitudinally polarized electron is usually circularly polarized in the same direction as the electron, giving rise to an apparent multiplication of the angular momentum. It is thus sometimes possible to detect the polarization of primary radiation by transferring it to a secondary one and then observing the latter.

Protons may also be polarized by nuclear scattering, especially at high energies (i.e., above 100 MeV). Detection of polarization is achieved most frequently by a double-scattering experiment. Energy loss by ionization occurs without appreciably affecting the polarization of protons. Low-energy polarized protons are formed in certain nuclear reactions.

Bibliography

The proof of several formulas contained in this chapter requires elaborate calculations. The student who is particularly interested should consult in the first place Bethe and Ashkin in (Se 59); (Ro 53); (He 54); and Fano, Spencer, and Berger in (Fl E).

Bethe, H. A., and J. Askin, "Passage of Radiations through Matter," in (Se 59), Vol. I.

Birks, J. B., *Scintillation Counters*, Pergamon Science Series, London, 1960.

Bohr, N., "The Penetration of Atomic Particles through Matter," *Kgl. Danske Videnskab. Selskab, Mat.-Fys. Medd.*, **18,** 8 (1948).

Burhop, E. H., *The Auger Effect and Other Radiationless Transitions*, Cambridge University Press, New York, 1952.

Burhop, E. H., and H. B. Massey, *Electronic and Ionic Impact Phenomena*, Oxford University Press, New York, 1952.

DeBenedetti, S., and H. Corben, "Positronium," *Ann. Rev. Nucl. Sci.*, **4,** 191 (1954).
Fagg, L. W., and S. S. Hanna, "Polarization Measurements on Nuclear Gamma Rays," *Rev. Mod. Phys.*, **31,** 711 (1959).
Fano, U., "Penetration of Protons, Alpha Particles, and Mesons," *Am. Rev. Nucl. Sci.*, **13,** 1 (1963).
Fano, Spencer, and Berger, "Penetration and Diffusion of X-rays," in (Fl E), Vol. 38.2.
Gentner, Maier-Leibnitz, and Bothe (GMLB 54).
Heitler, W. (He 54).
Jackson, J. D. (Ja 62).
Koch, H. W., and J. W. Motz, "Bremsstrahlung Cross-Section Formulas and Related Data," *Rev. Mod. Phys.*, **31,** 720 (1959).
Miller, Gibson, and Donovan, "Semiconductor Particle Detectors," *Ann. Rev. Nucl. Sci.*, **12,** 189 (1962).
Northcliffe, L. C., "Passage of Heavy Ions through Matter," *Ann. Rev. Nucl. Sci.*, **13,** 67 (1963).
Page, L. A., "The Polarization Measurements on Beta and Gamma Rays," *Rev. Mod. Phys.*, **31,** 759 (1959) and *Ann. Rev. Nucl. Sci.*, **12,** 43 (1962).
Rossi, B. (Ro 53).
Rutherford, E., *Radiations from Radioactive Substances*, Cambridge University Press, London, 1930.
Scott, W. T., "The Theory of Small Angle Multiple Scattering of Fast Charged Particles," *Rev. Mod. Phys.*, **35,** 231 (1963).
Tolhoek, H. A., "Electron Polarization, Theory, and Experiment," *Rev. Mod. Phys.*, **28,** 277 (1956).
Wapstra, Nijgh, and Van Lieshout, *Nuclear Spectroscopy Tables*, North-Holland Publishing Co., Amsterdam, 1959.
Willis, B. H., and J. H. Atkinson, Jr., *High-Energy Particle Data*, UCRL 2426, June 1957.
Yuan, L., and C. S. Wu, *Methods of Experimental Physics—Nuclear Physics*, Academic Press, New York, 1962.

Problems

2-1 Derive Eq. (2-2.10) for a small value of θ in the form $\theta = Ze^2/Eb$. Do the same for any value of θ by considering first the momentum transfer in any central force and specializing to the particular case of an inverse-square force.

2-2 What is the probability that an alpha particle of 5 MeV energy crossing a gold leaf of 1 mg cm^{-2} will be deflected through an angle between 10° and 11°?

2-3 If the alpha particle mentioned in Prob. 2-2 is deflected by 20°, what is its impact parameter and distance of maximum approach?

2-4 Prove Eq. (2-2.18) by introducing the relative coordinates of the colliding bodies and their reduced mass.

2-5 Find the maximum angle of scattering in the laboratory system for alpha particles impinging on protons.

2-6 Use Fig. 2-7 to find the range in copper of an alpha particle having an energy of 30 MeV and of a muon having an energy of 75 MeV. What is their specific energy loss in copper? Estimate the ranges of the same particles in aluminum, lead, and hydrogen, by considering the effect of the change in I (for hydrogen assume $I = 14.9$ eV). Note that the number of electrons per gram of absorber is approximately twice as large for hydrogen as for other substances and hence its mass stopping power is also twice as large.

2-7 Show by a dimensional argument based on the Thomas–Fermi atomic model that the constant I of Eq. (2-3.10) is proportional to Z [F. Bloch, *Z. Physik*, **81**, 363 (1933)].

2-8 Justify the following formula used in photographic emulsion studies. The number n of delta rays having an energy between W_1 and W_2, per unit length of the track, is

$$n = \frac{2\pi \mathcal{N} Z^2}{\beta^2}\left(\frac{e^2}{mc^2}\right)^2\left(\frac{mc^2}{W_1} - \frac{mc^2}{W_2}\right)$$

where $\mathcal{N}$ is the number of electrons per unit volume of emulsion and β and Z refer to the particle making the track.

2-9 The following equation has been given for the energy loss per centimeter by fission fragments,

$$\frac{1}{N}\frac{dE}{dx} = \frac{4\pi e^4}{mv^2}(Z_1^{\text{eff}})^2 Z_2 \log \frac{1.123 mv^3\hbar}{Ie^2 Z_1^{\text{eff}}} + \frac{4\pi e^4}{M_2 v^2} Z_1^2 Z_2^2 \times \log\left(\frac{M_1 M_2}{M_1 + M_2}\frac{v^2 a_{\text{scr}}}{Z_1 Z_2 e^2}\right)$$

where 1 refers to the fission fragment and 2 to the absorber material. The quantity a_{scr} is the impact parameter beyond which the energy loss resulting in nuclear collisions is zero because of screening. The first term refers to electron collisions, the second to nuclear collisions. Justify and discuss the equation.

2-10 Show that the probability of an energy loss dE by ionization for a particle of charge z traversing dx cm of a substance is approximately

$$\phi(E)\, dE\, dx = \pi N Z r_e^2 \frac{2mc^2 z^2}{\beta^2}\frac{dE}{E^2}\, dx$$

where N is the number of atoms per cubic centimeter, r_e is the classical radius of the electron, and E is the energy of the particle.

2-11 An absorption curve of a sample emitting beta and gamma rays was taken, using a Lauritsen electroscope, with aluminum absorbers. The data obtained were:

Absorber thickness, g cm^{-2}	Activity, divisions min^{-1}	Absorber thickness, g cm^{-2}	Activity, divisions min^{-1}
0	5.8	0.700	0.11
0.070	3.5	0.800	0.10
0.130	2.2	1.00	0.10
0.200	1.3	2.00	0.092
0.300	0.60	4.00	0.080
0.400	0.28	7.00	0.065
0.500	0.12	10.00	0.065
0.600	0.11	14.00	0.040

(*a*) Find the maximum energy of the beta spectrum (in MeV). (*b*) Find the energy of the gamma ray. (*c*) What would be the absorption coefficient of this gamma ray in lead?

2-12 Evaluate the angle θ_1 of Sec. 2-7 and find

$$\theta_1^2 = \frac{4\pi NZ(Z+1)z^2e^4}{p^2v^2}\,t$$

where t is in |cm|. See (Se 59), Vol. I, p. 285.

2-13 Calculate $\langle\Theta^2\rangle$ due to multiple scattering for 100-MeV protons crossing 2 mm of copper.

2-14 The discontinuities in absorption coefficients give a method for bracketing X-ray wavelengths in small intervals by measuring the absorption in elements with adjacent values of Z. Consider two absorbers: one with the K absorption edge above, the one with the edge below the wavelength to be measured. Plan experiments to identify by this method the K radiation of Tc and At.

2-15 A gamma ray is Compton-scattered backward ($\theta = 180°$). Calculate the energy of the scattered quantum for a primary quantum having $\hbar\omega = 0.01, 0.1, 1.0, 10, 100, 1{,}000$ MeV.

2-16 Calculate limiting expressions of the Klein–Nishina formula for $\hbar\omega \gg mc^2$ and $\hbar\omega \ll mc^2$.

2-17 A gamma ray has the absorption coefficient of 0.6 cm^{-1} in lead. Give its mass absorption coefficient and the absorption cross section per electron. What can you say about the energy of the gamma ray? If you measured the absorption coefficient in aluminum, what would you expect to find?

2-18 Electrons of 1 BeV energy pass through a lead plate 1 cm thick. Calculate the mean square of the linear deviation of the emergent points from the geometrical shadow point on the exit surface of the lead plate. What is the probability that the electron will produce a quantum? Repeat the calculation for a proton.

2-19 In the annihilation of positronium in the $^1S_0$ state, following the proof of Bethe and de Hoffmann, one finds two quanta with eigenfunctions

$$LL - RR$$

Show that the linear polarizations of the two quanta are perpendicular to each other. Repeat the analysis for the case $LL + RR$. See (BH 59).

2-20 To reduce the energy of a proton beam by using a copper moderator, what are the required thickness of copper, the fraction of the primary beam passing through, and the value of $\langle\Theta\rangle$ due to multiple scattering in the following cases:

E initial	*E* final
1 BeV	100 MeV
100 MeV	30 MeV
3 MeV	0.3 MeV

Discuss the effect of nuclear absorption in all three cases, and also estimate the final momentum spread, $\Delta p/p$, in each instance.

CHAPTER III

Detection Methods for Nuclear Radiations

EXPERIMENTS IN NUCLEAR PHYSICS depend upon the detection of nuclear radiations. This detection is made possible by the interaction of nuclear radiations with atomic electrons, which was treated in Chap. 2. Here we shall describe the main instruments which are used in practice.

3-1 Classification

For reasons of convenience, we shall classify them as shown in Table 3-1.

The same detector can be used in studies of various radiations, for the interaction of the radiations with the sensitive part of a detector may depend on different phenomena. Thus, a gas ionization chamber may detect heavy charged particles through their direct ionization effect; gamma rays through the photoelectrons, Compton electrons, or electron-positron pairs they produce in the gas or at the walls; high-energy neutrons through the ionization produced by recoil protons; and slow neutrons through the alpha particles produced by nuclear capture in boron or by the fission of U^{235}. Similarly, a Cerenkov counter

Table 3-1 Summary of Detection Methods

Type	Detection of single events	Detection of many particles
Electric	Ionization chamber	Ionization chamber
	Proportional counter	
	Geiger-Müller counter	
	Semiconductor counter	
Optical	Scintillation counter	Photographic blackening
	Cerenkov counter	
	Photographic emulsion	
	Cloud chamber	Chemical detectors
	Bubble chamber	
	Spark chamber	

can be used to detect charged particles and also gamma rays if the latter have enough energy to produce detectable electrons.

Instruments also differ widely in the information they yield. Some provide accurate determinations of the time at which an event occurs (say, within 1 nsec) but give little spatial resolution; a large Cerenkov counter is an example of this type. Other instruments provide excellent spatial resolution but no information about the time at which the event took place. Photographic emulsions used to record tracks of particles are a case in point. Instruments that make possible very precise measurements of the total energy released in an event may provide only a moderately accurate time resolution. An example would be a gas-filled ionization chamber or a solid-state counter used to detect the energy of alpha particles.

The efficiency of an instrument, i.e., the probability of its detecting a radiation crossing it, is another important characteristic. This may vary greatly. For most of the directly ionizing radiations, the efficiency is 1. In the detection of neutrons the efficiency depends strongly on their energy, ranging from a few per cent at high energy to nearly 1 for slow neutrons. There is a similar dependence of efficiency on energy in the case of gamma rays.

Almost all instruments, after detecting an event, lose their sensitivity for a certain period known as *dead time*. This period sets a limitation on the number of events per unit time that an instrument can count. It is clear that in order to count with high efficiency the reciprocal of the counting rate must be very small compared to the dead time.

Space, time, and energy resolution, efficiency, dead time, and other experimental requirements may depend on the size of the detector. The requirements often conflict, making compromises necessary in the choice and design of detectors. Typical numbers for parameters of different detectors are given in Table 3-2. Most of the radiation detectors listed in the table cannot function usefully without auxiliary electronic

Table 3-2 Numbers for Detector Parameters

Detector	Time resolution, sec	Dead time, sec	Space resolution, cm	Volume, cm^3
Ionization chamber	10^{-3}	10^{-2}	(a)	1–10^5
Geiger–Müller counter	10^{-6}	10^{-4}	(a)	1–10^4
Semiconductor counter	10^{-8}	10^{-6}	0.5	0.1
Scintillation counter	10^{-8}	10^{-6}	(a)	1–10^4
Cerenkov counter	10^{-9}	10^{-8}	(a)	10–10^4
Photographic emulsion			10^{-4}	10^3
Cloud chamber	10^{-2}	100	0.05	10^5
Bubble chamber	10^{-3}	1	5×10^{-3}	10^5
Spark chamber	10^{-6}	10^{-2}	0.05	5×10^5

[a] Depends on the size of the instrument.

equipment, such as amplifiers, discriminators, coincidence circuits, and scalers. For example, the light emitted by a single particle passing through a Cerenkov counter can be detected only by a sensitive photomultiplier tube; the electrical impulse of the photomultiplier must then be amplified so that it can be used in a coincidence circuit or recorded on a scaler. In complex experiments, even a computer can be considered as auxiliary equipment when it is used to record and analyze the data from a system of many counters or to interpret the data obtained from a bubble chamber.

3-2 Ionization Chambers

Ionization chambers are one of the oldest types of instruments used in nuclear physics and are extremely versatile. An ionization chamber is essentially a vessel containing some substance, usually gas, which becomes ionized when charged particles pass through it. The ions are collected with the aid of an electric field, and the ionization current is measured. We recall from Chap. 2 that it takes about 35 eV to form an ion pair in air. If the primary radiation loses 1 MeV in the chamber, it will form approximately 2.86×10^4 ion pairs—a quantity of electrical charge equal to 4.6×10^{-15} C for each sign. A minimum-ionizing, singly charged particle produces about 30 ion pairs in traversing 1 cm of air at atmospheric pressure. In general, ionization chambers are designed to collect all the ions produced in them, and a chamber is said to reach *saturation* when such total collection is made. At the same time, however, ion multiplication by secondary phenomena must be avoided. If it occurs, the apparatus works differently and is not called normally an ionization chamber (see Sec. 3-3). A schematic design of a typical ionization chamber is given in Fig. 3-1.

The rate of collection of the ions is determined by their mobility, which is defined as the ratio of the ion velocity to the electric field in the chamber. In air at STP, the ion mobility is of the order of 1 cm $\sec^{-1}$ per volt cm^{-1}. Values of the mobilities of positive and negative ions are listed in Table 3-3.

In cases where one is interested in integrating the current over a period of time long compared with the time for collecting the ions, the

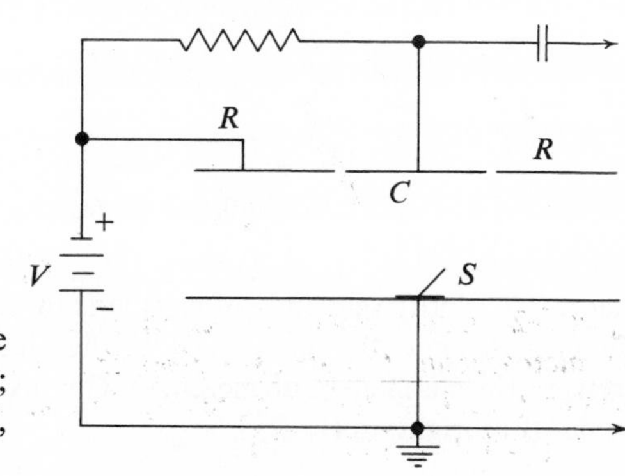

Figure 3-1 Typical ionization chamber. Parallel-plate ionization chamber with guard ring. *R*, guard ring; *S*, sample emitting an alpha particle; *V*, battery; *C*, collecting electrode.

Table 3-3 Mobility of Positive and Negative Ions in Gases

Gas	+ ion	− ion
	Mobility,[a] cm sec^{-1} per volt cm^{-1}	
Air	1.37	1.8
Hydrogen	5.7	8.6
Nitrogen	1.29	1.82
Oxygen	1.33	1.80
Helium	5.1	6.3
Argon	1.37	1.7
Carbon dioxide	0.79	0.95
Acetylene	0.71	0.86
Benzene	0.18	0.21
Methyl iodide	0.23	0.23

[a] At 760 mm pressure and 15°C.

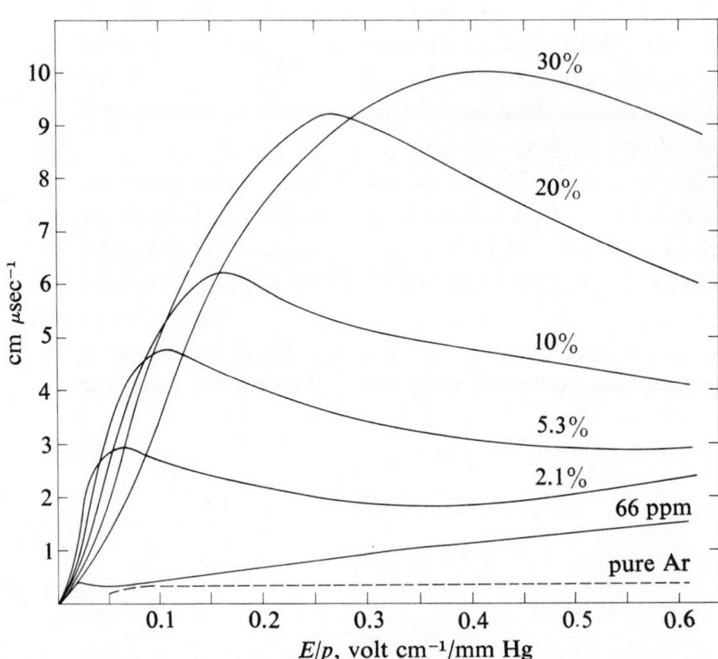

Figure 3-2 Drift velocities of electrons in argon-methane mixtures. The ordinate is in centimeters per microsecond; the abscissa gives the electric field (in volts per centimeter) divided by the gas pressure (in millimeters of mercury). Curves are labeled according to the percentage of methane in argon. [Fulbright, in (Fl E).]

mobility is unimportant. However, when one is interested in measuring the current produced by a single primary particle crossing the chamber, a short collecting time becomes desirable. A short collecting time is achieved by collecting only electrons whose velocity is about 1,000 times greater than that of the positive ions produced. For this purpose one uses pure noble gases or, better, mixtures such as Ar–CO_2, or Ar–CH_4 in which electrons remain free and hence, available for rapid collection. This can be seen in Fig. 3-2, where the electron velocity is plotted against the ratio of the electric field to the gas pressure. The comparatively high velocity allows the electrons to be collected in a time during which the positive ions barely move. As a consequence, with the usual type of apparatus (Fig. 3-3a) the output voltage depends on the site at which the ion is formed. In Fig. 3-3a, if only the negative charge q moves, the output voltage ΔV of the detector is given by

$$\Delta V = \frac{q}{C}\frac{x}{d} \tag{3-2.1}$$

where C is the electrical capacity of one electrode with respect to the other. The dependence of ΔV upon the site of ion formation is often undesirable and can be obviated by introducing an auxiliary grid, as shown in Fig. 3-3b. Since the electrons produce a significant output voltage only when they travel between grid a and the collecting electrode b, the same signal is obtained regardless of where the electron was liberated between a and c. An application of this method—a grid chamber used to measure very accurately the total ionization produced by alpha particles—is shown in Fig. 3-4.

Ionization chambers and other detectors depending on ionization by charged particles can also be used to detect uncharged particles, for instance, gamma rays and neutrons. Fast neutrons traversing a chamber filled with hydrogen gas can be detected through the ionization produced by the recoil protons that arise from neutron-proton collisions. For slow neutrons one can use a gas, such as BF_3, containing boron nuclei

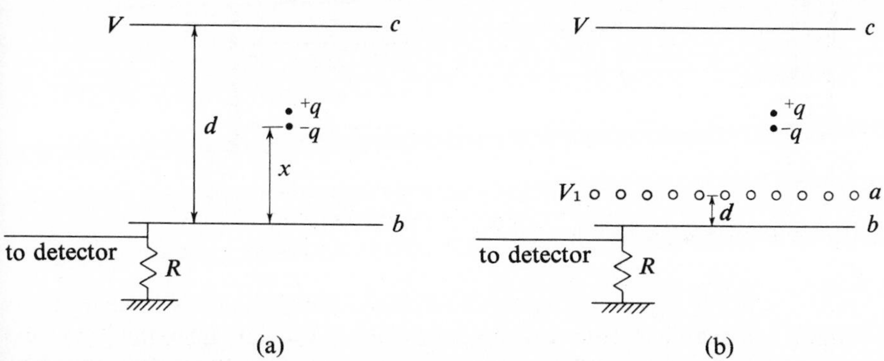

Figure 3-3 (a) Schematic drawing of an ion pair in a parallel-plate ionization chamber; (b) same as (a) but with an auxiliary grid. V, V_1 are the potentials of electrodes c and a.

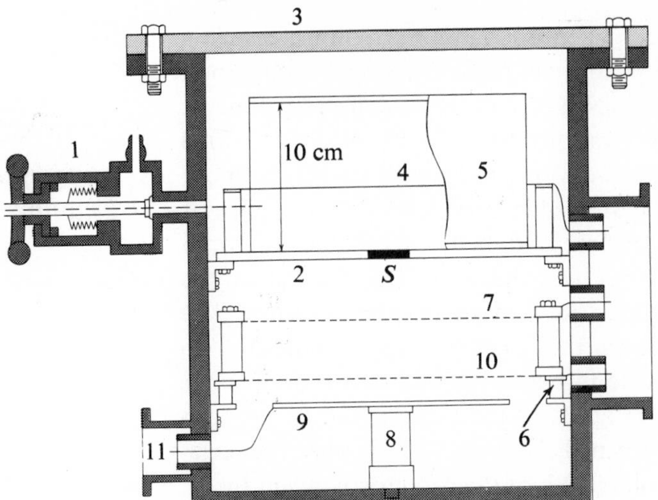

Figure 3-4 Ionization chamber for measuring the total energy of alpha particles. 1, valve; 2, electrode with source foil; 3, Plexiglas cover; 4, proportional counter filament; 5, cylindrical counter cathode; 6, insulator; 7, first grid for special measurements of angular correlations; 8, insulator; 9, collecting electrode; 10, second grid; 11, insulator; *S*, sample. [Komar, Korolev, and Kocharov, *Izv. Akad. Nauk SSSR*, **22,** No. 7, 824 (1958).]

that disintegrate under slow neutron bombardment emitting detectable alpha particles. Sometimes the chambers contain substances having special nuclear properties that make them sensitive only to particular radiations. For example, if the electrodes of a multielectrode chamber

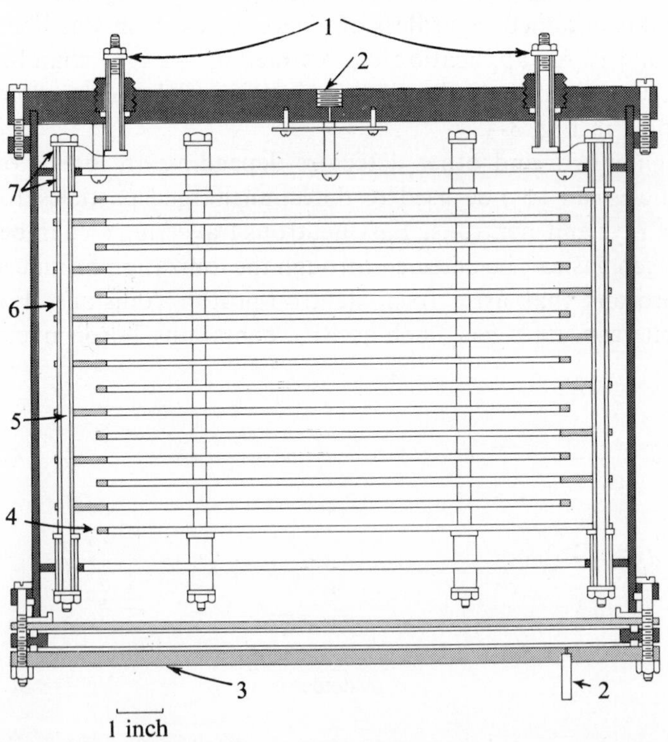

Figure 3-5 Multiple-plate fission chamber. 1, lead through insulators (Lucite); 2, gas inlet; 3, heavy second top plate, to be removed after filling of chamber; 4, aluminum rings supporting uranium-coated foils; 5, supporting rod and lead; 6, metal spacer; 7, Lucite spacers. [Courtesy C. E. Wiegand.]

are coated with U^{235}, the chamber becomes sensitive to slow neutrons, which cause the fission of the U^{235} nuclei. If the electrodes are coated with Bi, the chamber becomes sensitive to neutrons with energy greater than 50 MeV—the threshold for producing fission in bismuth by means of neutrons. Figure 3-5 gives an example of a multiplate fission chamber.

There are many possible geometric arrangements for ionization chambers, ranging from extremely small ones used for dosimetry to very large ones sometimes employed in cosmic-ray studies. Figure 3-6 shows an example of the first case, in which a small tube the size of a fountain pen contains the chamber and the electrode. Ionization chambers have also been made by substituting solids or liquids in place of gases.

Semiconductors have found an important application in the detection of nuclear events. In a *pn*-type semiconductor (for example, Si or Ge, Fig. 3-7) subjected to an electric field, an ionizing particle crossing the *pn* junction produces a current pulse and an associated voltage pulse. A very fast pulse ($\sim 10^{-8}$ sec) results when the ionizing particle passes through the thin junction region. The pulse amplitude is proportional to the energy lost in the junction layer over a very wide range of ionization density. Moreover, the energy required per ion pair is only about 3 eV compared with 30 eV in a gas. The result is that

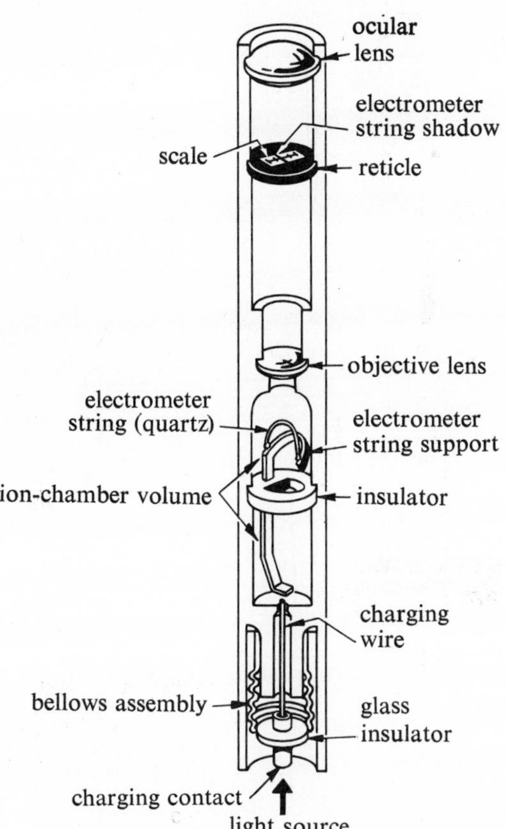

Figure 3-6 Pocket fiber electrometer. Victoreen direct-reading dosimeter. The charging wire contacts the electrometer string support for charging only. The electrometer string is of platinized quartz and moves when the electrometer is discharged. The optical system provides for measuring the displacement of the quartz fibre. [Courtesy Victoreen Company.]

semiconductor detectors provide excellent energy resolution (better than 1 per cent) and are especially suitable for experiments involving heavily ionizing particles such as alpha particles and fission fragments (see Fig. 3-43). At present, the thickness of the junction is limited to approximately 1 mm and the area of the counter to 4 cm^2.

3-3 Proportional and Geiger–Müller Counters

A schematic sketch of a gas-filled cylinder containing an isolated wire along its axis is shown in Fig. 3-8. When ionizing radiation enters such a cylinder, the current produced is a function of the impressed voltage V. At very low voltages, the current is proportional to V; then, over a certain voltage interval, the current is independent of V. At this point the apparatus performs as an ionization chamber, and the current is said to be saturated; i.e., only the primary ions are being collected.

If the voltage is now increased beyond the saturation interval, the primary ions begin to produce secondaries by collisions with the gas; consequently, the primary ionization is multiplied by a factor that depends on the geometry of the apparatus and on the applied voltage V, and the device functions as a *proportional counter*. In this way it is possible

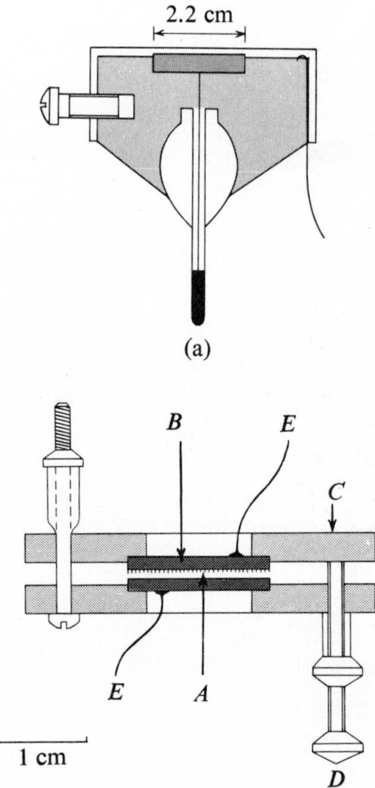

Figure 3-7 Solid-state detectors: (a) barrier counter (Au-coated Si wafer); (b) neutron sandwich spectrometer using the Li^6 $(n,\alpha)H^3$ reaction. In (b): *A*, Li^6 F; *B*, silicon wafer; *C*, Lavite ring; *D*, positioning screw; *E*, electrical leads. [Courtesy Ortec Company.]

to obtain multiplication factors up to several thousand. The effective time of collection which also depends on the geometry and V, can be reduced to microseconds. We shall not discuss here the mechanism of the multiplication process. Proportional counters can be used to investigate soft beta rays and also X rays through the photoelectrons they produce. When traversed by energetic particles, they also provide information on the ionization density produced by the particles.

Returning to the apparatus of Fig. 3-8, if we increase the voltage still further, a point is reached (the threshold) at which the presence of ions in the cylinder triggers a self-sustaining discharge that stops only if some special device lowers the potential difference across the counter. This procedure is called *external quenching*. The current in the discharge is independent of the primary ionization and the apparatus functions as a Geiger–Müller (G–M) counter. The ultraviolet-light quanta emitted in the discharge play an essential role in the working of a G–M counter. However, we shall not describe here the gas-discharge phenomena occurring in such counters.

Geiger–Müller counters are generally filled with argon-alcohol mixtures at pressures of about 10 cm Hg argon and 2 cm Hg ethyl alcohol. Occasionally other mixtures, consisting largely of a noble gas and an organic vapor, are used. The addition of the organic vapor renders the counter self-quenching; i.e., the discharge stops spontaneously without the necessity of lowering the voltage across the counter. If one sends a constant flux of ionizing particles through a G–M counter, one finds that the counting rate is independent of V over a certain voltage interval—that is, the counter has a "plateau." An example is shown in Fig. 3-9. Note that the threshold indicated for the G–M counter is above the voltage region where the tube works as a proportional counter. A G–M counter, after a discharge, has a certain dead time, of the order of 100 μsec, during which it cannot register a new pulse. One must therefore be careful not to send too high a flux through the counter; otherwise the successive ions arrive during the dead time, when the counter is *paralyzed.*

A G–M counter will respond to a single ion formed in the gas; thus any charged particles crossing the tube is certain to be detected.

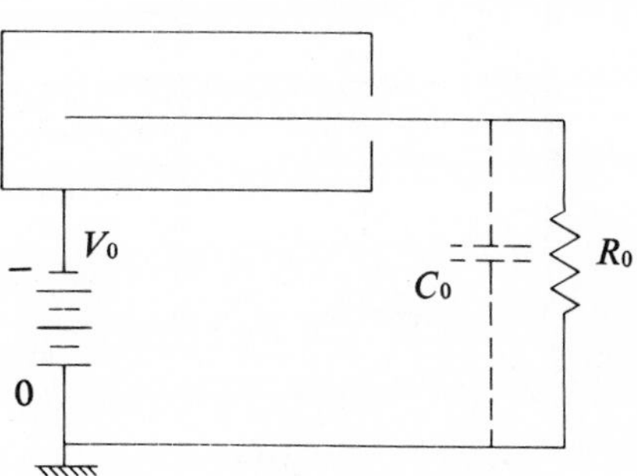

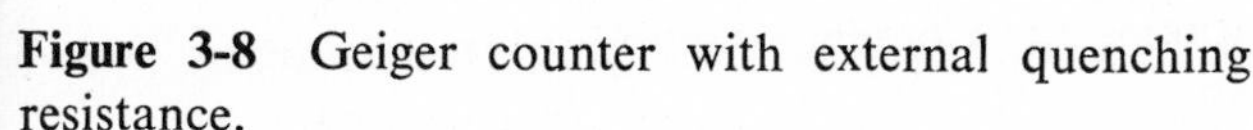

Figure 3-8 Geiger counter with external quenching resistance.

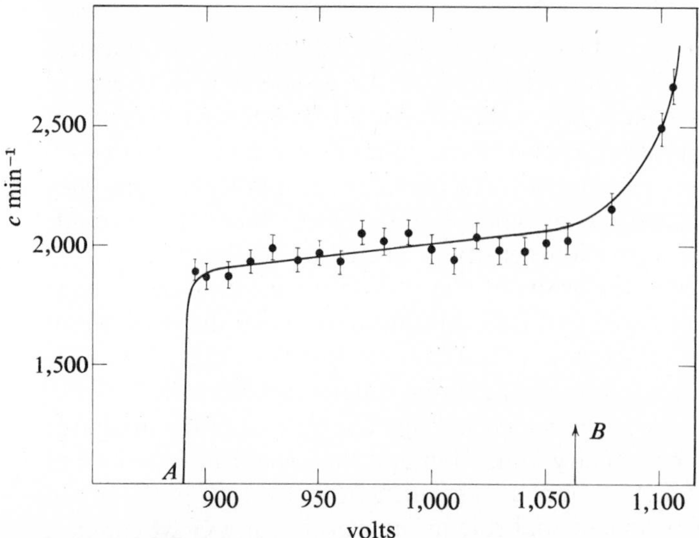

Figure 3-9 Dependence of counting rate of a Geiger counter on applied voltage. *A*, threshold voltage; *B*, limit of plateau. Plateau is 150 V long.

X rays, on the other hand, rarely form an ion pair, and their detection depends on the material of the counter walls from which electrons may be ejected by the X rays. Generally walls made of materials having high *Z*, such as lead, are the most favorable, but even then the efficiency for X rays or gamma rays is generally of the order of 1 per cent. Typical constructions of G–M counters are shown in Figs. 3-10, 3-11, and 3-12.

A G–M counter can be rendered sensitive to neutrons by filling it with a boron-containing gas, commonly BF_3. It is also possible to embed such a counter in paraffin (Fig. 3-13) in such a way that its sensitivity to neutrons is more or less independent of energy in the range from a few keV to a few MeV.

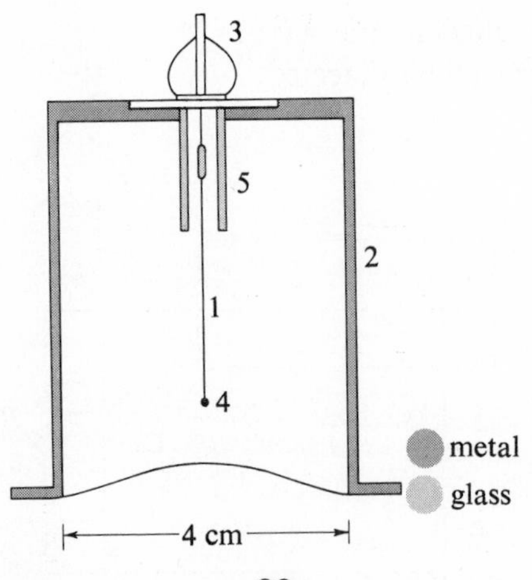

Figure 3-10 Thin mica-window counter. Window thickness 3 mg cm^{-2}. Diameter approximately 4 cm. 1, wolfram anode wire; 2, metal shell; 3, Kovar-glass seal; 4, glassbead; 5, glass sleeve. [Courtesy Radiation Counter Laboratories, Inc., Skokie, Ill.]

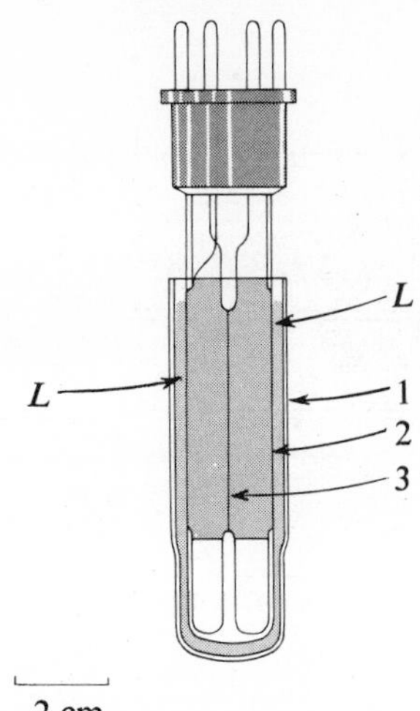

Figure 3-11 Dipping counter. Thin glass wall. Diameter approximately 2 cm. 1, Container of the liquid to be assayed (L); 2, glass wall metallized on the inside; 3, anode wire. [Courtesy Radiation Counter Laboratories, Inc., Skokie, Ill.]

3-4 Scintillation Counters

At the beginning of this century, Crookes introduced a device, which he called a *spinthariscope*, for counting single alpha particles. This instrument worked on the principle that an alpha particle impinging on a screen (covered with zinc sulfide containing additional activating impurities) produces scintillations that can be observed with a low-power microscope (Crookes; Elster and Geitel, 1903). The dials of luminous watches owe their luminosity to such scintillations; they are made by adding a small amount of a radioactive substance to a paste containing activated zinc sulfide.

The spinthariscope was an extremely important instrument in the hands of Rutherford and his pupils, who employed it extensively in establishing, for instance, Rutherford's scattering law. However, because the method was extremely laborious, it later fell into disuse with the development of G–M counters. Recently, modern versions have come to the forefront through the use of photomultipliers to detect scintillations, thus dispensing with dependence on the human eye and the accompanying labor and uncertainty of efficiency in detection. Many substances scintillate when bombarded by nuclear radiations, but those commonly used in practice fall into three classes: plastics, liquids, and organic and inorganic crystals. Noble gases (Kr, Xe) and liquid helium have been used for special purposes such as the detection

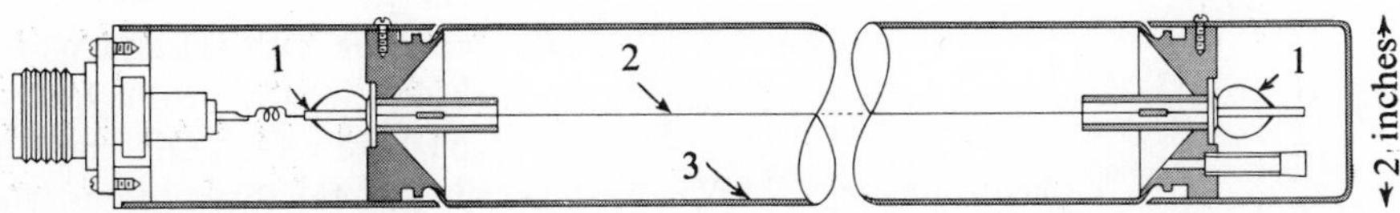

Figure 3-12 Cosmic-ray Geiger–Müller counter. Actual counter 30 inches long. 1, Kovar-glass seals; 2, anode wire; 3, metal cathode. [Courtesy Radiation Counter Laboratories, Inc., Skokie, Ill.]

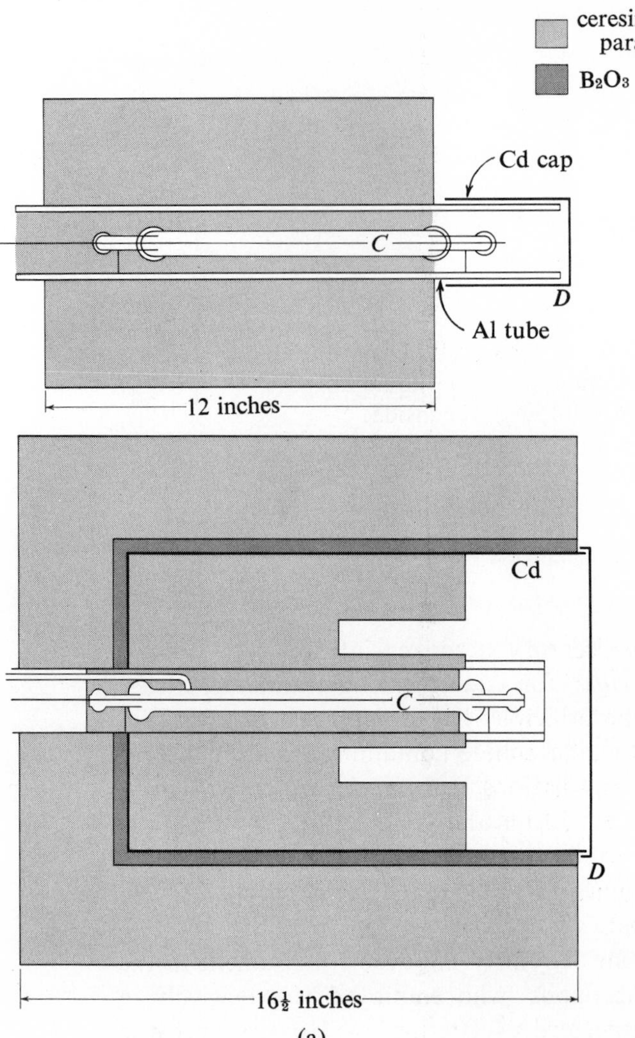

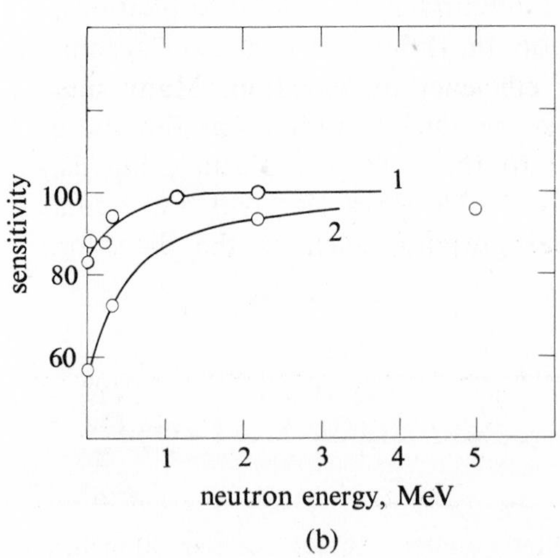

Figure 3-13 (a) Two neutron counters designed by Hanson and McKibben with uniform sensitivity (to within ~ 10 per cent) from 10 keV to 3 MeV. The second, or shielded, counter is designed to operate in a region of relatively high scattered neutron background. *C* are BF_3 counters; *D*, cadmium caps and shields. (b) Relative sensitivity in an arbitrary scale versus neutron energy of the shielded long counter with (1) and without (2) holes in the front face of the paraffin. [A. O. Hanson and J. L. McKibben, *Phys. Rev.*, **72**, 673 (1947).]

of fission fragments or alpha particles. Table 3-4 gives typical characteristics of a few scintillating substances. The scintillation light is emitted for the most part over a continuous spectrum with a maximum between 4,100 and 4,500 Å. When the scintillations occur in the extreme ultraviolet, one uses a light shifter, i.e., a substance that, when excited in the extreme ultraviolet, fluoresces in a more convenient spectral region.

It is possible with modern photomultipliers to detect a particle that loses only 4 keV in a scintillator. This is a practical figure and takes into account the problem of the collection of light. A phototube gives one electron at the cathode for about 20 light quanta, and the tube itself multiplies the electron by a factor of 10^8 in a period of a few pico seconds. The electron avalanche striking the anode may last $\sim 3 \times 10^{-9}$ sec. The fluctuations in this period depend on the structure of the photomultiplier tube. An example of a photomultiplier tube is shown in Fig. 3-14.

The density of ionization in some scintillating mediums influences the time dependence of light emission. If the ionization density is low, the light is emitted faster than if the ionization density is high. This effect has important applications in distinguishing different types of particles such as protons and alpha particles entering a scintillator. A very striking case is that of neutrons and gamma rays. The first act through recoil protons, the second mainly through Compton electrons. By measuring the total amount of light emitted in a time interval of the order of 0.5 μsec and the maximum instantaneous intensity (at about 0.1 μsec after the excitation), it is possible to distinguish clearly between scintillations produced by X rays and those produced by neutrons (Fig. 3-15).

Sodium iodide crystals activated with thallium are especially valuable for detecting X rays. They can be made nearly 100 per cent efficient, and the amount of light emitted can be related to the energy of the impinging radiation. This, however, may require a pulse-height analysis, like the one shown in Figs. 3-16 and 3-17, and an interpretation of the various peaks.

Table 3-4 Characteristics of Scintillators

Substance	Density, g cm^{-3}	Refractive index	Decay constant, nsec	Light (anthracene = 100)	Wavelength of max Å
Anthracene	1.25		32	100	4,470
Stilbene	1.16	1.62	4	60	4,100
Plastic[a]	1.04	1.58	3	36	4,500
Liquid[b]	0.88	1.50	3	40	3,820
NaI(Tl)	3.67	1.77	250	230	4,130
ZnS(Ag)	4.09	2.36	200	300	4,500

[a] Polystyrene + 16 g liter^{-1} *p*-terphenyl.
[b] Toluene + 3 g liter^{-1} 2-5-dyphenyl oxazole.

Large liquid scintillators, loaded with cadmium or boron and having a volume of hundreds of liters, are among the most efficient neutron detectors. Efficiencies greater than 95 per cent are possible.

Plastic and crystal scintillators can be made in all shapes and sizes. They are sometimes put in direct optical contact with a photomultiplier. However, for convenience they may be connected to the photomultiplier by *light pipes*. These are highly polished pieces of plastic (Plexiglas) in which the light travels by multiple reflections from the walls. The attenuation in light pipes is generally small (in the visible spectrum), but it must be remembered that it is not possible to funnel the light from a large scintillator to a small photocathode surface without an attenuation

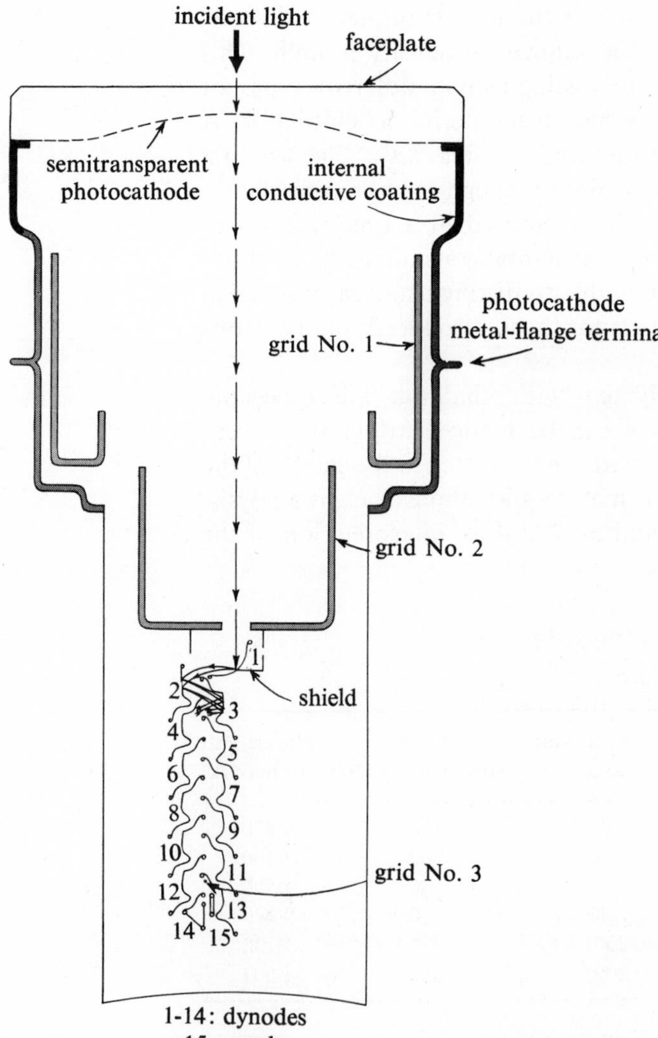

Figure 3-14 Schematic arrangement of a photomultiplier tube (RCA 7046). The electrons emitted from the illuminated curved cathode are directed by fixed electrostatic fields provided by grids No. 1 and No. 2 to the first dynode 1 (secondary emitter). The electrons impinging on the dynode surface produce many other electrons, the number depending on the energy of the impinging electrons. These secondary electrons are then directed by fixed electrostatic fields along curved paths to the second dynode 2, where they produce more electrons. This multiplying process is repeated in 14 stages until electrons emitted by the last dynode, No. 14, are collected by the anode and constitute the current utilized in the output circuit. Total multiplication 2×10^7. [Courtesy RCA Company.]

of light that is at least in the ratio of the surface areas at each end of the light pipe.

3-5 Cerenkov Counters

The Cerenkov counter works on the principle that radiation is emitted by charged particles whose velocity βc exceeds the velocity of light in a given medium, i.e., when $\beta > 1/n$, where n is the refractive index of the medium. The intensity of Cerenkov light in the visible spectrum is about 100 times weaker than typical scintillation light in a plastic. A particle moving with velocity c in a medium having $n = 1.5$ emits about 250 light quanta per centimeter of path (see Sec. 2-5).

Even though Cerenkov light is comparatively weak, Cerenkov counters are very useful in high-energy nuclear physics because of the directional property of the light. That is Cerenkov radiation is emitted in a cone of half angle θ, the axis of the cone being the incident-particle direction. The angle θ is given by the expression

$$\cos\theta = \frac{1}{n\beta} \tag{3-5.1}$$

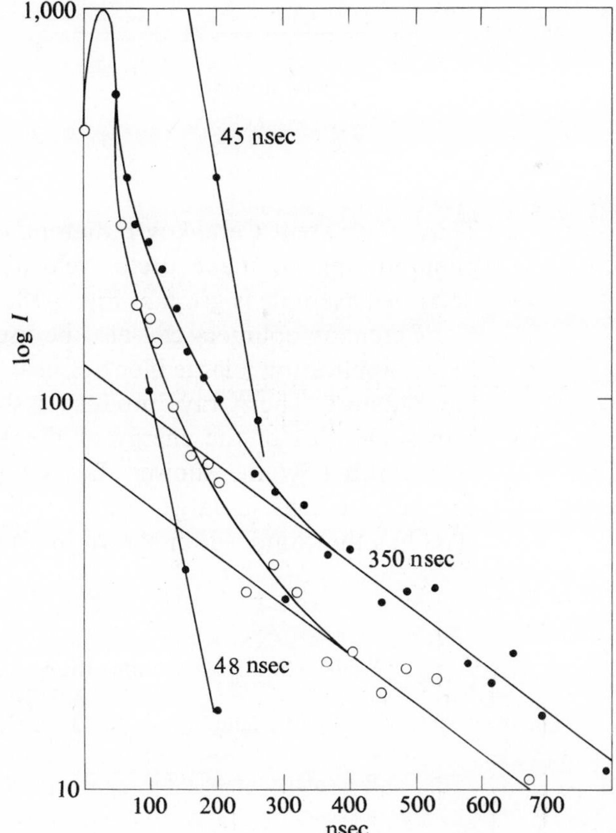

Figure 3-15 Light emission as a function of time for a scintillator (quaterphenyl) excited by neutrons or gamma rays. Ordinates are on a logarithmic scale. Open circles, gamma rays; closed circles, neutrons. [R. B. Owen, *IRE Trans.*, **NS-5**, 198 (1958).]

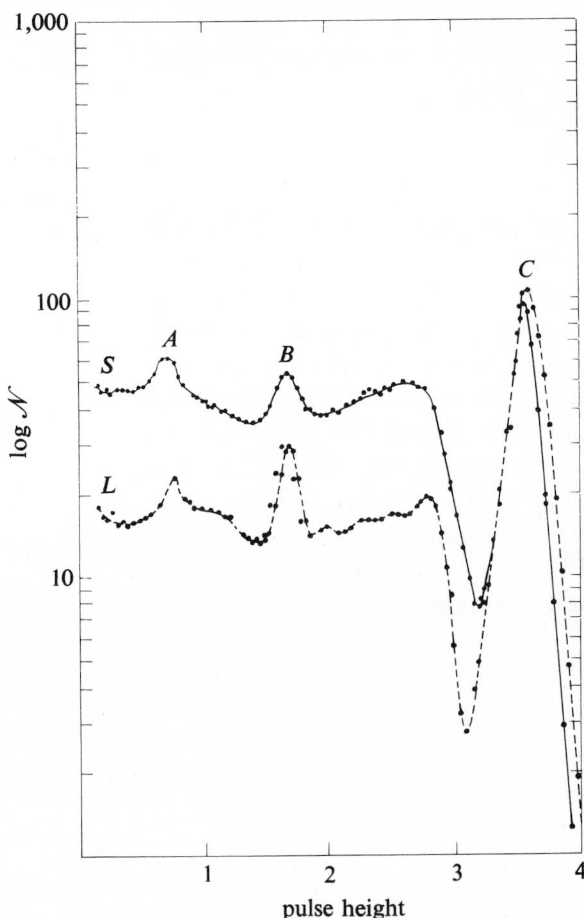

Figure 3-16 The pulse-height distributions for Zn^{65} on $1\frac{1}{2}$- by 1-in. (*S* curve) and 3- by 3-in. crystals (*L* curve) of activated sodium iodide. Ordinate is number of pulses on a logarithmic scale; abscissa, pulse height. The peaks observed are: *A*, backscattered radiation; *B*, annihilation radiation (0.51MeV); *C*, primary radiation (1.12 MeV). [P. R. Bell, in (Si 55).]

Thus transparent Cerenkov radiators, coupled with optical devices and photomultipliers, make useful velocity selectors for high-energy particles. An example is given in Fig. 3-18.

Cerenkov counters can also be used to detect high-energy X rays. In this application a large block of heavy glass is employed as the Cerenkov radiator. The X rays produce a shower in the glass, and one can gain some idea of the energy of the X ray from the total amount of light emitted by the shower. Glass especially suited for this purpose can be obtained in large blocks with good transparency. A typical glass has the composition shown in Table 3-5. This particular glass has

Table 3-5 Glass Composition

Compound	Na_2O	K_2O	PbO	SiO_2	As_2O_3
Percentage by weight	1.0	3.4	61.7	33.1	0.8

a density of 4.49 g cm^{-3}, n = 1.72, and radiation length X_0 = 2 cm. An example of such a glass Cerenkov counter is shown in Fig. 3-19.

3-6 Photographic Emulsions

The blackening of photographic plates was the first effect of nuclear radiation ever observed (Becquerel, 1896), and the blackening of plates or films is still a very important detection method. It is interesting to note that the reciprocity law according to which the blackening of a plate by X rays depends only on the product $I \cdot t$ (I = intensity, t = time of exposure) is valid in most cases. Special film for X rays is being manufactured currently and is used with or without reinforcing screens, which increase the photographic action of the primary radiation by emitting secondary light or electrons.

Single particles are detectable in special photographic emulsions rich in silver bromide. This old technique (Kinoshita, 1912) has been recently perfected and is now very useful. A typical modern emulsion (G–5 of Ilford) is described in Table 3-6.

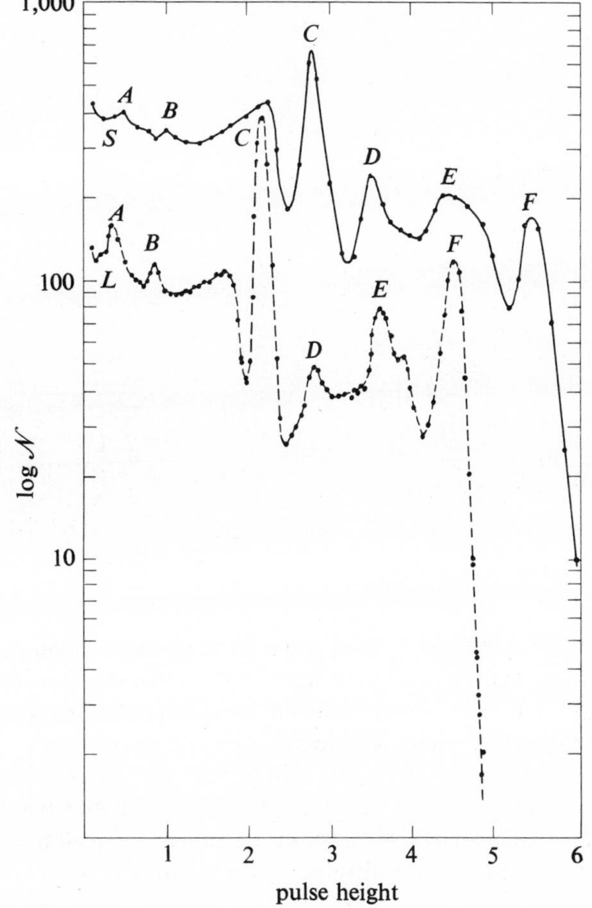

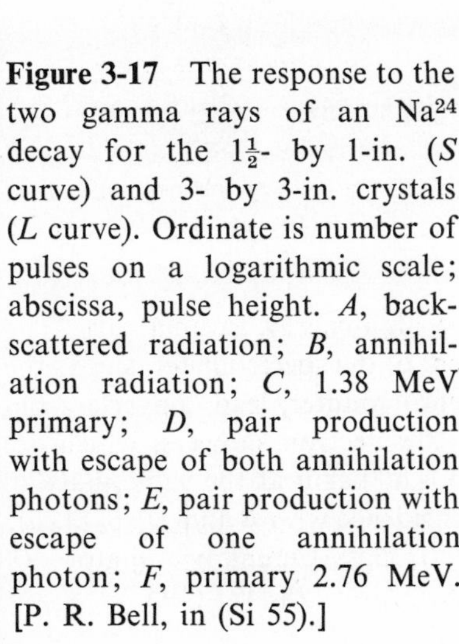
Figure 3-17 The response to the two gamma rays of an Na^{24} decay for the $1\frac{1}{2}$- by 1-in. (S curve) and 3- by 3-in. crystals (L curve). Ordinate is number of pulses on a logarithmic scale; abscissa, pulse height. A, backscattered radiation; B, annihilation radiation; C, 1.38 MeV primary; D, pair production with escape of both annihilation photons; E, pair production with escape of one annihilation photon; F, primary 2.76 MeV. [P. R. Bell, in (Si 55).]

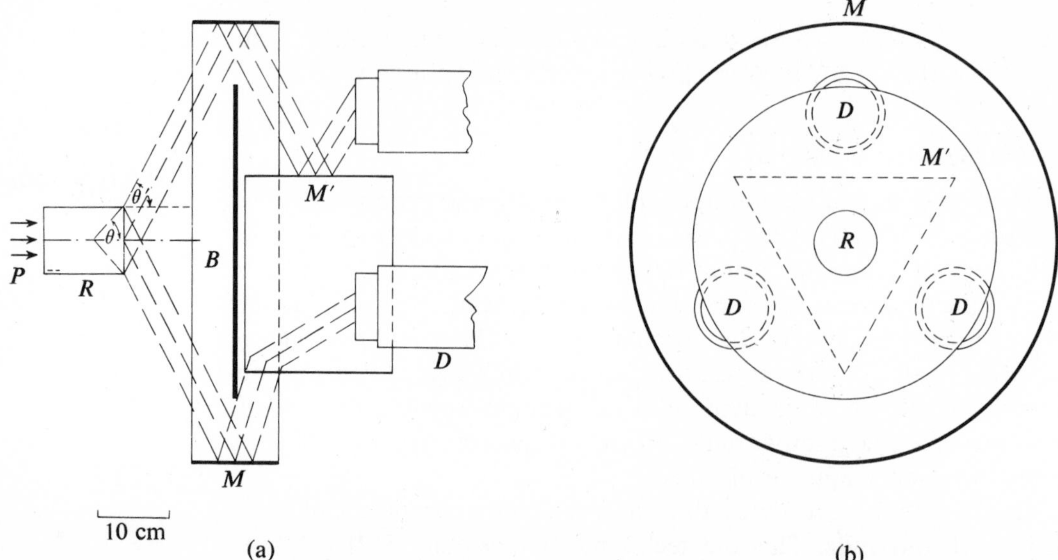

Figure 3-18 Schematic diagram of the velocity-selector Cerenkov counter: (a) side view; (b) front view. *R*, radiator; *M*, cylindrical mirrors; *M′*, plane mirrors; *D*, detectors (photomultipliers); *B*, black baffle; *P*, incident particles. [O. Chamberlain and C. E. Wiegand, UCRL 9288.]

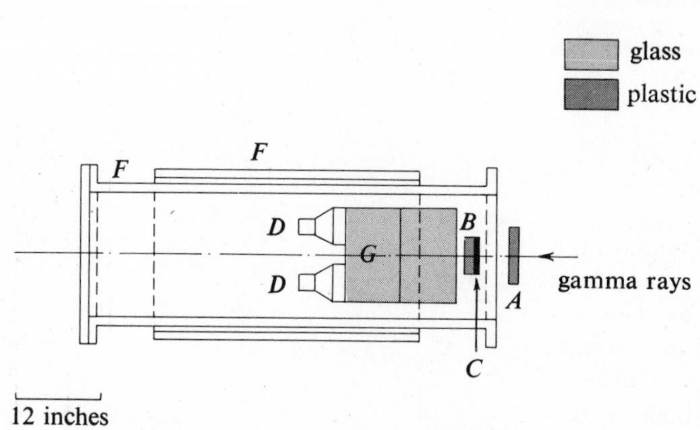

Figure 3-19 A large glass block used as a Cerenkov counter for high-energy gamma rays. The instrument can be used as a spectrometer. The schematic arrangement of the spectrometer, shows the glass, phototubes, and magnetic shield, as well as the anticoincidence counter, lead converter, and coincidence counter. These two scintillation counters ensure that the electron showers, which are pulse-height-analyzed, start in the 6-mm. lead converter *C*, and thus all begin at the same place in the system. *F*, iron magnetic shields; *A*, plastic scintillator in anticoincidence with *B* and *D*; *B*, plastic scintillator in coincidence with *D*; *C*, Pb converter 6 mm thick; *G*, glass Cerenkov radiator; *D*, detectors (photomultipliers). [Brabant, Moyer, and Wallace, *Rev. Sci. Instr.*, **28**, 421 (1957).]

Table 3-6 Data on Ilford G–5 Emulsion [a]

Density, g cm^{-3}	3.907	Ag, 1.85 g cm^{-3}
Atoms, cm^{-3}	8.12×10^{22}	Br, 1.36 g cm^{-3}
Mean A	28.98	I, 0.024 g cm^{-3}
Mean Z	13.17	C, 0.27 g cm^{-3}
Mean Z^2	456	H, 0.056 g cm^{-3}
Radiation length, cm	2.93	O, 0.27 g cm^{-3}
		S, 0.010 g cm^{-3}
		N, 0.067 g cm^{-3}

[a] The emulsion considered in the table is assumed to be in equilibrium with air of 50 per cent relative humidity.

A minimum-ionizing single charged particle produces about 30 developable grains per 100 μ of path length. The grain density is proportional to $-dE/dx$ and can thus be used to measure the velocity of a particle, at least so long as $v \ll c$ and the grain density does not reach saturation. Saturation occurs at $-dE/dx \simeq 10^3$ MeV g^{-1} cm^{-2}. For such a high specific energy loss and the consequent high specific ionization, all grains on the track are developable: a further increase of the specific ionization cannot increase the grain density. The determination of the specific ionization is often accomplished in practice by measuring the length of the gaps, i.e., of the regions free of

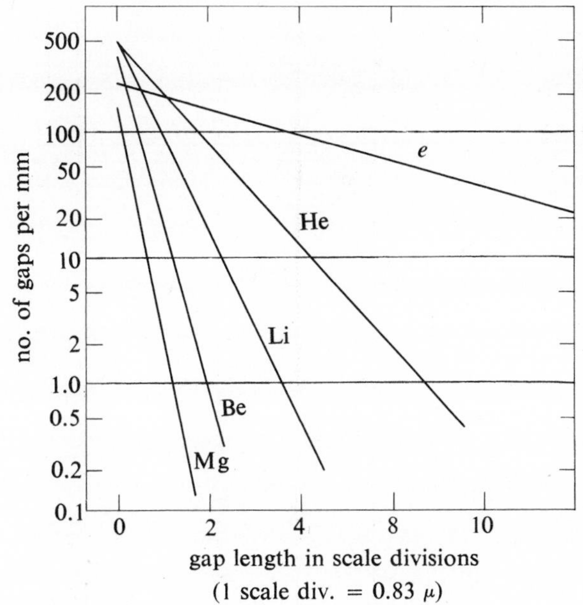

Figure 3-20 Graph for determining the specific ionization by measuring "gaps." Variation with gap length l of the number of gaps of length equal to or greater than l, for particles of different specific ionization. [(PFP 59).]

developed grains along a track (Fig. 3-20). The range of a particle traversing a photographic emulsion is also a function of the particle energy and can be found in range-energy tables (Fig. 3-21).

For velocities near c, it is still possible to measure the quantity $p\beta$ (where p is momentum) from the multiple scattering. One has approximately

$$\langle\alpha\rangle = K\left(\frac{l}{100\ \mu}\right)^{1/2} \frac{z}{p\beta} \tag{3-6.1}$$

where $\langle\alpha\rangle$ is the projected angle between chords of successive track segments of length l (in microns). For $l = 100\ \mu$ the constant K is 25.8° for single charged particles and for $p\beta$ in MeV/c (Fig. 3-22). The density of delta rays along a heavily ionizing track provides another means of measuring the energy of the particles.

Emulsions can be loaded with elements such as B, Bi, and U for special purposes; they can also be assembled in relatively large "stacks"

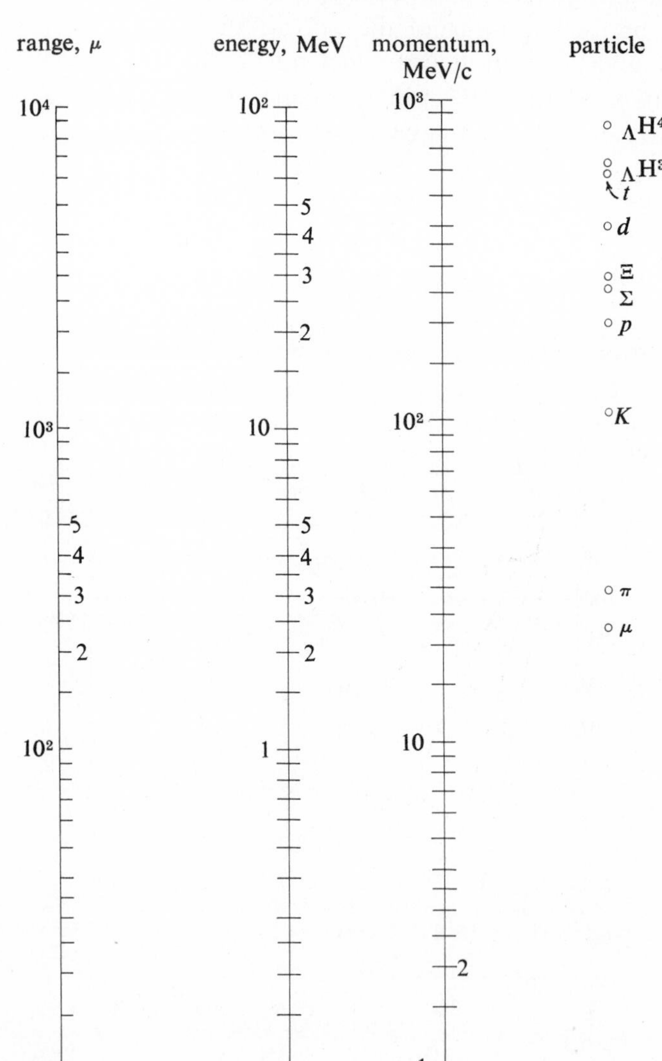

Figure 3-21 Nomogram for range, momentum, energy, and mass to be used in emulsion work. It relates to four variables by laying a straight edge across the scales. [Courtesy W. Barkas.]

(for example, 30 by 20 by 10 cm thick, with single layers 600μ thick) and subsequently disassembled for development. Each emulsion is then mounted on a glass plate and observed separately. With suitable markings, it is possible to follow the individual tracks through the successive emulsion layers. Figure 1-6 shows the historic photograph in which the pi meson was discovered.

3-7 Cloud Chambers

C. T. R. Wilson observed that a supersaturated vapor tends to condense on ions and that the resulting droplets become visible under bright illumination. He developed the first cloud chamber in 1912, with which he obtained the beautiful pictures of Fig. 3-23.

A cloud chamber is essentially a box, filled with a gas and a vapor (for example, air and H_2O), that can be expanded rapidly by a piston or a moving wall. Adiabatic expansion cools the gas and makes the vapor supersaturated. The saturated vapor pressure p^* on a drop of radius r having an electric charge e is greater than the saturated vapor pressure on a plane surface p according to the formula

$$\log \frac{p^*}{p} = \frac{M}{\rho r R T}\left(2\tau - \frac{e^2}{8\pi r^3}\frac{k-1}{k}\right) \tag{3-7.1}$$

where M is the molecular weight of the vapor and ρ, τ, and k are, respectively, the density, surface tension, and dielectric constant of the liquid. The vapor will therefore condense around charges, forming droplets that grow rapidly in size. The expansion ratio necessary to obtain suitable condensation conditions varies with the gas and vapor: for example, for air-alcohol mixtures at 20°C, a suitable expansion ratio is 1.31. The initial supersaturation, i.e., the pressure of the alcohol vapor divided by the pressure of the saturated alcohol vapor at the temperature immediately following expansion is then 5.7.

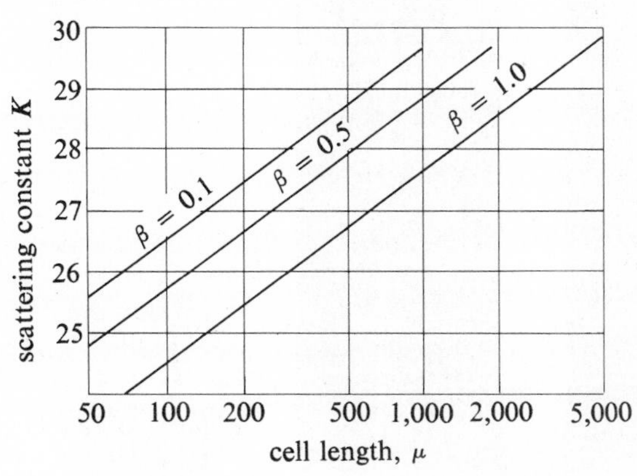

Figure 3-22 Values of the scattering constant as a function of cell size for different values of β. The scattering constant is measured in units such that if the value of $\langle\alpha\rangle$ is given in degrees per 100 μ, $K/\langle\alpha\rangle$ gives the value of $p\beta$ for singly charged particles in MeV/c. For multiple charged particles of any mass, the scattering constant given by the curve labeled $\beta = 0.1$ may be taken. But note the term z in the relation $p\beta = Kz/\langle\alpha\rangle$. [(PFP 59).]

The cloud chamber remains sensitive for about 0.1 sec after expansion, and the ions must be swept away by an electric field before a new compression-expansion cycle begins. Cloud chambers are usually illuminated by electric flashes in xenon, and the tracks are photographed stereoscopically in order to be able to reconstruct the event in three dimensions.

Magnetic fields of about 2×10^4 G are often applied to the chamber to measure the momentum of the particles producing the tracks. The accuracy of the measurement of curvature is limited by turbulence in the chamber and by the unavoidable multiple scattering in the gas. The first effect can be avoided by careful construction and operation. As an example of the cloud chamber see Fig. 3-24.

The expansion mechanism of a cloud chamber may be triggered at regular time intervals or in synchrony with the output of an artificial source such as an accelerator. It is also possible to arrange around a chamber counters or other devices that will trigger the chamber only when they detect a particular event. This is feasible because the chamber retains the ability of forming the tracks for long enough to allow the motion of the parts determining the expansion (Blackett and Occhialini, 1933; see Fig. 2-33).

It is also possible to build continuously operating cloud chambers which do not need any expansion mechanism. These are boxes having

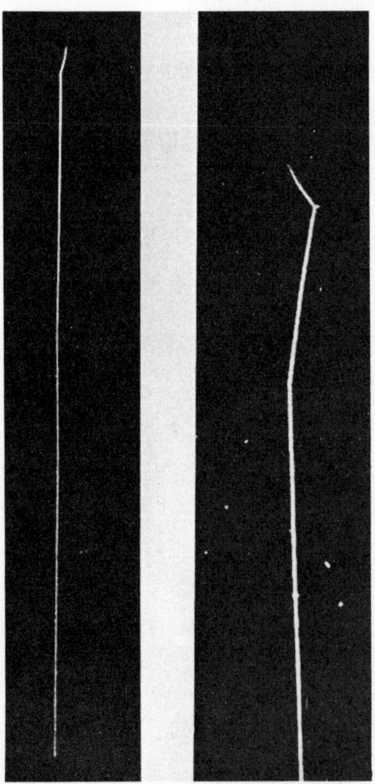

Figure 3-23 Original pictures of alpha particles obtained by C. T. R. Wilson in 1912.

a vertical temperature gradient, with the top warm and the bottom cold, and containing a mixture of gas and vapor. A layer is formed in which the vapor is supersaturated and in which tracks can be produced. This type of chamber can be operated with different mixtures of gas and vapor and at pressures up to several atmospheres. Demonstration chambers can be built very easily (Fig. 3-25).

3-8 Bubble Chambers

A recent important development (Glaser, 1952) in the art of detecting nuclear radiation has been the bubble chamber. This is a chamber full of a liquid at a pressure and temperature such that it is below the boiling point. The pressure is then suddenly lowered, thereby lowering the boiling point, and the liquid starts to develop bubbles, which form preferentially around ions. The bubbles are, like the droplets in a cloud chamber, visible under strong illumination. Bubble chambers are sensitive for times of the order of 10 msec. They have been operated

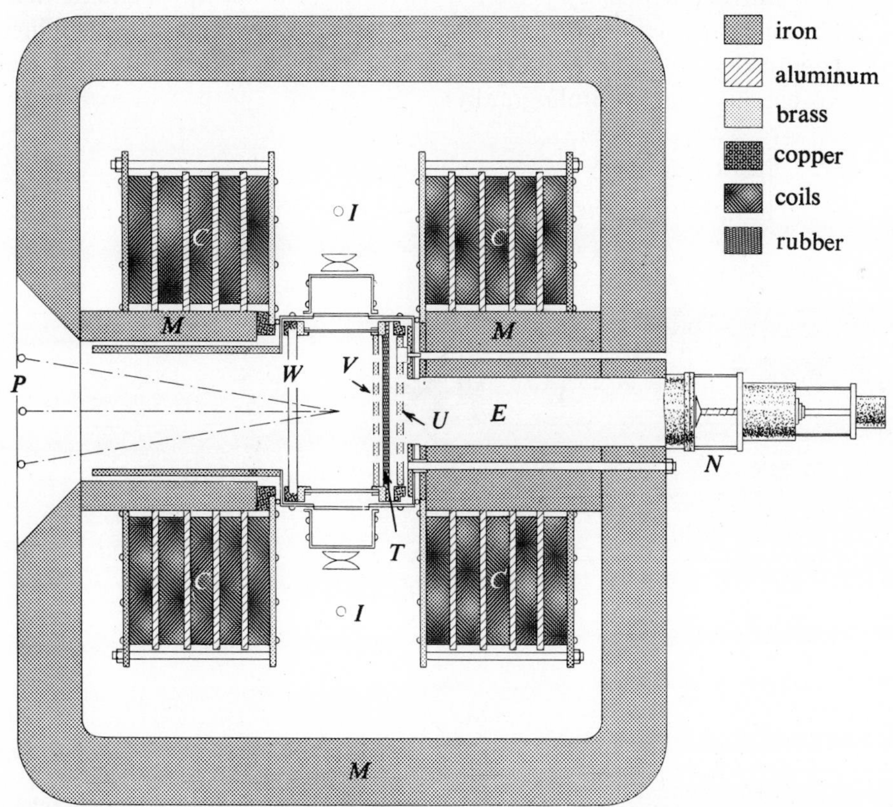

Figure 3-24 Top view of a cloud chamber with magnetic field. *M*, magnet; *C*, coils; *I*, illumination; *P*, photography. The rubber diaphragm *T* moves between the holey plates *U* and *V* when previously compressed air is released through *E* by opening valve *N*. [Thompson, Burwell, and Huggett, *Nuovo Cimento, Suppl.*, **4**, 286 (1956).]

with various liquids, including hydrogen, deuterium, helium, propane, and xenon. Their great advantage lies in the fact that the detecting material is much denser than the gas in cloud chambers and of simpler composition than photographic emulsions. For instance, in a hydrogen bubble chamber, hydrogen has a density of 0.07 g cm^{-3} at the boiling point under 1 atm pressure, whereas the density of the gas is 0.0899×10^{-3} g cm^{-3} at 0°C and 1 atm.

A hydrogen bubble chamber of very large dimensions has been developed by Alvarez and his co-workers. Figure 3-26 shows their chamber, which is 72 in. long and contains ~500 liters of liquid hydrogen. It is especially suited to the study of the complex phenomena that occur in the interactions of high-energy particles with hydrogen. Several of the illustrations in this book, notably those in Chap. 15, show the power of this method.

The cloud chamber and bubble chamber give a picture of the event being studied that must be analyzed to extract the pertinent information. The event is first reconstructed in space by using two or more photographs taken from different angles, i.e., a stereoscopic projection. The momenta of the particles involved are measured either from their range or from the curvature of their trajectories in a known magnetic field. The analysis is laborious and is greatly assisted by computing machines. The reader is referred to the literature for this special subject (see Rosenfeld, Chap. 3 Bibliography).

3-9 Spark Chamber

The spark chamber, a device based on old principles but developed

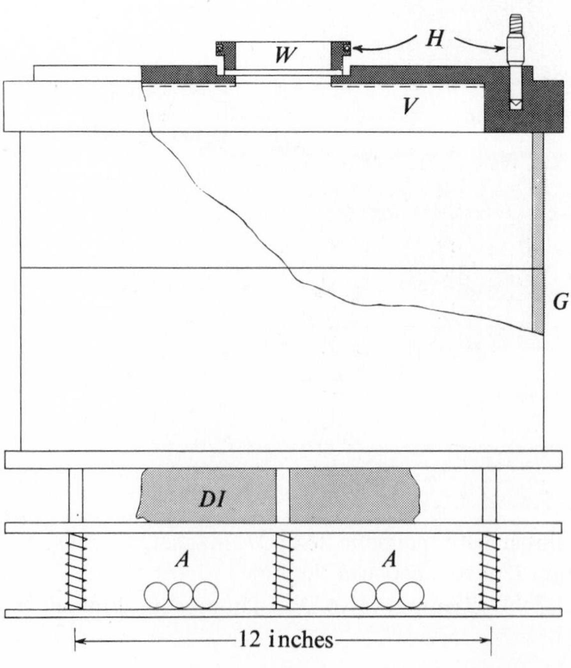

Figure 3-25 A simple, continuously sensitive cloud chamber. *W*, window; *V*, velvet pad; *G*, glass rings; *A*, counters; *DI*, dry ice; *H*, heaters. [E. W. Cowan, *Rev. Sci. Instr.*, **21**, 991 (1950).]

only in recent years (Cranshaw and De Beer, 1957; Fukui and Miyamoto, 1959), combines some of the features of counter arrays and of the bubble chamber. In its simplest form a spark chamber is an array of thin conducting plates. The even-numbered ones are grounded, and the odd-numbered can be brought to a high voltage. The gaps between plates are filled with a noble gas at atmospheric pressure. The gaps are about 8 mm wide, and a voltage of about 10 kV is applied across them for a short time ($\sim$ 0.2 μsec) at a chosen moment. The chamber is sensitive for about 0.5 μsec preceding the application of the voltage. Any charged particle passing through the chamber during this period produces along its path a visible and audible discharge which can be located by photographing and by acoustical or electrical methods. A clearing field is applied between the plates to sweep away unwanted electrons and ions.

From this description it is apparent that the chamber can be triggered with counters by applying the sensitizing field. The short interval during which the chamber is sensitive allows it to photograph the desired events without a serious background even when the flux of

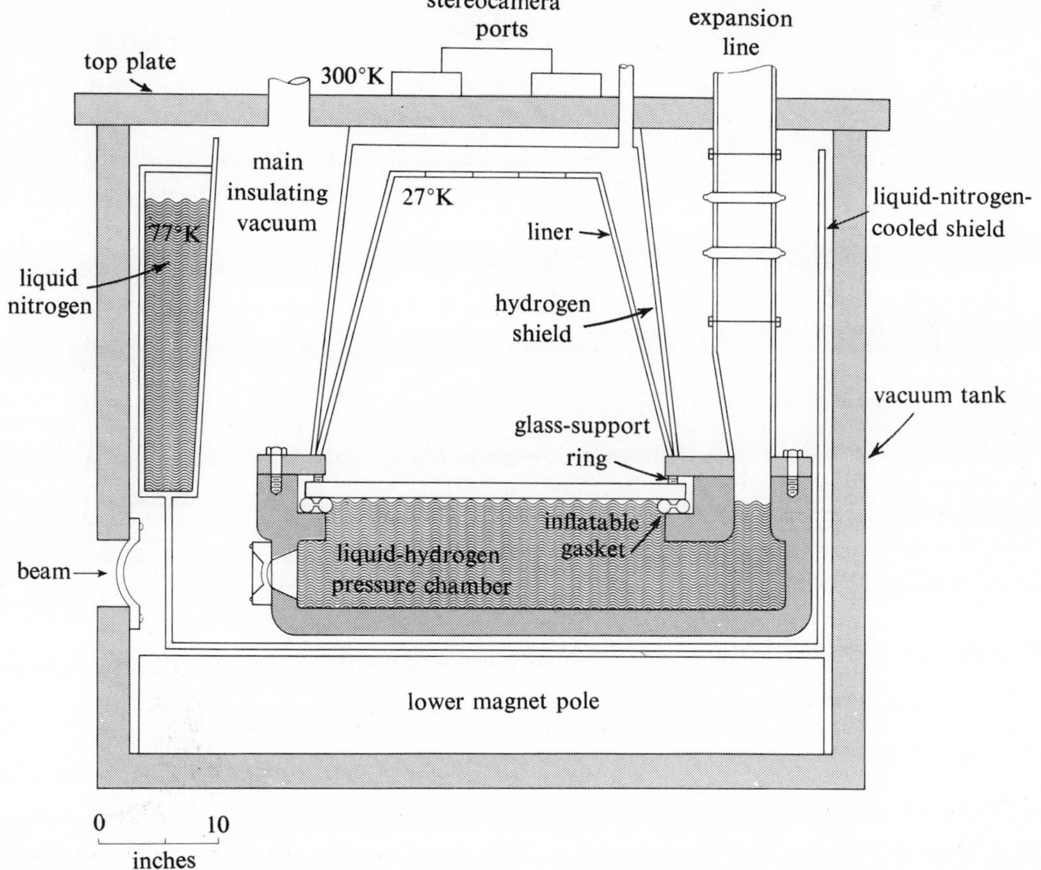

Figure 3-26 Longitudinal cross section of the 72-in. hydrogen bubble chamber. [Lawrence Radiation Laboratory; Alvarez group.]

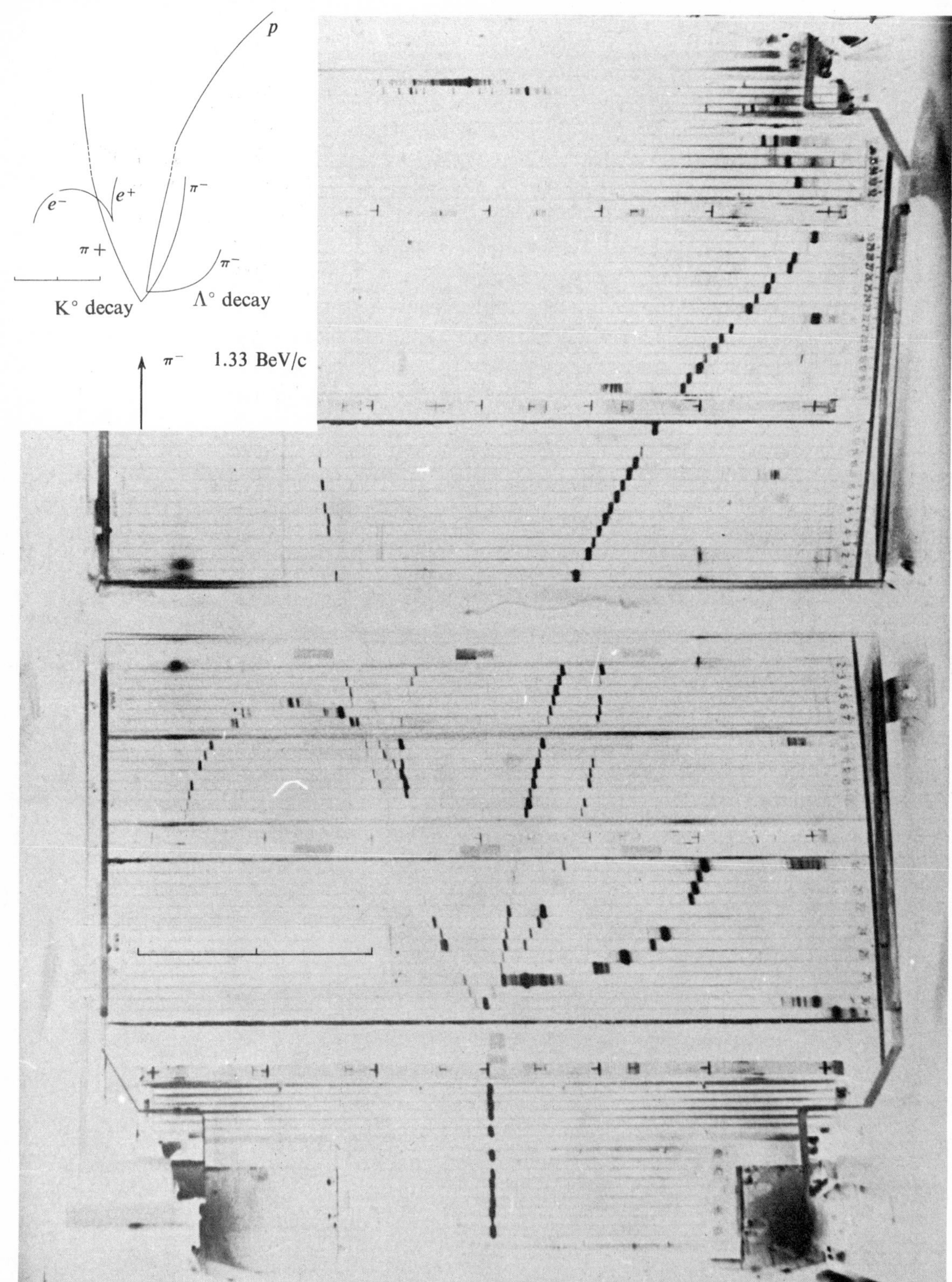

Figure 3-27 Spark-chamber picture of $\pi^- + p \to \Sigma^\circ + K^\circ$ reaction and subsequent reactions $\Sigma^\circ \to \Lambda^\circ + \gamma$; $\Lambda^\circ \to p^+ + \pi^-$; $K^\circ \to \pi^+ + \pi^-$; $\gamma \to e^+ + e^-$. The spark chamber is in a field of approximately 13.5 kG. [Courtesy A. Roberts.]

particles is several million per second. Ordinarily two cameras at right angles to one another are used to photograph an event in order to reconstruct the tracks in space (Fig. 3-27).

3-10 Electronics

In addition to actual detecting devices a wide variety of electronic apparatus and techniques form an integral part of nuclear instrumentation. Their detailed description falls outside the scope of this book. We shall confine ourselves to little more than a catalogue including some performance data. Many of the devices are now commercially available.

Almost all detecting devices include amplifiers, i.e., apparatus that multiply the voltage applied by the primary detector until it becomes easily measurable. The ratio between the output and the input voltage of the amplifier is called *voltage gain*, or simply, *gain*. It is often important that the gain be constant over a wide range of the input voltage. An apparatus with constant gain is called a *linear amplifier*. The constancy of the gain in time is another important characteristic: a gain drift of less than 1 per cent in 24 hours is a usual requirement.

Direct-current amplifiers are required for ionization chambers in a steady state. They are essentially different from pulse amplifiers, and their significant parameter is current sensitivity: 10^{-15} A is measurable to an accuracy of a few per cent.

For pulse-detecting instruments the output depends not only on the maximum voltage applied but also on the time dependence of the input voltage. A common way to characterize the time response of an amplifier is to give its *rise time*. If we suddenly apply a voltage v to the input terminal, the output will rise from 0.1 to 0.9 of its maximum value

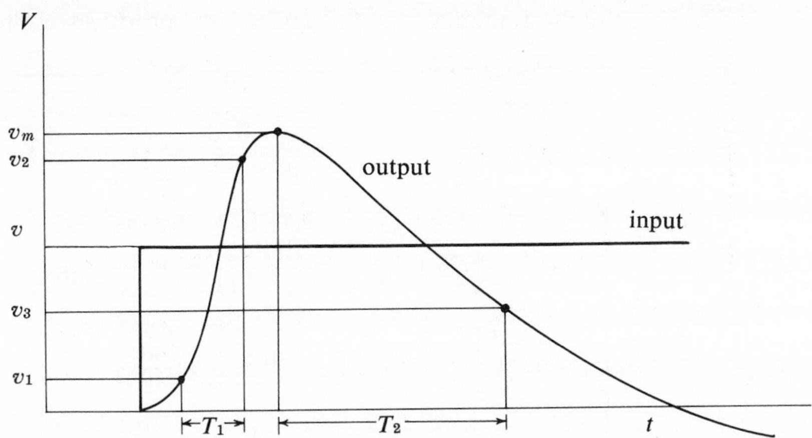

Figure 3-28 Input and output voltages in an amplifier v_m = maximum output voltage; $v_1 = 0.1v_m$; $v_2 = 0.9v_m$; $v_3 = v_m/e$; T_1 = rise time; T_2 = decay time.

within the rise time. The decay time of the amplifier is defined as the time taken to return to $1/e$ of the maximum value of the input voltage (Fig. 3-28). Rise times of 2×10^{-9} to 10^{-6} sec are used in practice. Decay times are usually 1 to 100 times as long as rise times. Generally speaking, speed of the amplifier and linearity of the output are mutually exclusive for high-gain devices.

Another important characteristic of an amplifier is its noise. The voltage at the output fluctuates, even in the absence of a signal, in an irregular fashion. Thermal agitation (Johnson noise) and the fluctuation in current due to the finite charge of the electron (shot effect) are unavoidable causes of noise. In a detector the signal-to-noise ratio must be kept as high as possible. For this reason, amplification of the primary signal is often performed in two stages: a first stage comprises a preamplifier of modest gain (5 to 10) but of very low noise. Its output is then fed through a transmission line, if necessary over a distance of many meters, to the amplifier proper. Another reason for using a preamplifier is that one can adapt it to any special purpose desired and join it to a main amplifier of standard design, the same for a variety of applications. The output voltages of common amplifiers are 10 to 100 volts. A typical high-gain amplifier is illustrated in Fig. 3-29 and its frequency response in Fig. 3-30. A typical preamplifier is shown in Fig. 3-31.

It is often important to register pulses following each other at very short intervals. This is accomplished by decreasing the decay time of the amplifier by various tricks, such as reflection of the original pulse on a terminated line. In this way dead time is minimized even for large saturating pulses.

In many applications it is also important to have automatic apparatus that will record the number of pulses applied to them. Such apparatus are called scalers. Their primary component is a flip-flop circuit (Fig. 3-32). This is a circuit with two stable states of current. An input pulse changes it from one state to the other. A switch manually operated every time that a pulse occurs is the most primitive kind of flip-flop circuit. Imagine, now, a device that produces a pulse when a

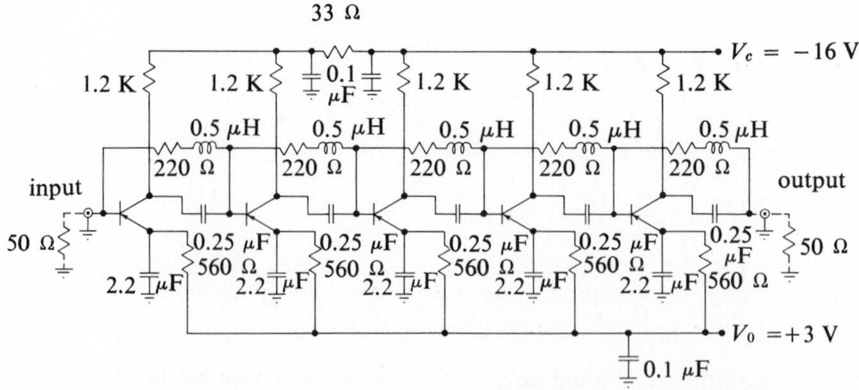

Figure 3-29 Wide-band transistor amplifier. [R.Scarlett.]

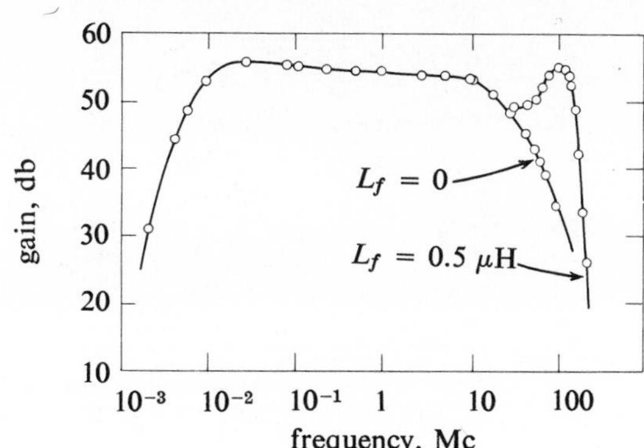

Figure 3-30 Frequency response of the wideband transistor amplifier shown in Fig. 3-29. Abscissa in logarithmic scale.

flip-flop circuit passes from state b to state a, but not when it passes from state a to state b. A series of flip-flop circuits connected to each other by the device mentioned above forms a scaling circuit, as shown in Fig. 3-33. Assume all the circuits to be initially in state a. Then each successive pulse will bring the scaler to the states indicated in Fig. 3-33.

It is clear that, if we interpret a as 0 and b as 1, the state of the boxes after n pulses will be given by the number representing n in a binary system of numbers, e.g.,

$$1 \quad 0 \quad 0 \quad 1 \quad 1$$

will indicate

$$(1 \times 1) + (0 \times 2) + (0 \times 4) + (1 \times 8) + (1 \times 16) = 25$$

if we put, as is usual with scalers, the highest power of 2 to the right.

The most important characteristic of a flip-flop circuit is its speed, i.e., how many times per second it can change from one state to the other; 10^6 times per second is a representative figure. It must be remembered, however, that this refers to equally spaced pulses. Random pulses occurring at the average rate of n per second are counted with

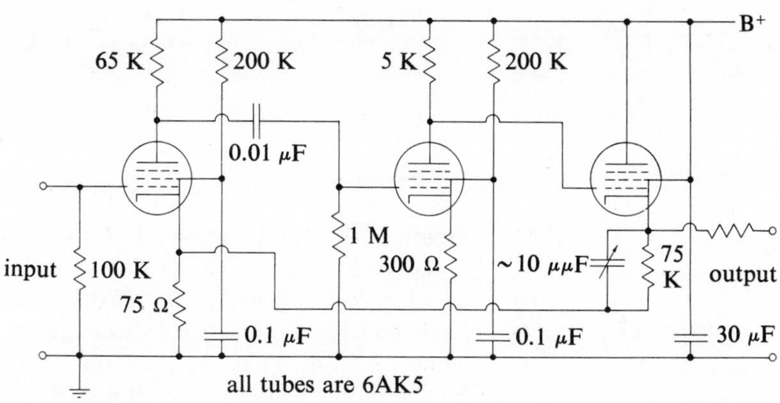

Figure 3-31 Preamplifier circuit containing feedback.

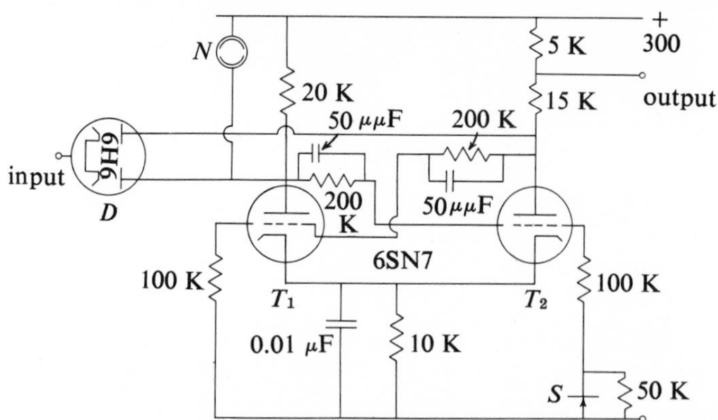

Figure 3-32 Flip-flop circuit (Higinbotham circuit). Its principle of operation briefly is as follows: Suppose that tube T_1 is conducting, T_2 is nonconducting. A negative signal of sufficient height, fed to the cathode of the twin diode D, will pass through only the upper half of D, since the anode of the lower half is at a potential much lower than the cathode. If the cross-coupling capacitor between the anode of T_2 and the grid of T_1 is sufficiently large, the signal will cause T_1 to be momentarily cut off, making T_2 conducting by way of the cross-feed capacitor between the anode of T_1 and the grid of T_2; T_1 will then remain nonconducting. The perfect symmetry of the circuit shows immediately that the action of the next pulse consists in flipping conductivity from T_2 to T_1.

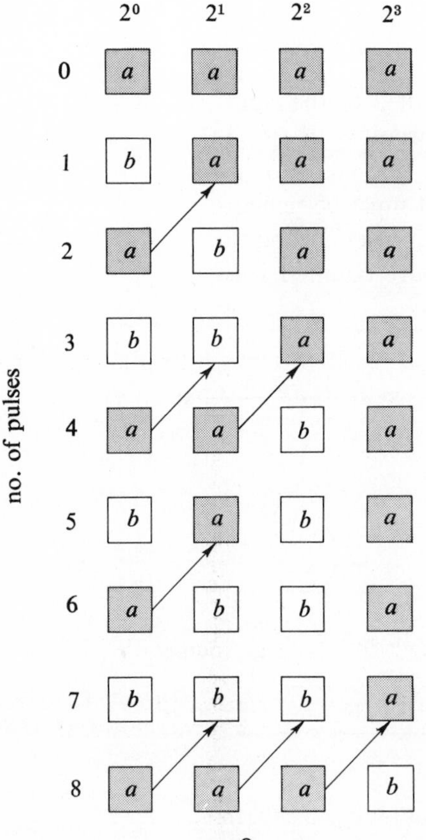

Figure 3-33 The functioning of a scaler on the arrival of successive pulses. The arrows show when a flip-flop circuit passes a pulse to the next circuit in the chain. Each box has the property of changing from gray to white or from white to gray on arrival of a pulse. Furthermore, if, and only if, a box changes from white to gray, it passes a pulse to the box at its right.

an approximate fractional counting loss $n\tau$, where τ is the minimum time required for a change from state a to state b, or vice versa. Generally, the voltage pulses (output of an amplifier) need be counted only if they are above a certain threshold. This is accomplished by a *discriminator* circuit. Discriminators are triggered only by pulses above their threshold and, once triggered, mostly, give a pulse of amplitude and duration independent of the triggering input. A typical discriminator circuit is shown in Fig. 3-34.

One of the most powerful electronic tools used in nuclear physics is the coincidence circuit (Rossi, 1930). Here we have an apparatus that responds only to two simultaneous input pulses. By "simultaneous" we mean within a very short time interval (resolving time), for example, 10^{-8} sec. After a pulse the circuit remains dead for a time of the same order of magnitude as the resolving time. The output for pulses occurring separately is appreciably smaller than the output for simultaneous pulses and will not trigger a discriminator. Thus the whole apparatus responds only to coincident pulses. Conversely, it is possible to form a circuit that responds only to separate pulses, but not to coincident pulses (anticoincidence). In all coincidence and anticoincidence circuits the input pulses must be similar in shape and amplitude in the two channels. The classical Rossi coincidence circuit is shown in Fig. 3-35.

The fundamental circuits described above may be combined into extremely versatile and complicated instruments, such as multichannel pulse analyzers. In such an instrument the input pulses are sorted according to their magnitude and counted in different channels (up to 4,000 channels are commercially available). A crystal scintillator connected

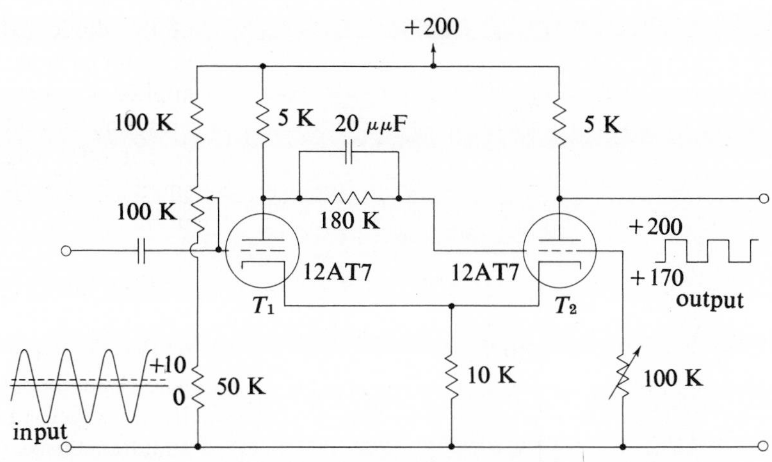

Figure 3-34 Discriminator of the Schmitt trigger-circuit type. Its principle of operation briefly is as follows: Normally only the right-hand tube T_2 is conducting, since the grid potential of T_1 is lower than that of T_2. A positive pulse of a magnitude equal to or larger than the difference of the two grid potentials will cause a complete transfer of the current to tube T_1, thereby producing a positive signal at the plate of T_2. This condition persists until the potential at T_1 is lowered sufficiently to make T_2 conducting.

to a multichannel pulse analyzer gives at once the whole gamma-ray spectrum emitted by a source.

Besides the fundamental apparatus mentioned above, a number of indispensable auxiliary apparatus are used in nuclear measurements: regulated power supplies of high and low voltage, electrostatic voltmeters, pulse generators for calibration purposes, and gating circuits that make a detector sensitive only for an assigned time after a given type of event are examples of the many circuits available.

We cannot give more details of these elaborate electronic techniques, which are in a state of continuous development. In recent years the use of transistorized equipment has greatly reduced the bulk and power required. Moreover, tunnel diodes (Esaki, 1958) are radically affecting such circuits as discriminators and scalers.

3-11 Complex Nuclear Instruments

The detectors described thus far are the fundamental components of the more elaborate instruments used in nuclear physics. It is obviously impossible to describe these in detail. In fact every experiment requires its own combination, and the design of such combinations is an important part of the experimental art. We shall confine ourselves to a few typical examples.

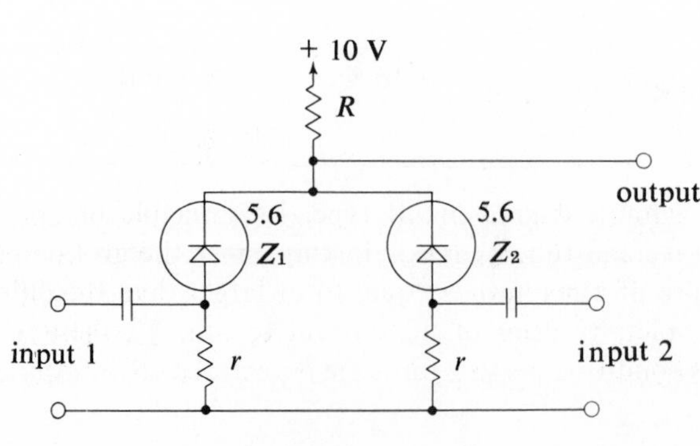

Figure 3-35 Rossi coincidence circuit. Normally both solid-state Zener diodes Z_1, Z_2 are conducting, and R is made large compared with the resistance r of the diodes. If large, positive noncoincidental pulses are applied to one of the diodes only, the current through it will be cut off. There will result a small voltage rise at the output of

$$\Delta V = V_R \frac{r}{2(R+r)} = \frac{V_R}{2}\frac{r}{R}$$

where V_R is the drop across R when both diodes are conducting. If, however, both tubes are simultaneously cut off by two coincident signals, the voltage rise will be

$$\Delta V' = V_R$$

and can consequently be much larger than ΔV.

A powerful auxiliary in all counting methods is the use of coincidence counters (Rutherford, 1912; Bothe, 1928). A single example will illustrate this method. Suppose that a radioactive substance emits a beta radiation and a gamma radiation and that we want to know whether the gamma radiation is emitted within a very short time of the beta disintegration, as would be the case if the nucleus were left in an excited state by the beta decay, or whether the gamma ray is uncorrelated in time with the beta decay, as would in fact happen if it preceded the beta decay. We could solve this problem by arranging a beta-ray counter (e.g., a thin-window G–M counter) and a gamma-ray counter (e.g., an NaI scintillator) as in Fig. 3-36. We count the single counts in the two counters and also the coincidences between them, i.e., the times when both counters register a pulse within a very short time interval τ. We assume now that the beta emission precedes the gamma emission by a

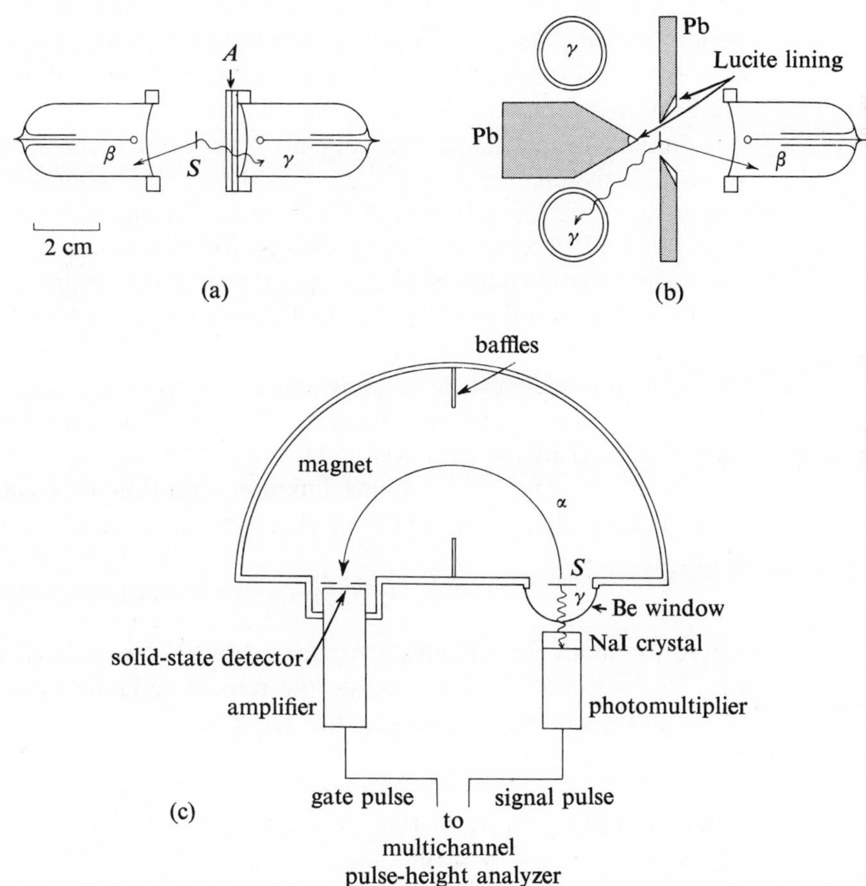

Figure 3-36 Types of coincidence measurements. (a) Simple coincidence arrangement, not suitable for gamma-gamma coincidences, because scattered quanta may produce spurious coincidences. (b) Coincidence arrangement for beta-gamma and gamma-gamma coincidences. The probability of scattering of electrons or soft gamma rays from one counter to another is reduced by the lead shields Pb. *S*, source; *A*, absorber. (c) Schematic diagram of an alpha spectrograph arranged for alpha-gamma coincidence studies.

time, on the average, $\ll \tau$ and that the emission of the beta and gamma rays is isotropic and uncorrelated in space. The number of counts per second registered by the beta counter is

$$\nu_\beta = \nu\eta_\beta \tag{3-11.1}$$

where η_β is the efficiency of the counter, i.e., the probability that a beta ray emitted by the source is counted by the detector, and ν is the rate of disintegrations in the source. The number of counts per second registered by the gamma counter is

$$\nu_\gamma = \nu\eta_\gamma \tag{3-11.2}$$

and the rate of coincidences if the β and γ emission are practically simultaneous, as happens when the beta ray precedes the gamma ray, is

$$\nu_c = \nu\eta_\beta\eta_\gamma \tag{3-11.3}$$

From these three equations it is possible to find ν, η_β, and η_γ. This example is extremely simple, but it illustrates the principle of the coincidence method. The time τ plays an essential part. In particular, when we use the terms "uncorrelated," "coincident," and so on, it is always with reference to τ.

Let us now consider what happens if the gamma emission precedes the beta emission. We may assume that the time between the two is on the average much larger than τ. The rate of coincidences is then the rate of "random," or "accidental," coincidences, which we evaluate as follows. Let us consider the number of times per second in which the beta counter is activated. This is given by Eq. (3-11.1). Similarly for the gamma counter we have Eq. (3-11.2). Now, every time that the beta counter is activated, the apparatus will register a coincidence if the gamma counter is also activated within a time τ_β. The time τ_β is the time during which the "gate" opened by the beta count stays open. During this time we shall have on the average $\nu\eta_\gamma\tau_\beta$ gamma impulses, and thus we have a rate of random coincidences, in which the beta ray precedes the gamma ray, given by

$$\nu_{\beta r} = \nu^2\eta_\gamma\eta_\beta\tau_\beta \tag{3-11.4}$$

where the index βr indicates a random coincidence initiated by a beta ray. In the same way we compute the rate of accidental coincidences, in which the gamma ray precedes the beta ray,

$$\nu_{\gamma r} = \nu^2\eta_\gamma\eta_\beta\tau_\gamma \tag{3-11.5}$$

Their sum gives the total rate of accidental coincidences. If, as often happens, $\tau_\beta = \tau_\gamma = \tau$, then

$$\nu_{\beta r} + \nu_{\gamma r} = \nu_r = 2\nu^2\eta_\gamma\eta_\beta\tau_\beta = 2\nu_\beta\nu_\gamma\tau \tag{3-11.6}$$

Note that the rate of accidental coincidences is proportional to ν^2, whereas that of true coincidences is proportional to ν.

In measuring coincidences the rate of accidental coincidences must be considered as a background and subtracted. A good way to check the rate of accidental coincidences is to use two separate sources, one for the beta counter, the other for the gamma counter, giving the same rate ν_β, ν_γ as the single common source. The coincidence rate obtained from the two separate sources is the rate of accidental coincidences.

Coincidence can also be used to locate events in space. Thus the coincidence between two counters can be used to trigger a cloud chamber located between them, which will show the particles that did the triggering. A system of this kind allowed Blackett and Occhialini (1933) to detect showers in a cloud chamber (Fig. 2-33).

The coincidence system can be refined to show the time of flight between two detectors, a system that was used for the identification of the antiproton and one that is frequently used in neutron spectroscopy. Correlation between the direction of emission of two particles can also be detected by coincidence methods. For instance, two-quanta annihilation of positrons with electrons at rest produces coincidences between two gamma-ray detectors only when these lie on a straight line with the source in between them.

The effective operation of a coincidence system depends mainly on its electronics. The important Rossi circuit mentioned previously has undergone many variations, but its principle is still the basis of most coincidence circuits. Anticoincidence circuits also have important uses. It is required of them that only one counter, not both of a pair, register a pulse. For example, if we want to be certain that a particle has stopped in a certain absorber, we can insert two counters in anticoincidence, as in Fig. 3-37.

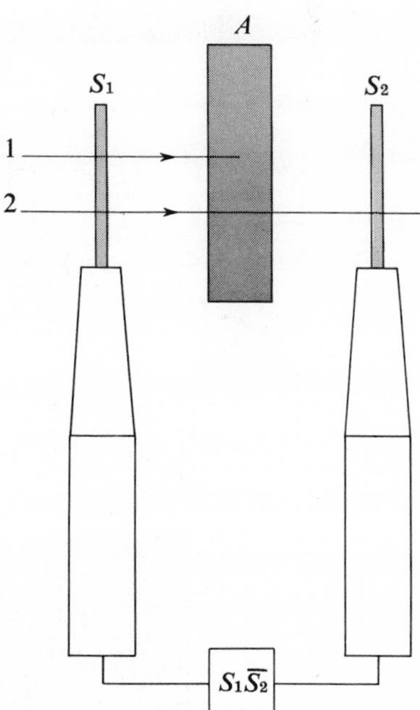

Figure 3-37 Method for selecting particles of a given range, i.e., stopping in *A*; S_1, S_2, scintillators; *A*, absorber; particle 1 triggers scintillator 1 but not 2; particle 2 triggers scintillators 1 and 2. Particle 1 of the desired kind is registered as $S_1\,\overline{S_2}$; particle 2 as $S_1\,S_2$. The bar on S_2 means that scintillator 2 does not give the signal.

3-12 Charged-Particle Spectrographs

A large group of instruments is devoted to the measurement of the energy of alpha and beta particles. These instruments almost always involve a magnetic field, which deflects the trajectory of the particle; the degree of curvature gives the momentum according to the equation

$$Br = \frac{c}{e}\, p \tag{3-12.1}$$

For electrons

$$Br = (3.335 \times 10^{3})p \tag{3-12.2}$$

where Br is in gauss cm and p in MeV/c.

The spectrographs are mainly of two kinds, according to whether high resolving power or high luminosity is the most important characteristic. One of the simplest of the first type is used in measurements of electron energies and is shown in Fig. 3-38. It focuses the electrons at 180° from the source, as indicated. The actual detection can be made by a photographic plate or by counters. The preparation of the source is extremely important, because its thinness, absence of back scattering from the support, and small dimensions determine primarily the quality of the spectrum (Fig. 8-7). For electrons spectrographs of high luminosity are often of the type illustrated in Figs. 3-39 and 3-40. The current in the magnet is varied and the counting rate in the detector is given as a function of the current in Fig. 3-41. Apertures up to 1 per cent are obtainable with $\Delta p/p \simeq 0.005$.

Alpha spectrographs generally follow the lines of beta spectrographs, except that much higher magnetic fields are ordinarily required. Figure 3-41 shows a spectrograph and a spectrum. Under the most favorable circumstances the absolute energy of alpha particles can be measured

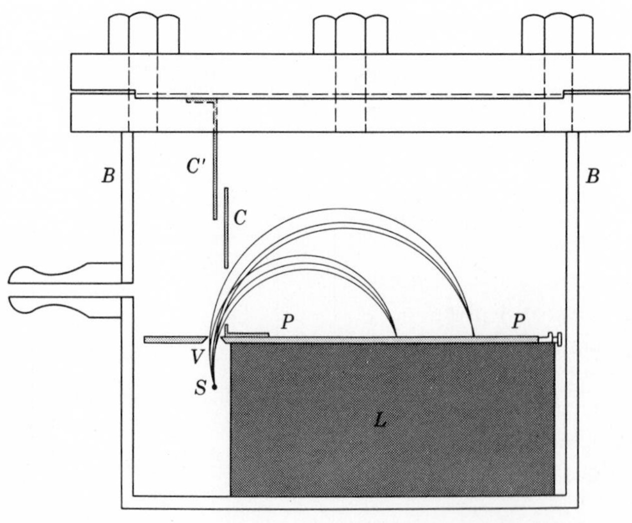

Figure 3-38 Rutherford's and Robinson's design for a beta spectrograph. Electrons from the source S, passing through the entrance slit V, are focused on the photographic plate P; L is a lead shield; C are baffles to stop scattered electrons.

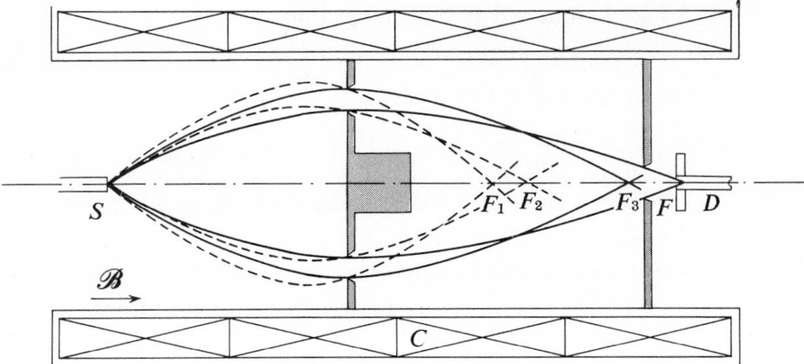

Figure 3-39 The principle of helical spectrometers. Coils C produce a uniform magnetic field B. Electrons emitted by source S, having different momenta, are focused in F_1, F_2, etc. When the focus coincides with the entrance of counter D, one has a maximum in the counting rate. By changing the current in C one obtains the peaks corresponding to different momenta.

to a few parts in 10^4. The planning of spectrographs is a problem in electron optics, and we shall not explore it further.

Alpha-particle spectrography can be carried out by magnetic spectrographs and also by a refined use of the ionization chamber through the measurement of the ionization produced by single alpha particles. About 50 to 100 keV can be resolved by this method (Fig. 3-42). Semiconductor counters have given even better results, as shown in Fig. 3-43.

Gamma rays and X rays are often measured through their conversion electrons; thus beta spectrographs also provide information on electromagnetic radiation. If internal conversion is used, extremely precise results (1 keV or better) can be obtained. External conversion is much less precise and generally can be used only for qualitative work.

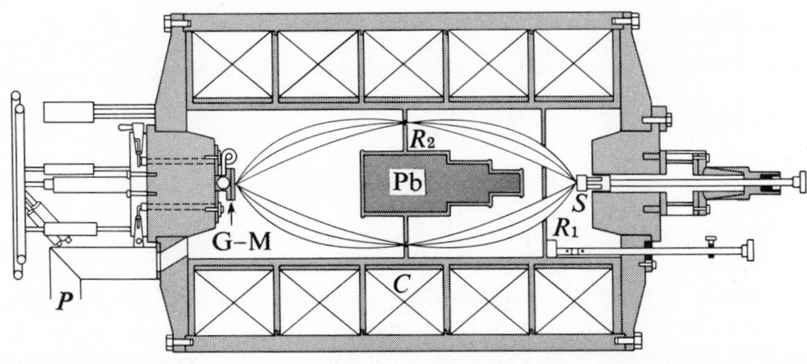

Figure 3-40 Axial section of the first intermediate-image, beta-ray spectrometer. S, source; C, coils; P, pump; R, shutter; G–M, detecting counter. A first ring image is formed at R_2. Remember that in both Figs. 3-39 and 3-40 trajectories of electrons are not plane curves. [K. Siegbahn and H. Slätis.]

3-13 Gamma-Ray Spectrographs

Spectrographs that measure the wavelength of gamma rays directly are of the crystal type, based on the Bragg equation

$$n\lambda = 2\,d \sin\theta \tag{3-13.1}$$

where λ is the wavelength to be measured, n is the order of the spectrum, d is the lattice constant of the crystal, and θ is the angle between the beam and the reflecting surface.

The main difficulty arises from the smallness of θ: for instance, for annihilation radiation (510.9 keV) $\lambda = 0.0243$ Å, and for a lattice constant of 3.02 Å (calcite), we have in the first order $\theta = 3.96 \times 10^{-3}$ rad, which means that special spectrographs have to be built. Conspicuous examples of precision instruments based on bent quartz crystal have been built by DuMond. The X rays are detected by counters.

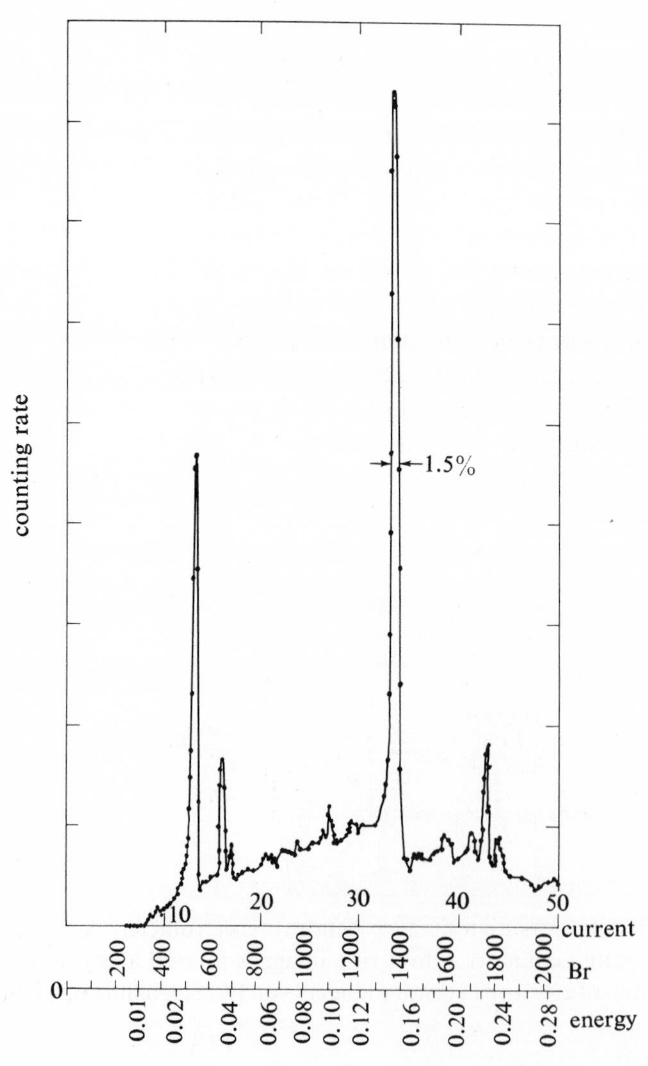

Figure 3-41 Beta spectrum of ThB taken with a spectrograph of the type illustrated in Fig. 3-40. On the abscissas: current in the coils is in amperes; Br in gauss cm; energy in MeV.

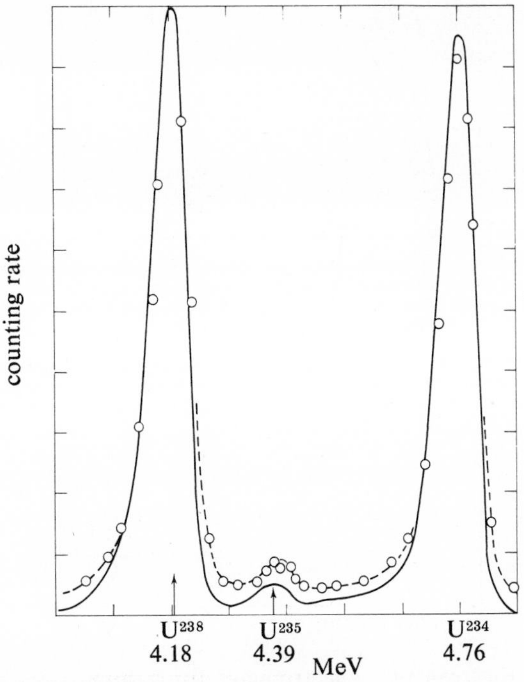

counting rate

U238
4.18
U235
4.39
U234
4.76
MeV

Figure 3-42 The characteristic alpha spectrum of natural uranium obtained by pulse-height analysis. The alpha particles of natural uranium (U^{238}, U^{235}, U^{234}) are visible in their natural abundance. [Baldinger and Huber, *Helv. Phys. Acta*, **22,** 365 (1949).]

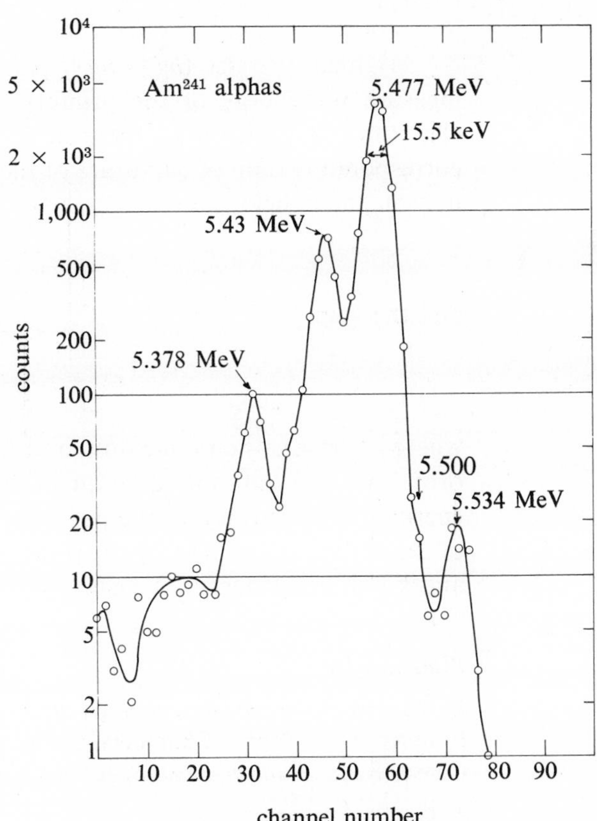

Figure 3-43 Energy spectrum of the alpha particle of Am^{241} obtained with a SiO_2 semiconductor detector. [F. S. Goulding, UCRL 11302.]

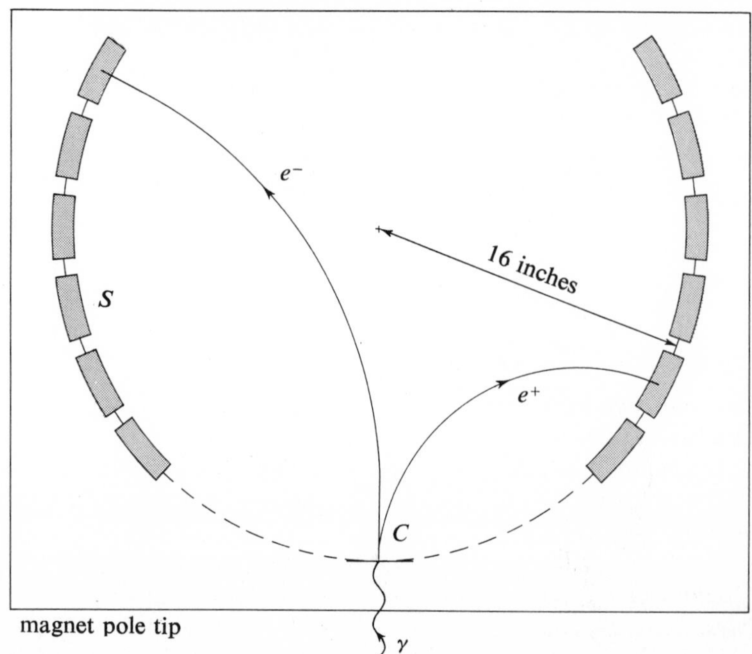

Figure 3-44 Electron-pair spectrometer for gamma rays having an energy up to 650 MeV. The converter *C* thickness is 0.1 to 0.4 g cm^{-2}; *S*, plastic scintillators. [Cence, Lind, Mead, and Moyer, *Phys. Rev.*, **131,** 2713 (1963).]

At high energies ($h\nu \gg mc^2$) pair production makes it possible to measure the energy of the primary X ray. The kinetic energy of the electron and positron in the pair is at the relativistic limit $cp^{\pm}$. The corresponding radii of curvature of the orbit of the electron and positron in a magnetic field are

$$r^{\pm} = \frac{c}{e}\frac{p^{\pm}}{B} \tag{3-13.2}$$

and the sum

$$r^{+} + r^{-} = \frac{h\nu}{eB} \tag{3-13.3}$$

where p^{+}, r^{+} are the momentum and radius of curvature of the positron orbit and p^{-}, r^{-} are the same quantities for the electron orbit. For high energies the electron and the positron move initially in the line of flight of the X ray, as required by the principle of conservation of momentum, and a pair spectrograph measures $r^{+} + r^{-}$ (Fig. 3-44).

Bibliography

Barkas, W., *Nuclear Research Emulsions*, Academic Press, New York, 1963.
Bradner, H., "Bubble Chambers," *Ann. Rev. Nucl. Sci.*, **10,** 109 (1960).
Chase, R. L., *Nuclear Pulse Spectrometry*, McGraw-Hill, New York, 1961.

Curran, S. C., *Luminescence and the Scintillation Counters*, Butterworths, London, 1953.
Dearnaley, G., and D. C. Northrop, *Semiconductor Counters, for Nuclear Radiations*, Wiley, New York, 1963.
Deutsch, M., and O. Kofoed-Hansen, "Gamma Rays" and "Beta-Rays," in (Se 59).
(Fl E), Vol. 45.
Fretter, W. B., "Nuclear Particle Detection," *Ann. Rev. Nucl. Sci.*, **5** (1955).
Gentner, Maier-Leibnitz, and Bothe (GMLB 54).
Glaser, D., "The Bubble Chamber," in (Fl E), Vol. 45.
Kendall, H. W., "Electronics Associated with Nuclear Research," *Ann. Rev. Nucl. Sci.*, **9,** 343 (1959).
Korff, S. A., *Electron and Nuclear Counters*, 2nd ed., Van Nostrand, Princeton, N.J., 1955.
Malmstadt, Enke, and Toren, *Electronics for Scientists*, Benjamin, New York, 1962.
Marshall, J., "Nuclear Particle Detection," *Ann. Rev. Nucl. Sci.*, **4** (1954).
Miller, Gibson, and Donovan, "Semiconductor Particle Detectors," *Ann. Rev. Nucl. Sci.*, **12,** 189 (1962).
Powell, Fowler, and Perkins (PFP 59).
Proceedings of the 1962 Conference on Instrumentation for High Energy Physics, *Nuclear Instruments and Methods*, **20** (1963).
Ritson, D. M., *Techniques of High Energy Physics*, Wiley-Interscience, New York, 1961.
Rosenfeld, A. H., "Data Reduction Methods for Bubble Chambers," *Ann. Rev. Nucl. Sci.*, **13** (1963).
Sayres, E., and C. S. Wu, "Gas Scintillators," *Rev. Sci. Instr.*, **28,** 758 (1957).
Snell, A. H. (ed.), *Nuclear Instruments and Their Uses*, Wiley New York, 1963.
Staub, H. H., "Detection Methods," in (Se 59), Vol. I.
Wilkinson, D. H., *Ionization Chambers and Counters*, Cambridge University Press, New York, 1950.
Yuan, L. C., and C. S. Wu, *Methods of Experimental Physics–Nuclear Physics*, Academic Press, New York, 1961 and 1963.

Problems

3-1 How much current would one obtain in an ionization chamber full of argon at atmospheric pressure traversed by 10^9 protons sec^{-1}? The energy of the protons is 300 MeV, the depth of the chamber 10 cm.

3-2 With the chamber of Prob. 3-1 what would be the current produced by 10^9 gammas per sec if the energy of the gammas is 5,000; 10,000; 10^5; and 10^7 eV? Neglect the effect of the walls. What would you do to make the wall effect negligible?

3-3 How would you measure the energy and intensity of a beam of protons in the energy domain from 100 KeV to 10 BeV? Indicate how to identify the particles, and devise appropriate systems for each energy region considered.

3-4 The same as Prob. 3-3 for electrons or positrons.

3-5 The same as Prob. 3-3 for gamma rays.

3-6 The same as Prob. 3-3 for neutrons from 0.01 eV to 10 BeV. Pay special attention to the differentiation from gamma rays.

3-7 Plan an experiment to measure the *p-p* scattering cross section at 100 MeV. Plan counters, target, beam geometry, etc.

3-8 Plan an experiment to detect the rare modes of decay

$$\pi^+ \rightarrow e^+ + \nu \text{ and } \pi^+ \rightarrow \pi^0 + e^+ + \nu$$

having the branching ratios 10^{-4} and 10^{-8}, respectively, compared with the decay $\pi^+ \rightarrow \mu^+ + \nu$.

3-9 Plan an experiment to measure the spontaneous fission of U^{238}. Consider all possible causes of background, the thickness of your sample, the time of observation, etc.

3-10 Plan an experiment for the precision measurement of the energy of the electron-positron annihilation radiation.

CHAPTER IV

Particle Accelerators

THE SUBJECT OF THIS CHAPTER is a branch of electromagnetism and mechanics. However, accelerators are an indispensable tool of nuclear experimentation, and a brief report on them is in order.

4-1 Introduction and Classification

The development of particle accelerators specifically designed for use in nuclear experiments began in the late 1920s. Several of the early accelerators involved the production of high voltages applied to an evacuated tube (Breit, Tuve, Lauritsen, Van de Graaff). The first nuclear disintegrations with artificially accelerated protons were achieved in 1930 by Cockcroft and Walton at the Cavendish Laboratory. Their apparatus, which accelerated protons to 300 keV, produced $Li^7(p,2\alpha)$ reactions.

The great difficulties connected with high voltages (arcs and corona discharges among others) prompted the invention of machines that do not require high electric fields and in which the high energy of the projectile is achieved by multiple accelerations or by electromagnetic induction. The first multiple accelerators were built by Wideroe in 1928 and, on the same principle, by Lawrence and Sloan in 1930. These machines, however, had no important practical applications at the time.

All the accelerators mentioned so far used only electric fields. The cyclotron (Lawrence, 1929) was the first accelerator to employ a magnetic field, which by bending the orbit of the particle in a spiral forces it to pass many times through an accelerating electric field. It is thus possible to achieve great energies with a relatively compact apparatus. The idea of the cyclotron occurred independently to several physicists (Thibaud, Lawrence, Szilard), but the development of an effective machine from small models into large cyclotrons was the work of E. O. Lawrence and his associates at Berkeley. Accelerators have had a majcr effect on the evolution of nuclear physics.

The cyclotron has inherent limitations that prevent it, in its simplest form at least, from accelerating particles to relativistic energies. These difficulties have been circumvented by the ingenious schemes of Veksler (1945) and McMillan (1946), which involved "phase stability" and made possible proton energies of 7×10^9 eV. Christophilos (1950) and, independently, Courant, Livingston, and Snyder (1952) invented a method (strong focusing) that has raised this limit to 3×10^{10} eV by means of very large but still practical machines.

At present, the cost of accelerators appears to be the main obstacle to the achievement of still higher energies.

The cyclotron and its derivative apparatus accelerate light nuclei. Electromagnetic induction was used by Kerst (1940) to accelerate electrons to many MeV. Kerst's apparatus is called the *betatron*. In later developments the betatron principle was combined with other acceleration methods (*synchrotron*).

All accelerators require an ion source. For electrons a hot filament is universally used; for nuclei many types of discharge tubes have been developed. As an example, we mention an ion source in which electrons coming from a hot filament oscillate in a volume occupied by hydrogen and ionize it by collision. The ions are "pulled out" by an electric field generating ion currents of the order of milliamperes (Fig. 4-1).

We shall limit our discussion to certain types of accelerators that are widely used and practically important, and for these we shall give only a summary of the principles, without technical details. To classify accelerators we shall divide them according to Table 4-1, partially illustrated in Fig. 4-2.

4-2 Potential-Drop Accelerators

The simplest accelerator, in principle, is an electrostatic machine connected to a discharge tube. The Van de Graaff accelerator (Fig. 4-3) is a modern realization of such an apparatus. A moving belt, charged by corona discharge, transports the charge inside a large conducting sphere. There another discharge removes the electricity from the belt, transferring it to the sphere. The sphere is the high-voltage electrode connected to the accelerating tube. The whole system is usually enclosed in a pressurized tank containing nitrogen, to which a few per cent freon

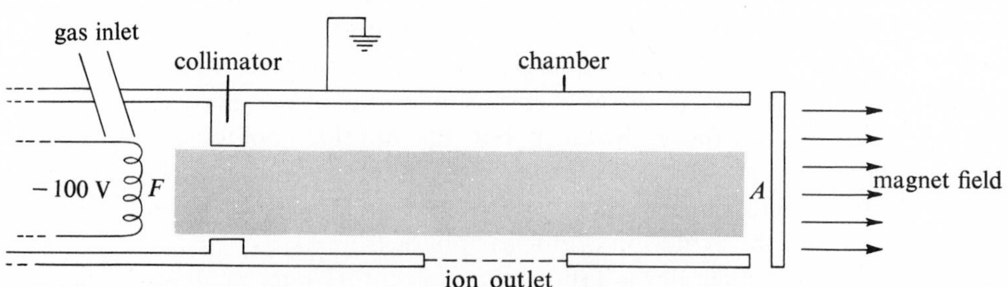

Figure 4-1 A typical positive-ion source. Electrons emitted by the filament F at -100 V oscillate between it and the anode A, while they curl around the lines of force of the containing magnetic field. The electrons form positive ions by impact in the gas present in the chamber. The mixture of positive ions and electrons, called plasma, fills the shaded region. Positive ions are extracted from the plasma through the aperture. [R. S. Livingston and R. J. Jones.]

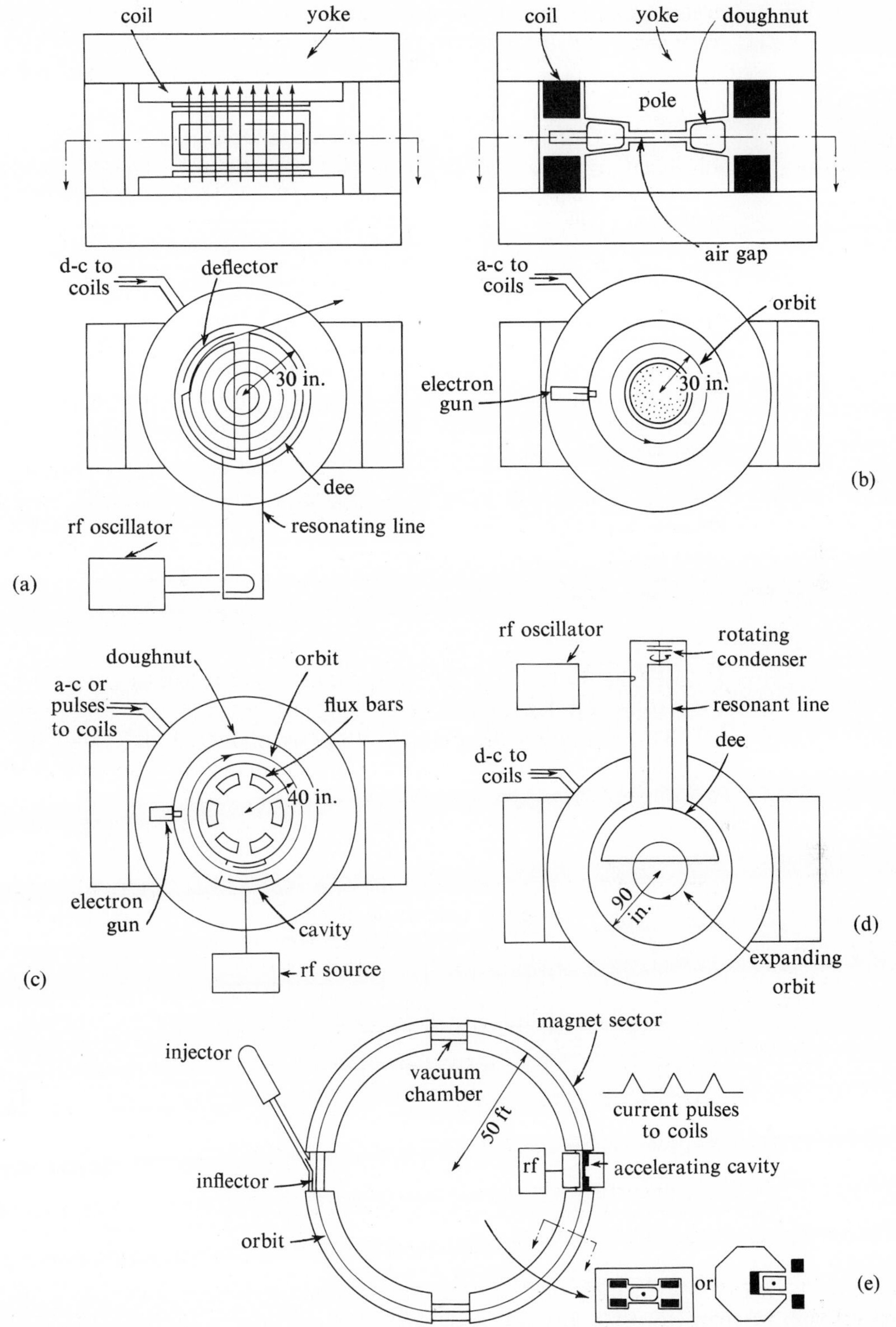

Figure 4-2 Diagrams of some of the most important circular (magnetic) accelerators, with typical dimensions: (a) cyclotron, (b) betatron, (c) electron synchrotron, (d) synchrocyclotron, (e) proton synchrotron (or electron race track). [*Nuclear Engineering Handbook*, McGraw-Hill, New York, 1958.]

Table 4-1 Classification of Accelerators

Accelerator	Particle accelerated	**E**	**H**	Orbit	Typical energy, MeV
Electrostatic, or Van de Graaff	e, p, d, α	Constant	None	Straight	12
Multiplier circuit, or Cockcroft–Walton	e, p, d, α	Constant	None	Straight	4
Betatron	e	None	Variable	Circular	300
Cyclotron	p, d, α	Fixed ω	Constant	Spiral	25
Synchrocyclotron	p	Variable ω	Constant	Spiral	700
Synchrotron	e	Fixed ω	Variable	Circular	10^3
Proton synchrotron	p	Variable ω	Variable	Circular	10^4
Strong-focusing	p	Variable ω	Variable	Circular	3×10^4
Linear accelerator, rf	p, d	$\omega \sim 200$ Mcps	None	Straight	30
Linear accelerator	e	$\omega \sim 3000$ Mcps	None	Straight	10^3
Heavy ions, Linac	C^{12}, O^{16}, etc.	$\omega \sim 70$ Mcps	None	Straight	$10 \times A$ of ion

(CCl_2F_2) has been added. The purpose of this choice of gases is to prevent discharges and destructive fires.

The maximum attainable voltage is about 10 MeV and may be measured by special voltmeters. Fixed points on the voltage scale

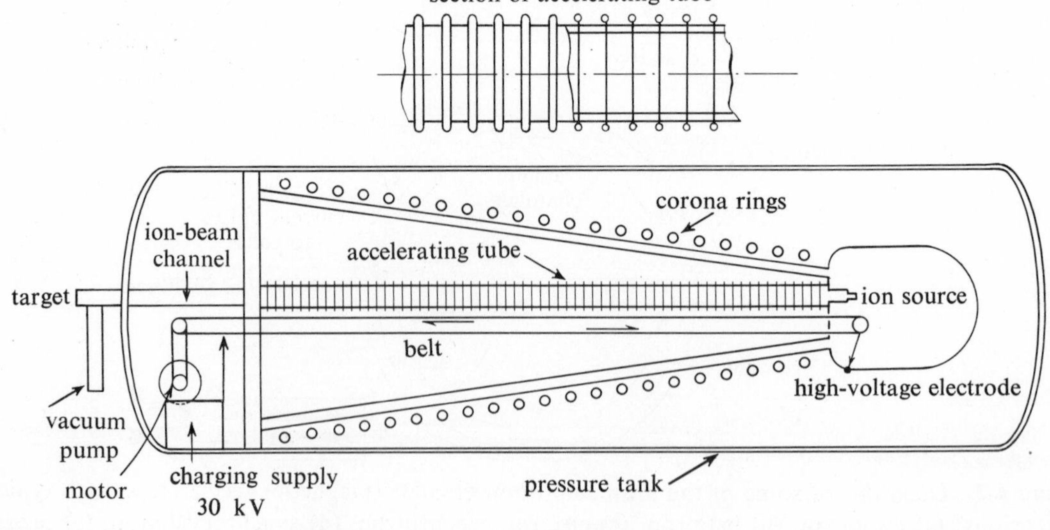

Figure 4-3 A Van de Graaff accelerator.

are given by certain sharp nuclear thresholds or resonances; for example, $Li^7(p,n)Be^7$ at 1880.7 ± 0.4 keV or $Li^7(p,\gamma)Be^{8*}$ at 441.2 ± 0.3 keV. The voltage produced is quite constant (within 1,000 V or less), and currents of the order of 100 μA are obtainable. An interesting device to double the energy attainable by an electrostatic accelerator is used in tandem accelerators, in which the charge of the ion is changed from negative to positive by electron capture (Fig. 4-5).

Another method of generating energies of about 10^6 eV involves voltage-multiplier circuits (Greinacher, Cockcroft, Walton), in which a transformer feeds alternating current of a certain voltage into a rectifying and multiplying apparatus (Fig. 4-4). The voltages obtainable are given in Table 4-1. Apparatus of the type described here are often used as injectors for larger accelerators.

4-3 The Betatron

As its name indicates, the betatron accelerates electrons. The particles circulate in an evacuated doughnut and the accelerating force is produced by electromagnetic induction rather than by an applied electric field (Fig. 4-6).

To keep a particle in its orbit in the doughnut, we need a magnetic field B_0 (at the orbit) such that

$$\frac{e}{c} B_0 R = p \tag{4-3.1}$$

where R is the radius of the orbit and e and p are the charge and momentum respectively, of the particle. This equation is relativistically correct.

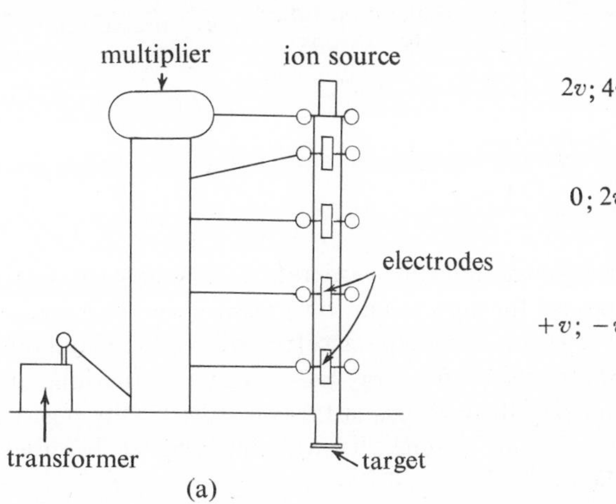

Figure 4-4 A Cockcroft–Walton accelerator. The general layout is shown in (a). The multiplication principle is indicated in (b). Alternating current travels up the line of capacitors to the left and is distributed to all the rectifiers R returning to ground through the capacitors to the right. The d-c flows through the rectifiers in series. When no current is drawn at V the potentials on the capacitors to the right are constant and have the values indicated on the figure. The potentials on the capacitors on the left oscillate between the limits indicated on the figure. The voltage V is four times as large as the peak input voltage v.

When the radius of an orbit changes slowly, i.e., when $\Delta R/R$ per revolution $\ll 1$, we shall speak of an *instantaneous orbit* and an *instantaneous radius*, meaning by this the orbit corresponding to the radius of curvature at time t.

If we increase the flux φ of $\mathbf{B}$ linked with the orbit, the particle experiences an electric field such that

$$\int E\,ds = \frac{-1}{c}\frac{d\varphi}{dt} \tag{4-3.2}$$

and hence its momentum increases according to

$$\frac{dp}{dt} = eE = -\frac{1}{c}\frac{e}{2\pi R}\frac{d\varphi}{dt} \tag{4-3.3}$$

Introducing now $\langle B\rangle$, the average value of B over the area enclosed by the orbit, we have by definition

$$\varphi = \langle B\rangle \pi R^2 \tag{4-3.4}$$

and, keeping the radius of the orbit constant,

$$\frac{d\varphi}{dt} = \pi R^2 \frac{d\langle B\rangle}{dt} \tag{4-3.5}$$

which combined with Eq. (4-3.3) gives

$$\frac{dp}{dt} = -\frac{e}{c}\frac{R}{2}\frac{d\langle B\rangle}{dt} \tag{4-3.6}$$

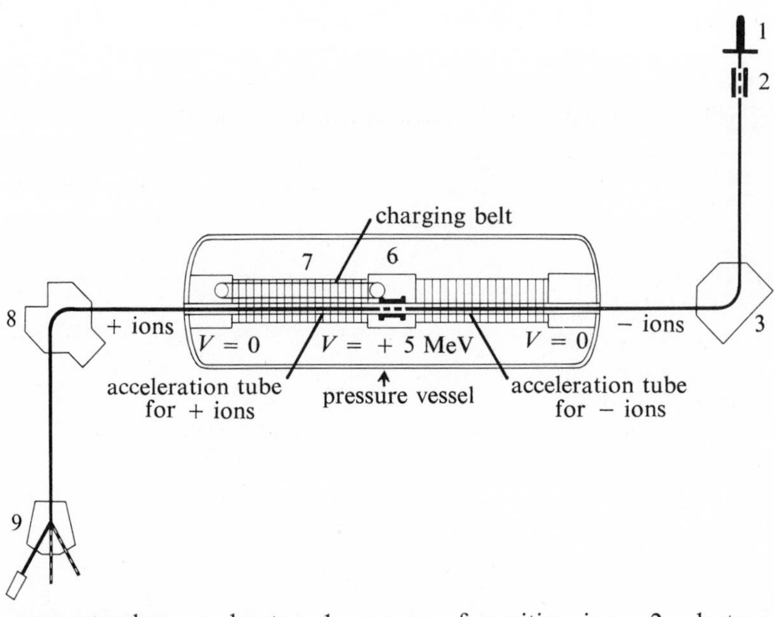

Figure 4-5 Two-stage tandem accelerator. 1, source of positive ions. 2, electron-adding canal. The ions are passed through gas at low pressure where they capture electrons and become negatively charged. 3, the negative ions are preaccelerated to 80 keV and injected into the Van de Graaff accelerator, where they acquire an energy of 5 MeV. 6, the ions are stripped of electrons and charged positively by passing through gas at low pressure. 7, the positive ions are accelerated to 10 MeV. 8, deflecting and analyzing magnet. 9, switching magnet. [Courtesy High Voltage Engineering Corp., Burlington, Mass.]

On the other hand, if we want to keep the radius of the orbit constant, Eq. (4-3.1) requires that

$$-R\frac{e}{c}\frac{dB_0}{dt} = \frac{dp}{dt} \tag{4-3.7}$$

and comparison with Eq. (4-3.6) gives

$$2\frac{dB_0}{dt} = \frac{d\langle B\rangle}{dt} \tag{4-3.8}$$

which is the fundamental condition for the betatron. The final momentum obtained by the electron is given by integrating Eq. (4-3.3),

$$p - p_0 = \frac{1}{2\pi R}(\varphi_0 - \varphi)\frac{e}{c} \tag{4-3.9}$$

where φ_0 and p_0 indicate, respectively, the initial momentum and initial flux associated with the orbit. Note that it is possible to choose independently the flux φ_0 and the initial guiding field B_0. For the *biased* betatron in particular the sign of φ_0 is opposite of that of φ, and such a machine may give, for the same magnet, about twice the momentum obtainable with a machine in which φ_0 is nearly 0.

The electron gains energy as it travels in its orbit. In the case of

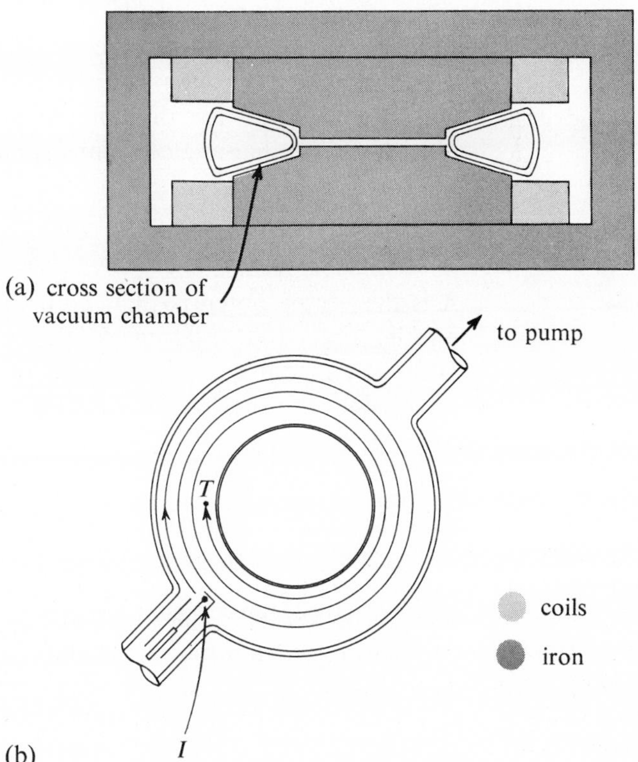

Figure 4-6 A betatron: (a) cross section; (b) plan view. The accelerating flux passes chiefly through the central gap. *I*, injector; *T*, target.

most betatrons the energy gained per turn is of the order of a few hundred eV. Hence, a large number of turns is required, and the beam must be focused. Otherwise it would spread out and dissipate by hitting the walls of the doughnut.

The focusing in the betatron, which is similar in many respects to that of other accelerators, will now be briefly discussed. Let us call the circle of radius R the desired orbit. This orbit thus has a constant radius in spite of the change of momentum as long as the betatron condition of Eq. (4-3.8) is satisfied. The field $\mathbf{B}$ at the orbit has two components: a z component, in the direction of the axis of symmetry of the machine, and a radial component B_r, in the radial direction. The plane of the orbit has $z = 0$. To achieve stability of particle orbits with respect to displacement in the z direction, there must be a restoring force, in first approximation, proportional to such a displacement.

We write the equations of motion of the electron subject to the Lorentz force (see Appendix H),

$$\mathbf{F} = -e\left(\mathbf{E} + \frac{1}{c}\mathbf{v} \times \mathbf{B}\right)$$

in cylindrical coordinates as

$$\frac{d}{dt}p_r - mr\dot{\theta}^2 = -e\frac{r}{c}\dot{\theta}B_z \qquad \textbf{(4-3.10)}$$

$$\frac{d}{dt}p_z = \frac{e}{c}r\dot{\theta}B_r \qquad \textbf{(4-3.11)}$$

where by m we indicate the relativistic mass and by p_r and p_z the momentum components in the r and z directions.

The equation for the component of the *canonical* momentum p_θ (θ is the azimuthal angle in our cylindrical coordinate system) is

$$p_\theta \equiv mr^2\dot{\theta} - \frac{e}{c}rA = \text{constant} \qquad \textbf{(4-3.12)}$$

$\mathbf{A}$ is the vector potential that points in the θ direction. $\mathbf{A}$ depends also on the time and $-(1/c)(\partial\mathbf{A}/\partial t)$ gives the accelerating electric field. However, in our consideration of the focusing action we do not need to consider the time variations of $\mathbf{A}$.

The z component of the magnetic field in the vicinity of the equilibrium orbit is described by

$$B_z = B_0\left(\frac{r}{R}\right)^{-n} \qquad \textbf{(4-3.13)}$$

where n is the field index and is positive. Equation (4-3.13) can be expanded to give in a first approximation

$$B_z = B_0\left(1 - n\frac{r-R}{R} + \cdots\right) \qquad \textbf{(4-3.14)}$$

B_r can now be determined from Maxwell's equation $\nabla \times \mathbf{B} = 0$, which in our case gives

$$\frac{\partial B_r}{\partial z} = \frac{\partial B_z}{\partial r} \tag{4-3.15}$$

Hence, remembering that $B_r = 0$ for $z = 0$, we have

$$B_r = z\frac{\partial B_r}{\partial z} = -\frac{nz}{R}B_0 + \cdots \tag{4-3.16}$$

Introducing new variables,

$$\rho = \frac{r - R}{R} \qquad \text{and} \qquad \zeta = \frac{z}{R} \tag{4-3.17}$$

we substitute the expressions of Eqs. (4-3.14) and (4-3.16) for B_z and B_r in Eqs. (4-3.10) and (4-3.11). Neglecting the change in mass during the motion considered here and quantities of the second order in ρ and ζ, we obtain after some reductions

$$\ddot{\rho} + \frac{eB_0}{mc}(1 - n)\rho\dot{\theta} = (1 + \rho)\dot{\theta}^2 - \frac{eB_0}{mc}\dot{\theta} \tag{4-3.18}$$

$$\ddot{\zeta} + \frac{eB_0}{mc}\dot{\theta}n\zeta = 0 \tag{4-3.19}$$

For the equilibrium orbit Eq. (4-3.1) gives

$$\frac{eB_0}{mc} = \omega_0 \tag{4-3.20}$$

where ω_0 is the angular velocity of the electron in this orbit, i.e.,

$$\omega_0 = \frac{v}{R} = \dot{\theta} \tag{4-3.21}$$

For this orbit the approximate azimuthal velocity $r\dot{\theta}$ is given by

$$r\dot{\theta} \simeq R\dot{\theta}(1 + \rho) \simeq v \tag{4-3.22}$$

whence

$$\dot{\theta} = \frac{v}{R}(1 - \rho) = \omega_0(1 - \rho) \tag{4-3.23}$$

Combining Eq. (4-3.23) with Eqs. (4-3.18) and (4-3.19) and neglecting higher terms, we obtain

$$\ddot{\rho} + \omega_0^2(1 - n)\rho = 0 \tag{4-3.24}$$

$$\ddot{\zeta} + \omega_0^2 n\zeta = 0 \tag{4-3.25}$$

For Eqs. (4-3.24) and (4-3.25) to describe oscillations, the coefficient of ρ and ξ must be positive, that is, $1 > n > 0$. This means that the field must decrease from the center to the periphery; or in other words that the lines of force must be concave toward the axis of the machine. This decrease, however, must not be too rapid ($n < 1$).

The oscillations described by Eqs. (4-3.24) and (4-3.25) are called *betatron oscillations*, and they are naturally damped as the field grows. The frequency of the radial oscillations is

$$\omega_{\text{radial}} = (1 - n)^{1/2}\omega_0 \tag{4-3.26}$$

That of the vertical oscillations is

$$\omega_z = n^{1/2}\omega_0 \tag{4-3.27}$$

and hence both frequencies are always less than ω_0. In the cyclotron radial oscillations are relatively unimportant. In the betatron the amplitude of both radial and vertical oscillations must be small, because if the oscillations exceed the dimensions of the cavity, the beam obviously strikes the walls and is lost.

In a betatron the energy necessary to energize the magnet travels between the magnet and a large bank of capacitors. The exchange occurs with a frequency of about 60 cps. Hence the magnet must be laminated in order to avoid too large eddy currents.

Electrons are injected with a special gun at energies of the order of 50 keV. After acceleration the orbit is either expanded or displaced and the electrons strike a target, producing a beam of bremsstrahlung (see Chap. 2). If the target is thin, this beam has a small angular aperture of the order of mc^2/E and can be very intense. For example, a 300-MeV betatron may give 15,000 roentgens min^{-1} at 1 m from the target.

The practical limit of betatron energies is about 300 MeV. The electrons traveling in a circular orbit radiate electromagnetic energy. The resulting energy loss per turn is given by

$$L = \frac{4\pi}{3}\frac{e^2}{R}\left(\frac{E}{m_0c^2}\right)^4\beta^3 \tag{4-3.28}$$

Inserting numbers for $R = 100$ cm, one obtains 8.91 eV per turn at 100 MeV. These losses, increasing with E^4, very quickly become prohibitive for electron accelerators, whereas they are negligible in all proton machines. The energy is radiated in a continuous spectrum that has a maximum for frequencies near

$$\nu_{\max} = \frac{3}{2}\left(\frac{E}{m_0c^2}\right)^3\frac{\omega_0}{2\pi} \tag{4-3.29}$$

For a 100-MeV betatron having $R = 100$ cm, the maximum occurs in the visible region and the corresponding light has been observed.

The radiation loss forces the electrons to spiral toward the center of the betatron where they can be caught by a target that "scrapes" the inner side of the beam.

4-4 The Cyclotron

In the Lawrence cyclotron a constant magnetic field guides the ions (nuclei) in a spiral path. The acceleration is imparted by an electric field that has the correct direction any time that the particle is subject to it (Fig. 4-7).

For the apparatus to function, it is essential that the particle arrive at the place where the electric field is applied at the right time. The two dees oscillate electrically with a period of $2\pi/\omega$. A particle between the dees at time 0 will again cross the slit between the dees at time

$$\frac{\pi r}{v} = t \tag{4-4.1}$$

where r is the radius of its orbit. At that time the electric field must be reversed from what it was at time 0. That is, t must be π/ω. We thus have

$$\frac{r}{v} = \frac{1}{\omega} \tag{4-4.2}$$

or, recalling (4-3.1),

$$\frac{eB}{mc} = \omega \tag{4-4.3}$$

This is the fundamental equation of the cyclotron. In any case m is the total *relativistic* mass. Note that r does not appear in the equation; hence the orbit may spiral (variation of r) while B and ω are kept constant in time. This is at least true as long as m is constant (non-relativistic energy).

From Eq. (4-4.3) it is apparent that, for a given frequency and field, a cyclotron can accelerate different particles having nearly identical values of e/m, such as deuterons and helium ions. In fact, by tuning the apparatus for different masses it has been possible to accelerate a number of ions up to carbon and nitrogen.

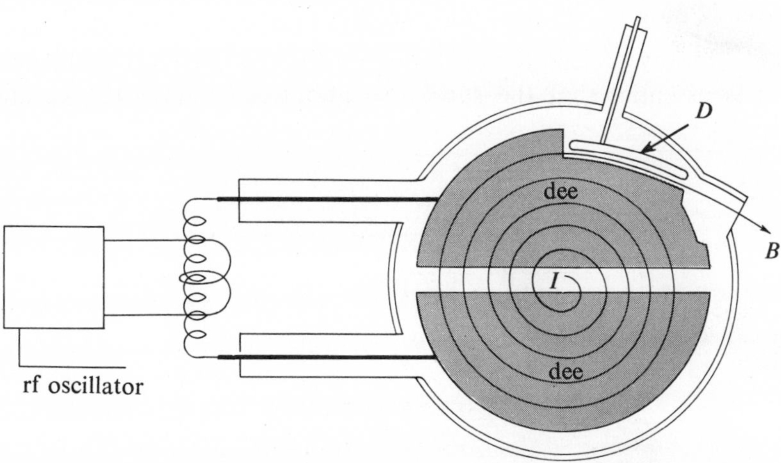

Figure 4-7 Essential parts of a cyclotron (not including the magnet), showing dees (hollow semi-circular accelerating electrodes), dee stem insulators, resonant circuit with an rf power source, and deflector plate D. The path of the ions from the source at the center I to the point of emergence at B is shown schematically.

In the cyclotron the ions must be focused, and the magnetic field of the cyclotron provides a weak focusing action as described for the betatron (Fig. 4-8). In addition, on crossing the gap between the dees there are vertical components of the electric force. Their main effect is focusing if the particle crosses the dee while the electric field is decreasing. Radial oscillations are less important for the cyclotron than for the betatron. After the particles have spiraled out toward the edge of the magnetic field, they are usually deflected electrically into a channel and may be brought out of the machine.

A cyclotron of this type can generate a circulating current of several milliamperes and a deflected beam of the same order of magnitude. Its energy is limited by relativistic considerations; for as the mass of the particle increases as it moves toward the edge of the magnetic field, we should also increase B in order to satisfy Eq. (4-4.3), with ω constant. This, however, conflicts with the focusing conditions, requiring that the magnetic lines of force be concave toward the symmetry axis of the machine. Relativity thus sets a limit to the maximum energy of a conventional cyclotron. For protons this limit is, in practice, about 30 MeV.

To reach higher energies, it is possible to introduce a magnetic field that increases with r (which, as we have seen, defocuses the ions), but to overcompensate for this defocusing action by making the magnetic field dependent on θ in such a way as to have a strongly focusing action. This possibility was indicated by L. H. Thomas in 1939, and there are now machines based on this method of focusing.

Another possibility is to vary the electrical frequency applied to the dees in order that a particle will always be in step with the accelerating field. This is accomplished by using the principle of phase stability (Veksler, 1945; McMillan, 1946).

4-5 Phase Oscillations and Stability

In any accelerator operating on the multiple-acceleration principle, it is essential that the successive impulses be imparted at the proper

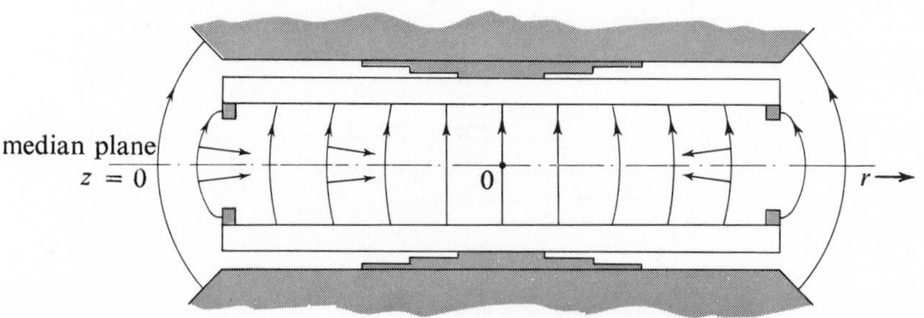

Figure 4-8 Restoring forces for particles in orbits above or below the median plane in the radially decreasing magnetic field of a cyclotron. The flat pyramidal shims shown in the shimming gaps are arranged to provide a small radial decrease in field in the center of the gap between holes. Ring shims at the periphery increase the region of useful field.

time. When an extremely large number of accelerations (many thousands) is required, the problem of keeping the circulating particles in step with the accelerating field appears to be formidable. Actually there is a mechanism that makes this possible. With suitable arrangements of fields the particles tend automatically to cross the accelerating gap at a time at which they receive the right energy necessary to keep them in resonance with the electric field. This is the principle of phase stability.

To understand the phenomenon qualitatively, let us consider first a particle circulating in an orbit through a constant magnetic field and passing a gap with an applied alternating electric field. Assume that the velocity of the particle is such as to cross the gap when the electric field is 0, and neglect radiation and other losses. The particle will circulate indefinitely in this orbit, at a constant velocity. The energy, frequency, and radius of this orbit are denoted by the adjective *synchronous*.

Suppose now that another particle arrives at the gap at time t_1, a little earlier than a synchronous particle (Fig. 4-9). It will then gain energy in crossing the gap. Having gained energy, its angular velocity (which is related to the energy by

$$\omega = \frac{eB}{mc} = \frac{eBc}{E} \tag{4-5.1}$$

where E = total energy) will be lowered, and the particle will next cross the gap at time t_2, a little later in phase than it did the first time. This process continues until the gap is crossed at the time when there is no electric field. However, the energy by now will be higher than that required to reach the gap at zero field, and after more turns the ion will cross the gap in the decelerating part of the cycle. Thus the particle will lose energy and hence its frequency will increase. This process will continue in the decelerating part of the cycle. However, the situation is now reversed, and the particle gains in frequency and loses energy until it is returned to the zero-phase position.

Thus the phase, frequency, energy, and radius of the orbit of a particle oscillate around the equilibrium situation. A group of particles

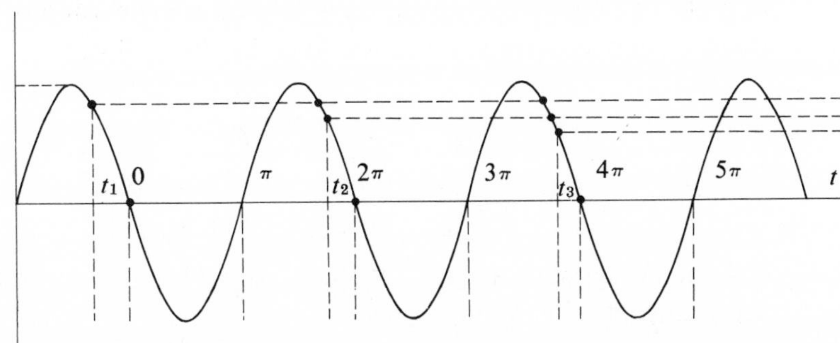

Figure 4-9 Variation of accelerating potential with time, showing origin of phase oscillations.

forms a "bunch" in the orbit, and each particle migrates back and forth within the bunch, requiring many thousands of revolutions to complete the cycle.

We may now take advantage of this property of the orbits in order to accelerate the particles by increasing the magnetic field very slowly, keeping the frequency constant. In the case of a relativistic particle (electron), the momentum increases as the radius of the orbit oscillates slightly around the equilibrium value. This is the principle of the synchrotron. Conversely, we may keep the magnetic field constant and slowly decrease the frequency of the accelerating field. The radius of the orbit then increases, along with the energy of the particle. This is the principle of the synchrocyclotron.

We may also keep the radius constant and slowly change both the frequency and the magnetic field (proton synchrotron). In every case the energy oscillates around the synchronous energy, which slowly increases with time.

We shall now consider this subject more quantitatively in a special example. Let us put the line $\theta = 0$ at the gap between the dees of a cyclotron. Call the potential difference at this gap

$$V \sin \omega_e t \tag{4-5.2}$$

and define the phase φ of a particle as the angle

$$\varphi = \pi + \theta - \omega_e t \tag{4-5.3}$$

where θ is the azimuthal angular position of the particle.

The particle has an instantaneous angular velocity $\omega = 2\pi/T$. If ω remains equal to ω_e, the phase is constant and the particle is a synchronous particle. On crossing the gap the particle is subject to an increase of potential

$$V \sin (\pi - \varphi) \qquad \text{at } \theta = 0 \tag{4-5.4}$$

or

$$V \sin (2\pi - \varphi) \qquad \text{at } \theta = \pi \tag{4-5.5}$$

In conclusion, a particle of charge e increases its energy by

$$\Delta E = eV \sin \varphi \qquad \text{at each gap } (\theta = 0 \text{ or } \theta = \pi) \tag{4-5.6}$$

Equation (4-5.6) shows the importance of the phase concept: the phase determines the increase of energy per revolution. For a synchronous particle having $\varphi = 0$ or π, ΔE is 0. For a synchronous particle the radius r_s and the energy are determined by the relations

$$\omega_s = \omega_e = \frac{eB_s c}{E_s} \tag{4-5.7}$$

$$r_s = \frac{c}{\omega_e} \beta = \frac{c}{\omega_e}\left[1 - \left(\frac{m_0 c^2}{E_s}\right)^2\right]^{1/2} \tag{4-5.8}$$

and the energy increase per revolution [Eq. (4-5.6)] may be rewritten by using Eqs. (4-5.7) and (4-5.8) as

$$2eV \sin \varphi_s = \frac{dE_s}{dt} T_s = \frac{2\pi ce}{\omega_e} \frac{d(B/\omega_e)}{dt} \tag{4-5.9}$$

• We shall now prove that, for a particle having the parameters r, ω, etc., near synchronism, the phase oscillates around a fixed value. This fact is of the greatest importance, because it tells us that it is not necessary to adjust all parameters in strict synchronism (a practically impossible task), but that the motion itself takes care of keeping the particle in phase (phase stability). Also by slowly changing B (increasing) or ω_e (decreasing) the synchronous energy increases, and hence the particles that are locked in the synchronous orbit are accelerated.

Let us indicate by

$$E - E_s = \delta E \qquad T - T_s = \delta T \qquad \text{etc.} \tag{4-5.10}$$

the difference between the energy, period, etc., of a particle and the corresponding quantity for a synchronous particle. Let us begin by finding some relations between δT, δE, δr, $\delta\beta$, and δp. Starting from

$$T = \frac{2\pi r}{\beta c} \tag{4-5.11}$$

we obtain by logarithmic differentiation

$$\frac{\delta T}{T} = \frac{\delta r}{r} - \frac{\delta\beta}{\beta} \tag{4-5.12}$$

We want to express $\delta r/r$ and $\delta\beta/\beta$ through $\delta E/E$. Assuming a field in accordance with Eq. (4-3.13), we have

$$cp = eB_0 r_0{}^n r^{1-n} \tag{4-5.13}$$

from which we get

$$\frac{\delta p}{p} = \frac{(1-n)\delta r}{r} \tag{4-5.14}$$

On the other hand, the relations $cp = \beta E$ and $E = E_0(1 - \beta^2)^{-1/2}$ give

$$\frac{\delta p}{p} = \frac{\delta\beta}{\beta} + \frac{\delta E}{E} \tag{4-5.15}$$

$$\frac{\delta\beta}{\beta} = \frac{(\beta^{-2} - 1)\delta E}{E} \tag{4-5.16}$$

Eliminating $\delta p/p$, $\delta\beta/\beta$, and $\delta r/r$ between Eqs. (4-5.14) and (4-5.16), we have, from Eq. (4-5.12),

$$\frac{\delta T}{T} = \left[1 - \frac{n}{\beta^2(n-1)}\right]\frac{\delta E}{E} = K\frac{\delta E}{E} \tag{4-5.17}$$

The quantity in brackets reduces to $(1 - n)^{-1}$ for $\beta = 1$. Moreover, if $0 < n < 1$, as is required for vertical and radial stability, $K > 1$. Taking the time derivative of Eq. (4-5.3), using Eq. (4-5.17) and the relation $\delta E = \omega_s r_s\, \delta p$, one finds

$$\dot{\varphi} = \omega - \omega_e = \delta\omega = -\omega_s\frac{\delta T}{T} = -Kr_s\omega_s{}^2\frac{\delta p}{E} \tag{4-5.18}$$

We return now to the problem of establishing the phase variation in time. The canonical equation gives

$$\dot{p}_\theta = \text{external torque} = \frac{2eV}{2\pi}\sin\varphi \tag{4-5.19}$$

in which we have replaced by a continuous torque the impulsive torque which the particle undergoes on crossing the slit between the dees.

Writing the expression for p_θ, we have

$$\frac{d}{dt}\left(mr^2\dot{\theta} + \frac{e}{c}rA_\theta\right) = \frac{e}{\pi}V\sin\varphi \tag{4-5.20}$$

This equation, for A_θ constant in time, states that the gain in energy per unit time is equal to the work done by the external electric torque. If A_θ contains the time explicitly, the gain in energy is determined by the sum of the external electric torque and the induced emf (betatron) acceleration. The equation neglects energy loss by radiation, which is unimportant for protons; it could be taken into account by subtracting $L/2\pi$ from the right side, where L is the energy lost, per turn, by radiation [Eq. (4-3.28)].

For a synchronous particle Eq. (4-5.20) is valid provided that we use the synchronous quantities p_s, r_s, etc. In order to see how a particle oscillates in a synchronous orbit, we "linearize" the problem by taking the difference between Eq. (4-5.20) and the corresponding equation for a synchronous particle. Recalling the definition of δ [Eq. (4-5.10)], we have, to the first order,

$$\frac{d}{dt}\left[\delta(mr^2\dot{\theta}) + \frac{e}{c}\,\delta(rA_\theta)\right] = \frac{e}{\pi}V(\sin\varphi - \sin\varphi_s) \tag{4-5.21}$$

Now, if A_θ does not contain the time explicitly, the quantity in brackets is

$$p\,\delta r + r\,\delta p + \frac{e}{c}\,\delta(rA_\theta) \tag{4-5.22}$$

This can be simplified by observing that $p = -(e/c)Br = -(e/c)[\partial(rA_\theta)/\partial r]$, from which $p\,\delta r = -(e/c)\,\delta(rA_\theta)$. We thus obtain

$$\frac{d}{dt}(r_s\,\delta p) = \frac{e}{\pi}V(\sin\varphi - \sin\varphi_s) \tag{4-5.23}$$

Taking $r_s\,\delta p$ from Eq. (4-5.18) and substituting it in Eq. (4-5.23), we have

$$\frac{d}{dt}\left(\frac{\dot{\varphi}E_s}{\omega_s^2K}\right) + \frac{e}{\pi}V(\sin\varphi - \sin\varphi_s) = 0 \tag{4-5.24}$$

Here φ is the unknown function of t and E_s, ω_s^2, K, and V are to be regarded as constant to the first approximations. Equation (4-5.24) then represents an oscillatory motion. If $\varphi - \varphi_s = \epsilon$ is small, Eq. (4-5.24) can be approximated by

$$\frac{E_s}{\omega_s^2K}\ddot{\epsilon} + \frac{eV}{\pi}\epsilon\cos\varphi_s = 0 \tag{4-5.25}$$

which gives the frequency of the phase oscillation as

$$\omega_\varphi = \omega_s\left(\frac{eVK}{\pi E_s}\cos\varphi_s\right)^{1/2} \tag{4-5.26}$$

The root is always $\ll 1$, because $eV \ll E_s$, and hence the phase oscillations are slow compared with the synchronous frequency. ●

Even if phase oscillations are not small, Eq. (4-5.24) may easily be discussed on the basis of the mechanical model shown in Fig. 4-10. The correspondence between the parameters of the model and the slowly varying quantities in Eq. (4-5.24) is given in the caption of the figure. It is clear that, if $\varphi_{\max} > \pi$, the motion loses its oscillatory character. The phase oscillations are accompanied by oscillations of radius, energy, etc. Equation (4-5.24) may be generalized to take into account radiation losses, and it may be transformed in various ways suitable for the synchrotron, linear accelerators, etc.

The main differences between the operation of the ordinary cyclotron and the synchrocyclotron are that:

1. In the latter the particles may turn around 10^5 times before reaching the maximum energy, instead of 10^2 times, as in the ordinary cyclotron. Thus the potential applied to the dees needs to be 10^{-5} of the maximum obtainable energy.
2. The frequency is modulated.
3. The ions form "slugs" that circulate in the machine and come out in spurts lasting about 50 μsec and repeating at the rate of 100 sec^{-1}.

The variable frequency is obtained by inserting in the radiofrequency oscillator a capacitor that periodically varies its capacitance either by a rotary mechanism or by a vibrating reed.

4-6 The Synchrotron and Proton Synchrotron

The synchrocyclotron requires magnetic-pole pieces of the diameter of the orbit. The maximum momentum obtainable is

$$\frac{e}{c}Br = p \qquad \text{or} \qquad T^2 + 2m_0c^2T = e^2B^2R^2 \tag{4-6.1}$$

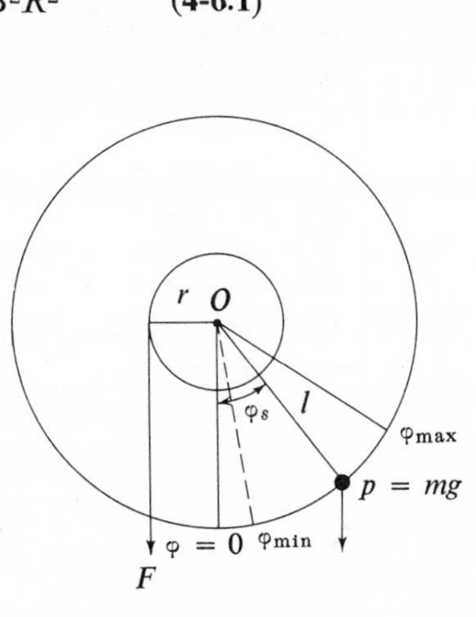

Figure 4-10 The weight mg gives a torque $mgl \sin \varphi$ with respect to O, which is opposed by the constant torque Fr. In the equilibrium position $\varphi = \varphi_s$. The equation of motion is

$$l\ddot{\varphi} = g(\sin\varphi - \sin\varphi_s)$$

and it is identical to Eq. (4-5.24), if

$$\frac{g}{l} = \frac{\text{eV}}{\pi}\frac{K}{E_s}\omega_s^2$$

$\varphi_{\min}$ and $\varphi_{\max}$ represent the minimum and maximum values of φ in an oscillation.

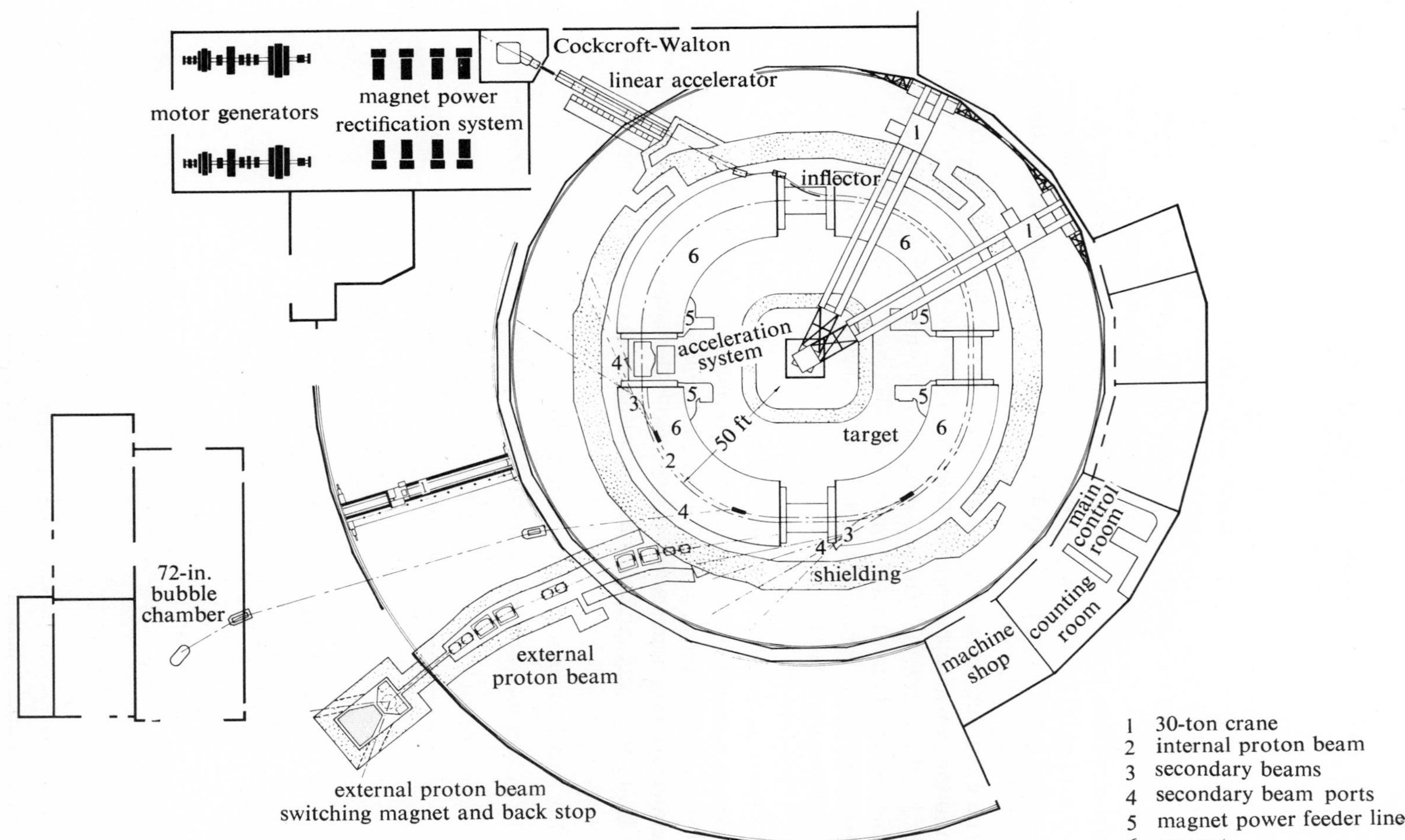

Figure 4-11 The bevatron (proton synchrotron) of the Lawrence Radiation Laboratory at Berkeley.

where T is the kinetic energy. Since B is limited in practice to about 22×10^3 G, the radius and hence the cost of the machine becomes prohibitive for protons above about 700 MeV.

The advantage of a ring-shaped machine is obvious, and the synchrotron is just such a machine. Its characteristic is a constant radius of orbit. The ions move in a doughnut-shaped, evacuated channel, to which is applied a magnetic field necessary to maintain the ions in an orbit of the proper radius. The accelerating electric field is provided in one or more gaps. For electrons, which are extremely relativistic, it suffices to increase the magnetic field and keep the frequency of the electric field constant. For protons, which are not extremely relativistic, it is necessary to increase the frequency as the magnetic field increases. In large machines, to avoid the problems of an extremely weak magnetic field at injection, it is necessary to inject the ions at an energy of many MeV. The injection is accomplished by auxiliary accelerators. The orbit of a large machine always has some field-free regions through which the ions move in a straight line. These regions are necessary for injection, acceleration, and deflection.

Figure 4-11, with Table 4-2, gives a description of a proton synchrotron; Fig. 4-12 shows an electron synchrotron.

4-7 Strong Focusing

In order to reach higher and higher energies, it is necessary to increase the radius of the accelerator, since B is limited by practical considerations. It is clear that it is then imperative to keep the ions in their trajectory with great precision, because in their extremely long path they could easily strike the wall of the doughnut. Moreover, the smaller the cross section of the tank, the cheaper it is to build and supply power

Table 4-2 Bevatron Characteristics

Maximum proton energy	6.2 BeV
Number of protons per pulse	3.2×10^{12}
Steel weight	9,500 tons
Air-cooled copper coil	350 tons
Magnetic field at injection	422 G
Magnetic field at 6.4 BeV	16,000 G
Power required	5,400 kW
Cockcroft–Walton injector—voltage	460 kV
Linear accelerator (proton injection energy to Bevatron)	19.6 MeV
Starting accelerating frequency	445 kc
Final accelerating frequency	2,500 kc
Average voltage gain per turn	1,500 eV
Time of acceleration	1.75 sec

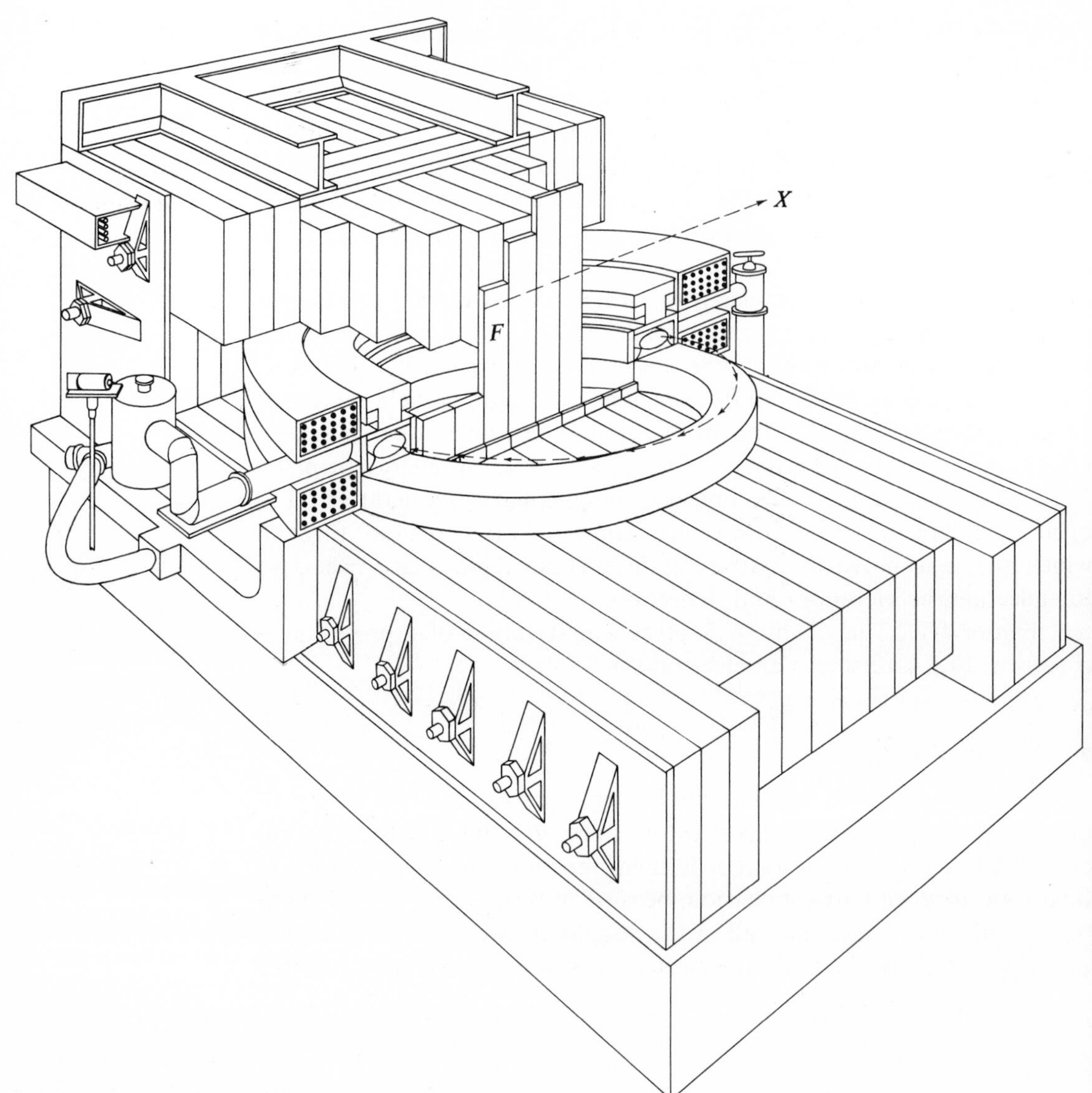

Figure 4-12 Cutaway view of the original Berkeley synchrotron. The laminated-iron magnet yoke is rectangular in outline, with a rectangular hole in the center through which pass the vertical "flux bars" that give the initial acceleration by betatron action. The magnet poles, coils, and vacuum chamber are circular. At the left is the *rf* oscillator, and at the far side of the vacuum chamber is the X-ray target, with an X-ray beam indicated by a straight arrow. The curved arrow is the path of an electron leaving the injector on its first trip around the orbit. [E. M. Macmillan in (Se 59).]

to the magnet. These considerations put a premium on keeping the amplitudes of the radial and vertical oscillations small.

This requirement is related to keeping the oscillation frequencies high. For instance, if at injection the ions start with $z = 0$, $\dot{z}(0)$ different from 0, the vertical oscillation will have the amplitude

$$z_{\max} = \frac{\dot{z}(0)}{\omega_z} \tag{4-7.1}$$

as can be seen immediately. Now $\omega_z = \omega_0(n)^{1/2}$, according to Eq. (4-3.27), and a large n is required to keep the value of $z_{\max}$ low. However, we know that radial stability requires $n < 1$, and it seems that the situation is hopeless.

Christofilos (1950) and, independently, Courant, Livingston, and Snyder (1952) found a way out of the difficulty. The magnet is built of successive segments having, alternately, n large and positive and n large in magnitude but negative. The first segment focuses vertically but defocuses horizontally. The opposite happens with the second segment. However, the sum total for both vertical and radial motion is focusing. This fact, unexpected at first sight, can be qualitatively understood by considering two optical lenses, one convergent and the other divergent. We have indicated in Fig. 4-19 the rays through a system of two magnetic lenses showing the resultant focusing action.

In an actual accelerator the vacuum tank is surrounded by a

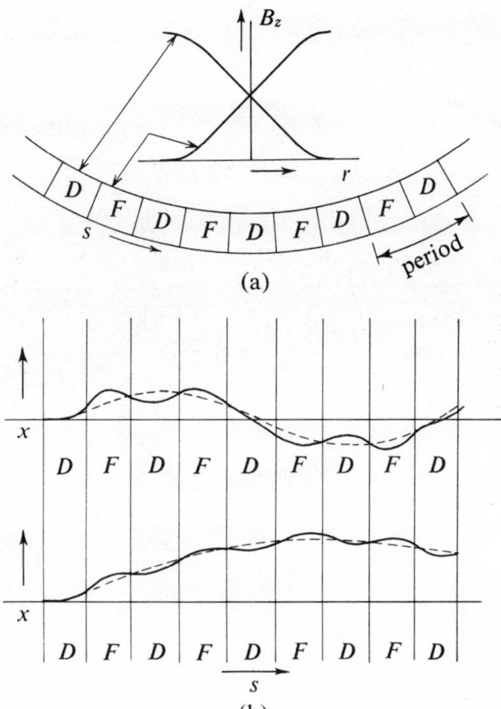

Figure 4-13 (a) A succession of focusing and defocusing lenses as arranged in a strong-focusing accelerator. (b) Two cases of the displacement of the beam along s showing focusing and defocusing actions. [Green and Courant, (Fl E).]

succession of magnets having alternately large n positive and negative. The magnets can be so arranged as to have a net focusing action. In Fig. 4-13 we show the trajectory in a section of the magnet. The whole ring is made by the periodic repetition of the elementary section. The precise arrangement must be calculated by taking the stability of the orbit into account. The combination of strong focusing and the principle of the proton synchrotron has made it possible to accelerate protons to energies of approximately 3×10^{10} eV. Figure 4-14 shows a section of the Brookhaven alternating gradient machine.

4-8 Linear Accelerators

The principle of multiple acceleration is also used in linear accelerators. The trajectory of the ions is approximately straight, however. There are many types of linear accelerators, for electrons, protons, and heavy ions such as C^{12}. We shall describe briefly only two types, one for electrons of very high energy, and the other for heavy ions.

As we have previously mentioned above a certain energy radiation

Figure 4-14 View of the alternating-gradient proton synchrotron of Brookhaven National Laboratory, showing a few of the 240 magnet sections. [Courtesy Brookhaven National Laboratory.]

losses become prohibitive for circular electron accelerators. In this respect linear accelerators have an obvious advantage. For heavy ions q/m is often low, because the atoms forming the ions are only partially ionized. A magnetic field would bend the trajectories of these ions only slightly, and it would be more costly to use a circular machine than a linear accelerator. At present energies of the order of 10 MeV per nucleon are secured for heavy ions by means of linear accelerators.

A linear accelerator of historical interest is shown in Fig. (4-15). The even and odd electrodes are connected to opposite poles of an oscillator. In the gaps between the drift tubes located on the axis of the cavity there is an electric-potential difference

$$V = V_0 \cos \omega t \qquad \textbf{(4-8.1)}$$

An ion in the gap is subject to the related field. An ion traveling inside a drift tube does not feel any field. If an ion crosses the gaps at the appropriate times, for example, at 0, $T = 2\pi/\omega$, $2T$, etc., it receives multiple accelerating impulses. The distance between gaps must increase if the ion is to cross the gap at the right time.

The distance L between gaps must be such that an ion enters a drift tube when the tube is negative and leaves it when it is positive, hence

$$L = \frac{vT}{2} \qquad \textbf{(4-8.2)}$$

where v is the velocity, in the drift tube. Nonrelativistically, after crossing j gaps, v is

$$\left(\frac{2e}{m} jV_0\right)^{1/2} \qquad \textbf{(4-8.3)}$$

Hence

$$L_j = \left(j\frac{2e}{m} V_0\right)^{1/2} \frac{T}{2}$$

Relativistically, for electrons of high energy, $v \to c$, and the distance between gaps is constant,

$$L = \frac{cT}{2} \qquad \textbf{(4-8.4)}$$

The type of accelerator illustrated in Fig. 4-15 was actually built and used by Lawrence and Sloan (1931) but has had little use in nuclear physics.

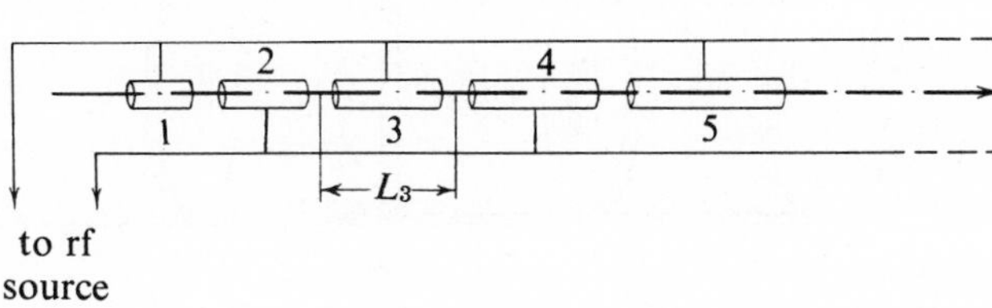

Figure 4-15 Linear accelerator, Lawrence–Sloan type. Drift tube 3 has a length $L_3 = [3(2e/m)V_0]^{1/2}(T/2)$.

Modern accelerators make use of waveguides to establish the electric field. High frequencies of up to 3,000 Mc are currently employed. A waveguide is a pipe of conducting material in which an oscillating electromagnetic field is established. The electromagnetic field can form a standing wave in the cavity, which then acts as a resonator, or it can form a traveling wave. The standing wave may of course be considered as the superposition of two traveling waves progressing in opposite directions. An ion that moves with the same velocity as the traveling wave is subject to a constant accelerating force.

In the case of high-energy electrons moving at a velocity very near c, the electromagnetic wave must move with a phase velocity c. Such modes of oscillation are achieved by inserting partitions in the cavity and exciting it at the proper frequency. Such a cavity is shown schematically in Fig. 4-16. The conducting disks give to the line the desired characteristic phase velocity.

In the Stanford electron accelerators, the wavelength used is of the order of 10 cm, and the disk spacing is one-fourth the wavelength. The power is supplied in pulses of 2-μsec duration, 60 pulses per second. The maximum energy reached thus far is 1 BeV.

As another example we mention the heavy-ion linear accelerators used to accelerate heavy ions (e.g., C, N, Ne) to energies of about 10 MeV per nucleon (Fig. 4-17). Positive ions of small charge are first accelerated in a Cockcroft–Walton type of accelerator having a potential drop of about 400 keV. On emerging from this accelerator, the ions are "bunched" so that they can be injected into the next section, a linear accelerator of the standing-wave type. In the second section the ions acquire an energy of about 1 MeV per nucleon. It is then possible to ionize them further by collision with mercury vapor and thus obtain a higher value of e/m, which is desirable for the next acceleration. The part of the machine where this process takes place is called the *stripper*. The ions now enter a new section, also of the standing-wave type, where they are further accelerated to an energy of about 10 MeV per nucleon ($v/c = 0.15$).

Linear accelerators, like circular accelerators, have phase stability, the most important difference being that phase stability in the former is achieved during the part of the cycle in which the potential increases,

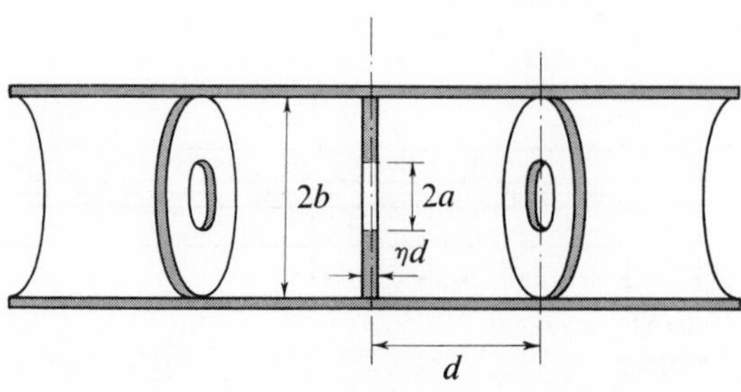

Figure 4-16 Structure of disk-loaded accelerator, showing important design dimensions.

rather than during the decreasing potential part of the cycle used in ordinary weak-focusing circular accelerators.

The ions are focused to prevent spreading of the beam by magnetic-quadrupole lenses (see Sec. 4-9) or other devices.

4-9 Beam-Transport Apparatus

For experimental purposes it is frequently necessary to generate beams of particles originating from a target. The art of producing and controlling such beams is rather similar to the art of optics. The optical components, lenses and prisms, are replaced by magnetic lenses and deflecting magnets.

One of the most useful magnetic lenses is a *quadrupole* (Fig. 4-18). In the vicinity of the axis of the quadrupole **B** has the form

$$B_x = by \qquad \textbf{(4-9.1)}$$

$$B_y = bx \qquad \textbf{(4-9.2)}$$

$$B_z = 0 \qquad \textbf{(4-9.3)}$$

satisfying Maxwell's equations and deriving from a scalar potential $V = -bxy$.

An ion moving in a region near the z axis and at a small inclination to this axis is subject to the forces

$$F_x = -\frac{e}{c}vbx \qquad \textbf{(4-9.4)}$$

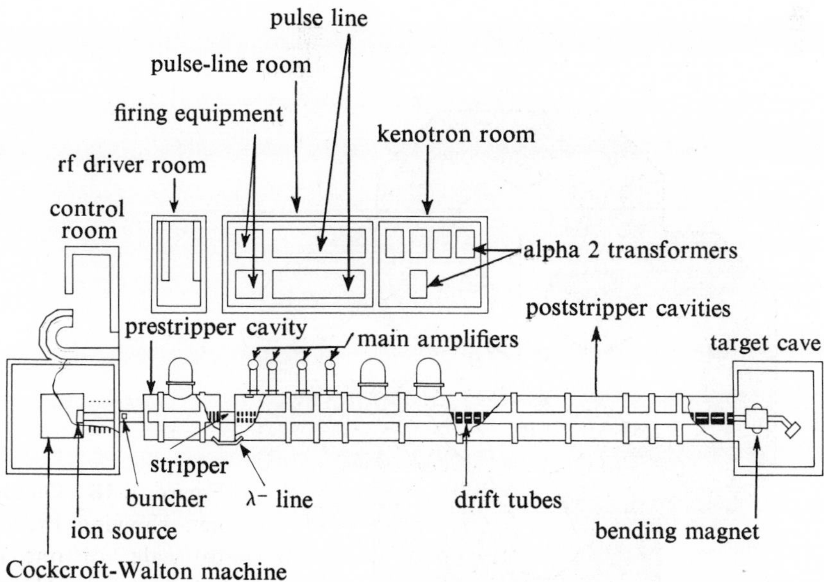

Figure 4-17 Plan view of heavy-ion linear accelerator of the Lawrence Radiation Laboratory in Berkeley.

$$F_y = \frac{e}{c} vby \tag{4-9.5}$$

$$F_z = 0 \tag{4-9.6}$$

In our approximation

$$\frac{d}{dt} = v \frac{d}{dz} \quad \text{and} \quad \frac{d^2}{dt^2} = v^2 \frac{d^2}{dz^2} \tag{4-9.7}$$

from which we have

$$\frac{d^2x}{dt^2} = -\frac{ev}{mc} bx = v^2 \frac{d^2x}{dz^2} \tag{4-9.8}$$

or

$$\frac{d^2x}{dz^2} = -k^2x \tag{4-9.9}$$

where $k^2 = (e/cp)(\partial B_y/\partial x)$.
Similarly one obtains

$$\frac{d^2y}{dz^2} = +k^2y$$

The difference in sign in the x and y equations shows that a lens focusing in the xz plane defocuses in the yz plane and vice versa.

If $dx/dz = 0$, $x = x_0$, $dy/dz = y_0 = 0$ at the entrance of the quadrupole ($z = 0$), and the quadrupole has length l, the ion crosses the z axis at $z = l + (1/k) \cot kl$, as can be verified by integrating Eq. (4-9.9). Figure 4-19 shows that the action of the quadrupole in the xz plane is the same as that of a lens of focal length

$$f = \frac{1}{k \sin kl} \tag{4-9.10}$$

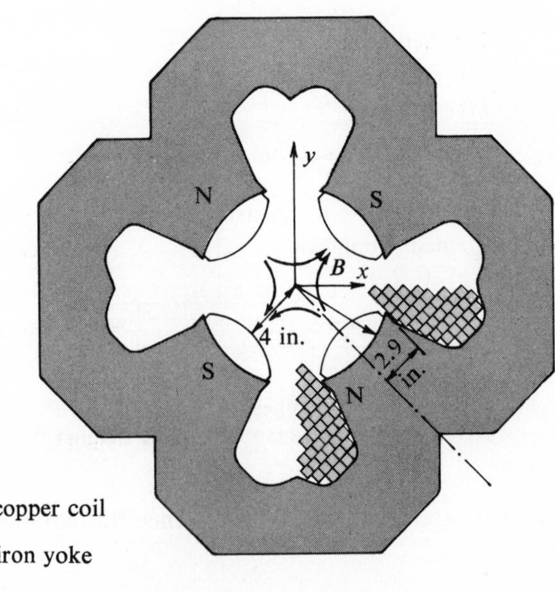

Figure 4-18 Quadrupole magnet, showing the cross section, to scale, of one of the most satisfactory quadrupole varieties. [O. Chamberlain, *Ann. Rev. Nucl. Sci.*, **10**, 161 (1960).]

and having its principal plane at a distance $-(1 - \cos kl)/(k \sin kl)$ from the image end of the quadrupole.

In the yz plane the quadrupole acts as a diverging lens because Eqs. (4-9.4) and (4-9.5) have different signs. It is possible to combine two or more quadrupoles in such a way as to give a real focus in both the vertical and the horizontal direction (Fig. 4-19). Generally such foci do not coincide, and the system is astigmatic. This, however, is not always undesirable in practice. Stigmatic systems may also be built, but they often have different magnifications in the x and y directions.

The combined action of several quadrupoles may be calculated by the following method. Consider first the x direction. A ray is then characterized by $x(z_0)$, $x'(z_0)$, where $dx/dz = x'$. The quantities $x(z)$, $x'(z)$ are linear functions of $x(z_0)$, $x'(z_0)$, the coefficients a, b, c, d, being functions of z.

$$x(z) = ax_0 + bx_0' \tag{4-9.11}$$

$$x'(z) = cx_0 + dx_0' \tag{4-9.12}$$

We can usefully represent this relation in the matrix form,

$$\begin{pmatrix} x \\ x' \end{pmatrix} = \begin{pmatrix} a & b \\ c & d \end{pmatrix} \begin{pmatrix} x_0 \\ x_0' \end{pmatrix} = X = MX_0 \tag{4-9.13}$$

The matrix M depends on the apparatus. For instance, for a free beam moving a distance b,

$$M = \begin{pmatrix} 1 & b \\ 0 & 1 \end{pmatrix} \tag{4-9.14}$$

Quadrupole lenses in the focusing and defocusing directions are represented between entrance and exit end by

$$\begin{pmatrix} \cos kl & \frac{1}{k} \sin kl \\ -k \sin kl & \cos kl \end{pmatrix} \quad \text{and} \quad \begin{pmatrix} \cosh kl & \frac{1}{k} \sinh kl \\ k \sinh kl & \cosh kl \end{pmatrix} \tag{4-9.15}$$

respectively.

A system is represented by the matrix product of the matrices corresponding to the components in the same order in which they are

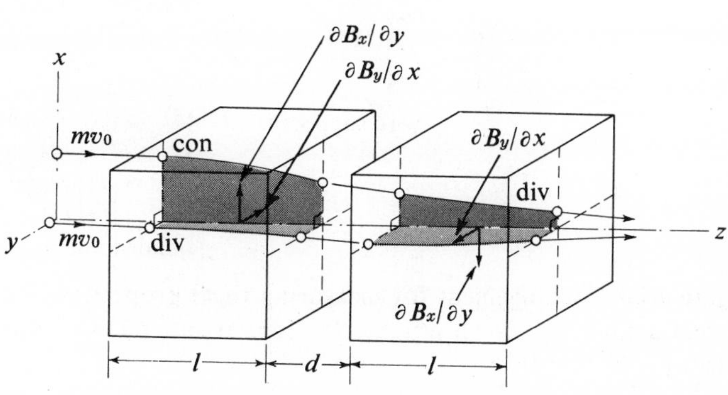

Figure 4-19 Double focusing by a pair of matched magnetic lenses in which the direction of the magnetic gradients is reversed. [From M. S. Livingston.]

traversed by the beam. For example, if the beam traverses components M_1, M_2, M_3, etc., the matrix describing the apparatus is M_3, M_2, M_1, etc. $= M$.

The matrix technique is also useful in calculating, for example, the effect of a series of magnets in an alternating gradient machine.

Experimentally rays traversing a complex system may often be traced by using a wire held under a tension T through which a current i passes. Such a wire in a magnetic field (Fig. 4-20) assumes the configuration of the orbit of an ion of charge e and momentum p provided that

$$\frac{i}{T} = \frac{e}{pc} \tag{4-9.16}$$

The magnetic systems thus far considered focus all particles having the same charge and momentum. In many experiments it is important to select particles of a given momentum and mass. This is accomplished by a combination of magnetic and electric deflection. In the Lorentz force

$$\mathbf{F} = e\left(\mathbf{E} + \frac{1}{c}\mathbf{v}\times\mathbf{B}\right) \tag{4-9.17}$$

the magnetic part depends on velocity, and the electric part does not. This permits distinguishing particles of the same momentum but of different velocity. A common method is to use electric and magnetic fields perpendicular to each other and to the direction of motion of the particle. When the electric and magnetic fields are in the ratio $E/B = v/c$, the particle traverses the velocity selector without deviation. Such an apparatus is called a *Wien filter*. Figure 4-21 shows a practical realization of a deflecting magnet, often used as a momentum selector. Figure 4-22 is a section of a Wien filter and Fig. 4-23 shows a complete setup for selecting a beam of particles having a given rest mass and velocity.

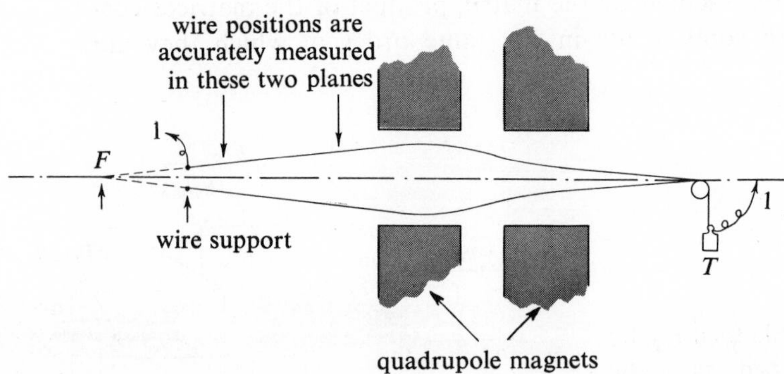

Figure 4-20 Arrangement for measuring focal properties of a pair of quadrupoles. 1 to regulated current source. T, known weight; F, focus point. [O. Chamberlain, *Ann. Rev. Nucl. Sci.*, **10,** 161 (1960).]

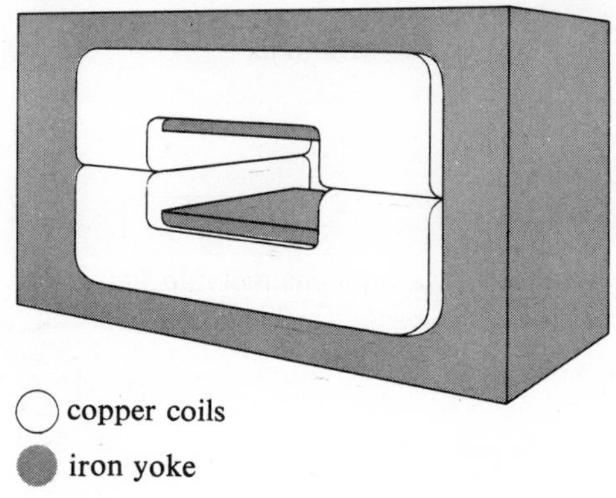

Figure 4-21 General-purpose deflecting magnet. This arrangement, with so-called "window-frame" construction, has proved very useful because it provides a very uniform field, even close to the coils, and may be used at high-magnetic-flux densities. [O. Chamberlain, *Ann. Rev. Nucl. Sci.*, **10,** 161 (1960).]

Bibliography

Baldinger, E., "Kaskadengeneratoren," in (Fl E), Vol. 44.

Chamberlain, O., "Optics of High-Energy Beams," *Ann. Rev. Nucl. Sci.*, **10,** 161 (1960).

Cohen, B. L., "Cyclotrons and Synchrocyclotrons," in (Fl E), Vol. 44.

Flügge, S. (Fl E).

Green, G. K., and E. D. Courant, "The Proton Synchrotron," in (Fl E), Vol. 44.

Herb, R. G., "Van de Graaff Generators," in (Fl E), Vol. 44.

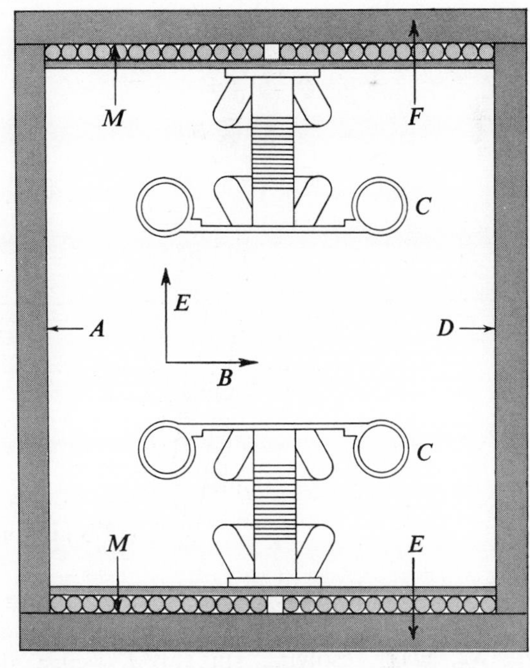

Figure 4-22 Mass selector for a high-energy accelerator. The beam moves perpendicularly to the plane of the figure. The electric field is obtained by establishing a potential difference between the plates of condensor *C*. The magnet field is generated by the coils *M*. *A* and *D* act as pole faces, *E* and *F* as return paths.

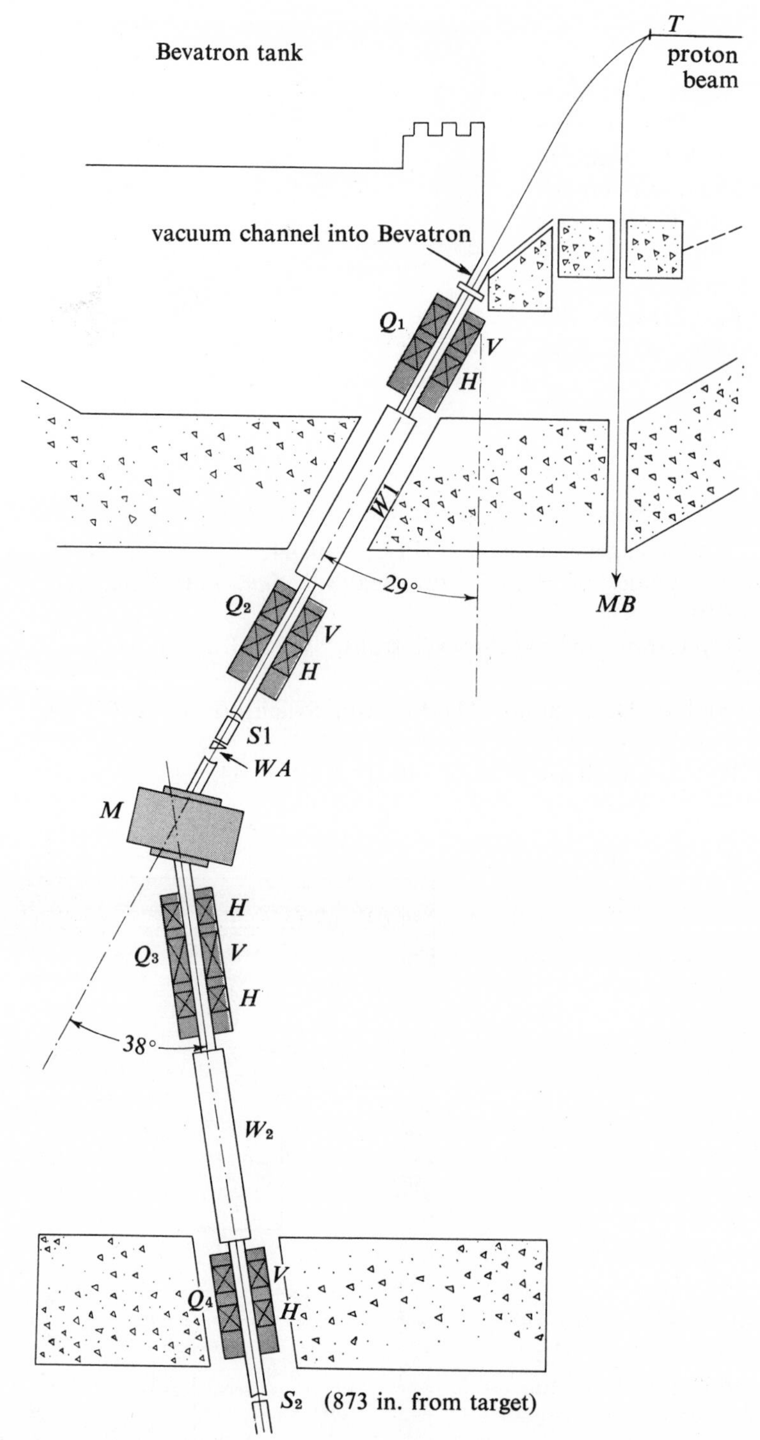

Figure 4-23 A complete beam selector for K^- having $p = 800$ MeV/c. *T*, target; *Q*1, *Q*2, *Q*3, *Q*4, 8-in. quadrupoles: *V*, vertical focusing; *H*, horizontal focusing; W_1, W_2, Wien filters; *M*, bending magnet; *S*1, *S*2, mass resolving slits; *WA*, wedge absorber. [Courtesy Lawrence Radiation Laboratory.]

Judd, D. L., "Conceptual Advances in Accelerators," *Ann. Rev. Nucl. Sci.*, **8**, 181 (1958).
Kerst, D. W., "The Betatron," in (Fl E), Vol. 44.
Livingood, J. J., *Principles of Cyclic Particle Accelerators*, Van Nostrand, Princeton, N.J., 1961.
Livingston, M. S., and J. P. Blewett, *Particle Accelerators*, McGraw-Hill, New York, 1962.
Marion, J. B., "Accelerator Energy Calibrations," *Rev. Mod. Phys.*, **33**, 139 (1961).
McMillan, E. M., "Particle Accelerators," in (Se 59), Vol. III.
Smith, L., "Linear Accelerators," in (Fl E), Vol. 44.
Wilson, R. R., "Electron Synchrotrons," in (Fl E), Vol. 44.

Problems

4-1 The loss of energy by an electron to radiation, given by Eq. (4-3.28), is associated with a radiation reaction force on the particle, given by

$$\mathbf{F}_L = -\frac{L}{2\pi r}\frac{\mathbf{v}}{v}$$

The components of the force that are transverse to the azimuthal direction produce damping. Calculate the *e*-folding time for this damping for electrons that have an energy of 10^9 eV and move in a magnetic field of 12 kG. Also calculate the power radiated per electron.

4-2 Linearized equations of motion for betatron oscillations, such as Eqs. (4-3.24) and (4-3.25), may be generalized by taking into account the slow changes in such parameters as mass, magnetic-field strength, orbit radius, and angular frequency which may occur during acceleration in various types of machines. Such changes are called *adiabatic* and lead in general to *adiabatic damping* of the oscillation amplitudes. It can be shown that the *action integral* J_i, given by

$$J_i = \oint p_i \, dq_i$$

(integrated over one cycle of an oscillation and neglecting slow changes) remains approximately constant when such changes occur. Assuming this, show that the amplitude of betatron oscillations in a betatron or electron synchrotron varies as the inverse square root of the magnetic-field strength B_0, for both nonrelativistic and relativistic particles.

4-3 Show that Eq. (4-5.24) for phase oscillations in a synchrocyclotron can be obtained from the hamiltonian function

$$H = \frac{eV}{\pi}(\cos\varphi + \varphi\sin\varphi_s) - \frac{\omega_s{}^2 K}{E_s}w^2$$

in which the canonically conjugate coordinate and momentum are φ and w, respectively. Sketch some of the curves of constant H in the $w - \varphi$ "phase plane," locating the two points at which both φ and w are zero, and the boundary, or *separatrix*, between regions of closed (phase-stable) and open (unbounded) curves. The variable w is the difference between actual and synchronous values of the function

$$W(E) = \int^{E} \frac{dE}{\omega(E)}$$

W is used because E itself is not canonically conjugate to the phase-angle coordinate φ, while w is introduced to display only changes relative to steadily varying synchronous quantities. Some advantages of this representation are: (1) it enables all phase motions to be visualized; (2) the adiabatic invariance of area contained within a closed curve (the action), referred to in Prob. 4-2, can be applied; and (3) the range of possible energies and phases within the phase-stable region at any energy can be readily determined. For further discussion see, for example, H. C. Corben and Philip Stehle, *Classical Mechanics*, 2nd ed., Wiley, New York, 1960, Sec. 98.

4-4 Plan a magnetic quadrupole lens having a 6-in. aperture. What is a reasonably attainable focal length for protons having $p = 400$ MeV/c?

4-5 Plan a separator for protons and K mesons. The momentum of the particles is 500 MeV/c. The angular separation required is 0.01 rad and the maximum field obtainable is 5×10^4 V cm^{-1}.

4-6 Make a general plan for a 10-MeV proton cyclotron. Estimate the diameter of the pole pieces of the magnet, the frequency and power of the oscillator, and the thickness of the shield. From these data make an approximate cost estimate. Add the cost of the building. Also estimate what crew will be needed, the power bill, and the yearly costs of operating the machine.

CHAPTER V

Radioactive Decay

HERE WE SHALL TREAT the laws of spontaneous radioactive decay, independent of the emission accompanying the transformation. This can be done because it happens that the law of decay is independent of the mechanism of the transformation. The results thus acquired apply to a great variety of cases and provide a phenomenological explanation of a vast category of experimental facts.

First, in Sec. 5-1 we shall neglect the fact that every substance contains an integral number of atoms and shall treat this number as a continuous variable. This procedure is legitimate if we deal with processes involving a great number of atoms. The continuum theory of radioactive decay is precise in the sense that, if we treat many systems of radioactive atoms initially identical, the average number of atoms contained in the various systems at any subsequent time is given exactly by the theory. On the other hand, each system may depart from the average, and for the study of these departures it is necessary to take into account the discontinuous, atomic nature of matter.

The decay law of radioactive substances was first clearly formulated and applied by Rutherford and Soddy as a result of their studies on the radioactivity of various substances, notably thorium, thorium X, and the emanations, although in more or less explicit form, it had also been known to earlier investigators.

5-1 Continuum Theory—One Substance

The fundamental law of radioactive decay can be formulated as follows: Given an atom, the probability that it will decay during the interval dt is $\lambda\, dt$. The constant λ is called the *decay constant*. Dimensionally it is a reciprocal time, and it is characteristic of the given substance and of the mode of the decay. The constant is independent of the age of the atom considered and, as we shall see later, being a nuclear property, is not affected by any of the usual physical agents. This type of law is characteristic of "casual" events and applies to all types of radioactive decay—alpha, beta, gamma, orbital electron capture, spontaneous fission—and also in the atomic process of light emission by excited atoms.

The simplest application of this law involves a single radioactive substance that has initially, $N(0)$ atoms. $N(0)$ is a large number, by hypothesis, so that we may consider $N(t)$, the number of atoms at time t, to be a continuously variable quantity. Then, according to our fundamental law, $-dN$, the increase in time dt of the number of atoms, is given by

$$-\,dN = \lambda N\,dt \tag{5-1.1}$$

which, integrated with the condition that initially we have $N(0)$ atoms, gives

$$N(t) = N(0)e^{-\lambda t} \tag{5-1.2}$$

Equation (5-1.2) is another formulation of the fundamental law of radioactive decay.

In practice one uses, in addition to the decay constant, its reciprocal $\tau = 1/\lambda$, called the *mean life*, and also the time T, in which the number of atoms initially present is reduced by a factor 2. T is often called the *period*, or *half-life*, of the substance. The period is related to the decay constant and to the mean life by

$$e^{-\lambda T} = e^{-T/\tau} = \tfrac{1}{2} \qquad \text{or} \qquad \lambda T = \frac{T}{\tau} = \log 2 = 0.6931472 \tag{5-1.3}$$

The term mean life is applied to τ because it is the average lifetime of the atoms. In fact, if we have initially $N(0)$ atoms, we shall have $N(t) = N(0)e^{-\lambda t}$ at time t, according to Eq. (5-1.2). Of these $N(t)\lambda\,dt$ will decay between times t and $t + dt$. The mean life is obtained by multiplying the last number by t, integrating with respect to dt between 0 and ∞, and dividing by the initial number of atoms present, $N(0)$:

$$\tau = \frac{1}{N(0)}\int_0^\infty \lambda t N(t)\,dt = \frac{1}{N(0)}\int_0^\infty N(0)e^{-\lambda t}\lambda t\,dt = \frac{1}{\lambda} \tag{5-1.4}$$

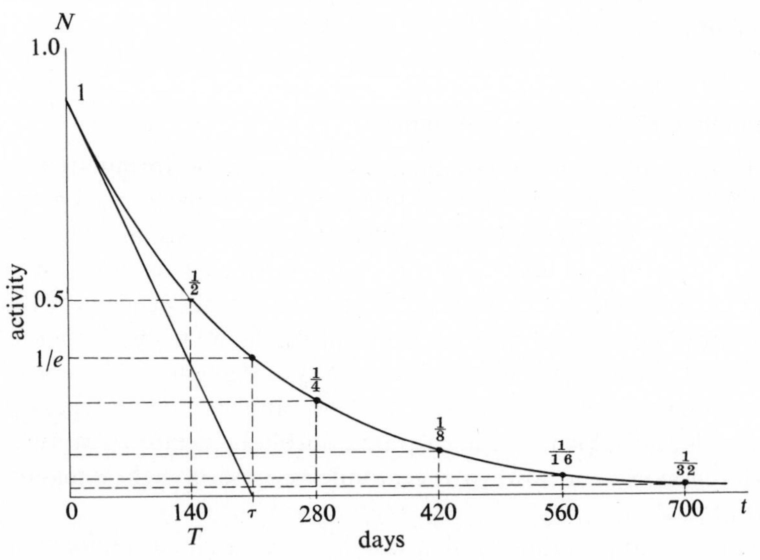

Figure 5-1 Decay of a radioactive substance.

It is also easily seen from Eq. (5-1.4) that, if a radioactive substance continues to decay at its initial rate $N(0)\lambda$, it will all disappear in a time τ (Fig. 5-1).

Graphically, if we plot $N(t)$ versus t, we obtain an exponential and the tangent to the curve at $t = 0$ intercepts the t axis at a time τ. If we plot $\log N(t)$ versus t, we obtain a straight line:

$$\log N(t) = \log N(0) - \lambda t$$

The slope of the straight line gives $-\lambda$. This second type of plot made directly on semilogarithmic paper is the most convenient and the most commonly used.

5-2 Continuum Theory—More than One Substance

Very often one radioactive substance decays into another that is also radioactive. The two substances are then said to be genetically related; the first is called the *parent*, or *mother*, substance, the second, the *daughter* substance. This relation is not limited to parent and daughter but extends sometimes over many "generations." Sometimes one substance can decay by two processes, e.g., by alpha and beta emission, giving rise to two different daughter substances: this occurrence is called *dual decay*, or *branching*.

Examples of long chains of radioactive decays are offered by the natural radioactive families (see Fig. 5-2) and also by the chains of successive beta decays typical of fission fragments.

Figure 5-2 shows that four alphas are expected from an atom of RdTh (Th^{228}) before reaching Th B (Pb^{212}) and their emission in succession is beautifully illustrated in Fig. 5-3. An atom of RdTh (Th^{228}) is embedded in a photographic emulsion, and each alpha particle emitted by it leaves its track in the emulsion.

We shall not consider in this section the case of branching, but we shall solve the following problem: Given that at time $t = 0$ we have $N_1(0)$, $N_2(0)$ atoms of the radioactive substances 1, 2, . . . etc., which are genetically related, find the number of atoms $N_1(t)$, $N_2(t)$ . . . present at any subsequent time.

Substance 1 decays according to the law expressed in Eq. (5-1.1): $dN_1 = -N_1\lambda_1\,dt$. For every atom of substance 1 that disintegrates, an atom of substance 2 is formed. Hence the number of atoms of substance 2 varies for two reasons: it decreases because substance 2 decays, but it increases because the decay of substance 1 continuously furnishes atoms of substance 2. The net change is given by

$$\frac{dN_2}{dt} = \lambda_1 N_1 - \lambda_2 N_2 \tag{5-2.1}$$

where λ_1 and λ_2 are the decay constants of the first and second substances, respectively. For a third substance we have, in a similar way,

$$\frac{dN_3}{dt} = \lambda_2 N_2 - \lambda_3 N_3, \text{ etc.} \tag{5-2.2}$$

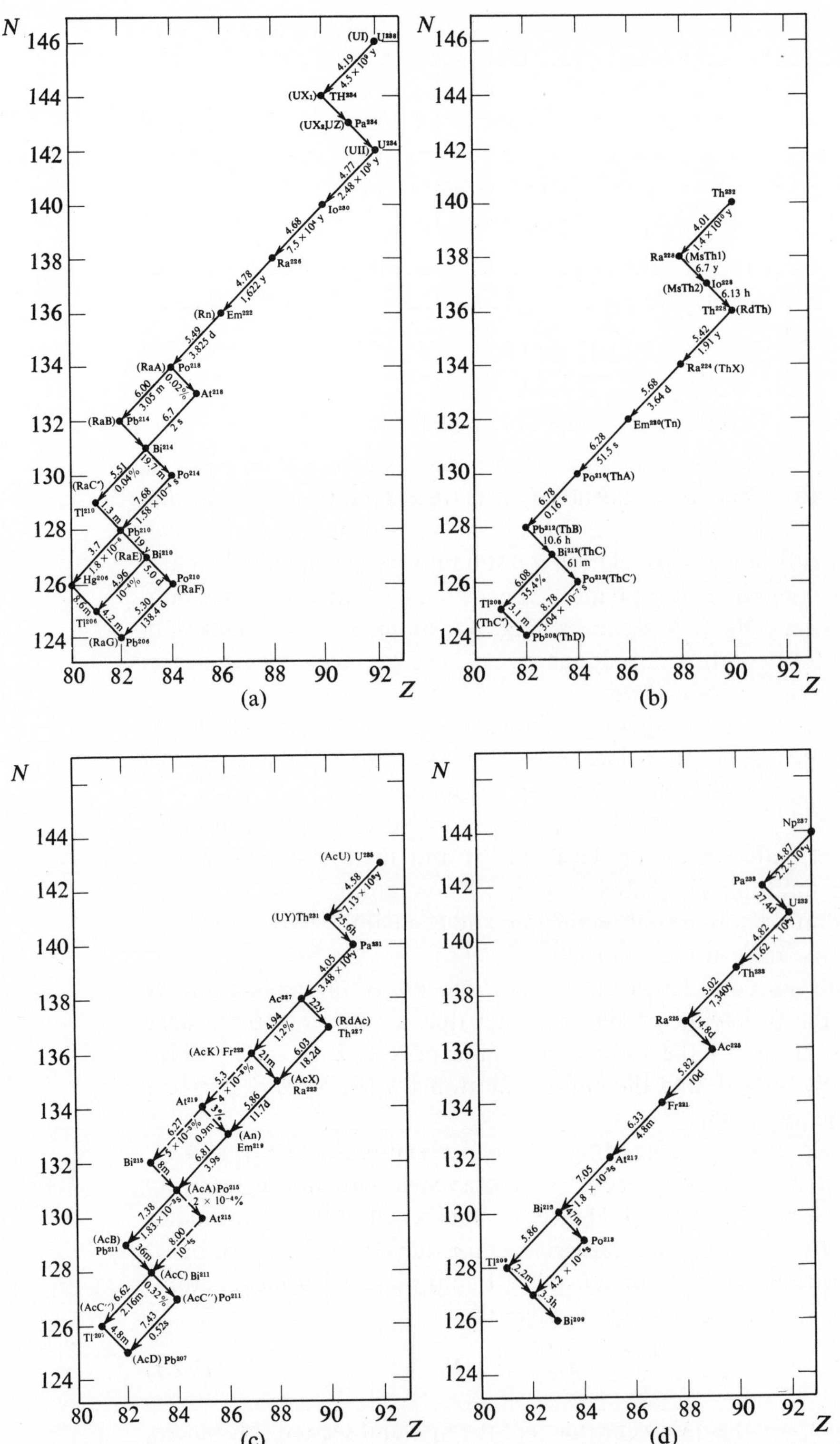

Figure 5-2 The natural radioactive families of U^{238}, Th^{232}, U^{235}, and of the artificially produced Np^{237} in a Z, N diagram, with the associated energies and half-lives.

This system of differential equations can be solved by putting

$$
\begin{aligned}
N_1 &= A_{11}e^{-\lambda_1 t} \\
N_2 &= A_{21}e^{-\lambda_1 t} + A_{22}e^{-\lambda_2 t} \\
N_3 &= A_{31}e^{-\lambda_1 t} + A_{32}e^{-\lambda_2 t} + A_{33}e^{-\lambda_3 t} \\
&\cdot \quad \cdot \quad \cdot \\
N_k &= A_{k1}e^{-\lambda_1 t} + A_{k2}e^{-\lambda_2 t} + \cdots + A_{kk}e^{-\lambda_k t}
\end{aligned} \tag{5-2.3}
$$

The constants A_{ki} are to be determined in such a way that the expressions of Eq. (5-2.3) satisfy the differential equations and the $N_k(0)$ have the prescribed initial values. Substituting the expressions of Eq. (5-2.3) into the differential equations (5-1.1), (5-2.1), (5-2.2), etc., we have

$$A_{ki} = A_{k-1,i}\frac{\lambda_{k-1}}{\lambda_k - \lambda_i} \tag{5-2.4}$$

This recursion formula is sufficient to determine all the A_{ki} with the exception of those with equal indexes.[1] These are determined by the

[1] If two or more of the decay constants involved should accidentally be equal, Eq. (5-2.4) cannot be applied and Eq. (5-2.3) has to be modified by replacing the exponentials with equal λ with terms of the form $te^{-\lambda t}$, $t^2e^{-\lambda t}$, etc.

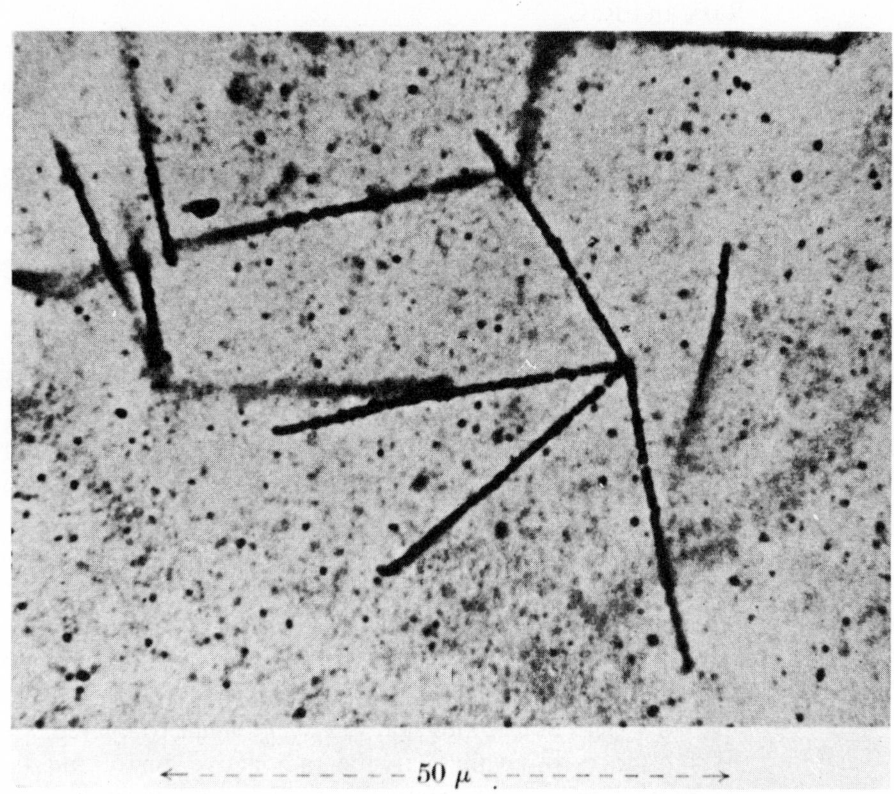

← 50 μ →

Figure 5-3 Radiothorium stars: The four tracks correspond to the alpha particles emitted by Th^{228}, Ac^{224}, Em^{220}, and Po^{216}. [Powell and Occhialini, *Nuclear Physics in Photographs*, Oxford University Press, London, 1947.]

initial conditions

$$N_k(0) = A_{k1} + A_{k2} + \cdots + A_{kk} \tag{5-2.5}$$

It will be noticed that in each of the expressions of Eq. (5-2.3) we have a sum of exponentials containing the decay constants of all the substances in the family preceding the one considered.

Some special cases of initial conditions are in practice very important, notably that in which only substance 1 is initially present and has $N_1(0)$ atoms initially. We have then, by a direct application of Eqs. (5-2.3) through (5-2.5),

$$\begin{aligned} N_1(t) &= N_1(0)e^{-\lambda_1 t} \\ N_2(t) &= N_1(0)\frac{\lambda_1}{\lambda_2 - \lambda_1}(e^{-\lambda_1 t} - e^{-\lambda_2 t}) \\ N_3(t) &= N_1(0)\lambda_1\lambda_2\left(\frac{e^{-\lambda_1 t}}{(\lambda_2 - \lambda_1)(\lambda_3 - \lambda_1)} + \frac{e^{-\lambda_2 t}}{(\lambda_3 - \lambda_2)(\lambda_1 - \lambda_2)}\right. \\ &\quad \left. + \frac{e^{-\lambda_3 t}}{(\lambda_1 - \lambda_3)(\lambda_2 - \lambda_3)}\right) \end{aligned} \tag{5-2.6}$$

This case occurs quite often, for example, in the active deposit of radium, where N_1, N_2, N_3 represent, respectively, the number of atoms of RaA, RaB, and RaC.

It is also important to see what happens to a mixture of radioactive substances left undisturbed for a long time. In Eq. (5-2.3) there will be terms containing the exponential with the smallest decay constant λ_s of the mixture. All atoms of species 1, 2, ..., s in a relatively short time become atoms of species s, and N_s itself is given by $N_s(t) = \mathcal{N}e^{-\lambda_s t}$, where $\mathcal{N} = N_1(0) + \cdots + N_s(0)$. If t is large enough ($t \gg 1/\lambda_s$), we have

$$\begin{aligned} N_1(t) &= N_2(t) = N_{s-1}(t) = 0 \\ N_s(t) &= \mathcal{N}e^{-\lambda_s t} \\ N_{s+1}(t) &= \mathcal{N}\frac{\lambda_s}{\lambda_{s+1} - \lambda_s}e^{-\lambda_s t} \end{aligned} \tag{5-2.7}$$

The ratio of the amount present of each of the substances following substance s to the amount of substance s itself is independent of time and is given by

$$\frac{N_t}{N_s} = \frac{\lambda_s\lambda_{s+1} \ldots \lambda_{t-1}}{(\lambda_{s+1} - \lambda_s)(\lambda_{s+2} - \lambda_s) \ldots (\lambda_t - \lambda_s)} \tag{5-2.8}$$

All substances decay according to the same time law, $e^{-\lambda_s t}$. When this situation obtains, we speak of *transient equilibrium*.

It happens sometimes that λ_s is very small compared with λ_t of all the substances following s in the radioactive family and that, during the interval under consideration $e^{-\lambda_s t} \simeq 1$. Then we write

$$\frac{N_t}{N_s} = \frac{\lambda_s}{\lambda_t} \tag{5-2.9}$$

and we speak of *secular equilibrium*. The interpretation of Eq. (5-2.9) is immediate: the number of atoms of substance s, $s + 1$, etc., disintegrating per unit time is the same, and hence the number of atoms present is inversely proportional to the decay constant. This situation occurs in ores containing uranium. The decay constant of U^{238} is extremely small compared with those of the products following it in the radioactive families, and the ores have been undisturbed for a long enough time to attain radioactive equilibrium. For all practical purposes the number of atoms in such an ore is independent of time as long as we limit ourselves to periods of no more than a few thousand years, and Eq. (5-2.9) holds for the radioactive families. However, it must be pointed out that the inactive lead isotopes that terminate the radioactive families are not necessarily present in an amount corresponding to the age of the mineral, because geochemical processes may have removed either the lead or the uranium in a different way.

A brilliant experiment on radioactive equilibrium is the following: Suppose that we have a solution containing U^{238} in equilibrium with its daughter product $UX_1(Th^{234})$, which has a period 24.1 days. By a chemical procedure we separate, almost instantaneously, UX_1 from U. The UX_1 fraction then decays with the period 24.1 days. On the other hand, since this fraction and the mother solution, when considered together, must remain in equilibrium, an amount of UX_1 must grow in the mother solution exactly equal to the amount disappearing from the separated fraction. This example was studied quantitatively by Rutherford and Soddy, and it helped to elucidate the theory of radioactive decay. The decay and growth curves (Fig. 5-4) were incorporated in Lord Rutherford's escutcheon.

Another important case occurring in practice is that of a radioactive substance (initially absent) formed at a constant rate. The differential equation for this process is

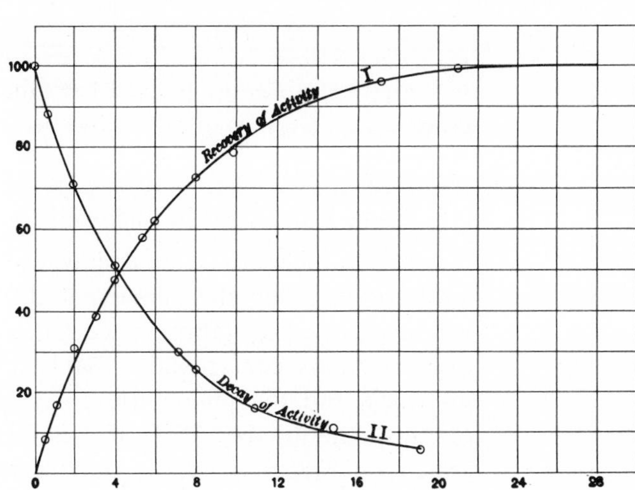

Figure 5-4 The original figure of decay of separated U and of the recovery of the activity in the mother solution. [E. Rutherford.]

$$\frac{dN}{dt} = Q - \lambda N \tag{5-2.10}$$

where Q is the number of atoms formed per unit time. Its solution when $N(0) = 0$ is

$$N(t) = \frac{Q}{\lambda}(1 - e^{-\lambda t}) \tag{5-2.11}$$

where Q/λ represents the number of atoms that one would obtain for $t \to \infty$ it is sometimes called the *saturation number* of atoms and is indicated by N_∞.

5-3 Branching

Several radioactive substances decay by more than one mechanism, for example, β^- and β^+ emission, alpha and beta emission. Let us consider alpha and beta branching and call the probability of alpha emission by one atom, in time dt, $\lambda_\alpha\, dt$ and the probability of beta emission by the same atom $\lambda_\beta\, dt$. Then the total probability of decay of the atom in time dt by either alpha or beta disintegration is $(\lambda_\alpha + \lambda_\beta)\, dt$. Hence

$$\frac{dN}{dt} = -(\lambda_\alpha + \lambda_\beta)N \tag{5-3.1}$$

and the mean life of the substance, defined as the time in which the amount initially present is reduced from 1 to $1/e$, is

$$\tau = \frac{1}{\lambda_\alpha + \lambda_\beta} \tag{5-3.2}$$

The ratio of the number of alpha to beta particles emitted during a certain time is called the *branching ratio* and is equal to $\lambda_\alpha/\lambda_\beta$. Sometimes the quantities $\tau_\alpha = 1/\lambda_\alpha$ and $\tau_\beta = 1/\lambda_\beta$ are used; these are called, not too accurately, the mean life of alpha and beta decay, respectively. From Eq. (5-3.2) it follows immediately that

$$\frac{1}{\tau} = \frac{1}{\tau_\alpha} + \frac{1}{\tau_\beta} \tag{5-3.3}$$

A similar terminology is used for other types of branching. Figure 5-2 gives some examples of alpha and beta branching.

5-4 Some Units Used in Radioactivity. Dosimetry

The number of atoms disintegrating per second in a given sample λN is often called the *activity* of the sample. Activities are generally measured in curies (abbreviated Ci). A sample undergoing 3.7×10^{10} disintegrations per second is said to have the activity of 1 Ci. The millicurie and the microcurie are 10^{-3} and 10^{-6} Ci, respectively. The origin of the number 3.7×10^{10} is as follows: In the early days of research on radioactivity the unit of activity was the amount of substance in equilibrium with 1 g of Ra and was called the curie in honor of P. and M. Curie. The unit was practical and convenient as long as all radioactive substances belonged to the Ra family. Later an attempt was made to determine the number of disintegrations per second in 1 Ci of a substance and, in particular, in 1 g of Ra. The results of many measurements gave approximately 3.7×10^{10} disintegrations per second. The definition of the curie was then changed to the number of disintegrations per second so as to make it applicable as well to substances that do not belong to the radium family.

Another approach to the definition of units of radioactivity considers the effect of the radiations instead of the number of disintegrations per unit time. We can speak, for instance, of 1 g radium equivalent for a MsTh sample, meaning that under certain conditions of filtration of the gamma rays (5 mm of lead) the ionization produced in a certain instrument by the two substances is the same. It is clear that this type of definition is dependent on the filtration of the radiations emitted by various substances and on the instrument used to detect the radiations. For this reason it must be used cautiously and with proper specification of the experimental conditions. However, it is often the only usable definition if the efficiency of the measuring instrument for the particular substance studied has not been determined. From this point of view it is possible to measure the ionizing action of a radioactive source emitting gamma rays by specifying that it produces a certain number of *roentgens* per hour at a distance of 1 m (Rhm). The roentgen (R) is defined as "that quantity of X or gamma radiation such that the associated corpuscular emission per 0.001293 g of air produces in air ions carrying 1 esu of quantity of electricity of either sign." The mass of air referred to is the mass of 1 cm³ of dry air at 0°C and 1 atm pressure. If we assume that an average of 32.5 eV is expended to produce a pair of ions in air, we find that 1 R corresponds to the absorption of

$$\frac{32.5 \times 1.60 \times 10^{-12}}{4.80 \times 10^{-10}} = 0.108 \text{ erg cm}^{-3} \text{ of air} \qquad \textbf{(5-4.1)}$$

or

$$\frac{0.108}{1.293 \times 10^{-3}} = 83.8 \text{ erg g}^{-1} \text{ of air} \qquad \textbf{(5-4.2)}$$

or 6.77×10^4 MeV cm^{-3} of air.

For several substances whose decay schemes are known it is possible, by using the data of Fig. 5-5, to calculate the Rhm corresponding to 1 disintegration per second and hence to deduce from an ionization measurement the activity of the sample. For example, Ra in equilibrium with its product gives 0.96 Rhm g^{-1}, without any filtration of the radiations; 0.25 mm of Pt reduces the Rhm to 0.88 per gram of Ra.

In practice, measurements of roentgens are obtained by using small air ionization chambers, the walls of which behave with respect to beta and gamma rays very much like air at very high pressure (see Fig. 3-6). One can then use an approximate theorem of Gray and Bragg, which states that the ionization produced by the gamma rays in the chamber is unaffected by the walls and is the same as would be obtained in an equal volume of an extended gaseous medium. This theorem is valid if the linear dimensions of the cavity are small compared with the range (in the gas-filling cavity) of the secondary corpuscular radiation (electrons) produced in the wall of the cavity. Chambers satisfying this condition, with walls made of suitable plastics, are called *air chambers* and are commercially available, being extensively used for medical X-ray dosimetry.

The Gray-Bragg relation can be written in the form

$$J = \frac{E}{\rho w} \tag{5-4.3}$$

where J is the number of ion pairs produced per unit volume of the gas, ρ is the ratio of the stopping power of the walls to the stopping power of the gas for the equilibrium radiation, E is the energy absorbed per unit volume of the walls, and w is the energy required to produce one ion pair. For an ideal air chamber ρ is simply the ratio of the densities of the walls and gas.

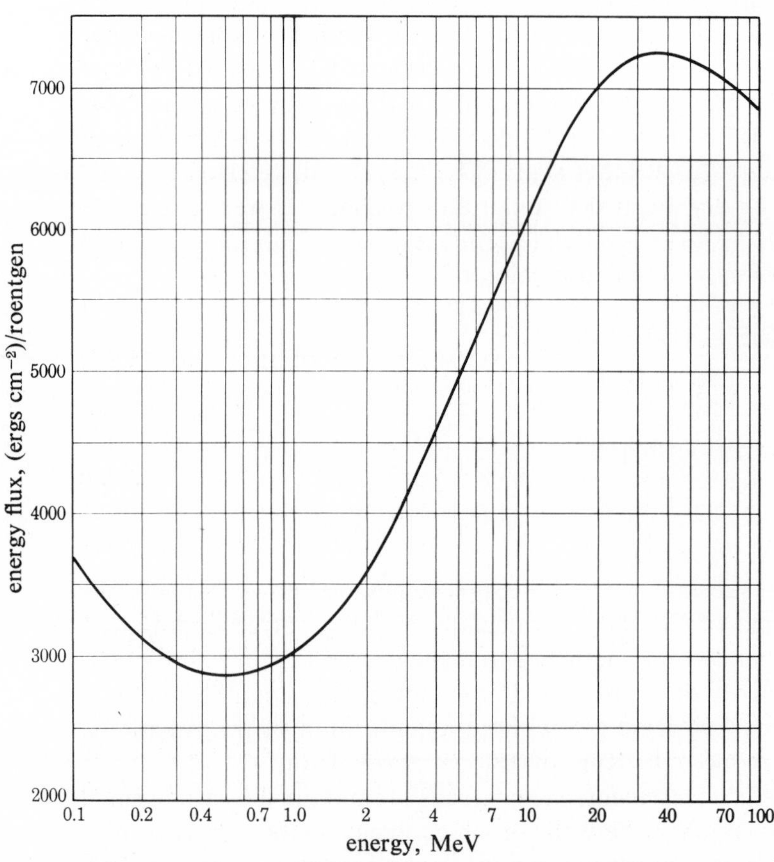

Figure 5-5 Energy flux per roentgen as a function of the energy of gamma radiation. [(Se 59).]

The energy flux required to produce 1 R depends on the frequency of the radiation considered. It has been calculated for a large energy interval, and the results are summarized in Fig. 5-5.

It must be borne in mind that to use this curve correctly the thickness of the wall must be great enough to establish equilibrium between the primary and secondary radiation; thus for 10 MeV about 4 g cm^{-2} of wall thickness is required. The ionization depends on the chemical composition of the walls, and according to the definition of the roentgen the walls should be of air. The data are computed for $w = 32.5$ eV.

Photographic dosimetry has been in use for many years. It is based on the blackening of photographic film under the action of radiations. For X rays it has been shown that the density obtained—that is, log (I_0/I), where I_0/I is the ratio between the incident and transmitted light for the film in question—is a function of the total dose to which the film has been exposed and not of the time distribution of the dose (reciprocity law). Photographic film is valuable in the dose range from about 10^{-2} to 10^4 R; it is available in a variety of emulsions and can be used for beta and gamma radiation. Radiation dosimetry, although of great importance in biological work, has not yet attained a fully satisfactory state of accuracy.

The roentgen as defined above is a perfectly precise unit, but it is not always a very convenient one. The definition specifically refers to air, and in most cases the irradiated objects are not air. In biological research, for example, it is often more convenient to define the dose as the number of ergs *absorbed* per gram of substance. From a beam delivering 1 R, 1 g of soft tissue will absorb approximately 93 ergs; from the same beam a different substance may absorb a different amount of energy—for instance, 1 g of air would absorb 83.8 ergs. The dose corresponding to the absorption of 93 ergs g^{-1} of soft tissue is called the *roentgen equivalent physical* (Rep). A similar unit of radiation is the rad, which corresponds to 100 ergs g^{-1}.

The biological effects of radiation are a function not only of the dose and type of radiation but also of the organ and tissue receiving the radiation. Whereas the measurement of the energy spent by the radiation is a relatively simple problem in physics, the evaluation of its biological effects is a much more difficult one, and one that is not even very well defined, because two radiations that are equivalent in producing a given biological effect may not be equivalent in other effects. Nevertheless, some tentative evaluations of *relative biological effectiveness* (RBE), have been made by the National Committee on Radiation Protection for various types of radiations; these are summarized in Table 5-1.

It has been found convenient in practical biological work to express doses of radiation of different specific ionizations in terms of a unit that incorporates both the magnitude of the dose and its biological effectiveness. This unit, the Rem, is defined by the relation

$$1 \text{ Rem} = 1 \text{ Rep} \times 1 \text{ RBE} \qquad \textbf{(5-4.4)}$$

Tolerance doses for safe conditions of work have been elaborated over

Table 5-1 Recommended Values of the Relative Biological Effectiveness (RBE) of Radiation of Different Specific Ionizations Applicable to Exposure to Radiation from External Sources[a,b]

(X rays, electrons, and positrons of any specific ionization: RBE = 1)

Heavy ionizing particles		
Average specific ionization,[c] ion pairs μ^{-1} of water	RBE[d]	Average linear energy transfer (LET) to water,[e] keV μ^{-1} water
100 or less	1	3.5 or less
100–200	1–2	3.5–7.0
200–650	2–5	7.0–23
650–1,500	5–10	23–53
1,500–5,000	10–20	53–175

[a] Present knowledge of the biological effectiveness of radiation of different specific ionizations does not warrant fine distinctions. Therefore ranges rather than individual figures are given in this table. For any range of specific ionization it is safer to use the higher of the two values of RBE given for that range, but a value obtained by linear interpolation is acceptable.

[b] The critical organs and effects considered are: skin with respect to cancer, blood-forming organs with respect to leukemia, gonads with respect to impairment of fertility, and lenses of the eyes with respect to cataracts.

[c] Specific ionization is expressed in ion pairs per micron of water in terms of its air equivalent.

[d] RBE is in terms of the permanent biological effectiveness of ordinary X rays for which the average specific ionization in the tissue of interest is assumed to be 100 ion pairs per micron of water.

[e] Linear energy transfer is given in keV per micron of water, using 35 eV per ion pair.

a period of years. Figure 5-6 summarizes these results graphically. The important tolerance dose to remember is 0.3 R per week for total body irradiation.

Cosmic rays at sea level and latitude 50° produce about 1.7 ion pairs per cm^3 sec^{-1}, or 5×10^{-3} R per week, which corresponds to about 1.7 per cent of the tolerance dose.

5-5 Fluctuations in Radioactive Decay. General Theory

At the beginning of this chapter we spoke of radioactive decay from the point of view of a continuous change in the number of atoms. Since this number is obviously an integer, it is clear that the theory previously given is only approximate. Although it holds exactly for the average values in the limit of a very large number of atoms, we may expect departures from it in cases in which the actual integral numbers of atoms or events are considered. It is the purpose of this section to treat the fluctuations or differences between the actual number of decaying atoms n and the average number $\langle n \rangle$.

The first problem is the following: We have a substance with an extremely long life (so long that we can neglect its average decay in the time considered) and emitting on the average $\langle n \rangle$ particles per second. What is the probability $P(n)$ that in a given second it emits n particles? This classical problem in the theory of probability is solved by *Poisson's formula:*

$$P(n) = \frac{\langle n \rangle^n}{n!} e^{-\langle n \rangle} \tag{5-5.1}$$

To prove this equation, we divide the time interval of 1 sec into K equal parts. K is an arbitrarily large number.

The probability of a disintegration occurring in any one of the K subintervals is then $\langle n \rangle / K$, and the probability that no disintegration

A. 300 mRem per week(1),(2),(3) to lens of eye. (Lens of eye considered to be at depth of 3 mm.) Significant volume is volume of entire lens.

B. Limit to entire body of 1,500 mRem per week if the half-value layer in tissue is <1 mm. (Thus rule applies especially to low-energy beta radiation.) Eye dose must not exceed 300 mRem per week.(1),(2)

C. 600 mRem per week(2),(3) to skin of total body. Basal layer of epidermis considered to be at depth of 0.07 mm.

D. 1,500 mRem per week to skin of head, neck, hands, forearms, feet and ankles—provided exposure to eyes is not over 300 mRem per week. In the case of X- or gamma-ray dose, the permissible 1,500 mR per week includes backscatter. Significant area is 1 cm² in region of highest dose rate.

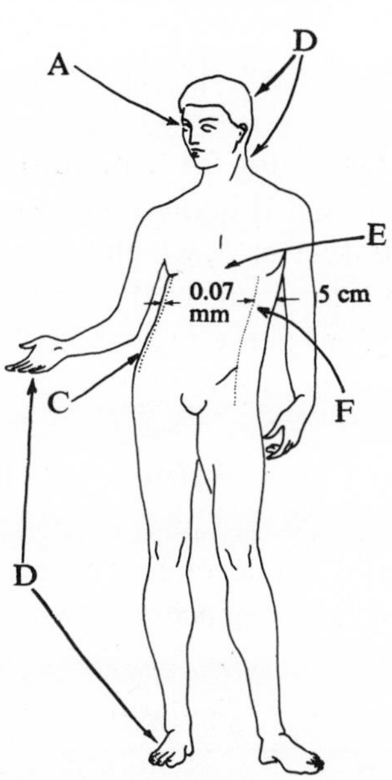

E. 300 mRem per week(2),(3) to portion of body inside 5 cm.

F. 300 mRem per week(2),(3) to blood-forming organs. These organs considered to be at depth of 5 mm. Significant volume 1 cm³ in region of highest dose rate.

G. Dose measured in air. Maximum permissible weekly dose of X or γ ($E < 3$ MeV) radiation may be 300 mR(1),(2) measured in occupied area.

(1) The 300 mR per week of X or γ radiation measured in air (when $E < 3$ MeV) may be increased to 450 mR per week to the lens of the eye, and about 400 mR per week to the bone, and to other tissues more than 5 cm inside the body with exception of the gonads, which are limited to 300 mRem per week until after age 45.

(2) When the exposures are continued over a period of several years, the integrated dose should not exceed one-third of the value indicated by these rates i.e.,

$$\int_0^T \text{rate } dt = \frac{(\text{basic permissible exposure rate}) \times \text{time}}{3}.$$

(3) An alternate rule is application of rule G to measurement of X or γ dose in air.

Figure 5-6 Basic permissible occupational exposure rates to external sources of ionizing radiation. [Natl. Bur. Standards (U.S.) Handbook 59.] [Figure from Etherington, *Nuclear Engineering Handbook*, McGraw-Hill, New York, 1958.]

occurs in any specified interval is $1 - (\langle n \rangle / K)$. The probability of a disintegration occurring in n, and only n, specified subintervals is

$$\left(\frac{\langle n \rangle}{K}\right)^n \left(1 - \frac{\langle n \rangle}{K}\right)^{K-n} \tag{5-5.2}$$

The first factor in Eq. (5-5.2) results from the requirement that n specified subintervals contain a disintegration and the second from the requirement that the remaining intervals $(K - n)$ do not contain a disintegration. If we now abandon the condition that the disintegrations must occur in specified subintervals and retain only the requirement that they must occur, we must sum Eq. (5-5.2) for all possible choices of the specified subintervals. These are equal in number to the combinations of K objects taken n at a time:

$$\binom{K}{n} = \frac{K(K-1)\cdots(K-n+1)}{n!} = \frac{K!}{n!(K-n)!} \tag{5-5.3}$$

We thus have

$$P_K(n) = \binom{K}{n}\left(\frac{\langle n \rangle}{K}\right)^n \left(1 - \frac{\langle n \rangle}{K}\right)^{K-n} \tag{5-5.4}$$

This formula (Bernoulli distribution) can be reinterpreted in a more general way. We repeat many times a certain experiment that must have one or two results, E or F, which are mutually exclusive. The probability of E occurring in each trial is p; the probability of F occurring is $1 - p = q$. What is the probability, in K trials, that E occurs n times and hence that F occurs $K - n$ times? The answer, as seen above, is

$$P_K(n) = \binom{K}{n} p^n q^{K-n} \tag{5-5.5}$$

Note that $P_K(n)$ is the term containing $p^n q^{K-n}$ in the binomial development of $(p + q)^K$, and hence

$$\sum_{n=0}^{K} P_K(n) = (p + q)^K = 1 \tag{5-5.6}$$

Equation (5-5.6) shows that the probabilities $P_K(n)$ are normalized correctly.

Before considering certain limiting cases of formula (5-5.3), we shall calculate the average $\langle n \rangle$ of the number of times that event E occurs in a series of K trials. Intuitively we expect it to be $\langle n \rangle = Kp$, and this is borne out by direct calculation. By definition,

$$\langle n \rangle = \sum_{n=0}^{K} n P_K(n) = \sum_{n=0}^{K} n \binom{K}{n} p^n q^{K-n} \tag{5-5.7}$$

On the other hand,

$$\frac{\partial}{\partial p}(p + q)^K = \frac{\partial}{\partial p} \sum_{n=0}^{K} \binom{K}{n} p^n q^{K-n} = \sum_{n=0}^{K} n \binom{K}{n} p^{n-1} q^{K-n} \tag{5-5.8}$$

and hence, upon using Eq. (5-5.7),

$$\langle n \rangle = p \frac{\partial}{\partial p}(p+q)^K = pK(p+q)^{K-1} = Kp \qquad \textbf{(5-5.9)}$$

because $p + q = 1$.

We now calculate the average value of $(n - \langle n \rangle)^2$, i.e., $\langle (n - Kp)^2 \rangle$, which is called the *variance* by statisticians. Its square root is the *standard deviation* indicated by σ. We have first

$$\begin{aligned}\sigma^2 &= \langle (n - pK)^2 \rangle = \langle n^2 \rangle - 2pK\langle n \rangle + p^2K^2 \\ &= \langle n^2 \rangle - p^2K^2 = \langle n^2 \rangle - \langle n \rangle^2 \end{aligned} \qquad \textbf{(5-5.10)}$$

and $\langle n^2 \rangle$ is evaluated, in a way similar to that used above for $\langle n \rangle$, as follows:

$$\begin{aligned}\langle n^2 \rangle &= \sum_{n=0}^{K} n^2 P_K(n) = \left(p^2 \frac{\partial^2}{\partial p^2} + p\frac{\partial}{\partial p}\right) \sum_{n=0}^{K} \binom{K}{n} p^n q^{-Kn} \\ &= \left(p^2 \frac{\partial^2}{\partial p^2} + p\frac{\partial}{\partial p}\right)(p+q)^K = K(K-1)p^2 + Kp \end{aligned} \qquad \textbf{(5-5.11)}$$

from which, remembering that $q = 1 - p$, we get

$$\sigma^2 = \langle n^2 \rangle - p^2K^2 = -Kp^2 + Kp = Kpq \qquad \textbf{(5-5.12)}$$

or

$$\sigma = (Kpq)^{1/2} \qquad \textbf{(5-5.13)}$$

The last expression for the standard deviation is of considerable importance.

We now make use of the fact that K is an arbitrarily large number, and we pass to the limit for K tending to infinity. We apply the well-known formulas

$$\lim_{K\to\infty} \binom{K}{n} = \frac{K^n}{n!} \qquad \text{and} \qquad \lim_{K\to\infty}\left(1 + \frac{1}{K}\right)^K = e$$

or

$$\lim_{K\to\infty}\left(1 - \frac{\langle n \rangle}{K}\right)^{K-n} = e^{\langle -n \rangle} \qquad \textbf{(5-5.14)}$$

Substituting these values in Eq. (5-5.4), we have

$$P(n) = \frac{\langle n \rangle^n}{n!} e^{-\langle n \rangle} \qquad \textbf{(5-5.15)}$$

where for $K \to \infty$, we have dropped the index K. This is the famous Poisson formula; it is illustrated in Fig. 5-7. From Eq. (5-5.15), remembering the development in power series of e^n, we also see immediately that

$$\sum_{n=0}^{\infty} P(n) = e^{-\langle n \rangle} \sum_{n=0}^{\infty} \frac{\langle n \rangle^n}{n!} = 1 \qquad \textbf{(5-5.16)}$$

which verifies that the sum of the probabilities for all possible numbers of disintegrations in a given time interval is 1.

If $\langle n \rangle$ is a large number, $P(n)$ has a sharp maximum in the vicinity of $n = \langle n \rangle$ and we may develop $\log P(n)$ in a power series of $n - \langle n \rangle$. Using *Stirling's asymptotic formula*, $\log (x!) = x \log x - x + \frac{1}{2} \log 2\pi x + \cdots$ we obtain for Eq. (5-5.15)

$$\log P(n) = n \log \langle n \rangle - \langle n \rangle - n \log n + n - \frac{1}{2} \log 2\pi n \quad \textbf{(5-5.17)}$$

and, taking the first and second derivatives with respect to n,

$$\frac{d \log P}{dn} = \log \langle n \rangle - \log n - \frac{1}{2n} \quad \textbf{(5-5.18)}$$

$$\frac{d^2 \log P}{dn^2} = -\frac{1}{n} + \frac{1}{2n^2} \quad \textbf{(5-5.19)}$$

The zero of the first derivative confirms the existence of the maximum[1] near $n = \langle n \rangle$ (neglecting terms in $1/n$ with respect to $\log n$ and terms in $1/n^2$ with respect to terms in $1/n$); the second derivative can be used to write the first terms of the power series for $\log P(n)$,

$$\log P(n) = \log P(\langle n \rangle) + \frac{(n - \langle n \rangle)^2}{2!} \left[\frac{d^2}{dn^2} \log P(n) \right]_{n=\langle n \rangle}$$

$$= -\frac{1}{2} \log 2\pi \langle n \rangle - \frac{(n - \langle n \rangle)^2}{2 \langle n \rangle} \quad \textbf{(5-5.20)}$$

[1]In a better approximation the maximum is near $n = \langle n \rangle - \frac{1}{2}$.

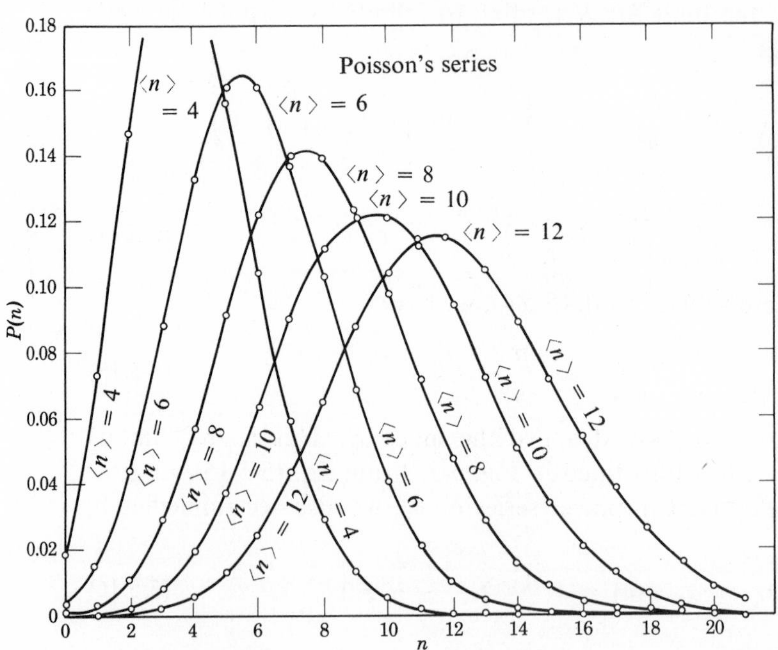

Figure 5-7 Poisson's formula: $P(n) = (\langle n \rangle^n / n!) \, e^{-\langle n \rangle}$ for different values of $\langle n \rangle$.

from which, passing from logarithms to numbers, we immediately get the famous *Gauss formula*,

$$P(n) = \frac{e^{-(n-\langle n\rangle)^2/2\langle n\rangle}}{(2\pi\langle n\rangle)^{1/2}} \tag{5-5.21}$$

(Examples of Poisson and Gauss distributions are shown in Fig. 5-8.) Recalling that

$$\int_{-\infty}^{\infty} e^{-x^2}\,dx = \pi^{1/2} \tag{5-5.22}$$

we readily see that

$$\int_{0}^{\infty} P(n)\,dn = 1 \tag{5-5.23}$$

which expresses again the normalization of the probability. Here we remember that $\langle n\rangle \gg 1$, and that the contributions to the integral for $n < 0$ are therefore negligible.

From Eq. (5-5.13), (5-5.15), or (5-5.21) it is possible to compute the root-mean-square (rms) deviation or standard deviation defined by Eq. (5-5.10). From Eq. (5-5.13), if K tends to ∞, p tends to 0 and q to 1; then Eqs. (5-5.13) and (5-5.9) give directly

$$\sigma^2 = Kp = \langle n\rangle \tag{5-5.24}$$

The same result is obtained if we insert for $P(n)$ the Poisson formula and use the identity

$$\sum_{n=0}^{\infty} n^2 \frac{\langle n\rangle^n}{n!} = \langle n\rangle(\langle n\rangle + 1)e^{\langle n\rangle} \tag{5-5.25}$$

which can be easily proved by comparing coefficients of equal powers of $\langle n\rangle$. Finally, the same result comes from the definition of σ^2 contained in Eqs. (5-5.10) and (5-5.11) and the gaussian distribution [Eq. (5-5.21)] if we remember that

$$\int_{-\infty}^{\infty} x^2 e^{-x^2}\,dx = \frac{1}{2}\pi^{1/2} \tag{5-5.26}$$

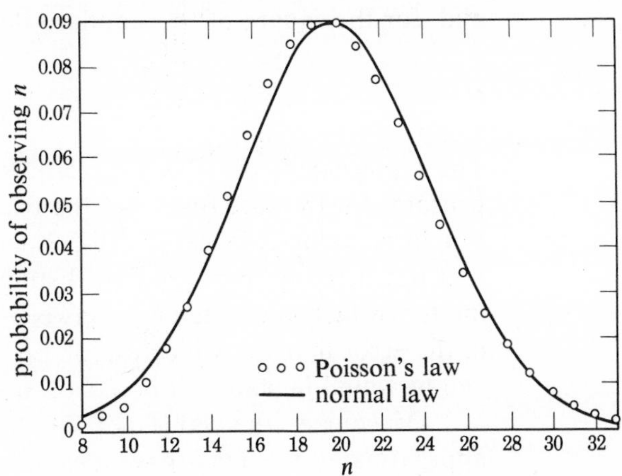

Figure 5-8 Comparison of Poisson's law for $n = 20$ with Gauss's law.

These expressions say that the average value of the square of the deviation from the average number of disintegrations to be expected in a certain time interval is equal to this same number, and hence

$$\sigma = \langle n \rangle^{1/2} \tag{5-5.27}$$

σ is known as the standard deviation of the distribution in n. Thus, if we have on the average 100 disintegrations per minute, we may expect deviations from this average, in every one-minute interval, such that the mean square of the deviations is again 100. Very often it is of great interest to know the relative standard deviation that results from Eq. (5-5.27),

$$\frac{\sigma}{\langle n \rangle} = \frac{1}{\langle n \rangle^{1/2}} \tag{5-5.28}$$

The relative standard deviation is inversely proportional to the square root of the number of counts used and is a measure of the precision of the determination.

One can also arrive at an estimate of σ by starting from its definition, Eq. (5-5.10), in which, however, we have not distinguished $\langle n \rangle$ from the "true" value of $\langle n \rangle$, which would be obtained from, for instance, an infinite number of observations. Let us indicate the true value of $\langle n \rangle$ by $\langle n_t \rangle$. In a sample giving n_i counts in each of N equally long time intervals, we should actually form

$$\sigma(n)^2 = \frac{1}{N} \sum_{i=1}^{N} (n_i - \langle n_t \rangle)^2 \tag{5-5.29}$$

Since the value $\langle n_t \rangle$ is actually unobtainable, we replace it with

$$\langle n \rangle = \frac{1}{N} \sum_{i=1}^{N} n_i \tag{5-5.30}$$

and we assume, for the square of the standard deviation of the single measurement,

$$\sigma^2(n) = \frac{1}{N-1} \sum_{i=1}^{N} (n_i - \langle n \rangle)^2 \tag{5-5.31}$$

and, for the square of the standard deviation of the average,

$$\sigma^2(\langle n \rangle) = \frac{1}{N(N-1)} \sum_{i=1}^{N} (n_i - \langle n \rangle)^2 \tag{5-5.32}$$

The replacement of N in Eq. (5-5.29) by $N - 1$ in Eq. (5-5.31) compensates for the fact that $\langle n_t \rangle$, the true value, has been replaced by $\langle n \rangle$. For large values of N, Eqs. (5-5.31) and (5-5.29) tend to coincide, and it is not actually important to distinguish between them, because, as a matter of fact, the difference between them is of the order of magnitude of the error in σ^2. Justification of Eq. (5-5.31) and of the last statement will be found in standard books on probability and statistics.

Of course, the values of σ^2 thus obtained are themselves only approximate; we may have examples in which σ^2 as calculated by

Eq. (5-5.31) comes out anomalously small. In fact, σ cannot be less, for our case, than $\langle n\rangle^{1/2}$; if our series of measures has given a lower value than this, we still must assume that the standard deviation is $\langle n\rangle^{1/2}$ and that we have obtained the lower value by accident. On the other hand, if we have found a standard deviation much larger than $\langle n\rangle^{1/2}$ we may suspect the existence of some cause of accidental errors.

We shall now illustrate these concepts by an actual example. A uranium sample was counted, and the number of alpha particles emitted in 1 min was recorded in 10 intervals each of 1 min duration. The first column of Table 5-2 shows the actual number of counts observed; the second column, the difference between the average number of counts and the specific 1-min count; and the third column, the square of the numbers written in the second column. The average count for a 1-min period is 35,946.4, with the standard deviation of any single measurement given by $(311{,}740/9)^{1/2} = 186$. If, according to Eq. (5-5.27), $\sigma = \langle n\rangle^{1/2}$, we find $\sigma = 189$, a satisfactory agreement. The average counting rate is 35,946.4 counts per minute, and the standard deviation of the average is given by $189/(10)^{1/2} = 60$, where 10 is the number of observations and the standard deviation of one observation is 189. In conclusion, the average counting rate of our sample is 35,946 $\pm$ 60 counts per minute.

The question may be asked: What is the probability that, in the case of a counting rate A with a standard deviation σ, the deviation from the "exact" result A^* will be larger than $\epsilon\sigma$? The exact result is defined, as above, as the one obtained by repeating the measurement of A a very great number of times. The answer to this problem in the case

Table 5-2 Numerical Example of Counting of a Sample

n	$n - \langle n\rangle$	$(n - \langle n\rangle)^2$
36,076	130	16,900
35,753	−193	37,249
35,907	− 39	1,521
36,116	170	28,900
35,884	− 62	3,844
36,136	190	36,100
35,741	−205	42,025
35,640	−306	93,636
36,124	178	31,684
36,087	141	19,881
$\langle n\rangle = 35{,}946.4$	Σ4	Σ311,740

$$\sigma(n) = \left(\frac{311{,}740}{9}\right)^{1/2} = 186$$

of a gaussian distribution is given in tables contained, for instance, in the *Handbook of Chemistry and Physics*. We quote here a few pertinent numbers.

The probability P of observing a counting rate differing from A^* by more than $\epsilon\sigma$ is given in Table 5-3. It will be noted that the probability of observing a counting rate differing from A^* by more than 0.6745σ is 0.5. This quantity is called the *probable error*.

If we want to know the standard deviation of a function f of two or more independently observed quantities x_1 and x_2 affected by the standard deviation σ_1 and σ_2, we use the fundamental formula of the *propagation of errors*,

$$\sigma_f = \left[\left(\frac{\partial f}{\partial x_1}\right)^2 \sigma_1^2 + \left(\frac{\partial f}{\partial x_2}\right)^2 \sigma_2^2\right]^{1/2} \qquad \textbf{(5-5.33)}$$

Of frequent application are the formulas for the standard deviations of the sum, difference, product, and quotient of two quantities. If the observed quantities are numbers of counts, Eqs. (5-5.27) and (5-5.33) give

$$\sigma(n_1 \pm n_2) = (n_1 + n_2)^{1/2} \qquad \textbf{(5-5.34)}$$

$$\sigma(n_1 n_2) = [n_1 n_2(n_1 + n_2)]^{1/2} \qquad \textbf{(5-5.35)}$$

$$\sigma\left(\frac{n_1}{n_2}\right) = \left(\frac{n_1}{n_2^2} + \frac{n_1^2}{n_2^3}\right)^{1/2} \qquad \textbf{(5-5.36)}$$

and

$$\frac{\sigma(n_1 n_2)}{n_1 n_2} = \frac{\sigma(n_1/n_2)}{n_1/n_2} = \left(\frac{1}{n_1} + \frac{1}{n_2}\right)^{1/2} \qquad \textbf{(5-5.37)}$$

where n_1 and n_2 are the observed numbers of counts. Expressions of the type of Eq. (5-5.36) are most rapidly obtained by use of the relation

$$\sigma(\log f) = \frac{\sigma(f)}{f} \qquad \textbf{(5-5.38)}$$

which is an immediate consequence of Eq. (5-5.33).

5-6 Fluctuations in Radioactive Decay. Applications

We shall now make some applications of the principles stated above, either in order to illustrate them or because the results are of practical importance:

1. Suppose that we have counted a sample that gives n_1 counts in

Table 5-3 Probability of a Given Multiple of the Standard Deviation

ϵ	0	0.6745	1	1.5	2.0	2.5	3	3.5	4
P	1	0.5000	0.3173	0.1336	0.0455	0.0124	0.0027	0.00046	0.000063

a certain counter in time t_1; the background of the counter gave n_2 counts in time t_2. We want to know the counting rate of the sample and the background counting rate of the counter. The times t_1 and t_2 are exactly known. For the background we have

$$\nu_2 = \frac{n_2}{t_2} \pm \frac{n_2^{1/2}}{t_2} \tag{5-6.1}$$

(The expressions following the ± sign are always standard deviations.)

We have, for the activity plus the background,

$$\nu_1 = \frac{n_1}{t_1} \pm \frac{n_1^{1/2}}{t_1} \tag{5-6.2}$$

for the net activity,

$$\nu = \nu_1 - \nu_2 \tag{5-6.3}$$

and, for its standard deviation according to Eq. (5-5.33),

$$\sigma(\nu) = [\sigma^2(\nu_1) + \sigma^2(\nu_i)]^{1/2} = \left(\frac{n_1}{t_1^2} + \frac{n_2}{t_2^2}\right)^{1/2} = \left(\frac{\nu_1}{t_1} + \frac{\nu_2}{t_2}\right)^{1/2} \tag{5-6.4}$$

Now we may ask: What is the best way to apportion a fixed counting time $T = t_1 + t_2$ between the counting of the sample and the counting of the background? From Eq. (5-6.4) we obtain

$$\sigma^2(\nu) = \frac{\nu_1}{t_1} + \frac{\nu_2}{T - t_1} \tag{5-6.5}$$

and, by minimizing with respect to t_1,

$$\frac{\nu_1}{\nu_2} = \frac{t_1^2}{t_2^2} \tag{5-6.6}$$

2. We want to check the existence of an effect that slightly changes the counting rate of a device. When can we reasonably conclude that the effect is real?

Counts in conditions *a*, n_1; counts in conditions *b*, n_2; with counting time the same for both conditions and equal to *t*,

$$\nu_1 - \nu_2 = \frac{n_1 - n_2}{t} \tag{5-6.7}$$

$$\sigma(\nu_1 - \nu_2) = \frac{(n_1 + n_2)^{1/2}}{t} \tag{5-6.8}$$

The effect is probably real if

$$3\sigma(\nu_1 - \nu_2) \leqslant (\nu_1 - \nu_2)$$

or

$$n_1 - n_2 \geqslant 3(n_1 + n_2)^{1/2} \tag{5-6.9}$$

More precisely the probability P that $|\nu_1 - \nu_2| > \epsilon\sigma(\nu_1 - \nu_2)$ is given by Table 5-3. For $\epsilon = 3$ we have $P = 0.0027$; hence, the probability that the effect is not due to a statistical fluctuation is $1 - P = 0.9972$. This last number is often called the *confidence level* of the result.

3. A certain sample gives ν counts per second on the average. What is the probability of finding an interval of t sec without counts? Equation (5-5.15) gives the answer if we make $n = 0$ and $\langle n \rangle = \nu t$,

$$P(0) = e^{-\nu t} \tag{5-6.10}$$

4. *Counting-loss problem.* Assume that a counting device is unable to register a pulse for a period τ after having registered a previous pulse (dead time). If we try to measure a sample giving rise to an average true counting rate ν_0, the device will show a counting rate $\nu < \nu_0$, because some of the pulses will occur during the dead time τ following each registered pulse and hence will not be registered. We want the relation between ν and ν_0. The total dead time per second is $\nu\tau$; the counts that should occur during this time but that cannot be registered are $\nu_0\nu\tau$, and from this

$$\nu = \nu_0 - \nu_0\nu\tau \tag{5-6.11}$$

or, upon assuming $\nu_0 - \nu \ll \nu$,

$$\nu_0 = \nu(1 + \nu\tau) \tag{5-6.12}$$

The practical procedure for correcting counting losses is to count two or more samples separately and then count them together. The count obtained from the sum of the samples is smaller than the sum of the counts obtained from the single samples because of the counting losses, and if Eq. (5-6.12) applies, the counting loss $\nu_0 - \nu$ is small compared with ν and the proportionality constant is determined empirically as stated above. It is not safe to correct for counting losses if these amount to more than about 20 per cent of the counting rate; it is better to subdivide the samples, reduce the solid angle of the detecting device, or otherwise arrange to use lower counting rates. If we go to the other limiting case of a pulse rate $\nu_0 \gg 1/\tau$, the apparatus is blocked and the counting rate decreases with increasing ν_0 or it counts at a counting rate $1/\tau$ according to its detailed construction. Under these conditions the apparatus is obviously unsuitable for making measurements.

5. *Fluctuations in ionization current.* Let us consider an ionization chamber containing a sample that emits alpha particles each of which gives a potential v to the collecting electrode. On the average ν particles per second are emitted, and we take a reading of the potential of the electrode every T sec. We compensate for the average charging effect of the source by using a leak resistor or by balancing it with another ionization chamber in opposition and an identical alpha source. The average potential reading $\langle p \rangle$ is then zero, but there are residual fluctuations of potential. We can calculate $\langle p^2 \rangle$ from Eq. (5-5.24). Calling n the actual number of particles emitted in time T and νT its average value, we have from Eq. (5-5.10)

$$\langle (p - \langle p \rangle)^2 \rangle = \langle (n - \nu T)^2 v^2 \rangle = v^2 \nu T \tag{5-6.13}$$

or, since $\langle p \rangle = 0$, owing to the compensating device,

$$\langle p^2 \rangle = v^2 \nu T \tag{5-6.14}$$

if the main effect is compensated with a resistor; or

$$\langle p^2 \rangle = 2v^2\nu T \tag{5-6.15}$$

if we have two balanced chambers. In this equation $\langle p^2 \rangle$ and T are directly measurable, and an experiment of this type can be used to determine the quantity $v\nu$.

Equations (5-6.14) and (5-6.15) are mainly qualitative because they do not consider the differences between the amounts of ionization produced in the various ionization acts and the electrical characteristics of the measuring instrument.

The fluctuations of p have been the object of several studies in which the influence of the electrical characteristics of the detecting apparatus has also been considered. Although most of these studies were performed with long-period electrometers and experimental devices that are now obsolete, the method of evaluating the results has wide applicability. If a particle emitted at time 0 produces in the instrument a deflection at time t indicated by $f(t)$, where the specific function depends on the characteristics of the apparatus, and if the apparatus is linear, the deflection at time T produced by k particles emitted at times $t_1, t_2, t_3, \ldots$ is given by

$$\phi = \sum_k f(T - t_k) \tag{5-6.16}$$

Now from the deflection of the apparatus at time T in a series of many experiments, we can obtain an average deflection $\langle \phi \rangle$. To calculate this quantity and its standard deviation, call ν the average rate of emission of the particles. In a small time interval τ the probability of emission of a particle is $\nu\tau$.

The contribution $\delta\langle \phi \rangle$ to the average deflection due to particles emitted in time τ is

$$\delta\langle \phi \rangle = f(T - t)\nu\tau \tag{5-6.17}$$

and, upon passing to the limit,

$$\langle \phi \rangle = \Sigma\, \delta\langle \phi \rangle = \int_0^T \nu f(T - t)\, dt \tag{5-6.18}$$

The standard deviation of $\langle \phi \rangle$ is obtained by using the theorem of the calculus of probability contained in Eq. (5-5.13), which states that the square of the standard deviation of the number $\nu\tau$ is $\nu\tau$ multiplied by the complementary probability $1 - \nu\tau$. Moreover, since the number of particles emitted in the single time intervals τ are statistically independent, the contributions to the square of the standard deviation from the various time intervals are to be added. We have then for the standard deviation of the deflection

$$(\phi - \langle \phi \rangle)^2 = \Sigma\, \nu\tau(1 - \nu\tau) f^2(T - t) \tag{5-6.19}$$

or, upon passing to the limit for $\tau \to 0$,

$$\langle (\phi - \langle \phi \rangle)^2 \rangle = \int_0^T \nu f^2(T - t)\, dt \tag{5-6.20}$$

Equation (5-6.20) can be applied to specific cases; e.g., if $f(t) = 0$ for $t < 0$ and $f(t) = ve^{-\gamma t}$ for $t > 0$, we have, for $T \gg 1/\gamma$,

$$\langle(\phi - \langle\phi\rangle)^2\rangle = \frac{v^2\nu}{2\gamma} \qquad \textbf{(5-6.21)}$$

which is similar to Eq. (5-6.14).

Equation (5-6.21) is often applied in the determination of the conditions under which a heavily ionizing radiation (e.g., fission fragments) can be measured over a background of an intense radiation the single particles of which ionize only slightly (beta rays). If the resolving time of the instrument, including the effect of the electronic components, is τ and the number of ions obtainable from the heavily ionized particle is F whereas each of the weakly ionizing particles, occurring with the frequency ν, produces f ions, we must have

$$F \gg (\nu\tau)^{1/2} f \qquad \textbf{(5-6.22)}$$

This relation, however, can be used only for qualitative estimates, because a detailed study of the experimental setup is required for more precise evaluations.

5-7 Method of Maximum Likelihood

Often, in order to measure a half-life, we measure the time at which the nuclei in a sample disintegrate, and then analyze the data by plotting a histogram of the number of decays in successive equal time intervals. This practical procedure does not extract all the information available in the experiment, and one wants a method that puts to best use all the information collected. This purpose is achieved by the method of maximum likelihood, which we shall illustrate by an example. We must emphasize, however, that in order to use it we must make an a priori hypothesis that drastically affects the results. For instance, in the following example it is essential to assume that we have only one radioactive substance present and that the decay law is a simple exponential.

Under these hypotheses, having observed M disintegrations at times $t_1, t_2, \ldots, t_M \leqslant T$ = total time of observation, we want to know the most probable value of the decay constant λ of the substance. We proceed as follows: For each disintegrating nucleus of the substance the probability of observing a decay between time t and $t + dt$ is

$$G(\lambda,t)\,dt = \lambda e^{-\lambda t}\,dt(1 - e^{-\lambda T})^{-1} \qquad \textbf{(5-7.1)}$$

where the denominator takes into account the finite time of observation T.

The probability of observing decays at times $t_1, t_2, \ldots, t_M$ is then proportional to

$$G(\lambda,t_1,t_2,\ldots,t_M) = \lambda^M \prod_{i=1}^{M} e^{-\lambda t_i}(1 - e^{-\lambda T})^{-1} \qquad \textbf{(5-7.2)}$$

This quantity is a function of the parameter λ, and we ask for which value of λ it has a maximum; the corresponding value of λ is the most likely one.

Explicitly we may look for the maximum of log G. We have then for the maximum

$$0 = \frac{\partial \log G(\lambda, t_1, t_2, ..., t_M)}{\partial \lambda}$$

$$= -\frac{\partial}{\partial \lambda}\left[\sum_{1=i}^{M} \lambda t_i + M \log (1 - e^{-\lambda T}) - M \log \lambda\right] \quad \text{(5-7.3)}$$

$$0 = \sum_{i=1}^{M} t_i + MT(e^{\lambda T} - 1)^{-1} - \frac{M}{\lambda} \quad \text{(5-7.4)}$$

This equation may be solved for λ by iteration. In the limiting case where $\lambda T \gg 1$ it gives the obvious result

$$\frac{1}{\lambda} = \tau = \frac{\sum_{i=1}^{M} t_i}{M} \quad \text{(5-7.5)}$$

As a figure of merit for the value of the parameter λ obtained by solving Eq. (5-7.5), it is reasonable to assume

$$\mathscr{E}(\lambda) = \left[-\frac{\partial^2}{\partial \lambda^2} \log G(\lambda, t_1, ..., t_M)\right]^{-1/2} \quad \text{(5-7.6)}$$

We verify this result in the case in which G considered as a function of λ has a gaussian distribution with standard deviation σ,

$$G = Ke^{-(\lambda-\lambda_0)^2/2\sigma^2} \quad \text{(5-7.7)}$$

Then

$$\log G = \log K - \frac{(\lambda - \lambda_0)^2}{2\sigma^2} \quad \text{(5-7.8)}$$

and

$$-\frac{\partial^2 \log G}{\partial \lambda^2} = \frac{1}{\sigma^2} \quad \text{(5-7.9)}$$

In this case $\mathscr{E}$ of Eq. (5-7.6) coincides with the standard deviation of λ.

5-8 Methods of Measuring Decay Constants

The simplest way to measure a decay constant is by direct application of Eq. (5-1.1) or (5-1.2). This is very simple if τ is a convenient interval of anywhere from about 1 min to a few years. Outside this range practical difficulties arise. Even if τ is convenient, however, it may happen that the radiation emitted in the decay is difficult to detect (for example in RaD), in which case it is sometimes possible to measure, not the decay of the substance under investigation, but the production of a daughter product, from which one can calculate τ of the mother substance.

If τ is very short, it is still possible to employ mechanical methods in making the measurements (such as the container propelled by compressed air, used in piles), down to intervals of approximately 1 sec. For intervals of this duration, flow methods are effective if the substance is gaseous. The substance is produced in a certain place at a constant rate and is blown through a tube in a stream of gas with velocity v, measurable from the area of the tube and the rate of flow of the gas. The activity of the gas in the steady stream in the tube is measured at two points at distance d from each other. These activities are in the ratio $e^{-d/v\tau}$, from which τ can be obtained. Sometimes in experiments of this type the formation of an active deposit can be observed, and τ of the gas can be obtained from the distribution of the active deposit on the walls of the tube. Classical experiments by this method were performed by Rutherford. There have been many modifications of the method; noteworthy is the artifice employed by Jacobsen in which the velocity of recoiling atoms imparted by the emission of a particle is used.

In recent times electronic methods have been used for the direct measurement of very short lifetimes, down to $\tau \simeq 10^{-9}$ sec. The principle of the methods requires that the decay to be studied be preceded by another event, which is used to actuate an electronic gate and establish the origin of time. The gate stays open for a time t. The probability of a count in the gate is then

$$k \int_0^t \lambda e^{-\lambda\xi}\, d\xi = k(1 - e^{-\lambda t}) \qquad \textbf{(5-8.1)}$$

in which we have included in k geometric and efficiency factors, which, however, are constant. The apparatus is arranged to count the number of gates formed, and also the number of gates during which a particle is detected. By measuring the ratio between the number of times a particle is detected while the gate is open and the total number of gates formed as a function of t one obtains λ, from Eq. (5-8.1).

One may also keep the duration of the gate t constant but small compared with τ and vary the time T after the first triggering pulse at which the gate opens. This procedure is called *measurement of delayed coincidences*. The number of delayed coincidences per disintegration is proportional to $e^{-\lambda T}(1 - e^{-\lambda t})$ or, for $t \ll 1/\lambda$, to $\lambda t e^{-\lambda T}$ (Fig. 5-9).

Sometimes it is possible to feed the pulses of the detector into a cathode-ray oscilloscope with a calibrated time sweep. Pulses appear characteristically in pairs. By measuring the number of pairs corresponding to a time interval between t and $t + \Delta t$ as a function of t, one obtains an exponential curve $e^{-\lambda t}$, or, more directly, if one can neglect the background, the average time interval between the pulses gives τ.

For values of τ up to a few years, direct measurements are still practicable. For larger τ, direct measurement of the number of disintegrations undergone by a weighed amount of radioactive substance is generally used. Aside from the necessity of starting with a chemically and radioactively pure substance the method is easily applied to alpha emitters where the absolute counting of the alpha particles does not offer great difficulties and where one alpha particle is emitted per disintegration.

Finally the condition of secular equilibrium [Eq. (5-2.9)] between two genetically related substances can also be used for the determination of the ratio of their decay constants. A classical example is that of radium and uranium: in an old, unaltered ore the ratio is 3.66×10^{-7} by weight (Boltwood's number).

The precision that has been attained up to now in measurements of λ is of the order, in the most favorable cases, of a few parts in 10,000, but the great majority of radioactive decay constants are not known to within 1 per cent.

Extensive collections of data on radioactive decay are available in tabular and graphical form. For instance, an excellent table of isotopes is given by Strominger, Hollander, and Seaborg; General Electric has also published a useful isotope chart (see the Bibliography).

5-9 Chronological and Geological Applications

Radioactive decay has found very interesting applications to the problem of establishing dates of events remote in time.

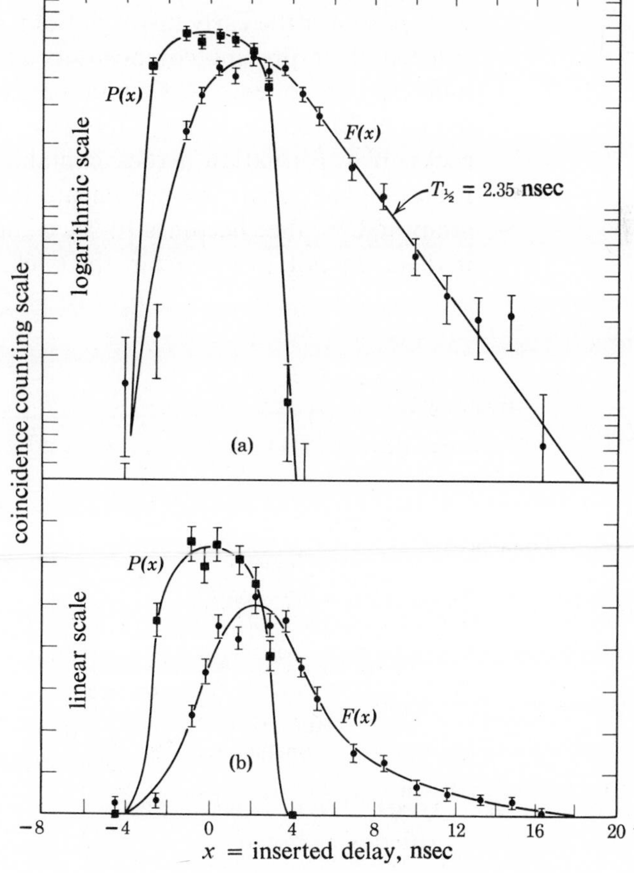

Figure 5-9 Delayed coincidence resolution curve $F(x)$ for the 158-keV gamma ray of Hg^{199} with a prompt curve $P(x)$ for comparison: (a) logarithmic scale; (b) linear scale. The half-life of the gamma ray can be measured by the slope of the right-hand part of log $F(x)$ in (a) or by the shift of the centroid of $F(x)$ to the right in (b). The result is $T_{1/2} = (2.35 \pm 0.20) \times$ nsec. The standard deviations of the points are indicated by vertical bars. [R. L. Graham and R. E. Bell, *Can. J. Phys*, **31,** 377 (1953).]

On the archaeological scale this has been established by C^{14} dating. Cosmic rays in the atmosphere continuously form C^{14} by nuclear reactions. C^{14} itself is chemically combined with oxygen and finally finds its way into all organic material. Carbon in a living plant or animal has the same isotopic composition as atmospheric carbon. When the animal or plant dies, its exchange of carbon stops and in due course C^{14} disappears with a half-life of 5,570 years. Thus coal or petroleum has lost all its C^{14}, whereas the carbon in a young tree has the same activity as atmospheric carbon (15 dis g^{-1} sec^{-1}). It is thus clear that one can date an object containing organic carbon by measuring the specific activity of the carbon. The sensitivity of the method sets a limit of about 30,000 years to the determinable ages. Older samples are too inactive to be accurately dated. A calibration curve is shown in Fig. 5-10. (There are some indications that carbon in wood produced today has a little lower specific activity than carbon derived from wood of a century ago. This has been attributed to the dilution of atmospheric carbon by inactive carbon originating from fossil fuels.)

On the geological scale, radioactivity has given the most reliable information on absolute time. The substances commonly employed are uranium and its isotopes, thorium, potassium, and rubidium.

We shall briefly describe some of the methods used. First, however, let us define what we mean by the age of a rock. We do not know what has been the early history of our planet, but at a certain time rocks reached their present composition, crystallizing and segregating their different components. A slow process of metamorphosis continues even today. Radioactive dating refers essentially to the time of formation of rocks. If at formation a rock contained a certain amount of uranium, it accumulated in it the helium produced by uranium decay. For each atom of U^{238} that becomes Pb^{206}, eight alpha particles are formed, and if these do not escape from the rock, the ratio between the uranium

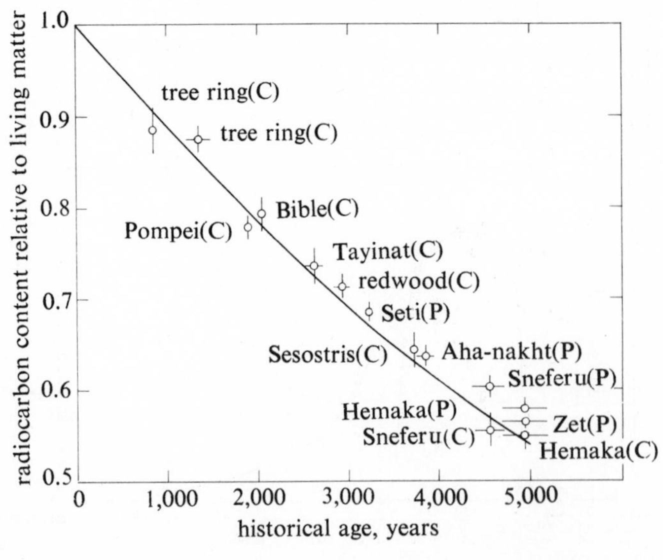

Figure 5-10 Calibration curve of C^{14} method. Curve calculated from $T = 5{,}568 \pm 30$ years. Key: Samples of known age: (C), Chicago dates; (P), Pennsylvania dates (Ralph). [W. F. Libby, in *Les Prix Nobel en 1960*, Stockholm, 1961.]

present and the helium accumulated gives the age of the rock. A similar procedure is applicable to thorium. The most important consideration is always to make certain that no helium or uranium has escaped the sample during the life of the rock. The uranium-lead ratio may be used in a similar way and is less subject than the helium methods to errors caused by differences in diffusion or escape from the rocks of lead and uranium. Other methods use the Pb^{206}/Pb^{207} isotopic ratio of radiogenic lead or the ratio of radiogenic lead to Pb^{204}. Finally K/Ar ratios and Rb^{87}/Sr^{87} ratios are also used and are becoming increasingly important. Occasionally it is possible to date the same rock by several methods; the results show reasonable agreement.

The oldest surface rocks have an age of about 2.7×10^9 years. The same methods have been applied to the determination of the age of meteorites and the oldest of these are 4.5×10^9 years. This should be the age of formation of the earth, as distinguished from the segregation of the surface rocks.

Bibliography

Aldrich, L. T., and G. W. Wetherill, "Geochronology by Radioactive Decay," *Ann. Rev. Nucl. Sci.*, **8,** 257 (1958).

Anders, E., "Meteorite Ages," *Rev. Mod. Phys.*, **34,** 287 (1962).

Annis, M., "Maximum Likelihood," *Rev. Mod. Phys.*, **25,** 818 (1953).

Burbidge, G., "Nuclear Astrophysics," *Ann. Rev. Nucl. Sci.*, **12,** 507 (1962).

Feller, W., *An Introduction to Probability Theory and Its Application*, Wiley, New York, 1957.

General Electric Nuclear Chart, 6th ed., rev. to December 1964.

Lal, D., and B. Peters, "Cosmic Ray Produced Isotopes and Their Application to Problems in Geophysics," *Progr. Elem. Particle Cosmic Ray Phys.*, **6,** 3 (1962).

Libby, W. F., *Radiocarbon Dating*, 2nd ed., University of Chicago Press, Chicago, 1955.

Moyer, B. J., "Practical Control of Radiation Hazards in Physics Research," *Ann. Rev. Nucl. Sci.*, **8,** 327 (1958).

Nuclear Processes in Geologic Settings, Publication 400, National Academy of Sciences, Washington, 1956.

Rankama, K., *Progress in Isotope Geology*, Wiley–Interscience, New York, 1963.

Segrè, E., "Radioactive Decay," in (Se 59), Vol. III.

Strominger, Hollander, and Seaborg, "Table of Isotopes," *Rev. Mod. Phys.*, **30,** 585 (1958).

Suess, H. E., "The Radioactivity of the Atmosphere and Hydrosphere," *Ann. Rev. Nucl. Sci.*, **8,** 243 (1958).

Sullivan, W. H., *Trilinear Chart of Nuclear Species*, U.S. Government, 1949–1963.

Problems

5-1 Calculate the volume of 1 Ci of radon at 0°C and 760 mm Hg pressure.

5-2 Calculate the weight of 1 Ci of Pu^{239}.

5-3 A piece of gold 1 mm thick is bombarded for 15 h by a slow neutron beam having 10^6 neutrons per sec. How many disintegrations per second of Au^{198} occur in the sample 24 h after the end of bombardment?

5-4 Ba^{140} decays into La^{140} with a half-life of 12.5 days. La^{140} has a half-life of 40 h. A sample initially contains pure Ba^{140}. Call this amount 100 in arbitrary units. Using semilogarithmic paper, plot the amounts of Ba and La formed (as a function of time) over a period of 15 days.

5-5 An atomic explosion forms isotopes of U^{238} by successive neutron capture. The capture cross sections are $\sigma(238)$, $\sigma(239)$, etc. The flux of neutrons through the material is φ, and it lasts a short time t. How much U^{250} is formed per atom of U^{238}?

5-6 As light a shield as possible is required for a very large source (1,000 Ci) of a beta emitter having beta rays of 2 MeV, in order that a person can work near it safely. Give your suggestions.

5-7 Prove that for a Poisson distribution $\langle n^2 \rangle - \langle n \rangle^2 = \langle n \rangle$.

5-8 One milligram of iron does not emit any fission fragment for a month. The decay constant of iron for spontaneous fission has an even chance of being smaller than λ. Find λ, assuming every λ in a $d\lambda$ interval a priori equally probable.

5-9 A certain sample that gives a counting rate of 107 counts per min on a Geiger–Müller counter has been observed for 23 min. The background of the counter is 42 counts per min, based on an observation lasting 40 min. Find the probable net counting rate of the sample and its probable error.

5-10 In a given time T you want to measure the absorption coefficient of a substance for neutrons. The approximate value of this absorption coefficient is μ_0. The beam gives approximately N_0 counts per sec in the detector, with no absorber. Determine the thickness of absorption you will use and the apportionment of the time between measurements on a purely statistical basis. Consider also the case of a background of approximate value n_0 counts per sec.

5-11 A Geiger counter, after counting one particle, becomes dead for a time τ. A counting rate ν is observed for a certain sample; the true counting rate ν_0 is often calculated by the formula $\nu_0 = \nu(1 + \beta\nu)$. Justify the formula and find the relation between β and τ. The formula is an approximate one, valid if ν is close to ν_0.

5-12 Two ionization chambers are mounted in opposition on a compensating circuit. A certain sample is put in one chamber and gives a deflection of 180 arbitrary units per min.Two samples identical to it are put in the two chambers and the deflections obtained in 1-min periods are observed. The results are 0, +40, −12, −19, +48, −31, −25. How many ionization events occur in the chamber per minute, assuming that all ionization events give equal deflection?

5-13 In polarization measurements one scatters protons on a target. The protons may go to the left or right of the target. One is interested in the "asymmetry," that is, $p_L - p_R = \epsilon$, where p_L and p_R are the probabilities of scattering to the left and right. One measures the actual numbers scattered to the left, N_L, or to the right, N_R. Calling

$$p_L' = \frac{N_L}{N_L + N_R} \qquad p_R' = \frac{N_R}{N_L + N_R}$$

and

$$\epsilon' = p'_L - p'_R$$

one has approximately

$$p'_L - p'_R = p_L - p_R$$

In setting up an experiment it is desired that $|\epsilon' - \epsilon| < 0.005$ with 95 per cent probability, or, as one says, a confidence level 0.95. How many counts should one collect?

5-14 Set up the equation for finding the value of α in an angular correlation distribution. Gamma rays are emitted in a cascade of 2, and we know that their angular correlation is given by

$$W(\varphi) = 1 + \alpha \cos^2 \varphi$$

M pairs have been observed making the angles $\varphi_1, \ldots, \varphi_M$.

PART II

The Nucleus

CHAPTER VI

Elements of the Nuclear Structure and Systematics

In order to obtain a picture of the nucleus in the ground state, we must first measure its "global" properties; charge, mass, radius, spin, magnetic moment, and so on. Some of these, such as charge and mass, require refined techniques but present no conceptual difficulties. We cannot take too naive a view of the radius, thinking simply in terms of the radius of a macroscopic object, but we must be careful about its definition. Spin is quantized and, apart from being a quantum-mechanical vector, it offers no special conceptual difficulties. Magnetic and electric multipole moments in a quantum-mechanical system must also be defined; here the main idea is to take their expectation value for the case of maximum orientation in an external field. In this chapter we shall describe briefly the techniques used for these measurements.

The empirical findings must then be interpreted, although both historically and conceptually the two processes of accumulation of empirical data and of their interpretation go hand in hand. Having established the fundamental fact that nuclei consist of protons and neutrons, one might hope to repeat the feat accomplished by atomic physics in the interpretation of the atom, where the application of quantum mechanics to the Rutherford–Bohr models solved virtually all problems. We could set out to find the force between nucleons and from that derive all nuclear properties. This program is at present impossible for two reasons: first, the force between nucleons is not as simple as the Coulomb force and is not known precisely. Second, the mathematical problem of solving the Schrödinger equation for a nucleus is beyond our present powers, nor are there approximations that offer hopes of quantitative results of a precision comparable to that attainable in atomic problems.

The usual remedy in a situation of this kind is to introduce models that simulate, more or less accurately, nuclear behavior, and when necessary to introduce empirically parameters that help in the description. From the systematics of the results one then tries to improve the model. This procedure is very commonly employed in all experimental sciences.

As a consequence of this approach, we may find useful various models, depending on the property under consideration and also on the mass number of the nucleus studied. The models, however, are not independent of each other. Ultimately they are all facets or approximations of a theory that does not yet exist. For this reason the study of limiting cases and of the relations between the models is especially important.

Some of the models, for example the liquid-drop static model, are very simple and require relatively few experimental data; however, they do not give detailed information, although they are valuable for over-all systematic studies. Other models provide detailed information but only in special mass intervals or on special properties.

In this chapter we discuss the models as soon as the relevant empirical material has been treated. This parallels to a certain extent the historical development. The interrelations between the models are set forth in Fig 6-1, which also includes models, such as the optical model, to be discussed in later chapters. Although the knowledge of nuclear reactions is necessary for an understanding and appreciation of some of these models, they are included in Fig. 6-1 for completeness.

6-1 Charge

The Rutherford planetary model of the atom made possible, very

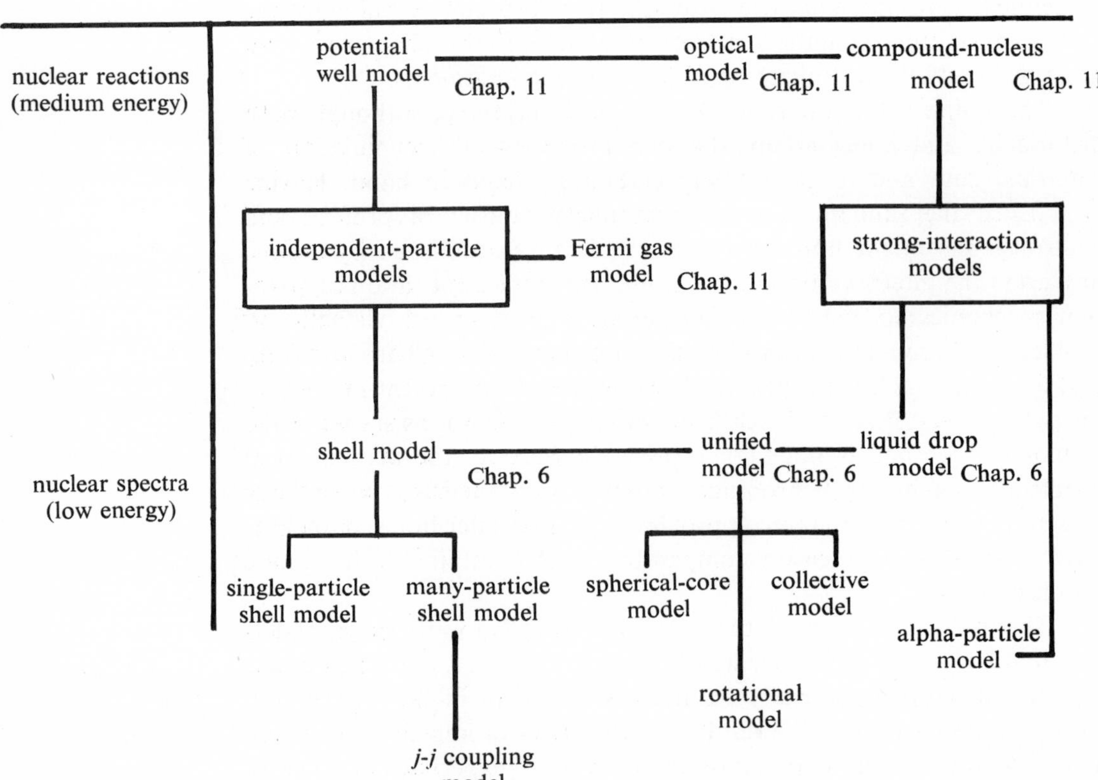

Figure 6-1 Models of the nucleus. The models are treated in different chapters as indicated in the figure. [From Moszkowski, in (Fl E).]

early, an interpretation of X-ray spectra of many elements obtained by Moseley in 1912. It was apparent from the spectral data (Fig. 6-2), that the nucleus has a positive charge Ze, where Z is the atomic number and $|e| = (4.80298 \pm 0.00007) \times 10^{-10}$ esu is the magnitude of the charge on the electron. The atomic number Z is exactly an integer; subelectronic charges have never been observed. The fact that single atoms are exactly neutral has been checked with great precision by sending a molecular beam of cesium or potassium atoms through an electric field. The total

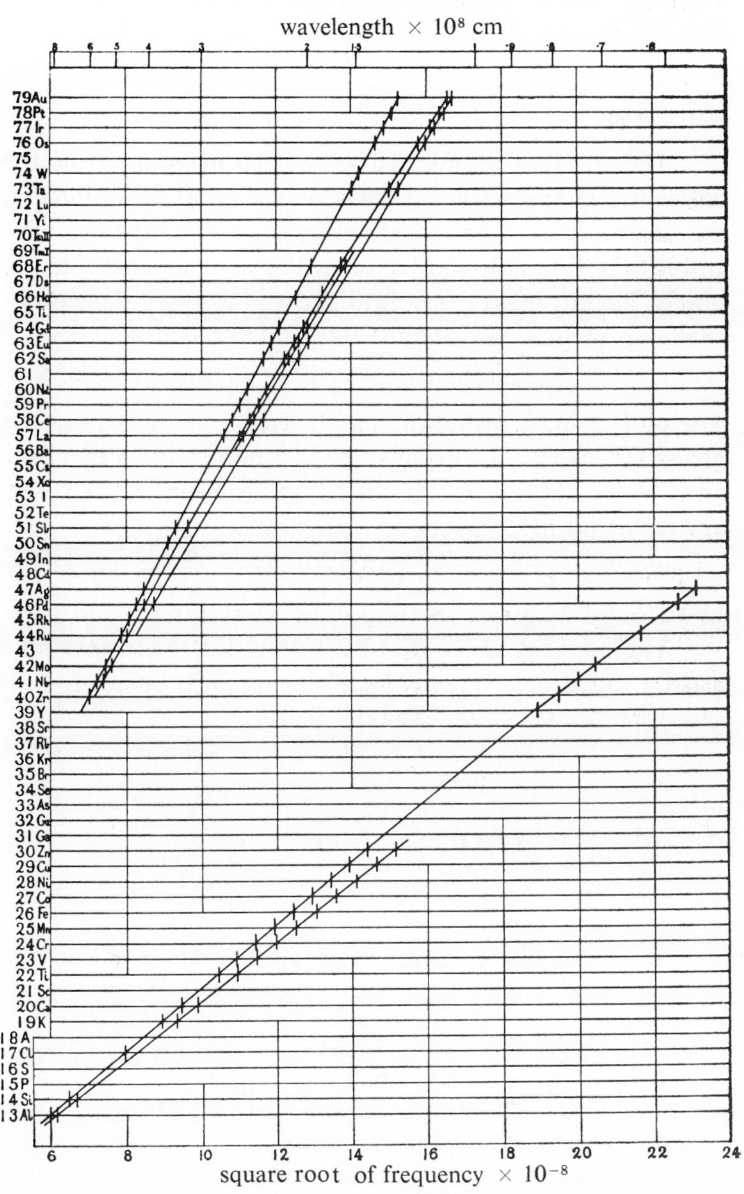

Figure 6-2 Original figure, from a paper by Moseley [*Phil. Mag.*, **26**, 1024 (1913)] showing the relation between Z and $\nu^{1/2}$ of X rays.

charge of the atom that resulted from these experiments is less than 10^{-18} electron charge. Furthermore, the electron-proton charge difference has been determined to be less than 5×10^{-19} electron charges and the charge of the neutron less than 2×10^{-15}, in the same units. Experiments on the average charge of atoms or molecules set limits about 100 times smaller. The identity of all electrons is further proved by the applicability to them of Pauli's exclusion principle. Namely, it has been verified that electrons emitted in beta decay cannot enter orbits already occupied by atomic electrons. This is an absolutely stringent test and rules out, for example, the possibility of a difference between orbital electrons and electrons emitted in beta decay. The identity of all protons has also been verified (see Sec. 6-4).

6-2 Mass

The study of atomic masses by the mass spectrograph shows that each nuclear species has a mass nearly equal to an integral multiple of the proton mass. The integer in question is called the mass number A. In 1961 the International Union of Physics and Chemistry adopted as the unit of nuclear mass the twelfth part of the mass of the atom C^{12}, and we shall use this unit consistently. Its absolute value is

$$1.660420 \times 10^{-24}\ \text{g} = 931.478 \pm 0.004\ \text{MeV}$$

The unit of mass ordinarily employed by physicists until 1960 was one giving $O^{16} = 16$. The chemists used a unit of mass in which the average mass of the natural mixture of oxygen isotopes was 16. These two units and the new unit $C^{12} = 12$ are in the ratio

$$1\ \text{mu}(C^{12} = 12) = 1.000317917\ \text{mu}(O^{16} = 16) = 1.000043\ \text{mu}(O = 16)$$

In Table 6-1 we give a few important masses in units of $C^{12}/12$ and MeV.

The quantity $A - M$, where M is the exact mass of the atom, is usually called the "mass defect," the quantity $M - A = \Delta M$ is usually called the "mass excess," and the quantity

$$\frac{M - A}{A} = f \tag{6-2.1}$$

is called the "packing fraction" (Fig. 6-3).

Table 6-1 Some Important Masses

	$C^{12}/12$	MeV
$C^{12}/12$	1	931.478 ± 0.004
1 MeV	1.07356×10^{-3}	1
Electron	5.48597×10^{-4}	0.511006 ± 1.4 eV
Neutron	1.0086654	939.550 ± 0.004
Proton	1.0072766	938.256 ± 0.004
Deuterium atom	2.01410	1,876.093
Helium atom	4.00260	3,728.33

If, by a nuclear reaction, atoms 1 and 2 of masses M_1 and M_2 combine to form a third atom of mass M_3, then $(M_1 + M_2 - M_3)c^2$ is the binding energy that has escaped from the system, perhaps as gamma radiation, during the synthesis. Conversely it might be necessary to supply energy to atoms 1 and 2 in order to combine them.

These energy relations are expressed by the equation

$$M_1 + M_2 = M_3 + Q \tag{6-2.2}$$

a positive Q meaning that we obtain work by combining M_1 and M_2 into M_3, and a negative Q meaning that it takes work to combine M_1 and M_2 into M_3. For instance,

$$n + p = d + Q \qquad Q = 2.225 \text{ MeV} \tag{6-2.3}$$

A neutron and a proton at rest combine to form a deuteron, the excess energy of 2.23 MeV escaping as a gamma ray and as recoil energy of the deuteron formed.

By convention the tables of masses give atomic masses. To obtain nuclear masses, one must subtract from them Z electron masses (m_e) and, to be exact, must also add the binding energy of the electrons. For instance,

$$M(\text{hydrogen atom}) = M(\text{proton}) + m_e - 13.60 \text{ eV}$$

In most equations the use of atomic or nuclear masses gives the same result except for the small and often negligible differences of electronic binding energy; if positrons are involved, however, the orbital electrons must be taken into account.

Thus, if an atom of mass $M(A,Z)$ undergoes a beta decay, we have

$$M(A,Z) = M(A, Z + 1) + Q$$

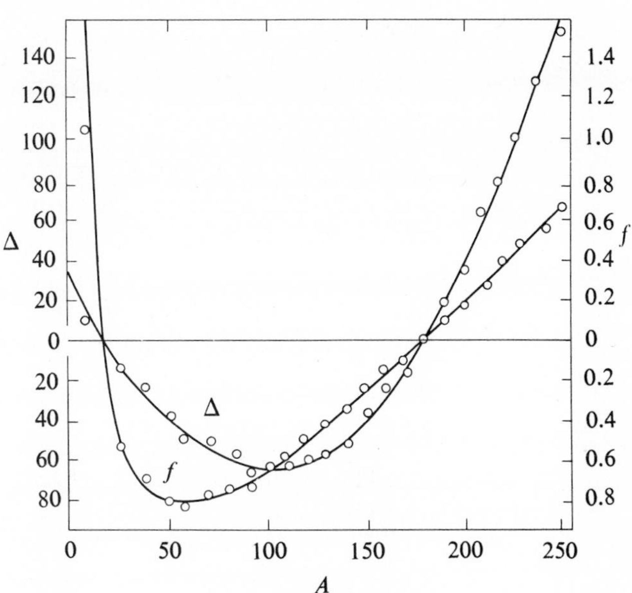

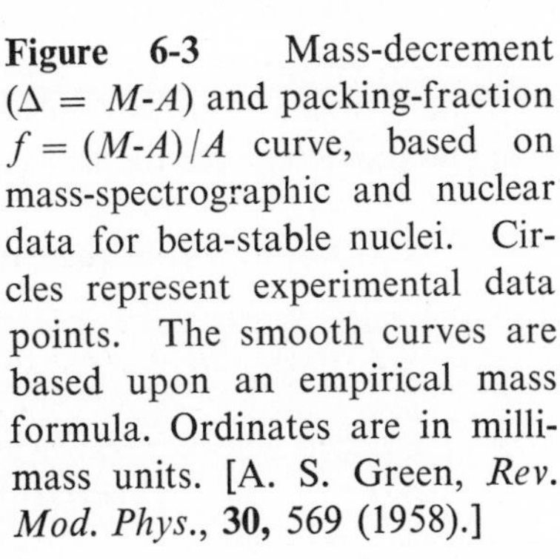

Figure 6-3 Mass-decrement ($\Delta = M\text{-}A$) and packing-fraction $f = (M\text{-}A)/A$ curve, based on mass-spectrographic and nuclear data for beta-stable nuclei. Circles represent experimental data points. The smooth curves are based upon an empirical mass formula. Ordinates are in millimass units. [A. S. Green, *Rev. Mod. Phys.*, **30**, 569 (1958).]

In this case $M(A, Z + 1)$ contains the rest mass of $Z + 1$ electrons, and Q is the maximum kinetic energy of the escaping electron (the neutrino then does not carry away any energy). If we have a positron decay,

$$M(A,Z) = M(A, Z - 1) + 2m_e + Q \tag{6-2.4}$$

where Q is again the maximum kinetic energy of the positron. Clearly unless

$$M(A,Z) > M(A, Z - 1) + 2m_e \tag{6-2.5}$$

positron emission is impossible (see also Chap. 9).

There are several methods for determining the mass of a nucleus. The most important are by means of the mass spectograph and by energy measurements in nuclear reactions.

The mass spectrograph connected with earlier experiments by J. J. Thomson (1912), was developed by F. W. Aston (1920) and has been brought to a high degree of perfection. In order to determine the mass m of an ion of known charge ze, it is enough to determine ze/m. As is well known, a magnetic field produces on a charge ze moving in it a force $\mathbf{F}$,

$$\mathbf{F}_B = \frac{ze}{c}\mathbf{v} \times \mathbf{B} \tag{6-2.6}$$

where $\mathbf{B}$ is the magnetic induction and $\mathbf{v}$ is the velocity of the particle. An electric field $\mathbf{E}$ gives a force

$$\mathbf{F}_E = ze\mathbf{E} \tag{6-2.7}$$

The orbit of a particle is affected by both fields, and a combination of these fields can be used to determine any two of the following three quantities: momentum p of the particle, velocity v, and its kinetic energy T. For instance, if we have a magnetic and an electric field perpendicular to each other and to the velocity of a particle and of magnitudes such that

$$\frac{v}{c} = \frac{E}{B} \tag{6-2.8}$$

then the particle moves in a straight line, since the electric and magnetic forces compensate each other. Adding two slits to the system, we have a "Wien filter." Particles that have passed through such a Wien filter must all have the same velocity v. If we now pass the beam through a uniform magnetic field B and measure the radius r of the circular orbit described by the particles, we obtain the momentum of the particles. We then have

$$r = \frac{cp}{zeB} \tag{6-2.9}$$

The momentum and velocity yield, the rest mass, $m = p/v$, or relativistically,

$$m = \frac{p}{\gamma v} \tag{6-2.10}$$

where

$$\gamma = \left[1 - \left(\frac{v}{c}\right)^2\right]^{-1/2} \qquad \textbf{(6-2.11)}$$

There are many combinations of electric and magnetic fields suitable for mass spectrographs. Of particular importance are the focusing properties of the arrangement: it is desirable that particles emerging from one point into a small angle converge on one point or one line. It is even possible to obtain double focusing, whereby particles emerging within a small angle from a slit and having slightly different velocities converge in an image. Figure 6-5 shows a modern type of double-focusing mass spectrograph and Fig. 6-6 the lines obtainable. An interesting variation of these arrangements is the time-of-flight method, in which the velocity of an ion is determined by its period of revolution in a magnetic field.

Mass spectroscopy has many applications. Of greatest immediate interest to nuclear physics are precise mass determinations and the identification and abundance measurements of various isotopes.

The isotopic composition of an element as found in nature is usually fixed, because the different isotopes behave identically from the physico-chemical point of view. This is not always precisely true, although

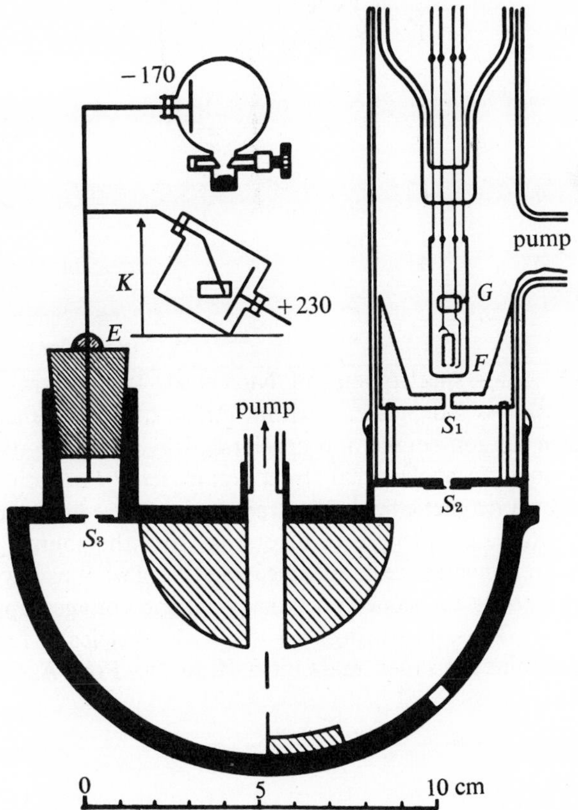

Figure 6-4 Mass spectrograph of Dempster. The electric field between G and S_1 determines the energy of the ions, and the magnetic field determines their momentum.

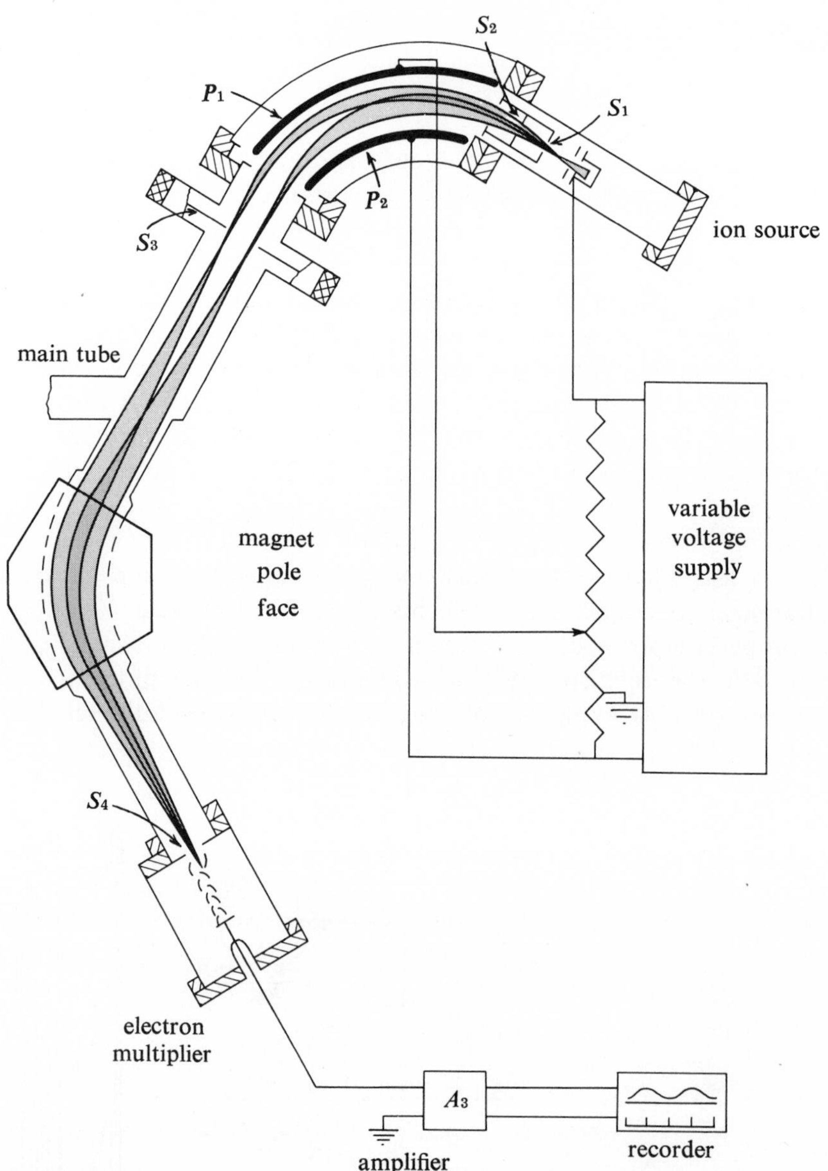

Figure 6-5 Mass spectrometer of Nier et al. The spectrometer focuses ions of a given mass; the focusing action is independent, within limits, of kinetic energy and of the entrance angle. Ions are produced in the ion source and accelerated by a voltage of about 40 kV. They are electrically deflected through an angle of 90° by a condenser P_1P_2 (radius 20 in.), and refocused on an electron multiplier by a magnetic field. The trajectories in the figure represent two beams of ions, of the same mass but different velocity and diverging from the source. The double-focusing action is demonstrated by the convergence of such beams at S_4. Two ions having a mass ratio m/m' and starting from rest follow exactly the same trajectory if all the voltages applied in the two cases are in the ratio $V'/V = m/m'$. Thus, measuring the ratio V'/V electrically for which two ions (e.g., CH_4^+,O^+) arrive at the same point gives their mass ratio. [Courtesy Prof. A. O. Nier.]

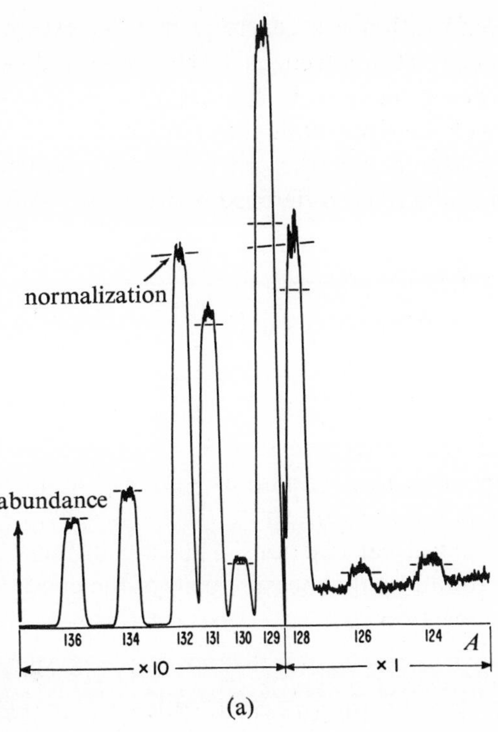

(a)

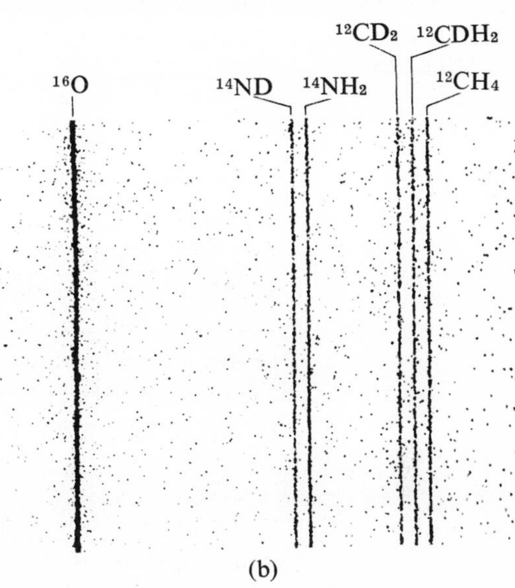

(b)

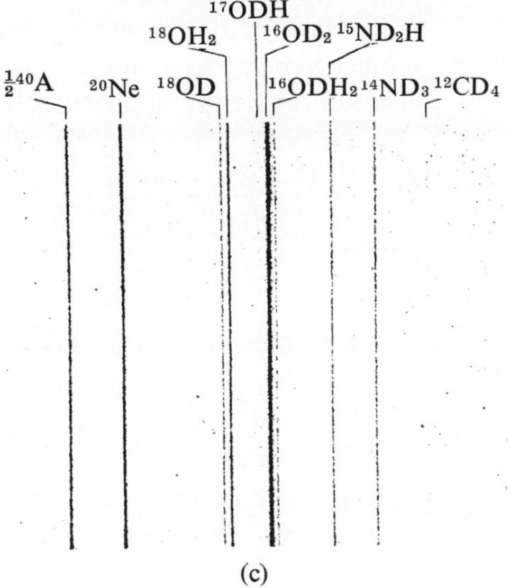

(c)

Figure 6-6 (a) Mass spectrum showing anomalous isotopic composition of Xe from a meteorite. The horizontal lines give the normal abundance of Xe isotopes in gas from the earth's atmosphere. The excess Xe^{129} demonstrates the presence in the meteorite of a radioactive I^{129} at the time of the meteorite's formation. [J. H. Reynolds, *Phys. Rev. Letters*, **4,** 8 (1960).] (b) and (c) Mass spectra-multiplet at $A = 16$ and $A = 20$ showing several molecules and O^{16}. Resolution about 1/80,000. [From Bieri, Everling, and Mattauch, *Z. Naturfors.*, **10a,** 659 (1955).]

departures from the normal composition are generally minute, except when radioactive-decay phenomena are involved, as in the case of radiogenic lead. For all practical purposes chemical inseparability of isotopes is absolute and forms the basis of the important tracer method.

Mass determinations are now precise to the order of 1 part in 10^8. The quantity directly measured is the mass difference between two ions of approximately the same ze/m, one has:

$$\begin{aligned} H_2^1 - H_1^2 &= 1.54825 \pm 0.0010 \text{ millimass units} \\ H_3^2 - \tfrac{1}{2}(C_1^{12}) &= 42.3065 \pm 0.004 \text{ millimass units} \\ (C_1^2\, H_4^{11}) - O_1^{16} &= 36.38594 \pm 0.0002 \text{ millimass units} \end{aligned} \tag{6-2.12}$$

It is just by the study of these three doublets that the masses of H^1, H^2, and O^{16}* have been determined with reference to $C^{12} = 12$. The procedure may be extended to many other nuclei and thus a table of atomic masses is built. Moreover, it is possible to integrate the mass spectroscopic data with data derived from nuclear reactions. Thus, for instance, the mass of the neutron may be found by the measurement of the energy of the gamma rays emitted in the reaction

$$n^1 + H^1 = H^2 + \gamma \tag{6-2.13}$$

if the mass of the deuteron and proton are known. In this case, if the neutron is captured at rest, we have

$$n^1 + H^1 - H^2 = Q = \hbar\omega + \frac{\hbar^2\omega^2}{2m_d c^2} \tag{6-2.14}$$

where the last term is the recoil kinetic energy of the deuteron. As another example, consider an atom of mass M_1 and kinetic energy T_1 colliding with an atom of mass M_0 at rest. The reaction products are an atom of mass M_2, which escapes with a kinetic energy T_2 at an angle θ to the direction of the impinging particle and an atom of mass M_3, with a kinetic energy T_3 at angle φ. The conservation of energy and momentum, in nonrelativistic approximation, gives on elimination of φ

$$Q = \frac{M_2 + M_3}{M_3} T_2 - \frac{M_3 - M_1}{M_3} T_1 - \frac{2(M_1 M_2 T_1 T_2)^{1/2}}{M_3} \cos\theta \tag{6-2.15}$$

where

$$Q = M_0 + M_1 - M_2 - M_3 \tag{6-2.16}$$

In Eq. (6-2.15) T_1, T_2, θ are directly measurable from the experimental conditions. A typical reaction, which can be treated by Eq. (6-2.15), is

$$Li^6 + H^1 = He^3 + He^4 + Q \qquad Q = 4.023 \text{ MeV} \tag{6-2.17}$$

Relativistic corrections are of the order of T/Mc^2 and are sometimes necessary. The masses of many stable and unstable isotopes have been

* In the notation X_n^A, X stands for the chemical symbol, A for the mass number, n for the number of atoms in the molecule, and the whole symbol for the molecular mass.

measured with high precision by a combination of mass-spectrographic measurements and measurements of energy in nuclear reactions.

Other branches of physics have also contributed to precise mass spectrometry. Microwave spectrometry in particular often permits the precision measurement of mass ratios of isotopes.

Another important application of mass spectrometry is the determination of the relative abundances of isotopes in a mixture. This measurement of the natural mixture of isotopes, combined with the masses of the single isotopes, allows ordinary chemical atomic weights to be found with a precision generally superior to that of chemical determinations. Even extremely rare isotopes with an abundance of only a few parts in 10^4, have been detected, and for many undetected ones low upper limits of the abundance have been set. In this field other branches of physics have contributed in a notable way: the important isotopes H^2, C^{13}, N^{15}, and O^{18} were discovered spectroscopically, and He^3 in the atmosphere was discovered by using the resonant properties of the cyclotron.

Everling, König, Mattauch, and Wapstra have calculated an extensive table of masses, taking into account all available experimental data and adjusting them by a least-squares procedure. All of these data are of importance for the development of nuclear systematics. Some of the more striking results are as follows:

1. Nuclei with odd Z have only one or two stable isotopes.
2. Nuclei with odd Z and even A are unstable (the only exceptions are H^2, Li^6, B^{10}, N^{14} and Ta^{180}).
3. In any group of isobars with A and Z odd, there are only one or two nuclei stable against beta decay.

Table 6-2, which refers to stable nuclei, shows the preference for the Z-even–A-even composition. A similar conclusion is reached by a study of nuclear abundances.

6-3 Nuclear Radii

The definition of a nuclear radius is somewhat arbitrary, because the result of a measurement depends on the phenomenon used to define the nuclear radius; however, all the results agree qualitatively and to a certain extent quantitatively also. This is especially remarkable considering the variety of methods used. Here we consider first the scattering of alpha particles, neutrons, and protons of widely different energies.

Table 6-2 Number of Stable Nuclei

	A even	A odd
Z even	156	48
Z odd	5	50

The dominant force in these cases is of nuclear origin. Next we mention electron scattering, the isotope shift of optical spectral lines, mu-mesic atoms, and the electrostatic term in the nuclear masses. These involve only electric interaction. The concordance of the results shows among other things that at least approximately the bulk of nuclear matter has a constant specific charge, although there may be variations on the surface of the nucleus.

Historically the first measurement of nuclear size was made by Rutherford and Chadwick, who determined the angle of scattering at which the scattering cross section of alpha particles from a nucleus starts to show departures from Rutherford's law. There is a minimum distance of approach in a collision that corresponds to this angle, and the fact that the scattering law based on the pure electric Coulomb interaction breaks down is interpreted as evidence that at this minimum distance specific nuclear forces become effective. The alpha particle and the target nucleus have "touched" each other. In this way it was found by Rutherford that the nuclear radius of light elements could be represented by the formula

$$R = r_0 A^{1/3} \qquad \text{with} \qquad r_0 = 1.2 \times 10^{-13}\ \text{cm} \tag{6-3.1}$$

Although the method is a crude one, the result has been confirmed by later studies.

Using neutrons instead of charged particles as projectiles, we find the range of the nuclear forces directly, disregarding the Coulomb field. There are many such measurements. However, at low energies, where the de Broglie wavelength of the neutron is comparable to or larger than the nuclear radius, these measurements are not usable; and, at very high energies, nuclei are transparent to neutrons. Hence, intermediate energies (10 to 20 MeV) must be used. Figure 6-7 shows a graph of the nuclear radius obtained from neutron measurements. Here we use the relation

$$\sigma = 2\pi R^2 \tag{6-3.2}$$

where σ is the total nuclear cross section. The justification of the factor 2

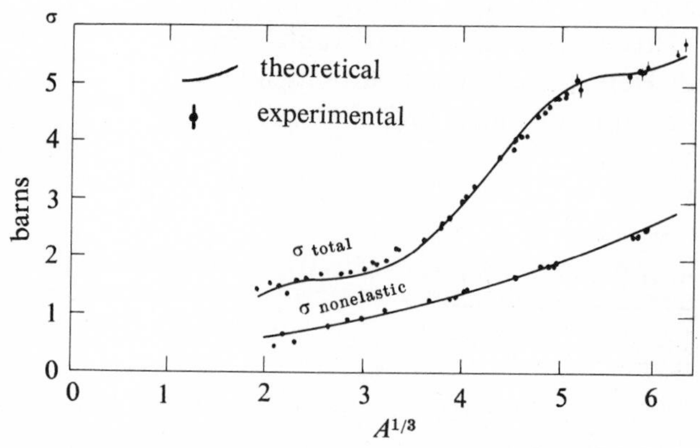

Figure 6-7 Experimental and theoretical total and nonelastic cross sections of 14-MeV neutrons as a function of $A^{1/3}$. [S. Fernbach, *Rev. Mod. Phys.*, **30,** 414 (1958).]

in Eq. (6-3.2) comes from the so-called diffraction scattering (see Chap. 11).

Diffraction scattering itself gives another method of determining the nuclear radius. If we assume for the sake of simplicity that the nucleus is a black disc of radius R, diffracting the de Broglie wave of the incident particle according to the laws of optics,[1] we should obtain a differential scattering cross section

$$\frac{d\sigma}{d\omega} = \frac{4\pi^2 R^2}{\sin^2\theta} J_1^2\left(\frac{R\sin\theta}{\lambda\!\!\!^{-}}\right) \tag{6-3.3}$$

where $J_1(x)$ is the Bessel function of order unity and $\lambda\!\!\!^{-} = \hbar/mv$ is the de Broglie wavelength of the incident particle. The function $J_1(x)$ has the first zero at

$$x = 0.610 \times 2\pi \tag{6-3.4}$$

and the asymptotic form for large x

$$J_1(x) \to \left(\frac{2}{\pi x}\right)^{1/2} \sin\left(x - \frac{\pi}{4}\right) \tag{6-3.5}$$

The first minimum of scattering thus occurs for an angle such that

$$\sin\theta = 0.610 \times 2\pi \frac{\lambda\!\!\!^{-}}{R} \tag{6-3.6}$$

and from its measurement we have another method of obtaining R (Fig. 6-8).

In addition to the specific nuclear methods mentioned above, it is possible to deduce the nuclear radius from the scattering of high-energy electrons on the assumption that the electron is subject to electromagnetic interactions only. This gives the distribution of the electric charge of the nucleus, and the result is again approximately represented by Eq. (6-3.1), with $r_0 = 1.2$.

It will be noted that Eq. (6-3.1) is an approximation, in that the nucleus is not a homogeneous sphere but has a density distribution decreasing gradually near the surface. An electric-charge density distribution (Saxon) that is widely used and is in agreement with experiment is

$$\rho(r) = \frac{\rho_1}{\exp[(r - C)/Z_1] + 1} \tag{6-3.7}$$

with

$$C = 1.07A^{1/3} \times 10^{-13}\ \text{cm} \qquad \text{and} \qquad Z_1 = 0.545 \times 10^{-13}\ \text{cm} \tag{6-3.8}$$

ρ_1 is determined by the normalization condition

$$Ze = \int_0^\infty \rho(r) 4\pi r^2\, dr \tag{6-3.9}$$

[1] See, e.g., Jenkins and White, *Fundamentals of Optics*, McGraw-Hill, New York, 1957, or (Ja 62).

(Fig. 6-9). This formula is valid, with small variations of C, for any nucleus having $A > 30$. A measure of the surface thickness is provided by the difference of the radii for which $\rho(r)$ is 0.1 and 0.9 of its maximum value. For the Saxon distribution this is $4.4Z_1 \sim 2.4 \times 10^{-13}$ cm.

Electron-scattering measurements give probably the most detailed information at present obtainable on the nuclear-charge distribution. Using high-energy electrons (1 BeV), one has a de Broglie wavelength $\lambdabar = 1.95 \times 10^{-14}$ cm, small enough to start exploring the nuclear structure.

The experimental data obtained are $d\sigma/d\omega$ as a function of the scattering angle θ; we shall consider only elastic scattering. The calculations may be carried out to various degrees of approximation. In the simplest case, including the spin of the electron and recoil effects, one has for a point nucleus

$$\left(\frac{d\sigma}{d\omega}\right)_{\text{point}} = \left(\frac{Ze^2}{2E_0}\right)^2 \frac{1}{\sin^4(\theta/2)} \frac{\cos^2(\theta/2)}{1 + (2E_0/Mc^2)\sin^2(\theta/2)} \tag{6-3.10}$$

where θ is the laboratory scattering angle, E_0 the total energy of the electron in the laboratory, and M the mass of the nucleus. Here the last

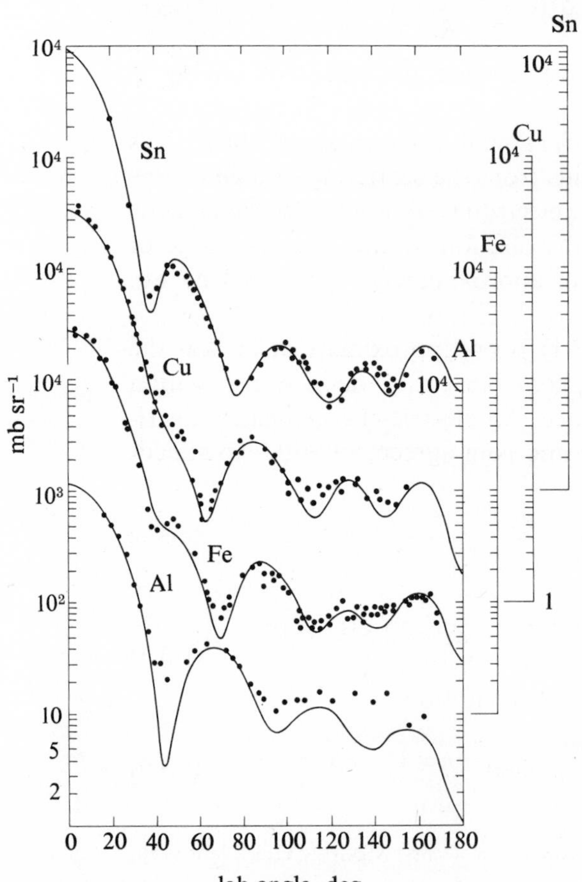

Figure 6-8 Experimental and theoretical differential cross sections for 14-MeV neutrons scattered from Sn, Cu, Fe, and Al. The experimental data presented are not completely corrected for multiple scattering, nor have angular and energy resolution been taken into account. [S. Fernbach, *Rev. Mod. Phys.*, **30,** 414 (1958).]

factor originates from the kinematics of nuclear recoil. Equation (6-3.10) naturally cannot give any information on nuclear size, since the nucleus has been assumed to be represented by a point charge.

However, the finite dimensions of the nucleus affect the scattering. For zero magnetic moment and an extended distribution of electric charge, we show in Appendixes B and C that the differential scattering cross section is given by

$$\frac{d\sigma}{d\omega} = \frac{d\sigma}{d\omega}_{\text{point}} |F(q)|^2 \tag{6-3.11}$$

where, for elastic collisions,

$$q = \frac{|\mathbf{p} - \mathbf{p}'|}{\hbar} = |\mathbf{k} - \mathbf{k}'| = \frac{2}{\hbar} p \sin\frac{\theta}{2} \qquad (|\mathbf{p}| = |\mathbf{p}'|) \tag{6-3.12}$$

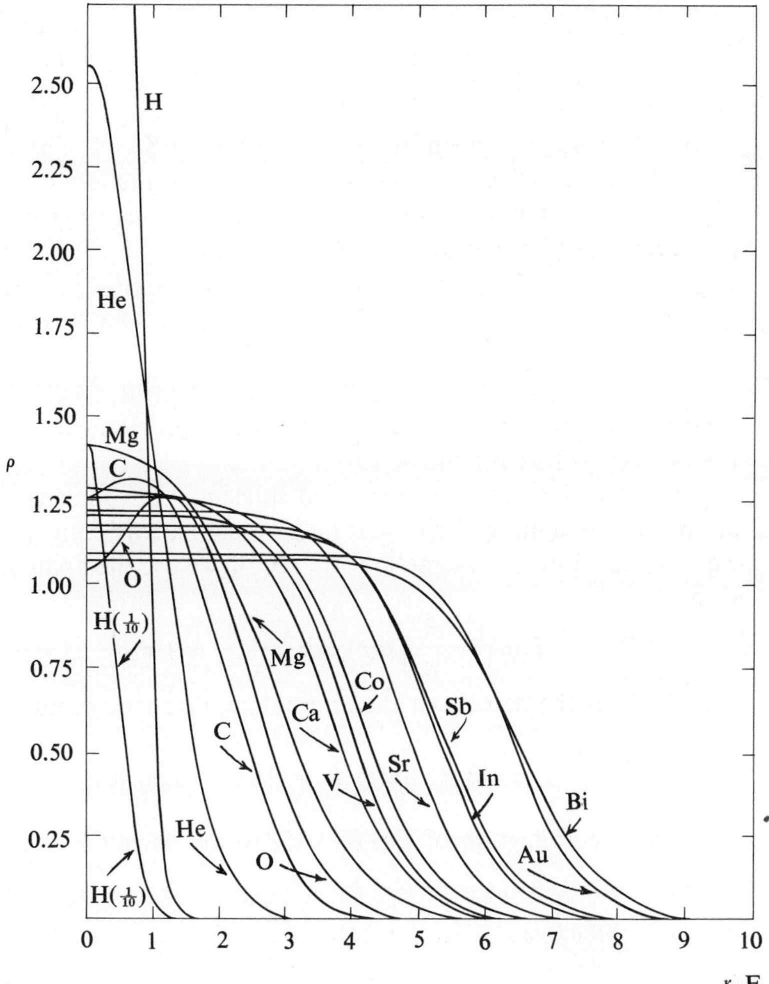

Figure 6-9 Nuclear charge density as a function of distance from the center of the nucleus found by electron scattering methods. Ordinates unit: 10^{19} coulomb cm^{-3}. [R. Hofstadter, *Ann. Rev. Nucl. Sci.*, **7**, 231 (1957).]

is proportional to the momentum transferred. The function $F(q)$ is called the form factor, and its expression is, in Born approximation,

$$F_1(q) = \frac{1}{Ze}\int \rho(r) \exp i\,[(\mathbf{k} - \mathbf{k}')\cdot\mathbf{r}]d\tau \tag{6-3.13}$$

where the integral is extended over the volume of the nucleus and ρ is the electric-charge density. Note that F_1 is normalized so as to give $F_1(0) = 1$.

A hypothetical charge distribution can be tested against experiment by comparing the observed $d\sigma/d\omega$ with the one calculated through Eqs. (6-3.11) and (6-3.13) and the assumed charge distribution.

The proton and the neutron are of special interest. Even for them it has been possible to measure form factors. But in order to obtain meaningful results, it is also necessary to take into account the magnetic moments of the particles. Let us first consider a "Dirac proton" with spin $\frac{1}{2}$ and magnetic moment $e\hbar/2Mc$. Its electron scattering has been calculated to be

$$\left(\frac{d\sigma}{d\omega}\right)_d = \left(\frac{d\sigma}{d\omega}\right)_{\text{point}} \left[1 + \left(\frac{\hbar q}{2Mc}\right)^2 2\tan^2\frac{\theta}{2}\right] \tag{6-3.14}$$

where $(d\sigma/d\omega)_{\text{point}}$ is given by Eq. (6-3.10), with $Z = 1$. The second term in the brackets reflects scattering due to the magnetic moment.

The next step is to introduce the anomalous magnetic moments (see Sec. 6-6) (Rosenbluth, 1950), obtaining

$$\left(\frac{d\sigma}{d\omega}\right)_{\text{Rosenbluth}} = \left(\frac{d\sigma}{d\omega}\right)_{\text{point}} \left\{1 + \left(\frac{\hbar q}{2Mc}\right)^2 \left[2(1 + K)^2 \tan^2\frac{\theta}{2} + K^2\right]\right\} \tag{6-3.15}$$

where K is the anomalous part of the magnetic moment: $K = 1.79$ for the proton, -1.91 for the neutron.

We can now consider extended nucleons, introducing appropriate electric and magnetic form factors. For the electric form factor we use Eq. (6-3.13). For the magnetic form factor we use the analogous expression

$$F_2(q) = \frac{1}{K}\int \mu(r) \exp\left[i(\mathbf{k} - \mathbf{k}')\cdot\mathbf{r}\right]d\tau \tag{6-3.16}$$

where $\mu(r)$ is the density of the anomalous magnetic moment. Thus

$$F_2(0) = \int \mu(r)\, d\tau = 1 \text{ for the proton} \tag{6-3.17}$$

The generalization of Eq. (6-3.15) to an extended source is then

$$\frac{d\sigma}{d\omega} = \left(\frac{d\sigma}{d\omega}\right)_{\text{point}} \left\{F_1^2 + \left(\frac{\hbar q}{2Mc}\right)^2 \left[2(F_1 + KF_2)^2 \tan^2\frac{\theta}{2} + K^2F_2^2\right]\right\} \tag{6-3.18}$$

This formula reduces to Eq. (6-3.15) for $F_1 = F_2 = 1$.

Hofstadter (1955) and others conducted experiments on the scattering of high-energy (500 to 1,000 MeV) electrons by protons and measured the angular distribution of the electrons. Similar scattering experiments on deuterons give information on the neutron by subtraction procedures. Such studies clearly have important implications. They reveal directly the "meson clouds" (see Chap. 14) surrounding the nucleons. They also show that the charge and magnetic moment densities have different and complicated radial dependencies. The use of higher electron momenta and hence smaller de Broglie wavelengths is likely to yield further information on this important subject.

As a first approximation, the electric-charge density of the proton may be represented by an exponential,

$$\rho = \rho(0)\, e^{-r/a} \tag{6-3.19}$$

with $a = 0.23 \times 10^{-13}$ cm. The root of the mean-square radius for this distribution is $\sqrt{12}\, a = 0.8 \times 10^{-13}$ cm. The value of this density distribution formula is chiefly qualitative. The detailed study of proton and neutron form factors has become very important for particle physics (see Part III of this book). For this purpose it is more convenient to use, instead of the quantities F_1 and F_2 mentioned above, the combinations $F_{\text{charge}} = F_1 - (\hbar q/2Mc)^2 K F_2$ and $F_{\text{magnetic}} = (F_1 + KF_2)/(1 + K)$. These are shown as functions of q^2 in Fig. 6-10 (a) and (b).

In addition to the direct methods mentioned above, variations in the nuclear radius can be found spectroscopically by a study of the isotope shifts in atomic spectra. It is well known that in the case of hydrogen the spectral lines of isotopes are slightly displaced, because the reduced mass of the electron enters in Bohr's formula. In fact, observation of this isotope shift was used in 1931 by Urey, Brickwedde, and Murphy to discover deuterium. Other light elements show an isotope effect of similar origin, but it was found by Schüler, Kopfermann, and others in 1931 that heavy nuclei, for which the mass effect is negligible, show an isotope shift. Here the important effect is the nuclear volume. Within the nucleus the electric potential varies not as $1/r$ but, in the case of a uniformly charged sphere, as r^2. The conditions of continuity for field and potential at $r = R$ (nuclear radius) give for the potential φ, for $r < R$,

$$\varphi(r) = \left(+\frac{3}{2} - \frac{1}{2}\frac{r^2}{R^2}\right)\frac{Ze}{R} \tag{6-3.20}$$

Two isotopes have slightly different radii, and hence the corresponding potentials show a slight difference, $\delta\varphi$. The energy difference for the atomic levels is then, according to standard perturbation theory,

$$\delta W = e \int \psi^*\psi\, \delta\varphi\, d\tau \tag{6-3.21}$$

where $\psi^*\psi$ is the density of the atomic electrons in the nucleus. In the case of a single s electron, neglecting relativistic corrections (which, however, are important in practice), we can evaluate Eq. (6-3.21), assuming that $\psi^*\psi$ is constant and equal to $|\psi(0)|^2$. We obtain

$$\delta W = \frac{4\pi}{5} Ze^2\, |\psi(0)|^2\, R\, \delta R \tag{6-3.22}$$

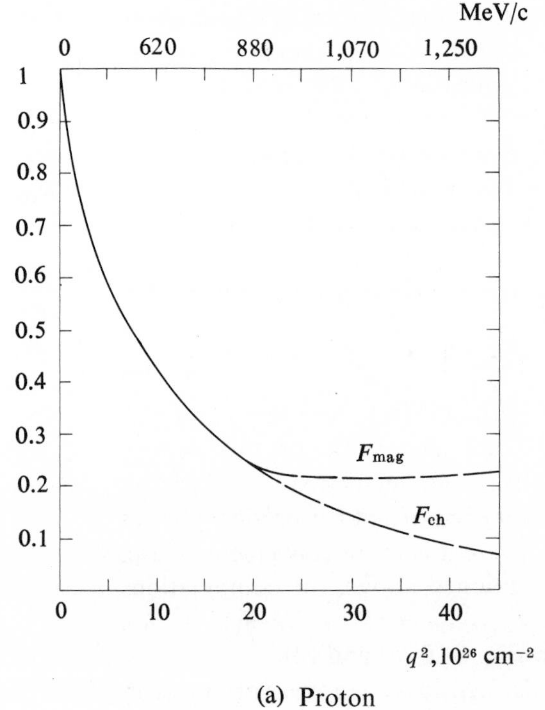

(a) Proton

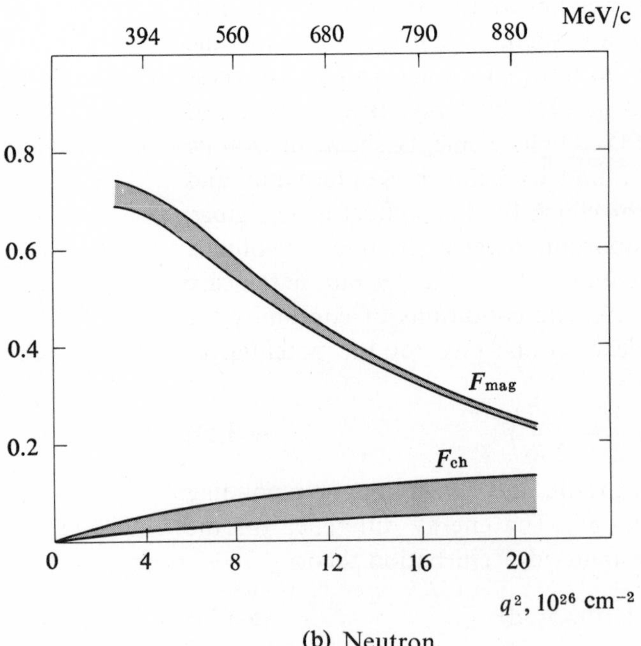

(b) Neutron

Figure 6-10 Neutron and proton form factors as derived from electron scattering. The abscissa is the square of the momentum transfer $q = (2p/\hbar) \sin (\theta/2)$. $1/q = 10^{-13}$ cm corresponds to a momentum of 197 MeV/c. The forms factor F_{charge} and $F_{magnetic}$ are connected to F_1 and F_2 of Eqs. (6-3.13) and (6-3.16) by $F_{charge} = F_1 - (\hbar q/2Mc)^2 KF_2$ and $F_{magnetic} = (F_1 + KF_2)/(1 + K)$. [Courtesy R. Hofstadter.]

This equation relates δW to the change in nuclear radius and, if we assume constant density for nuclear matter, to the difference in mass number.

After relativistic corrections and other refinements have been made, it is possible to compare the observed isotope shifts with those calculated on the basis of a model. This type of consideration is clearly only approximate, as shown by the observation (Sumner Davis, 1959) that there is an "isotope" shift even between isomeric states of the same nucleus. If we want to ascribe this isomeric shift to a change in nuclear volume, we must consider finer details, such as the specific orbits of the constituent nucleons.

Nuclear radii are also obtained from the study of the departure from the simple Bohr hydrogen-atom formula that is observed in the mu-mesic atoms. These atoms are similar to a hydrogen atom but are formed by a nucleus and a mu meson. The meson orbit is about 200 times smaller in radius than the corresponding electron orbit. For sufficiently high Z the bulk of the meson wave function is inside the nucleus and thus permits us to probe the electric potential within the nucleus. For more details see articles quoted in the Bibliography of Chap. 13.

Another line of evidence concerning the nuclear radius derives from measurements of the electrostatic energy of the nucleus due to the accumulation of the positive charge in the nuclear volume. If all the charge were uniformly distributed over the surface of the nucleus, this

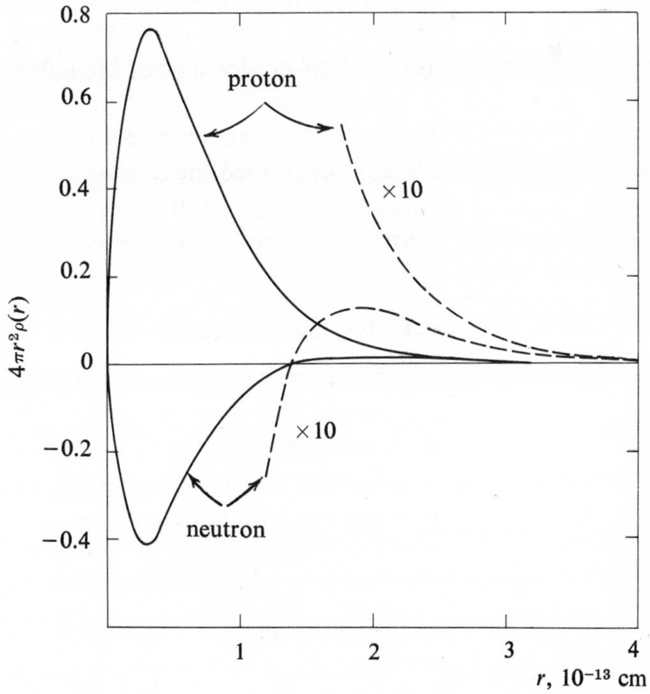

Figure 6-11 The proton and neutron charge density distributions given by the Fourier transforms of the form factors. At the origin an additional very narrow peak (practically a delta function) has been omitted. It contains about 0.3 of the total charge for the proton and neutralizes the total charge for the neutron. [R. Hofstadter and R. Herman, *Phys. Rev. Letters*, **6,** 293 (1961).]

energy would be $Z^2e^2/2R$. Assuming that the charge is uniformly distributed in the nuclear volume, we obtain

$$\frac{3}{5} Z^2 \frac{e^2}{R} = \text{electrostatic energy} \tag{6-3.23}$$

Now there are pairs of nuclei having the same A such that either nucleus can be obtained from the other by transforming all the neutrons of one into protons and all the protons into neutrons. Examples of these "mirror nuclei," as they are called, are H^3 and He^3, B^{11} and C^{11}, C^{13} and N^{13}, and S^{20} and P^{20}. There is reason to believe that the specific nuclear forces acting in such nuclei are practically identical and that the energy difference, apart from the different rest mass of neutron and proton, is entirely of electrostatic origin. When the nuclei differ by one unit in Z, Eq. (6-3.23) gives for the difference in their electrostatic energy,

$$\frac{3}{5} \frac{(2Z + 1)e^2}{R} = \Delta E \tag{6-3.24}$$

and if they have also $Z = (A \pm 1)/2$, respectively, as, for example, C^{11} and B^{11}, we rewrite Eq. (6-3.24) as

$$\Delta E = \frac{3e^2}{5} \frac{A}{R} = \frac{3}{5} \frac{e}{r_0} A^{2/3} \tag{6-3.25}$$

if, as we have repeatedly assumed,

$$R = r_0 A^{1/3} \tag{6-3.26}$$

From this relation it is clear that a plot of ΔE versus $A^{2/3}$ should give a straight line. From its slope we obtain $r_0 = 1.30 \times 10^{-13}$ cm (Fig. 6-12). The departures from the straight line are due to finer effects (shell closure), which will be discussed later on. All these methods give results in agreement with Eq. (6-3.1), with constants r_0 varying between 1.2 and 1.5×10^{-13} cm for all but the lightest nuclei.

Equation (6-3.1) and its refinements cannot be properly applied to the proton, neutron, deuteron, or to the lightest nuclei. We have already mentioned the case of the proton. The deuteron will be discussed in detail in Chap. 10; it has an especially loose structure, and its "radius," defined in Chap. 10, is 4.31×10^{-13} cm.

6-4 Nuclear Statistics

Systems containing identical particles show, according to quantum mechanics, a peculiar behavior that affects many of their properties. We shall treat here the simplest cases of direct interest to nuclear physics.

Given two identical particles (e.g., two alphas, two electrons, two protons, etc.) we write the Schrödinger equation for the system:

$$\frac{\hbar^2}{2m} (\nabla_1^2 + \nabla_2^2)\, u(r_1,r_2) + [E - V(r_1,r_2)]\, u(r_1,r_2) = 0 \tag{6-4.1}$$

or, symbolically,

$$H(1,2)u(r_1,r_2) = Eu(r_1,r_2) \tag{6-4.2}$$

indicating by r_1 or 1, r_2 or 2, all coordinates, including the spin of particles 1 and 2.

We now find that the solutions are degenerate. That is, if $u\ (r_1,r_2)$ is a solution of the problem for a certain eigenvalue, so necessarily is $u(r_2,r_1)$ for the same eigenvalue. This follows from the fact that

$$H(1,2) = H(2,1) \tag{6-4.3}$$

because of the indistinguishability of identical particles. Hence a linear combination

$$U(r_1,r_2) = \alpha u(r_1,r_2) + \beta u(r_2,r_1) \tag{6-4.4}$$

is also a solution for the same eigenvalue. The choice of constants $\alpha = \pm\beta$, real has the important property that if $\alpha = \beta$,

$$U(r_1,r_2) = U(r_2,r_1) \tag{6-4.5}$$

If $\alpha = -\beta$,

$$U(r_1,r_2) = -U(r_2,r_1) \tag{6-4.6}$$

In the first case, the eigenfunction is symmetrical with respect to the exchange of the particles; in the second, it is antisymmetrical. If the system is initially described by a symmetrical or by an antisymmetrical

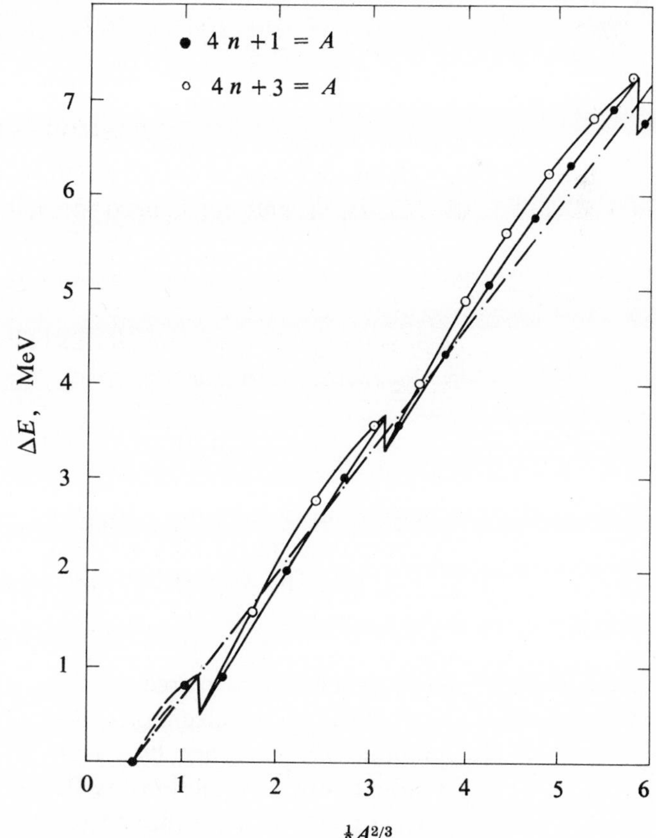

Figure 6-12 Experimental Coulomb energy differences for mirror nuclei as a function of $\frac{1}{2}A^{2/3}$. The dashed-and-dotted line shows the simple classical approximation for $r_0 = 1.30$ F. The curved lines are based on more refined models. [Kofoed-Hansen, *Rev. Mod. Phys.*, **30**, 449 (1958).]

eigenfunction, it will be described by the same type of eigenfunction forever, because the change of the eigenfunction is determined by a symmetrical hamiltonian, and this ensures the preservation of the symmetry or antisymmetry. In order to see this, observe that according to Schrödinger's equation

$$-\frac{\hbar}{i}\frac{\partial\psi}{\partial t} = H\psi \tag{6-4.7}$$

and hence the change in time of ψ, $\partial\psi/\partial t$ is a symmetrical or antisymmetrical function together with $H\psi$. But since H is symmetrical, $H\psi$ has the same symmetry as ψ and consequently the time variation of ψ also has the same symmetry as ψ. Observation demonstrates that natural particles have eigenfunctions that are either symmetrical or antisymmetrical with respect to the exchange of two identical particles. For instance, electrons, protons, neutrons, and, in general, particles with spin $\frac{1}{2}$ all have eigenfunctions which are antisymmetrical with respect to the exchange of the coordinates, whereas particles with spin 0, 1, or, in general, with integral spin, as the alpha particles or deuterons, have eigenfunctions that are symmetrical with respect to the exchange of the coordinates. These facts are among the most important in quantum mechanics and have far-reaching consequences. For instance, consider two noninteracting identical particles. The hamiltonian then separates into the sum of the two terms

$$H(1) + H(2) = H(1,2) = H(2,1) \tag{6-4.8}$$

If

$$u_1(1),\ u_2(1),\ u_3(1),\ \ldots$$
$$u_1(2),\ u_2(2),\ u_3(2),\ \ldots$$

are the eigenfunctions of $H(1)$, $H(2)$, etc., corresponding to eigenvalues E_1, E_2, E_3, ... and normalized in such a way that

$$\int |u_1|^2\, d\tau = \int |u_2|^2\, d\tau \cdots = 1 \tag{6-4.9}$$

then the eigenfunction of $H(1,2)$ belonging to the eigenvalue $E_n + E_m$ is degenerate and has the form

$$u_{nm}(1,2) = \frac{1}{\sqrt{2}}\,[u_n(1)u_m(2) \pm u_m(1)u_n(2)] \tag{6-4.10}$$

where we must take the plus sign if the eigenfunctions are symmetrical or the minus sign if they are antisymmetrical.

If only antisymmetrical solutions are admissible, for m equal to n, $u(1,2)$ vanishes. Hence it is not possible for two identical antisymmetrical particles to be in the same state. This is the original formulation of Pauli's exclusion principle.

In statistical mechanics, particles having antisymmetrical eigenfunctions are governed by Fermi–Dirac statistics, and particles having symmetrical eigenfunctions by Bose–Einstein statistics. For this reason, particles having antisymmetrical wave functions are called fermions, and particles having symmetrical wave functions are called bosons.

Whether a particle is a boson or a fermion depends on its spin. The empirical evidence accumulated over a long period of years shows that bosons have integral spin and fermions have half-integral spin. This striking connection between spin and statistics has very deep theoretical reasons which were finally elucidated by Pauli (1940). Before Pauli's argument it was important to establish empirically whether a given nucleus was a boson or a fermion. This can be done in several ways. One of the historically most important and most ingenious methods is based on the analysis of alternating intensities in the rotational spectra of homonuclear diatomic molecules.

● Consider the eigenfunction of a diatomic molecule having identical nuclei. It can be factored, approximately, into four eigenfunctions: one containing the electronic coordinates, a second the relative distance of the two nuclei and corresponding to the vibration of the nuclei, a third the rotational coordinates of the nuclei, and a fourth the nuclear spin coordinates:

$$u = u_{\text{el}} u_{\text{vib}} u_{\text{rot}} u_{\text{spin}} \tag{6-4.11}$$

where u_{el} depends on the coordinates of the electrons, and its symmetry character on the exchange of the nuclei can be analyzed by a detailed study of the molecule. For the sake of definiteness, let us assume that it is symmetrical. The u_{vib} factor is symmetrical because it depends only on the magnitude of the distance between the nuclei. The rotational part of the eigenfunction is the eigenfunction of a free rotator in space,

$$u_{\text{rot}} = P_l^m (\cos\theta)\, e^{im\varphi} \tag{6-4.12}$$

where θ and φ are the colatitude and the longitude of the axis joining the two nuclei. The function u_{rot} is symmetrical for even l and antisymmetrical for odd l. This follows from the fact that $P_l^m(\cos\theta)\, e^{im\varphi}$ is a spherical harmonic of order l that is r^{-l} times a polynomial in x, y, z, of degree l, homogeneous and harmonic. The interchange of the nuclei corresponds to a change in the variables of the function: θ goes to $\pi-\theta$ and φ to $\pi+\varphi$; or, in cartesian coordinates, x, y, z change sign. This leaves the function unchanged if l is even or changes its sign if l is odd.

In order to analyze the fourth factor we need spin eigenfunctions. For spin $\frac{1}{2}$ the functions have only two values (spin up or spin down), indicated as $\alpha \equiv$ spin up or $\beta \equiv$ spin down. The particle considered is indicated as the argument of the function. Thus, $\alpha(2)$ means spin up for the second particle. For a complete explanation we refer the reader to texts on quantum mechanics. In the case of two spin $\frac{1}{2}$ particles, the last factor concerning the nuclear spins can then be written as follows: If the two spins are parallel, the eigenfunction u_{spin} has one of the three following forms corresponding to the three triplet states:

$$\alpha(1)\alpha(2); \qquad \frac{1}{\sqrt{2}}[\alpha(1)\beta(2) + \alpha(2)\beta(1)]; \qquad \beta(1)\beta(2) \tag{6-4.13}$$

If the spins are antiparallel, the eigenfunction has the form

$$\frac{1}{\sqrt{2}}[\alpha(1)\beta(2) - \alpha(2)\beta(1)] \qquad \textbf{(6-4.14)}$$

The triplet states are therefore symmetrical, and the singlet state is antisymmetrical with respect to the exchange of the spins only. If the whole eigenfunction has to be antisymmetric with respect to the exchange of the nuclei, it is clear that eigenfunctions with l odd must be associated with triplet states. Conversely, states of even l are all associated with singlet states. It follows that the statistical weights of states with l odd are three times as large as those of states with l even.

In the emission or absorption of electromagnetic radiation the symmetry character of the level must be preserved, as shown at the beginning of this section. Moreover, electromagnetic radiation, in practice, produces transitions that change only the factor of the eigenfunction containing ordinary coordinates. It follows that spectral lines are divided between those connecting states that are symmetrical with respect to the exchange of ordinary (not spin) coordinates of the nuclei (symmetric lines) and those connecting states antisymmetric with respect to the exchange of ordinary coordinates (antisymmetric lines). The intensity of the spectral lines, other things being equal, is proportional to the statistical weight of the states. From this it follows that, in a band in which the rotational states do not change, we find a characteristic alternation of intensities. In the example considered above lines corresponding to l odd would be three times as strong as those corresponding to l even. It is clear that in this argument it is essential to assume that the two nuclei are fermions; if they were bosons, the lines with even l would have been stronger. Similar alternations of intensities are shown in the Raman effect of homonuclear diatomic molecules. An example (N_2^{14}) is shown in Fig. 6-13.

The reasoning may be generalized to include the treatment of

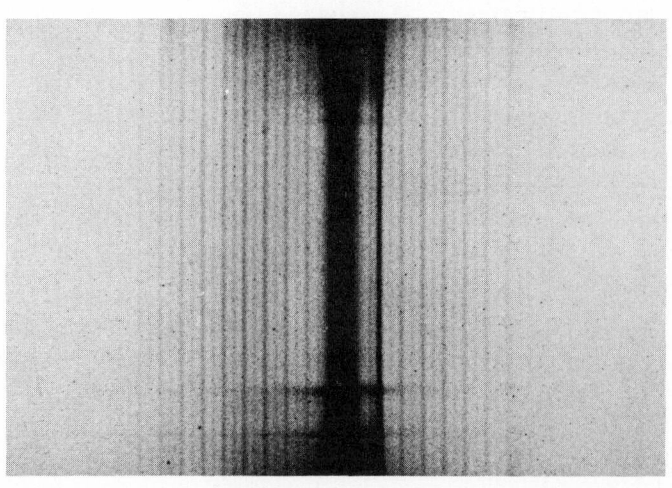

Figure 6-13 Alternating intensities in the Raman spectrum of the N_2^{14} molecule (as observed by F. Rasetti).

an arbitrary nuclear spin. The statistical weights of neighboring rotational states are in the ratio

$$\frac{I+1}{I} = \rho \tag{6-4.15}$$

For fermions the greater weight belongs to the states that are antisymmetrical with respect to the exchange of the spatial coordinates (spin thus excluded) of the identical nuclei. For bosons the smaller weight belongs to the same type of state. The ratio of the intensities giving ρ of Eq. (6-4.15) may be used to determine I. Note that for $I = 0$, half the levels are missing. ●

The main results of this and other methods are that all nuclei with A even have an integral spin and are bosons; all nuclei with odd A have a half-integral spin and are fermions. These rules have been of great importance in establishing the model of the nucleus formed by neutrons and protons.

6-5 Liquid-Drop Model

We are now in a position to discuss a crude nuclear model that has the advantage of great simplicity combined with the ability to reproduce many of the salient features of nuclear matter. Until about 1931 nuclear models treated the proton and the electron as fundamental constituents of the nucleus. These particles were the simplest known to exist in the free state; and electrons, since they are ejected by nuclei in beta decay, could reasonably be expected to be present inside nuclei. A nucleus of mass number A and charge Z was supposed to contain A protons and $A - Z$ electrons. This hypothesis accounted for the charge and mass of the nucleus, because electrons are very light and the Z electrons did not greatly affect the nuclear mass. It was the most natural hypothesis in many respects, but two very serious stumbling blocks were discovered about 1930. It was shown by Rasetti in 1929 (Fig. 6-13) by a study of the Raman spectrum of the N_2^{14} molecule that N^{14} is a boson (see Sec. 6-4) and hence must contain an even number of fermions. Later the same was shown to be true of H^2. Now it is clear that according to the electron-proton hypothesis N^{14} contains 14 protons and 7 electrons and H^2 contains 2 protons and 1 electron, that is, 21 or 3 fermions, respectively, in contradiction to experiment, which requires them to contain an even number of fermions. A second difficulty arose from the fact that a nucleus supposed to contain an odd number of fermions such as N^{14} was found experimentally to have an integral spin instead of the expected half-integral spin.

In addition, the confining of the electron to a region in space of nuclear dimensions (10^{-13} cm) presented serious difficulties because, through the uncertainty principle of quantum mechanics, it implied an implausibly high kinetic energy for the electron.

All these difficulties were removed by Chadwick's discovery, in

1931, of the free neutron, of mass nearly equal to that of the proton. Immediately thereafter Ivanenko and Heisenberg independently proposed a nuclear model containing neutrons and protons as fundamental constituents. This model assumes that the neutron is a fermion of spin $\frac{1}{2}$. Nuclei contain Z protons and $A - Z = N$ neutrons and thus, in the case of N^{14}, 7 neutrons and 7 protons, i.e., an even number of fermions, which agrees with the boson character of N^{14} and with its integral spin. Moreover, the relatively large mass of the neutron and proton removes the difficulties created by the uncertainty principle. The neutron-proton model of the nucleus has been universally accepted and forms the basis of all studies of nuclear structure.

If we plot the number of neutrons contained in the nucleus as a function of Z for all stable nuclei, we obtain the diagram of Fig. 6-14, sometimes called the "Segrè chart." Postponing the consideration of fine points, we see that there is a relation between Z and N, because representative points are restricted to a small region, one would say almost a curve, of the ZN plane. An important requirement for a nuclear model is thus to account for this regularity.

Figure 6-3 shows the packing fraction and mass decrement as a function of A. The packing fraction and mass decrement are smooth functions of A. If the packing fraction were zero, the binding energy per nucleon would be about 7.6 MeV, this being the average mass excess of neutron and proton. The actual values found indicate that the average binding energy per nucleon varies between about 6 and 8 MeV, as shown in Fig. 6-15.

The fact that both the binding energy per nucleon and the density of nuclear matter are almost independent of A shows the resemblance of nuclei to liquid droplets, where the heat of vaporization and the density of the liquid are independent of the size of the droplet. Pursuing this analogy rather literally, we shall try to express the mass of the stable nuclei as a function of A and Z, in agreement with the experimental facts.

The largest term in the mass will clearly be

$$ZM_p + NM_n = (A - Z)M_n + ZM_p \qquad \textbf{(6-5.1)}$$

However, since nuclei are bound, the nuclear mass must be smaller than this quantity. Since the binding energy per nucleon is almost constant, for a first approximation we should subtract from $(A - Z)M_n + ZM_p$ a positive quantity proportional to A in order to represent the total binding energy. Thus we add to Eq. (6-5.1) the quantity

$$-a_1A = M_1 \qquad a_1 > 0 \qquad \textbf{(6-5.2)}$$

The droplet analogy suggests the possibility of the existence of surface effects. Actually a nucleon near the nuclear surface is not expected to be bound as strongly as a nucleon in the interior, because it has nucleons only on one side instead of all around. In subtracting a_1A, we have thus overcorrected, and we must add a term proportional to the number of nucleons on the nuclear surface, We know that the

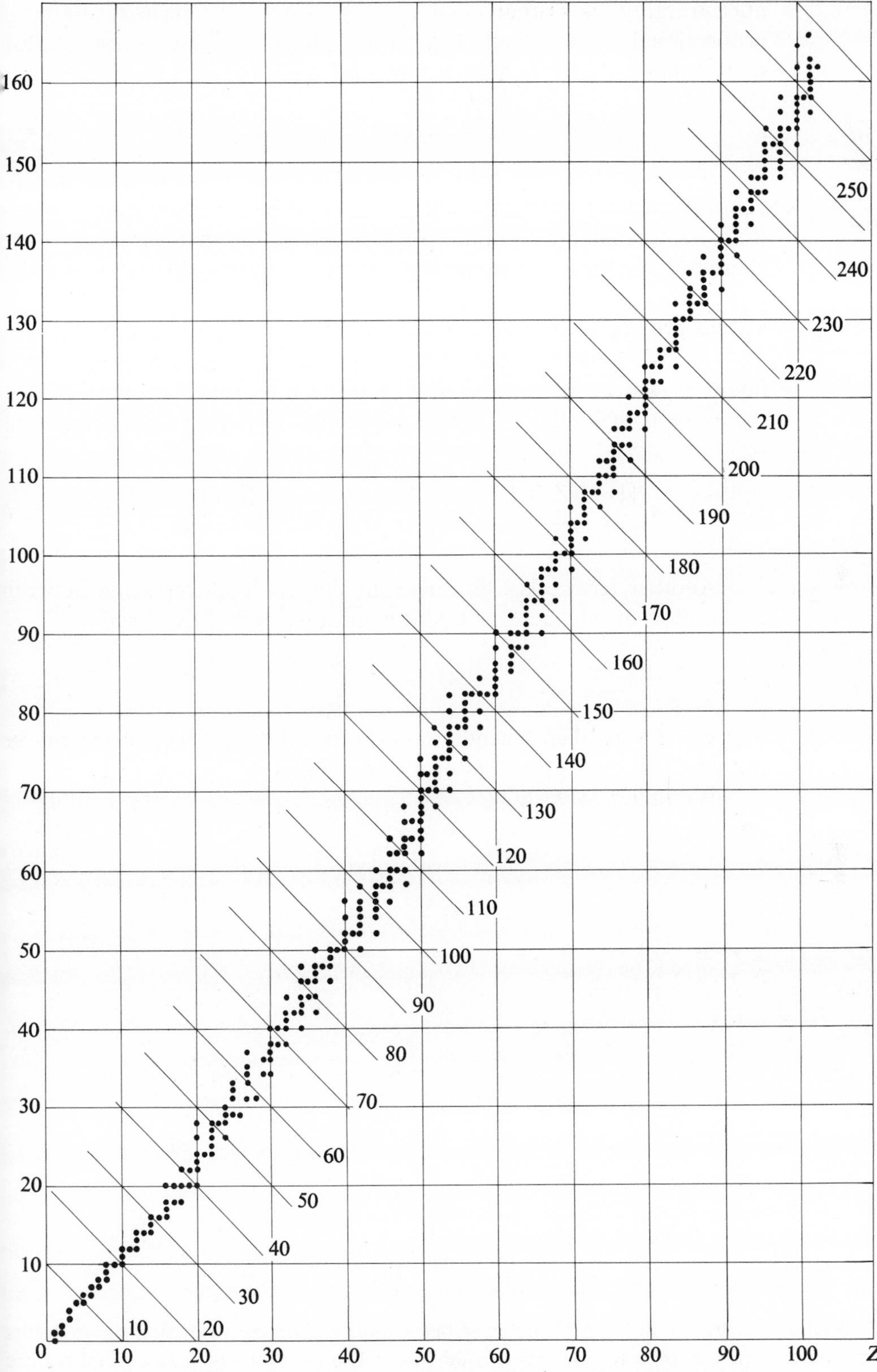

Figure 6-14 Chart of all β-stable nuclei in a Z–N plane.

nuclear radius is proportional to $A^{1/3}$, hence, the nuclear surface is proportional to $A^{2/3}$, and this surface effect will give a contribution to the mass, $+a_2A^{2/3}$, of opposite sign from $-a_1A$. We thus add a term

$$M_2 = a_2A^{2/3} \qquad a_2 > 0 \tag{6-5.3}$$

If we examine Fig. 6-14, we see that there is a tendency for Z to equal N, at least for light nuclei. For heavy nuclei Z becomes smaller than N, because the Coulomb repulsion requires energy to accumulate charge in the nuclear volume. We want to express the fact that there is a tendency to favor $N = Z$. This can be done by adding to the mass a term proportional to A and depending on N/Z, with a minimum for $N = Z$. We want this term to be proportional to A by analogy with a liquid in which, given the composition, the energy is proportional to the amount of liquid. A simple expression satisfying these conditions is

$$M_3 = \tfrac{1}{4}a_3A\frac{[1-(Z/N)]^2}{[1+(Z/N)]^2} = \tfrac{1}{4}a_3\frac{(N-Z)^2}{A} = a_3\frac{[(A/2)-Z]^2}{A} \qquad a_3 > 0 \tag{6-5.4}$$

Another term takes into account the Coulomb repulsion between the protons in the nucleus. It will be positive and of the form

$$M_4 = \xi\frac{Z^2e^2}{r_0A^{1/3}} \tag{6-5.5}$$

where ξ is a number depending on the radial dependence of the charge distribution; e.g., for a uniform density $\xi = \frac{3}{5}$.

We prefer to write

$$M_5 = \frac{a_4Z^2}{A^{1/3}} \qquad a_4 > 0 \tag{6-5.6}$$

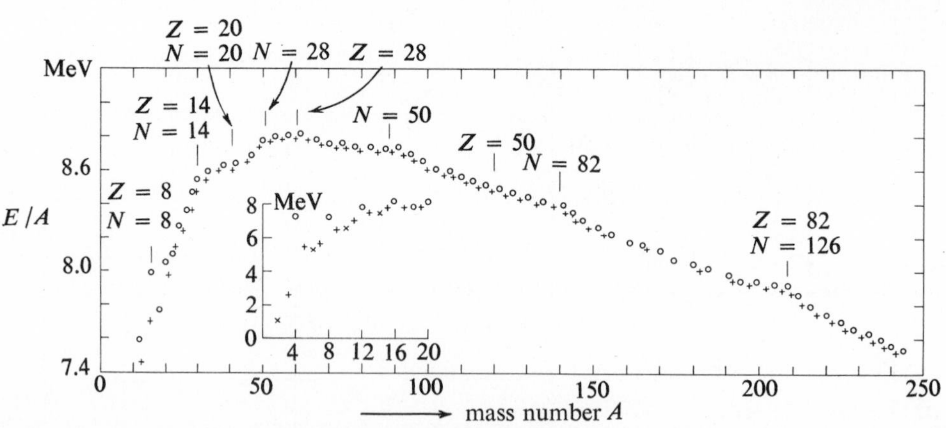

Figure 6-15 Binding energy per nucleon of the most beta-stable isobars as a function of A. Points refer to even-even nuclides, crosses to nuclides of odd mass. The positions of magic numbers are indicated. Insert detailed picture for the lowest masses. Here the four known beta-stable odd-odd nuclides are indicated by oblique crosses. [From A. H. Wapstra.]

Finally there is a term $\delta(A - Z, Z)$ which takes into account the increased stability when N and Z are even, as opposed to cases where either Z or N or both are odd (see Sec. 6-2). The final formula for the atomic mass neglecting the binding energy of the electrons is thus

$$M(A,Z) = (A - Z)\,M_n + ZM_p + Zm_e - a_1A + a_2A^{2/3} + a_3\frac{[(A/2) - Z]^2}{A} + \frac{a_4Z^2}{A^{1/3}} + \delta = 1.008665(A - Z) + 1.007825Z - a_1A + a_2A^{2/3} + a_3\frac{[(A/2) - Z)]^2}{A} + \frac{a_4Z^2}{A^{1/3}} + \delta \qquad \textbf{(6-5.7)}$$

Equation (6-5.7) is called the "Weizsäcker mass formula."

The determination of the constants a_1, a_2, a_3, a_4 must take into account as many facts as possible. For instance, one could take all the measured masses and fit them by a least-squares adjustment of the constants. Considerable effort has been spent on this determination. Green (1953) has calculated a set of constants that is often used (Table 6-3). The units are millimass units (1 mmu = 931.478 keV). $\delta(e, o)$ means δ for $A - Z = N$ even, Z odd, etc.

To study the δ term further, consider isobaric nuclei, which can be transformed one into the other by beta decay (A constant, $\Delta Z = +1$) or by orbital-electron capture or positron emission (A constant, $\Delta Z = -1$). If Eq. (6-5.7) contained all but the last term, as in the case for A odd, where the δ term is zero, the masses of a series of isobars, considered as a function of Z, would have a minimum for a certain value of $Z = Z_0$ and would lie on a parabola on a ZM plane (Fig. 6-16). The only stable nucleus of mass A would then be the one with $Z = Z_0$. Rarely, it may happen that two neighboring nuclei with $Z = Z_0$ and $Z_0 + 1$ or $Z = Z_0$ and $Z_0 - 1$ have very nearly the same energy; thus whereas one is stable the other has such a long life as to be semistable. Strictly speaking, however, only one nucleus of a given odd A is expected to be stable. On examining a table of isotopes we find that this is true.

The situation is different for nuclei with even A. Here we find that there may be several stable isobars, which however have values of Z differing by at least two units. The last term of Eq. (6-5.7) describes this situation. If N and Z are both odd, the masses are increased by δ above the dotted line (Fig. 6-17), which represents Eq. (6-5.7) without the δ term. If N and Z are both even, the mass is decreased by δ and

Table 6-3 Constants for the Weizsäcker Mass Formula

a_1	a_2	a_3	a_4	$\delta(e,o)$	$\delta(o,e)$	$\delta(e,e)$	$\delta(0,0)$
16.710	18.500	100.00	0.750	0	0	$-36A^{-3/4}$	$36A^{-3/4}$

lies on the lower line. It is clear from the figure that under these circumstances there may be more than one beta-stable isotope of mass A, and also that such isotopes must differ by at least two units in Z. These stability rules account for, among other things, the fact that there are no stable isotopes of elements 43 (Tc) and 61 (Pm).

The average accuracy of Eq. (6-5.7) is about 2 MeV except at places where there are strong shell effects (see Sec. 6-4). Figure 6-18 shows the differences between the results of Eq. (6-5.7) with the Green constants and the actual experimental masses.

An interesting application of the mass formula is the determination of the nuclear radius by using it as a parameter in a_2 and a_4 and fitting the constants to the experimental masses. Green obtained a value determined solely by mass measurements of $r_0 = 1.237 \times 10^{-13}$ cm, which is in excellent agreement with the other methods previously mentioned.

Equation (6-5.7) is very useful any time that a panoramic view of nuclear properties is needed. For instance, it gives the relation between A and Z for stable nuclei: by setting $(\partial M/\partial Z)_A = 0$, we obtain the Z for which a series of isobars has the minimum mass. Using Eq. (6-5.7) we have

$$-0.000840 - \frac{2a_3}{A}\left(\frac{A}{2} - Z\right) + a_4 \frac{2Z}{A^{1/3}} = 0 \qquad \textbf{(6-5.8)}$$

which, recalling that $A = Z + N$, we can interpret as the equation of the "curve" of Fig. 6-14. Other interesting applications of Eq. (6-5.7) involve the calculations of the energy released in the fission of heavy nuclei and the calculations of the limits (Fig. 7-7) of alpha stability (see Chap. 7).

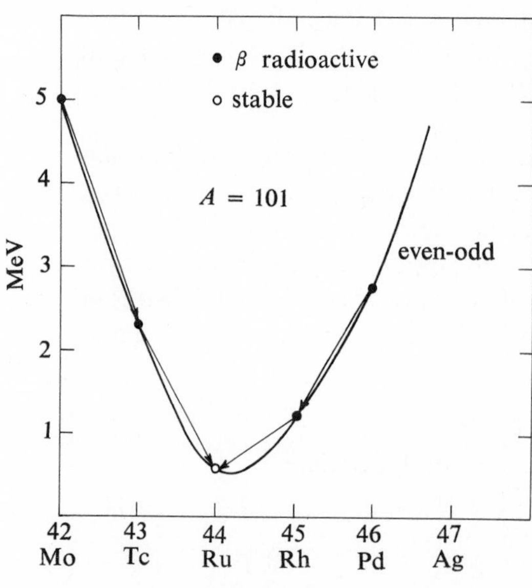

Figure 6-16 Energy (in MeV) of nuclei of mass number 101. The zero point on the energy scale is arbitrary.

Seeger (1961) has used a semiempirical mass formula to compute and tabulate 7479 atomic masses. The formula used is basically similar to Eq. (6-5.7) with a slight modification in the third term but is further corrected to take shell effects into account. The differences between the observed and tabulated masses are shown in Fig. 6-19. This table of masses extends to many nuclides as yet undiscovered.

6-6 Spin and Magnetic Moments I

Definitions and Interaction with a Magnetic Field

Many nuclei show an intrinsic angular momentum, or "spin." This is always a multiple of $\hbar$ for nuclei of even mass number and always an odd multiple of $\hbar/2$ for nuclei of odd mass number, as is to be expected if the nucleus consists of neutrons and protons. The spin in $\hbar$ units is indicated by the vector **I**. We must remember here that **I** has the properties of a quantum-mechanical angular-momentum vector. In particular the measurement of $\mathbf{I}^2$ always gives the result $I(I + 1)$, and the measurement of one component of **I**, say I_z, can give as a result any of the numbers $I, I - 1, \ldots, -I$. A component of **I**, such as I_z and I^2 can be measured simultaneously, but I_x and I_z or two other different components of **I** are not compatible observables. The vector **I** can be treated by the "vector model" as **L**, **S**, and **J** in atomic physics.

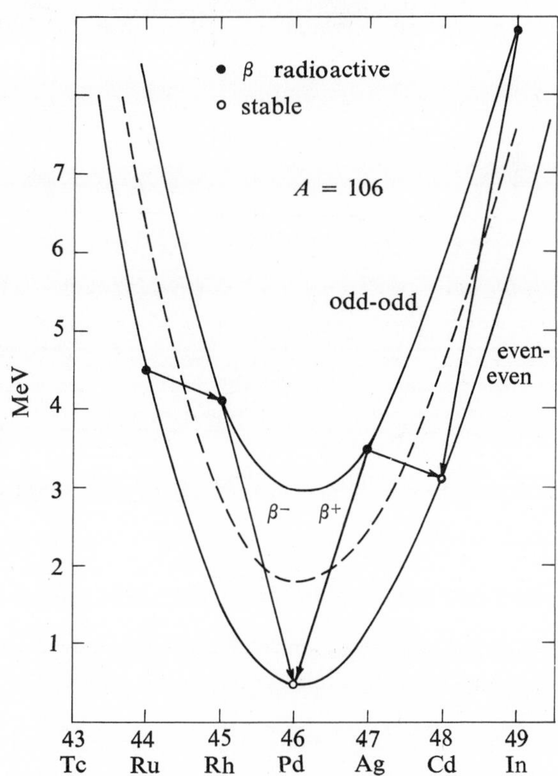

Figure 6-17 Energy (in MeV) of nuclei of mass number 106. The zero point on the energy scale is arbitrary.

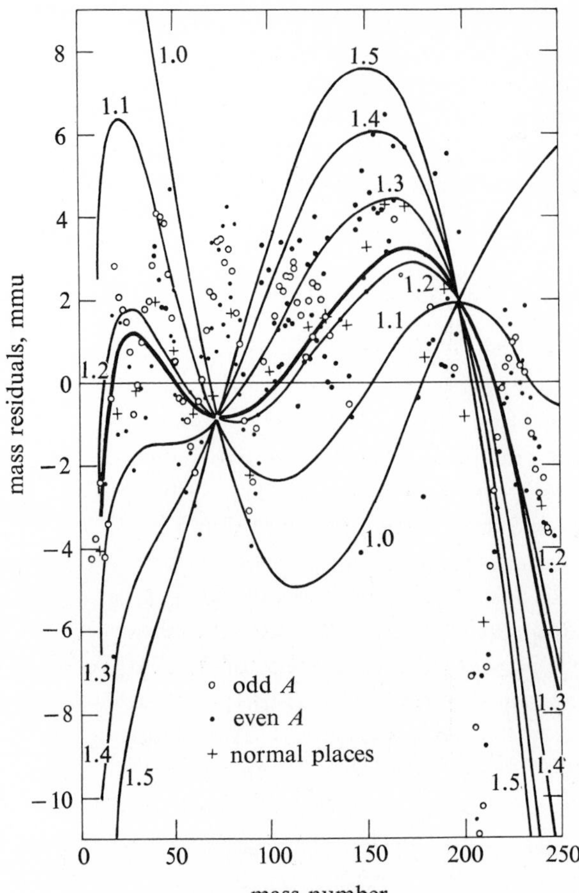

Figure 6-18 The mass residuals of beta-stable nuclides in relation to the semiempirical functions obtained by least squares. The heavy curved line corresponds to the "best" fit to the normal places. The light curved lines represent the best fits attainable when the radius constant is fixed at the values indicated. All points are plotted as deviations from the reference values. [A. E. S. Green, *Rev. Mod. Phys.*, **30**, 569 (1958).]

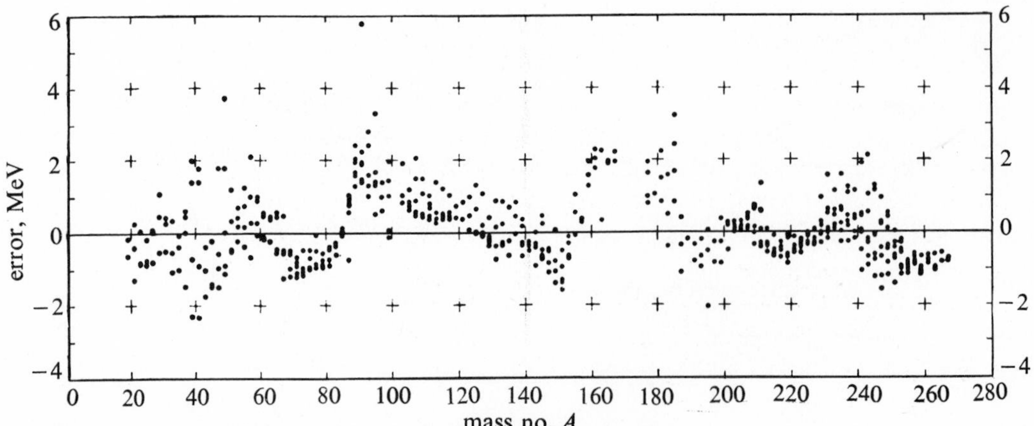

Figure 6-19 Errors of 488 atomic-mass excesses for odd-mass atoms, calculated by Seeger according to his semiempirical mass formula, and plotted against atomic mass number A. [P. A. Seeger, *Nucl. Phys.*, **25**, 1 (1961).]

Its main quantum-mechanical properties are embodied in the commutation relations:

$$I_xI_y - I_yI_x = iI_z \qquad (6\text{-}6.1)$$

$$I_zI^2 - I^2I_z = 0 \qquad (6\text{-}6.2)$$

$$\text{eigenvalue of } I^2 = I(I + 1)$$

$$\text{eigenvalues of } I_z = I, I - 1, \ldots, -I$$

Associated with the spin is a magnetic moment. The magnitude of the magnetic moment μ_I is not quantized and can take any value. The natural unit for measuring magnetic moments is the nuclear magneton

$$\frac{|e|\hbar}{2M_pc} = \mu_n = 0.50505 \pm 0.00002 \times 10^{-23} \text{ erg gauss}^{-1} = \frac{\mu_B}{1{,}836.09}$$

where M_p is the mass of the proton. In addition to the magnetic moment we shall often consider the nuclear g_I number, defined by

$$\frac{\boldsymbol{\mu}_I}{\mu_n} = \mathbf{I}g_I \qquad (6\text{-}6.3)$$

and the gyromagnetic ratio γ_I, defined by

$$\mu_I = \gamma_I \hbar I \qquad (6\text{-}6.4)$$

Note that by convention $g_I > 0$ means nuclear spin and magnetic moment parallel to each other. By a similar convention we call the magnetic moment due to electrons $\boldsymbol{\mu}_J/\mu_B = \mathbf{J}g_J$. The g_J are mostly negative. For instance, an electron in an *s* state has $g_J = -2$ (Fig. 6-20). The sign conventions used in the literature vary.

Historically nuclear spins and magnetic moments were first postulated by Pauli in 1924 to explain the hyperfine structure of the atomic spectral lines. The spin $\frac{1}{2}$ of the proton was recognized by Dennison in 1927.

Proceeding to establish systematically the static electromagnetic properties of nuclei, we consider in general the electromagnetic field produced by a nucleus outside a region containing the nuclear charge. The electric potential produced by a system of charges confined to a region of space can be developed in spherical harmonics. In the special

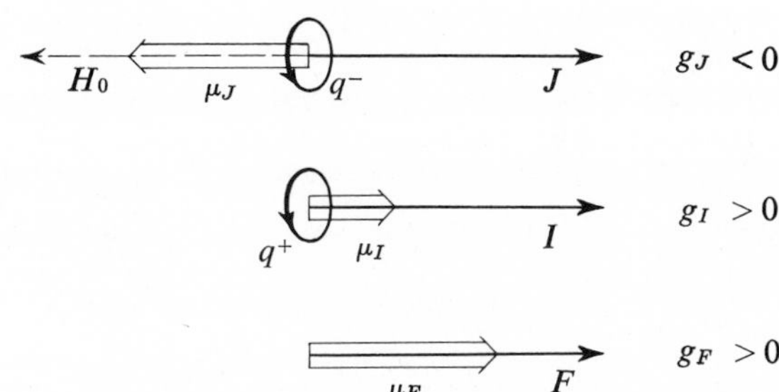

Figure 6-20 Sign conventions for **I**, **J**, **μ**, **H**, and *g* numbers.

case of a nucleus we shall take advantage of the fact that the charges are axially symmetrical around the direction of the spin **I**. Actually it may be considered that the rapid rotation around this axis averages the charge distribution (Fig. 6-21).

The potential outside a region containing the charges obeys the Laplace equation $\nabla^2 V = 0$, which we shall express in polar coordinates. We shall choose as the z axis the axis of rotation (direction of **I**). The potential at a point P outside the nucleus is a function of R and θ, the symmetry around the z axis precluding φ dependence. The potential V thus satisfies the equation

$$\nabla^2 V = \frac{1}{R^2}\frac{\partial}{\partial R}\left(R^2\frac{\partial V}{\partial R}\right) + \frac{1}{R^2 \sin\theta}\frac{\partial}{\partial\theta}\left(\sin\theta\frac{\partial V}{\partial\theta}\right) = 0 \qquad \textbf{(6-6.5)}$$

Now the general solution of Eq. (6-6.5), with the prescribed symmetry, is

$$V(P) = V(R,\theta) = \frac{1}{R}\sum_{n=0}^{\infty}\frac{a_n}{R^n}P_n(\cos\theta) \qquad \textbf{(6-6.6)}$$

where $P_n(\cos\theta)$ is a Legendre polynomial and the a_n are constants dependent on the system of charges producing the potential. The Legendre polynomials may be defined by the identity

$$\sum_{n=0}^{\infty}\left(\frac{r}{R}\right)^n P_n(\cos\theta) \equiv \frac{1}{[1 + (r/R)^2 - 2(r/R)\cos\theta]^{1/2}} \qquad \textbf{(6-6.7)}$$

with $r \leqslant R$. The first three are

$$P_0(\cos\theta) = 1 \qquad P_1(\cos\theta) = \cos\theta \qquad P_2(\cos\theta) = -\tfrac{1}{2} + \tfrac{3}{2}\cos^2\theta \qquad \textbf{(6-6.8)}$$

All P_n have the property

$$P_n(1) = 1 \qquad \textbf{(6-6.9)}$$

In order to find the a_n, consider the potential at a point S on the z axis. Using Eqs. (6-6.6) and (6-6.9) we have

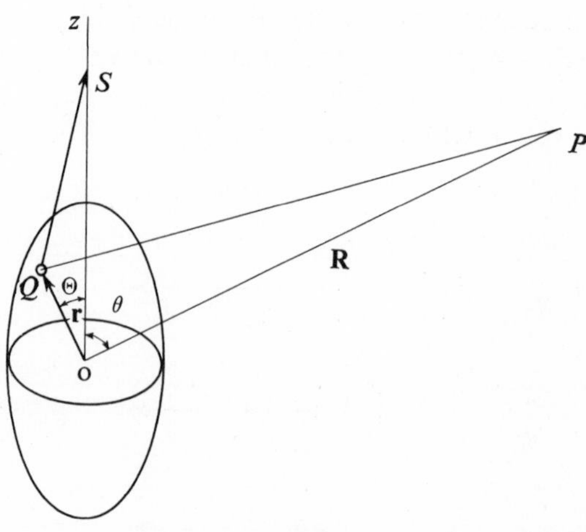

Figure 6-21 Notations relevant to the calculation of the electric potential produced at a point P by a system of charges located near the origin.

$$V(S) = \frac{1}{R} \sum_{n=0}^{\infty} \frac{a_n}{R^n} \tag{6-6.10}$$

We can also calculate $V(S)$ directly (see Fig. 6-21),

$$V(S) = \int \frac{\rho(r)}{r_{SQ}} \, d\tau \tag{6-6.11}$$

or, using Eq. (6-6.7),

$$V(S) = \sum_{n=0}^{\infty} \int \rho(r) \frac{r^n}{R^n} P_n(\cos\Theta) \, d\tau \tag{6-6.12}$$

where $R = OS$, from which by comparison with Eq. (6-6.10) we obtain

$$a_n = \int \rho(r) r^n P_n(\cos\Theta) \, d\tau \tag{6-6.13}$$

Remembering that $r\cos\Theta = z$, we see immediately that

$$a_0 = \int \rho \, d\tau = Ze = \text{charge} \tag{6-6.14}$$

$$a_1 = \int \rho z \, d\tau = \text{electric dipole moment} \tag{6-6.15}$$

$$a_2 = \int \tfrac{1}{2} \rho(3z^2 - r^2) \, d\tau = \tfrac{1}{2} eQ \tag{6-6.16}$$

Equation (6-6.16) defines the quantity Q, dimensionally an area, which is called the magnitude of the nuclear electric quadrupole moment. Similarly, if we consider the electric currents in the nucleus, we can calculate the magnetic vector potential outside the nucleus; this will contain terms corresponding to a magnetic dipole in the nucleus and other, higher terms, which we usually neglect. Experimentally the electric charge, the electric quadrupole moment, and the magnetic dipole moment have been observed and measured extensively. Some examples of magnetic octupoles are also known.

An electric dipole moment cannot appear if the state has a definite parity, that is, when $u_n(x,y,z) = \pm u_n(-x,-y,-z)$. Then the expectation value of z,

$$\langle z \rangle = z_{nn} = \int u_n^* z u_n \, d\tau \tag{6-6.17}$$

is identically zero. Although definite parity is a sufficient, but not a necessary condition for the vanishing of the electric dipole moment, current theories predict a vanishing electric dipole moment for all nuclei. The condition that all motions in the nucleus are "time reversible" (see Chap. 9) is sufficient for this.

We shall now discuss the determination of some of the quantities mentioned above. The electric charge is most directly seen in X-ray spectra or in Rutherford scattering (Sec. 6-1), and we shall not discuss it further. The electric dipole moment of the neutron—according to the results of a direct measurement—(Smith, Purcell, and Ramsey, 1957) is equal to the charge of the electron multiplied by $(-0.1 \pm 2.4) \times 10^{-20}$ cm. Hence, this moment could be exactly zero, in agreement with present theory.

The magnetic dipole moment manifests itself in many phenomena, most directly in the hyperfine structure of spectral lines. Atomic spectral lines, when examined by means of high-resolution apparatus, often show splitting of the order of magnitude of a fraction of a wave number (Fig. 6-22). We have already seen in Sec. 6-2 that different isotopes may radiate light at slightly different spectral frequencies (isotope shift). However, we are concerned here with structures shown in the spectra of monoisotopic substances. The energy levels giving rise to them show what is called a "hyperfine" structure (hfs), to distinguish it from the fine structure due to the electron spin-orbit coupling. The hfs is attributed to the magnetic energy of the magnetic moment of the nucleus immersed in the magnetic field due to the atomic electrons. This magnetic energy is given by

$$W_{\text{mag}} = -\boldsymbol{\mu}_I \cdot \mathbf{H}(0) \qquad \textbf{(6-6.18)}$$

where $\mathbf{H}(0)$ is due to the atomic electrons and possibly to an external field, and the nuclear magnetic moment is considered to be concentrated in a point at the origin of the coordinates. We shall first consider the case where the external field is absent. For the atomic electrons the contribution to the magnetic field by a single s electron is especially important (see Table 6-5). The field $\mathbf{H}$ at the nucleus is antiparallel to the electronic resultant angular momentum $\mathbf{J}$. Using the vector model of the atom (Fig. 6-23) we expect the nuclear spin $\mathbf{I}$ to couple with $\mathbf{J}$ to give a resultant $\mathbf{F}$. The vector $\mathbf{F}$ is fixed in space and takes the values

$$F = I + J, I + J - 1, \ldots, |I - J| \qquad \textbf{(6-6.19)}$$

These are $2J + 1$ or $2I + 1$ values, whichever is smaller. Terms with different $\mathbf{F}$ vectors have slightly different energies and form an hfs multiplet. There is a close analogy between an ordinary multiplet in Russell–Saunders (spin-orbit) coupling and an hfs multiplet. The vectors correspond to each other, as in Table 6-4.

The energy levels of the hfs multiplet are given by

$$\Delta W_{I,J} = \frac{A}{2}[F(F + 1) - I(I + 1) - J(J + 1)] \qquad \textbf{(6-6.20)}$$

Table 6-4 Correspondence between Fine Structure and HFS Multiplets

Ordinary multiplet	Hfs multiplet
L	J
S	I
J	F

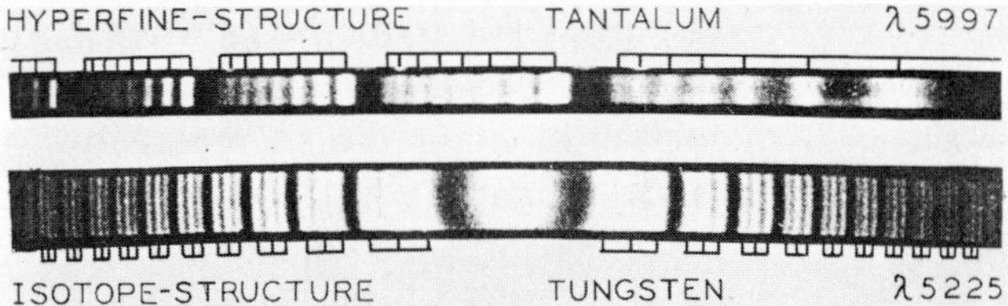

Figure 6-22 Hyperfine structure in the visible spectrum of tantalum. Isotope structure in the visible spectrum of tungsten. [Original from Harvey E. White.]

which is exactly analogous to the ordinary spin-orbit multiplet. Equation (6-6.20) derives from Eq. (6-6.18) as follows: Since **H**(0) is proportional to **J**, we can write it as $H(0)\mathbf{J}/J$; similarly

$$\boldsymbol{\mu}_I = \frac{\mu_I \mathbf{I}}{I} \tag{6-6.21}$$

Substituting in Eq. (6-6.18) we have

$$\Delta W = \frac{-\mu_I H(0)}{IJ} \mathbf{I}\cdot\mathbf{J} = -\mu_I H(0) \cos \mathbf{IJ} \tag{6-6.22}$$

In order to calculate the quantum-mechanical value of cos IJ, we note that

$$\mathbf{F} = \mathbf{I} + \mathbf{J} \tag{6-6.23}$$

or, squaring and isolating $\mathbf{J}\cdot\mathbf{I}$,

$$\mathbf{I}\cdot\mathbf{J} = IJ \cos IJ = \tfrac{1}{2}(F^2 - I^2 - J^2) \tag{6-6.24}$$

The quantum-mechanical vectors **F**, **I**, and **J** give as expectation value for F^2 the numbers $F(F + 1)$, etc. Substituting in Eq. (6-6.24) we find for the expectation value of IJ cos IJ,

$$\tfrac{1}{2}[F(F + 1) - I(I + 1) - J(J + 1)] = \frac{C}{2} \tag{6-6.25}$$

Equation (6-6.25) inserted in Eq. (6-6.22) gives

$$\Delta W_{I,J} = \frac{-\mu_I}{2}\frac{H(0)}{IJ}\; F(F+1) - I(I + 1) - J(J + 1)] = \frac{A}{2}C \tag{6-6.26}$$

with

$$A = -\mu_I \frac{H(0)}{IJ} \tag{6-6.27}$$

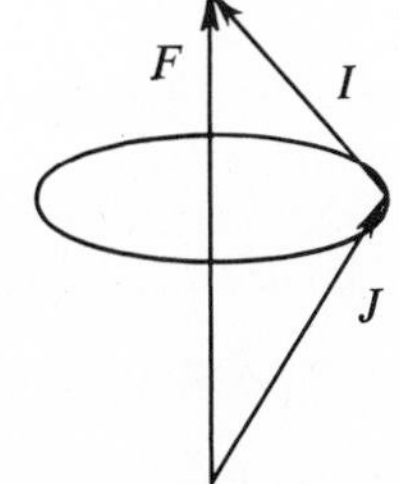

Figure 6-23 Vector model for an atom having nuclear spin. **J** is the total angular momentum of the electrons, **I** the nuclear spin, and **F** the total angular momentum of the atom.

The sign of A is such that when $H(0)$ and $\mathbf{J}$ are antiparallel, as usually happens (because of the negative electron charge), then for a positive nuclear moment the energy is lowest when $\boldsymbol{\mu}_I$ is parallel to $\mathbf{H}(0)$ and hence antiparallel to J.

If we introduce in Eq. (6-6.26) the values of F given by Eq. (6-6.19), we obtain the levels of the hfs multiplet. These obey the interval rule, which states that the intervals in an hfs multiplet are in the ratios

$$I + J : I + J - 1 \cdots |I - J| + 1 \qquad \textbf{(6-6.28)}$$

It is clear that the analysis of an hfs multiplet will give the value of I simply by counting the number of components if $J \geqslant I$; if $J < I$, application of the interval rule or measurement of the intensity of spectral lines gives I if J is known.

The calculation of $H(0)$ is a problem of atomic physics; the solution is simple in the case of a single s electron outside a closed shell, as, for instance, in the ground state of an alkali atom. This case is of practical importance. One obtains

$$H(0) = -\tfrac{8}{3}\pi\mu_B\,|\psi(0)|^2 \qquad \textbf{(6-6.29)}$$

where μ_B is the Bohr magneton.[1] Equation (6-6.29) can be made plausible by a semiclassical argument as follows: We assume that the Schrödinger ψ is associated not only with an electric-charge density but also with a magnetization intensity; an element of volume $d\tau$ has associated with it a magnetic moment $-\mu_B|\psi(x)|^2\,d\tau\,\mathbf{k}$, where $\mathbf{k}$ is a unit vector in the spin direction. We must now calculate the field produced at the origin. To obtain the correct answer, we cannot use the scalar potential but must use the vector potential. The physical reason for this is that the electron spin corresponds to a current loop and not to a permanent dipole.

● The vector potential from our electron distribution is given by

$$-\mu_B \int |\psi(r)|^2\,\mathbf{k} \times \nabla \frac{1}{r}\,d\tau = \mathbf{A} \qquad \textbf{(6-6.30)}$$

To calculate

$$\nabla \times \mathbf{A} = \mathbf{H} \qquad \textbf{(6-6.31)}$$

we exchange the order of integration and differentiation in Eqs. (6-6.30) and (6-6.31) and use the vector equation

$$\int \nabla \times \mathbf{a}\,d\tau = -\int \mathbf{a} \times \frac{\mathbf{r}}{r}\,d\sigma \qquad \textbf{(6-6.32)}$$

We have then

$$\mathbf{H} = \mu_B \int |\psi(r)|^2 \left(\mathbf{k} \times \nabla \frac{1}{r}\right) \times \frac{\mathbf{r}}{r}\,d\sigma \qquad \textbf{(6-6.33)}$$

[1] The minus sign means that the direction of the spin and of J are antiparallel.

with $d\sigma = r^2\, d\Omega$ and $\nabla(1/r) = -\mathbf{r}/r^3$. The rule for the double vector product

$$(\mathbf{v}_1 \times \mathbf{v}_2) \times \mathbf{v}_3 = \mathbf{v}_2(\mathbf{v}_1 \cdot \mathbf{v}_3) - \mathbf{v}_1(\mathbf{v}_2 \cdot \mathbf{v}_3) \tag{6-6.34}$$

gives

$$\mathbf{H} = \mu_B \int |\psi(r)|^2 \left[\left(-\frac{\mathbf{r}}{r}\left(\mathbf{k} \cdot \frac{\mathbf{r}}{r}\right)\right) + \mathbf{k}\right] d\Omega \tag{6-6.35}$$

Introducing unit vectors **i**, **j**, and **k**,

$$\frac{\mathbf{r}}{r} = \sin\theta \sin\varphi \mathbf{i} + \sin\theta \cos\varphi \mathbf{j} + \cos\theta\, \mathbf{k} \tag{6-6.36}$$

we obtain

$$\mathbf{k} - \frac{\mathbf{r}}{r^2}(\mathbf{k} \cdot \mathbf{r}) = \mathbf{k}(1 - \cos^2\theta) - \mathbf{i} \sin\theta \cos\theta \cos\varphi$$
$$- \mathbf{j} \sin\theta \cos\theta \cos\varphi \tag{6-6.37}$$

Integrating in $d\Omega = \sin\theta\, d\theta\, d\varphi$ over a small sphere containing the origin, the terms involving **i** and **j** vanish and the **k** term gives

$$\mathbf{H} = \mathbf{k}\mu_B \int_0^{\pi} |\psi(r)|^2\, 2\pi \sin^3\theta\, d\theta \tag{6-6.38}$$

Performing the integration and then replacing $\psi(r)$ by $\psi(0)$, we obtain

$$H(0) = -\frac{8\pi}{3}\mu_B |\psi(0)|^2 \tag{6-6.39}$$

It is useful to express $\psi(0)$ in a simple way that is a fair approximation. Such an expression [see, e.g., (Ko 58)] is

$$|\psi(0)|^2 = \frac{1}{\pi a^3} \frac{Z(1+z)^2}{n^2_{\text{eff}}} \tag{6-6.40}$$

where a is Bohr's hydrogen-atom radius, Z is the atomic number of the nucleus, z is the degree of ionization of the atom, and n_{eff} is the effective quantum number. The accuracy of this formula for $|\psi(0)|^2$ is of the order of 10 per cent. ●

As an example we give in Table 6-5 some values of $H(0)$ for the

Table 6-5 Magnetic Field at the Nucleus Produced by the Atomic Electrons

Atom	$^2S_{1/2}$, n	$H(0)$, gauss	n	$H(0)$, gauss	$H(0)$, gauss
H	1	1.74×10^5		$^2P_{1/2}$	$^2P_{3/2}$
Li	2	1.3×10^5			
Na	3	4.4×10^5	3	4.2×10^4	2.5×10^4
K	4	6.3×10^5	4	7.9×10^4	4.6×10^4
Rb	5	1.3×10^6	5	1.6×10^5	8.6×10^4
Cs	6	2.1×10^6	6	2.8×10^5	1.3×10^5

ground state of the alkali atoms where the field is due to one s electron and also for the ^2P states where the field is due to a p electron.

Thus far we have considered the nucleus as interacting only with the atomic electrons, in the absence of external fields. It is important also to consider how the hfs multiplet is affected by the perturbation caused by a constant external magnetic field H_e. We must distinguish two limiting cases in which the external field is such that

$$\frac{|\mu_B g_J \mathbf{J}\cdot\mathbf{H}_e|}{|\boldsymbol{\mu}_I\cdot\mathbf{H}(0)|} \gg 1 \text{ or } \ll 1 \tag{6-6.41}$$

The first case corresponds to the atomic Zeeman splitting of a level large compared with the hfs splitting; the second corresponds to the Zeeman splitting small compared with hfs splitting. For the first limiting case (strong field) the vector diagram is that shown in Fig. 6-24a, and the magnetic energy is

$$\Delta W = (-m_I g_I \mu_n - m_J g_J \mu_B) H_e \tag{6-6.42}$$

where the first term is negligible compared with the second. To the magnetic energy must be added the energy of the interaction between I and J. The approximate result is

$$\Delta W = -m_J g_J \mu_B H_e + A m_I m_J \tag{6-6.43}$$

In the second case (weak field) the vector diagram of the atom is given by Fig. 6-24b. The hfs multiplet undergoes a Zeeman effect with a magnetic energy given by

$$\begin{aligned}\Delta W &= -H_e F \cos FH_e[(J/F)\mu_B g_J \cos JF + (I/F)\mu_n g_I \cos IF] \\ &\simeq -\mu_B g_F m_F H_e\end{aligned} \tag{6-6.44}$$

where m_F indicates, as usual, $F \cos FH_e$. The second term in parentheses is about 2,000 times smaller than the first and can be neglected.

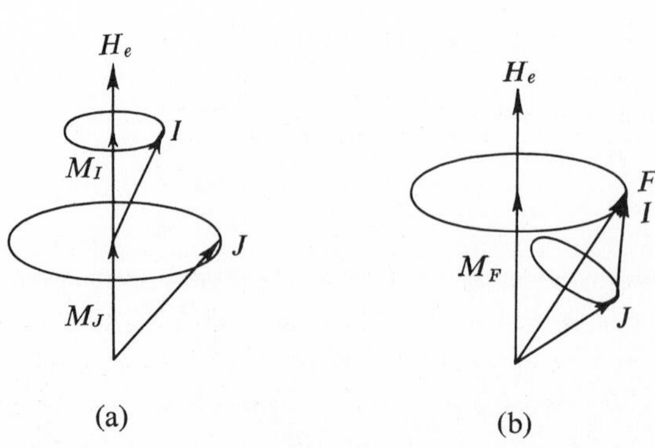

Figure 6-24 (a) Vector diagram of an atom with nuclear spin in a strong magnetic field. The interactions $\mathbf{I}\cdot\mathbf{H}_e$ and $\mathbf{J}\cdot\mathbf{H}_e$ are large compared to the $\mathbf{I}\cdot\mathbf{J}$ interaction. I and J precess independently around H_e. (b) Vector diagram of an atom with nuclear spin in a weak magnetic field. The interaction between $\mathbf{J}$ and $\mathbf{H}_e$ is small compared to the $\mathbf{J}\cdot\mathbf{I}$ interaction. I and J precess around F, which in turn precesses around H_e.

Using the quantum-mechanical expression for the cosines, we can then write

$$g_F = g_J \frac{F(F+1) + J(J+1) - I(I+1)}{2F(F+1)} \tag{6-6.45}$$

Figure 6-25 gives the magnetic energy, calculated exactly, also for intermediate fields.

The atomic magnetic moment can be defined by

$$\mu_{\text{eff}} = \frac{\partial W}{\partial H_e} \tag{6-6.46}$$

This is given in Fig. 6-26 for the cesium atom. For a given hfs multiplet the atomic magnetic moment is a function of F, m_F, and H, and, for certain values of the field, it may vanish.

Radiative transitions between different hfs levels are subject to selection rules similar to those governing ordinary multiplets (refer to Fig. 6-27). In the case of electric dipole radiation (see Chap. 8), in the absence of an external field, we have

$$\Delta F = \pm 1, 0 \tag{6-6.47}$$

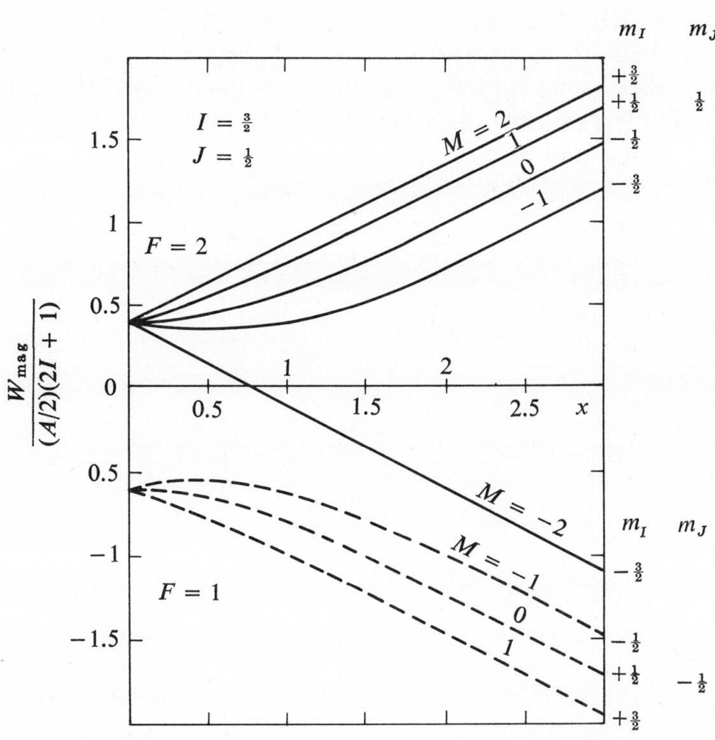

Figure 6-25 Variation of energy levels with magnetic field H of an atom in a $^2S_{1/2}$ state for a nuclear spin of $\frac{3}{2}$. The solid and dashed lines correspond to the levels arising from the states $F = 2$ and $F = 1$, respectively. The parameter x is $(-\mu_J J + \mu_I I)\, H/\Delta W \sim \mu_B H/\Delta W$, where ΔW is the energy difference between states $F = 2$ and $F = 1$ at zero magnetic field: $\Delta W = (A/2)(2I+1)$ [see Eq. (6-6.20).]

In the presence of an external magnetic field, if the field is weak, we have

$$\Delta m_F = 0 \tag{6-6.48}$$

for components polarized parallel to the field (π components) and

$$\Delta m_F = \pm 1 \tag{6-6.49}$$

for components polarized perpendicular to the field (σ components). In the case of a strong field we have

$$\Delta m_I = 0 \tag{6-6.50}$$

$$\Delta m_J = 0 \text{ for } \pi \text{ components} \tag{6-6.51}$$

$$\Delta m_J = \pm 1 \text{ for } \sigma \text{ components} \tag{6-6.52}$$

In every case the parity must change. All this is shown in Fig. 6-27. For magnetic dipole radiation we have the same selection rules, except that the parity must not change.

6-7 Spin and Magnetic Moments II

Methods of Measurement

In the preceding section we briefly outlined the spectroscopic method of measuring spin and magnetic moment. This method was the first to be used and it is still important. However, over the years different techniques have been invented. In particular, O. Stern, I. I. Rabi, and others have developed methods based on the application of

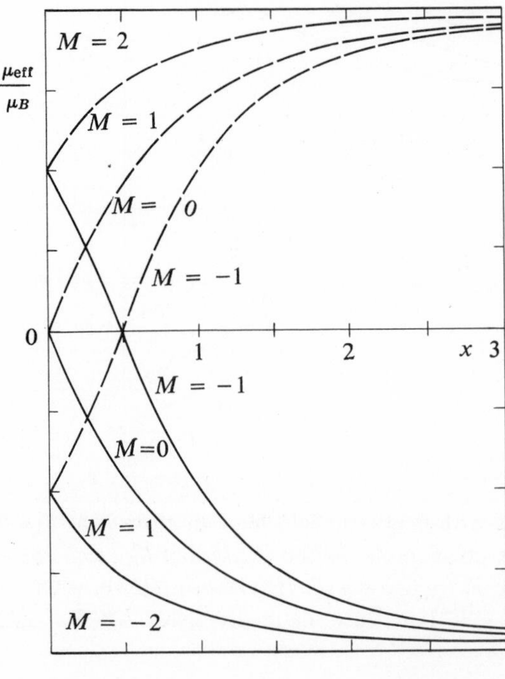

Figure 6-26 Dependence (on the magnetic field) of the magnetic moment of an atom in a $^2S_{1/2}$ state with a nuclear spin of $\frac{3}{2}$. The solid lines refer to M levels of the state $F = 2$ and the dashed lines to $F = 1$ levels. x has the same meaning as in Fig. 6-25.

molecular beams. These are beams of molecules moving in a vacuum (Fig. 6-28); as the figure indicates, the molecules leave the oven O, are collimated by the slit S, and are finally detected at the detector D. The detector may have a variety of forms; for instance, it may be a hot wire that ionizes impinging molecules, or a Pirani manometer in which the molecules are trapped and which shows an increase in pressure, or it may be a detector of radioactivity if the substance used is radioactive. The molecule in the free beam can be subjected to forces and hence can be deflected. In the original experiment of Stern and Gerlach silver atoms were sent into an inhomogeneous magnetic field and were deflected in the z direction by a force

$$F = \mu_{\text{eff}} \frac{\partial H_z}{\partial z} \tag{6-7.1}$$

where $\partial H_z/\partial z$ is called the inhomogeneity of the field. This force produces a deflection that can be calculated from elementary mechanics; we have immediately

$$\ddot{z} = \mu_{\text{eff}} \frac{\partial H_z}{\partial z} \frac{1}{M} \tag{6-7.2}$$

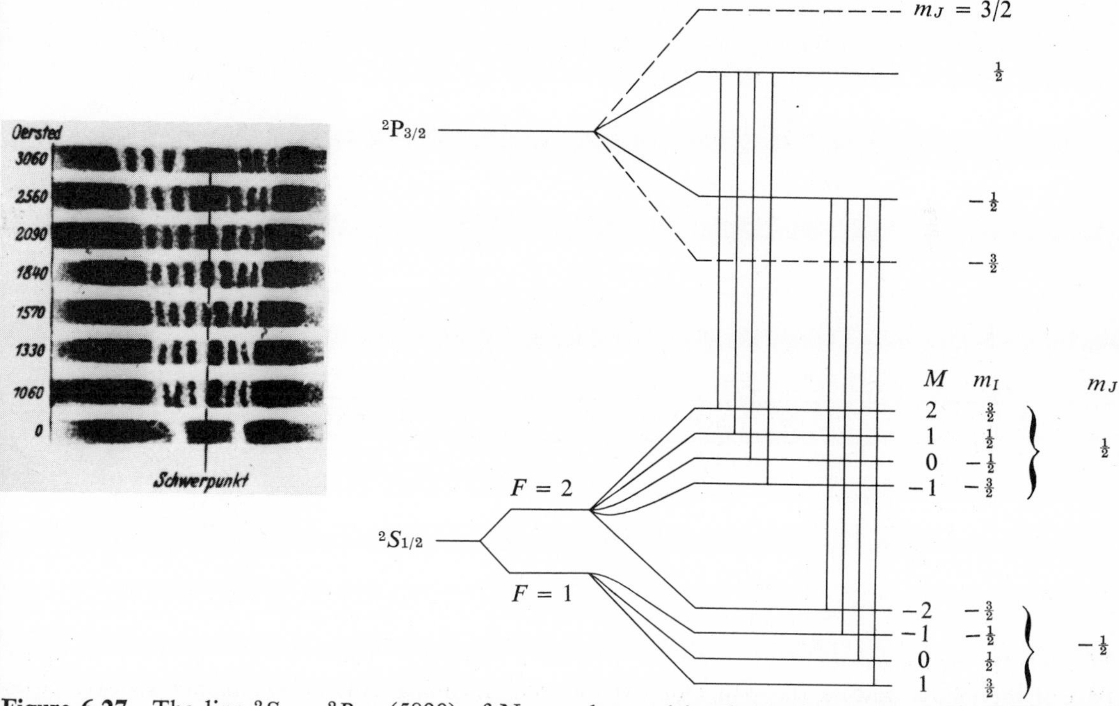

Figure 6-27 The line $^2S_{1/2} - {}^2P_{3/2}$ (5890) of Na as observed in absorption. The nuclear spin $I = \frac{3}{2}$ splits the terms as indicated in the right side of the figure. Note that in the $^2P_{3/2}$ term the hfs is so small that the strong external field case applies always. The observations have been made for various values of an external field H as indicated in the right part of the figure. [D. A. Jackson and H. Kuhn, *Proc. Roy. Soc.* (*London*), **167,** 210 (1938).]

$$z = \tfrac{1}{2}\mu_{\text{eff}} \frac{\partial H_z}{\partial z} \frac{1}{M}\left(\frac{x}{v}\right)^2 \tag{6-7.3}$$

where x is the length of the field, M the mass of the molecule, and v its velocity.

Now, if molecules are deflected from the beam, the beam intensity decreases and this is experimentally detectable. Subjecting the molecules to a magnetic field H_z having an inhomogeneity $\partial H_z/\partial z$ thus results, in general, in a decrease of intensity in the undeflected beam. However, if H_z is such that $\mu_{\text{eff}}(H_z) = 0$, the intensity does not decrease and, as a function of H, it has a maximum value because the beam is undeflected. The field value at which this occurs can be seen in Fig. 6-26 for a special case. This experiment thus gives $H_e/\Delta W$ or A. In order to find μ_I, we still need information about the atomic field of the nucleus, according to Eq. (6-6.26).

There are other methods, developed by Rabi and his group, which

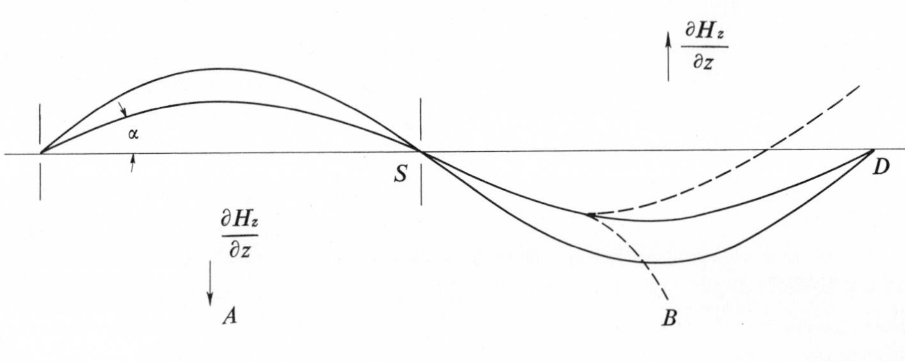

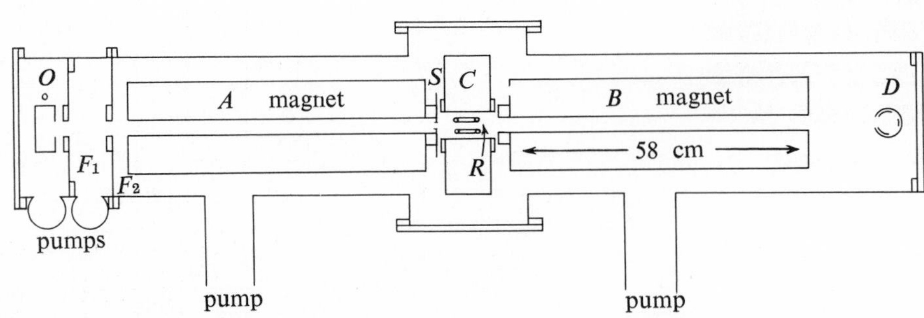

Figure 6-28 Schematic diagram of a molecular-beam apparatus. The two solid curves in the upper part of the figure indicate the paths of two molecules having different moments and velocities and whose moments are not changed during passage through the apparatus. The two dashed curves in the region of the B magnet indicate the possible changes in path for one of these molecules if its component of magnetic moment has been either increased or decreased in the region of the C field. The motion in the z direction has, in each of the curves, been greatly exaggerated. [J. B. M. Kellogg and S. Millman, *Rev. Mod. Phys.*, **18**, 323 (1946).]

dispense with this requirement. These involve measuring the interactions of the nucleus with an externally applied, directly measurable field. The method is illustrated in Fig. 6-28. A beam is deflected in the inhomogeneous magnetic field A and refocused on the detector D by the inhomogeneous field B. Between the A and B fields is a C field that has a constant component H_z and a component perpendicular to it, variable in time, proportionally to sin ωt. This component induces transitions between various levels of the hfs multiplet according to the selection rules given in Sec. 6-6 when the frequency ω is such that resonance occurs—in other words, such that the energy difference between the levels is equal to the energy of the quanta of the field, $\hbar\omega$. Equation (6-6.42) gives, for instance, in the case of strong field, the resonance condition

$$\hbar\omega = g_I \mu_n H_z \Delta m_I \tag{6-7.4}$$

When such transitions occur, the B magnet may not refocus, because the molecule has changed magnetic moment and the beam arriving at D is weakened. As can be seen from Eq. (6-7.4) the g_I factor can be determined solely from the external field, H_z, and ω.

This method can give extremely precise results. In particular, the diatomic molecules of the hydrogen isotopes have been analyzed in great detail by this method (Kellogg, Rabi, Ramsey, and Zacharias, 1934). The same principle has also been applied by Alvarez and Bloch (1939) to the free neutron; and recently many radioactive nuclei also have been investigated by it. In the latter instances the molecular-beam intensity was determined by measuring the radioactivity deposited on a catcher target.

Another method for measuring magnetic moments, developed by Bloch and Hansen (1946) and independently by Purcell (1946), employs bulk amounts of matter. A simplified, schematic version of the form developed by Bloch is as follows (Fig. 6-29). Suppose that we have some ordinary water and that we consider the hydrogen nuclei in a

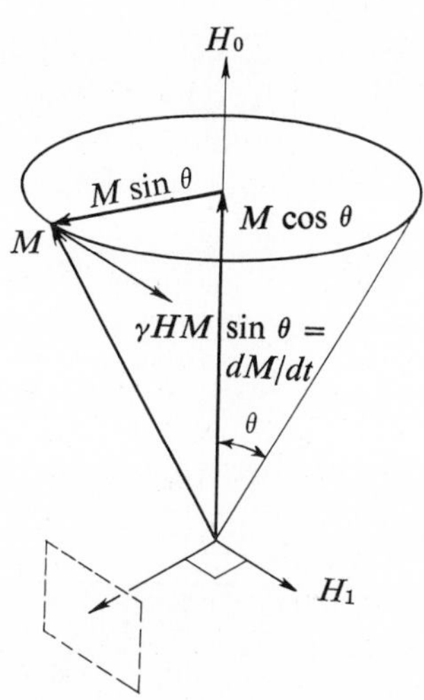

Figure 6-29 Schematic diagram of spin precession in a magnetic field and the Bloch method of measuring magnetic moments.

constant magnetic field H_0 in the z direction. Because of the Boltzmann factor there are more protons oriented with their magnetic moment parallel than antiparallel to the field. This gives rise to a very small average magnetization of matter in bulk, given by Langevin's theory,

$$P_0 = N\mu_I{}^2 \frac{H}{kT} \frac{I+1}{I} = \chi_0 H_0 \tag{6-7.5}$$

where N is the number of nuclei per cm³ and P_0, the magnetization, is the magnetic moment per unit volume. This magnetization would be imperceptibly small if we tried to measure it by a static-field method. If, however, we apply a field that rotates in a plane perpendicular to H_0, we can render it observable. Consider classically the mechanical angular momentum per unit volume $\mathbf{M}$ associated with P_0; according to Eq. (6-6.4) it is

$$\gamma\mathbf{M} = \mathbf{P}_0 \tag{6-7.6}$$

with γ equal to the gyromagnetic ratio.

The equation of motion for $\mathbf{M}$ (per unit volume) is

$$\frac{d\mathbf{M}}{dt} = \text{torque} = \gamma\mathbf{M} \times \mathbf{H} \tag{6-7.7}$$

Bloch showed that Eq. (6-7.7) is also valid in quantum mechanics if we interpret $\mathbf{M}$ as the average value of the angular momentum and $\gamma\mathbf{M}$ as the average value of the magnetic moment.

For constant H_0 we have, taking the dot product of both sides by $\mathbf{M}$ that $d(M^2)/dt = 0$ or M^2 = constant; similarly taking the dot product by $\mathbf{H}$ we have $\mathbf{M}\cdot\mathbf{H}$ = constant. The conclusion is that $\mathbf{M}$ precesses around $\mathbf{H}_0$ with a period T such that [Fig. 6-29 and Eq. (6-7.7)]

$$T\gamma M H_0 \sin\theta = 2\pi M \sin\theta \tag{6-7.8}$$

i.e., with a circular frequency

$$\gamma H_0 = \omega_L \tag{6-7.9}$$

If we use a reference system with the z axis on H_0 and rotating around H_0 with a frequency ω_L, the motion is the same as that which would occur without $\mathbf{H}_0$ in a nonrotating system (Larmor's theorem). Now add a small field $\mathbf{H}_1$ normal to $\mathbf{H}_0$ and rotating with a frequency ω. If $\omega \neq \omega_L$, the field $\mathbf{H}_1$ will sometimes tend to increase θ and will sometimes tend to decrease it, having on the average no effect. If $\omega = \omega_L$, this field will follow the vector $\mathbf{M}$ and will act on it as a constant field, tending to vary the angle θ. Thus for $\omega = \omega_L$ the angle θ after a while will become large, and $\mathbf{M}$ will precess on cones of increasing aperture, executing complete rotations about the z axis until it becomes antiparallel to z. From there it again starts to precess until it once more becomes parallel to the z axis, and so on (Fig. 6-30). In practice the small field $\mathbf{H}$ is not a rotating field but an alternating field in the y direction, varying as $\mathbf{H}_1 \cos \omega t$. This field is equivalent to two fields of amplitude

$\frac{1}{2}\mathbf{H}_1$ and rotating at angular frequences of $+\omega$ and $-\omega$ around the z axis. Of these only one is effective if $\omega = \omega_L$; the other can be neglected because for it $\omega = -\omega_L$ and hence is out of resonance. When $\mathbf{M}$ forms a large angle with $\mathbf{H}_0$, it can induce an emf of frequency ω_L in a fixed coil lying in a plane parallel to $\mathbf{H}_0$ and perpendicular to H_1. The induced emf is detected, and from the value of $\mathbf{H}_0$ and of the frequency ω_L one finds, using Eq. (6-7.9), the value of γ. In the Purcell method the resonance is detected by measuring the radiofrequency energy absorbed in the material placed in a magnetic field. This absorption has a sharp maximum when the radiofrequency coincides with the ω_L.

In this oversimplified description we have not yet considered the very important role of the relaxation times of the substance. The study of relaxation times and other peculiarities of these phenomena has extensive ramifications in chemistry, in studies of molecular structure, and in solid-state physics. The method has undergone many developments and is now extensively applied even in the measurement of magnetic fields (using the known magnetic moment of hydrogen). Figure 6-31 is a diagram of a typical apparatus for measuring magnetic moments by the Purcell method.

The methods described above give the spin and magnetic moment

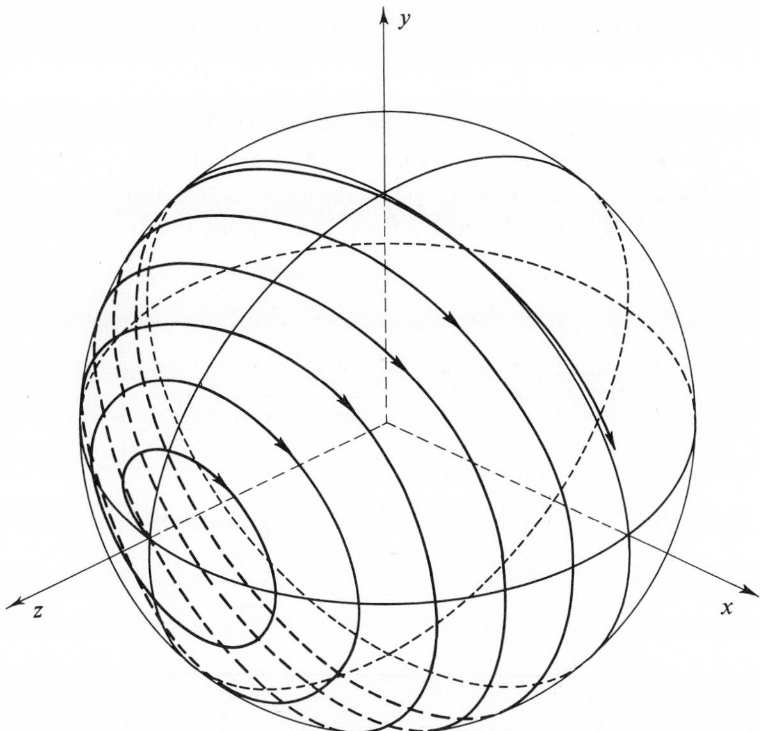

Figure 6-30 Trajectory of the end point of the magnetic polarization vector of hydrogen nuclei subject to an alternating field at the resonance frequency. The strong field is in the z direction, the alternating field in the x or y direction. The relaxation time is infinite. [From (Fl E).]

of stable and radioactive nuclei. Another group of methods applies only to radioactive nuclei, and especially to short-lived states (see also Chap. 8). We shall explain them by a simplified example that will show the essential principles of the method. Suppose that the nucleus has three levels connected by two gamma rays in cascade and that the intermediate state has a mean life τ. With two counters in coincidence we find the probability that the two gamma rays of the cascade will form an angle between θ and $\theta + d\theta$. This probability has the form

$$P(\theta)\,d\theta = A + B\cos^2\theta + \cdots \tag{6-7.10}$$

a series with even powers of $\cos\theta$. For the sake of simplicity we shall stop at the term in $\cos^2\theta$. The existence of an angular correlation is explained by the fact that in the first gamma emission the nucleus is left with its spin in a direction correlated with the direction of the outgoing gamma. For instance, in a macroscopic dipole radio antenna the quanta are emitted preferentially in a direction perpendicular to the antenna. Thus the emission of the first quantum gives some information on the nuclear orientation. The second quantum is then emitted anisotropically with respect to the first, because an oriented nucleus emits, in general, gamma rays in a pattern which is oriented with respect to the spin.

Now introduce a magnetic field **H** perpendicular to the plane in which we measure the correlation. This field will force the spins of the intermediate state to precess with an angular velocity

$$\omega_I = g_I \mu_n \frac{H}{\hbar} \tag{6-7.11}$$

and during the mean life of the intermediate state τ the spin will rotate through an angle $\omega_I\tau$. The angular correlation will thus change, the angle θ being replaced by $\theta - \omega_I\tau$, and at the same time a damping of

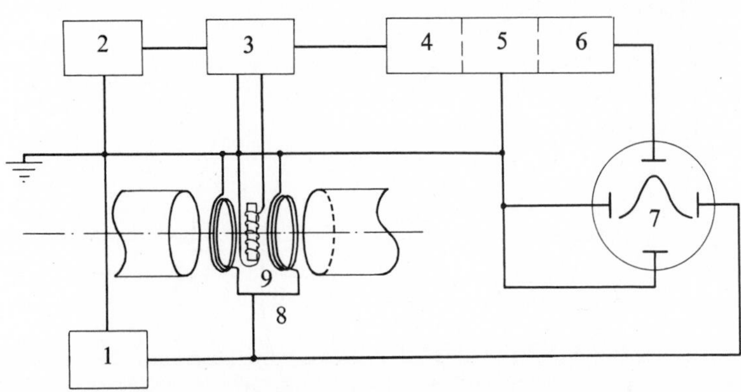

Figure 6-31 Principle of a Purcell apparatus for observing nuclear precession motions: 1, low-frequency generator; 2, high-frequency generator; 3, bridge; 4, high-frequency amplifier; 5, high-frequency rectifier; 6, low-frequency amplifier; 7, oscilloscope; 8, Helmholtz coils; 9, solenoid on sample.

the correlation occurs, because different nuclei emit the gamma rays at different times. $P(\theta)$ is replaced by

$$P(H,\theta,T) = \int_0^T P(\theta - \omega_I t)\, e^{-t/\tau}\, \frac{dt}{\tau} \Big/ \int_0^T e^{-t/\tau} \frac{dt}{\tau} \qquad \textbf{(6-7.12)}$$

where T is the time during which the apparatus is sensitive after the emission of the first quantum. By varying T and H, it is possible to determine, in favorable cases, both τ and g_I. The method has many variations. It is useful in dealing with problems in solid-state physics because in the field H one must also consider crystalline fields. It has been applied to Cd^{111} and several other radioactive nuclides (Fig. 6-32).

Finally it has become possible, in some cases, to observe the nuclear Zeeman effect directly by using nuclear "recoilless" emission (see Chap. 8).

6-8 Electric Quadrupole Moments

The first indication of nuclear electric quadrupole moments came when it was found that the interval rule did not apply to the hfs multiplet (Schmidt and Schüler, 1935). We shall now calculate classically the energy due to an electric quadrupole moment of the nucleus. The electric field due to the atomic electrons has J as a cylindrical axis of symmetry. The nuclear charge has a cylindrical symmetry axis in I. We introduce two coordinate systems, the atomic one with the z axis parallel to J and the nuclear one with the ζ axis parallel to I.

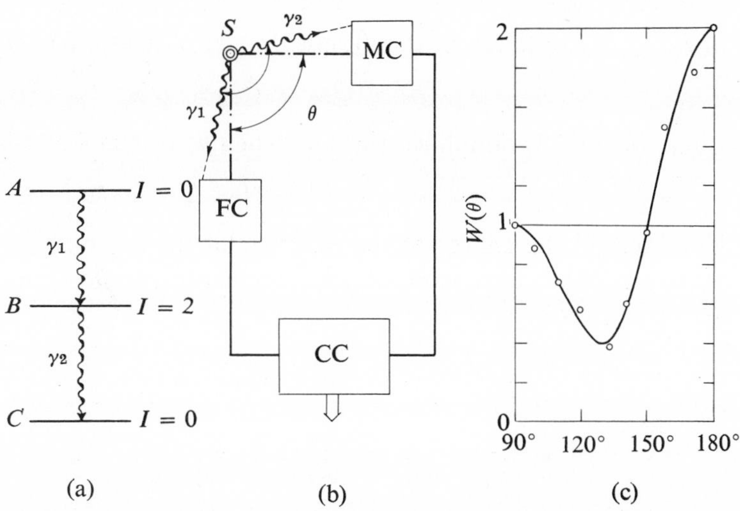

Figure 6-32 Example of a directional correlation measurement: (a) level diagram; (b) apparatus: *S*, source; *FC*, fixed counter; *MC*, movable counter; *CC*, coincidence circuit; (c) result. [H. Frauenfelder in (Si 55).]

The electrostatic energy of the nucleus is

$$W_E = e\int \rho_n \varphi \, d\tau \tag{6-8.1}$$

where $e\rho_n$ is the nuclear electric-charge density, φ is the potential due to the atomic electrons, and the integral is extended over the nuclear volume. We have thus

$$\int \rho_n \, d\tau = Z \text{ (atomic number)} \tag{6-8.2}$$

Call $\varphi(0)$ the potential at the origin of our reference system, which is at the center of the nucleus, and expand this potential in a power series in the vicinity of the origin. We have

$$W_E = e\int \rho_n[\varphi(0) + (\nabla\varphi)\cdot\mathbf{r} + \tfrac{1}{2}(\varphi_{xx}x^2 + 2\varphi_{xy}xy + \cdots)] \, d\tau \tag{6-8.3}$$

where $\varphi_{xy} = \partial^2\varphi/\partial x \, \partial y$, etc. The first term is clearly the term that would occur if the nuclear charge were all at the center and the nucleus were a point. The second term is zero because nuclei have no electric dipole—the third term is the interesting one.

In order to evaluate Eq. (6-8.3) we consider it first in the atomic coordinate system. Here terms containing φ_{xy}, φ_{xz}, φ_{yz} vanish because of the rotational symmetry of the atomic charge around **J**. We thus have

$$W_Q = \frac{e}{2}(Q_{xx}\varphi_{xx} + Q_{yy}\varphi_{yy} + Q_{zz}\varphi_{zz}) \tag{6-8.4}$$

$$Q_{xx} = \int \rho_n x^2 \, d\tau, \text{ etc.} \tag{6-8.5}$$

and x, y, z are taken in the atomic system of axes. We define also

$$Q_{rr} = Q_{xx} + Q_{yy} + Q_{zz} \tag{6-8.6}$$

Equation (6-8.4) simplifies further, when we remember that

$$\nabla^2\varphi = 0 \tag{6-8.7}$$

if we neglect the charge of the electrons at the nucleus. (This approximation is valid, as a more detailed discussion would show.) The axial symmetry gives

$$\varphi_{xx} = \varphi_{yy} \tag{6-8.8}$$

We then have

$$\varphi_{zz} = -2\varphi_{yy} = -2\varphi_{xx} \tag{6-8.9}$$

These last relations, inserted in Eq. (6-8.4), give

$$W_Q = \frac{\varphi_{zz}}{4} e\int (3z^2 - r^2)\rho_n \, d\tau \tag{6-8.10}$$

• In this formula it is desirable to express the integral as a nuclear integral referred to the nuclear coordinate system. We shall call

$$Q = \int \rho_n(3\zeta^2 - r^2)\,d\tau = 3Q_{\zeta\zeta} - Q_{rr} \qquad \textbf{(6-8.11)}$$

the nuclear quadrupole moment, and we use it to express the integral of Eq. (6-8.10). Observe first that, the nuclear-charge distribution being symmetric around ζ, we have

$$Q_{\xi\xi} = Q_{\eta\eta} \qquad \textbf{(6-8.12)}$$

and

$$Q_{\xi\eta} = Q_{\eta\zeta} = Q_{\xi\zeta} = 0 \qquad \textbf{(6-8.13)}$$

where the $Q_{\xi\xi}$, etc., are defined as in Eq. (6-8.5) with x, y, x interchanged with ξ, η, ζ. The relations between the x, y, z and ξ, η, ζ give

$$\xi^2 + \eta^2 + \zeta^2 = x^2 + y^2 + z^2 = r^2 \qquad \textbf{(6-8.14)}$$

whence

$$Q_{rr} = Q_{xx} + Q_{yy} + Q_{zz} = Q_{\xi\xi} + Q_{\eta\eta} + Q_{\zeta\zeta} \qquad \textbf{(6-8.15)}$$

Moreover,

$$z = \xi \cos \xi z + \eta \cos \eta z + \zeta \cos \zeta z \qquad \textbf{(6-8.16)}$$

with

$$\cos^2 \xi z + \cos^2 \eta z + \cos^2 \zeta z = 1 \qquad \textbf{(6-8.17)}$$

Calculating z^2 and Q_{zz} by using Eqs. (6-8.5), (6-8.12), (6-8.13), and (6-8.16) we have

$$Q_{zz} = Q_{\xi\xi}(1 - \gamma^2) + Q_{\zeta\zeta}\,\gamma^2 \qquad \textbf{(6-8.18)}$$

where

$$\gamma = \cos \zeta z = \cos IJ = \cos \theta \qquad \textbf{(6-8.19)}$$

From Eq. (6-8.17) we obtain, by Eqs. (6-8.12), (6-8.10), and (6-8.15),

$$3Q_{zz} - Q_{rr} = Q(\tfrac{3}{2}\gamma^2 - \tfrac{1}{2}) = QP_2(\cos\theta) \qquad \bullet\ \textbf{(6-8.20)}$$

Equation (6-8.18) inserted in Eq. (6-8.10) finally yields the expression for W_Q,

$$W_Q = \frac{eQ}{4}\,\varphi_{zz}\,P_2(\cos\theta) \qquad \textbf{(6-8.21)}$$

The quadrupole moment of a nucleus, Q, vanishes obviously for a spherically symmetrical nucleus. Quantum mechanically we must define Q in a more precise way as the expectation value

$$\langle 3z^2 - r^2 \rangle$$

for a given wave function. The wave function to be chosen is the one for which $M_I = I$, that is, the one corresponding to the maximum alignment of the total angular momentum along the z axis. We see then that according to quantum mechanics Q vanishes also for $I = \frac{1}{2}$, as can be found by calculating its average value, mentioned above. In order to do this note, using laboratory coordinates, that

$$z = \frac{\mathbf{r}\cdot\mathbf{I}}{I} = \frac{xI_x + yI_y + zI_z}{I} \tag{6-8.22}$$

Equations (6-6.1) and (6-6.2) for $I = \frac{1}{2}$ give

$$\begin{aligned} I_x^2 + I_y^2 + I_z^2 &= I(I+1) = \tfrac{3}{4} \\ I_x^2 = I_y^2 = I_z^2 &= \tfrac{1}{4} \\ I_xI_y + I_yI_x &= 0, \text{ etc.} \end{aligned} \tag{6-8.23}$$

Using these relations in Eq. (6-8.22) we find

$$z^2 = \frac{1}{4}(x^2 + y^2 + z^2)\frac{4}{3} = \frac{r^2}{3} \tag{6-8.24}$$

which implies $3z^2 - r^2 = 0$, or using Eq. (6-8.11),

$$Q = 0 \tag{6-8.25}$$

A positive Q indicates a cigar-shaped nucleus and a negative Q a lens-shaped nucleus.

Equation (6-8.21) is semiclassical, and the spherical harmonic $P_2(\cos\theta)$ can be written

$$\frac{3}{2}\left(\frac{\mathbf{I}\cdot\mathbf{J}}{IJ}\right)^2 - \frac{1}{2} = \frac{\frac{3}{2}(C^2 - 2I^2J^2)}{4I^2J^2}$$

To transform it into a quantum-mechanical expression (Casimir, 1936), the spherical harmonic must be replaced by

$$P_2(\cos\theta) \to \frac{\frac{3}{2}C(C+1) - 2I(I+1)J(J+1)}{I(2I-1)J(2J-1)} \tag{6-8.26}$$

where C is given in Eq. (6-6.25) as $F(F+1) - I(I+1) - J(J+1) = 2\mathbf{I}\cdot\mathbf{J}$. We have, in conclusion,

$$W_Q = \frac{B}{4}\,\frac{\frac{3}{2}C(C+1) - 2I(I+1)\,J(J+1)}{I(2I-1)\,J(2J-1)} \tag{6-8.27}$$

with

$$B = eQ\varphi_{zz}(0) \tag{6-8.28}$$

Equation (6-8.27) seems to give an indeterminate result for $J = \frac{1}{2}$ or $I = \frac{1}{2}$, but in these cases $W_Q = 0$ because either φ_{zz} or Q vanishes.

In order to obtain Q from the energy, we need to know $\varphi_{zz}(0)$. This is an atomic problem for which, to date, only approximate solutions have been found.

The spectral terms of an atom having a nucleus with $Q \neq 0$ are shifted by the amount W_Q and thus do not follow the interval rule. A detailed spectroscopic study, either in the optical or in the microwave region, can give values of B and, if $\varphi_{zz}(0)$ can be calculated, of Q. Other methods using matter in bulk, similar to the Bloch–Purcell methods for μ_I, can also be applied to find B (Dehmelt and Kruger).

Molecular-beam methods have also been extensively applied, and through them Q of the deuteron has been measured with great precision. We have limited our discussion to methods for directly measuring magnetic moments and electric quadrupole moments of nuclei, making no assumptions from the nuclear model. There are other methods, which we shall not describe but which allow us to relate certain experimental data (such as the cross section for Coulomb excitation; see Chap. 8) to nuclear moments, provided that a given nuclear model is valid. These methods can be used either to check the model, if one measures all the quantities involved, or to measure the moment, if one accepts the model.

6-9 Nuclear Polarization

Nuclei with $I \neq 0$ may be oriented in such a way that the substates with different m have different populations. For instance, in the case $I = \frac{1}{2}$ we may have $a_{1/2}$ nuclei with spin pointing up and $a_{-1/2}$ nuclei with spin pointing down relative to an external magnetic field. We call the expression

$$P = \frac{a_{1/2} - a_{-1/2}}{a_{1/2} + a_{-1/2}} \tag{6-9.1}$$

the "polarization" of our system of nuclei.

For arbitrary values of I we consider the quantities

$$\begin{aligned} f_1 &= \frac{1}{I} \sum_{m_I} m_I a_{m_I} \\ f_2 &= \frac{1}{I^2} \left[\sum_{m_I} m_I^2 a_{m_I} - \tfrac{1}{3} I(I+1) \right] \\ f_3 &= \frac{1}{I^3} \left[\sum_{m_I} m_I^3 a_{m_I} - \tfrac{1}{5}(3I^2 + 3I - 1) \sum_{m_I} m_I a_{m_I} \right], \quad \text{etc.} \end{aligned} \tag{6-9.2}$$

where the a_{m_I} are normalized so as to make

$$\sum_{m_I} a_{m_I} = 1 \qquad -I \leqslant m_I \leqslant I \tag{6-9.3}$$

The number f_k is called the "degree of orientation of order k." If all a_{m_I} are equal, all $f_k = 0$. For spin I, only the f_k with $k \leqslant 2I$ may differ from zero. In particular, for $I = \frac{1}{2}$, f_1 is the polarization. For larger spins one may have

$$a_{m_I} = a_{-m_I} \tag{6-9.4}$$

for every m_I, but $a_{m_I} \neq a_{m'_I}$ ($|m_I| \neq |m'_I|$). When this occurs, all f_k with k odd vanish, but some of the f_k with k even are different from zero, and the system is "aligned." For instance, a system of deuterons all with $m_I = 0$ is aligned but not polarized.

The energy differences associated with nuclear orientation are generally of the order of magnitude $\mu_n H$, where H is an external magnetic field. The thermal agitation determines energy fluctuations of order kT, and when kT is comparable with $\mu_n H$, the nuclear orientation will be destroyed by the thermal agitation. For $H = 20 \times 10^4$ gauss,

$\mu_n H/kT \simeq 10^{-3}/T$, which indicates the necessity of using temperatures in the range of 10^{-2} to 10^{-3} °K. These may be achieved by methods of adiabatic demagnetization. The simplest method, often called the "brute-force" method, is to cool the material in a magnetic field (Gorter and Simon, 1934).

For spin $\frac{1}{2}$ nuclei, the ratio of the number of nuclei oriented parallel or antiparallel to an external field H at a temperature T is given by Boltzmann's law,

$$\frac{a_{1/2}}{a_{-1/2}} = e^{g_I \mu_n H/kT} \tag{6-9.5}$$

and the polarization obtainable is approximately

$$f_1 = g_I \mu_n \frac{H}{2kT} \tag{6-9.6}$$

The nuclear relaxation time, often inconveniently long, and the low temperature required make this method technically difficult.

Indirect methods (Gorter, 1948; Rose, 1949) proceed by polarizing the atomic magnetic moments of paramagnetic salts. These are about 1,000 times larger and easier to polarize than the nuclear moments. They produce, in turn, oriented magnetic fields of the order of 10^6 gauss at the nucleus, and these last fields produce the nuclear orientation.

It is possible to obtain alignment but not polarization by using the anisotropic properties of crystals; at sufficiently low temperatures, the nuclear moments set themselves parallel to a crystal axis, but without producing any net polarization. For instance, the nuclear electric quadrupole moment will align with an ionic local electric field due to the lattice of the crystal. Methods of this type have been tested successfully in several cryogenic laboratories (Pound and Bleaney, 1951).

There are also dynamic processes of orientation that make it possible, when the appropriate electromagnetic radiation is applied, to increase the population of one of the substates of an hfs multiplet and thus achieve a nuclear polarization. This field is being rapidly developed, and we must refer to current literature for more details.

If the oriented nuclei are radioactive, the alignment or the polarization may be checked by observing the anisotropy of the radiations emitted. The technique is one of great and increasing importance.

6-10 Values of Spin, Magnetic Moments, and Quadrupole Moments

In Table 6-6 we summarize some of the results of the measurement of spins, magnetic moments, and electric quadrupole moments. Note the striking rule that all even-even nuclei in the ground state have zero spin and hence no magnetic moment or electric quadrupole moment. For this reason they have been omitted from Table 6-6.

Table 6-6 Selected Examples of Values of Nuclear Spins, Magnetic-Dipole Moment, and Electric-Quadrupole Moment[a]

Z	element	A	Half-life	Spin	Dipole moment μ	Quadrupole moment Q
0	n	1	11.7 m	$\frac{1}{2}$	−1.91315	
1	H	1		$\frac{1}{2}$	2.79290	
		2		1	0.85741	0.00274
		3	12.4 y	$\frac{1}{2}$	2.97884	
2	He	3		$\frac{1}{2}$	−2.12755	
3	Li	6		1	0.82201	−0.002
		7		$\frac{3}{2}$	3.25631	−0.1
4	Be	9		$\frac{3}{2}$	1.1774	0.03
5	B	10		3	1.8008	0.06
9	F	19		$\frac{1}{2}$	2.6285	
11	Na	22	2.6 y	3	1.747	
		23		$\frac{3}{2}$	2.2176	0.10
13	Al	27		$\frac{5}{2}$	3.6414	0.155
15	Cl	35		$\frac{3}{2}$	0.82181	−0.078
		36	3×10^5 y	2	1.2854	−0.017
19	K	39		$\frac{3}{2}$	0.39146	0.11
		40	1.3×10^9 y	4	−1.2981	−0.006
		41		$\frac{3}{2}$	0.21517	0.1
		42	12.5 h	2	−1.137	
		43	22 h	$\frac{3}{2}$	0.163	
35	Br	76	17 h	1	0.5480	0.26
		77	57 h	$\frac{3}{2}$		
		79		$\frac{3}{2}$	2.1056	0.33
						$\Omega = 0.11$
		80	18 m	1		
		80^m	4.5 h	5		
		81		$\frac{3}{2}$	2.2696	0.28
						$\Omega = 0.13$
		82	35.5 h	5	1.626	0.77
43	Tc	99	2.1×10^5 y	$\frac{9}{2}$	5.6805	0.3
49	In	109	4.3 h	$\frac{9}{2}$	5.53	1.20
		110^m	5.0 h	7		
		111	2.8 d	$\frac{9}{2}$	5.53	1.18
		113	$>10^{14}$ y	$\frac{9}{2}$	5.5232	1.14
		113^m	1.7 h	$\frac{1}{2}$	−0.2105	
		114^m	50 d	5	4.7	
		115	6×10^{14} y	$\frac{9}{2}$	5.5344	1.16
		115^m	4.5 h	$\frac{1}{2}$		
		116^m	54 m	5	4.3	
55	Cs	127	6 h	$\frac{1}{2}$	1.43	
57	La	138	1×10^{11} y	5	3.706	0.9
71	Lu	176	4×10^{10} y	7	2.8	8
72	Hf	177		$\frac{7}{2}$	0.61	3
		178		0		
		178^m	4.8 s	8		
		179		$\frac{9}{2}$	0.47	3
		180^m	5.5 h	8		

Table 6-6 (*continued*)

Z	element	A	Half-life	Spin	Dipole moment μ	Quadrupole moment Q
73	Ta	181		$\frac{7}{2}$	2.1	6
80	Hg	197	65 h	$\frac{1}{2}$	0.5240	
		197^m	24 h	$(\frac{13}{2})$	−1.032	1.5
		199		$\frac{1}{2}$	0.50267	0.4
92	U	233	1.6×10^5 y	$\frac{5}{2}$	0.52	3.4
		235	7×10^8 y	$\frac{7}{2}$	0.34	4.0
94	Pu	239	24,300 y	$\frac{1}{2}$	0.27	
		241	460 y	$\frac{5}{2}$	1.4	4.9

[a] The unit of magnetic moment is the nuclear magneton. The electric-quadrupole moments are measured in units of 10^{-24} cm^2. A recent, complete table of the same quantities, containing references to the original literature, is given by Lindgren in (Si 65). The symbol Ω represents magnetic-octupole moment in units $\mu_n \times 10^{-24}$ cm.

Turning to the nuclei with A odd, beginning with the proton, we should expect the proton to have, according to Dirac's theory the magnetic moment of exactly 1 nuclear magneton, but instead we find an experimental value of 2.793, and for the neutron, which should have no magnetic moment whatsoever, the value is −1.91. It is interesting to note that the difference between the magnitudes of the magnetic moment of the neutron and the proton is approximately 1 nuclear magneton. This might be explained, qualitatively at least, by the hypothesis that the magnetic moment of the proton is composed of two parts: one a Dirac moment, of 1 nuclear magneton for the proton and 0 for the neutron; the other an additional moment resulting from mesonic effects. The part attributable to the mesonic effects is then $2.79 - 1 = 1.79$ for the proton and −1.91 for the neutron. This may be qualitatively explained as originating from the virtual dissociation of the nucleon into a "bare Dirac nucleon" and a meson. The mesonic orbital motion gives rise to a magnetic moment of $+\mu_\pi$ if the meson is positive and of $-\mu_\pi$ if the meson is negative. We now write the dissociations of proton and neutron as

$$p \to n + \pi^+$$
$$n \to p + \pi^-$$

and the fraction of the time during which the nucleon is dissociated as τ. We then have, indicating by μ_p, μ_n the magnetic moments of proton and neutron:

$$\mu_p = +\mu_\pi\tau + (1 - \tau)1 = (\mu_\pi - 1)\tau + 1$$
$$\mu_n = (1 - \mu_\pi)\tau$$

This relation would give

$$\mu_p + \mu_n = 1$$

whereas experimentally one finds

$$\mu_p + \mu_n = 0.88$$

The agreement is surprisingly good for such a simple argument. One of the problems of meson theory is to account precisely for the magnetic moment of the proton and neutron.

The deuteron has a magnetic moment which is almost exactly the algebraic sum of the magnetic moment of the proton and neutron. Remembering that the deuteron has spin 1 and that it is composed of a neutron and a proton with parallel spins and no relative angular momentum (s state), one should not be surprised at the result for the magnetic moment. The next problem is to study why the magnetic moment is not exactly equal to the sum of the two moments. The discrepancy is reasonably accounted for by the admixture of d states into the ground state of the deuteron, as will be seen in Chap. 10. Turning to heavier nuclei, we find in several cases values of the magnetic moment that are fairly easily explained. For example, in the case of He^3 and H^3 we should expect to find the magnetic moment of a neutron in the first and of a proton in the second, because the identical nucleons have opposite spin and the only effective nuclide is the unpaired one.

A general regularity has been observed by Schmidt (1937) and can be explained by assuming that odd-A nuclei are composed of a core forming a closed shell plus one nucleon. The closed shell must contain an even number of neutrons and an even number of protons and has no angular momentum or magnetic moment. To this shell we now add one nucleon with angular momentum l and spin $\frac{1}{2}$. Clearly the total I of the nucleus is then equal to $l \pm \frac{1}{2}$. According to the vector model $\mathbf{l}$ and $\frac{1}{2}$ combine to form $\mathbf{I}$. Each one precesses around $\mathbf{I}$ independently, and the magnetic moment in nuclear magnetons along $\mathbf{I}$ is

$$\mu_I = g_l \frac{\mathbf{l} \cdot \mathbf{I}}{I} + g_s \frac{\mathbf{s} \cdot \mathbf{I}}{I} \qquad \text{(6-10.1)}$$

The scalar product of $\mathbf{l} \cdot \mathbf{I}$ is given by

$$s^2 = l^2 + I^2 - 2\mathbf{l} \cdot \mathbf{I} \qquad \text{(6-10.2)}$$

or quantum mechanically by

$$\frac{\mathbf{l} \cdot \mathbf{I}}{I^2} = \frac{l(l+1) + I(I+1) - s(s+1)}{2I(I+1)} \qquad \text{(6-10.3)}$$

and a similar expression is obtained for $(\mathbf{s} \cdot \mathbf{I})/I^2$. Inserting them in Eq. (6-10.1) we find

$$g_I = g_s \frac{I(I+1) + s(s+1) - l(l+1)}{2I(I+1)} + g_l \frac{I(I+1) + l(l+1) - s(s+1)}{2I(I+1)} \qquad \text{(6-10.4)}$$

From this formula we obtain for $I = l + \frac{1}{2}$

$$\mu_I = \tfrac{1}{2} g_s + l g_l \qquad \text{(6-10.5)}$$

and, for $I = l - \frac{1}{2}$,

$$\mu_I = -\tfrac{1}{2} g_s \frac{2l - 1}{2l + 1} + g_l \frac{(l + 1)(2l - 1)}{2l + 1} \qquad \textbf{(6-10.6)}$$

The two formulas can be combined to give

$$\mu_I = I\left[g_l \pm \frac{1}{2l + 1}(g_s - g_l)\right] \qquad \textbf{(6-10.7)}$$

where the upper sign is valid for $I = l + \frac{1}{2}$ and the lower for $I = l - \frac{1}{2}$. The g_l and g_s values are given in Table 6-7.

The experimental values of nuclear moments are plotted in Fig. 6-33, together with the values predicted by Eq. (6-10.7).

The observed values do not fall exactly on the Schmidt lines but lie between them. Several explanations have been offered to account for this deviation. For instance, it has been assumed that a neutron and a proton in the nucleus do not have the same magnetic moment as they do when free. It is not surprising, however, that a theory based on such a crude model fails to give quantitative results; in fact it is rather encouraging to find that the agreement is as good as it is.

6-11 Shell Model

In the liquid-drop model we have emphasized the properties of "nuclear matter" and have said nothing about single nucleons. This is a great departure from the atomic model, where the emphasis is on the motion of the electrons in the field provided by the nucleus.

The atomic model, however, has been so successful that one is tempted to find a way to extend at least some of its features to the nucleus. Indeed, there are reasons for suspecting that nucleons have well-defined individual orbits. For certain numbers of neutrons or protons, called "magic numbers," nuclei exhibit special characteristics of stability reminiscent of the properties shown by noble gases among the atoms. In the latter case the closure of a shell (*K*, *L*, *M*, ... shells for 2, 10, 18, ... electrons) is responsible for the peculiarities of the noble gases, such as their chemical inertness, diamagnetism, and high ionization potential. M. Mayer, and Haxel, Jensen, and Suess (1949), surmised that nuclear shells might close at some magic numbers that are revealed in nuclear phenomena.

Table 6-7 *g* Numbers for Neutron and Proton

	Neutron	Proton
g_l	0	1
g_s	−3.826	5.586

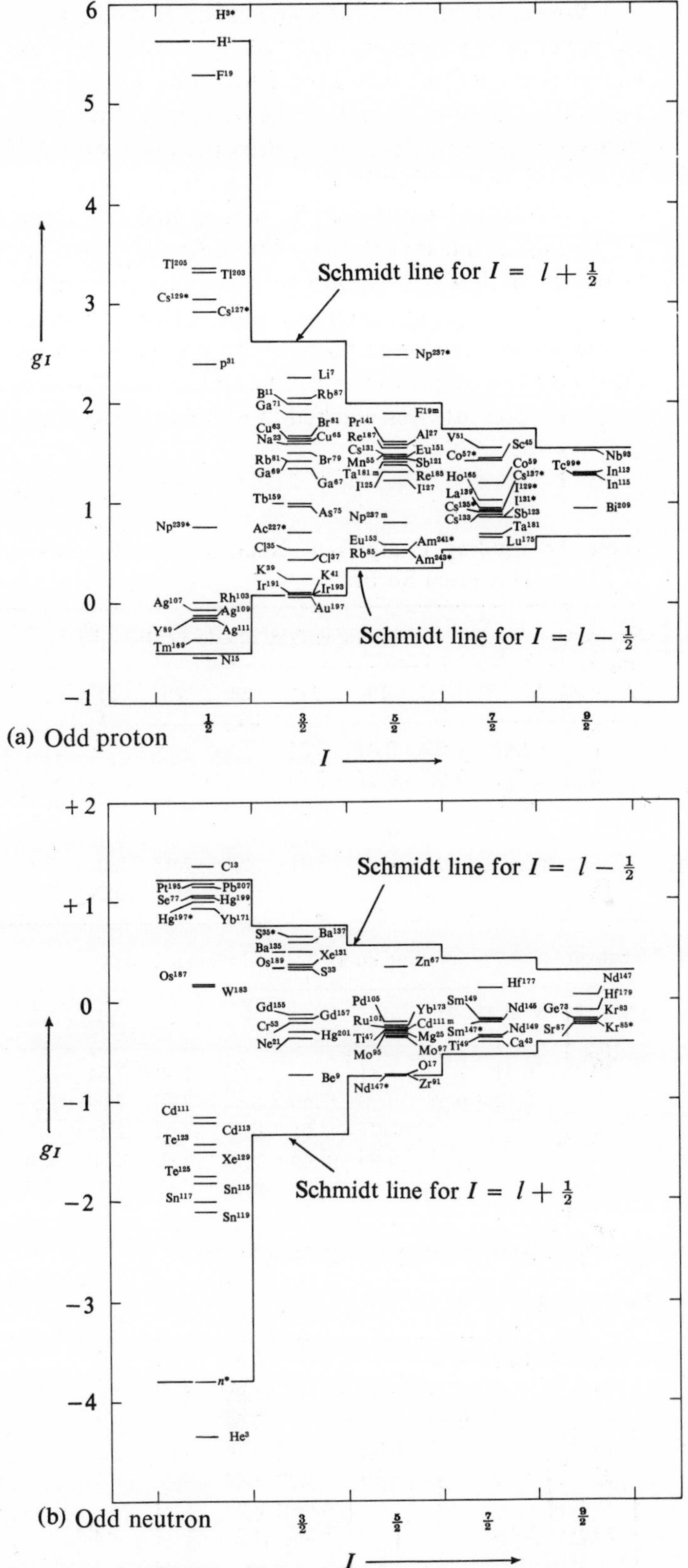

Figure 6-33 Schmidt lines and experimental nuclear magnetic *g*-factors (*, radioactive nuclei; *m*, metastable states).

We shall mention here some of the evidence supporting the "magic" character of the numbers: 2, 8, 20, 28, 50, 82, and 126. The fundamental fact is that the 3rd, 9th, 21st, 29th, 51st, 83rd, and 127th nucleons are especially loosely bound. The decrease from the average binding energy of these nucleons is approximately 1 or 2 MeV (see Table 6-8). We can note this effect by observing the jumps in the differences between the experimental values of the masses and the values predicted by the semiempirical mass formula. The differences are particularly large for values of A that correspond to magic numbers of neutron and proton (Fig. 6-18). An exaggerated example is He^4, in which the second neutron or the second proton is bound with an energy of about 20 MeV and a third neutron or proton is not bound at all. Other shells at low magic numbers present less-marked anomalies, but the doubly magic O^{16}

Table 6-8 Binding Energies of Neutrons and Protons in the Region of Closed Shells[a]

Neutron excess	Binding energy of odd neutron, MeV									
$(N-Z)$	$N = 15$	17	19	21	23	25	27	29	31	33
1	8.47	8.65	8.84	8.37						
2	7.73	7.93	8.57	7.79						
3	6.44	6.60	7.02	6.64	7.94	8.79	9.11	9.29	9.00	8.91
4			6.54	6.11	7.37	8.91	9.13	9.10	8.40	8.64
5				5.01	5.96	7.43	8.02	7.93	7.64	8.51
6						6.91	8.21	7.30	7.26	7.50

Neutron excess	Binding energy of odd neutron, MeV							
$(N-Z)$	$N = 41$	43	45	47	49	51	53	55
10	6.94	7.32	7.81		8.95	8.39	7.64	
11	6.12	6.48	6.98	7.49	8.41	7.16	7.09	7.37
12			7.07	7.81	8.70	7.32	7.19	
13			5.86	6.88	6.93	6.60	6.96	6.91
14					6.79	6.11	6.71	6.91

Neutron excess	Binding energy of odd neutron, MeV					
$(N-Z)$	$N = 75$	77	79	81	83	85
23	6.45	6.51		7.81	6.00	6.40
24		6.45	6.73		5.82	
25		6.99	6.82		5.74	
26			6.36		5.14	
27			6.30		5.24	
28				6.84	5.57	
29				5.96	3.57	

Table 6-8 (*continued*)

Neutron excess $(N - Z)$	Binding energy of odd neutron, MeV $N = 121$	123	125	127	129	131	133
42	5.25	6.76	6.85	5.13			
43		7.31	6.73	4.55	5.09	5.55	5.97
44			6.54	4.67	5.10	5.56	6.21
45			5.54	3.87	4.32	4.59	5.33

Neutron excess $(N - Z)$	Binding energy of odd proton, MeV $Z = 23$	25	27	29	31
0	5.14	4.60	3.91	1.50	
2	6.80	6.44	5.76	4.34	3.79
3	6.83	6.55	6.34	5.50	3.97
4	7.84	7.73	7.10	5.63	5.12
5	8.09	8.16	7.15	5.84	5.13

[a] The binding energies of the last odd neutron in the regions $N = 20$, 28, 50, 82, and 126 are shown in the first four tables for various neutron excesses. In the fifth table the odd-proton binding energies near $Z = 28$ are given. The tabulated neutron binding energies are defined by $\mathrm{BE}(N + 1, Z) - \mathrm{BE}(N,Z)$, where $\mathrm{BE}(N,Z)$ is the total binding energy of the nucleus with Z protons and N neutrons. A similar definition holds for the proton binding energies. (From R. D. Lawson.)

is well known for its stability. The evidence for the magic character of the higher numbers is less direct. To cite some of the relevant facts, nuclei with 50 protons or 50 neutrons are especially abundant, and isotones with 28, 50, or 82 neutrons extend over a larger range of Z than the neighboring isotonic series. Similarly, tin ($Z = 50$) has the greatest number of stable isotopes, 10.

The magic character of the number 126 for neutrons is strikingly shown in alpha decay (Fig. 7-11). When alpha emission separates the 126th neutron from a nucleus—necessarily together with the 125th neutron—the energy of alpha particles is markedly lower than when the 128th and 127th neutrons are ejected. This is explained by the sudden decrease in binding energy for neutrons after the 126th.

Similar phenomena occur in beta decay. Consider the energy released in beta decay, during which process the difference between the number of neutrons and the number of protons in the nucleus decreases by two units. We find rather regular curves if we plot this energy as a function of A for a given value of $N - Z$ in the original nucleus. However, obvious jumps appear in the curves when a nucleus with a magic number of neutrons or protons is involved (Fig. 6-34).

Neutron-capture cross sections are particularly low for nuclei containing 50, 82, or 126 neutrons, because the neutron to be captured will be only slightly bound and this indirectly decreases probability of capture (Fig. 6-35).

The phenomena mentioned above are consequences of the jumps in binding energy shown in Table 6-8; moreover, the spin and magnetic moment of nuclei, as we shall see presently, also are related to the shell structure of the nuclei. There are many more facts in nuclear physics that affirm the shell structure or find a plausible explanation on the basis of this model.

However, we immediately encounter a serious difficulty of principle; there is no obvious fixed center which provides a potential for the nucleons, as the nucleus does for atomic electrons. However, one may postulate that all the nucleons together could provide a potential well in which the nucleons move and that by some mechanism, not yet fully analyzed, the sum of the interactions between the single nucleon pairs (which are known by direct proton-proton and neutron-proton scattering experiments) is equivalent to a potential well. While an analysis to demonstrate this equivalence has been the goal of complicated investigations by Brueckner, Watson, Bethe, and others, the result can be stated very simply: Each nucleon is subject to a potential $V(r)$ that—in extremely oversimplified form—can be represented by a rectangular well,

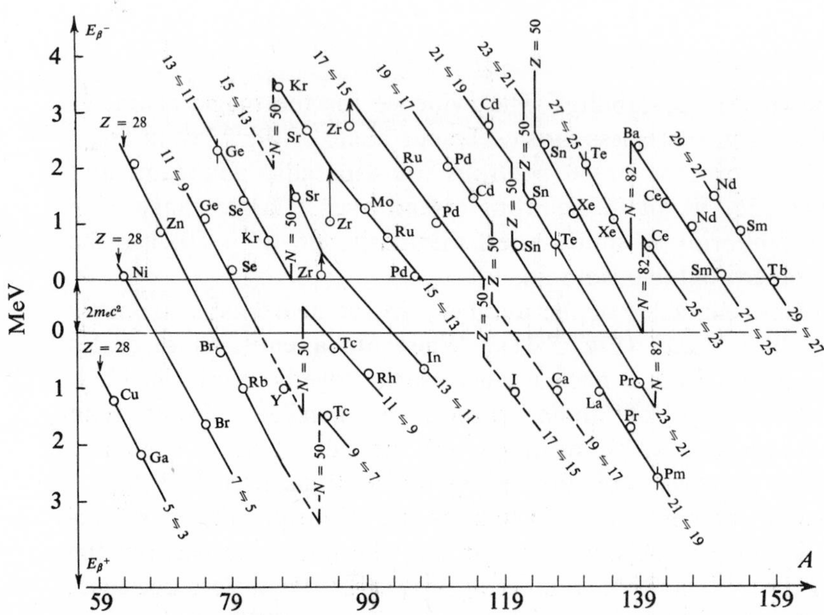

Figure 6-34 Beta energy of the reaction

$$ {}_{Z}X_{N+1}{}^{A} \underset{\beta^{+}\text{capture}}{\overset{\beta^{-}}{\rightleftarrows}} {}_{Z+1}X_{N}{}^{A} \quad 28 \leqslant Z \leqslant 64 $$

The lines are labeled according to *N*-*Z* before and after the decay. The decay energy varies regularly on a line except when *N* or *Z* = 50, when there is a jump. [From (MJ 55).]

$$V(r) = -V_0 \qquad r \leqslant R$$
$$V(r) = 0 \qquad r > R \tag{6-11.1}$$

If we assume that the nucleons move in this well, we can establish a series of levels. But with the potential of Eq. (6-11.1) or with simple modifications of it, we find that the shells do not close at the magic numbers. To account for the experimental results it is necessary to introduce the additional hypothesis of a strong spin-orbit coupling. This is an interaction between nuclear orbital angular momentum and spin; it is formally analogous to the well-known spin-orbit interaction of atomic electrons (Jensen and Mayer, 1949). However, the nuclear spin-orbit coupling is different from one commonly present in atoms (*L-S* or Russell–Saunders coupling), where the orbital angular momenta of all electrons combine into a total **L** and all spins into a total **S**, and **L** and **S** combine to form **J**. In nuclei the interaction between the spin and the orbit of a single nucleon is usually greater than the interaction between orbital momenta or spins of different nucleons; thus, each **l** and **s** combine to form a **j**. All **j** thus gives the resultant total angular momentum (*j-j* coupling). There are also other types of coupling but for more details we refer to the original literature.

We must also note that, whereas the electron Coulomb interaction is repulsive and has a long range favoring states of minimum spatial symmetry, the attractive nuclear interaction favors a maximum of spatial symmetry. Moreover the short range of this interaction gives special stability to each pair of identical nucleons coupling to zero angular momentum [pairing effect; compare the δ term in Eq. (6-5.7)]. If nucleons couple as described, we expect and find that ground states of most odd-*A* nuclei have I equal to the j of the last bound nucleon. This is verified in odd-*A* nuclei that have nearly closed neutron or

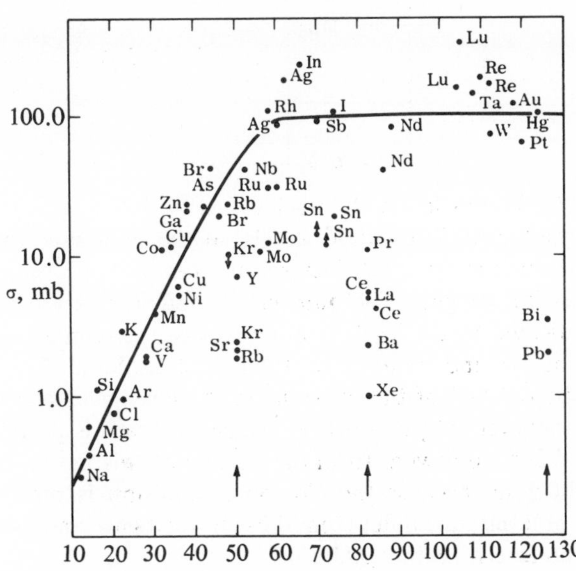

Figure 6-35 Neutron capture: cross sections as a function of neutron number of target nucleus. Ordinate, logarithmic scale.

proton shells. Finally, for nuclei with even Z and even A, I must equal 0 in the ground state, a striking empirical regularity.

The order of levels shown in Fig. 6-36, with spin-orbit coupling taken into account, is fundamental to the interpretation of nuclear phenomena according to the shell model. Actually there are minor differences between the case of an unpaired neutron and of an unpaired proton. However, one may neglect them in a first approximation and

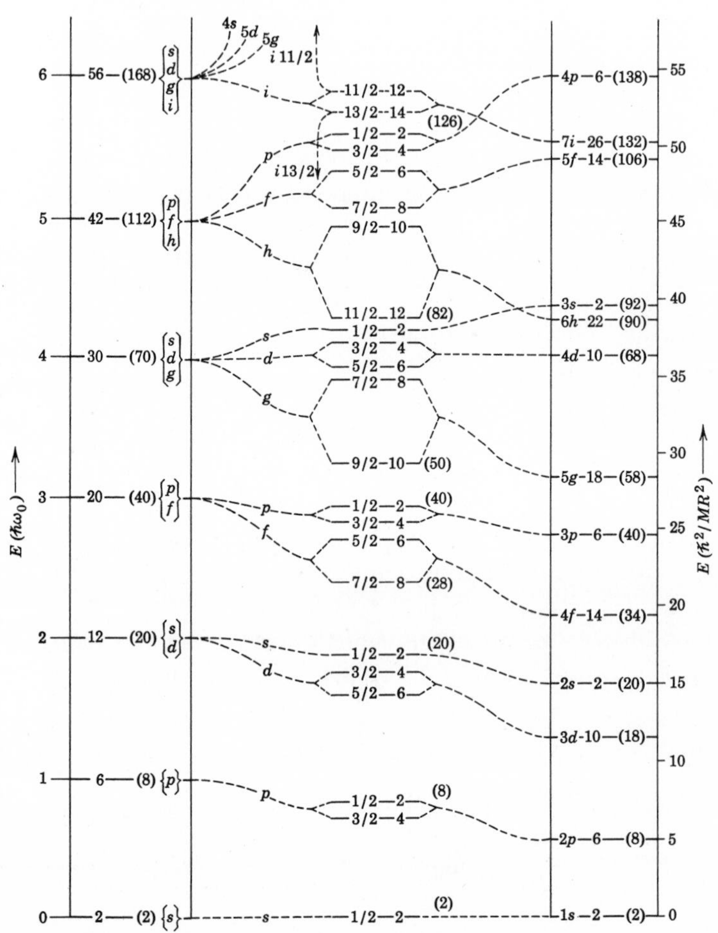

Figure 6-36 Energy levels of a nucleus. At the left side, in the limiting case of a parabolic potential, we have the harmonic oscillator levels; at the right side, the limiting case of a square well; in the center, the nuclear case. The integral number on the level gives the number of sublevels contained in it (statistical weight). The numbers in parentheses are the total number of sublevels below the energy indicated by the level, in other words, the number of nucleons in a nucleus necessary to fill all states below, and inclusive to, the level considered. The half-integral numbers give the angular momentum $j = l \pm \frac{1}{2}$ of the nucleons in the level. A magic number corresponding to a closed shell appears whenever the jump between adjacent levels is particularly large. The actual filling of orbits in nuclei differs somewhat from the scheme of this figure. First, the neutron and proton levels are slightly different, because the Coulomb repulsion is present only for protons. Furthermore, the splittings of levels may differ from those of the figure and produce alterations in the order of appearance of the levels. [From (MJ 55).]

use Fig. 6-36 for neutrons and protons alike. Then the **l** and **j** of the extra nucleon outside the closed even-even shell are predictable from the shell model (Fig. 6-36), and thus the systematics of nuclear spins and magnetic moments is accounted for by the shell model, because the spins are simply the spin of the unpaired nucleon and the magnetic moments are obtained from Eq. (6-10.7).

For example, O^{17} has an extra neutron, the ninth, that should be in a state $d_{5/2}$; and the spin of O^{17} is 5/2, as expected. Its magnetic moment, lying very close to the Schmidt line, also confirms this interpretation.

The shell model can also be used to give information on the spin of odd-odd nuclei. We require here the "Nordheim rules." Define the Nordheim number as $N = j_p - l_p + j_n - l_n$, where p and n refer to the odd proton and neutron, respectively.

The rules say that if $N = 0$, then $I = |j_n - j_p|$ and that if $N = \pm 1$, I is either $|j_n - j_p|$ or $j_n + j_p$. There are exceptions to these rules, however, especially among light nuclei.

It would be desirable to derive the shell model, which is clearly successful, from fundamental facts such as the nucleon-nucleon interaction. Even without going into this complicated subject we must point out a serious difficulty in the shell model. How can a nucleon move in an orbit in nuclear matter? The mean free path of a nucleon would appear to be short compared with the distance it would have to travel before we would be justified in speaking of an orbit. A partial answer to this difficulty is given by the fact that collisions within a nucleus are inhibited by Pauli's principle; the final states that the colliding nucleons should reach are already occupied.

We close with a remark on the potential V of Eq. (6-11.1). The nucleus, with its strong central force, gives rigidity to the atomic structure. In a nucleus there is no fixed center of force. The surface tension (compare Sec. 6-5) tends to make the nucleus spherical. However, the fractional increase in surface of an ellipsoid of rotation over a sphere of equal volume is of the order of the square of the fractional differences of the axes and is thus small in practical cases. The nucleus as a whole then, is, fairly easily deformed and nonspherical nuclei are well known.

6-12 Collective Nuclear Model

The shell model has been most successful in explaining a number of nuclear features, some of which have been mentioned and some of which will be considered later. However, it does not provide a complete description of the nucleus. It is particularly successful in the case of nuclei composed of a closed shell plus one or a few additional nucleons. In the closed-shell configuration the nucleus is spherical. The addition of one or more nucleons produces only small deformations. However, midway between closed shells the situation is different. The nuclei depart appreciably from the spherical form, and collective motions involving many nucleons become important.

This is clearly seen, for instance, in nuclear quadrupole moments (Fig. 6-37). Near a closed shell the values obtainable by ascribing the quadrupole to a single particle outside a shell agree reasonably well with experiment; but in the middle of the shell the quadrupole moments are many times larger than can be accounted for by a single particle. Rainwater (1950) suggested that the single particle deforms the whole nucleus, and that the observed quadrupole results from the collective deformation of many orbits. Very crudely, the effect would be similar to that produced by a small heavy ball rotating inside a rubber balloon. The pressure produced by the centrifugal force of the small ball would determine the deformation of the rubber envelope. The nucleons then move in a potential that is not spherically symmetrical. We thus have two types of motion: motion of the entire nucleus as though all the nucleons occupied an ellipsoidal box that might rotate or even

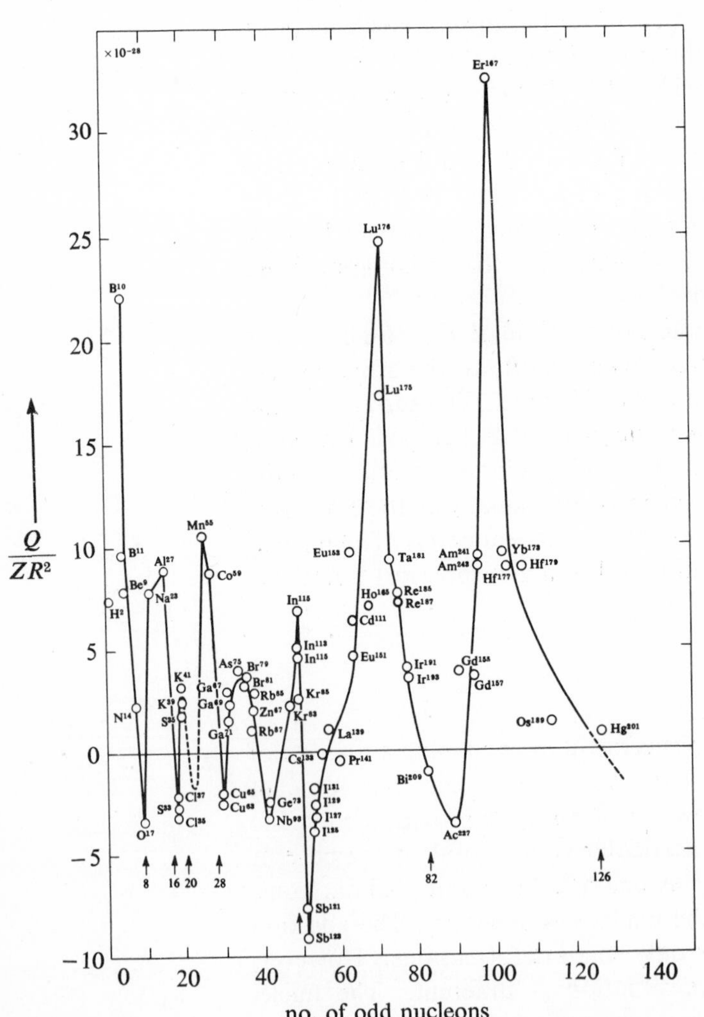

Figure 6-37 Reduced nuclear quadrupole moments as a function of the number of odd nucleons. The quantity Q/ZR^2 gives a measure of the nuclear deformation independent of the size of the nucleus.

deform itself by vibrations; and motions of the nucleons inside the box. The two types of motion are coupled more or less strongly to each other. The mathematical development of these ideas (A. Bohr, B. Mottelson, and others from 1952 on) is the basis for the "collective model," which has been particularly successful for $A \sim 24$, $150 < A < 190$, and $A > 230$.

An example of this type has long been known in the case of diatomic molecules, the motions of which are naturally classified as rotational, vibrational, and electronic in order of increasing energy. As typical magnitudes we may take 0.005 eV for a rotational level spacing, 0.1 eV for a vibrational level spacing, and 2 eV for an electronic level spacing. The motions are clearly separable and, correspondingly, the wave function can be factored into rotational, vibrational, and electronic terms. Mathematically this means that the hamiltonian is composed of three additive parts containing: (1) electronic coordinates, (2) vibrational coordinates, and (3) rotational coordinates. The wave function is then the product of three wave functions (compare Sec. 6-4), each containing the respective coordinates.

In the nucleus we can attempt a similar separation of the motions. We consider first a central "core" containing the nucleons of a closed shell. Outside of this core there are n nucleons forming a "cloud." If $n = \pm 1$ (we consider one nucleon missing from a closed shell as $n = -1$) we have the case to which the shell model applied best. For such a nucleus the excited states are given by the excited levels of the single nucleon of the cloud (Fig. 6-38).

For larger even values of n the nucleons in the cloud are subject

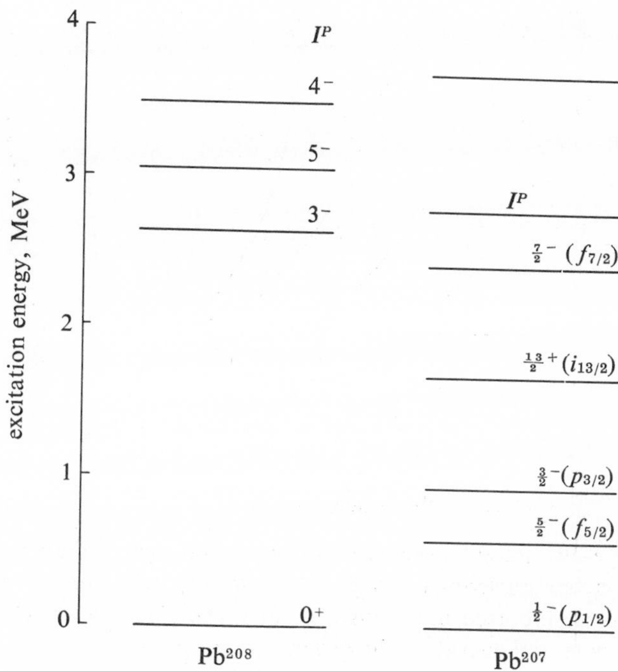

Figure 6-38 Spectra of lead isotopes. The figure shows the observed levels labeled for the experimentally determined spins and parities. The configuration assignment is shown in parentheses. Pb^{208} ($N = 126$, $Z = 82$) with both kinds of nucleons in closed shells represents a core spectrum. Pb^{207} with $n = -1$ gives a single-particle spectrum.

to two types of forces: short-range forces responsible for orienting the spins of pairs of identical nucleons. Under their influence nuclei tend to a spherical form and zero spin; and long-range forces which tend to produce an overlap of the eigenfunctions of all n particles. If the latter forces predominate they push the nucleons in certain special directions, thereby deforming the cloud.

In this case the potential in which the nucleons move ceases to be spherically symmetrical, as Fig. 6-39 shows. Corresponding to this change of potential the energy levels of the shell model lose their degeneracy and shift as shown in the examples of Fig. 6-40; the corresponding wave functions have been extensively studied by Nilsson (1955).

A spherical cloud is subject to vibrations around its equilibrium shape. Excited states corresponding to one, two, or three vibrational quanta in the cloud are often found. They are equally spaced and their angular momentum and parity are 2^+; 0^+, 2^+, 4^+, and 0, 2, 3, 4, 6^+. They are most easily observed when n is small (Fig. 6-41).

Deformed nuclei corresponding to large even values of n show prominent rotational levels. These have the spacing

$$\frac{\hbar^2}{2\mathscr{I}} I(I+1)$$

characteristic of rotational levels. However, for $\mathscr{I}$ one must consider

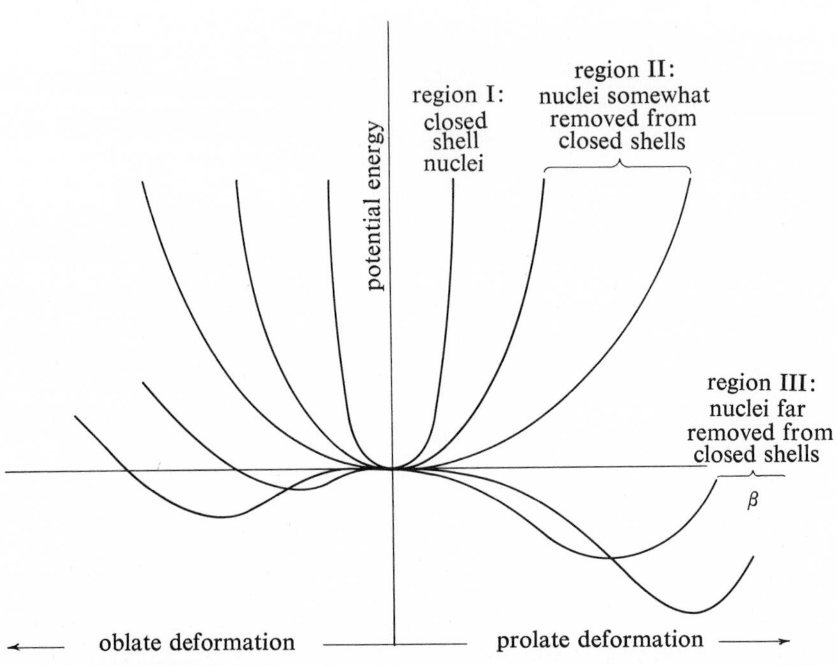

Figure 6-39 Potential energy $V(\beta)$ as a function of deformation for even-even nuclei near closed shells, a few nucleons removed from closed shells, and far removed from closed shells where the nucleus is stabilized in a nonspherical shape. The curves are schematic only, and all of them refer to the potential energy of the ground state.

Figure 6-40 Energy spectrum for single-particle motion in an ellipsoidal potential. The spectra are drawn as a function of the deformation $\delta = \Delta R/R$. For $\delta = 0$, the potential is spherical and we have the usual sequence of orbitals corresponding to a spherical shell model, that is, $1s_{1/2}$ (which comes lower than the lowest orbit drawn in this figure), $1p_{3/2}$, $1p_{1/2}$, $1d_{5/2}$, $2s_{1/2}$, $1d_{3/2}$, and then a little above the region covered in the figure $1f_{7/2}$. For $\delta \neq 0$ the states are labeled by the quantum numbers K and parity, which are indicated on the right. A complete characterization of the states requires additional quantum numbers besides K and parity and these are given in the square brackets. Each of the orbits is doubly degenerate. [From S. G. Nilsson, *Kgl. Danske Videnskab. Selskab, Mat.-Fys. Medd.*, **29**, No. 16 (1955).]

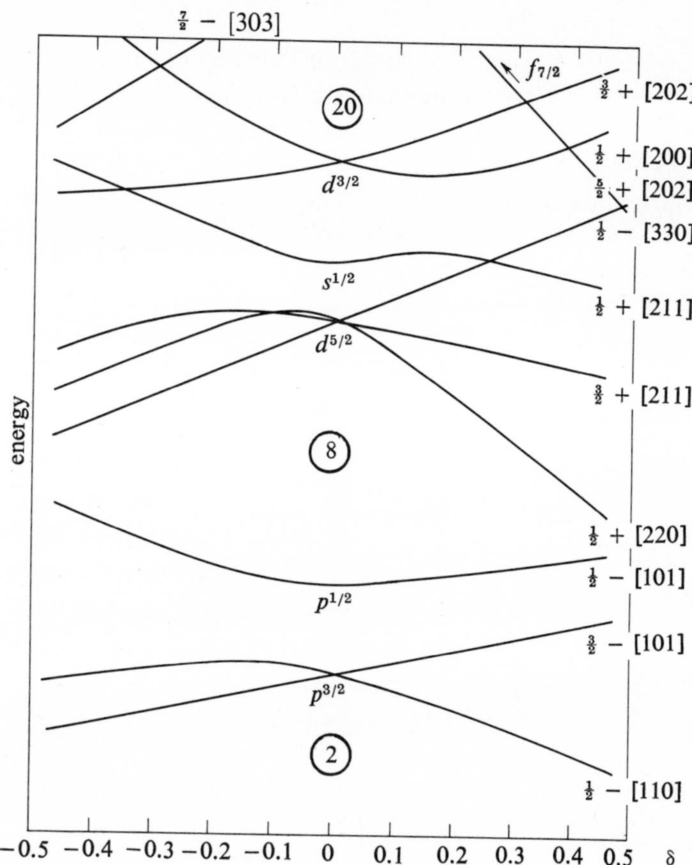

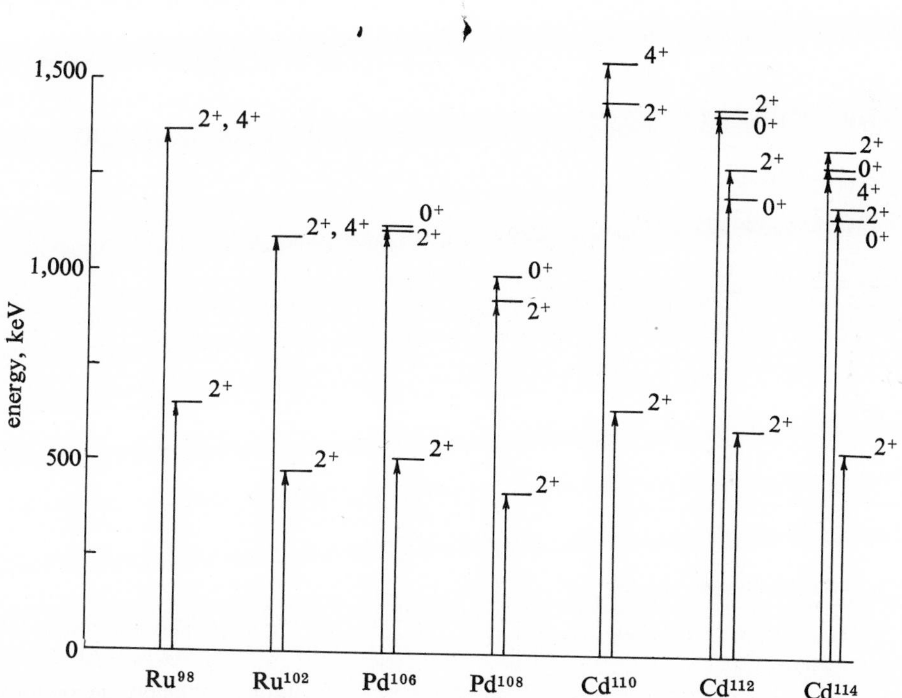

Figure 6-41 Examples of vibrational levels of nuclei of even A.

not the total moment of inertia of the nucleus, which we shall call $\mathscr{I}_0$, but that part associated with the nuclear deformation. For a spherical nucleus $\mathscr{I}$ is zero. The angular momentum I is an even integral number (Fig. 6-42).

For *odd n* the situation is more complicated. If the odd nucleon is added to a deformed cloud the result is a rotational spectrum of a single particle in a nonspherical well (Fig. 6-43). If the odd nucleon is added to a spherical cloud, the cloud is excited.

The levels considered thus far are relatively low (several MeV at most). At much higher energies the core itself may be excited. Such levels are found up to about 20 MeV, at which level gamma absorption may cause vibration of all the protons against the neutrons (see Chap. 11). There are other ways of exciting the core, for instance, by electron or alpha particle bombardment. (Figure 6-44 summarizes in an idealized fashion the energy levels discussed above.)

The distinction between the different types of motion in nuclei is not always clear-cut, because the coupling of the motions is often strong. In other words, if, for example, the energy difference between vibrational levels is not large compared with that between rotational levels, it is not possible to consider rotation as a structure superimposed on vibrations. Consequently, the expression of the wave function as a product of the functions of the different coordinates is not always a good approximation.

We shall now discuss the rotational levels in somewhat greater detail. Single particles in the nucleus having an axis of rotational symmetry z' possess angular momenta that precess rapidly around z', preserving, however, a constant component Ω_p in this direction. The values of Ω_p are half-integral numbers, positive or negative. States with Ω_p differing only in sign are degenerate because they correspond to rotations differing only in sense. The sum of all Ω_p values is called

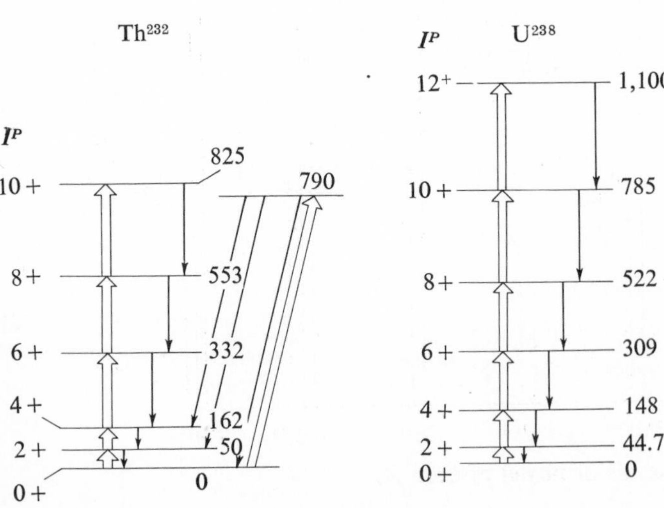

Figure 6-42 Examples of rotational levels observed in even-A nuclei of heavy elements by the Coulomb excitation process.

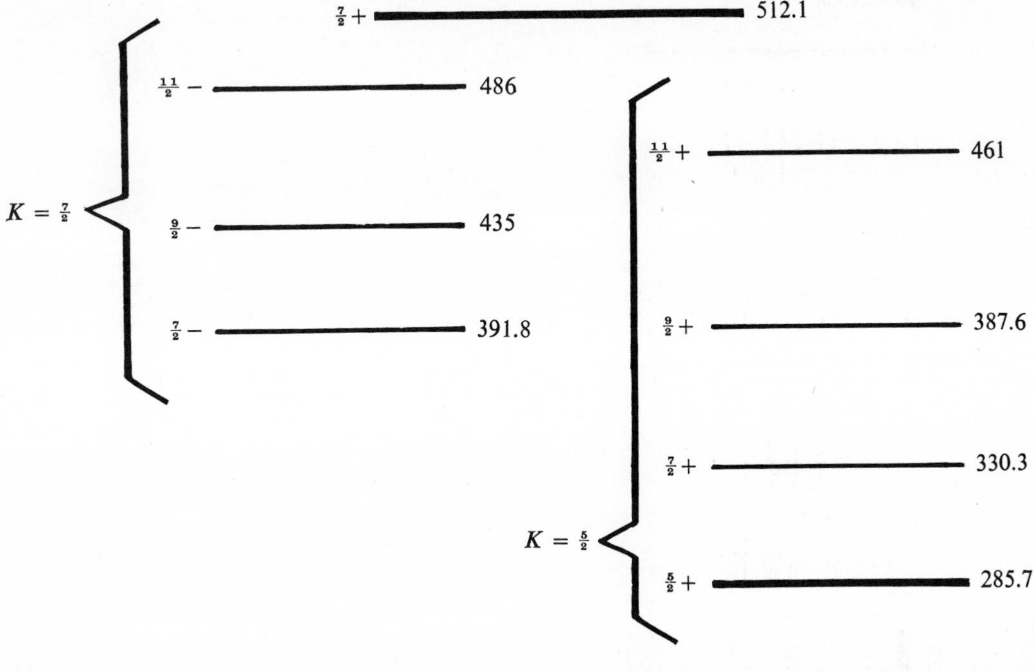

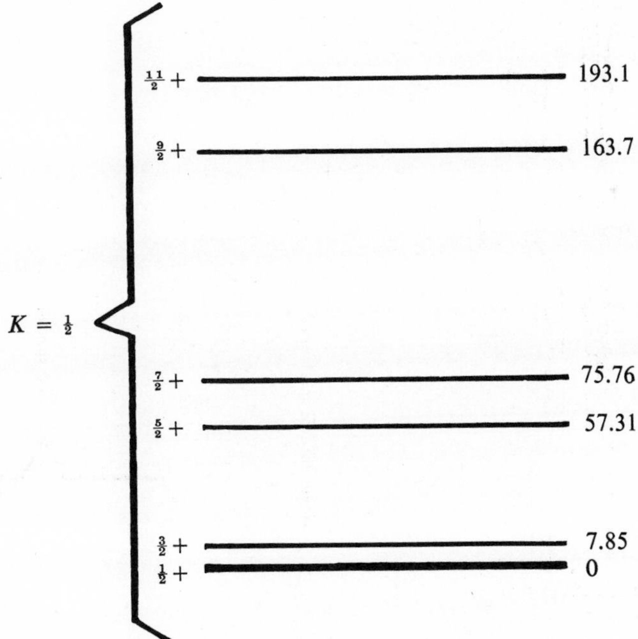

Figure 6-43 Energy levels of Pu^{239} with associated levels of rotational excitation.

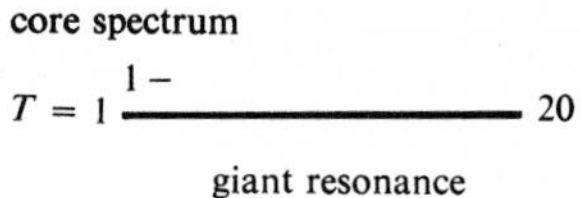

$T = 0$ 2^+ 12

quadrupole deformation

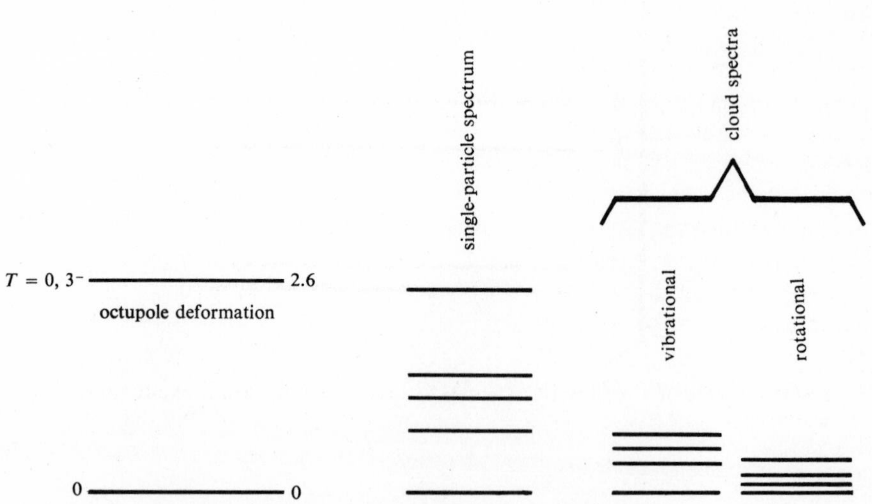

Figure 6-44 Schematic idealized representation of core, single-particle, and cloud spectra. Note typical energy scale. [V. Weisskopf, *Phys. Today*, **14,** No. 7 (1961).]

Ω. In the ground state of even-even nuclei the nucleons are paired, in couples, with Ω_p numbers of opposite sign so that $\Omega = 0$.

The rotations of a symmetrical nucleus are described by quantum vectors **I**, **K**, and **M** (see Fig. 6-45). The first is the angular momentum. Vector **K** is the component of **I** along the symmetry axis z' and M is the component of **I** in a fixed arbitrary direction. The component of **I** perpendicular to **K** is called **R**, and is due to the rotation of the nucleus as a whole. In the rotational ground state of nuclei $\mathbf{K} = \mathbf{\Omega}$.

The energy levels of the system are those of a symmetrical top, but the moment of inertia $\mathscr{I}$ that appears in the formula does not necessarily correspond to the entire nucleus, considered as a rigid body. It is better left as a parameter to be determined experimentally.

With reference to Fig. 6-45 we see that the rotational energy levels are given by

$$E_R = \frac{\hbar^2}{2\mathscr{I}} \langle \mathbf{R}^2 \rangle \tag{6-12.1}$$

but $\mathbf{I} = \mathbf{j} + \mathbf{R}$, and therefore, by the cosine rule and insertion of the quantum-mechanical expectation values, we have

$$\langle R^2 \rangle = [I(I+1) + j(j+1) - 2I_{z'}j_{z'} - 2I_y j_y - 2I_x j_x] \tag{6-12.2}$$

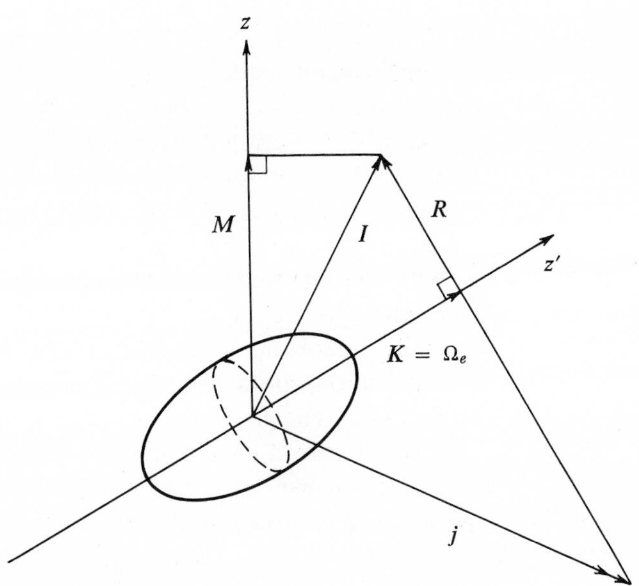

Figure 6-45 Coupling scheme for deformed nuclei. Strongly deformed nuclei still have an axis of symmetry (indicated by z'). The angular momentum properties are characterized by three vectors, constants of the motion: **I, M,** and **K. I** and **M** are the total angular momentum and its components along a fixed axis z. **K** is the component of the angular momentum of a single nucleon (**j**) in the direction of z'. It is thus the same as Ω_p of Sec. 6-12 and is also the component of **I** in the direction of the nuclear axis of symmetry z'. The collective rotational angular momentum **R** is perpendicular to z'. Since there are no collective rotations around a symmetry axis, K is a constant in a rotational band and represents an intrinsic angular momentum. For even-even nuclei, $K = 0$ in the ground state.

The quantity $I_{z'} j_{z'}$ is simply K^2, as is apparent from Fig. 6-45. The last two terms give zero except in the important case, where $K = \frac{1}{2}$. If $K \neq \frac{1}{2}$, we then obtain for the rotational part of the energy the well-known formula

$$E_{\text{rot}} = \frac{\hbar^2}{2\mathcal{I}} I(I + 1) \tag{6-12.3}$$

In this formula, we repeat, $\mathcal{I}$ represents an empirically determined moment of inertia associated with the nuclear deformation.

In the ground state of an even-even nucleus $\Omega = 0$, as we have seen above, K is also zero and hence I vanishes, as has always been found. Furthermore, by exciting the lowest rotational states, we find only even values of I. This can be justified by considering the Sommerfeld quantization rule $\oint p\, dq = 2\pi n\hbar$, where the integral is extended over one period of the motion. In the case considered here, the angular momentum and the angle of rotation are the conjugate variables and the period of the motion is a rotation by π, not by 2π, because such a rotation about I is sufficient to restore the original configuration. This symmetry thus has the consequence that I can take only even values; $I = 0, 2, 4, \ldots$ with even parity. We show in Fig. 6-43 the energy levels corresponding to nuclear rotation for some even-even nuclei. These levels are given with excellent approximation by the formula (6-12.3), and thus for $I = 0, 2, 4, 6$, etc., the rotational energies are in the ratios $E_2{:}E_4{:}E_6{:}E_8 = 6{:}20{:}42{:}72$ (see Fig. 6-42).

In odd-A nuclei with $K \neq \frac{1}{2}$, or in excited states of even-even nuclei with $\Omega \neq 0$, the ground state has

$$I_0 = K = \Omega \tag{6-12.4}$$

and the rotational spectrum has

$$I = I_0, I_0 + 1, I_0 + 2, \text{etc.} \tag{6-12.5}$$

as shown in Fig. 6-45. The case $K = \frac{1}{2}$ is more complicated, and we omit it here.

We have said repeatedly that the effective moment of inertia appearing in the rotational levels is due to nuclear deformation. We can now try to account for its values by models. For instance, we could consider the nucleus as a rigid body or as a liquid in irrotational motion within the nuclear surface. It is at once clear that a deformed nucleus will have an electric quadrupole moment, and thus a connection between $\mathcal{I}$ and Q is apparent and affords a test of the model. This test is especially interesting considering that the large values of certain electric quadrupole moments were the starting point of the idea of collective motions. The first step in evaluating $\mathcal{I}$ is to express the nuclear deformation by a deformation parameter β, defined through the expansion of the nuclear surface in spherical harmonics. Calling $R(\theta)$ the nuclear radius in a direction at angle θ to the symmetry axis, we write

$$R(\theta) = R_0\,(1 + \beta Y_{20}(\cos\theta) + \cdots) \tag{6-12.6}$$

or, stopping at Y_{20},

$$R(\theta) = R_0 \left[1 + \beta \left(\frac{5}{4\pi}\right)^{1/2} (\tfrac{3}{2}\cos^2\theta - \tfrac{1}{2})\right] \tag{6-12.7}$$

For instance, in ellipsoidal nuclei the deformation parameter is approximately related to the difference between the semiaxes ΔR by

$$\frac{\Delta R}{R} = \frac{3}{2}\left(\frac{5}{4\pi}\right)^{1/2}\beta = \delta \tag{6-12.8}$$

Early theories attempted to relate the moment of inertia $\mathcal{I}$ to the deformation parameter β by the model of an irrotational fluid, giving $\mathcal{I}$ proportional to β^2, as shown by the dashed curve in Fig. 6-46. As the data on actual deformation (obtained from electric quadrupole moments and transition probabilities) accumulated, it appeared that the moment of inertia to be used in Eq. (6-12.3) lay between the values predicted by the rigid-body and the irrotational-fluid models. Moments of inertia close to experimental ones have now been calculated by using wave functions of single nucleons, with correlations between different nucleons (see Fig. 6-47). To connect the nuclear deformation with the electric quadrupole moment remember that we must find the expectation value

$$\langle \rho_n(3z^2 - r^2)\rangle = \int \psi^*(3z^2 - r^2)\psi \, d\tau \tag{6-12.9}$$

To compute it we must state which ψ are to be used. In Sec. 6-8 we specified that we must have $M_I = I$, that is, maximum alignment of the nucleus as a whole. This gives the quadrupole moment Q.

It is interesting to compute the expectation value for a nonspherical nucleus in two steps. We define an intrinsic quadrupole moment Q_0 with respect to the rotational-symmetry axis by using as the eigenfunction, not the complete eigenfunction, but only the factors that do not

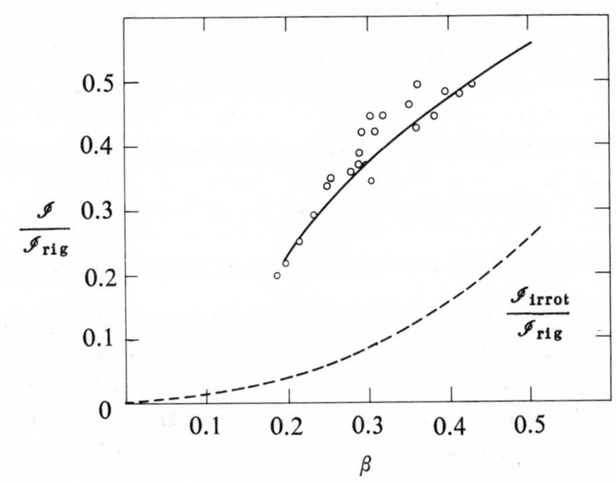

Figure 6-46 Empirical moments of inertia of deformed nuclei, expressed in units of the rigid-body moment, are plotted against the nuclear quadrupole deformations. The dashed curve indicates the curve expected in the case of irrotational flow of a liquid in rotational motion, which is evidently far from the actual situation.

involve the rotation of the nucleus as a whole. In the classical limit Q_0 is simply

$$Q_0 = \int \rho_n(3\xi^2 - r^2)\, d\tau \tag{6-12.10}$$

For example, for a rotation ellipsoid it has the value

$$Q_0 = \frac{4}{5} ZR\, \Delta R \tag{6-12.11}$$

or, introducing β,

$$Q_0 = \frac{4}{5} ZR^2 \frac{3}{2} \left(\frac{5}{4\pi}\right)^{1/2} \beta \tag{6-12.12}$$

Next we pass from Q_0 to Q, multiplying Q_0 by a "projection factor" that is a function of I and K. This projection factor depends on the model chosen.

By using the coupling scheme of Fig. 6-45, a rather complicated calculation gives

$$Q = Q_0 \frac{3K^2 - I(I+1)}{(I+1)(2I+3)} \tag{6-12.13}$$

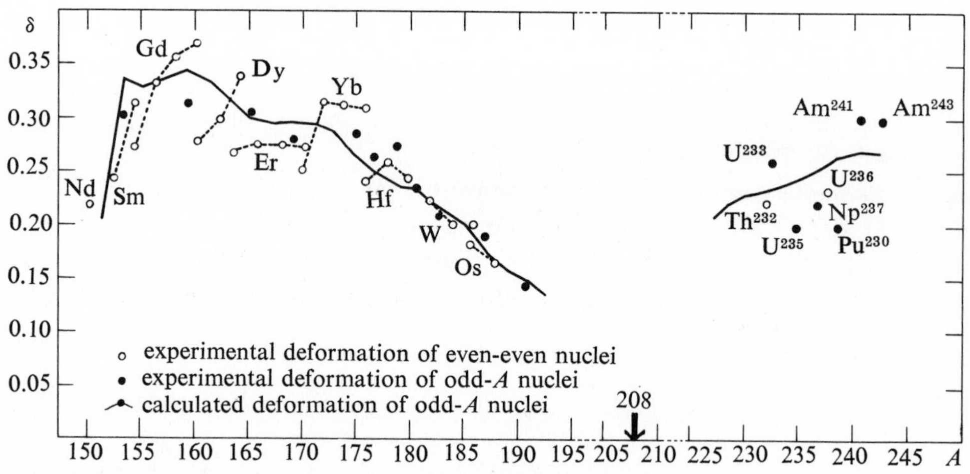

Figure 6-47 Comparison of equilibrium ground-state nuclear deformation calculated from Nilsson wave functions with experimental values. The solid line represents calculated values of the equilibrium deformation for the odd-A nuclei along the valley of beta stability. The experimental data corresponds to δ values obtained by means of the equation

$$Q_0 = \tfrac{4}{5}\, \delta Z R_0^2 (1 + \tfrac{1}{2}\delta + \cdots)$$

using measured Q_0 values. The latter are based on observed $E2$ transition probabilities, and their experimental uncertainty is usually of the order of 10 to 20 per cent. Values of δ corresponding to odd-A nuclides are denoted by dots. Even-even nuclei, denoted by circles, are included for com pleteness. The deformations of the americium isotopes are obtained from hfs measurements. [From B. R. Mottelson and S. G. Nilsson, *Kgl. Danske Videnskab. Selskab, Mat.-Fys. Medd.*, **1,** No. 8 (1959).]

which in the ground state, when $K = I$, reduces to

$$Q = Q_0 \frac{I(2I - 1)}{(I + 1)(2I + 3)} \qquad \text{(6-12.14)}$$

Measurement of Q provides thus means of finding directly the deformation parameter β of Eq. (6-12.8). We can then compute the value of $\mathscr{I}$ to be expected for a rigid body, or for a fluid in irrotational motion contained in an ellipsoidal surface and compare the result with the experimental values of $\mathscr{I}$.

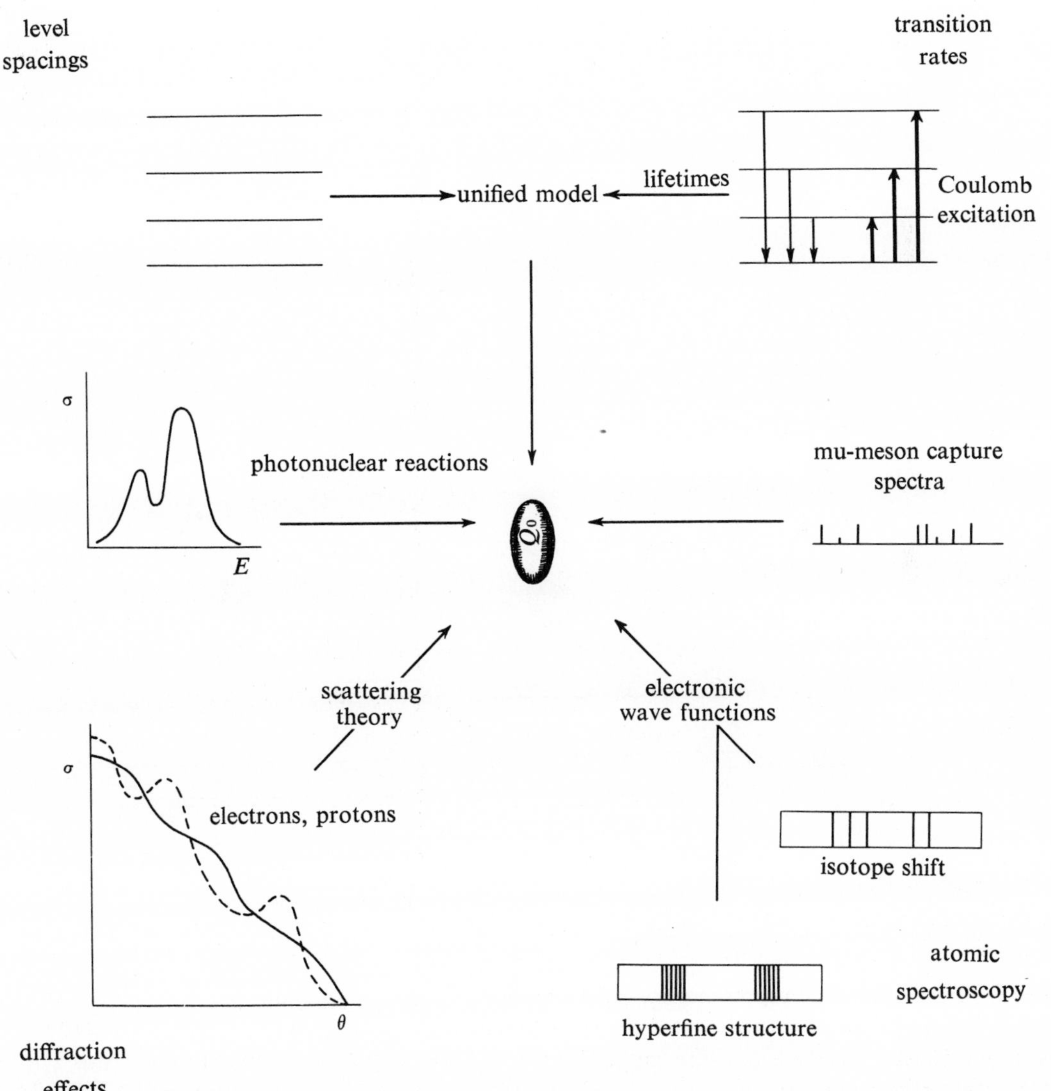

Figure 6-48 Schematic summary of various experimental conditions leading to the intrinsic nuclear quadrupole moment Q_0, and the theoretical concepts involved to obtain Q_0 from its experimental manifestations. [G. Temmer, *Rev. Mod. Phys.*, **30,** 498 (1958).]

The intrinsic quadrupole moment manifests itself not only through Q but also in several other phenomena, such as the isotope shift of spectral lines, the nuclear scattering of electrons or protons and, most prominently, the probability of exciting low rotational levels of a nucleus by the electric field of a heavy particle passing near it (Coulomb excitation; see Chap. 8). This probability is proportional to Q_0^2, which is the same for the initial and final rotational states, in agreement with the definition.

Equation (6-12.14) again shows that, for $I = \frac{1}{2}$, Q is zero even for a finite Q_0. Physically this is due to the fact that if Q_0 cannot be oriented with respect to the total angular momentum I, it averages out to zero owing to the nuclear motions. This result is shown in another form by the argument given in Eqs. (6-8.22) to (6-8.25). The interrelation between the phenomena in which Q or Q_0 play an important role is illustrated in Fig. 6-48.

We close this incomplete outline of current ideas on nuclear models

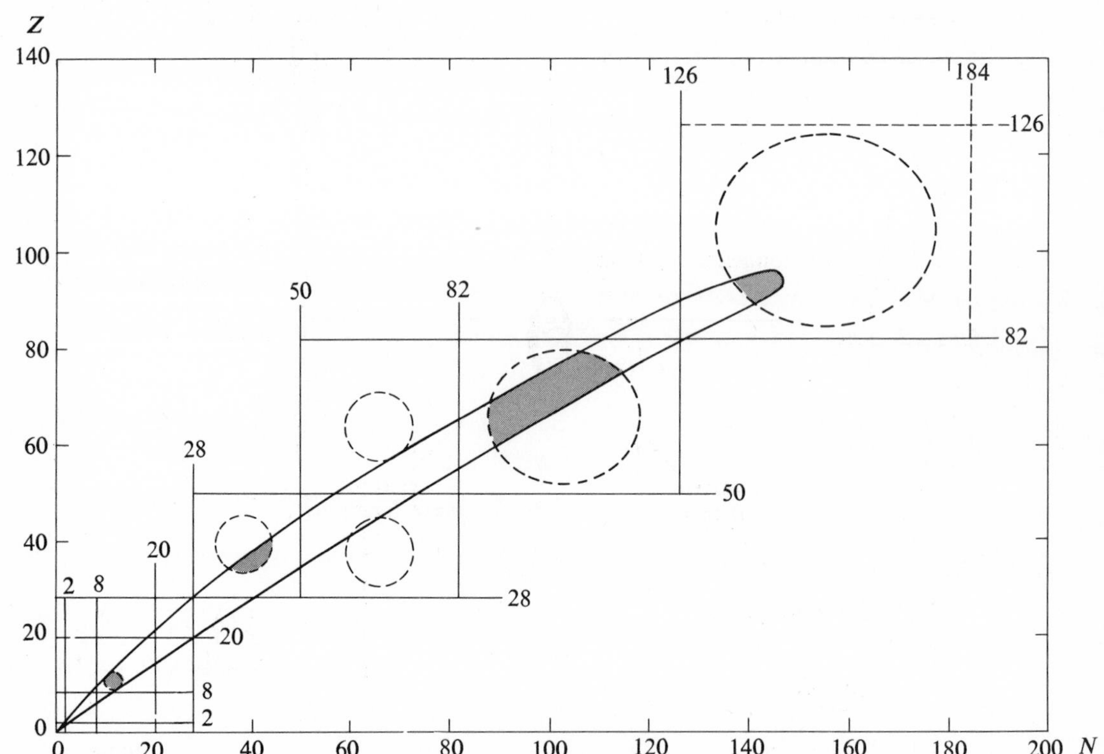

Figure 6-49 A schematic representation of a Z-versus-N chart of the nuclides showing the neutron (vertical lines) and proton (horizontal lines) closed-shell lines. The outer, irregular boundary encloses those nuclei having a half-life longer than 1 minute. The line of beta stability runs approximately down the center of this area. The groups of nuclides where rotational spectra of the type predicted for deformed nuclei have been observed are indicated by shading. Additional regions where it may be possible to find such nuclei are also indicated by dashed lines. [From Marshalek, Person, and Sheline, *Rev. Mod. Phys.*, **35**, 108 (1963).]

showing in Fig. 6-49 the regions to which the different models are applicable, and with a general remark.

The study of the nuclear shell model introduces into nuclear physics many ideas familiar in atomic physics. Similarly the collective model introduces into nuclear physics ideas familiar in molecular physics, and ideas borrowed from the solid-state theory of super conductivity have found their application in nuclear models. Table 6-9 illustrates the point.

Even stereochemistry has inspired an interesting and simple model, although one of limited application. This is the alpha-particle model applicable to light nuclei having the same number of neutrons and protons, this number being a multiple of 4. Evidently one can think of these nuclei (Be^8, C^{12}, O^{16}, etc.) as being composed of He^4 nuclei. The interesting feature here is that such a simple idea can be used to predict successfully several properties of these nuclei (see Fig. 6-50). We cannot further enlarge upon these rapidly developing subjects. However, it is noteworthy that they demonstrate once again the formal relations existing between apparently remote branches of physics.

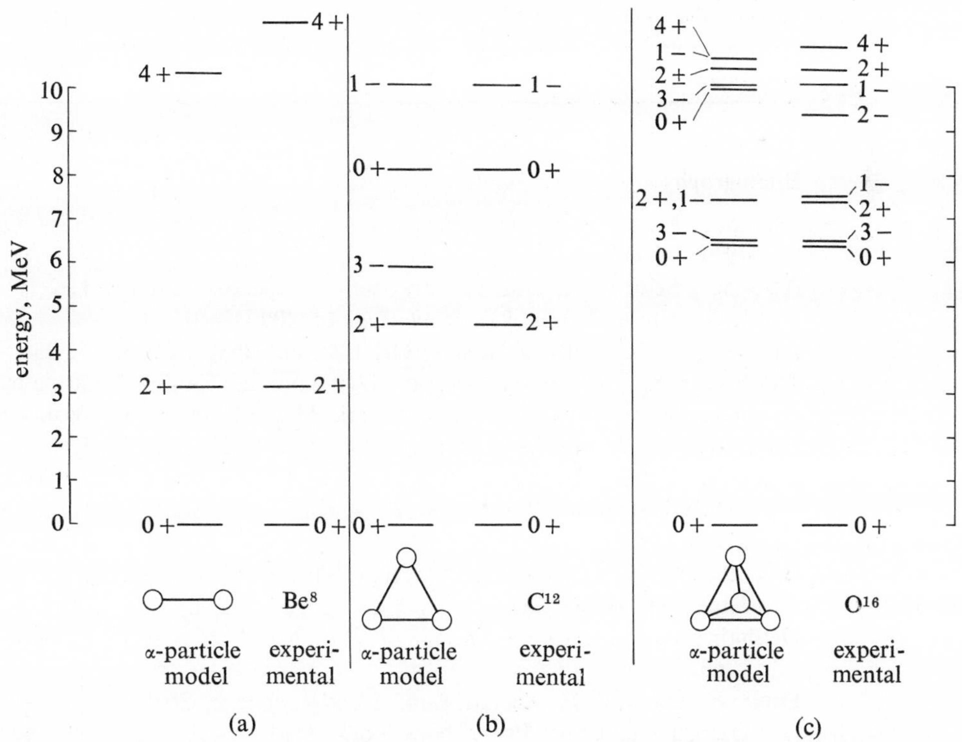

Figure 6-50 Level schemes of Be^8, C^{12}, and O^{16} and a comparison with the alpha-particle model. [From (Fl E).]

Table 6-9 Intrinsic and Collective Motions in Metals, Molecules, and Nuclei (from Moszkowski, with some changes)

Property	Metals	Molecules	Nuclei
Single-particle state occupied by	Electrons	Electrons	Nucleons
Slowly varying parameters that affect motion of single particles	Nuclear lattice constants	Nuclear positions	Form of the nucleus as a whole and its deformations
Intrinsic motions	The electrons move in the periodic field of the lattice	The electrons move in the field of the nuclei	The nucleons move independently in the field formed by the nucleons themselves
Energy levels	Brillouin zones	Electronic levels	Shell levels
Collective motions	Lattice vibrations	Vibrations and rotations	Energies of nucleons in deformed potential
Energy levels	Specific heat	Energy localized in nuclei	Rotational and vibrational energy of the collective motion
Coupling of intrinsic to collective motion	Weak	Strong	Moderate to strong
$\omega_{\text{coll}}/\omega_{\text{part}}$	>1	$\ll 1$	$\leqslant 1$

Bibliography

Abragam, A., *The Principles of Nuclear Magnetism*, Clarendon Press, Oxford, 1961.

Ajzenberg-Selove, F., and T. Lauritsen, "Appendix: Energy Levels of the Light Nuclei," *Ann. Rev. Nucl. Sci.*, **10,** 409 (1960).

Ambler, E., "Methods of Nuclear Orientation," *Progr. Cryog.*, **2,** 235 (1960).

Bainbridge, K. T., "Charged Particle Dynamics and Optics, Relative Isotopic Abundances of the Elements, Atomic Masses," in (Se 59), Vol. I.

Blin-Stoyle, R. J., and M. A. Grace, "Oriented Nuclei," in (Fl E), Vol. 42.

Bohr, A., and B. Mottelson, "Collective and Individual Particle Aspects of Nuclear Structure," *Kgl. Danske Videnskab. Selskab, Mat.-Fys. Medd.*, **27,** 16 (1953).

Brix, P., and H. Kopfermann, "Isotope Shift Studies of Nuclei," *Rev. Mod. Phys.*, **30,** 517 (1958).

DeShalit, A., and I. Talmi, *Nuclear Shell Theory*, Academic Press, New York, 1963.

Drell, S. D., and F. Zachariasen, *Electromagnetic Structure of Nucleons*, Oxford University Press, New York, 1961.

Duckworth, H. E., *Mass Spectroscopy*, Cambridge University Press, New York, 1958.

Elliott, J. P., and A. M. Lane, "The Nuclear Shell-Model," in (Fl E), Vol. 39.

Everling, König, Mattauch, and Wapstra, "Relative Nuclidic Masses," *Nucl. Phys.*, **18,** 529 (1960).

Fernbach, S., "Nuclear Radii as Determined by Scattering of Neutrons," *Rev. Mod. Phys.*, **30,** 414 (1958).

Foldy, L. L., "Neutron-Electron Interaction," *Rev. Mod. Phys.*, **30,** 471 (1958).

Geschwind, S., "Determination of Atomic Masses by Microwave Methods," in (Fl E), Vol. 38.1.

Goldhammer, P., "The Structure of Light Nuclei," *Rev. Mod. Phys.*, **35,** 40 (1963).

Green, A. E. S., "Nuclear Sizes and the Weizsäcker Mass Formula," *Rev. Mod. Phys.*, **30,** 569 (1958).

Hand, Miller, and Wilson, "Electric and Magnetic Form Factors of the Nucleon," *Rev. Mod. Phys.*, **35,** 335 (1963).

Hill, D. L., "Matter and Charge Distribution within Atomic Nuclei," in (Fl E), Vol. 39.

Hintenberger, H., "High-Sensitivity Mass Spectroscopy in Nuclear Studies," *Ann. Rev. Nucl. Sci.*, **12,** 435 (1962).

Hofstadter, R., "Nuclear and Nucleon Scattering of High-Energy Electrons," *Ann. Rev. Nucl. Sci.*, **7,** 231 (1957).

Hofstadter, R., *Nuclear and Nucleon Structure*, Benjamin, New York, 1963.

Jeffries, C. D. *Dynamic Nuclear Orientation*, Wiley-Interscience, New York, 1963.

Kelly, F. M., "Determination of Nuclear Spins and Magnetic Moments by Spectroscopic Methods," in (Fl E), Vol. 38.1.

Kofoed-Hansen, O., "Mirror Nuclei Determinations of Nuclear Size," *Rev. Mod. Phys.*, **30,** 449 (1958).

Kopfermann, H. (Ko 58).

Laukien, G., "Nuclear Magnetic High Frequency Spectroscopy," in (Fl E), Vol. 38.1.

Mack, J. E., and H. Arroe, "Isotope Shift in Atomic Spectra," *Ann. Rev. Nucl. Sci.*, **6,** 117 (1956).

Marshalek, Person, and Sheline, "Systematics of Deformation of Atomic Nuclei," *Rev. Mod. Phys.*, **35,** 108 (1963).

Mayer, M. G., and J. H. D. Jensen, (MJ 55).

Moszkowski, S. A., "Models of Nuclear Structure," in (Fl E), Vol. 39.

Nemirowsky, P. E., *Nuclear Models*, Spon Ltd., London, 1963.

Nierenberg, W. A. "Measurement of the Nuclear Spins and Static Moments of Radioactive Isotopes," *Ann. Rev. Nucl. Sci.*, **7,** 349 (1957).

Preston, M. A. (P.62).

Ramsey, N. F. (Ra 56).

Ramsey, N. F., "Nuclear Moments and Statistics," in (Se 59), Vol. I.

Rasmussen, J. O., "Nuclear Radii from Alpha-Particle Scattering and Alpha Radioactivity," *Rev. Mod. Phys.*, **30,** 424 (1958).

Roberts, L. D., and J. W. T. Dabbs, "Nuclear Orientation," *Ann. Rev. Nucl. Sci.*, **11,** 175 (1961).

Seeger, P. A., "Semiempirical Atomic Mass Law," *Nucl. Phys.*, **25,** 1 (1961).

Sheline, R. K., "Vibrational States in Deformed Even-Even Nuclei," *Rev. Mod. Phys.*, **32,** 1 (1960).

Talmi, I., "Effective Interactions and Coupling Schemes in Nuclei," *Rev. Mod. Phys.*, **34,** 704 (1962).

Talmi, I., and I. Unna, "Theoretical Interpretation of Energy Levels of Light Nuclei," *Ann. Rev. Nucl. Sci.*, **10,** 353 (1960).

Townes, C. H., "Determination of Nuclear Quadrupole Moments," in (Fl E), Vol. 38.1.

Wapstra, A. H., "Atomic Masses of Nuclides," in (Fl E), Vol. 38.1.

Weisskopf, V. F., "Problems of Nuclear Structure," *Phys. Today*, **14,** 18 (1961).

Wilets, L., "Isotope Shifts," in (Fl E), Vol. 38.1.

Problems

6-1 Show that ions of the same charge starting from rest in static electric fields follow the same trajectory, irrespective of their mass.

6-2 Show that ions of the same charge starting from rest in any combination of static electric and magnetic fields follow the same trajectories if their mass is multiplied by a fixed number K while all electric fields are multiplied by $1/K$ and the magnetic fields are left unchanged.

6-3 From the mass doublets given in Sec. 6-2 find the masses of H_1^1 and D_1^2.

When neutrons are captured by H_1^1 to form D_1^2, gamma rays of 2.230 ± 0.005 MeV are observed. Find the mass of the neutron.

6-4 The following two nuclear reactions have been observed:

$$N^{14} + He^4 = O^{17} + H^1 - 1.26 \text{ MeV}$$

$$O^{16} + H^2 = N^{14} + He^4 + 3.13 \text{ MeV}$$

Bombarding O^{16} with H^2, $O^{17} + H^1$ is also formed. Calculate the energy of the protons ejected at 90° and at 0° with respect to the direction of the deuterons, in the laboratory system, as a function of the deuteron energy.

6-5 Find the threshold for the (γ,n) reaction on N^{14} from the following data:

N^{13} is a positron emitter with an upper energy limit of 1.2 MeV.

Mass of N^{14} = 14.00307 Mass of C^{13} = 13.00335

6-6 Find the threshold for the p,n reaction of Cu^{63} given that

$$Cu^{63} + H = Zn^{63} + n$$

$$Zn^{63} = Cu^{63} + e^+ + \nu$$

and the upper limit for the positron energy is 2.3 MeV.

6-7 At what value of Z does the lowest Bohr orbit of a μ meson just fall inside the nuclear radius?

6-8 Given that the proton has a root-mean-square radius of 0.8 F, and assuming a uniform charge distribution (*a*) calculate the radius R for the proton, (*b*) what value of momentum transfer (express as $\hbar q$ in MeV/c) is required to observe a decrease from the point-charge cross section by a factor of 10? What is the minimum electron energy required to produce this effect?

6-9 The form factors in electron scattering can be written as

$$F(q) = \frac{1}{Ze}\int \rho e^{-i\mathbf{q}\cdot\mathbf{r}}\, d\tau$$

Show that for a spherically symmetric $\rho(r)$ this reduces to

$$F(q) = \frac{4\pi}{q}\int_0^\infty \rho r \sin(qr)\, dr$$

Further, show that

$$F(q) = 1 - \frac{q^2 \langle r^2 \rangle}{6} \ldots$$

where

$$\langle r^2 \rangle = 4\pi \int_0^\infty \rho r^4 \, dr$$

6-10 Calculate $F(q)$ for the distribution

$$\rho = \rho_0 \qquad 0 < r < R$$
$$\rho = 0 \qquad r > R$$

6-11 In order to find $F_1{}^2(q)$ and $F_2{}^2(q)$ [Eq. (6-3.18)], measurements of $d\sigma/d\omega$ at different values of θ, but at the same value of q, are useful. One procedure is to measure the quantity in the braces of Eq. (6-3.18), called R, and plot curves with F_1 as abscissa and F_2 as ordinate for constant q, giving the number R. Vary θ, at constant q, and consider a new curve for the new measured R. From these measurements F_1 and F_2 are found (with some ambiguities). Discuss the algebra of the problem.

6-12 Show that two identical nuclei of spin I give rise to $(2I + 1)^2$ linearly independent spin eigenfunctions. Of these $I(2I + 1)$ are antisymmetric and $(I + 1)(2I + 1)$ are symmetric with respect to nuclear exchange. Apply to the case $I = 1$ and construct the eigenfunctions.

6-13 Show that the electrostatic energy of a uniformly charged sphere of radius R is $\frac{3}{5}(Q^2/R)$, where Q is the total charge of the sphere.

6-14 Apply the mass formula to the isobaric pairs $(\text{Cd-In})^{113}$, $(\text{Os-Re})^{187}$, $(\text{Sb-Te})^{123}$ and discuss what types of activities you would expect.

6-15 With the mass formula calculate the energy to be expected in a uranium fission. Compare the instantaneous energy release to that due to beta and gamma activity of the fission products. Assume that U splits into equal fragments.

6-16 Calculate the magnetic field at the nucleus of a hydrogen atom and of an atom of Fr in their ground states.

6-17 Discuss methods for producing elements with $Z > 100$, taking into account α, β, and spontaneous fission decay. Use a table of masses for the new isotopes.

6-18 Calculate the surface energy of a nucleus, assuming that the binding energy of a nucleon B is the surface energy corresponding to the small bulge produced in the nuclear surface by a nucleon before it escapes the nucleus.

6-19 Suppose we consider a proton as a uniformly dense sphere of radius $R = 1 \times 10^{-13}$ cm. (*a*) What angular velocity is needed to give it an angular momentum of $(3/4)^{1/2}\hbar$? (*b*) What rotational kinetic energy does this correspond to? (*c*) How many amperes are going around the axis of rotation of the proton?

6-20 (*a*) Consider two particles of masses m_1, m_2 revolving in a circular orbit about their common center of mass. If their charges are e_1, e_2 respectively, calculate the gyromagnetic ratio of the system; neglect spins. (*b*) Apply this result to the calculation of the orbital g factor, g_l, for the following systems: (i) The neutron and proton in a deuterium nucleus. (ii) A μ^- meson (charge e^-, mass $= 207m_e$) bound to a proton.

6-21 Back and Wulff [*Z. Physik*, **66**, 31 (1930)] measured the hyperfine structure of the line 3775, $7s^2S_{1/2} - 6p^2P_{1/2}$ of Tl^{205} and found three components, as shown in the figure below.

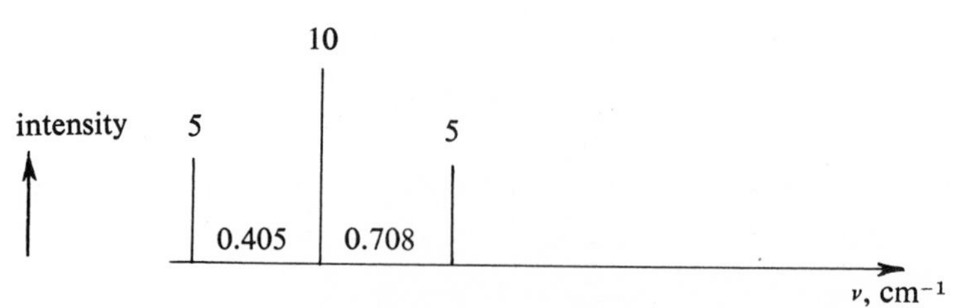

Deduce all that you can about the spin and magnetic moment of the nucleus. The $^2P_{1/2}$ has a larger term splitting than $^2S_{1/2}$. Calculate the Zeeman effect of this hyperfine structure.

6-22 Show that for an atom having $J = \frac{1}{2}$, the hyperfine-structure energy levels in an external field H are given by

$$W_M = -\frac{\Delta W}{2(2I+1)} - \frac{\mu_I}{I} Hm \pm \frac{\Delta W}{2}\left(1 + \frac{4m}{2I+1}x + x^2\right)^{1/2}$$

where $\Delta W = (A/2)(2I + 1) = W(F = I + \frac{1}{2}) - W(F = I - \frac{1}{2}) = 2\pi\hbar\ \Delta\nu$, $x = [(-\mu_J/J) + (\mu_I/I)]H/\Delta W$, and the upper sign is used for $F = I + \frac{1}{2}$, the lower for $F = I - \frac{1}{2}$. (Breit–Rabi formula). Show that this exact relation has as limiting cases Eqs. (6-6.43) and (6-6.44). Calculate from the Breit–Rabi formula μ_{eff}.

6-23 Figure out how the apparatus of Fig. 6-31 works.

6-24 An atomic-beam experiment was performed to measure the spin of 3.2h Ag^{112}. A resonance of the flop-in type, that is a transition from a state $F' = F'' = I + \frac{1}{2}$, $M_F' = -I + \frac{1}{2}$, to $M_F'' = -I - \frac{1}{2}$ was observed for a frequency of 5.825 Mc/sec. In the same beam Rb^{85} gave the same type of resonance for a frequency of 4.685 Mc/sec. I of Rb^{85} is $\frac{5}{2}$. Find I of Ag^{112}.

6-25 With the same substances, Ag^{112} and Rb^{85}, one observed, at a higher magnetic field than in the previous problem, the same type of transition at frequencies 91.739 Mc/sec for Rb^{85} and 204.920 Mc/sec for Ag^{112}. Calculate a and $\Delta\nu$ for Ag^{112}. $g_J = -2.00238$ for Rb and $-$ 2.00233 for Ag.

6-26 For Ag^{107}, $\Delta\nu = -1{,}712.56$ Mc/sec, $I = \frac{1}{2}$, $g_I = -0.2261$ nuclear magnetons. Find using the previous results g_I and μ_I for Ag^{112}.

6-27 Show that for a homogeneous ellipsoid of semiaxes a, a, b the quadrupole moment is given by $Q = \frac{2}{5}(b^2 - a^2)$.

6-28 The nuclear electric quadrupole moment due to one proton is defined as the expectation value of $\langle 3z^2 - r^2 \rangle = Q$ for the state in which $M_I = I$ (which is the state of maximum alignment).

Giving an explicit form to the eigenfunction of the proton,

$$R(r)\, Y_l^l(\theta,\varphi)\alpha$$

where R is the radial function, Y_l^l the spherical harmonic, and α the spin function, show that for $I = l + \frac{1}{2}$,

$$Q = -\frac{2l}{2l+3}\langle r^2 \rangle = -\frac{2I-1}{2I+2}\langle r^2 \rangle$$

The same expression of Q as a function of I is valid for $I = l - \frac{1}{2}$.

6-29 Show that the values of

$$Q(M) = \langle 3z^2 - r^2 \rangle$$

for $M \neq I$ are given by

$$Q(M) = Q(I)\frac{3M^2 - I(I+1)}{I(2I - 1)}$$

6-30 Show that for a rotational ellipsoid of small eccentricity and uniform charge density $Q_0 = \frac{4}{5} ZR\,\Delta R$ and that the parameters β, δ and the eccentricity of the ellipsoid are connected by

$$\pm e = \frac{|a^2 - b^2|^{1/2}}{a} = \left(\frac{2\Delta R}{R}\right)^{1/2} \qquad \frac{\Delta R}{R} = \delta = \frac{3}{4}\left(\frac{5}{\pi}\right)^{1/2}\beta$$

where $2a$ is the length of the rotational axis and $2b$ the length of the other two axes. Signs are such that for a cigar shape $e > 0$, for a lens shape $e < 0$; $\Delta R = a - b$.

6-31 Calculate the alignment coefficients f_1, f_2 for a system of deuterons at $T = 10^{-2}$ °K in a field of 10^5 gauss.

6-32 A dynamic scheme of proton polarization envisages hydrogen atoms in a magnetic field giving levels as illustrated below, where the magnetic moment of the electron is opposite to H in (1) and (2) and the magnetic moment of the proton is parallel to H in (1) and opposite in (2). Find the orientations of these moments in levels (3) and (4). Now consider a tuned radio frequency (calculate its frequency) that, given sufficient intensity, equalizes the populations of states (2) and (3). Calculate the populations of states (1) and (4) taking them to be in thermal equilibrium with (3) and (2), respectively. From this show that the nuclear polarization is $-\tanh(\delta/2kT) \approx -\delta/2kT$.

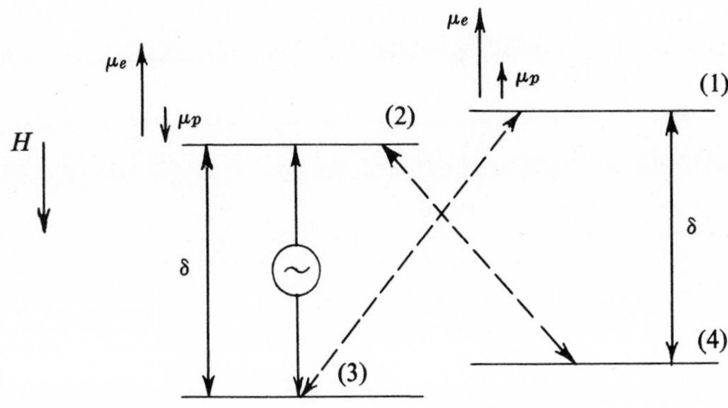

6-33 Consider two particles with magnetic moments μ_1 and μ_2, each having the same spin **s**. Calculate their total magnetic moment in a state of zero orbital angular momentum and total spin **I**. (Express the result in terms of μ_1, μ_2, s, and I.) What is the magnetic moment when $I = 0$?

6-34 (*a*) Suppose that we try to interpret the $_2He^3$ nucleus (spin $\frac{1}{2}$) as a two-body system consisting of a deuteron bound to a proton, in a state of zero orbital angular momentum (s state). From the known deuterium magnetic moment ($0.857\mu_n$) and proton moment ($2.79\mu_n$), calculate the $_2He^3$

magnetic moment expected on this model. (*b*) What is the Schmidt model prediction for $_2He^3$, assuming the odd nucleon to be in an $s_{1/2}$ state? (*c*) Which agrees better with the measured value of $-2.13\,\mu_n$?

6-35 For the following nuclei the spins and parities of the ground state are given. Justify the observed values by shell-model considerations:

$He^3(\frac{1}{2}+)$ $Ne^{21}(\frac{3}{2}+)$ $Al^{27}(\frac{5}{2}+)$ $K^{38}(3+)$ $Ga^{66}(1+)$ $Ga^{69}(\frac{3}{2}-)$
$Bi^{209}(\frac{9}{2}-)$ $Bi^{210}(1-)$

Remember that *s*, *d*, *g* nucleons have + parity and *p*, *f*, etc., have − parity. [From (P 62).]

6-36 Show that Nordheim rules forbid the existence of odd-odd nuclei with ground states 0+ or 1−. Find some exceptions. [From (P 62).]

6-37 Describe the physical conditions under which $I = K \to \infty$ or $I \to \infty$, with K constant and small, and explain why in the first case $Q = Q_0$ and in the second $Q = -Q_0/2$. Note in the second case the opposite sign of Q and Q_0 and explain it.

CHAPTER VII

Alpha Emission

NUCLEI SUBJECTED to nuclear bombardment are known to emit many types of heavy particles, such as neutrons, protons, alpha particles, and deuterons. We shall not consider bombardment in this chapter but shall concentrate instead on spontaneous processes, that is, processes arising from metastable states that have a relatively long life. These involve only the emission of alpha particles and spontaneous fission, as far as heavy particles are concerned. The emission of delayed neutrons is really an instantaneous process; its apparent slowness is caused by the fact that it must be preceded by the emission of a beta ray. The emission of delayed neutrons will be treated in Chap. 11.

The study of alpha-particle emission is a rather large and important chapter of nuclear physics. The accumulation of experimental material, which continues to increase at a rapid pace, has helped considerably in the formulation and refinement of nuclear models. The theory still leaves many interesting problems unsolved, mainly those of trying to understand the hindrance factors (see Sec. 7-2) and to correlate them to specific models.

7-1 Introduction

Why are alpha particles emitted by nuclei? Why do we not have a proton or deuteron radioactivity? The answer to this question is found in the release of nuclear energy accompanying the reactions. The alpha particle has such a large mass defect that emission of an alpha particle is energetically possible when proton emission is not. This feature is clearly shown by the semiemperical mass formula given in Sec. 6-5. It is also apparent from the formula that alpha radioactivity is expected only for heavy nuclei; however, the sharpness of the boundary of the zone of alpha radioactivity at $Z = 83$ is an effect of the shell structure of the nucleus (see Sec. 6-11). A few alpha emitters—Pt^{190}, Hf^{174}, Gd^{152}, Sm^{147}, and Nd^{144}—occur at lower Z (Fig. 7-1).

If we want to treat alpha emission by classical arguments, we face the following paradox: by scattering alpha particles on heavy nuclei and observing whether or not they follow Rutherford's law, it is possible to map the electrostatic potential to which the alpha particle is subject as a function of its distance from the center of the nucleus (Fig. 7-2). We thus find a potential energy

$$V(r) = \frac{Ze}{r} \quad \text{for} \quad r > R \tag{7-1.1}$$

For $r < R$, nuclear forces become effective, and the potential is not simply the electrostatic one. However, we might try to represent the attractive force that retains the alpha particle in the nucleus by a potential well of suitable depth. The total energy E of the alpha particle is known, because we can measure its kinetic energy directly once it leaves the nucleus. If we try to reconcile these facts with classical mechanics, we confront a paradox. We know that alpha particles remain in the nucleus a long time—a very long time compared with the period necessary for them to cross it if they are moving with a velocity corresponding to their kinetic energy outside the nucleus. One would conclude that if the potential barrier preventing their escape is low enough they should be emitted in a time of the order of magnitude of the nuclear radius divided by their velocity. Conversely, if with the energy available, the potential barrier is insurmountable, they should never be able to leave the nucleus.

This paradox was resolved by Gamow and by Condon and Gurney (1929), who, treating the problem quantum mechanically, showed that there is a finite probability of escape even in the case for which classical mechanics would predict an absolutely impenetrable barrier and hence

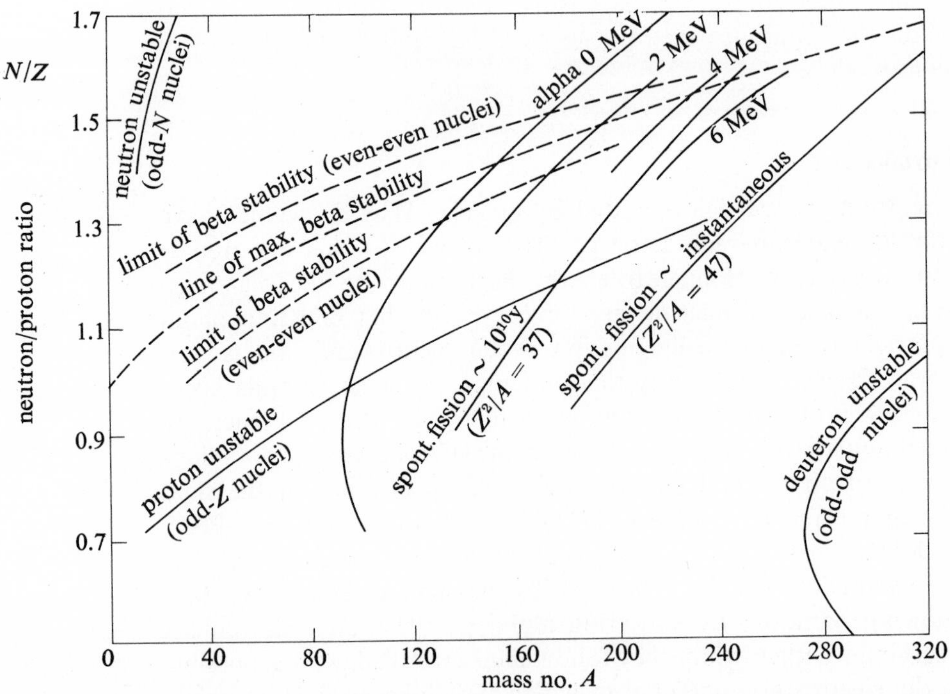

Figure 7-1 Nuclear stability limits predicted by the liquid-drop model. The curves are calculated from the semiempirical mass formula of Chap. 6. [After G. C. Hanna, from (Se 59).]

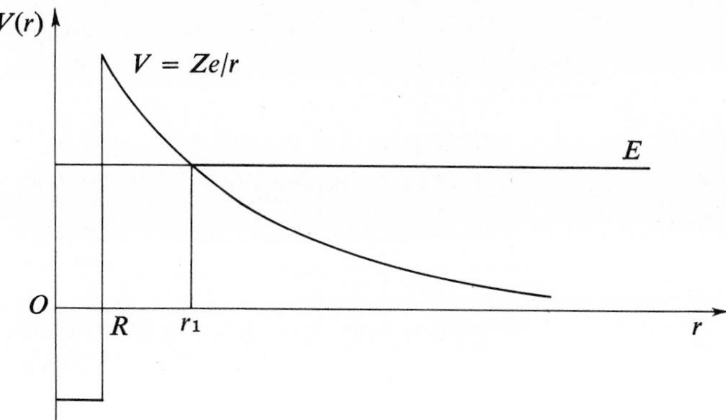

Figure 7-2 Electrostatic potential energy of an alpha particle as a function of the distance from the center of the nucleus.

nuclear stability. In order to show the essential points of the argument without becoming involved in mathematical difficulties, we shall proceed in several steps. First, we shall use a semiclassical argument developed by von Laue, which will give an estimate of the decay constant of an alpha emitter. Second, we shall study some important characteristic features of the quantum-mechanical problem.

It is known that if we try to find a stationary solution to the one-dimensional problem of a potential energy barrier (Fig. 7-3) we find that even a barrier higher than the total energy of the particles has a finite transparency.

Assume a barrier of the form shown in Fig. 7-3 with width a. We shall consider only the case of interest to us, $V > E$. A set of solutions to Schrödinger's equation

$$\frac{d^2u}{dx^2} + \frac{2m}{\hbar^2}(E - V)\,u = 0 \tag{7-1.2}$$

in zones I, II, and III is

$$u_{\text{I}} = A_{\text{I}}\,e^{ikx} + B_{\text{I}}\,e^{-ikx} \qquad -\infty < x < 0 \tag{7-1.3}$$

$$u_{\text{II}} = A_{\text{II}}\,e^{+Kx} + B_{\text{II}}\,e^{-Kx} \qquad 0 < x < a \tag{7-1.4}$$

$$u_{\text{III}} = A_{\text{III}}\,e^{ikx} + B_{\text{III}}\,e^{-ikx} \qquad a < x < \infty \tag{7-1.5}$$

with

$$k = \frac{(2mE)^{1/2}}{\hbar} = \frac{p}{\hbar} = \frac{1}{\lambda\!\!\!^{-}} \tag{7-1.6}$$

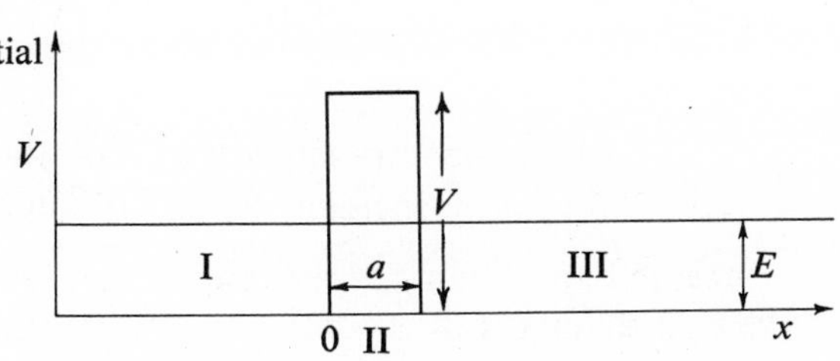

Figure 7-3 A barrier of thickness a, corresponding to the potential energy V. The solutions of Eq. (7-1.2) for the zones I, II, and III are given in the text.

$$K = \frac{(2m|E - V|)^{1/2}}{\hbar} \tag{7-1.7}$$

where p is the momentum and λ the de Broglie wavelength. We must determine the A's and B's in such a way that

$$u \text{ and } u' = \frac{du}{dx} \tag{7-1.8}$$

are continuous, as known from elementary quantum mechanics. Moreover, in region III we want to have only particles moving to the right, which means

$$B_{\text{III}} = 0 \tag{7-1.9}$$

The calculation gives at $x = a$

$$A_{\text{III}}\, e^{ika} = A_{\text{II}}\, e^{Ka} + B_{\text{II}}e^{-Ka} \tag{7-1.10}$$

$$ik\, A_{\text{III}}e^{ika} = K(A_{\text{II}}e^{Ka} - B_{\text{II}}e^{-Ka}) \tag{7-1.11}$$

Solving for A_{II} and B_{II} one obtains

$$A_{\text{II}} = \frac{A_{\text{III}}}{2}\left(1 + \frac{ik}{K}\right) e^{(ik-K)a} \tag{7-1.12}$$

$$B_{\text{II}} = \frac{A_{\text{III}}}{2}\left(1 - \frac{ik}{K}\right) e^{(ik+K)a} \tag{7-1.13}$$

At the other side of the barrier for $x = 0$ one has

$$A_{\text{I}} + B_{\text{I}} = A_{\text{II}} + B_{\text{II}} \tag{7-1.14}$$

$$A_{\text{I}} - B_{\text{I}} = (A_{\text{II}} - B_{\text{II}})\frac{K}{ik} \tag{7-1.15}$$

We should eliminate A_{II} and B_{II} between Eqs. (7-1.12), (7-1.13), (7-1.14), and (7-1.15), and find the relation between A_{I}, amplitude of an incoming wave; B_{I}, amplitude of a reflected wave; and A_{III}, amplitude of a transmitted wave. In practical cases $Ka \gg 1$, and this condition, equivalent to small transparency of the barrier, permits us to simplify considerably the formulas. In fact, if $Ka \gg 1$, we can neglect A_{II} compared with B_{II} and obtain

$$2A_{\text{I}} = B_{\text{II}}\left(1 - \frac{K}{ik}\right) = \frac{A_{\text{III}}}{2}\left(1 - \frac{ik}{K}\right)\left(1 - \frac{K}{ik}\right) e^{(ik+K)a} \tag{7-1.16}$$

The ratio

$$\frac{|A_{\text{III}}|^2}{|A_{\text{I}}|^2} = \frac{16k^2K^2 \exp(-2Ka)}{(k^2 + K^2)^2} \sim e^{-2Ka} = T \tag{7-1.17}$$

gives the "transmissivity" of the barrier, that is, the flux transmitted for unity incident flux. To calculate the reflectivity

$$R = \frac{|B_{\text{I}}|^2}{|A_{\text{I}}|^2} \tag{7-1.18}$$

one must use the exact solution of the problem. As is to be expected, one finds

$$R + T = 1 \tag{7-1.19}$$

In the case of a variable potential the transparency is approximately expressed by a simple generalization of Eq. (7-1.17),

$$T = \exp\left[-\frac{2}{\hbar}\int_R^{r_1}(2m|E - V|)^{1/2}\,dx\right] = e^{-2G} \tag{7-1.20}$$

The integral is to be extended through the region in which $E - V < 0$, that is, to the forbidden region of classical mechanics.

Passing to the tridimensional case without angular momentum and for the Coulomb potential,

$$V = \frac{zZe^2}{r} \tag{7-1.21}$$

we have

$$E = \frac{zZe^2}{r_1} \tag{7-1.22}$$

where E is the kinetic energy of the alpha particle for large separation. We also define the barrier height as

$$B = \frac{Zze^2}{R} \tag{7-1.23}$$

We can then calculate G explicitly, finding

$$G = \frac{(2m)^{1/2}}{\hbar}\int_R^{r_1}\left(\frac{Zze^2}{r} - E\right)^{1/2} dr = \frac{(2mZze^2r_1)^{1/2}}{\hbar} \times \left[\arccos\left(\frac{R}{r_1}\right)^{1/2} - \left(\frac{R}{r_1} - \frac{R^2}{r_1^2}\right)^{1/2}\right] \tag{7-1.24}$$

This formula may be rewritten using $x = R/r_1 = E/B$ and $v = (2E/m)^{1/2}$ as

$$G = \left(\frac{1}{\hbar}\right)\left(\frac{2m}{E}\right)^{1/2} zZe^2\,[\arccos(x^{1/2}) - x^{1/2}(1 - x)^{1/2}] \tag{7-1.25}$$

or

$$G = \frac{2zZe^2}{\hbar v}\,\gamma(x) \tag{7-1.26}$$

with

$$\gamma(x) = \arccos(x^{1/2}) - x^{1/2}(1 - x)^{1/2}$$

The function $\gamma(x)$ has been tabulated and is found, for example, in Bethe, and in Perlman and Rasmussen. For $x \ll 1$ it is approximately $\gamma(x) \to (1/2)\pi - 2x^{1/2} + \cdots$. For $x = E/B \ll 1$, G can be crudely approximated by

$$G \approx \frac{\pi zZe^2}{\hbar v} - \frac{2e}{\hbar}(2zZmR)^{1/2} \tag{7-1.27}$$

From the transparency we pass to the decay constant of the nucleus by assuming that an alpha particle moves inside the potential well with a certain velocity v_0 and hence hits the wall $v_0/2R$ or, in a tridimensional case, v_0/R times per second. At each "hit" it has the probability T of leaking out; hence the decay constant

$$\lambda = \frac{v_0}{R} e^{-2G} \tag{7-1.28}$$

Here v_0 and R can be inferred crudely from the velocity of the alpha particle outside the nucleus and from any estimate of the nuclear radius, but the really important factor is e^{-2G}.

The velocity v_0 is of the order of 10^9 cm/sec, and R is about 10^{-12} cm. Hence, the alpha particle may make 10^{21} attempts per second to escape; e^{-2G} must range from 10^{-13} to 10^{-39} to encompass the decay constants of short-lived substances such as ThC′(Po^{212}) with a period of 3.0×10^{-7} sec, and long-lived substances such as U^{238} with a period of 4.5×10^9 years. The factor v_0/R might vary a little from nucleus to nucleus, but it is clear that a variation of 26 powers of 10 can come only from the transparency, where $2G$ in the exponential is a function of R and E.

In the one-dimensional model the angular momentum is automatically zero; however, in the real case the centrifugal potential energy $\hbar^2 l(l+1)/mr^2$ ($l\hbar$ is the angular momentum) must be added to the Coulomb potential. Its effect is generally very small in the case of the alpha decay, and it has been neglected in the previous analysis.

Using the approximate expression of G [Eqs. (7-1.24) and (7-1.27)], we can write, for $E/B \ll 1$,

$$\log \lambda = \frac{-(2mB)^{1/2}}{\hbar} R\left[\pi\left(\frac{B}{E}\right)^{1/2} - 4\right] + \log\frac{v_0}{R} \tag{7-1.29}$$

where we have neglected terms containing positive powers of E/B. Remembering the dependence of B on R [Eq. (7-1.23)] and the fact that R is proportional to $A^{1/3}$, we recognize that for a series of isotopes we can expect that $\log \lambda$ will be approximately a linear function or $E^{-1/2}$ (Fig. 7-4). A numerical formula for the half-life T (in years) given by Taagepera and Nurmia is

$$\log_{10} T = 1.61\,(ZE^{-1/2} - Z^{2/3}) - 28.9 \tag{7-1.30}$$

E is in MeV and Z refers to the daughter substance. It is derived from Eq. (7-1.29) using suitable semiempirical formulas for the dependance of R on Z. One can use Eqs. (7-1.25) and (7-1.28) to calculate R from the experimentally known decay constants and energies of the alpha particles. This has been done extensively and one finds that the R value calculated from ground transitions of even-even nuclei show great uniformity, corresponding to values of about $1.5 \times 10^{-13} A^{1/3}$ cm. Nuclei below the neutron closed shell of 126 show rates slower by an order of magnitude, hence they give effective R values somewhat smaller than other nuclei do. Decay rates of odd nuclei tend to be smaller than would be predicted by systematics of even-even rates.

This method of determining the nuclear radius was one of the earliest used. It gives a value higher than others by about 20 per cent. It should be remembered, however, that the definition of nuclear radius used here applies to a special model. One could argue that the radius measured is near the sum of the alpha-particle radius plus the nuclear radius itself.

Geiger and Nuttall as early as 1911 had plotted the logarithm of the half-life versus the range of the alpha particles, observing a remarkable regularity (Fig. 7-5). The range is in fair approximation proportional to $E^{1.5}$, and hence the old Geiger–Nuttall plot is in principle similar to the plot of Fig. 7-4. It shows in a striking way the importance of energy in determining the decay constant.

7-2 Fine Structure of Alpha Spectra

Alpha decay usually involves a nucleus in the ground state. However, many alpha emitters show a line spectrum of alpha particles (Rosenblum, 1929), owing to the fact that there are several final levels for the alpha transition. This explanation is confirmed by the fact that

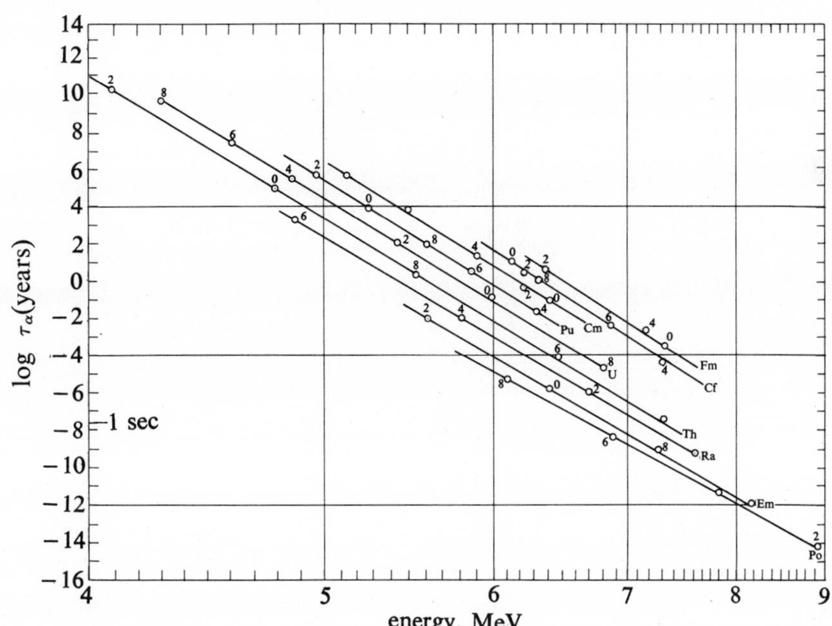

Figure 7-4 Plot of logarithms of partial alpha half-lives for ground-state transitions vs. the inverse square root of the total alpha-decay energy (alpha-particle energy + recoil energy). The points are experimental, and the straight lines are based on a least-squares analysis of the points where energies have been determined by magnetic spectrographs. The prints are numbered with the last figure of the mass number. [C. J. Gallagher and J. O. Rasmusen, *J. Inorg. Nucl. Chem.*, **3,** 333 (1957).]

one finds gamma rays of energy corresponding to the energy difference between the alpha lines. An example of this situation is given in Fig. 7-6. It will be noted that the lower levels of U^{234} have angular momenta 0, 2, 4 and energy separations in the ratio expected for rotational levels of a rigid rotator, as was mentioned in Sec. 6-12.

The different alpha lines have intensities determined primarily by their energy, which affects the transparency of the barrier, and to a lesser extent by the influence on the barrier of the angular momentum. Other factors, not all clearly understood, alter in specific cases the decay constant expected in the simple penetration picture.

In the case of Po^{212} (ThC′) and Po^{214}(RaC′) we have the instance of a structure in the upper level. The alpha decay is so rapid that it can compete with the gamma transitions between the upper levels. We thus have "exceptionally long range alpha particles" (Figs. 7-7 and 7-8). They are very rare, and they are interesting because they afford a method of measuring gamma-decay rates, if one knows the alpha-decay rate. One has for the upper state

$$\frac{\lambda_\gamma}{\lambda_\alpha} = \frac{N_\gamma}{N_{lr}} \tag{7-2.1}$$

The ratio N_γ/N_{lr} is the same as the ratio N_α/N_{lr} between the number of normal and long-range alpha particles, because each gamma ray is immediately followed by a "normal" alpha particle. The ratio N_α/N_{lr}

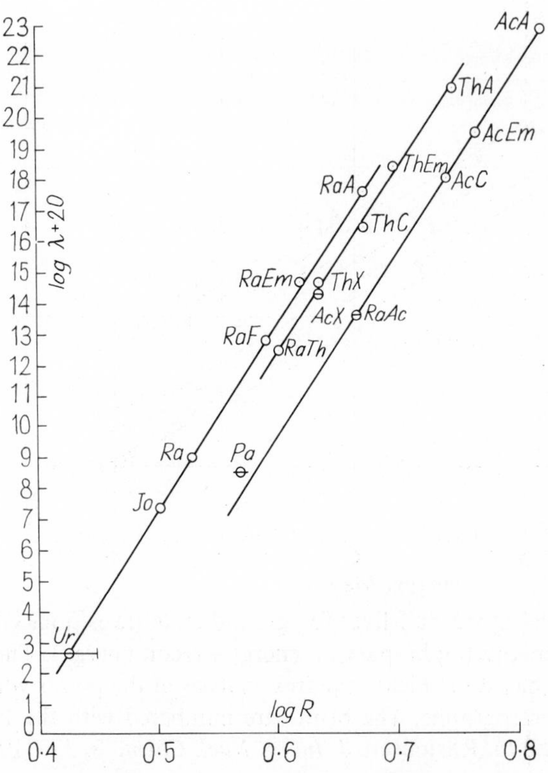

Figure 7-5 Original figure of Geiger and Nuttall showing the connection between range and decay constant in alpha-particle decay. [From Rutherford, Chadwick, and Ellis, *Radiations from Radioactive Substances*, Cambridge University Press, New York, 1930.]

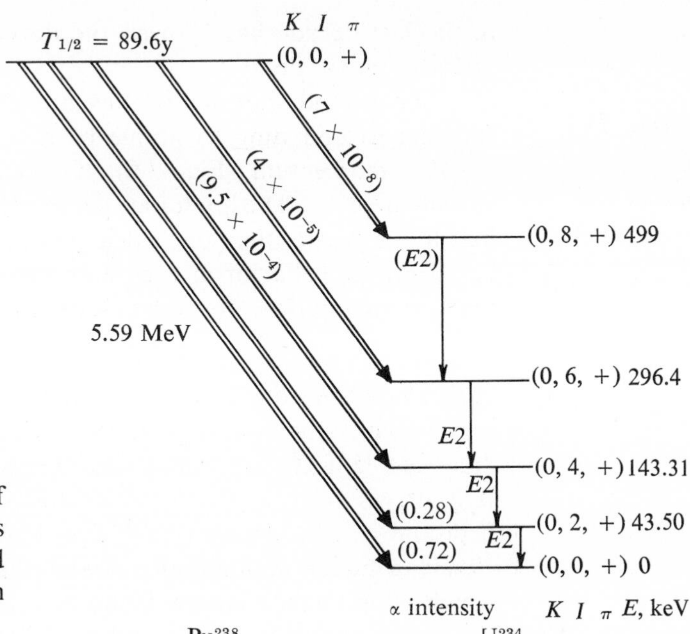

Figure 7-6 Decay scheme of Pu^{238} showing alpha transitions starting from one level and ending in different levels. [From F. S. Stephens in (AS 60).]

may be measured directly. The probability per unit time of alpha emission by the excited state, λ_α, may be estimated from the energy of the transition and other factors, and λ_γ is then obtained from Eq. (7-2.1). The λ_γ obtained in the case of ThC′ are of the order of 10^{12} sec^{-1}. The λ_α are about 0.21×10^7 sec^{-1} for the ground state and 0.9×10^8 sec^{-1} and 10^{10} sec^{-1} for the states at 0.73 and 1.8 MeV. The method is not quantitative, but it is interesting and historically important.

7-3 Systematics of Alpha Decay

The great accumulation of experimental material on alpha decay

Figure 7-7 Excited states of alpha emitters: long range from RaC′ and alpha rays from RaC. [K. Philipp, *Naturwiss.*, **14**, 1203 (1926).]

in the last decade has allowed the development of an elaborate systematics of alpha decay.

The ground states of even-even nuclei show the largest decay constants, corresponding to simple barrier penetration with no change in angular momentum (Fig. 7-9). Other transitions are "hindered" in varying degrees. The hindrance factor is the factor by which the observed half-life is greater than one calculated according to certain prescriptions based on the behavior of even-even nuclei. To arrive at definite standards, semiempirical formulas such as

$$\log T = AE^{-1/2} + B \tag{7-3.1}$$

are used. The constants A and B taken from tables like Table 7-1.

The introduction of hindrance is thus equivalent to considering a "reduced half-life" in which the energy effect is taken into account. It is very similar to the ft values and reduced gamma widths used in beta and gamma decays (see Chaps. 8 and 9).

One factor in hindrance is the change of angular momentum l, which adds to the Gamow factor G a term

$$\frac{l(l+1)\hbar^2}{R(2mB)^{1/2}} \tag{7-3.2}$$

This term for $l = 4$ increases the mean life for the case $R = 9.3 \times 10^{-13}$ cm, $Z = 88$, $A = 226$ by a factor of 6.7. It is thus relatively unimportant.

The study of hindrances is useful in connection with nuclear models. Even-even nuclei, between ground states, where both states have $I = 0$

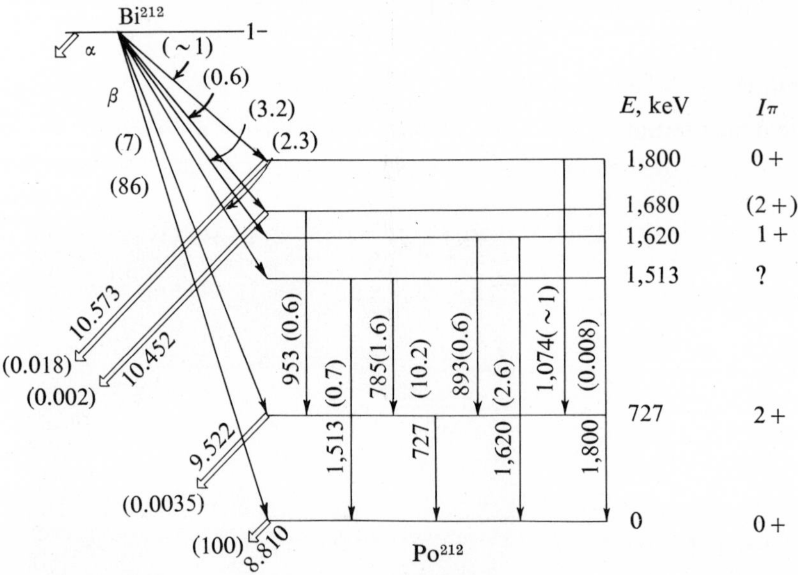

Figure 7-8 Level scheme and decay scheme of Po^{212}. E_α in MeV and E in keV. All intensities (in parentheses) relative to 100 Po^{212} ground-state transitions. [G. T. Emery and W. R. Kane, *Phys. Rev.*, **118**, 755 (1960).]

nd are even, have, by definition, a hindrance of 1. Even-even nuclei ften have "rotational levels" 2^+, 4^+, 6^+, etc. The hindrances for ransitions to these increase rapidly and are only in part accounted for y the effect of angular momentum.

Even-odd nuclei, when they depart from sphericity, show more han one system of rotational bands. Among the levels there are then ome that correspond to the same configuration in the upper and lower tates, except for the additional alpha particle in the upper state. In his last case the transition to the base level is practically unhindered, nd it is believed that it does not involve the unpaired nucleon at all Fig. 7-10).

A factor which might be important in determining hindrances but vhich is hard to estimate is the probability of finding a preformed alpha

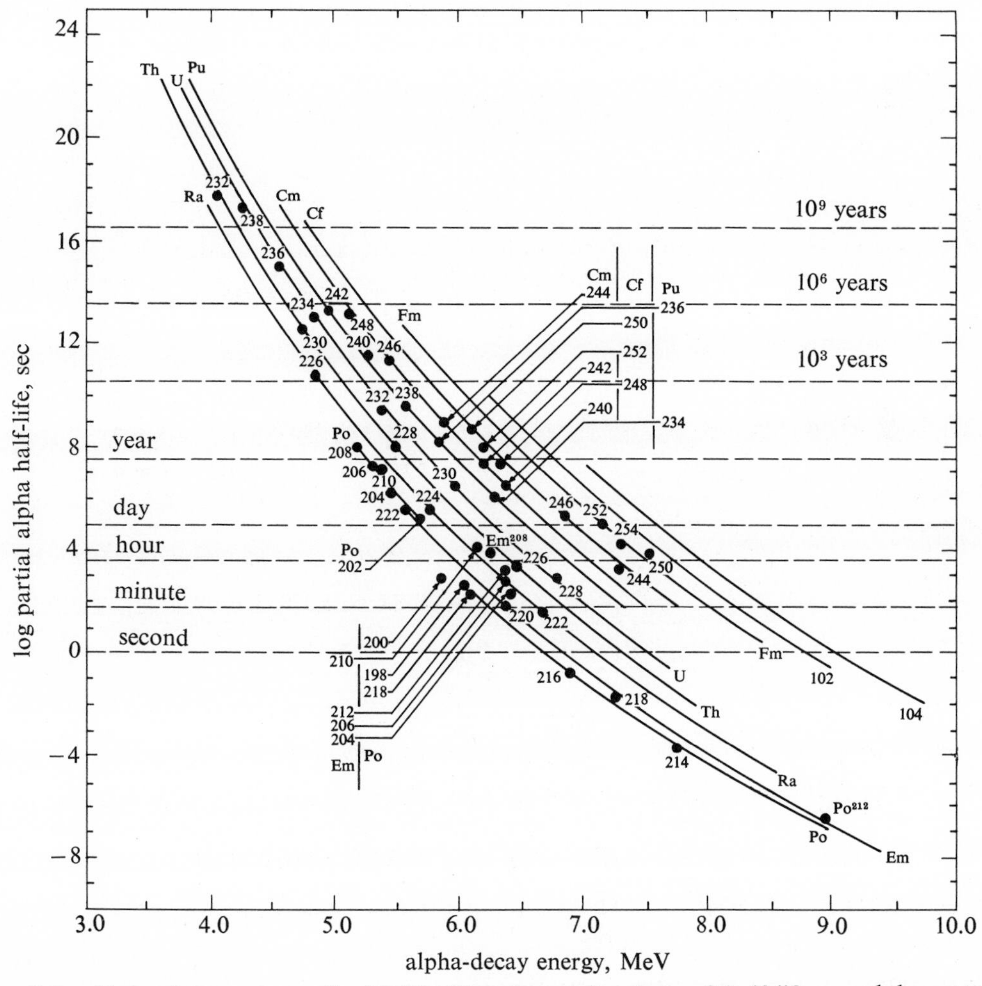

Figure 7-9 Alpha-decay energy (in MeV). Experimental values of half-life vs. alpha energy for even-even nuclei.

Table 7-1 Constants for Eq. (7-3.1)[a]

Z of parent element		A_Z	B_Z
84	Po	129.35	−49.9229
86	Em	137.46	−52.4597
88	Ra	139.17	−52.1476
90	Th	144.19	−53.2644
92	U	147.49	−53.6565
94	Pu	146.23	−52.0899
96	Cm	152.44	−53.6825
98	Cf	152.86	−52.9506

[a] For precise work E is not the energy of the alpha particle E_α but the energy of the disintegration. Correcting for the recoil of the disintegrating nucleus and for the energy given to the electron cloud, one has $E = E_\alpha A/(A - 4) + 6.5 \times 10^{-5} Z^{7/5}$ MeV. T is in seconds.

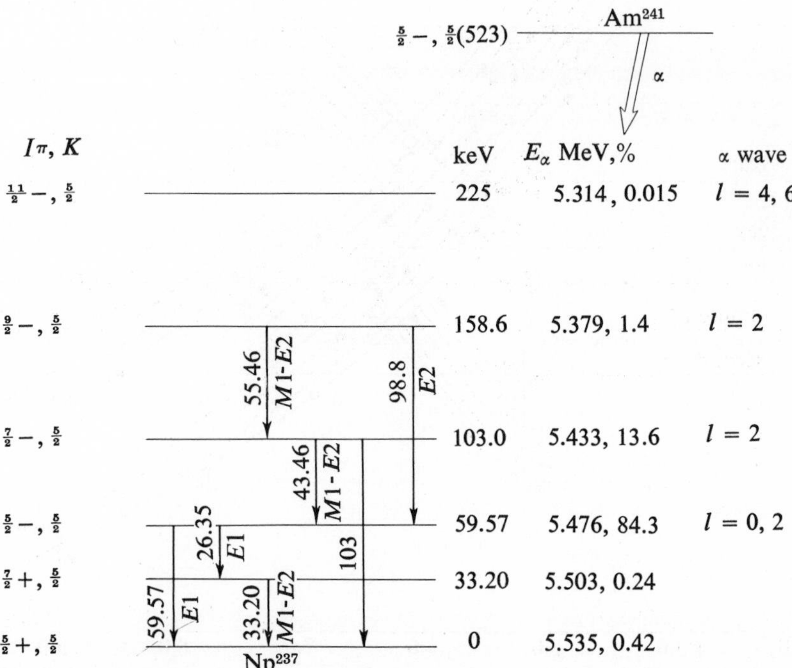

Figure 7-10 Decay scheme of Am^{241}, illustrating particularly the favored alpha decay to the 5/2 band. The l values are the alpha waves believed to contribute to the population of each member of the favored rotational band. [From F. S. Stephens in (AS 60).]

particle in the nucleus. Indeed the striking probability of Eq. (7-1.28) might occasionally be considerably overestimated, because the nucleons might not be in the proper configuration corresponding to an alpha particle. The influence of this effect is shown conspicuously in the branching ratios of the fine structure of the alpha decay of Po^{211} (Mang, 1957), where the probability of finding an alpha-particle configuration can be calculated to a good approximation by using the shell model. Departures of the nucleus from the spherical form may also produce hindrance.

Finally, huge discontinuities in the energy-mass number diagram occur in connection with closed shells for all nuclei in which $Z < 84$, $N < 128$, or both (Fig. 7-11). These discontinuities, however, are explained by energy changes due to the shell model and do not involve any anomaly in the alpha decay.

7-4 Virtual Binding

We shall now give a supplementary treatment of the problem of a particle in a well that will show qualitatively features sometimes called "virtual binding." Although the example we shall treat is oversimplified, we shall try to preserve the essential physical features of the phenomenon, which is very important in several phases of nuclear physics (see also Flügge and Marschall).

We shall again treat a one-dimensional problem, with a potential as shown in Fig. 7-12. At $x = 0$ and at $x = l$ we have infinitely high potential walls. At $x = a$ we have an extremely thin but very high wall, such that

$$\frac{2m}{\hbar^2}\int_{a-\varepsilon}^{a+\varepsilon} V(x - a)\, dx = \frac{1}{g} \tag{7-4.1}$$

[$V(x)$ is a delta function of Dirac; elsewhere $V = 0$.]

The Schrödinger equation

$$u'' + \frac{2m}{\hbar^2}(E - V)\, u = 0 \tag{7-4.2}$$

gives, on integration over a small interval containing $x = a$,

$$u'_{\mathrm{II}} - u'_{\mathrm{I}} + \frac{2m}{\hbar^2}\int_{a-\varepsilon}^{a+\varepsilon} [E - V(x - a)]u(x)\, dx = 0 \tag{7-4.3}$$

$$u'_{\mathrm{II}} - u'_{\mathrm{I}} = \frac{u(a)}{g} \tag{7-4.4}$$

where u'_{I}, u'_{II} are the derivatives of $u(x)$ left and right of a. We thus have a discontinuity in $u'(x)$ at $x = a$. We also have the boundary conditions for $u(x)$,

$$u_{\mathrm{I}}(0) = u_{\mathrm{II}}(l) = 0 \tag{7-4.5}$$

and

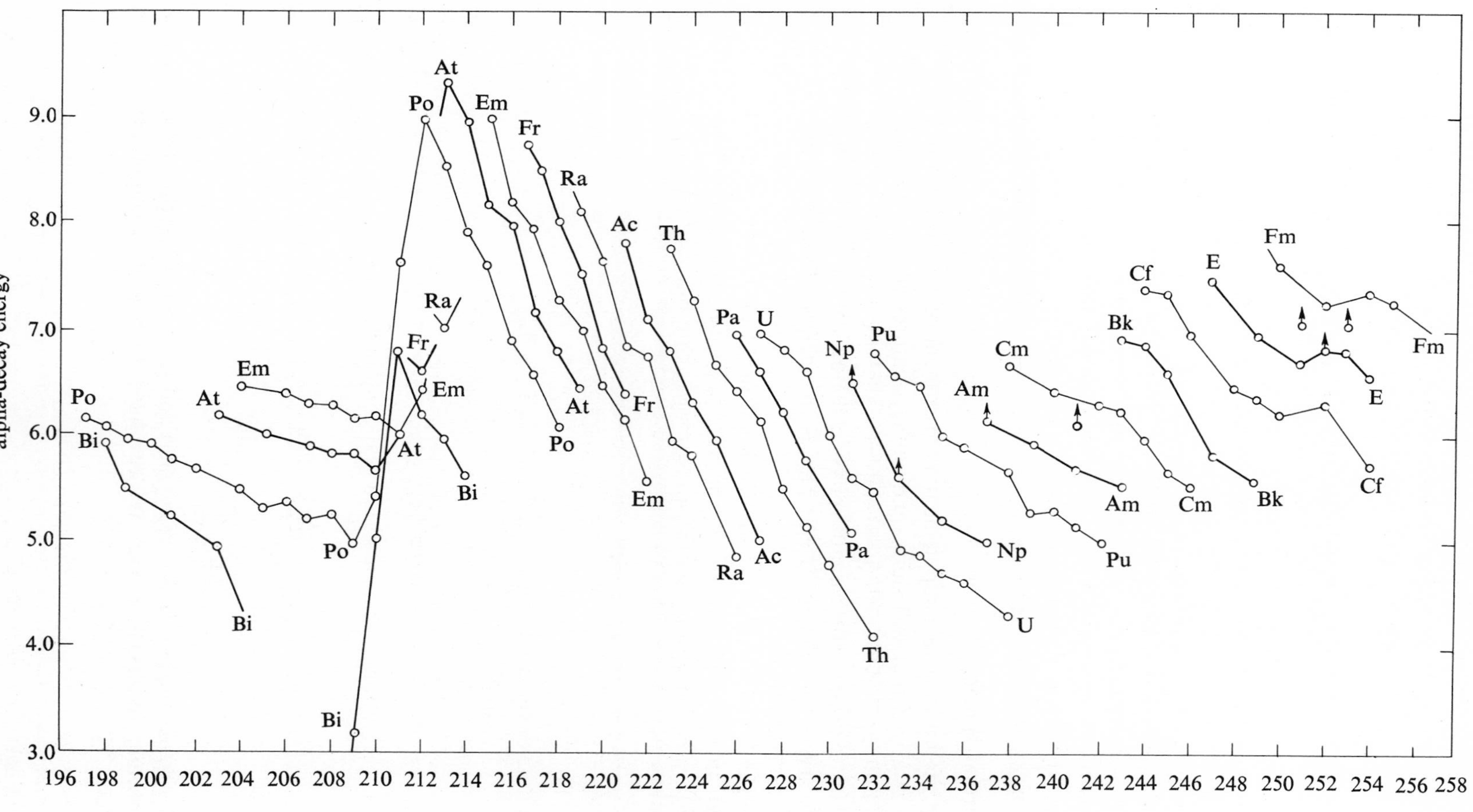

Figure 7-11 Alpha-decay energy versus mass number for the heavy elements. The lines connect isotopic nuclei. The breaks in the lines of Bi, Po, At, Em, and Fr are due to shell effects associated with the magic number 126 (neutrons).

$$u_{\mathrm{I}}(a) = u_{\mathrm{II}}(a) \tag{7-4.6}$$

In general,

$$u(x) = A \sin kx + B \cos kx \tag{7-4.7}$$

with

$$k = \frac{(2mE)^{1/2}}{\hbar} = \frac{1}{\lambda} \tag{7-4.8}$$

We can satisfy the boundary conditions for $u(x)$ by putting

$$u_{\mathrm{I}}(x) = A \sin kx \qquad x \leqslant a \tag{7-4.9}$$

and

$$u_{\mathrm{II}}(x) = B \sin k(l - x) \qquad x \geqslant a \tag{7-4.10}$$

with

$$B = A \frac{\sin ka}{\sin k(l - a)} \tag{7-4.11}$$

The condition of Eq. (7-4.4) gives the eigenvalues of k. We find from Eqs. (7-4.4) and (7-4.6)

$$\cot ka + \cot k(l - a) = \frac{-1}{kg} \quad \text{or} \tag{7-4.12}$$

$$k \sin kl = -(1/g) \sin ka \sin k(l - a)$$

These relations give the eigenvalues of k and the relative amplitudes of A and B. Instead of discussing them in general, we shall treat the case $kg \ll 1$, which corresponds to a small transparency of the barrier. If

$$kg = 0 \text{ exactly} \tag{7-4.13}$$

we have two separate compartments. The boundary conditions then require that $u(x)$ be zero at 0, a, l, and we have for the eigenvalues of k,

$$\sin k_n a = 0 \tag{7-4.14}$$

$$k_n = \frac{n\pi}{a} \tag{7-4.15}$$

$$\sin k_m(l - a) = 0 \tag{7-4.16}$$

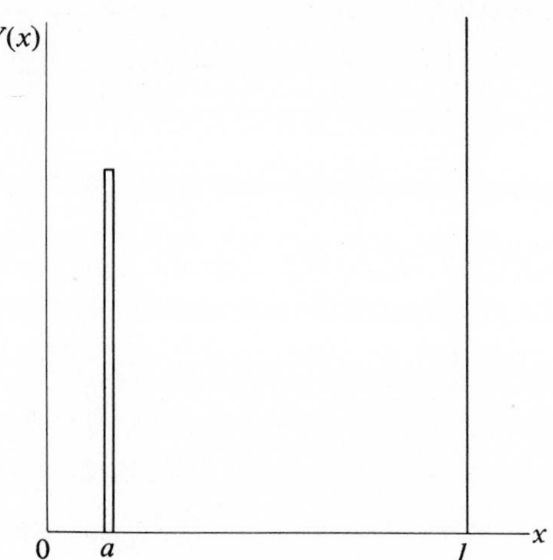

Figure 7-12 A box of length L divided at a by a barrier of the form of a delta function to give a simple example of virtual binding.

$$k_m = \frac{m\pi}{l - a} \tag{7-4.17}$$

with n, m integral numbers.[1] The normalized eigenfunctions corresponding to Eq. (7-4.14) are

$$u_{\text{I}} = \left(\frac{2}{a}\right)^{1/2} \sin \frac{n\pi x}{a} \qquad u_{\text{II}} = 0 \tag{7-4.18}$$

whereas those corresponding to Eq. (7-4.16) are

$$u_{\text{II}} = \left(\frac{2}{l - a}\right)^{1/2} \sin \frac{m\pi(l - x)}{l - a} \qquad u_{\text{I}} = 0 \tag{7-4.19}$$

Equation (7-4.18) asserts that the particle is somewhere in the left compartment, and certainly not in the right compartment. Equation (7-4.19) asserts that the particle is not in the left compartment, but somewhere in the right one. The two compartments are completely separate, and the energy levels of the whole system are the ensemble of the energy levels of the two component parts.

We shall now consider the case of $kg \neq 0$, but small. We shall also make the assumption that $l \gg a$, which implies that the levels corresponding to Eq. (7-4.18) are widely separated, whereas those corresponding to Eq. (7-4.19) almost form a continuum. The model thus has the essential features of a nucleus containing an alpha particle (zone I) confined by a barrier of small transparency. The nucleus itself is contained in a large box, $l \gg a$, the purpose of the box being only to avert mathematical complications arising from the continuous spectrum of eigenvalues that occurs for an infinite l.

We are mainly interested in what happens to Eq. (7-4.18), which corresponds to the physical conditions of an alpha particle in a nucleus. The eigenvalue k of Eq. (7-4.14) is now changed to

$$k_n^{(1)} = k_n + \epsilon_n = \frac{n\pi}{a} + \epsilon_n \tag{7-4.20}$$

and we determine ϵ_n by satisfying the condition expressed in Eq. (7-4.12) up to terms in ϵ_n^2. This gives

$$\epsilon_n = -\frac{n\pi g}{a^2} = -\frac{k_n}{a} g \tag{7-4.21}$$

The corresponding eigenfunction in the left compartment is

$$u_{\text{I}}(x) = A \sin k_n^{(1)} x = A(\sin k_n x + \epsilon_n x \cos k_n x) \tag{7-4.22}$$

It joins smoothly with the eigenfunction in the right compartment:

$$\begin{aligned} u_{\text{II}}(x) &= A(-1)^n \frac{\epsilon_n a}{\sin k_n(l - a)} \sin k_n(l - x) \\ &= -A(-1)^n k_n g \frac{\sin k_n(l - x)}{\sin k_n(l - a)} \end{aligned} \tag{7-4.23}$$

[1] To avoid complications we assume $k_n \neq k_m$.

These eigenfunctions represent a stationary state in which there are currents from the left to right and from right to left in both compartments. The eigenfunction is large in the left compartment and small but finite in the right one.

The amplitude in the left compartment is approximately A; in the right compartment

$$\frac{Ak_n g}{\sin k_n(l - a)} \tag{7-4.24}$$

The amplitude in the left compartment is hence much greater than the amplitude in the right compartment. However, this situation represents an exceptional case. The eigenvalues of k for which this situation obtains as pointed out before are widely separated, the distance between them being approximately π/a, as seen from Eq. (7-4.20). There are also the eigenvalues of k that correspond to Eq. (7-4.19), which are quite frequent, being spaced approximately π/l apart. For them the amplitude is large in the right compartment and small in the left compartment.

For energies

$$\frac{\hbar^2 k^2}{2m} = \frac{\hbar^2}{2m}\left(\frac{n\pi}{a}\right)^2 \tag{7-4.25}$$

or energies in their immediate vicinity, the ratio of the probabilities per unit length of finding the particle in the left rather than in the right compartment is the order of $1/k^2g^2$. For other energies this ratio is k^2g^2. The states corresponding to the exceptional energies $E = (\hbar^2/2m)(n\pi/a)^2$ are called "virtual states."

Suppose now that in a virtual state we could suppress the wave travelling from right to left in the right, large compartment, leaving the other waves unaffected. The state would not be stationary any more, and the amplitude in the small compartment must decrease, because it is not replenished by the incoming wave. The decrease in amplitude in the left compartment is such as to maintain the current from left to right in the large compartment.

The initial situation would be described by

$$u_{\text{I}} = A \sin k_n x \tag{7-4.26}$$

and

$$u_{\text{II}} = -A(-1)^n \frac{gk_n}{\sin k_n(l - a)} \frac{e^{-ik_n(l-x)}}{2i} \tag{7-4.27}$$

where Eq. (7-4.27) is obtained from Eq. (7-4.23) by writing the $\sin k(l-x)$ as the sum of two exponentials and suppressing the one corresponding to the incoming wave.

The outgoing flux corresponding to $u_{\text{II}}(x)$ is

$$\varphi = \tfrac{1}{2} A^2 g^2 k_n^2 \left(\frac{\hbar k_n}{m}\right) \tag{7-4.28}$$

where we have averaged over $\sin^2 k_n(l - a)$, replaced it by $\frac{1}{2}$, and used the relation

$$v_n = \frac{\hbar k_n}{m} \tag{7-4.29}$$

This means that we consider a small interval of k in the neighborhood of k_n. The level k_n is indeed broad, as will be seen later, and this justifies our procedure.

We now consider A slowly variable with time, corresponding to the leaking of the particle from the small compartment to the large one. The principle of conservation of matter requires that the outgoing flux φ be equal to the rate of decrease of the probability of finding the particle in the left compartment:

$$-\frac{d}{dt} A^2 \int_0^a \sin^2 k^{(1)}x \, dx = \varphi \tag{7-4.30}$$

and

$$-\tfrac{1}{2}\frac{dA^2}{dt} = \tfrac{1}{2} A^2 g^2 {k_n}^2 \frac{v_n}{a}$$

or (7-4.31)

$$-\frac{dA^2}{A^2} = g^2 {k_n}^2 \frac{v}{a}\, dt$$

This last formula can be easily interpreted semiclassically. dA^2/A^2dt is the decay constant of the particle in the small box, and this is equal to the number of collisions on the wall per unit time v/a multiplied by the transparency of the barrier, here g^2k^2. We return thus to the point of view expressed in Eq. (7-1.27), but with considerably deeper insight into the situation.

The fact that the amplitude decreases exponentially in time can be expressed mathematically by writing the complete Schrödinger function as

$$\psi(x,t) = u(x)e^{-(iE/\hbar)t}e^{-(\lambda/2)t} \tag{7-4.32}$$

or by formally considering a complex eigenvalue of the energy $E - i\lambda\hbar/2$, where λ is the decay constant.

A more elaborate, complete, and rigorous treatment, which brings us to the same result, is to construct, out of stationary solutions by superposition a $\psi(x,0)$ that is zero outside the small compartment and then to follow its evolution in time by using the time-dependent Schrödinger equation. It is noteworthy that, in order to construct the initial $\psi(x,0)$, it is necessary to superpose states of different energies, lying in an interval of order of magnitude ΔE around the virtual state, with ΔE connected to the decay constant λ by

$$\frac{\Delta E}{\lambda} = \hbar \tag{7-4.33}$$

The relation of Eq. (7-4.33) to the uncertainty principle is clear. We have at our disposal for measuring the energy of the virtual state a time τ of the order of $1/\lambda = \tau$ and hence $\tau \Delta E = \hbar$.

In practice, for many natural alpha emitters, τ is of the order of seconds or more. Hence ΔE is of the order of 10^{-27} erg, which means practically an infinitely sharp energy interval. But in nuclear reactions one meets situations where τ is extremely short and thus produces large ΔE. For example, $\Delta E = 1$ eV corresponds to $\tau = 6 \times 10^{-16}$ sec, and times as short as 10^{-22} sec occur.

Bibliography

Ajzenberg-Selove, F. (AS 60).

Bethe, H. A., "Nuclear Physics," *Rev. Mod. Phys.*, **9**, 69 (1937).

Flügge, S., and H. Marschall, *Rechenmethoden der Quantentheorie*, Springer, Berlin, 1952.

Hanna, G. C., "Alpha Radioactivity," in (Se 59), Vol. III.

Hyde, E. K., and G. T. Seaborg, "The Transuranium Elements," in (Fl E), Vol. 42.

Perlman, I., and F. Asaro, "Alpha Radioactivity," *Ann. Rev. Nucl. Sci.*, **4,** 157 (1954.)

Perlman, I., and J. O. Rasmussen, "Alpha Radioactivity," in (Fl E), Vol. 42.

Rasetti, F., *Elements of Nuclear Physics*, Prentice-Hall, Englewood Cliffs, N.J., 1936.

Rasmussen, J. O., "Alpha Radioactivity," to be published in a new edition of (Si 55); available as UCRL 3424.

Stephens, F. S., "The Study of Nuclear States Observed in Alpha Decay," in (AS 60).

Problems

7-1 Consider a particle of mass M and energy E in the potential

$$V = V_0 \qquad 0 < x < a$$
$$V = 0 \qquad x < 0 \quad \text{or} \quad x > a$$

Show that transmission through the potential barrier is approximated by

$$T = \frac{16E}{V_0} \exp\left[\frac{-2a}{\hbar}(2MV_0)^{1/2}\right]$$

7-2 Show that for constant V, Eq. (7-1.20) gives approximately the same result as Eq. (7-1.17).

7-3 In beta decay, the emission of low-energy positrons is inhibited by the Coulomb barrier. Show that for very low energy positrons ($E \sim 100$ keV), the inhibition factor is approximately $e^{-2\pi Ze^2/\hbar v}$, where v is the positron speed and Z is the atomic number of the daughter nucleus.

7-4 The considerations used in alpha-decay theory also apply to nuclear reactions in which charged particles coming from the ouside must penetrate the Coulomb barrier to interact with the nucleus. Compute the penetration probability (i.e., the transmission) of a 1-MeV proton through the Coulomb barrier surrounding a $_{92}U^{238}$ nucleus.

7-5 The centrifugal force of a spinning nucleus makes it more stable with respect to alpha decay. Show by a drawing of the potential barrier why this is the case.

7-6 $_{84}Po^{212}$ decays by emission of an 8.8-MeV alpha particle with a half-life of 0.3×10^{-6} sec. Estimate the probability that an 8.8-MeV alpha particle, in a head-on collision with a $_{82}Pb^{208}$ nucleus, will penetrate its Coulomb barrier.

7-7 The nucleus $_{84}Po^{216}$ has a half-life of 0.16 sec for the emission of an alpha particle of energy 6.77 MeV. From the theory of alpha decay and these measured quantities, estimate the radius of this nucleus.

7-8 Compute the hindrance factors for the rotational band in and compare with the experimental numbers of Fig. 7-6.

7-9 Justify Eq. (7-1.30) including its numerical coefficients.

7-10 Prove Eq. (7-4.20).

CHAPTER VIII

Gamma Emission

GAMMA RAYS were discovered very early among the radiations emitted by nuclei and their electromagnetic nature was established at the same time as that of X rays (von Laue, 1912). The study of gamma rays has always played an important role in nuclear physics. They yield information on the energy and quantum numbers of nuclear states; and for this reason they are, like other nuclear radiations, a powerful tool in analyzing nuclear phenomena. In particle physics we find that some particles, the neutral pi meson, for instance, can convert themselves into pairs of gamma rays. This fact is sufficient to give considerable information about the original particle, as we shall see in Chap. 14. It is thus clear that the study of electromagnetic radiation is very important in nuclear or particle physics. We must here distinguish two aspects of this study: one is essentially electromagnetic theory, the other its application to nuclear problems. In this book we are mainly concerned with the second aspect; however, we shall also treat some areas that are, in the main, the subject of electromagnetic theory. For further details and a reference book on electromagnetism consult, for example (Ja 62).

8-1 Introduction

We shall start with a semiclassical description of the radiation process. We imagine that the nucleus consists of a charge-current distribution confined to a region about the nuclear origin and undergoing periodic motion, whose frequency ω is related to the energies involved in a nuclear transition between two levels by $\omega = (E_1 - E_2)/\hbar$. We shall, as far as is possible, apply to the radiating system concepts taken from classical electromagnetism, which we shall translate into their quantum-mechanical equivalents. A rigorous but less intuitive theory is arrived at by starting from the quantum theory of radiation.

As we shall see shortly, it is important whether or not the wavelength of the electromagnetic radiation considered is large compared with nuclear dimensions. In the case of long wavelength, which obtains for gamma-ray energies up to several MeV (i.e., for most nuclear gamma rays), the treatment is much simplified by using the "long-wavelength" approximation. Even so, a fairly exact treatment is possibly only for the deuteron, which will be treated in Chap. 10; nuclear photoreactions will be considered in Chap. 11. Here we shall deal primarily with emission and absorption of gamma rays occurring in transitions between nuclear levels of low or moderate excitation.

Remember that for a system of periodically moving charges, located at the origin of the coordinates, we can distinguish a zone for which $r \ll \lambda\!\!\!^{-} = c/\omega$, in which the electric and magnetic fields can be calculated from the instantaneous velocity and position of the charges, and a radiation zone for $r \gg \lambda\!\!\!^{-}$, where retardation effects must be considered. Here r is the distance from the radiator, $\lambda = 2\pi\lambda\!\!\!^{-}$ is the wavelength of the emitted radiation, ω is the angular frequency of motion, and c is the velocity of light.

In the radiation zone, the electric and magnetic fields $\mathscr{E}$ and $\mathscr{H}$ in gaussian units are related by the following fundamental equations:

$$|\mathscr{E}| = |\mathscr{H}| \qquad \mathscr{H} \cdot \mathscr{E} = 0 \qquad \mathscr{E} \cdot \mathbf{r} = \mathscr{H} \cdot \mathbf{r} = 0 \tag{8-1.1}$$

Moreover, they decrease as $1/r$ and give rise to a Poynting vector,

$$\mathbf{S} = \frac{\mathscr{E} \times \mathscr{H}}{4\pi} c \tag{8-1.2}$$

decreasing as $1/r^2$, which ensures a flow of energy toward infinity. A detailed study of the electric-dipole radiation gives the following expressions for $\mathscr{E}$ in the radiation zone: $\mathscr{E}$ is directed along the meridian, and its magnitude is

$$\mathscr{E}_\theta = \frac{\sin\theta}{rc^2} \ddot{p}\left(t - \frac{r}{c}\right) \tag{8-1.3}$$

where p is the retarded value of the electric dipole moment directed in the z direction and located at the origin. The dipole varies in time according to $p = p_0 \cos \omega t$ and θ is the angle between r and the direction of the dipole. $\mathscr{H}$ is equal in magnitude to $\mathscr{E}$ and is directed along the parallels (Figs. 8-1 and 8-2). The average power radiated according to Eq. (8-1.2), with $d\Omega$ the element of solid angle, is

$$\langle W \rangle = \frac{c}{4\pi} \int \mathbf{r}^2 \cdot (\mathscr{E} \times \mathscr{H})\, d\Omega = \int \frac{\sin^2\theta}{c^3 4\pi} \langle (\ddot{p})^2 \rangle\, d\Omega = \frac{2}{3} \frac{\langle (\ddot{p})^2 \rangle}{c^3} = \frac{\omega^4}{3c^3} p_0^2 \tag{8-1.4}$$

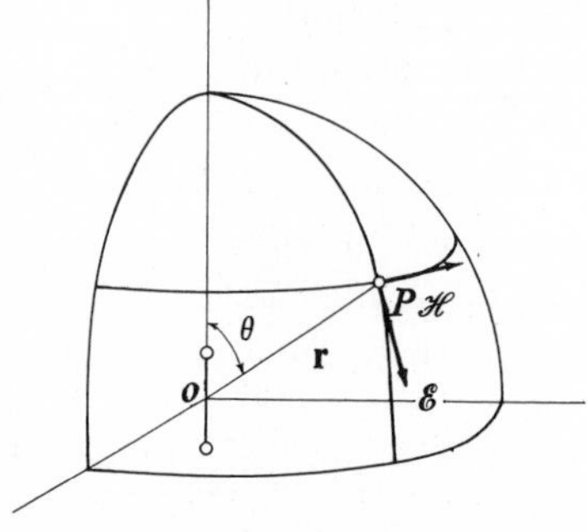

Figure 8-1 Schematic diagram of the electric dipole field in the radiation zone for a given ($\mathbf{r}$, θ, t). The field has a cylindrical symmetry with respect to the z axis. The direction of the electric field is the tangent to a meridian, while the direction of the magnetic field is the tangent to a parallel for the sphere of radius r.

This is a particular case of Larmor's important formula,

$$\langle W \rangle = \frac{2}{3} \frac{e^2 \langle (\ddot{r})^2 \rangle}{c^3} \tag{8-1.5}$$

which is valid for $\dot{r} \ll c$.

Consider now two identical dipoles oriented in the z direction, having the same frequency ω but opposite phase, and shifted with respect to each other by a length $\Delta x \ll \lambda\!\!\!^{-}$. The system is called a quadrupole (Fig. 8-3). The dipole moment of the system is zero at all times, but the system nevertheless radiates energy. The field $\mathscr{E}_Q$ generated by the quadrupole at each point of space is equal to $-(\partial\mathscr{E}/\partial x)\Delta x = \mathscr{E}_Q$, where $\mathscr{E}$ is the field produced by one of the dipoles alone. It is easily

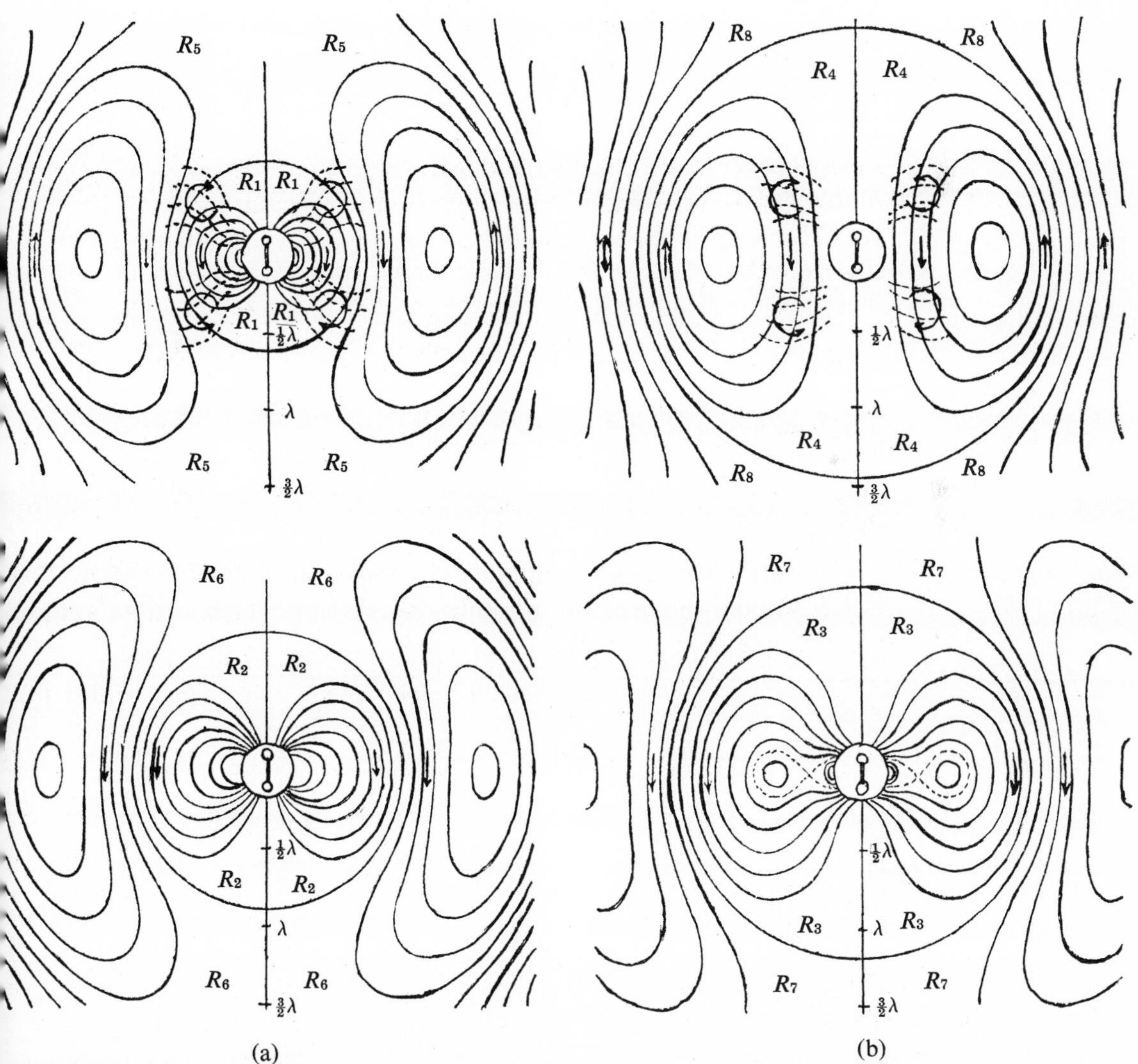

Figure 8-2 Hertz's original figures. Electric field lines produced by an oscillating dipole at various times as a function of r and θ. These pictures show mainly the induction zone ($r \ll \lambda$) and the transition to the radiation zone ($r \gg \lambda$).

seen that on the x axis the quadrupole field is $\mathscr{E}(\Delta x/\lambdabar)$ and that the same relation obtains as an order of magnitude in all directions. Hence the ratio of the energy radiated by our quadrupole to that radiated by one of the constituent dipoles alone is of the order $(\Delta x/\lambdabar)^2$. However, the angular distribution of the intensity per unit solid angle is radically different from that of the dipole. For a nuclear system $\Delta x/\lambdabar$ is a number of the order of magnitude of the nuclear dimensions divided by $\lambdabar$. Using the relations

$$\lambdabar = \frac{197}{E_{\text{MeV}}} \times 10^{-13}\text{ cm} \tag{8-1.6}$$

and

$$R = 1.2A^{1/3} \times 10^{-13}\text{ cm}$$

we find

$$\frac{R}{\lambdabar} = 6.1 \times 10^{-3} A^{1/3} E\,(\text{MeV}) \tag{8-1.7}$$

For low levels with $E = 0.1 - 1$ MeV and for $A^{1/3}$ of several units, the ratio $R/\lambdabar$ is of the order of 10^{-2}. The quadrupole radiation is thus 10^4 times weaker than the dipole radiation and is important only if the dipole radiation is forbidden (i.e., has intensity zero).

The very important condition $\Delta x/\lambdabar \ll 1$ can be transformed to illustrate another aspect of its physical meaning. For a nucleon moving in a nucleus of radius R we have the order-of-magnitude relation

$$\omega \approx \frac{v}{R} \tag{8-1.8}$$

where v is the velocity of the nucleon and hence

$$\frac{\Delta x}{\lambdabar} \approx \frac{v}{c} \tag{8-1.9}$$

Returning to dipole radiation, its emission is determined by the electric-dipole moment of the radiating system, which is a vector of components

$$\Sigma ex,\ \Sigma ey,\text{ and }\Sigma ez \tag{8-1.10}$$

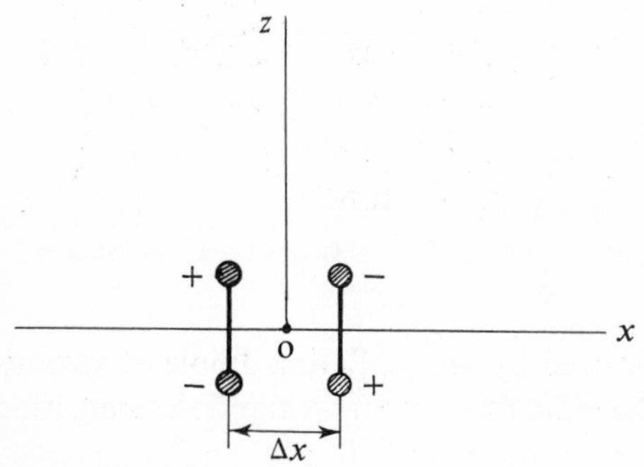

Figure 8-3 A configuration of electric charges having a net electric quadrupole but no monopole or dipole.

where the sum is extended to all the nuclear charges. To calculate the transition probabilities quantum mechanically, the quantities x of the classical formulas must be replaced by matrix elements,

$$x \to x_{if} = \int \psi_f^* x \psi_i \, d\tau \tag{8-1.11}$$

where ψ_f and ψ_i are the wave functions of the final and initial states, respectively.

Thus, for example, Eq. (8-1.5) gives the average power radiated by a linear dipole as

$$\langle W \rangle = \frac{4e^2\omega^4}{3c^3} |x_{if}|^2 \tag{8-1.12}$$

Note that p_0^2 has been replaced by $2e^2|x_{if}|^2$.[1] Dividing by the energy content of one quantum $\hbar\omega$, we obtain the radiative decay constant

$$\lambda_\gamma = \frac{4}{3\hbar} \frac{e^2}{c^3} \omega^3 |x_{if}|^2 \tag{8-1.13}$$

It is possible to jump from one quantum-mechanical stationary state to another by different types of electromagnetic radiation, but it turns out that, if $\lambdabar \gg R$, only one or two types of radiation are important. The particular type depends on the angular momentum and "parity" of the stationary states considered. We thus have selection rules, which we shall discuss shortly.

We shall now develop the classical theory by looking first at the electromagnetic field and afterward at its source.

The main purpose of the analysis of the electromagnetic fields in electric and magnetic multipoles is to separate the different parts with definite parity and angular momentum so as to be able to establish

[1] This was done because we should Fourier-analyze the coordinate x and write it as

$$x = \sum_{-\infty}^{+\infty} x_\omega e^{i\omega t}$$

where $x_\omega = x_{-\omega}^*$ because x is real. When we calculate $(\ddot{x})^2$, we find

$$(\ddot{x})^2 = \sum_{\omega,\omega'} \omega^2\omega'^2 x_\omega x_{\omega'} e^{i(\omega+\omega')t}$$

and making the time average, we find that only terms with $\omega = -\omega'$ contribute, giving

$$\langle(\ddot{x})^2\rangle = \sum_{\omega=-\infty}^{\infty} \omega^4|x_\omega|^2 = 2\sum_0^{\infty} \omega^4|x_\omega|^2$$

In Eq. (8-1.11) x_{if} corresponds to x_ω, and hence we have Eq. (8-1.12).

selection rules with the help of the conservation theorems. Using this approach, we derive from Maxwell's equations in vacuum the vector equations for the electric and magnetic fields. Let $\mathscr{E}$ and $\mathscr{H}$ be the electric and magnetic time-dependent fields,

$$\mathscr{E}(x,y,z,t) = \mathbf{E}(x,y,z)\, e^{-i\omega t} \tag{8-1.14}$$

and

$$\mathscr{H}(x,y,z,t) = \mathbf{H}(x,y,z)\, e^{-i\omega t} \tag{8-1.15}$$

Maxwell's equations as shown in electricity give the relations

$$\nabla^2\mathbf{E} + k^2\mathbf{E} = 0 \quad \text{and} \quad \nabla^2\mathbf{H} + k^2\mathbf{H} = 0 \tag{8-1.16}$$

where $k = \omega/c$, with the subsidiary condition $\nabla \cdot \mathbf{E} = \nabla \cdot \mathbf{H} = 0$. We try to solve these equations in polar coordinates. The procedure is to obtain a complete set of solutions of the vector equations by solving first the simple scalar equation

$$\nabla^2\Phi + k^2\Phi = 0 \tag{8-1.17}$$

This is accomplished by setting

$$\Phi_l^m(r,\theta,\varphi) = j_l(kr)\; Y_l^m(\theta,\varphi) \tag{8-1.18}$$

where $j_l(kr)$ is the "spherical Bessel function," defined in terms of the ordinary Bessel function of half-odd-integer order as

$$j_l(kr) = \left(\frac{\pi}{2kr}\right)^{1/2} J_{l+1/2}(kr) \tag{8-1.19}$$

and $Y_l^m(\theta,\varphi)$ is the spherical harmonic. Note that the spherical harmonics form an orthonormal set obeying the relation

$$\int Y_{l'}^{*,m'}(\theta,\varphi)\; Y_l^m(\theta,\varphi)\, d\Omega = \delta_{l'l}\, \delta_{m'm} \tag{8-1.20}$$

Application of the operators

$$\mathbf{L} = -i(\mathbf{r} \times \nabla) \quad \text{and} \quad \frac{-i}{k}(\nabla \times \mathbf{L}) \tag{8-1.21}$$

to Φ_l^m gives the vectors

$$\mathbf{F}_{lm}{}^{(0)} = \mathbf{L}\Phi_l^m \quad \text{and} \quad \mathbf{F}_{lm}{}^{(1)} = \frac{-i}{k}(\nabla \times \mathbf{L})\,\Phi_l^m \tag{8-1.22}$$

which are solutions of Eq. (8-1.16) if we put

$$\mathbf{H}_{lm} = -\,\mathbf{F}_{lm}{}^{(0)} \qquad \mathbf{E}_{lm} = \mathbf{F}_{lm}{}^{(1)} \tag{8-1.23}$$

for an electric multipole El or

$$\mathbf{H}_{lm} = \mathbf{F}_{lm}{}^{(1)} \qquad \mathbf{E}_{lm} = \mathbf{F}_{lm}{}^{(0)} \tag{8-1.24}$$

for a magnetic multipole Ml.

The calculations necessary to show these results are found in (BW 52) and (Ja 62). Note that the operator **L** is essentially the angular momentum operator of quantum mechanics.

The relation between the fields of an electric multipole and those of a magnetic multipole is simple. We pass from one to the other by interchanging electric and magnetic fields and changing the sign of the electric field. This transformation is called a "dual" transformation and is expressed by

$$\mathscr{E}' = -\mathscr{H} \qquad \mathscr{H}' = \mathscr{E} \tag{8-1.25}$$

where the primed field is the dual of the unprimed one.

We can now determine what kind of source located at the origin of the coordinates would give a field described by Eqs. (8-1.23) and (8-1.24). We would find in the case of Eq. (8-1.23) that an electric 2^l pole is necessary, whereas the field of Eq. (8-1.24) would be generated by a type of source which we have not yet considered, but which is necessary to account for the most general radiation field: a 2^l magnetic pole. We can think of an oscillating magnetic dipole as generated by a small loop of alternating current or by two magnetic poles changing their distance periodically (Fig. 8-4). The field outside a sphere containing the system of currents or of magnetic poles is of course identical. From the magnetic dipole we can pass to the magnetic quadrupole in the way we did for the electric multipoles, etc. The field created by an electric dipole is designated $E1$; the one created by an electric quadrupole, $E2$. In general, the field created by an electric 2^l pole is commonly designated as El. Similar nomenclature applies to the fields created by magnetic multipoles.

El and Ml fields have different symmetry properties, and this fact is extremely important in establishing selection rules. For example, let us consider an $E1$ and an $M1$ field. These are generated by charges or currents, and we shall consider the fields produced at a time t and at a point $\mathbf{r}(x,y,z)$ by a distribution of moving charges having the coordinates $\mathbf{s}_i$.

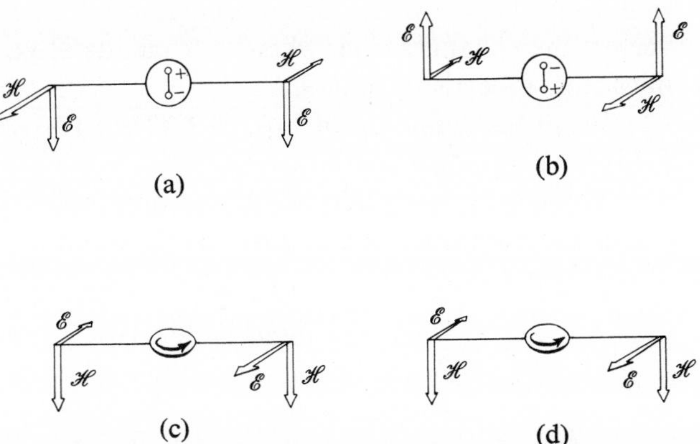

Figure 8-4 Dual fields of electric and the magnetic dipoles. (a) and (b) show the electric dipole field and illustrate its symmetry properties on reflection of the source, or of the observation point through the origin. (c) and (d) show the magnetic dipole field in like manner. Comparison of (a) with (c) shows how the dual transformation changes the $E1$ field into the $H1$ field and vice versa.

The fields are a function of **r** and **s**, where the **s** are all the coordinates of the charges. We can thus write $\mathscr{E}(\mathbf{r},\mathbf{s})$, $\mathscr{H}(\mathbf{r},\mathbf{s})$. Now suppose that we change the coordinates of the charges from **s** to $-\mathbf{s}$, which means that we reflect the position of the charges with respect to the origin. For an electric-dipole field we have (cf. Fig. 8-4a and b)

$$\begin{aligned}\mathscr{E}(\mathbf{r},\mathbf{s}) &= -\,\mathscr{E}(\mathbf{r},-\,\mathbf{s})\\ \mathscr{H}(\mathbf{r},\mathbf{s}) &= -\,\mathscr{H}(\mathbf{r},-\,\mathbf{s})\end{aligned} \tag{8-1.26}$$

If, on the other hand, we look at the same electric-dipole field at points **r**, $-\mathbf{r}$ without changing the source, we have (Fig. 8-4a and b)

$$\begin{aligned}\mathscr{E}(\mathbf{r},\mathbf{s}) &= +\,\mathscr{E}(-\mathbf{r},\mathbf{s})\\ \mathscr{H}(\mathbf{r},\mathbf{s}) &= -\,\mathscr{H}(-\mathbf{r},\mathbf{s})\end{aligned} \tag{8-1.27}$$

Fields obeying Eqs. (8-1.26) and (8-1.27) are called *odd*.

On the other hand, for a magnetic-dipole field we have (cf. Fig. 8-4c and d)

$$\begin{aligned}\mathscr{E}(\mathbf{r},\mathbf{s}) &= \mathscr{E}(\mathbf{r},-\,\mathbf{s})\\ \mathscr{H}(\mathbf{r},\mathbf{s}) &= \mathscr{H}(\mathbf{r},-\,\mathbf{s})\end{aligned} \tag{8-1.28}$$

because reflection through the origin does not change the sense of rotation of the charges. Changing **r** to $-\mathbf{r}$ (Fig. 8-4c and d) gives

$$\begin{aligned}\mathscr{E}(\mathbf{r},\mathbf{s}) &= -\mathscr{E}(-\mathbf{r},\mathbf{s})\\ \mathscr{H}(\mathbf{r},\mathbf{s}) &= +\mathscr{H}(-\mathbf{r},\mathbf{s})\end{aligned} \tag{8-1.29}$$

Fields, such as the magnetic-dipole field, that obey Eqs. (8-1.28) and (8-1.29) are called *even* fields. From Eqs. (8-1.26) to (8-1.29) it follows that for all radiation fields, even or odd,

$$\begin{aligned}\mathscr{E}(\mathbf{r},\mathbf{s}) &= -\mathscr{E}(-\mathbf{r},-\,\mathbf{s})\\ \mathscr{H}(\mathbf{r},\mathbf{s}) &= \mathscr{H}(-\mathbf{r},-\,\mathbf{s})\end{aligned} \tag{8-1.30}$$

Equation (8-1.30) is a consequence of the fact that the combined operation $\mathbf{r}\to-\mathbf{r}$, $\mathbf{s}\to-\mathbf{s}$ is an inversion of all coordinates. $\mathscr{E}$, a polar vector, then changes sign, whereas $\mathscr{H}$, an axial vector, or pseudo vector, does not. (See also Chap. 9.)

From the definition of Eqs. (8-1.23) to (8-1.25) it follows that dual fields have opposite parity.

The classical oscillating electric multipoles, located at the source, which generate the fields of Eqs. (8-1.23) and (8-1.24) have expressions of the form

$$Q_{lm} = \int \rho(r) r^l Y_l^m(\theta,\varphi)\, d\tau, \qquad \text{for } El \tag{8-1.31}$$

and

$$M_{lm} = -\frac{1}{c(l+1)}\int r^l Y_l^m(\theta,\varphi)\, \nabla\cdot(\mathbf{r}\times\mathbf{j})\, d\tau \quad \text{for } Ml \tag{8-1.32}$$

where $\rho(r)e^{-i\omega t}$ is the electric density, **j** is the electric-current density connected to ρ by

$$i\omega\rho = \nabla\cdot\mathbf{j}(\mathbf{r}) \tag{8-1.33}$$

at r, and the integral is extended to the whole region containing the charges. The continuity equation (8-1.33) necessarily connects a time variation of ρ with a current density. Hence, electric and magnetic radiation are present together. However, they cannot be of the same order, as we shall see presently.

Let us first consider electric-multipole transitions. We shall assume that we have only one charged particle of coordinates **r**. The results obtainable in this very special case are true in general. To obtain the transition probabilities in quantum mechanics, we replace $\rho(r)$ by

$$e\psi_f^*(\mathbf{r})\psi_i(\mathbf{r}) \tag{8-1.34}$$

In the special case of $E1$, it is easily recognized that Eq. (8-1.31) gives, apart from constants, the matrix elements of Eqs. (8-1.12) and (8-1.13). To see this it suffices to replace the spherical harmonics by their expressions in cartesian coordinates. This equivalence is true for any l.

8-2 Selection Rules

If, for a certain order of multipole, the matrix elements that determine the transition probability vanish exactly, the transition is forbidden and that multipole component of the electromagnetic field is absent. We thus have *selection rules.*

A simple selection rule derives immediately from the property of ψ for any central system expressed by

$$\psi(\mathbf{r}) = \pm\psi(-\mathbf{r}) \tag{8-2.1}$$

This relation results from the fact that, for a system in which the potential depends on $|\mathbf{r}|$ only (central system), the hamiltonian does not change if we change **r** into $-$**r**. If a solution of the corresponding Schrödinger equation is not degenerate, we then have

$$\begin{aligned} \mathrm{H}(\mathbf{r})\psi(\mathbf{r}) &= \mathrm{E}\psi(\mathbf{r}) \\ \mathrm{H}(-\mathbf{r})\psi(\mathbf{r}) &= \mathrm{E}\psi(\mathbf{r}) \\ \mathrm{H}(\mathbf{r})\psi(-\mathbf{r}) &= \mathrm{E}\psi(-\mathbf{r}) \end{aligned} \tag{8-2.2}$$

which implies that $\psi(\mathbf{r}) = k\psi(-\mathbf{r})$, with k constant. If we now perform the operation of inversion (change from **r** to $-$**r**) twice, which obviously gives the identity, we have

$$\psi(\mathbf{r}) \underset{\text{1st inv.}}{\rightarrow} k\,\psi(-\mathbf{r}) \underset{\text{2nd inv.}}{\rightarrow} k^2\,\psi(\mathbf{r}) = \psi(\mathbf{r}) \qquad \text{or } k = \pm 1 \tag{8-2.3}$$

If $k = 1$, the eigenfunction is called *even*, or of parity $+1$; if $k = -1$, it is called *odd*, or of parity -1. If the eigenfunction is degenerate, one can always form linear combinations $\psi(\mathbf{r}) \pm \psi(-\mathbf{r})$ that have the property indicated in Eq. (8-2.3).

The parity of the product of two even functions or of two odd functions is even; the parity of the product of an even function multiplied by an odd one is odd. The integral over all space of an odd function is zero, because the contributions to the integral of elements of volume at **r** and $-\mathbf{r}$ cancel each other out.

The function $r^l Y_l^m(\theta,\varphi)$ is itself even or odd, according to whether l is even or odd, irrespective of m (see Sec. 6-4).

Assume now that $\psi_i(\mathbf{r})$ and $\psi_f(\mathbf{r})$ have the same parity. Then the integrand in Eq. (8-1.31) will have the parity $(-1)^l$, and the integral will vanish for l odd. Similarly, if ψ_i and ψ_f have opposite parity, the integral will vanish for l even.

We thus have the selection rule that El radiation for l odd (even) is accompanied by a (no) change of parity in the eigenfunction. We shall designate by $\Delta\pi = 1$ (or yes), $\Delta\pi = 0$ (or no) a transition with or without a change of parity.

In addition to the selection rules connected with the change of parity, there are very important selection rules associated with the change of angular momentum of the nucleus. We cannot give here a general proof for these rules, but we shall give examples to show how they arise, and then state the general case.

Assume that the initial and final states of the nucleus have angular momenta l' and l'', respectively, with l integer, and z components of the angular momenta m' and m'', respectively. The initial and final states will thus have eigenfunctions of the form

$$u_i = f_{n'l'}(r)\; Y_{l'}^{m'}(\theta,\varphi) \tag{8-2.4}$$

and

$$u_{\text{fin}} = f_{n''l''}(r)\; Y_{l''}^{m''}(\theta,\varphi) \tag{8-2.5}$$

If we consider electric-dipole radiation ($E1$), the matrix elements will be given by Eq. (8-1.31) and will contain integrals of the type

$$\int Y_{l''}^{m''*}(\theta,\varphi)\; Y_1^{1,0,-1}(\theta,\varphi)\; Y_{l'}^{m'}(\theta,\varphi)\, d\Omega \tag{8-2.6}$$

It suffices then to remember that $Y_1^{0,\pm1}$ are proportional to $\cos\theta$, $\sin\theta e^{\pm i\varphi}$, and the general form of Y_l^m to see immediately that the integrand will contain a factor $e^{i(m'-m'')\varphi}$ or $e^{i[(m'-m'')\pm1]\varphi}$ and thus that the integral will vanish unless

$$m' = m'' \tag{8-2.7}$$

or

$$m' = m'' \pm 1 \tag{8-2.8}$$

Similarly one finds that the integral vanishes also unless

$$l' = l'' \pm 1 \tag{8-2.9}$$

by using properties of $Y_l^m(\theta,\varphi)$ mentioned in Problem 8-8. Now, if we recall the meaning of l and m, we see that in the emission of electric-dipole radiation the total angular momentum of the nucleus changes by one unit and that its z component changes by zero or one unit. This argument may be extended to noninteger spin and arbitrary radiation, with the result that for El radiation we must have

$$|J' - J''| \leqslant l \leqslant J' + J'' \tag{8-2.10}$$

In this chapter J', J'' are the total angular momentum in the initial and final nuclear states. [For the proof refer to (Ma 57) or (BW52).] Equation (8-2.10) has the geometrical interpretation that it must be possible to construct a triangle of sides J', J'', and l. The principle of conservation of angular momentum suggests that the outgoing wave of El light carries an angular momentum of magnitude l with respect to the center of mass of the nucleus. This is borne out by direct calculation of the density of angular momentum for the quantized electromagnetic field.

Thus far we have been concerned only with electric multipoles. Magnetic multipoles arise from the electric currents caused by the motions of the charges in the nucleus and from the intrinsic magnetic moments connected with the spins. Remember in this connection that the neutron, although neutral, has a magnetic moment. In the simplest case of the dipole due to the motion of a spinless charged particle, the z component of the matrix element for magnetic radiation is proportional to

$$\int \psi_f^*(xp_y - yp_x)\psi_i \, d\tau \tag{8-2.11}$$

because the operator $xp_y - yp_x = L_z$ is proportional to the component of the magnetic moment produced by the electric current associated with the transition. This is to be compared to the electric-dipole matrix element given by Eq. (8-1.11). We shall shortly see the effect of the intrinsic magnetic moment.

In the specific case mentioned above, the $M1$ matrix element is not zero only if ψ_f^*, ψ_i have the same parity, because the operator L_z does not change the parity of ψ_i. Moreover, as with $E1$ transitions, selection rules for $M1$ are $\Delta l = \pm 1$ and $\Delta m = \pm 1, 0$, as can be easily verified.

The selection rules for magnetic radiation can be generalized and can be interpreted as representing conservation of angular momentum if one associates with $M1$, $M2$, $M3$ radiation 1, 2, 3 units of angular momentum, just as in the case of $E1$, $E2$, and $E3$. In fact, from the relation between the fields of El and Ml expressed by Eqs. (8-1.23) and (8-1.24) and the expression for the density of momentum $\mathbf{p}$ in an electromagnetic field,

$$\mathbf{p} = \frac{\mathscr{E} \times \mathscr{H}}{4\pi c} \tag{8-2.12}$$

we see that the magnitude of the density of momentum of El and Ml is the same, and hence the magnitude of the density of angular momentum is also identical in the two cases.

We can now make an order-of-magnitude estimate of the relative importance of electric- and magnetic-dipole radiation. The amplitude of the electric-dipole field produced by a charge e confined to a volume $\sim R^3$ is proportional to $eR/r\lambda\!\!\!^{-2}$ according to (8-1.3). The uncertainty relation applied to the coordinate of the charge gives

$$Rmv \approx \hbar \tag{8-2.13}$$

or

$$R = \frac{\hbar}{mv} \tag{8-2.14}$$

where m and v are the mass and velocity of the charge. Hence, the electric field due to the electric dipole is of the order

$$\mathscr{E}^{(E)} \approx \frac{e\hbar}{mv}\frac{1}{r\lambda\!\!\!^{-2}} \tag{8-2.15}$$

The nuclear magnetic moment originating from the same system of charges is of the order $e\hbar/mc$. The associated electric field is therefore proportional to

$$\mathscr{E}^{(M)} \approx \frac{e\hbar}{mc}\frac{1}{r\lambda\!\!\!^{-2}} \tag{8-2.16}$$

$$\frac{\mathscr{E}^{(E)}}{\mathscr{E}^{(M)}} = \frac{c}{v} \tag{8-2.17}$$

which means by comparison with Eqs. (8-1.5) and (8-1.9) that the electric field due to the magnetic dipole is comparable to that due to the electric quadrupole. This estimate is also true for higher-order multipoles and is not altered by taking into account the intrinsic magnetic moment, which is of the same order of magnitude as the orbital one.

In Table 8-1 we sum up the results for the lowest-order radiation possible between two states of angular momentum J', J'' and parity π', π''. It must be remembered that the triangular relation [Eq. (8-2.10)] must always be obeyed. Hence, the table gives conditions that are necessary but not sufficient for radiative transitions. Thus, for example, transitions from $J' = 0$ to $J'' = 0$ are always forbidden, and transitions $J' = \frac{1}{2}$ to $J'' = \frac{1}{2}$, $\Delta\pi = 0$ cannot occur as $E2$, because the triangular relation is violated. Transitions from $J' = 0$ to $J'' = 0$ can occur only by mechanisms different from electromagnetic radiation, namely, by the emission of conversion electrons or by the formation of electron-positron pairs.

Table 8-1 Selection Rules for Electromagnetic Multipole Radiation

	$E1$	$E2$	$E3$	$E4$	...
$\Delta\pi$	1	0	1	0	
$\|\Delta J\| \leqslant$	1	2	3	4	...
	$M1$	$M2$	$M3$	$M4$	...
$\Delta\pi$	0	1	0	1	
$\|\Delta J\| \leqslant$	1	2	3	4	...

In practice the types of radiation observed up to now are $E1$ to $E5$ inclusive and $M1$ to $M4$ inclusive. In almost all cases, except the pairs $E2$-$M1$ and $E1$-$M2$, only a single type of radiation occurs in a given transition.

8-3 Transition Probabilities

Generalizing the results obtained in Sec. 8-2, the structure of the complete formulas for the transition probabilities will appear plausible to the reader. The detailed calculation (BW 52) yields

$$\lambda^{(E)}(l,m) = \frac{8\pi(l+1)}{\hbar l[(2l+1)!!]^2}\left(\frac{\omega}{c}\right)^{2l+1}|\mathcal{Q}_{lm} + \mathcal{Q}'_{lm}|^2 \qquad \textbf{(8-3.1)}$$

$$\lambda^{(M)}(l,m) = \frac{8\pi(l+1)}{\hbar l[(2l+1)!!]^2}\left(\frac{\omega}{c}\right)^{2l+1}|\mathcal{M}_{lm} + \mathcal{M}'_{lm}|^2 \qquad \textbf{(8-3.2)}$$

Here l is the order of the transition, and $n!!$ means $1\cdot3\cdot5\cdots n$. The first formula is valid for El and the second for Ml radiation. $\mathcal{Q}_{lm}$ and $\mathcal{M}_{lm}$ are the parts of the matrix element containing the ordinary coordinates, and $\mathcal{Q}'_{lm}$ and $\mathcal{M}'_{lm}$ are the parts of the matrix elements containing the intrinsic magnetic moment.

We can write them formally as

$$\mathcal{Q}_{lm} = e\sum_{1}^{Z}{}_k\int r_k^l Y_l^{m*}(\theta_k,\varphi_k)\psi_f^*\psi_i\,d\tau \qquad \textbf{(8-3.3)}$$

$$\mathcal{M}_{lm} = -\frac{1}{l+1}\frac{e\hbar}{Mc}\sum_{1}^{Z}{}_k\int r_k^l Y_l^{m*}(\theta_k,\varphi_k)\nabla\cdot(\psi_f^*\mathbf{L}_k\psi_i)\,d\tau \qquad \textbf{(8-3.4)}$$

$$\mathcal{Q}'_{lm} = -\frac{i(\omega/c)}{l+1}\frac{e\hbar}{2Mc}\sum_{1}^{A}{}_k\int \mu_k r_k^l Y_l^{m*}(\theta_k,\varphi_k)\nabla\cdot(\psi_f^*\mathbf{r}_k\times\boldsymbol{\sigma}_k\psi_i)\,d\tau \qquad \textbf{(8-3.5)}$$

$$\mathcal{M}'_{lm} = -\frac{e\hbar}{2Mc}\sum_{1}^{A}{}_k\int \mu_k r_k^l Y_l^{m*}(\theta_k,\varphi_k)\nabla\cdot(\psi_f^*\boldsymbol{\sigma}_k\psi_i)\,d\tau \qquad \textbf{(8-3.6)}$$

Here the symbols have the following meanings: i and f indicate initial and final states; k is the number of the nucleon: 1 to Z for protons, $Z+1$ to A for neutrons; ψ refers to the eigenfunction of the whole nucleus; the vector operator $\mathbf{L}_k$ is $-i\mathbf{r}_k\times\boldsymbol{\nabla}_k$; the μ_k are the magnetic moments of the nucleons in units $e\hbar/2Mc$; the $\boldsymbol{\sigma}$ are Pauli matrix operators. The spherical harmonics are evaluated for the position of each nucleon in turn. The $\lambda(l,m)$ averaged over the initial m' states and summed over the final m'' states correspond to the average transition probability from an unpolarized source irrespective of the polarization of the emitted radiation. We call

$$B(l,J_i,J_f) \qquad \textbf{(8-3.7)}$$

the expression

$$|\mathcal{Q}_{lm} + \mathcal{Q}'_{lm}|^2 \qquad \textbf{(8-3.8)}$$

or

$$|\mathcal{M}_{lm} + \mathcal{M}'_{lm}|^2 \qquad \textbf{(8-3.9)}$$

averaged and summed up as indicated. We introduce correspondingly the symbol

$$\lambda(l) = \frac{1}{2J_i + 1} \sum_{m_i} \sum_{m_f} \lambda(l,m) \tag{8-3.10}$$

and we have

$$\lambda(l) = \frac{8\pi(l + 1)}{l[(2l + 1)!!]^2} \left(\frac{\omega}{c}\right)^{2l+1} \frac{1}{\hbar} B(l,J_i \to J_f) \tag{8-3.11}$$

If we need to distinguish electric and magnetic transitions, we shall use $\lambda(El)$, $B(El)$, etc.

The evaluation formulas such as Eqs. (8-3.3) to (8-3.11) would clearly require a detailed knowledge of the nucleus such as is not available today. Calculations are possible only for some simple models; a notable case is that of only one nucleon radiating. In particular we shall consider a nucleus of odd A according to the shell model. Its angular momentum is then due to the odd nucleon alone, and we assume $j - j$ coupling. The radiation is emitted only because the single nucleon changes orbit. We write the interesting part of the eigenfunction as

$$\psi_i = R_{nl}(r)\phi_{j,l,m}(\theta,\varphi) \tag{8-3.12}$$

and a similar one for ψ_f.

By inserting Eq. (8-3.12) into the multipole formulas (8-3.3) to (8-3.6), the parts containing the spherical harmonics can be integrated and factored out. They give a result that we indicate by

$$S(J_i,J_f,l) \tag{8-3.13}$$

The numerical value of this expression has been explicitly calculated (Moszkowski, 1951) and tabulated. In general, it is of the order of magnitude of unity. The matrix element $\mathcal{Q}$, $\mathcal{Q}'$ and $\mathcal{M}$, $\mathcal{M}'$ have the dimensions of er^l and $(e\hbar/Mc)\, r^{l-1}$, respectively. The integrals expressing them are extended over the nuclear volume; thus the variable r appearing in them has the order of magnitude of the nuclear radius R. This suggests introducing dimensionless quantities

$$\mathfrak{Q}(El,J_i,J_f) = (\mathcal{Q} + \mathcal{Q}')/eR^l \quad \text{and}$$
$$\mathfrak{M}(Ml,J_i,J_f,) = (\mathcal{M} + \mathcal{M}')/[(e\hbar/Mc)R^{l-1}]$$

One then obtains for the transition probabilities

$$\lambda(El) = \left(\frac{e^2}{\hbar c}\right) \frac{l + 1}{l} \frac{\omega}{[(2l + 1)!!]^2} \left(\frac{\omega R}{c}\right)^{2l} (2J_f + 1)\, S|\mathfrak{Q}(El)|^2 \tag{8-3.14}$$

and

$$\lambda(Ml) = \left(\frac{e^2}{\hbar c}\right) \frac{l + 1}{l} \frac{\omega}{[(2l + 1)!!]^2} \left(\frac{\omega R}{c}\right)^{2l} (2J_f + 1) S\left(\frac{\hbar}{McR}\right)^2 |\mathfrak{M}(Ml)|^2 \tag{8-3.15}$$

In the case in which a single proton changes state in the transition,

$$\mathfrak{Q}(El) = \int_0^\infty R_i(r)\left(\frac{r}{R}\right)^l R_f^*(r)r^2\,dr \tag{8-3.16}$$

and

$$\mathfrak{M}(Ml) = \left(\mu_p l - \frac{l}{l+1}\right)\int_0^\infty R_i(r)\left(\frac{r}{R}\right)^{l-1} R_f^*(r)r^2\,dr \tag{8-3.17}$$

where $\mu_p = 2.79$, the magnetic moment of the proton in nuclear magnetons, and R_i and R_f are the radial eigenfunctions of the initial and final states. For the single-neutron case

$$\mathfrak{Q}(El) = 0 \tag{8-3.18}$$

because the neutron has no charge, and

$$\mathfrak{M}(Ml) = \mu_n l \int R_i(r)\left(\frac{r}{R}\right)_0^{l-1} R_f^*(r)r^2\,dr \tag{8-3.19}$$

The radial integrals may be approximated by assuming $R_{nl}(r) =$ constant $= (3/R^3)^{1/2}$ from $r = 0$ to $r = R$, as required by normalization and zero for $r \gg R$. We then have immediately, for example,

$$\mathfrak{Q}(El) = \int R_f^*(r)\frac{r^l}{R^l}R_i(r)r^2\,dr = \frac{3}{3+l} \tag{8-3.20}$$

and similar expressions for the other matrix elements

On the usual assumption that $R = r_0A^{1/3}$ the transition probabilities have been evaluated. They are shown in Fig. 8-5. The transition probabilities depend strongly on the energy of the transition through the factor ω^{2l+1} and on A, which enters through the radius R at the power $2l$. The approximations involved are crude, and one cannot expect good numerical agreement. Important effects such as the recoil of the rest of the nucleus except the nucleon considered have been entirely neglected, and an oversimplified model has been used. We gain an impression of the measure of agreement between the experimental results and our schematization, comparing the values of the experimental mean life for gamma transitions with the values predicted by Eqs. (8-3.14) and (8-3.15). To facilitate the comparison, we use the "reduced mean life," or "comparative mean life," i.e., the mean life corrected by the factors due to transition energy and nuclear size (Fig. 8-6).

Experimentally the mean life of a gamma emission can be measured directly down to approximately 10^{-10} sec. Indirect measurements involve the observation of Coulomb excitation (see Sec. 8-7) and the observation of level width either through resonance fluorescence or otherwise. Here one can reach values of about 10^{-12} sec.

To show the influence of the type of motion on the gamma transition probabilities, we shall mention a case almost opposite to the one-particle model: the liquid-drop model. According to this model, neutrons and protons in a nucleus are bound in such a way that the local composition of nuclear matter is practically constant. The electric

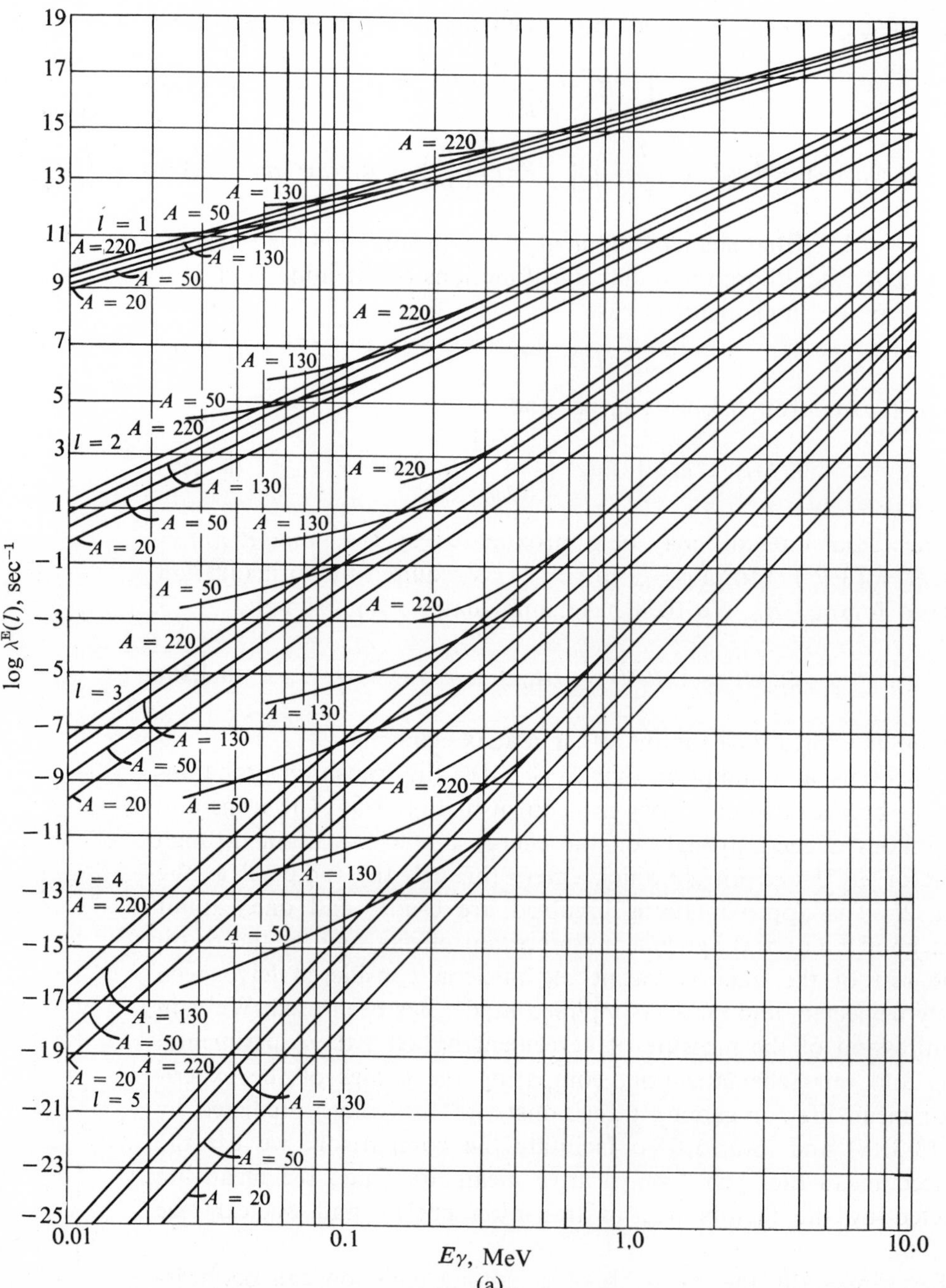

(a)

Figure 8-5 The transition probability for gamma-ray emission [as a function of the transition energy E_γ (MeV)] based on the single-particle model. Part (a) plots the transition probability for *El* radiation ($l = 1, \ldots, 5$) for nuclei of mass 20, 50, 130, and 220 according to the formula

$$\lambda(El) = \frac{4(l+1)}{l[(2l+1)!!]^2}\left(\frac{3}{3+l}\right)^2\left(\frac{E_\gamma}{140}\right)^{2l+1} A^{2l/3}\frac{mc^2}{\hbar}$$

Part (b) plots the transition probability for *Ml* radiation ($l = 1, \ldots, 5$) according to the formula

$$\lambda(Ml) = \frac{0.088(l+1)}{l[(2l+1)!!]^2}\left(\frac{3}{2+l}\right)^2\left(\frac{E_\gamma}{140}\right)^{2l+1} A^{(2l-2)/3}\left(\frac{\mu_p l}{2} - \frac{l}{l+1}\right)^2\frac{mc^2}{\hbar}$$

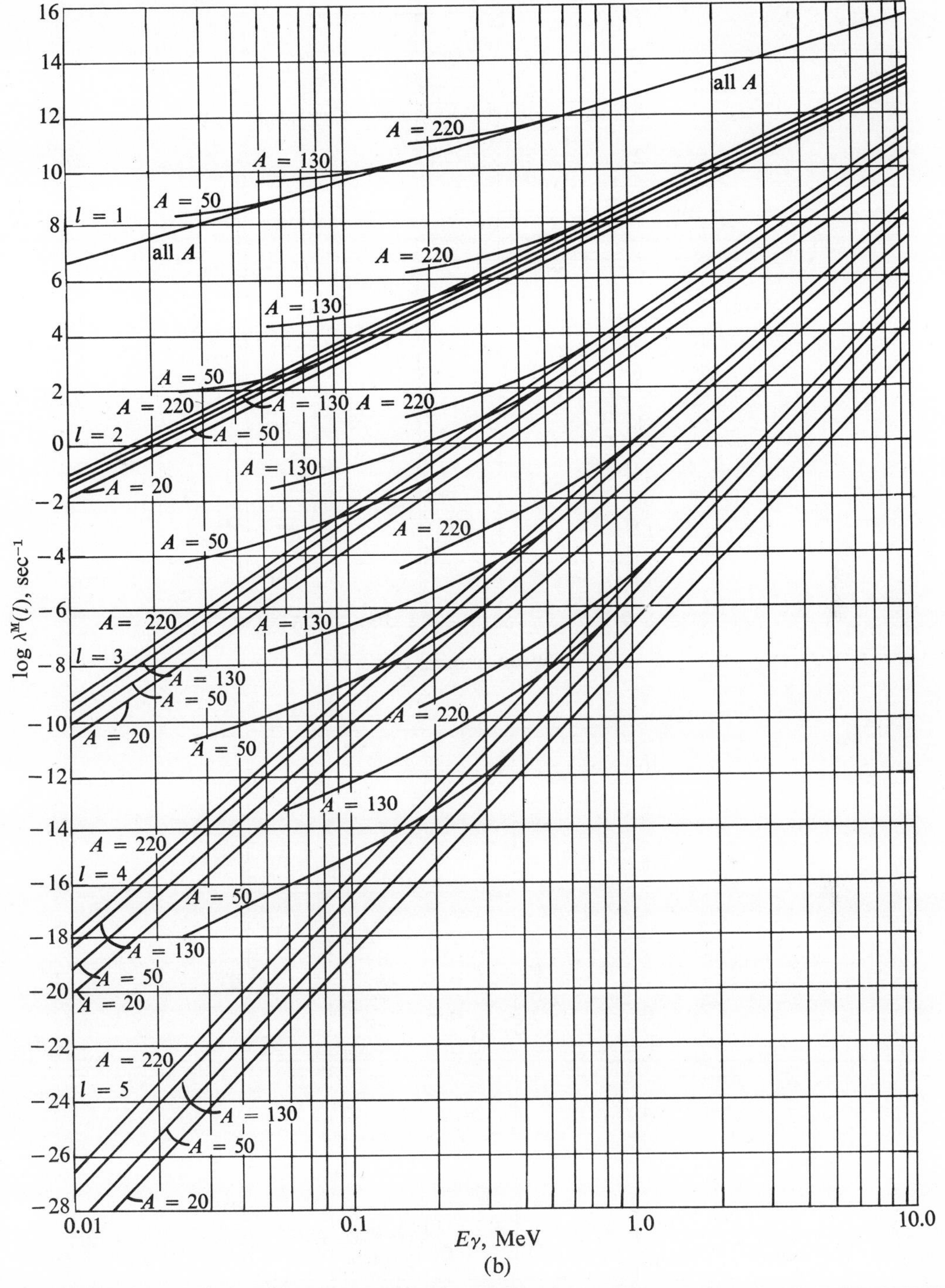

(b)

The formulas neglect the factor $S(J_i,J_f,l)$ of Eq. (8-3.13) and assume

$$R = 1.40A^{1/3}\ \text{F}$$

The curves represent the additional contributions to the total transition probability by the internal conversion process. [From Condon and Odishaw, *Handbook of Physics*, McGraw-Hill, New York, 1958.]

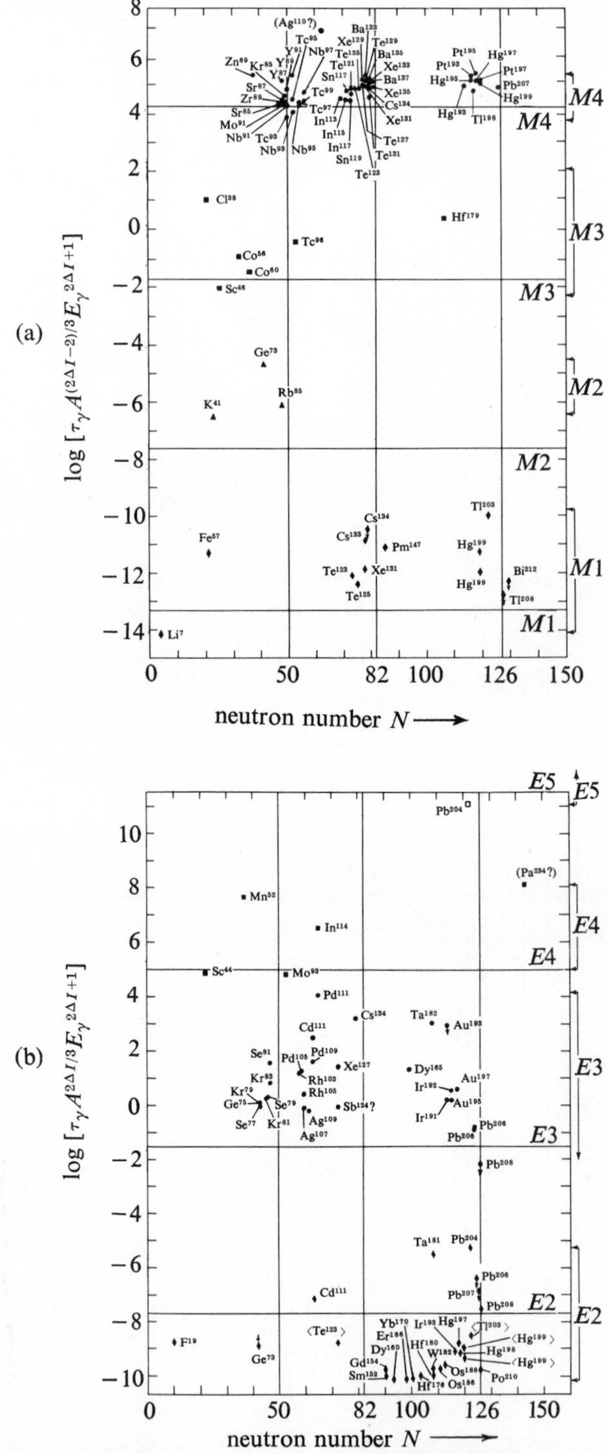

Figure 8-6 Comparison of experiment with the "reduced half-life" of gamma transition. The "reduction" should eliminate the influence of energy and ΔI. [M. Goldhaber and J. Weneser, *Ann. Rev. Nucl. Sci.*, **5**, 1 (1955).]

center of charge then has the same coordinates as the center of mass and cannot move under the action of internal forces, because of the principle of the conservation of momentum. It follows that the electric-dipole moment is zero, and dipole radiation is strictly forbidden. This situation exists in many low-energy transitions in which the dipole radiation is much weaker than would be expected on the basis of Eq. (8-3.14).

At high energy (~20 MeV) there seems to be a different type of motion, in which all protons together oscillate relative to all neutrons. This motion gives rise to a large electric-dipole moment that enables the nuclei to absorb electromagnetic energy strongly in that frequency range and hence gives rise to large cross sections for the (γ,n), (γ,p) reactions. The absorption has the character of a broad resonance, sometimes called the "giant" resonance, and will be treated in Chap. 11.

Finally, special types of surface motion in the nucleus occasionally favor electric-quadrupole radiation (see Secs. 6-12 and 8-7).

8-4 Internal Conversion

In the preceding section we have considered the transition of a nucleus from one level to another by emission of electromagnetic radiation. This and, given sufficient energy, pair production would be the only ways to execute the transition for an isolated nucleus deprived of all its atomic electrons. The presence of the electrons makes possible a different process: the nucleus can lose its excitation and transfer it directly to one of the atomic electrons which is ejected with a kinetic energy equal to the energy of the gamma transition minus the binding energy of the electron. Electrons ejected by this mechanism are called "conversion electrons," and one speaks of conversion in the K shell, in the L shell, etc., according to the shell vacated by the conversion electron. The conversion coefficient

$$\frac{N_e}{N_\gamma} = \alpha \qquad \textbf{(8-4.1)}$$

is the ratio between the average number of electrons and the average number of gamma rays emitted in connection with a given transition. It is possible also to distinguish "partial conversion coefficients" according to the shell from which the electron is taken. Thus one has

$$\alpha_K + \alpha_L \cdots = \alpha \qquad \textbf{(8-4.2)}$$

where α_K, α_L, etc., are the partial conversion coefficients (Fig. 8-7).

The possibility of decay of an excited state by internal conversion adds to its decay constant; thus the total decay constant λ is equal to the sum of the partial decay constants λ_γ and λ_e for gamma emission and conversion electron emission. As a consequence of Eq. (8-4.1) one has

$$\lambda = \lambda_\gamma + \lambda_e = \lambda_\gamma(1 + \alpha) \qquad \textbf{(8-4.3)}$$

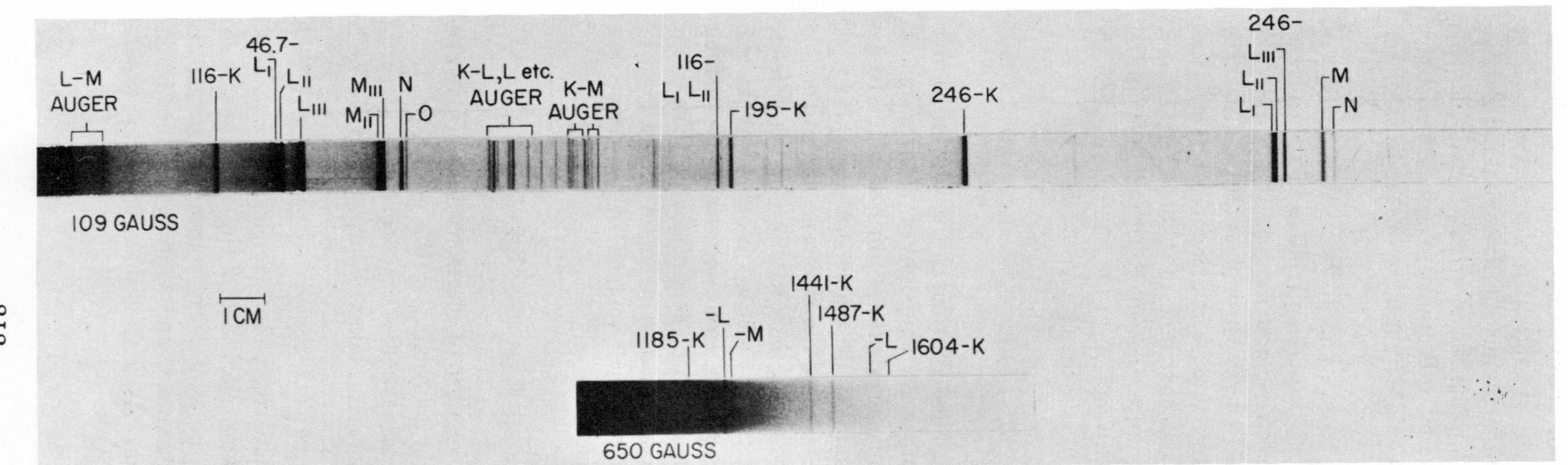

Figure 8-7 Internal conversion spectrum of $At^{209,\ 210,\ 211}$, showing *K*, *L*, *M*, and *N* conversion. [Mihelich, Schardt, and Segrè, *Phys. Rev.*, **95,** 1508 (1954).]

A direct experimental proof of the last relation is given by the decay of an excited state in Tc^{99}, which proceeds with a slightly longer mean life if some of the surrounding electrons are removed by chemical bonding.

If there are two radioactive emissions in rapid succession, e.g., β (negative electrons) and gamma emission, the energy of the conversion electrons tells which emission is the first. Starting with a nucleus of atomic number Z, if the beta emission precedes the gamma emission, the binding energies of the conversion electrons correspond to an atom with atomic number $Z + 1$ and not Z (L. Meitner and H. J. von Baeyer, 1919). Similar considerations obtain for alpha emission or orbital electron capture associated with gamma emission.

The internal conversion coefficients depend on the atomic number of the nucleus, on the energy, and on the character of multipolarity of the transition, but not on the specific nuclear model. Thus their study is a powerful aid to the classification of nuclear levels. Their values as a function of the energy, of the type of radiation, and of A have been extensively tabulated. We shall now calculate one of the simplest possible cases, which will bring out the essentials of the phenomenon.

Suppose that the nucleus is in an excited state from which it can pass to the ground state by the emission of $E1$ radiation. The nucleus can then be compared with an electric dipole of frequency ω. The presence of this dipole may induce transitions from the ground state of the atom to an excited state; specifically, the K electrons, which are in a $1s$ state, can be brought by dipole radiation to a p state, possibly in the continuum. The probability of this transition is calculable with golden rule No. 2,

$$w = \frac{2\pi}{\hbar}|M_{if}|^2 \frac{d\mathscr{N}}{dE} \tag{8-4.4}$$

We have to evaluate the matrix element M_{if} and the density of the accessible final states. Call the initial eigenfunction of the electron in the $1s$ state

$$\psi_i(\mathbf{r},t) = u_i(r) \exp\left(-\frac{iE_i}{\hbar}t\right) \tag{8-4.5}$$

and the final eigenfunction of the electron in the continuum

$$\psi_f(\mathbf{r},t) = u_f(\mathbf{r}) \exp\left(-\frac{iE_f}{\hbar}t\right) \tag{8-4.6}$$

The transition from the initial to the final state is induced by the electric field of the nucleus, which is described as an electric dipole of moment $\mathbf{P}$ directed along the z axis and varying in time with frequency ω. The electric potential of this dipole is

$$V(\mathbf{r},t) = p_0 \frac{\cos\theta}{r^2} \cos\omega t = p_0 \frac{\cos\theta}{r^2}\frac{1}{2}(e^{i\omega t} + e^{-i\omega t}) \tag{8-4.7}$$

where θ is the angle between $\mathbf{r}$ and the z axis. The matrix element of the induced transitions is

$$M_{if} = e \int \psi_f^*(\mathbf{r},t) V \psi_i(\mathbf{r},t)\, d\tau \tag{8-4.8}$$

M_{if} is of appreciable magnitude only if

$$|E_i - E_f| = \hbar\omega \tag{8-4.9}$$

Moreover, since u_i corresponding to an s state does not contain θ, while V contains the factor $\cos\theta = P_1(\cos\theta)$, ψ_f^*, when expanded in spherical harmonics, will contribute to the integral only through the term containing also $P_1(\cos\theta)$, all the other terms being orthogonal to $u_i V$. This shows that the transition will occur only to p levels. The density of the final states in Eq. (8-4.4) must thus be limited to the density of the p states.

At this point we can already see the important qualitative conclusion mentioned above. The probability of internal conversion and the radiation probability are both proportional to p_0^2; hence this quantity will disappear from the internal conversion coefficient. The internal conversion coefficient is a function of the energy of the transition and of the atomic number of the atom, because they appear in the initial and final wave functions, but not of the complicated nuclear wave functions. For other multipole fields the same qualitative conclusion obtains: the internal conversion coefficients depend on the character of the radiation El or Ml, the atomic shell in which it occurs, the atomic number, and the energy.

Note that this result is not absolutely exact. There are some additional effects depending on nuclear size and internal motions, which in special cases affect the conversion coefficient appreciably. In the main, however, it is correct to assume that the internal conversion coefficient is a purely atomic property.

In order to take the calculation a little further in our simple example, we take as the wave function of the final state that of a free electron and expand it in spherical harmonics (see Appendix D). We are, however, interested only in the p-wave component, because all other components give zero matrix elements with the initial s state. We thus write

$$u_f = N \frac{\cos\theta}{(kr)^{1/2}} J_{3/2}(kr) \tag{8-4.10}$$

or, asymptotically for large kr,

$$u_f = -N\cos\theta \left(\frac{2}{\pi k^2 r^2}\right)^{1/2} \cos kr \tag{8-4.11}$$

We have indicated by N a normalization factor, which we evaluate by enclosing the system in a very large sphere of radius R and using the asymptotic expression for the eigenfunction. We find

$$N = k\left(\frac{3}{4R}\right)^{1/2} \tag{8-4.12}$$

For the initial state we take the hydrogen-type s-wave function

$$u_i = \frac{1}{\pi^{1/2}}\left(\frac{Z}{a_0}\right)^{3/2} \exp\left(-\frac{Zr}{a_0}\right) \qquad \text{with } a_0 = \frac{\hbar^2}{me^2} \tag{8-4.13}$$

The matrix element is then

$$M_{if} = p_0(\cos\omega t)\, ek \left(\frac{3}{4R}\right)^{1/2} \frac{1}{\pi^{1/2}}\left(\frac{Z}{a_0}\right)^{3/2} \int_0^\infty \exp\left(-\frac{Zr}{a_0}\right) \times \frac{\cos\theta}{r^2}\frac{J_{3/2}(kr)}{(kr)^{1/2}}\cos\theta\, d\tau \tag{8-4.14}$$

$$= p_0(\cos\omega t)\left(\frac{4\pi}{3R}\right)^{1/2} ek \left(\frac{Z}{a_0}\right)^{3/2} I \tag{8-4.15}$$

with

$$I = \int_0^\infty \exp\left(-\frac{Zr}{a_0}\right)\frac{J_{3/2}(kr)}{(kr)^{1/2}}\, dr \tag{8-4.16}$$

The density of the final states must be limited to p states only. From the asymptotic expression [Eq. (8-4.11)] and the condition $u_f(R) = 0$ we find the quantization condition

$$kR = (n + \tfrac{1}{2})\,\pi \tag{8-4.17}$$

with n an integral number. Thus in the k interval Δk there are

$$R\frac{\Delta k}{\pi} = \Delta\mathcal{N} \tag{8-4.18}$$

states. From this equation we get

$$\rho = \frac{d\mathcal{N}}{dE} = \frac{R}{\hbar\pi v} \tag{8-4.19}$$

Combining Eqs. (8-4.15) and (8-4.19) we obtain for one of the K electrons

$$\lambda_e = \frac{8\pi}{\hbar} p_0^{\,2} \frac{4e^2k^2}{3}\left(\frac{Z}{a_0}\right)^3 \frac{I^2}{\hbar v} \tag{8-4.20}$$

On the other hand λ_γ is given by

$$\lambda_\gamma = \frac{4}{3}\frac{p_0^{\,2}\omega^3}{\hbar c^3} \tag{8-4.21}$$

according to Eq. (8-1.5) or (8-3.1) and hence the internal conversion coefficient is, for the two K electrons,

$$\alpha = \frac{4\pi}{\hbar}\frac{k^2e^2}{v}\left(\frac{Z}{a_0}\right)^3 \frac{c^3}{\omega^3} I^2 \tag{8-4.22}$$

A closed-form evaluation can be obtained in the special case of $a_0/Z \gg 1/k$, which means that the energy of the transition is very large compared with the electron binding energy. We shall assume, moreover, that the ejected electron is not relativistic. To be consistent, then, we assume for the electron that $mv^2/2 \simeq (\hbar k)^2/2m \simeq \hbar\omega$.

The integral I can be calculated by elementary means on the assumption that $e^{-Zr/a_0} = 1$, and we have

$$I = \int_0^\infty J_{3/2}(kr) \frac{dr}{(kr)^{1/2}} = \left(\frac{2}{\pi k^2}\right)^{1/2} \tag{8-4.23}$$

Replacing in Eq. (8-4.22) with the approximations mentioned above, we have

$$\begin{aligned}\alpha_K &= \frac{8}{\hbar} \frac{e^2 m^{1/2}}{(2\hbar\omega)^{1/2}} \left(\frac{Z}{a_0}\right)^3 \frac{c^3}{\omega^3} \\ &= \frac{1}{2} Z^3 \left(\frac{e^2}{\hbar c}\right)^4 \left(\frac{2mc^2}{\hbar\omega}\right)^{7/2}\end{aligned} \tag{8-4.24}$$

This formula, valid under the hypothesis mentioned for dipole radiation, may be extended to El radiation, giving

$$\alpha_K^l = Z^3 \left(\frac{e^2}{\hbar c}\right)^4 \frac{l}{l+1} \left(\frac{2mc^2}{\hbar\omega}\right)^{l+5/2} \tag{8-4.25}$$

The approximations used here are too crude to give valuable numerical results. However, it is possible to obtain good accuracy by employing relativistic wave functions and other necessary refinements. The extension to higher electric and magnetic multipoles becomes increasingly cumbersome. Typical numerical results are shown in Figs. 8-8, 8-9, and 8-10. Extensive tables of internal coversion coefficients are reported in the literature, for instance in (Se 59).

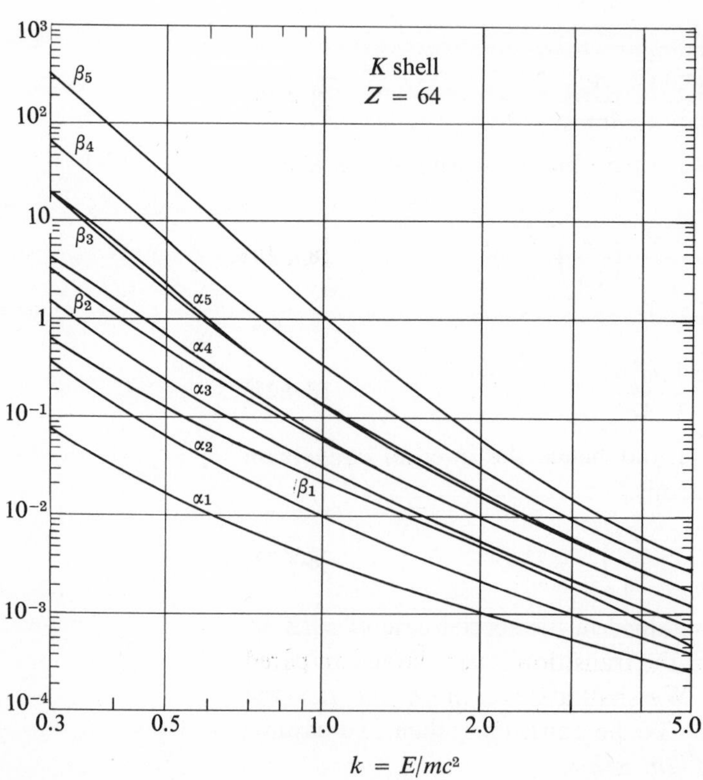

Figure 8-8 Electric (α_L) and magnetic (β_L) conversion coefficients for the K shell and for $Z = 64$. Energy scale gives $E/mc^2 = k$. [From (Si 55).]

The measurement of internal conversion coefficients is performed by counting the number of gamma rays, for instance, with a scintillation counter, and the number of conversion electrons with a Geiger-Müller counter or photographically, often with the help of beta spectrographs (Fig. 8-10). The measurement of the ratios of the conversion coefficients for the different X-ray levels $\alpha_K:\alpha_{LI}:\alpha_{LII}$, etc., can be made with a beta spectrometer without measuring gamma rays. The ratios by themselves give valuable information for classifying the type of radiation.

8-5 Nuclear Isomerism

The selection rules described in Sec. 8-2 can slow down electromagnetic transitions to such a point that the excited state has a very long mean life, "very long" meaning from 0.1 sec to years. In this case, the excited state is called a "metastable" or an "isomeric" state in analogy with the chemical isomers. It is clear from the definition that the limit of 0.1 sec is completely arbitrary. There are gamma transitions of mean lives ranging from 10^{-16} to 10^8 sec; thus the point at which one starts to call a state metastable is arbitrary.

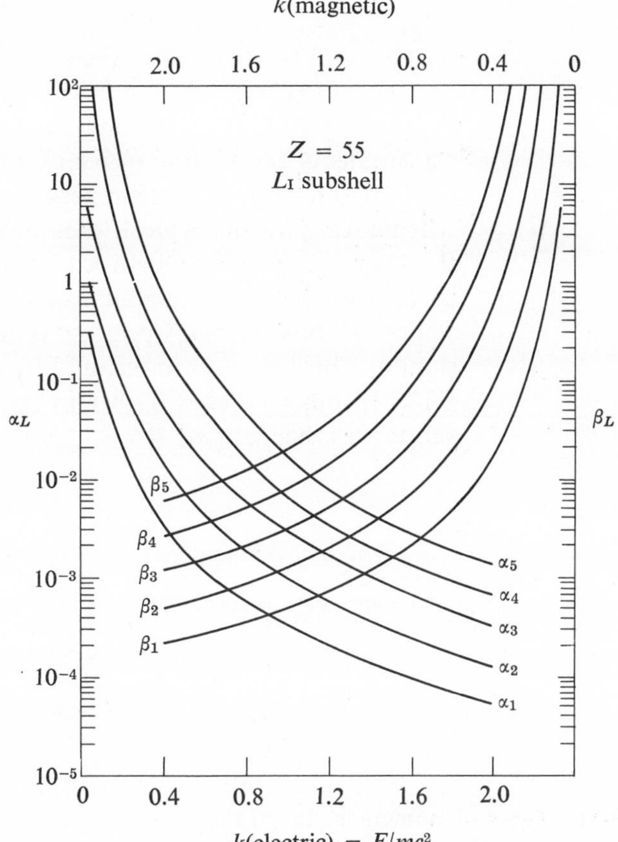

Figure 8-9 Electric and magnetic conversion coefficients for the L_I subshell and for $Z = 55$. For clarity the electric and magnetic curves have been separated by using the separate energy scales (in units of E/mc^2) given at the bottom and top of the figure. [From (Si 55).]

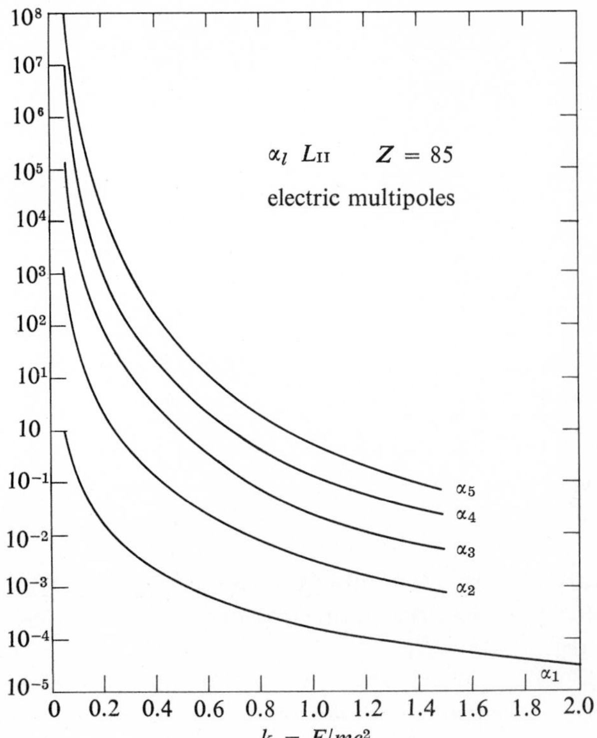

Figure 8-10 Electric conversion coefficients for the L_{II} subshell, $Z = 85$. Energy scale in E/mc^2. [From (Si 55).]

The phenomenon of nuclear isomerism was discovered in Pa^{234} by O. Hahn (1921). The explanation in terms of forbidden gamma transitions is due to von Weizsäcker (1936).

Often nuclear isomerism accompanies beta transitions, as indicated schematically in the typical level diagrams of Fig. 8-11. In Fig. 8-11a the isomeric transition between levels a and b is very probable compared with the beta transition between a and c. If $\lambda_{ia} \ll \lambda_{\beta b}$, the substance exhibits the beta spectrum typical of level b, with the decay constant λ_{ia}. Br^{80} is an example, and its level diagram is illustrated in Fig. 8-12. In other cases (Fig. 8-11b) levels a and b decay as independent substances, because $\lambda_{ia} \ll \lambda_{\beta b}$.

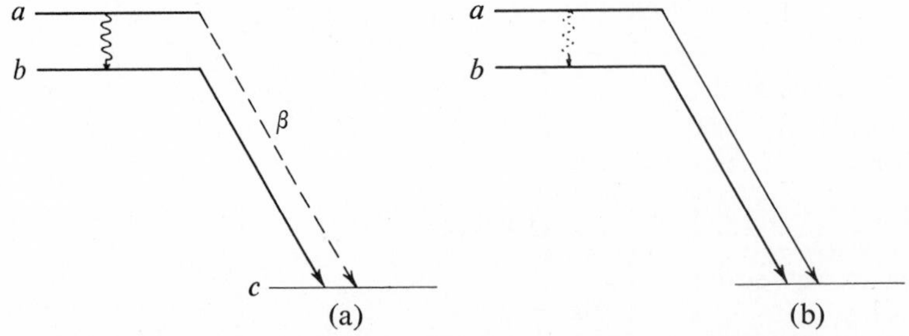

Figure 8-11 Types of isomerism. In (a) the upper level decays prevalently by gamma emission to the ground state, which decays by beta emission. In (b) upper and lower states decay independently by beta emission.

Isomeric transitions, being highly forbidden, must correspond to large ΔJ and small energy. Both circumstances favor high internal conversion, and this is another characteristic of isomeric transitions. In fact, the large internal conversion may be used to separate chemically nuclear isomers. In the case of Br^{80}, for instance, the 4.4-hr excited level emits a gamma ray of 49 keV, which is highly converted and leaves a vacancy in an inner shell subsequently filled by an outer electron. This process proceeds until one of the valence electrons is used. If the Br^{80} atom is bound in an organic compound, loss of the valence electron sets it free as a Br^- ion, which can be chemically separated by precipitation of AgBr. It is thus possible to separate the nuclei that have undergone isomeric transition from the others.

To be metastable an excited level must differ from lower energy levels by three or more units of J; the radiation emitted is thus $E3$, $M3$, or of higher multipolarity. The condition mentioned is satisfied only for $A \geqslant 39$, and there are no isomers of the light elements. Even at higher A, nuclear isomeric states are not spread uniformly among all nuclei but are preferentially concentrated in "islands" of nuclei with Z or N just below the magic numbers 50, 82, 126 and even A. Isomers with both N and Z even are very rare (Fig. 8-13).

These facts are accounted for satisfactorily by the shell model. First, in an even-even nucleus, the excitation of a nucleon involves the pairing energy, which is too large to allow the formation of isomers. Second, the islands of isomerism are explained by a study of Fig. 6-36. For low A up to 40 nucleons the orbits involved have $j \leqslant 5/2$, and there are no possibilities of large spin differences between energetically close orbits. Shortly before the numbers 50, 82, or 126, there are energetically neighboring orbits with $j = 1/2, 9/2; 1/2, 11/2; 1/2, 13/2$ and these give rise to the "islands of isomers."

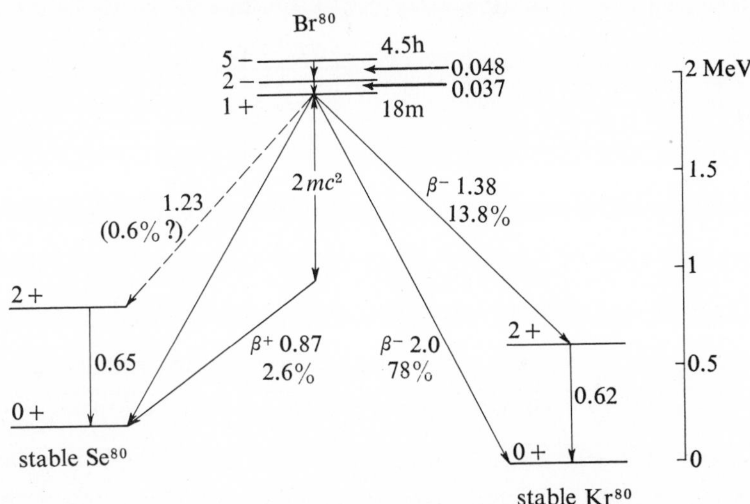

Figure 8-12 Energy-level diagram for Br^{80}, illustrating isomeric transition. All energies in MeV.

8-6 Angular Correlations in Gamma Emission

Often, when two gamma rays are emitted in rapid succession by the same nucleus, one finds that the directions of emission of the two rays are correlated. This means that upon assuming the direction of the first gamma as z axis, the probability of the second falling into the element of solid angle $d\omega$ is not constant but depends on the angle θ between the two directions. This type of correlation, already mentioned in Chap. 6, is not restricted only to $\gamma - \gamma$ emission. The principles that we shall repeat here may be generalized to other cases.

Suppose that we have nuclei emitting light quanta through electric-dipole transitions. We place the nuclei in a magnetic field, which orients them in such a way that the electric dipole is along the z axis. We know that no quanta will be emitted in the direction of the z axis and that the maximum probability of emission will be in the xy plane. Conversely, in the absence of an orienting field, the fact that a gamma quantum is emitted in a certain direction tells us that that direction is *not* the direction of the electric dipole and makes it a priori more probable that the electric dipole is perpendicular to the direction of the first

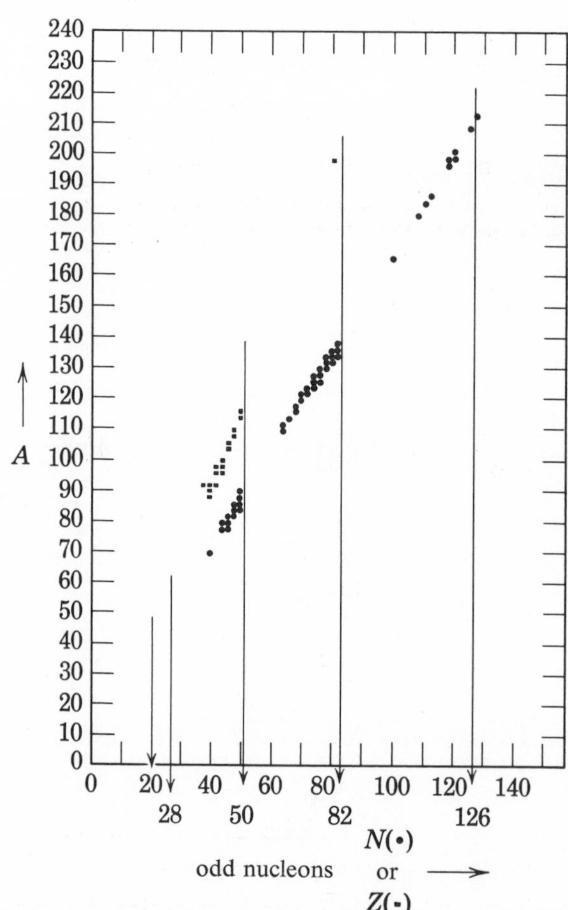

Figure 8-13 Distribution of long-lived isomers of odd mass number A plotted against the number of odd nucleons (N or Z). (Isomerism islands.) [M. Goldhaber and J. Weneser, *Ann. Rev. Nucl. Sci.*, **5**, 1 (1955).]

quantum. A second quantum is thus less likely to be emitted in a direction perpendicular to the first quantum than in any other. This argument can be made quantitative. For the probability $P(\theta)$ of successive emissions having an included angle θ, one finds

$$P(\theta)\,d\omega = A(1 + \cos^2\theta)\,d\omega \tag{8-6.1}$$

where $d\omega$ is the element of solid angle and

$$A = \frac{3}{16\pi} \tag{8-6.2}$$

is a normalization constant.

The quantum-mechanical treatment of the correlation for more complicated cases shows that $P(\theta)$ is a polynomial of even degree in $\cos\theta$. This is apparent from the fact that $P(\theta)$ and $P(\pi - \theta)$ must be equal, if parity is conserved, that is, if the correlation is not altered on reflection through the origin, as is the case for electromagnetic interactions. The degree of the polynomial in $\cos^2\theta$ and its coefficients depend on the spins of the three states involved and on the character of the two radiations connecting them.

We have already discussed in Chap. 6 the effect of a magnetic field on angular correlations. A typical apparatus is illustrated in Fig. 8-14. Despite the apparent simplicity of the equipment, considerable care must be exercised in order to avoid the numerous sources of error, such as scattering of radiation from one counter into the other, finite solid angles, efficiency of counters, etc. (See also Fig. 6-32.)

8-7 Coulomb Excitation

Nuclear levels can be excited by bombarding nuclei with charged

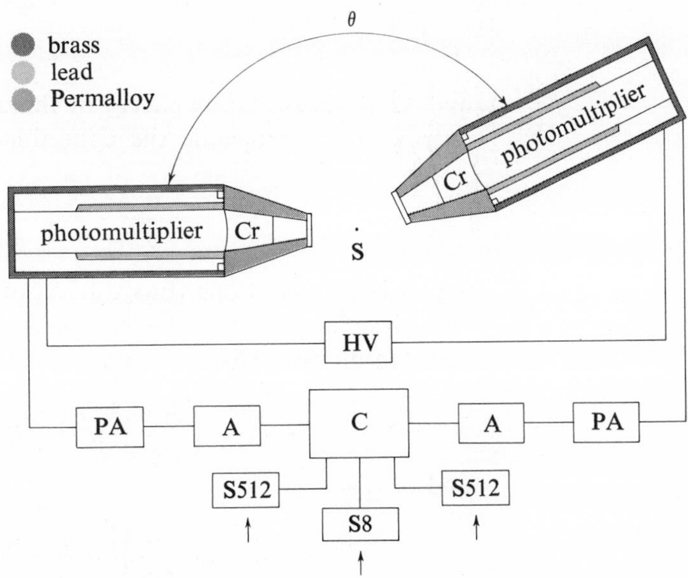

Figure 8-14 Apparatus for measuring angular correlations of gamma rays. PA, preamplifiers; A, amplifiers; C, coincidence circuit, 0.1-μ sec resolution; S 512, scale of 512; Cr, crystals; S, source.

heavy particles such as protons or alpha particles. This method of study is experimentally preferable to the use of electrons where there are background difficulties from the bremsstrahlung. Keeping the energy of the heavy charged particles below the nuclear Coulomb barrier, we avoid specific nuclear reactions, and the backgrounds due to unwanted effects are small. Projectiles used have some MeV of energy; the levels excited, some tenths of MeV of energy. The electric field of the projectile induces transitions in the target, and the effect can be calculated semiclassically by considering the field produced by the projectile moving in its hyperbolic trajectory as a perturbation on the nucleus. The matrix elements involved are the multipole electric moments of the nucleus connecting initial and final states. The calculation is rather involved, but the underlying physical concepts are simple. For the method of calculation to be valid, the orbit concept must be applicable, and hence the de Broglie wavelength $\lambda\!\!\!^{-}$ of the projectile must be small compared with the distance of closest approach to the target. Now calling a half this distance, one has

$$a = \frac{Z_1 Z_2 e^2}{mv^2} \tag{8-7.1}$$

where Z_1, Z_2 are the atomic numbers of projectile and target and m, v are mass and velocity of the projectile. The condition $a/\lambda\!\!\!^{-} \gg 1$ is then

$$\eta \equiv \frac{a}{\lambda\!\!\!^{-}} = \frac{Z_1 Z_2 e^2}{\hbar v} \gg 1 \tag{8-7.2}$$

Furthermore, the collision must be nonadiabatic; otherwise no transition occurs. This means that the collision time a/v must be short compared with the nuclear periods τ to be excited, where

$$\tau = \frac{1}{\omega} = \frac{\hbar}{\Delta E} \tag{8-7.3}$$

and ΔE is the excitation energy of the target. Indicating by E the kinetic energy of the projectile the condition of nonadiabatic collision gives

$$\xi = \frac{a}{v}\frac{\Delta E}{\hbar} = \frac{Z_1 Z_2 e^2}{\hbar v^3}\frac{\Delta E}{2E} \ll 1 \tag{8-7.4}$$

When both conditions [Eqs. (8-7.2] and (8-7.4)] are satisfied, calculation gives for the total cross section for Coulomb excitation the approximate result for $\Delta E/E \ll 1$:

$$\sigma_{El} = \left(\frac{Z_1 e}{\hbar v}\right)^2 a^{-2l+2}\, B(El, J_i \to J_f)\, f_{El}(\xi)$$

and

$$\sigma_{Ml} = \left(\frac{Z_1 e}{\hbar c}\right)^2 a^{-2l+2}\, B(Ml, J_i \to J_f)\, f_{Ml}(\xi) \tag{8-7.5}$$

Note that the transition is characterized by its multipolarity and that the matrix element in B is the same as the one entering into the spontaneous emission formulas (8-3.11) and (8-3.15). The function $f(\xi)$ takes into account details of the orbit and is tabulated. For

$$\xi \ll 1, \qquad f_{E2} = 1 \tag{8-7.6}$$

One of the most important cases of Coulomb excitation is that of $E2$ excitation of rotational levels 0^+, 2^+, 4^+, etc., in even-even nuclei with

$$\Delta J = 2 \tag{8-7.7}$$

The matrix elements derived from experiment are sometimes many times larger than can be accounted for by single-particle models and are due to collective motions. They are connected with the intrinsic quadrupole moment Q_0 of such nuclei; e.g., for a $0^+ \rightarrow 2^+$ transition,

$$B(E2) = \frac{5}{16\pi} Q_0^2 \tag{8-7.8}$$

We see here a connection through the intrinsic quadrupole moment between the moment of inertia, the transition probability, and the observable electric-quadrupole moment (cf. Sec. 6-12).

8-8 Nuclear Fluorescence

In atomic physics, resonance and fluorescence radiation are important and easily observed phenomena. We would also expect to observe resonance radiation from nuclei; however, many early attempts to detect it failed. The reason for this is that the nuclear absorption lines are very narrow and thus absorb very little radiation from a continuum. On the other hand, if one tries to excite resonance radiation by the corresponding emission light as in the optical case, the recoil of the emitting nucleus shifts the light out of resonance with the absorber. Let us first consider a strictly monochromatic line. If the initial excited state has an energy E above the ground states in the laboratory system, we have, by the principle of conservation of energy and momentum,

$$\hbar\omega + \frac{p^2}{2m} = E \tag{8-8.1}$$

with

$$\hbar\omega = pc \tag{8-8.2}$$

where ω is the frequency of the light emitted and p and m are the recoil momentum and the mass of the nucleus supposed initially at rest. These relations give approximately

$$\hbar\omega = E\left(1 - \frac{E}{2mc^2}\right) \tag{8-8.3}$$

On the other hand, for absorption we need

$$\hbar\omega = E\left(1 + \frac{E}{2mc^2}\right) \tag{8-8.4}$$

to conserve energy and momentum. We see that, to have resonance, we must multiply the frequency of emission by

$$\sim \left(1 + \frac{E}{mc^2}\right) \tag{8-8.5}$$

or

$$1 + \frac{\hbar\omega}{mc^2} \tag{8-8.6}$$

to find the necessary absorption frequency.

However, spectral lines have a natural width $\delta\omega$ associated with the mean life τ of the excited state by

$$\delta\omega = \frac{1}{\tau} \tag{8-8.7}$$

If this width is large compared to $\hbar\omega^2/mc^2$ the emission line will overlap sufficiently with the absorption line so as to produce resonance radiation. This is the usual case in visible light. If, however, the natural width is insufficient to produce the desired overlap, as is the case in nuclear gamma rays, one can still modify the frequency, as seen by the absorber, with the help of the Doppler effect. If the source moves toward the absorber with velocity

$$v = \frac{\hbar\omega}{mc} \tag{8-8.8}$$

the Doppler shift compensates the recoil effects and resonance is obtained. For instance, in the case of Au^{198}, $\hbar\omega = 0.41$ MeV, and v must be equal to 0.67×10^5 cm/sec, which is attainable by mechanical means or by thermal agitation in a hot vapor. Actually nuclear resonance radiation has been observed (Moon, 1951) by using a source of radioactive gold 198 in rapid motion with respect to a mercury resonator. The study of the intensity of the resonance radiation as a function of velocity of the source can be made to yield information on τ, which, in the case of Au^{198}, is of the order of 10^{-11} sec.

Resonance absorption has been demonstrated in Ir^{191} by Mössbauer (1958) by a different system. He used an Os^{191} source and Ir^{191} as the absorber, both cooled at low temperature. The source decays by beta emission to an excited state at 129 keV of the stable Ir^{191}. The half-life of this state is 1.3×10^{-10} sec and its natural width $(\delta\omega/\omega)_{nat} = 3 \times 10^{-11}$. The recoil energy of the free nucleus would be 0.047 eV, corresponding to a Doppler shift $(\Delta\omega/\omega)_{Doppler} = 3.6 \times 10^{-7}$. However, when the nucleus is bound in a crystal its motion may be crudely compared to that of an oscillator. If the recoil energy is insufficient to raise the oscillator from its ground state to the first excited state, no energy can be transferred to the crystal lattice, and we speak of recoilless emission.

Thus, if we replace the crystal by an ensemble of oscillators of frequency ω_E (as in Einstein's theory of specific heat), there will be recoilless emission only if $\hbar\omega_E \gg \hbar^2\omega^2/mc^2$ (see Fig. 8-15). The momentum $\hbar\omega/c$ is always transferred to the lattice, but if the emission is recoilless the mass receiving it is practically infinite and no energy is delivered to the lattice. The actual spectrum of the lattice vibrations is much more complicated than in the Einstein schematization and as a better approximation we use a Debye spectrum, replacing $\hbar\omega_E$ by $k\Theta$, where Θ is the Debye temperature. At temperatures higher than absolute zero, crystal oscillators are excited and the probability of energy transfer to the lattice increases. The development of these ideas in a quantitative form gives a formula for the probability f of recoilless emission:

$$f = \exp -\left\{\frac{3}{2}\frac{\hbar^2\omega^2/2mc^2}{k\Theta}\left[1 + 4\left(\frac{T}{\Theta}\right)^2\int_0^{\Theta/T}\frac{x\,dx}{e^x - 1}\right]\right\}$$

$$\simeq \exp -\left\{\frac{3}{2}\frac{\hbar^2\omega^2/2mc^2}{k\Theta}\left[1 + \frac{2}{3}\left(\frac{\pi T}{\Theta}\right)^2\right]\right\} \qquad (T \ll \Theta) \qquad \textbf{(8-8.9)}$$

The first term is independent of temperature and shows that, even at absolute zero, the fraction of recoilless decays is large only if the recoil

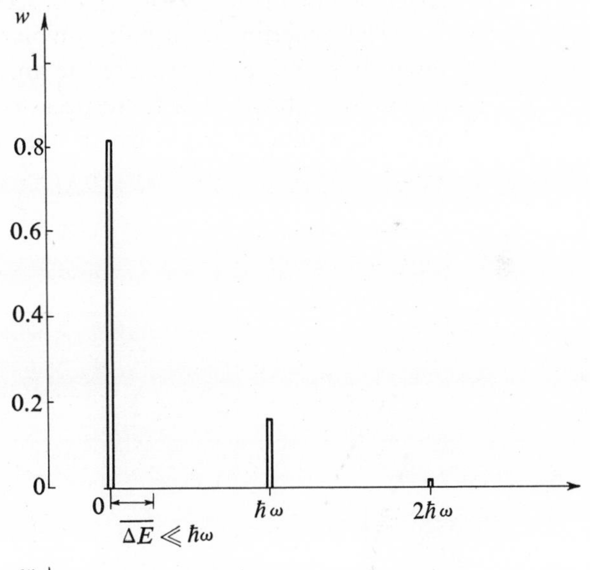

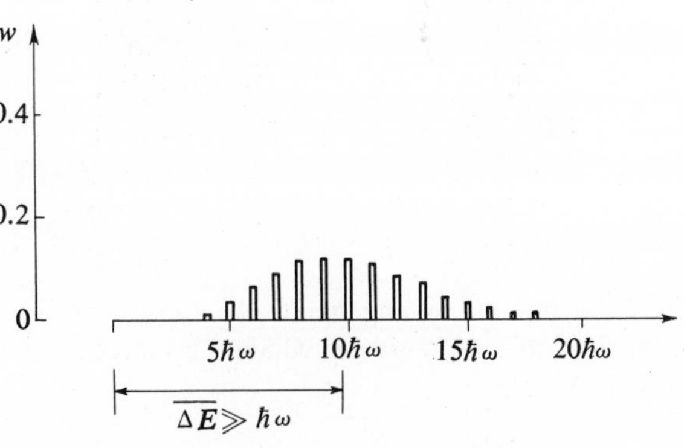

Figure 8-15 Relative probability for a gamma-ray transition simultaneous with the excitation of 1, 2, . . ., n oscillators in the crystal lattice. The figures refer to two values of the ratio between the recoil energy ΔE and $\hbar\omega_E$, $T = 0$°K (after R. L. Mössbauer). [*Les Prix Nobel en* 1961, Stockholm, 1962.]

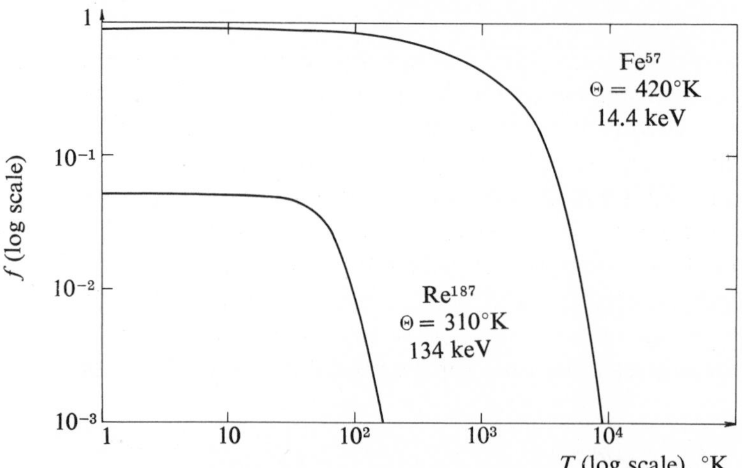

Figure 8-16 Fraction of recoilless transitions in iron or rhenium as a function of the temperature. [R. L. Mössbauer, *Ann. Rev. Nucl. Sci.*, **12,** 123 (1962).]

energy of the free nucleus is small compared with $k\Theta$. The probability of recoilless decay decreases with increasing temperature and it is negligible for temperatures large compared with Θ (Fig. 8-16). Similar effects occur in the absorption process.

The experiments usually involve a source and an absorber of the same substance and measure the amount of radiation absorbed. If one moves the absorber with respect to the source, the frequency of the absorption line changes by an amount

$$\frac{\Delta\omega}{\omega} = -\frac{v}{c} \tag{8-8.10}$$

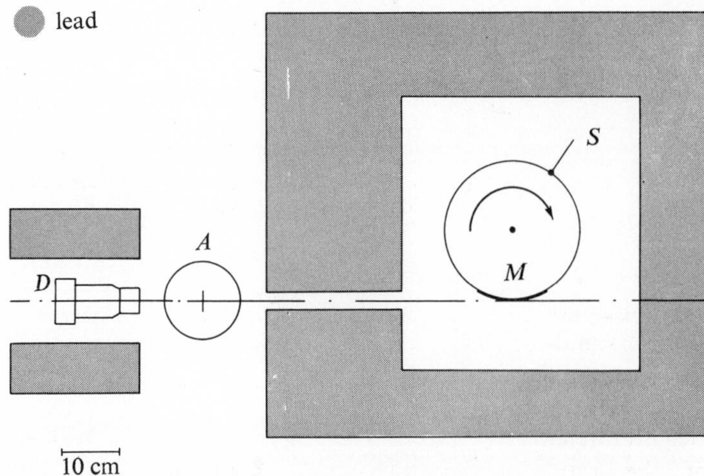

Figure 8-17 Experimental arrangement: *A*, cryostat of absorber; *S*, rotating cryostat with source; *D*, scintillation detector; *M*, region in which the source is seen from *D*. [R. L. Mössbauer, *Naturwiss.*, **45,** 538 (1958).]

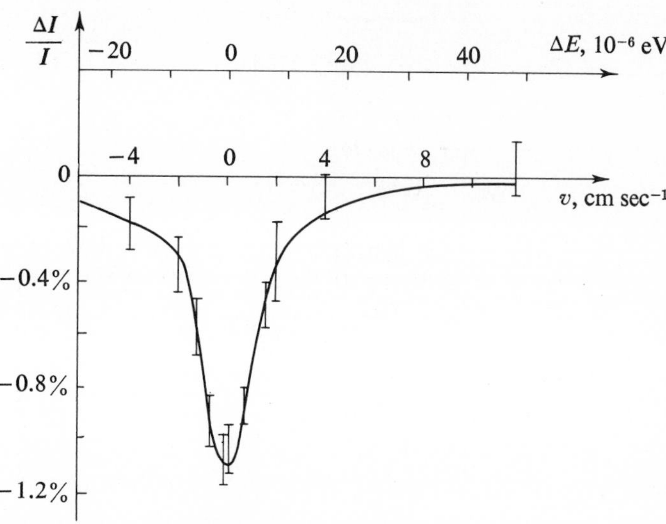

Figure 8-18 Fluorescent absorption in Ir^{191} as a function of the relative velocity between source and absorber. The upper scale on the abscissa shows the Doppler energy that corresponds to the velocity on the lower scale. $T = 88°K$. [R. L. Mössbauer, *Naturwiss.*, **45,** 538 (1958).]

and less radiation is absorbed, because the overlap of the emission and absorption curves is less complete (Figs. 8-17 and 8-18). It is thus possible to analyze the structure, or form, of a line by using "Doppler spectrometry." Some lines are so sharp that Doppler effects due to velocities of a few tenths of a millimeter per second are visible. Even sharper lines probably exist, but are difficult to detect.

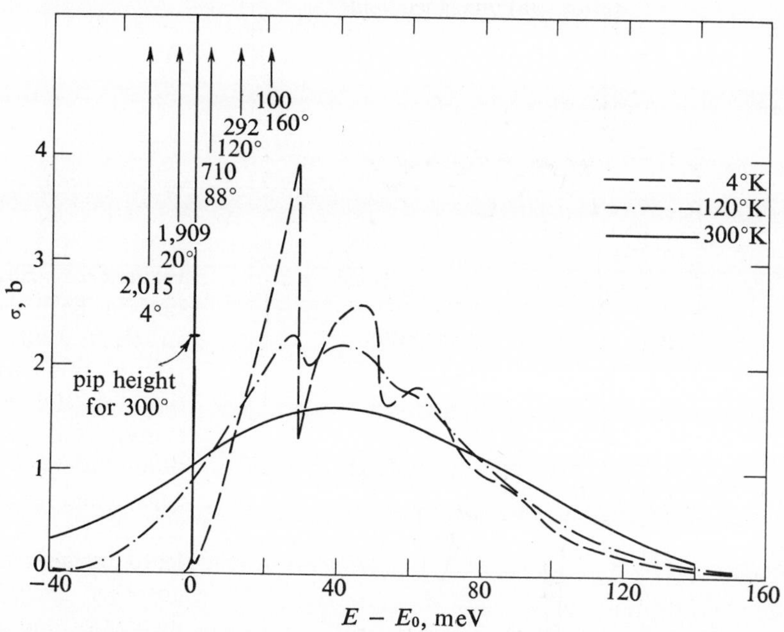

Figure 8-19 The absorption cross section per nucleus in a crystal of natural iridium, for a monochromatic gamma-ray beam and phonons having a Debye spectrum. The arrows give the cross section at zero relative velocity for the temperatures indicated.

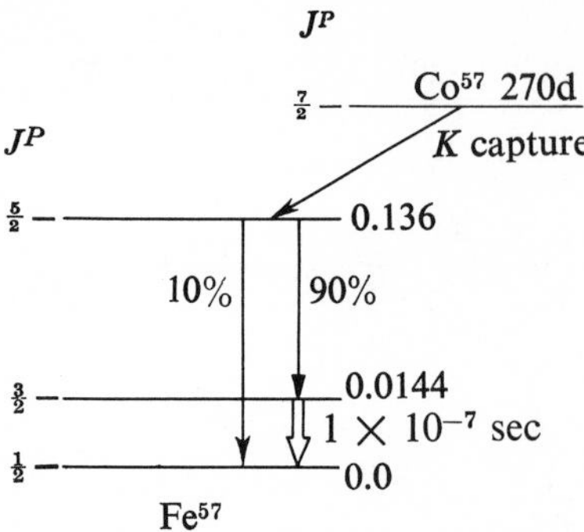

Figure 8-20 Decay scheme of Fe^{57}. The data to the left of the levels are their spins and parities, those to the right their energies. The times shown are the half-lives.

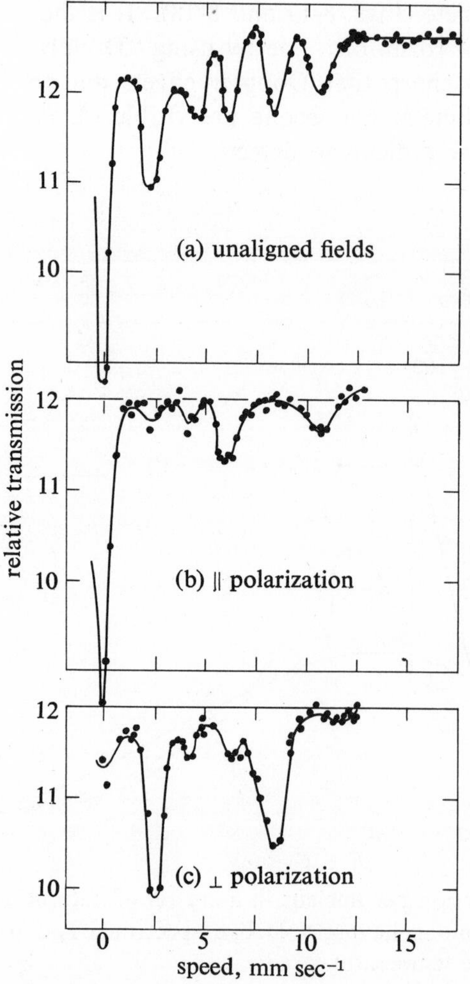

Figure 8-21 Fluorescent absorption in Fe^{57} showing hyperfine structure. Plotted is the observed relative transmission as a function of the velocity between source and absorber. (a) Randomly oriented magnetic field in source and absorber. (b) Source and absorber fields aligned parallel to one another. (c) Source and absorber fields aligned perpendicular to one another. [Hanna, Littlejohn, Perlow, Preston, and Vincent, *Phys. Rev. Letters*, **4**, 177 (1960).]

A quantitative illustration of the form of an emission line as a function of the temperature of the lattice is given in Fig. 8-19. For an absorption line one would have the same figure, but it would be reflected on the spike of the line, corresponding to the frequency of the recoilless transition.

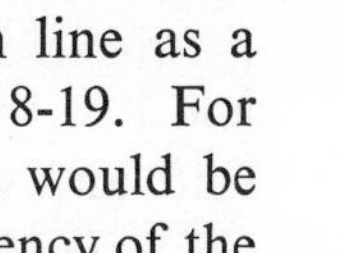

The absorption of the radiation is naturally accompanied by the emission of fluorescent radiation from the absorbing nucleus and also by the connected emission of conversion electrons, etc. One of the examples of recoilless radiation most often studied is afforded by a line of 14.4-keV energy emitted by Fe^{57} in an $M1$ transition. It has a mean life of 10^{-7} sec and hence

$$\left(\frac{\Delta\omega}{\omega}\right)_{\text{nat}} = 3 \times 10^{-13} \tag{8-8.11}$$

The Doppler effect corresponding to this width is achieved with a velocity of 0.1 cm sec^{-1} (Fig. 8-20).

Such an unprecedented degree of monochromaticity has already

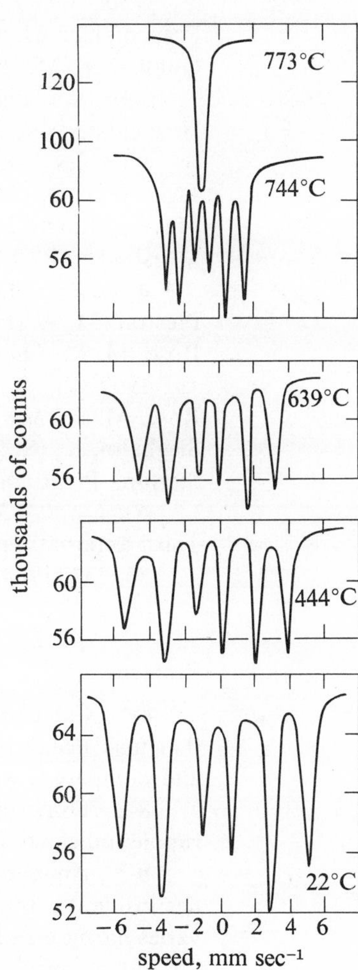

Figure 8-22 Absorption spectra for metallic Fe^{57} between room temperature and the Curie temperature. The single-line source (Co^{57} in Cu) was at the temperature of liquid nitrogen. [Preston, Hanna, and Heberle, *Phys. Rev.*, **128,** 2207 (1962).]

permitted the observation of the nuclear Zeeman effect (Fig. 8-21 and it is an important tool in several fields of physics (gravitational re shift and solid-state investigations, for example Fig. 8-22).

Bibliography

Ajzenberg-Selove, F. (AS 60).

Alburger, D. E., "Nuclear Isomerism," in (Fl E), Vol. 42.

Alder, Bohr, Huus, Mottelson, and Winther, "Study of Nuclear Structur by Electromagnetic Excitation with Accelerated Ions," *Rev. Mod. Phys.* **28,** 432 (1956).

Blatt, J. M., and V. Weisskopf (BW 52).

Burhop, E. H., *The Auger Effect and Other Radiationless Transitions*, Cam bridge University Press, New York, 1952.

Church, E. L., and J. Weneser, "Nuclear Structure Effects in Internal Con version," *Ann. Rev. Nucl. Sci.*, **10,** 193 (1960).

Deutsch, M., and O. Kofoed-Hansen, "Gamma-Rays," in (Se 59), Vol. III

Devons, S., and J. B. Goldfarb, "Angular Correlations," in (Fl E), Vol. 42

Frauenfelder, H., "Angular Correlation of Nuclear Radiation," *Ann. Rev Nucl. Sci.*, **2,** 129 (1952).

Frauenfelder, H., *The Mössbauer Effect*, Benjamin, New York, 1962.

Goldhaber, M., and J. Weneser, "Electromagnetic Transitions in Nuclei," *Ann. Rev. Nucl. Sci.*, **5,** 1 (1955).

Heydenburg, N. P., and G. M. Temmer, "Excitation of Nuclei by Charge Particles," *Ann. Rev. Nucl. Sci.*, **6,** 77 (1956).

Jackson, J. D. (JA 62).

Mayer, M., and H. D. Jensen (MJ 55).

Mössbauer, R. L., "Recoilless Nuclear Resonance Absorption," *Ann. Rev Nucl. Sci.*, **12,** 123 (1962).

Preston, M. A. (P 62).

Rose, M. E., *Internal Conversion Coefficients*, North-Holland, Amsterdam 1959.

Rose, M. E., *Multipole Fields*, Wiley, New York, 1955.

Siegbahn, K. (Si 55).

Stelson, P. H., and F. K. McGowan, "Coulomb Excitation," *Ann. Rev Nucl. Sci.*, **13,** 163 (1963).

Third International Conference on the Mössbauer Effect, *Rev. Mod. Phys.* **36,** 333 (1964).

Problems

8-1 Calculate from Eq. (8-1.5) the mean life of a nuclear excited stat that may decay by electric dipole radiation. Develop a numerical exampl and compare it with atomic radiation.

8-2 Draw the figures corresponding to Fig. 8-4 for the electric quad rupole indicated in Fig. 8-3.

8-3 An almost spherical surface defined by $R(\theta) = R_0\,[1 + \beta P_2(\cos\theta)$ has inside it a total charge Q uniformly distributed. The small parameter varies harmonically in time with frequency ω. Keeping only lowest-order term in β and making the long-wavelength approximation, calculate the nonvanishin multipole moments, the angular distribution of radiation, and the power radiated. [From (Ja 62); compare Sec. 6-12 for collective nuclear motions.]

8-4 Suppose that part of the electromagnetic radiation emitted by a nucleus arises from an intrinsic magnetization:

$$\mathbf{M}(\mathbf{r}',t) = \mathbf{M}_\omega(\mathbf{r}')\, e^{-i\omega t} + \text{complex conjugate}$$

(*a*) Obtain the general formula for the total radiation rate from such a system. (*b*) Show that the electric dipole contribution from this magnetization is zero.

8-5 Let us assume that we can crudely represent a nucleus as two oscillating currents in opposite directions, as shown in the figure below.

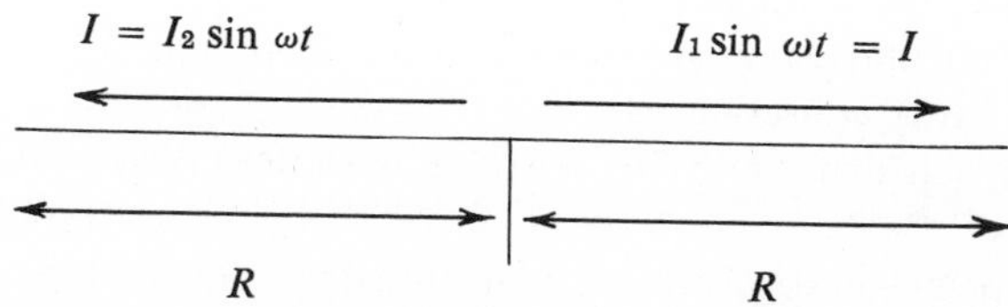

(*a*) If $I_1 = 2\,(e\omega/c)$, $I_2 = e\omega/c$ determine the multipole nature of the radiation, and obtain expressions for the angular distribution and the total decay rate. (*b*) Do the same for $I_1 = I_2 = e\omega/c$. (*c*) In part (*b*) let $R = 5 \times 10^{-13}$ cm, $\hbar\omega = 1$ MeV, and determine the mean life of the excited state of the nucleus.

8-6 $_{28}\mathrm{Ni}^{60}$ has an excited state that decays to a lower excited state and then to the ground state in two successive electric quadrupole transitions. On the basis of this information, what are the possible spin and parity assignments for these two excited states of the Ni nucleus?

8-7 The lithium nucleus Li^7 emits a 0.48-MeV gamma ray in a transition that goes from an excited state with angular momentum $\frac{1}{2}$, odd parity, to the ground state with angular momentum $\frac{3}{2}$, odd parity. (*a*) What are the possible choices for the multipolarity and nature of the emitted radiation? (*b*) Of these possibilities which one is likely to be the principal contributor to the transition? (*c*) Estimate the lifetime of the excited state.

8-8 Using the formulas

$$\left(\frac{8\pi}{3}\right)^{1/2} Y_1^1\, Y_l^{m-1} = \left[\frac{(l+m)(l+m+1)}{(2l+1)(2l+3)}\right]^{1/2} Y_{l+1}^m - \left[\frac{(l-m)(l-m+1)}{(2l+1)(2l-1)}\right]^{1/2} Y_{l-1}^m$$

$$\left(\frac{4\pi}{3}\right)^{1/2} Y_1^0\, Y_l^m = \left[\frac{(l+1)^2-m^2}{(2l+1)(2l+3)}\right]^{1/2} Y_{l+1}^m + \left[\frac{l^2-m^2}{(2l+1)(2l-1)}\right]^{1/2} Y_{l-1}^m$$

$$\left(\frac{8\pi}{3}\right)^{1/2} Y_1^{-1}\, Y_l^{m+1} = \left[\frac{(l-m)(l-m+1)}{(2l+1)(2l+3)}\right]^{1/2} Y_{l+1}^m - \left[\frac{(l+m)(l+m+1)}{(2l+1)(2l-1)}\right]^{1/2} Y_{l-1}^m$$

calculate explicitly the integral (8-2.6) entering $E1$ radiation. Prove the formulas given above from the definition of $Y_l^m(\theta,\varphi)$ and properties of $P_l(x)$ as given in (Sc 55).

8-9 Discuss the conditions of energy and quantum numbers under which a nucleus can decay by electron-positron emission.

8-10 Y^{89} has an excited level 0.915 MeV above the ground state; it decays to the ground state with a half-life of about 16 seconds. The initial state has spin $\frac{9}{2}$, the final state spin $\frac{1}{2}$, and there is a parity change in the transition. (*a*) What is the lowest multipole order which can contribute? Calculate the expected rate and compare it with the experimental result. (*b*) Suppose that we wanted to check whether, in the ground state, there was any mixture of other angular momenta than $\frac{1}{2}$ (i.e., check angular momentum conservation). Set a rough upper limit to the amplitude of an angular momentum $= \frac{3}{2}$ component in the final state, using as experimental data only the measured lifetime and transition energy. Assume strict parity conservation.

8-11 Plan an experiment to measure the internal conversion coefficient for the lines of Br^{80}.

8-12 In a mu-mesic atom the transition from the $2p$ to the 1s mesic orbit may occur by radiation or by an Auger process, in which an electron of the atom is emitted. Estimate the ratio of the probability of the second process with respect to the first one. Note the analogy to internal conversion.

8-13 Draw a diagram illustrating why the correlation between two γ emissions can depend only on even powers of cos θ.

8-14 Three states having spins J_1, J_2, J_3 are connected by two gamma rays γ_1, γ_2 having an electric or magnetic multipolarity l_1, l_2. Show (or make a plausible argument) that the angular correlation between them does not depend on the energy of γ_1 and γ_2 or on their electric or magnetic character. Moreover, the cascade $J_1 \xrightarrow{l_1} J_2 \xrightarrow{l_2} J_3$ gives the same correlation as the cascade $J_3 \xrightarrow{l_2} J_2 \xrightarrow{l_1} J_1$. If $J_2 = 0$, there is no correlation.

8-15 Using protons or alpha particles one produces Coulomb excitation in a thin target. Adjust the velocities of the projectiles so that they have the same ξ in both cases. What is the ratio of the cross sections and how does it depend on the electric multipole order?

8-16 Consider the resonance absorption of the 0.014-MeV gamma ray from Fe^{57}. (*a*) If there were no Mössbauer effect, and resonance absorption were to be observed by moving the source with respect to the absorber, how large would the relative speed have to be? How well controlled would it have to be; i.e., what speed variations would destroy the effect? (*b*) Considering the Mössbauer effect, suppose that the excited state has a magnetic moment of 0.5 nuclear magnetons, the ground state has none, and the nucleus is in a field of 10^5 gauss. For what values of the relative velocity of emitter and absorber will absorption peaks be observed? (*c*) Would you expect the 0.136-MeV gamma ray from the higher state of Fe^{57} to give rise to recoil-free emission? If not, why not?

CHAPTER IX

Beta Decay

BETA DECAY is a *nuclear* transformation accompanied by the emission of an electron. The same name has been applied to other types of transformations, notably the emission of positrons or the capture by the nucleus of orbital electrons. During nuclear transformations, electrons may be emitted by an *atom* for different reasons, for instance, as conversion electrons in a gamma transition. Beta decay does not refer to such secondary emission of orbital electrons.

9-1 Introduction

In the early studies of radioactivity there was considerable confusion as to the origin of the electrons observed in nuclear transformations. A clear distinction between nuclear electrons, or beta rays, and conversion electrons was made in 1919, when Chadwick showed that, besides the monoenergetic line spectrum of conversion electrons, there was also a continuous spectrum of disintegration electrons. This continuous spectrum at once presented a serious difficulty: the decay is a transition between two definite states, yet the kinetic energy of the electron is not always the same. Now, to uphold the principle of energy conservation, it is necessary to account for the energy which does not appear as kinetic energy of the electrons. Many hypotheses were formulated to account for this missing energy; for instance, it was suggested that an associated gamma emission carried off the energy missing in the beta spectrum. Careful investigations, with calorimeters that should have observed any known radiation, failed to reveal any energy besides that visible in the continuous beta spectrum.

It was also found that the beta spectrum has a definite upper energy limit corresponding to the total energy available in the disintegration. For instance, if we consider the transformation of H^3 into He^3, the mass spectrographic data for the nuclear masses of the two substances shows us that the reaction

$$H^3 = He^3 + e + Q \tag{9-1.1}$$

balances exactly if we make Q the upper limit of kinetic energy of the electrons of the continuum. Similarly, there are several cases of substances that decay as shown in Fig. 9-1. Now the sum of energy of the alpha particles plus the upper limit of the beta energy, not the energy of the single beta rays, is equal in the two branches of the disintegration diagram.

Beta decay presents other grave difficulties as well, because it apparently violates not only the principle of conservation of energy but also the principle of conservation of angular momentum and the rule for the statistics of a composite system. For example, if the beta decay were

$$H^3 \rightarrow He^3 + e$$

the angular momentum of H^3 is $\frac{1}{2}$ and the angular momentum on the right hand is 0 or 1 from the spins, plus an integer from a possible orbital angular momentum; but in any case the total is an integer. As far as the statistics are concerned, H^3 is a fermion and the system $He^3 + e$ is a boson.

All these difficulties are eliminated by assuming the existence of an additional undetected particle which accompanies the electron in beta decay and carries off an amount of energy equal to the difference between the observed energy for a given electron and the maximum energy of the beta spectrum. This new particle, postulated by Pauli as early as 1930, is the neutrino.

To preserve not only the principle of energy conservation but also the principle of conservation of electric charge and of angular momentum and the rules governing statistics, we must ascribe certain properties to the neutrino. First of all, conservation of charge requires that the neutrino be electrically neutral; also, if the particle were not neutral it would leave a detectable ionization. This last consideration ensures that the particle's magnetic moment, if present, must also be extremely small (actually $< 10^{-6}\,\mu_n$). The balance of energy in the case of the $H^3 \rightarrow He^3$ transformation shows that the neutrino rest mass is less than 500 eV. A limit of $\simeq$ 200 eV is derived from the shape of the beta spectra. In fact, its rest mass is, in all likelihood, exactly 0, as will be shown by arguments to be discussed later. The balance of angular momenta in beta decay requires a spin $\frac{1}{2}$ for the neutrino; and in order to satisfy the statistical requirements, the neutrino must be a fermion. This can be seen from the fact that H^3 and He^3 are both fermions and transform into each other by the emission of an electron, which is a fermion, and a neutrino, which therefore must also be a fermion. Relativity requires the relation $E = cp$ between energy and momentum of any zero-rest-mass particle. Thus in beta decay it should be possible to measure neutrino momentum by observing the nuclear recoil from the combined neutrino and the electron emission. This in fact is the case.

All these properties of the neutrino were ascribed to it in order to preserve the validity of some of the fundamental conservation laws of physics. In addition, a particle with these properties can be made to account quantitatively for the phenomena of beta decay (Fermi, 1934).

At this point we shall anticipate some results, the importance of which will be shown later. A neutrino is a fermion of charge 0 and as such has an antiparticle that may or may not be identical to it. The

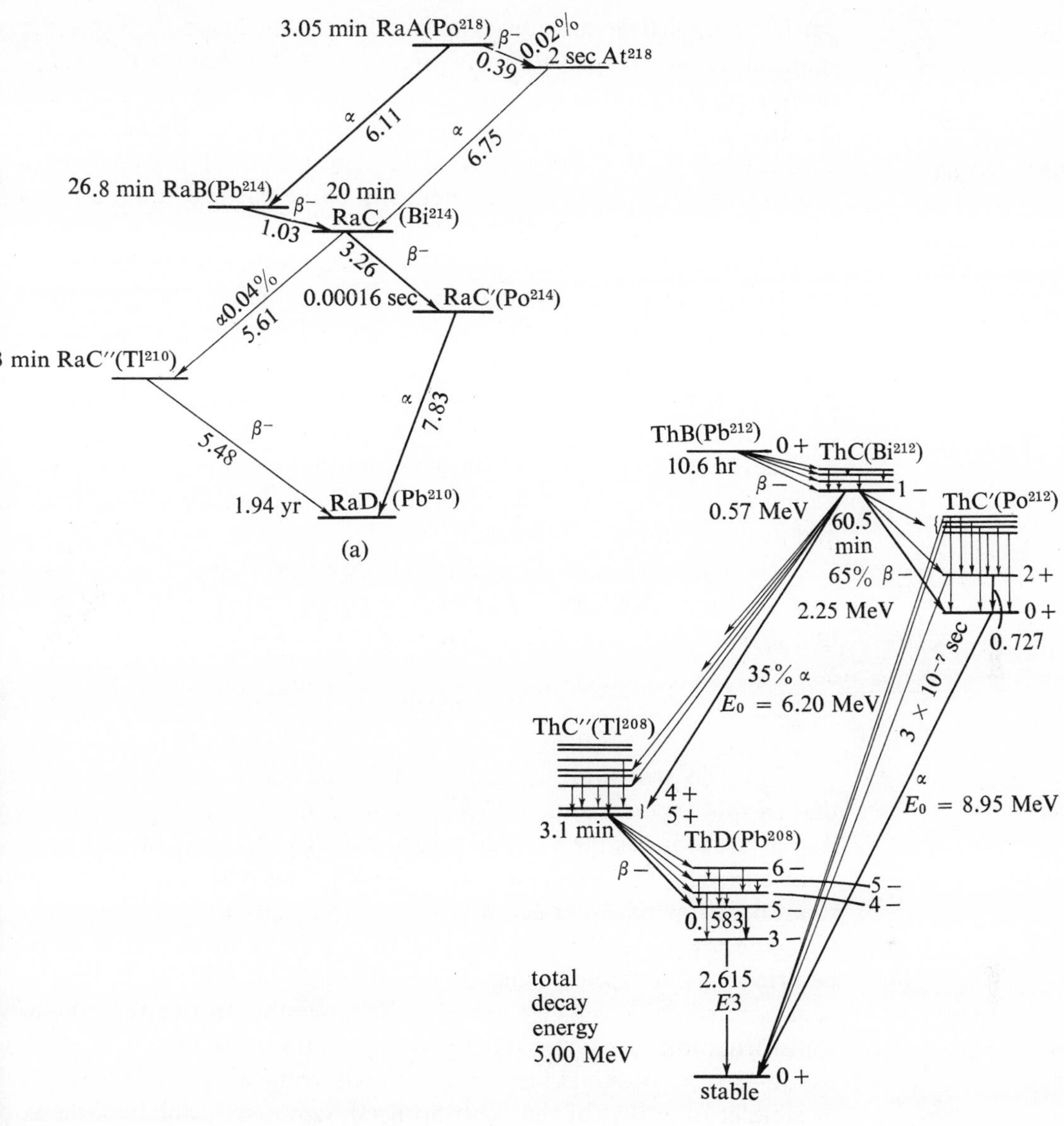

Figure 9-1 Cycles in which the energy of the alpha particles, plus that of the upper limit of the beta spectrum, balance, along two different paths. (a) Decay scheme of the radium active deposit of rapid change. Details of the complex radiations are not shown. The total disintegration energy of each mode of decay is given in MeV. (b) Decay schemes for the principal transitions in the "thorium active deposit" ThB $\xrightarrow{\alpha}$ ThC $\xrightarrow{\alpha\beta}$ . . . Note that the short-range alpha rays of ThC are alpha transitions *to* excited levels, while the long-range alpha rays of ThC′ are alpha transitions *from* excited levels. Note the origin of the very important and useful 2.62-MeV gamma ray, which is in cascade with a preceding 0.58-MeV gamma ray and the beta transition. When all alpha- beta-, and gamma-ray energies are summed, the total disintegration energy is the same (11.19 MeV) in the two competing branches: ThC $\xrightarrow{\beta}$ ThC′ $\xrightarrow{\alpha}$ ThD and ThC $\xrightarrow{\alpha}$ ThC″ $\xrightarrow{\beta}$ ThD. The angular momentum and parity assignments in ThD are as determined by Elliott and co-workers. [From E. K. Hyde, "Natural Radioactivity of the Heavy Elements," UCRL 10612.]

particle-antiparticle relation assigns to the antineutrino the same mass, spin, charge, and magnitude of magnetic moment as those of the neutrino. Moreover, in all processes where a neutrino is emitted, an antineutrino can be absorbed with the same result, and vice versa. By definition the antineutrino is the particle emitted in beta decay, for instance, when a neutron becomes a proton; the neutrino is the particle emitted in positron decay or in orbital-electron capture.

At first sight it might appear that the neutrino and the antineutrino are strictly indistinguishable. The question of whether neutrino and antineutrino are the same particle or not can be solved only by experiment. Experiments to be described later answer this question in a startling way. The spin of the neutrino is always antiparallel to its momentum; the spin of the antineutrino is parallel to its momentum. This property gives to the neutrino a "handedness" (in the sense that a screw has), introducing a fundamental asymmetry in its behavior. It is clear, then, that neutrino and antineutrino are different.

The handedness of the neutrino is best described by using the concept of helicity. Helicity is the scalar product of the spin and the momentum divided by the product of the modulus of these quantities:

$$\mathscr{H} = \text{helicity} = \frac{\mathbf{p}\cdot\boldsymbol{\sigma}}{|\mathbf{p}||\boldsymbol{\sigma}|} \tag{9-1.2}$$

For the neutrino the helicity has the value -1, which means that its spin vector is antiparallel to its momentum direction. To compare it to a screw, it has the sense of a left-handed screw (ordinary screws are right-handed). The antineutrino has helicity $+1$ and may be compared to an ordinary right-handed screw.

One consequence of the fixed helicity of the neutrino and of the antineutrino is that the rest mass of both must be exactly 0; thus they always move with velocity c, and it is impossible to overtake them by transformation to a faster-moving frame. If this were not so, a neutrino would have opposite helicity in systems moving with a velocity greater or smaller than that of the neutrino itself, contrary to the hypothesis of fixed intrinsic helicity.

If we assume the hypotheses of (1) mass 0 for the neutrino and antineutrino and (2) helicity of neutrino and antineutrino, -1 and $+1$, respectively, it is possible to develop a two-component theory of the neutrino (Weyl, 1929; Lee and Yang; Landau; A. Salam, 1957) which is based on a degeneracy of Dirac's theory for a spin-$\frac{1}{2}$ particle occurring when the rest mass of the particle is 0. In the ordinary Dirac theory there are four components, corresponding to two possible spin orientations of positive or negative energy (or particle and antiparticle). According to the two-component theory, half the states are suppressed, and the particle is associated with one helicity ($\mathscr{H} = -1$), the antiparticle with the other ($\mathscr{H} = +1$). This theory describes a particle having the two properties listed, and in many respects it is the simplest of the theories that account for the known phenomena of beta decay. It requires nonconservation f parity, as will be explained, and was rejected until this fact was experimentally demonstrated.

-2 Experiments on the Neutrino

The neutrino is the most elusive of the nuclear particles, and most of the evidence concerning it is indirect. We have already mentioned how its energy appears in beta decay as a deficit in the electron kinetic energy. Associated with this energy is a momentum that can be determined by measuring the vector momentum of the decay electron and the vector momentum of the recoil nucleus. Their sum must be equal and opposite to the vector momentum of the undetectable neutrino. On the assumption of 0 rest mass for the neutrino, as indicated above, the momentum of the neutrino is E_ν/c and is calculable from the energy of the other two particles. The main difficulty in experiments of this type is that the momentum of the recoil nucleus is of the order of 1 MeV/c, and hence the recoil energy, even in favorable cases, is only about 100 eV. This makes accurate measurements very difficult.

The recoil experiments have been performed with the neutron, He^6, Be^7, Ne^{19}, Ne^{23}, A^{35}, and Eu^{152}. In some cases attempts have been made to observe the nuclear recoil in a low-pressure cloud chamber. A picture obtained with He^6 is shown in Fig. 9-2. Most of the measurements require very difficult and ingenious techniques, involving the

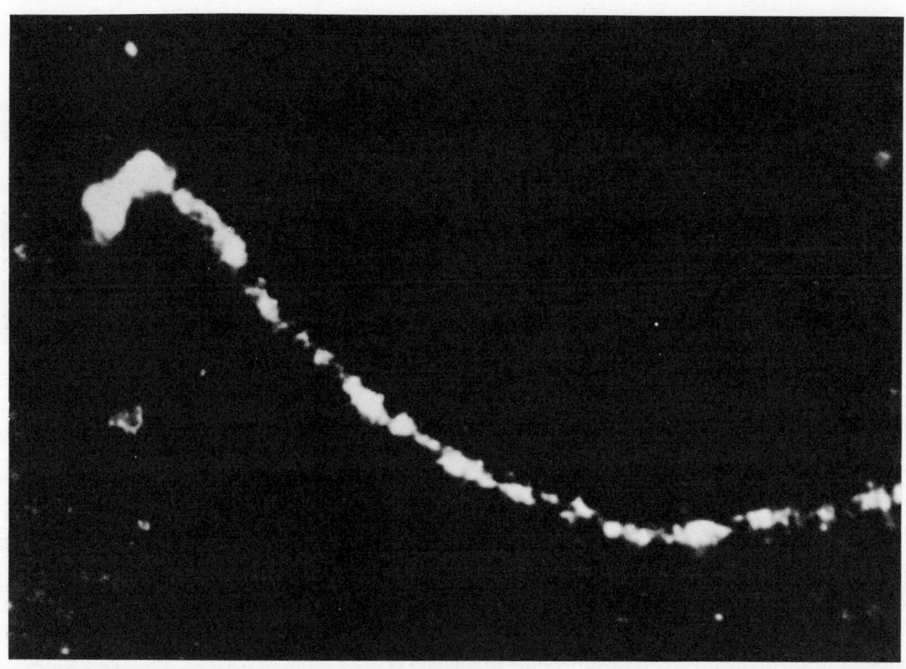

Figure 9-2 Recoil of He^6 in beta decay. [J. Csikay and A. Szalay, *Nuovo Cimento, Suppl.*, Padova Conference, 1957.]

further acceleration of the recoil nucleus in an external field. Figure 9-3 shows an experimental arrangement used and Fig. 9-4 the results obtained.

In the case of *K* capture the recoil situation is simpler than in beta decay. Only a monoenergetic neutrino is emitted, and hence the recoil nuclei all have the same momentum. However, even in a very favorable case, the transformation of Be^7 to Li^7, the recoil energy is only 57.3 eV.

The properties ascribed to the neutrino to satisfy the conservation laws of momentum and energy are verified by the recoil experiments. This verification is of fundamental importance, but it does not add to our knowledge of the neutrino. After all, the particle was initially postulated in order to satisfy the conservation laws.

Another type of experiment, in which the direct interaction of the free neutrino is observed, was performed by Cowan and Reines in 1953.

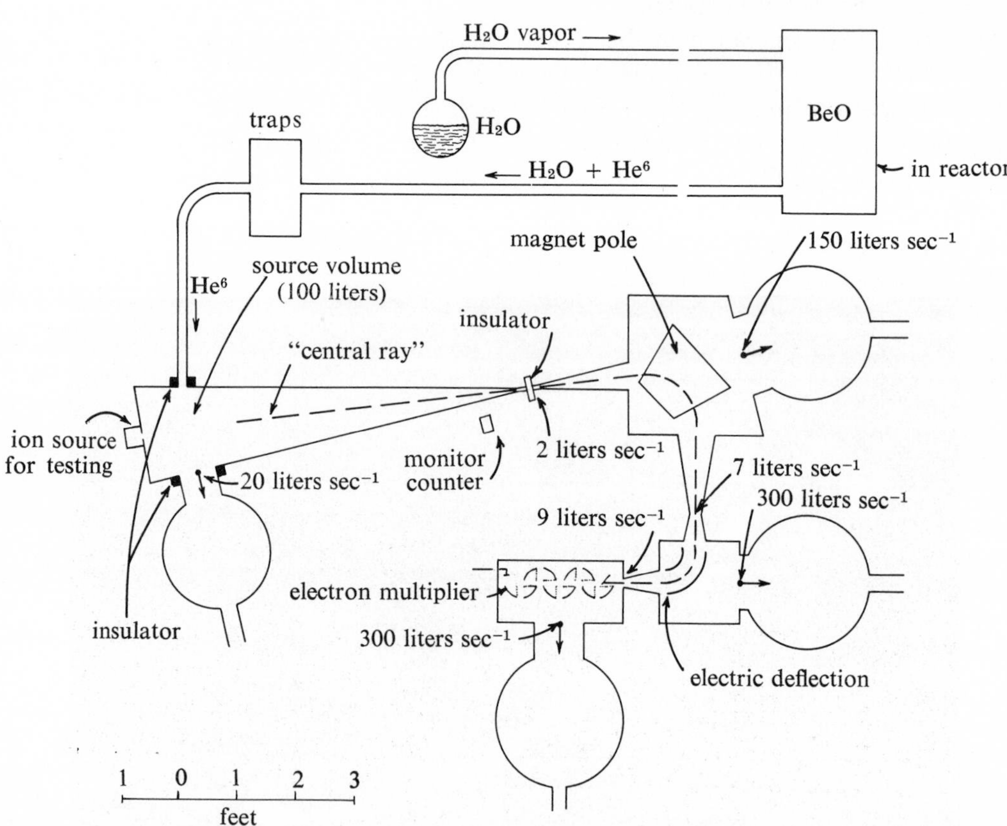

Figure 9-3 Experimental apparatus. The He^6 produced in a reactor by the $Be^9(n, \alpha)He^6$ reaction is carried by a continuous stream of water vapor to the laboratory where the vapor is removed and the He^6 is left to decay in the conical source volume. A proportional counter monitors the source activity. Recoil Li^6 ions undergo magnetic and electrostatic analysis and are detected by a secondary electron multiplier. Three stages of differential pumping reduce the background of atoms which decay near the detector. [From Johnson, Pleasonton, and Carlson, *Phys. Rev.*, **132,** 1149 (1963).]

demonstrates properties of the neutrino which go beyond those re-
uired by the conservation laws and which are implied in Fermi's theory.
ı this sense it gives independent proof of the existence of the neutrino.
'he reaction

$$n \rightarrow p + e + \bar{\nu} \qquad \textbf{(9-2.1)}$$

ıay be inverted by bombarding protons with antineutrinos, causing the
rotons to emit a positron and become neutrons.

$$\bar{\nu} + p \rightarrow n + e^{+} \qquad \textbf{(9-2.2)}$$

'his reaction was observed with a nuclear reactor as the source of anti-
eutrinos. A large vat containing a hydrogenous substance with Cd
dded was bombarded by antineutrinos and the following sequence of
vents was recorded: The positron is emitted, and its annihilation radia-
.on, which follows rapidly ($\sim 10^{-9}$ sec), is observed. The neutron itself

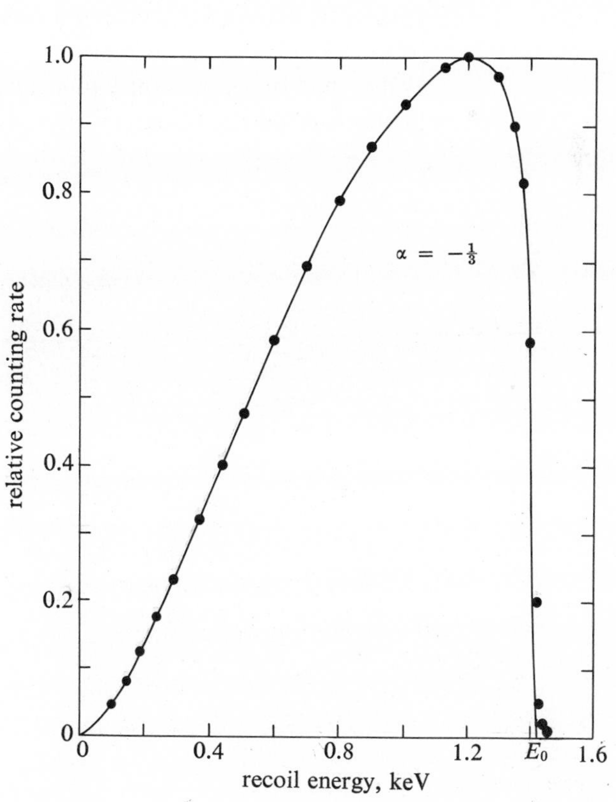

igure 9-4 Spectrum of singly harged Li^6 ions from the beta ecay of He^6 as a function of the verage recoil energy of the ions 'ansmitted by the analyzers. ɔns were accelerated to about vice their recoil energy before nalysis. Uncertainties from ɔunting statistics are less than ıe point sizes.

The form of this spectrum epends on the angular correla-on between the momenta of ıe electron p and of the neutrino In the case of He^6 the correla-on is approximately $P(\mathbf{p}, \mathbf{q})$ $E\,d\omega$ = const. $pEq^2\,[1 + \alpha(cp/E)$ ɔs $\theta]\ dE\ d\omega$, where E is the ɔtal energy of the electron, is the angle between p and , and $d\omega$ is the element f solid angle. The constant α is nportant because its value indi-ates the type of interaction ffective in the decay (see Sec. -8). The theoretical curve is lotted for $\alpha = -1/3$ with the ormalization constant and the nd point E_0 chosen to give a ood fit of theory to experiment. 'ohnson, Pleasonton, and Carl-ɔn, *Phys. Rev.*, **132,** 1149 (1963).]

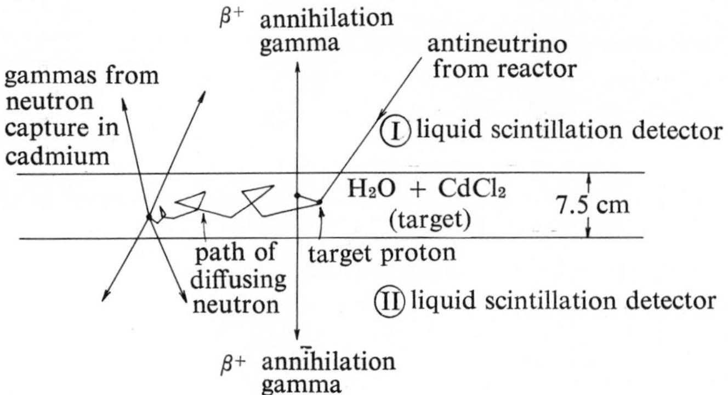

Figure 9-5 Schematic diagrai of neutrino detection. An ant neutrino from a reactor produce a neutron and a positron by th reaction $\bar{\nu} + p \rightarrow n + e^+$. Th positron is detected by its ann hilation with an electron. Th neutron is detected by the gamm rays emitted upon its captur [After C. L. Cowan and F Reines.]

is captured much later (10^{-5} sec) by the Cd and capture gamma ray are then seen (Figs. 9-5 and 9-6). This sequence is sufficiently character istic to be unmistakable. The cross section for the process indicated b Eq. (9-2.2) can be estimated by detailed balance (see Chap. 11) fron the observed mean life of the neutron (17.3 min) and is expected to b of the order of 10^{-43} cm^2 for antineutrinos originating in fission. Thi number agrees with the experimental observations of Cowan and Reines Note that the cross section is energy-dependent; at energies of severa BeV it reaches values of the order of 10^{-38} cm^2. This increase follow merely from the increased density of final states, which varies as $p_\nu{}^2$.

Finally the question of the identity or nonidentity of neutrino an antineutrino has been tested experimentally in two other ways, asid from the determination of the helicity. The emission of a neutrin always has the same consequences as the absorption of an antineutrinc If neutrino and antineutrino are identical, we have the further fact tha

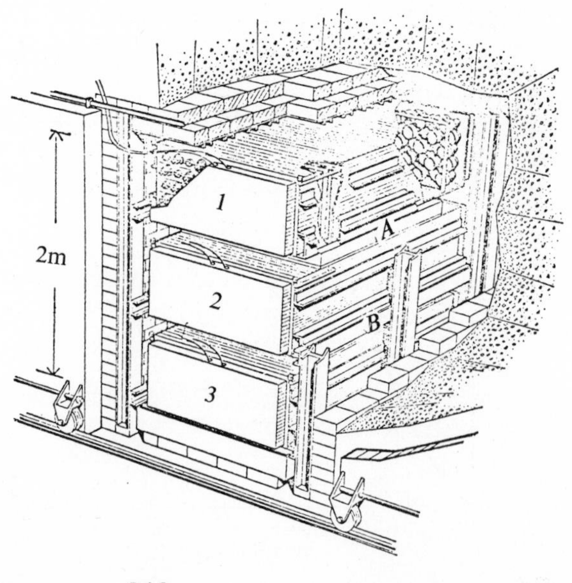

Figure 9-6 Sketch of detecto inside their lead shield. Th detector tanks marked 1, 2, an 3 contained 1,400 liters of liqui scintillator solution. The scin tillations were viewed in eac tank by 110 5-in. photomultiplie tubes. The white tanks *A* and *B* about 28 cm deep, contained 20 liters of water-cadmium chlorid target.

bsorption of a neutrino has the same consequences as absorption of the ntineutrino. For a concrete application (first assuming the neutrino and ntineutrino to be distinct), consider three nuclei such as Sn^{124}, Sb^{124}, and e^{124}. Their masses are such that Sn^{124} (Fig. 9-7) could conceivably ansform into Te^{124}, with the simultaneous emission of two electrons nd two antineutrinos having 2.3 MeV of energy. The whole process, a cond-order process with respect to the beta decay, is highly improbable. he mean life would be of the order of $10^{22\pm2}$ years, and the two electrons ould not balance the momentum between them.

Now consider the antineutrino as identical to the neutrino. Sn^{124} ay then transform directly into Te^{124}, with the emission of only the vo electrons, which balance the momentum between them. We may ink that, in the second-order process giving rise to this transformation, e antineutrino was emitted and reabsorbed, the reabsorption counting as e second emission of the previous case. Under this hypothesis the half-fe turns out to be much shorter than in the previous case, $10^{16\pm2}$ years.

The only certain case of double beta decay is demonstrated in a mass pectrographic experiment by Inghram and Reynolds. They found a ean life of 10^{20} years for Xe^{130}. Experiments on this substance and on r^{96}, Nd^{150}, Sn^{124}, and Ca^{48} favor the nonidentity of the neutrino and ntineutrino. Furthermore, if and only if the antineutrino is identical to he neutrino, the reaction

$$\bar{\nu} + Cl^{37} \rightarrow A^{37} + e^- \tag{9-2.3}$$

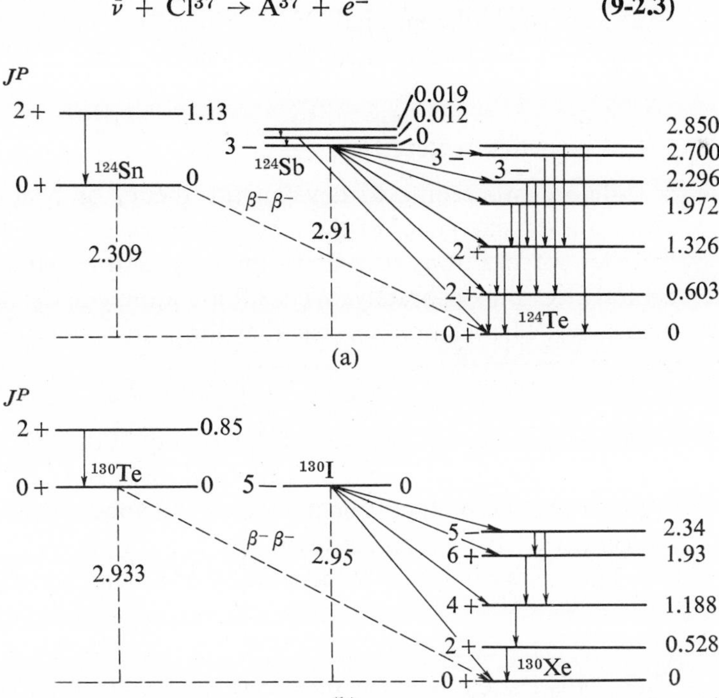

igure 9-7 Level diagrams for double beta decay. (a) $A = 124$; $_{50}Sn \rightarrow {}_{51}Sb \rightarrow {}_{52}Te$. (b) $A = 130$; Te → I → Xe. Energies in MeV. [From G. F. Dell'Antonio and E. Fiorini, *Nuovo Cimento, Suppl.*, **7**, 132 (1961).]

is the inverse of

$$Cl^{37} \rightarrow A^{37} + e^- + \bar{\nu} \tag{9-2.}$$

and therefore the bombardment of Cl^{37} with antineutrinos should b effective in producing A^{37}. Again the experimental results are agains the identity of the two particles (Davis, 1955). Thus the ν and $\bar{\nu}$ appear t be two different particles.

Neutrinos appear, not only in beta decay, but also in the decay c pi mesons, mu mesons, and other particles (see Chap. 13). The questio then arises whether all neutrinos are identical or whether there are differ ent species. The example of the electron and the mu meson points to th possibility of particles that have the same interactions and the sam spin and charge but which differ in some other way, in the electron muon case, in the mass. In other words, there seems to be some other still unknown property (see Chaps. 12 and 13), which is needed to charac terize a particle completely. Experiments (Lederman, Schwartz, Stein berger, et al., Brookhaven, 1962) have indeed shown that the neutrin of beta decay is different from the neutrino arising in pi-meson decay The latter type of neutrino was used to bombard aluminum in a spar chamber. It was found that the pi-meson neutrino can produce m mesons, but not electrons. If there were only one species of neutrinos electrons and muons would be produced in about the same abundance Hence, the result of this experiment is taken to indicate the occurrenc of at least two different kinds of neutrinos. (In what follows, "neutrinos" always mean a neutrino arising in beta decay, unless otherwise indicated.

9-3 Energetics of Beta Decay

Before proceeding to develop the theory of beta decay, we shal point out the energetics of the reactions involved. We shall consider th emission of electrons, the emission of positrons, and the capture o orbital electrons separately. We shall use atomic masses M_Z and nuclea masses N_Z. The relation between the atomic mass and the nuclear mass is

$$M_Z = N_Z + Zm - B_Z \tag{9-3.1}$$

where B_Z is the binding energy of the totality of the atomic electrons and m is the mass of the electron. This binding energy and, especially, the difference between binding energies that will appear in the final equations are generally small compared with the beta-ray energies.

The energy balance for beta decay of a bare nucleus is

$$N_Z = N_{Z+1} + m + Q \tag{9-3.2}$$

where m is the electron (or positron) mass and Q the kinetic energy of the electron, neutrino, and recoil nucleus, the last being almost always negligible. The equivalent form for atomic masses is

$$M_Z = M_{Z+1} + (B_{Z+1} - B_Z) + Q \tag{9-3.3}$$

'he energy balance for positron emission is

$$N_Z = N_{Z-1} + m + Q \quad (9\text{-}3.4)$$

r, with atomic masses,

$$M_Z = M_{Z-1} + 2m + (B_{Z-1} - B_Z) + Q \quad (9\text{-}3.5)$$

'inally the energy equation for orbital-electron capture is

$$N_Z + m - B_Z{}^K = N_{Z-1} + Q \quad (9\text{-}3.6)$$

r

$$M_Z = M_{Z-1} + (B_{Z-1} - B_Z) + B_Z{}^K + Q \quad (9\text{-}3.7)$$

Iere $B_Z{}^K$ means the binding energy of the K electron if the electron aptured by the nucleus is in a K shell. It is apparent that if

$$B_Z{}^L < (M_Z + B_Z) - (M_{Z-1} + B_{Z-1}) - Q < B_Z{}^K \quad (9\text{-}3.8)$$

he case might present itself in which K capture is impossible but L apture might occur. In orbital-electron capture Q is the energy of the eutrino plus the very small recoil energy of the nucleus. Figure 9-8 hows the neutrino energy spectrum in a case when all three, positron mission, K and L capture, occur.

-4 Classification of Interactions. Parity

In physics there are four types of forces acting:

1. The electromagnetic interactions—familiar from macroscopic nd atomic physics and responsible for phenomena such as Coulomb cattering and gamma emission.

2. The specific strong nuclear interactions—responsible for phenomena such as neutron-proton scattering.

3. The weak interactions—responsible for beta decay and allied henomena.

4. The gravitational interactions, which are negligible and will ot be considered here.

The electromagnetic interactions are treated by Maxwell's equations nd the quantum-mechanical generalizations of these equations. The harge of the electron is the universal constant that appears whenever

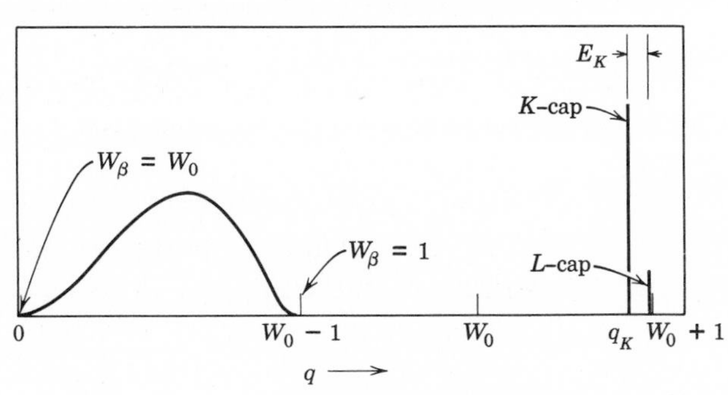

'igure 9-8 Neutrino spectrum rom combined β^+ decay and K and L capture. Abscissa, nomentum or energy of neutrino. W means total energy. W_0 is he disintegration energy in mc^2 mnits. $W_\beta = W_0$ corresponds to he upper limit of the positron pectrum; $W_\beta = 1$ corresponds to ositrons at rest. [From (Se 59).]

electromagnetic interactions are considered. Instead of the elementary charge, one often considers the dimensionless quantity $e^2/\hbar c \simeq 1/137$ as representative of the coupling strength of the electromagnetic interaction. The ordinary photons are the quanta of the electromagnetic field; they are bosons of zero rest mass.

The most typical example of a strong interaction is the Yukawa interaction:

$$N \to N + \pi \tag{9-4.1}$$

in which a nucleon transforms into a nucleon and a pion. Whenever this type of interaction occurs, another universal constant appears which performs a role similar to the electric charge in the case of the electromagnetic field. This constant, expressed in a dimensionless fashion as $f^2/\hbar c$, has a value close to one. The strong interactions have a short range; that is, their force acts within a characteristic distance of the order of 10^{-13} cm. This fact, as Yukawa pointed out, forces the quanta of the field to have a finite rest mass; the quanta are identified with pi mesons which are bosons of spin zero.

Weak interactions are characterized by the participation of four fermions in a given process. Examples are:

$$n \to p + e^- + \bar{\nu} \qquad \text{(beta emission)} \tag{9-4.2}$$

$$C^{11} \to B^{11} + e^+ + \nu \qquad \text{(positron emission)} \tag{9-4.3}$$

$$Be^7 + e^- \to Li^7 + \nu \qquad (K\text{ capture}) \tag{9-4.4}$$

$$\mu^- \to e^- + \nu + \bar{\nu} \qquad (\mu\text{-meson decay}) \tag{9-4.5}$$

Weak interactions have a coupling constant G or, in more complete theories, several coupling constants which, expressed like those used for strong and electromagnetic interactions, are of the order of $G^2/\hbar c = 10^{-14}$. In all the cases cited, beta decay, positron emission, orbital-electron capture, and mu-meson decay, we find a neutrino or antineutrino participating. However, there are also weak interactions, such as the decay of a K meson into pions, which do not involve a neutrino or antineutrino.

In 1956 the study of certain mesons (then called τ and θ) presented a great puzzle. Experimentally they were found to have the same mass, half-life, and spin, which suggested that they were the same particle. On the other hand, they decayed into pion systems of opposite parity; hence, if parity was conserved they had to be different. The acuteness of the dilemma led Lee and Yang to question the conservation of parity in weak interactions. It was then found that all weak interactions seem to have in common the nonconservation of parity (Lee and Yang, 1957). This is a major difference between weak interactions on the one hand and strong and electromagnetic interactions on the other.

Conservation of parity can be described at different levels of sophistication. In the simplest terms it can be defined as follows: If the mirror image of a physical phenomenon represents another possible physical situation, the phenomenon is said to conserve parity. All phenomena involving strong and electromagnetic interactions alone *do* conserve parity. An example, shown in Fig. 9-9, will make the meaning of these statements clear. The upper half of the figure shows the intensity of beta emission from cobalt placed in a magnetic field generated by the coil. The magnetic field orients the nuclear spin of cobalt in such a way that the current of the solenoid and the current in the nucleus generating its magnetic moment are parallel. The lower part of the figure gives the mirror image of the upper part, which *is not* what is observed. In fact the lower part of the figure can be realized experimentally as far as solenoid and nucleus are concerned by simply inverting the direction of the current in the solenoid. What happens then is that the maximum intensity goes from left to right and not from right to left, as indicated by the dashed arrows in the figure (mirror image of the upper half). Thus parity is not conserved. Conservation of parity would require equal probability of emission of beta rays to the right or to the left of the figure. This is what happens for gamma-ray emission.

The invariance on mirroring was assumed, incorrectly, to have a logical necessity a priori, such as is usually accepted for the invariance of the result of an experiment repeated in different places, in different orientations in space, or at different times. The experiment shows that this invariance on mirroring is not verified in beta decay.

We now present these remarks in a different form by noting that the vectors used in physics are of two different kinds. The distinction becomes clear when we consider the same physical quantity in two coordinate systems derived from each other by reflection through the origin,

$$x \to -x' \qquad y \to -y' \qquad z \to -z' \tag{9-4.6}$$

If a vector such as displacement, velocity momentum, acceleration, electric field, etc., has components

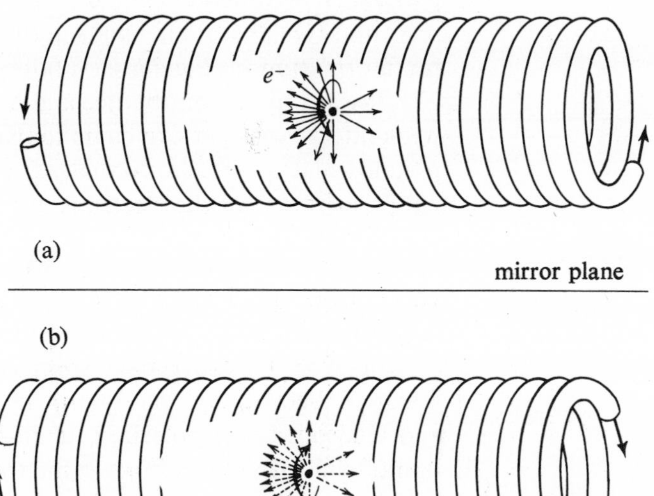

Figure 9-9 (a) Beta decay of polarized cobalt. (b) Mirror image of experiment (a). This is not what happens in fact, because if the current in the solenoid is reversed [which is equivalent to going from (a) to (b)], the beta rays go preferentially to the right. On the other hand, if one observes gamma rays, the probability of emission at an angle θ or $\pi-\theta$ with the axis of the solenoid is the same, and thus parity is conserved for gamma emission.

$$X \quad Y \quad Z$$

in the first (unprimed) system, then in the second system the reference of the same vector has components

$$X' = -X \qquad Y' = -Y \qquad Z' = -Z \tag{9-4.7}$$

Vectors of this type are called polar vectors. Consider now the angular momentum

$$\mathbf{L} = \mathbf{r} \times \mathbf{p} \tag{9-4.8}$$

and remember the definition of vector product. In components one has $L_x = yp_z - zp_y$ and the similar formulas for L_y and L_z. In the primed system both **r** and **p** change sign. Hence the components of **L** in the primed and unprimed system are the same. This result derives also from the geometrical definition of vector product, which involves the convention of the right-hand thread rule or its equivalent.

A vector such as **L** is called a pseudovector or axial vector. Torque, angular momentum, spin, magnetic field and magnetic moments are examples of pseudovectors. Vectors and pseudovectors behave in the same way for translations or rotations of the coordinate system; it is only on inversion that they behave differently.

The scalar product of two polar vectors or of two axial vectors is a number, invariant upon reflection of the coordinate system, and is called a true scalar, or simply a scalar. The scalar product of a polar vector and an axial vector is a number that changes sign upon inversion of the coordinate system. Such numbers are called pseudoscalars.

The result of a physical measurement is always a number, which, however, may behave as a scalar or as a pseudoscalar. The mirror reflection mentioned above leaves true scalars unchanged, but it changes the sign of pseudoscalars. Hence if the image and the object must be indistinguishable, all pseudoscalars must vanish. The observation of pseudoscalars different from 0 thus implies the breakdown of parity conservation. On the other hand, until a pseudoscalar has been observed, no information on the conservation of parity is available.

It was pointed out by Lee and Yang in 1956 that all experiments on weak interactions performed up to that time were not designed to observe pseudoscalar quantities. Actually Cox in 1928 had observed a longitudinal polarization of the electrons in beta decay; i.e., the quantity

$$\mathbf{v} \cdot \boldsymbol{\sigma} \tag{9-4.9}$$

had not been 0. This observation was disbelieved at the time and later forgotten.

In 1956 an experiment specifically designed to detect a pseudoscalar in beta decay was set up by Wu, Ambler, Hayward, Hoppes, and Hudson. Using polarized cobalt-60 nuclei, they found that the direction of emission of electrons in the transformation to nickel-60 is preferentially opposite to the spin direction. Thus the expectation value of the pseudoscalar $\langle \mathbf{v} \cdot \mathbf{I} \rangle$, where **I** is the nuclear spin and **v** the electron velocity, was measured and found to be different from 0.

The discovery of this startling phenomenon was made by the experi-ent illustrated in Fig. 9-10. The cobalt nuclei were oriented by cooling a magnetic field (Chaps. 6 and 10). The extremely low temperature).01°K) required was obtained by adiabatic demagnetization, and the egree of orientation ascertained by observing the anisotropy in the emis-ion of the gamma rays. The beta rays were then counted, with the results hown in Fig. 9-11. If parity were conserved the intensity pattern should e symmetrical with respect to a horizontal plane passing through the ource, as the gamma-ray pattern is.

Mathematically, the principle of conservation of parity rules out ertain terms in the expression of the hamiltonian, which is the operator hat governs the time dependence of the wave function, because these erms would not be invariant on a reflection through the origin or, more xplicitly, if x, y, and z were changed into $-x$, $-y$, and $-z$, respectively; hus the parity of the wave function would be changed as time went on. 'or example, in the expression of the energy of the electromagnetic field, erms like $\mathbf{H}^2$ and $\mathbf{E}^2$ (scalars) are permissible, but a term such as $\mathbf{E} \cdot \mathbf{H}$ pseudoscalar) would change sign on inversion of the coordinates nd is not permissible if parity is to be conserved. In strong and

'igure 9-10 Schematic diagram f lower portion of the cryostat sed for polarization of Co^{60} uclei, the specimen used. The eta particles are detected by a hin anthracene crystal ~ 2 cm bove the Co^{60} source. The cintillations from the crystal re transmitted through the lucite od to a photomultiplier tube bove. The two NaI counters one in the equatorial plane and ne near the polar position) vere used to measure the gamma-ay anisotropy and thus the mount of polarization of the Co^{60}. [From Wu, Ambler, Hay-vard, Hoppes, and Hudson.]

electromagnetic interactions, terms that do not conserve parity are absen from the hamiltonian. By analogy all terms that do not conserve parit were omitted in writing the hamiltonian for weak interactions unti experiment showed that they must be present.

9-5 Fermi's Theory of Beta Decay

In constructing his theory of beta decay, Fermi was guided by th analogy to electromagnetic gamma-ray emission. In the latter, a nucleu passes from an excited state to the ground state, creating a photon. I beta decay, a neutron is transformed into a proton, and an electron an an antineutrino are created. The object of a theory of beta decay is t give a dynamical description of this process.

Fermi assumed the conservation of parity, but his calculation

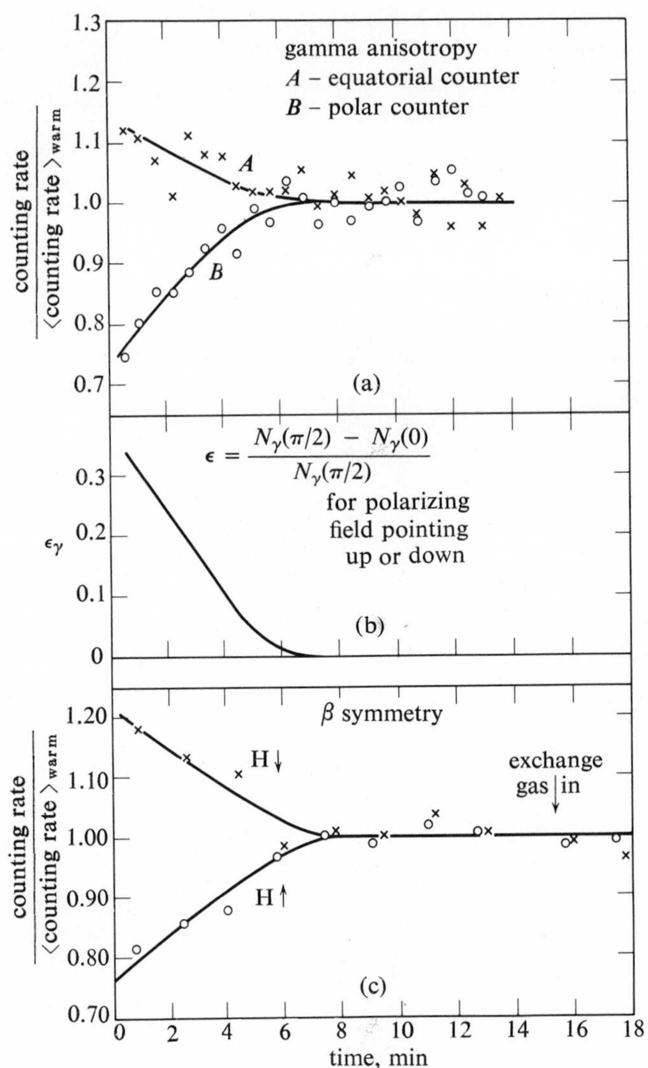

Figure 9-11 Gamma anisotrop (as determined from the tw NaI counters) and beta asymmetry for the polarizing fiel pointing up and down as function of time. The times fo disappearance of the beta an gamma asymmetry coincide; thi is the warm-up time. The warm up time for the sample is approxi mately 6 minutes and the count ing rates for the warm unpolarize sample are independent of the fiel direction. [From Wu, Ambler Hayward, Hoppes, and Hudson.

involved only scalar quantities, and it turns out that the results of his theory still stand in large measure, in spite of the fundamental changes produced by the discovery of the nonconservation of parity.

The main results of Fermi's theory are the explanation, by the introduction of only one new parameter (the g coupling constant) of:

1. The form of the beta spectra, i.e., number of electrons per energy interval.
2. The relation between the maximum energy of the decay and the mean life.
3. The classification of beta transitions and the establishment of selection rules.

The fundamental ideas of Fermi's theory are general enough to be easily adapted to changes of the interaction (e.g., to parity nonconservation), still preserving the validity of many of his results.

The starting point is golden rule No. 2 (Appendix A), which gives the transition probability

$$w = \frac{2\pi}{\hbar} |H_{if}|^2 \rho \tag{9-5.1}$$

To apply this formula we need to know the expression for the matrix element between the initial and final states and to calculate the density of the final states:

$$\rho = \frac{dN}{dW} \tag{9-5.2}$$

The last assignment will be performed shortly.

It is found that the density of final states completely determines the form of the beta spectrum, the matrix element in allowed transitions being a constant independent of the energy of the electrons. The matrix element must be guessed at and this, of course, represents the most difficult part of the theory. We postulate that the wave functions of the four particles intervening in the reaction appear linearly in H_{if}. This postulate, which excludes the appearance of higher powers or derivatives of the wave functions, is justified by experience and suggested by analogy with the electromagnetic field. Relativistic invariance is assumed. The matrix element, by definition, has the form

$$H_{if} = \int \psi_{\text{fin}}{}^* H \psi_{\text{in}} \, d\tau \tag{9-5.3}$$

Here H is the operator representing the unknown interaction. This operator is more general than the ordinary operators of nonrelativistic quantum mechanics, because the initial and final states do not refer to the same particles. The operator must be able to "destroy" the initial particles and "create" the final ones. The initial wave function $\psi_{\text{in}} = u_i$ describes the nucleus before decay; the final eigenfunction ψ_{fin} is the product of u_f (describing the nucleus in the final state) times ψ_e times $\psi_{\bar{\nu}}$, the wave functions of the electron and antineutrino appearing in the final state. The unstarred states are destroyed in the transition, an the starred states are created. Moreover, the emission of a neutrino an the absorption of an antineutrino of opposite momentum are equivalent and we may replace $\psi_{\bar{\nu}}^*$ by ψ_ν to make the equations more symmetrica To a good approximation (for exceptions see below) ψ_e and $\psi_{\bar{\nu}}$ ar constant throughout the nuclear volume.

The matrix element is then tentatively written as

$$H_{if} = g \int u_f^* u_i \psi_e^* \psi_\nu \, d\tau \tag{9-5.4}$$

Here the integral is extended only over the nuclear coordinates and th nuclear wave functions take into account the transformation of a neutro into a proton in the nucleus. Thus it would be simply $\psi_e^*\psi_\nu$ if a neutro became a proton, without any other appreciable change in the nuclea wave function, as, for example, in the $H^3 \rightarrow He^3$ transformation. A mor formal description of the nuclear integral is obtainable with the help o the isotopic spin operators (see Chap. 10), but we shall omit this development.

The new universal constant g, characteristic of beta decay, has th dimensions of energy $\times$ volume. Its numerical value can be determined b experiment, as we shall see shortly, and is of the order of 10^{-49} erg cm^3 To get an idea of its size, we divide g by the volume corresponding to th nuclear radius; the result is about 1 eV. The nuclear potential betwee neutron and proton for a well of the same radius is about 10^7 time greater.

In this first study we shall assume that the wave functions of th electron and the neutrino have the form (neglecting spin)

$$\psi_e(\mathbf{r}) = \frac{1}{\Omega^{1/2}} e^{i\mathbf{k}_e \cdot \mathbf{r}} \qquad \psi_\nu(\mathbf{r}) = \frac{1}{\Omega^{1/2}} e^{-i\mathbf{k}_\nu \cdot \mathbf{r}} \qquad \mathbf{k} = \mathbf{p}/\hbar \tag{9-5.5}$$

where Ω is the volume of a big box in which we enclose the system fo normalization purposes. The use of a nonrelativistic expression for a neutrino of mass 0 is certainly objectionable. Nonetheless the results obtained are, in spite of this inconsistency, useful for orientation, and they represent a first approximation to the relativistic theory. By assuming the plane wave form for the wave function of the electron and neutrino, we have neglected their possible interactions with the nucleus; this is an exceedingly good approximation for the neutrino, and a fai approximation for the electrons, which are actually subject to electromagnetic forces from the nuclear charge. The correction for the latte effect is mathematically involved but does not offer difficulties in principle; it will later be taken into account numerically.

We now observe that for the momenta occurring ordinarily in beta decay,

$$k^{-1} = \frac{\hbar}{p} \sim 2 \times 10^{-11} \text{ cm} \tag{9-5.6}$$

is large compared with the nuclear dimensions over which the integrals appearing in the matrix element extend; we can thus write

$$e^{i\mathbf{k}\cdot\mathbf{r}} = 1 + i\mathbf{k}\cdot\mathbf{r} - \cdots \qquad (9\text{-}5.7)$$

and the second term will be, in the nuclear region, between 0.1 and 0.01. We then stop with the first term of the expansion unless it should happen that the corresponding matrix element becomes exactly 0, in which case we must consider higher terms. This classification generates transitions of various orders (allowed, first forbidden, etc.) closely analogous to the multipole expansion of electromagnetic radiation. We shall consider only allowed transitions, for which we then write, according to Eqs. (9-5.4) and (9-5.5),

$$H_{if} = g\frac{M_{if}}{\Omega} \qquad (9\text{-}5.8)$$

We have represented by M_{if} the integral $\int u_f^* u_i \, d\tau$, about which we shall make no hypothesis at present, and have introduced a volume Ω in which the system is enclosed in order to simplify the normalization. M is dimensionally a pure number.

What we have said up to now concerning H_{if} is still vastly oversimplified. We mention here the necessary improvements: (1) The u_i, u_f, ψ_e, ψ_ν must be treated relativistically with Dirac spinors. This brings about the possibility of several different interactions (cf. Sec. 9-8). (2) H_{if} must cover not only electron emission but also positron emission and orbital-electron capture. This is achieved by adding to H_{if} its hermitian conjugate. (3) The interaction as written is parity-conserving; in order to describe transitions that do not conserve parity, further terms have to be added to it.

Leaving these points for the present, we must now consider the density of final states, i.e., the number of states per energy interval of the total energy W. Three bodies participate in the disintegration: the final nucleus, the electron, and the neutrino. Energy and momentum must be conserved. The momenta of the three particles are generally of comparable magnitudes and balance to 0, but the energy taken up by the recoil nucleus is very small compared with the energy of the electron and the neutrino, and we can neglect it.

We can thus say that the sum of the energies of electron and neutrino, E_e and E_ν, is equal to the total disintegration energy W, without worrying about the energy imparted to the nucleus by conservation of momentum,

$$W = cp_\nu + (m^2c^4 + c^2p_e^2)^{1/2} = E_\nu + E_e \qquad (9\text{-}5.9)$$

We now want the number of states of the electron having a momentum in the interval between p_e and $p_e + dp_e$ irrespective of the momentum of the neutrino. The number of states in which the neutrino has a momentum in the interval dp_ν and the electron has a momentum in the interval dp_e is

$$dN_e\,dN_\nu = \frac{16\pi^2\Omega^2}{(2\pi\hbar)^6}\,p_\nu^2\,dp_\nu\,p_e^2\,dp_e \qquad (9\text{-}5.10)$$

We eliminate dp_ν and p_ν from Eq. (9-5.10) by noting that for constant p_e Eq. (9-5.9) gives

$$W - E_e = E_\nu = cp_\nu \tag{9-5.11}$$

and

$$dW = dE_\nu = c\, dp_\nu \tag{9-5.12}$$

which, replaced in Eq. (9-5.10), yields

$$dN_e \frac{dN_\nu}{dW} = \frac{16\pi^2\Omega^2}{(2\pi\hbar)^6 c^3}(W - E_e)^2 p_e^2\, dp_e \tag{9-5.13}$$

This is the density of final states, for which the electron has a momentum between p_e and $p_e + dp_e$ irrespective of the neutrino momentum, while the total energy is between W and $W + dW$. It is the appropriate density to be used in Eq. (9-5.1), which then gives (for the probability of a disintegration yielding an electron of momentum between p_e and $p_e + dp_e$)

$$w(p_e)\, dp_e = \frac{2\pi}{\hbar c} g^2|M_{if}|^2 \frac{(4\pi)^2}{(2\pi\hbar)^6} \frac{(W - E_e)^2}{c^2} p_e^2\, dp_e \tag{9-5.14}$$

The volume Ω disappears, as it must, by cancellation in Eq. (9-5.14).

We may ask also what the total decay rate λ is, irrespective of the electron momentum. This is obtained from Eq. (9-5.14), by integrating with respect to dp_e from 0 to the maximum possible momentum of the electron,

$$p_{e\,\max} = \frac{1}{c}(W^2 - m^2c^4)^{1/2} \tag{9-5.15}$$

giving

$$\lambda = \frac{g^2|M_{if}|^2}{2\pi^3 c^3 \hbar^7} \int_0^{p_e \max} [W - (m^2c^4 + c^2p_e^2)^{1/2}]^2\, p_e^2\, dp_e \tag{9-5.16}$$

It is convenient to measure energies in units of mc^2 and momenta in mc, putting

$$E_e = \epsilon\, mc^2 \tag{9-5.17}$$

$$p_e = \eta\, mc \tag{9-5.18}$$

$$W = \epsilon_0\, mc^2 \tag{9-5.19}$$

$$p_{e\,\max} = \eta_0\, mc \tag{9-5.20}$$

Equation (9-5.14) takes the form

$$w(\eta)\, d\eta = \frac{g^2 m^5 c^4}{2\pi^3\hbar^7} |M_{if}|^2 (\epsilon_0 - \epsilon)^2 \eta^2\, d\eta \tag{9-5.21}$$

or

$$w(\eta)\, d\eta = \frac{g^2 m^5 c^4}{2\pi^3\hbar^7} |M_{if}|^2 [(1 + \eta_0^2)^{1/2} - (1 + \eta^2)^{1/2}]^2\, \eta^2\, d\eta \tag{9-5.22}$$

Actually we have oversimplified our discussion on several counts besides the matrix element. For instance, we neglected the Coulomb interaction between nucleons and electrons when we assumed a plane wave for the electron [Eq.(9-5.3)]. This can be corrected by introducing the $\psi_e^2(0)$ calculated numerically with the eigenfunctions of positive energy (continuous spectrum). The factor thus obtained is a function of the product of the charge of the particle emitted, $\pm e$, multiplied by the nuclear charge Ze of the final nucleus and E. We shall call it $F(Z, \epsilon)$ for electrons. For positron emitters Z must be taken as negative.

An approximate expression of $F(Z, \epsilon)$ is

$$F(Z,\epsilon) = 2\pi n[(1 - \exp(-2n\pi)]^{-1} \tag{9-5.23}$$

where n is $Ze^2/\hbar v_e$, and v_e is the velocity of the electron far from the nucleus. For n small compared with 1, $F(Z, \epsilon)$ is unity.

Equation (9-5.21) is thus corrected to

$$w(\eta)\, d\eta = \frac{g^2m^5c^4|M_{if}|^2}{2\pi^3\hbar^7} F(Z,\epsilon)(\epsilon_0 - \epsilon)^2\eta^2\, d\eta \tag{9-5.24}$$

or its equivalent

$$w(\epsilon)\, d\epsilon = \frac{g^2m^5c^4}{2\pi^3\hbar^7} |M_{if}|^2F(Z,\epsilon)(\epsilon_0 - \epsilon)^2\epsilon\eta\, d\epsilon \tag{9-5.25}$$

Since M_{if} is independent of p_e and p_ν (at least for allowed transitions), we have from Eq. (9-5.24) the "form" of the beta spectrum; that is, the probability that an electron is emitted in a momentum interval $d\eta$ around η and from (Eq. 9-5.25) the similar expression for the probability of emission in an energy interval $d\epsilon$. This form is shown in Fig. 9-12. Often one plots

$$\left[\frac{w(\eta)}{\eta^2F(Z,\epsilon)}\right]^{1/2} \text{versus } (\epsilon_0 - \epsilon) \tag{9-5.26}$$

From Eq. (9-5.24) it is clear that this plot should give a straight line (Kurie plot, Fig. 9-13). Departures from the straight line are attributed to a dependence of M_{if} on p_e such as occurs in forbidden transitions according to Eq. (9-5.7) (Fig. 9-14).

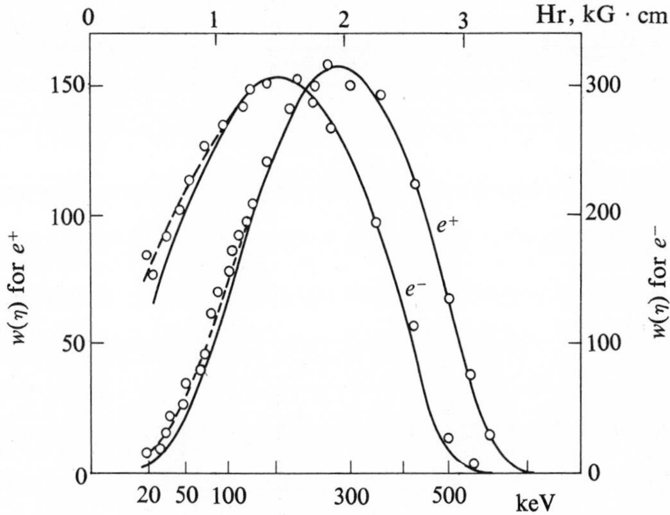

Figure 9-12 Momentum spectra of Cu^{64} electrons and positrons. Circles are experimental points, solid curves are theoretical. Curves not normalized. [C. S. Wu and R. D. Albert, *Phys. Rev.*, **75**, 315 (1949).]

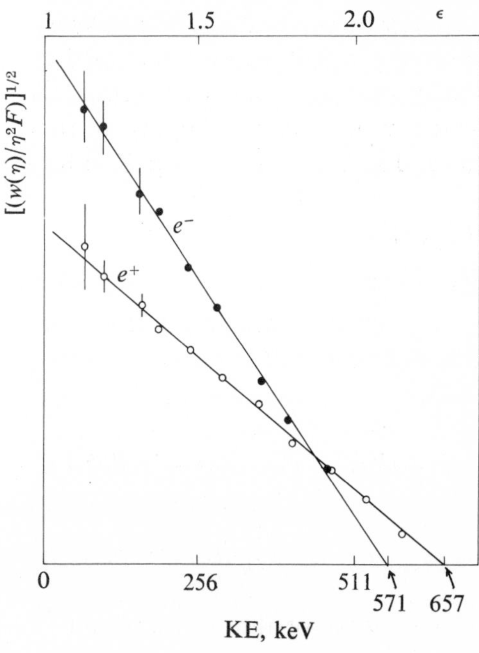

Figure 9-13 The Kurie plots of the Cu^{64} beta spectra. Both positron and electron spectra are shown. End points are at 571 keV for e^- and at 657 keV for e^+. Points are not normalized. [G. E. Owen and C. S. Cook, *Phys. Rev.*, **76,** 1726 (1949).]

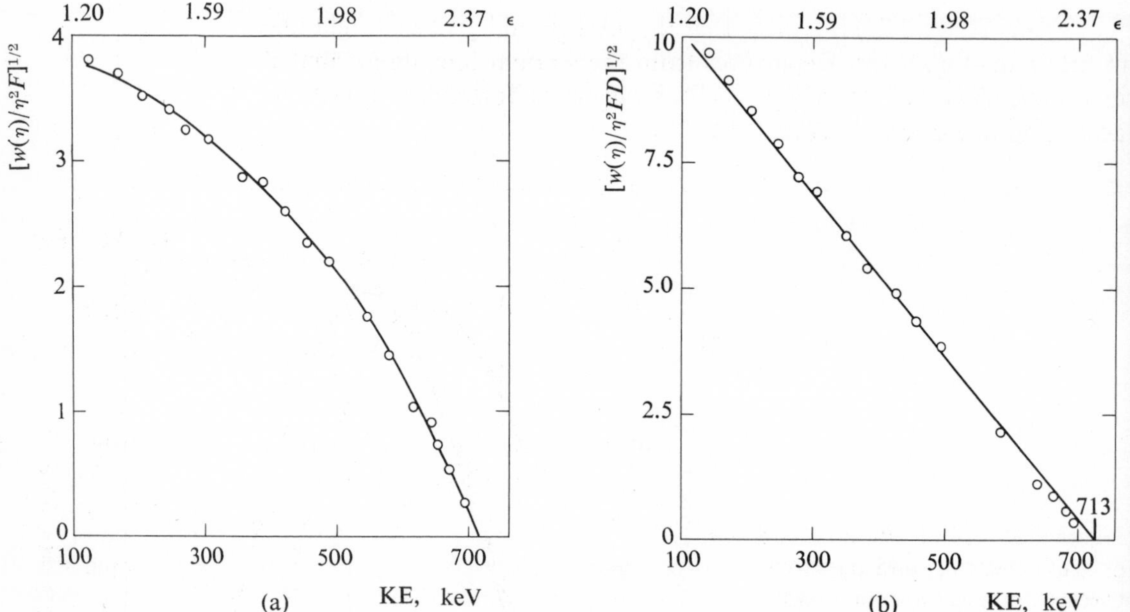

Figure 9-14 (a) The conventional Kurie plot for Cl^{36} beta spectrum is given. (b) Forbidden Kurie plot for Cl^{36} beta spectrum. The correction factor used in this case was

$$D = (\epsilon_0 - \epsilon)^4 + (10/3)(\epsilon^2 - 1)(\epsilon_0 - \epsilon)^2 + (\epsilon^2 - 1)^2$$

(curves not normalized). [C. S. Wu and L. Feldman, *Phys. Rev.*, **76,** 693 (1949).]

In this discussion we have assumed that the neutrino has a zero rest mass. If this were not the case, Eqs. (9-5.9) to (9-5.13) would be slightly different, and the form of the beta spectrum, especially near the upper energy limit, would be characteristically affected (Fig. 9-15). The experimental data from this type of information helps to put an upper limit on the neutrino mass of $\simeq$ 200 eV.

The decay constant λ is obtained by integration of Eq. (9-5.24) from 0 to η_0 [or integration of Eq. (9-5.22) for $F(Z, \epsilon) = 1$]. The result for $F(Z,\epsilon) = 1$ is

$$\lambda = \frac{g^2 m^5 c^4}{2\pi^3 \hbar^7} |M_{if}|^2 f(\eta_0) \tag{9-5.27}$$

where

$$f(\eta_0) = \int_0^{\eta_0} [(1 + \eta_0^2)^{1/2} - (1 + \eta)^{1/2}]^2 \, \eta^2 \, d\eta$$

$$= -\frac{1}{4}\eta_0 - \frac{1}{12}\eta_0^3 + \frac{1}{30}\eta_0^5 + \frac{1}{4}(1 + \eta_0^2)^{1/2} \log [\eta_0 + (1 + \eta_0^2)^{1/2}] \tag{9-5.28}$$

which has the limiting forms

$$f(\eta_0) \simeq \frac{1}{30}\eta_0^5 \qquad \eta_0 \gg 5 \tag{9-5.29}$$

and

$$f(\eta_0) \simeq \frac{2}{105}\eta_0^7 \qquad \eta_0 \ll 0.5 \tag{9-5.30}$$

For quantitative calculations and Z not too small the Coulomb correction of the electron wave function must be considered. From Eq. (9-5.25) we have, on integration,

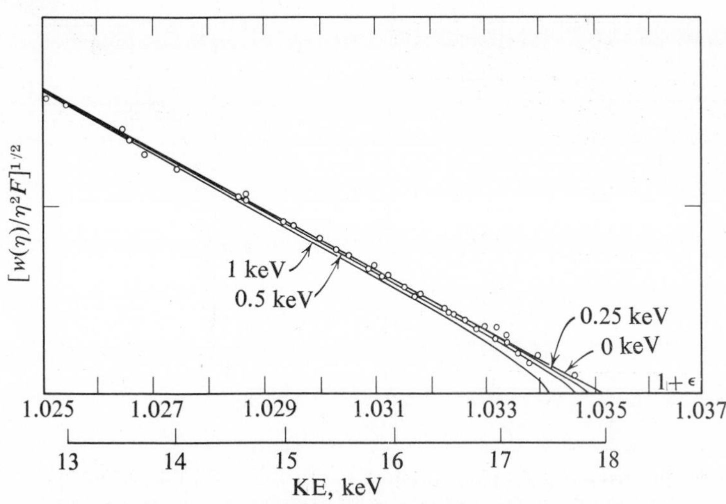

Figure 9-15 Upper end of Fermi plot for H^3 compared with curves for different neutrino rest masses. [L. M. Langer and R. D. Moffat, *Phys. Rev.*, **88**, 689 (1952).]

$$\lambda = \frac{g^2}{2\pi^3}\frac{m^5c^4}{\hbar^7}|M_{if}|^2 f(Z,\epsilon_0) = \frac{G^2}{2\pi^3}\frac{mc^2}{\hbar}|M_{if}|^2 f(Z,\epsilon_0) \tag{9-5.31}$$

where $f(Z, \epsilon_0)$ is now a complicated function which includes the Coulomb correction. Figure 9-16 shows a typical example of $f(Z\epsilon_0)$.

Equation (9-5.31) could be used to determine g or G from the energy and decay constant of a beta emitter if $|M_{if}|^2$ were known. To anticipate a result to be discussed later, in some simple cases the expression $|M_{if}|^2$ may be evaluated and from this one obtains, by using the experimental values of f/λ, a value of g of the order of 10^{-49} erg cm^3. A more quantitative treatment must take into account various types of interactions, as will be seen later.

9-6 Matrix Element

To obtain from mean-life experiments a more quantitative insight into the beta interaction we must reduce the data in such a way as to separate the influence of the energy of the transition, the atomic number involved, etc., from the relevant nuclear data.

Equation (9-5.31) can be rewritten as

$$\frac{\text{const}}{|M_{if}|^2} = f(Z,\epsilon_0)t \tag{9-6.1}$$

where t is the half-life of beta decay. On the right we have directly measurable quantities, t and f, which are functions of Z and ϵ_0; on the

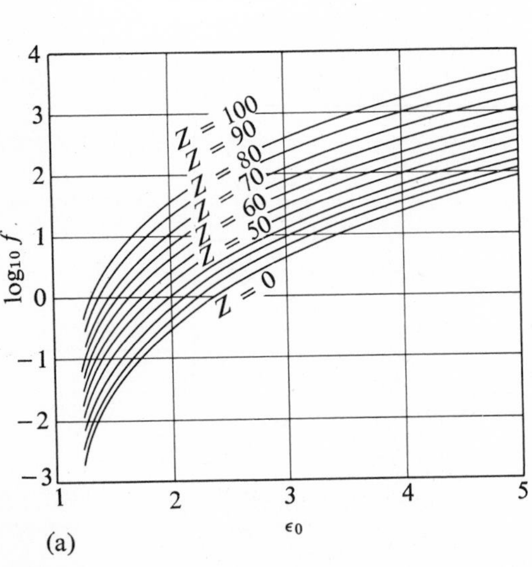

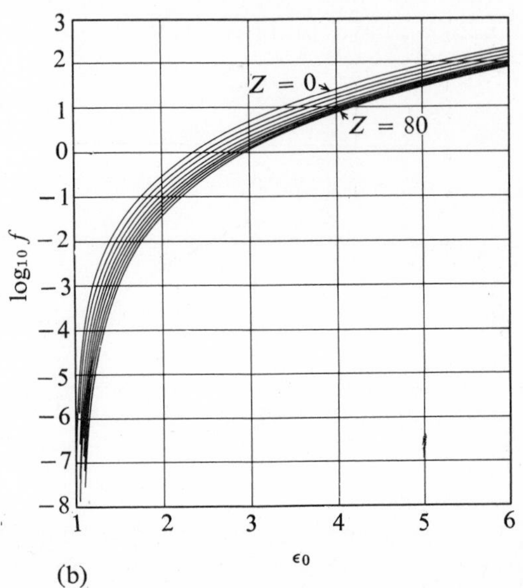

Figure 9-16 The quantity $\log f$ as a function of atomic number and energy for electrons (a) and positrons (b). ϵ_0 is the total energy of the upper limit of the spectrum. [E. Feenberg and G. Trigg, *Rev. Mod. Phys.*, **22**, 399 (1950).]

left we find $1/|M_{if}|^2$, which depends on the nuclear structure. Equation (9-6.1) allows us to extract from the experimental data, which is affected by the energy of the decay and Z, the information about $|M_{if}|^2$ that is relevant to the nuclear problem. Some examples of values of ft for typical decay are given in Table 9-1. The quantity ft is sometimes called "comparative half-life." Nomograms for the rapid evaluation of ft are given in Fig. 9-17.

From the table it is apparent that ft varies over a great range of values and that small values of ft, that is, large matrix elements, occur only if

$$\Delta I = \pm 1, 0 \tag{9-6.2}$$

This is strongly reminiscent of the selection rules of electromagnetic radiation. A qualitative nonrelativistic argument gives some insight into the situation. In the interaction [Eqs. (9-5.4) and (9-5.8)] $\psi_\nu(0)$ and $\psi_e(0)$ appear: these are different from 0 only for states having $j = \frac{1}{2}$. Nonrelativistically we could say that only s states have $\psi(0)$ different from zero.

Table 9-1 Some Typical Beta Decays

Decaying nucleus	Initial spin and parity	Product nucleus	Final spin and parity	$T/2$, sec	E max, MeV	Log, ft	$\|M_{GT}\|^2$	$\|M_F\|^2$
n	$\frac{1}{2}+$	H	$\frac{1}{2}+$	11.7 ± 0.3 m	0.782	3.0744	3	1
H^3	$\frac{1}{2}+$	He^3	$\frac{1}{2}+$	12.4 y	0.0194	3.03	3	1
He^6	0+	Li^6	1+	0.813	3.50	2.77	2	0
O^{14}	0+	N^{14*}	0+	71.1	1.811	3.4873	0	2
Al^{26*}	0+	Mg^{26}	0+	6.60	3.202	3.4843	0	2
Cl^{34}	0+	S^{34}	0+	1.53	4.50	3.4928	0	2
C^{14}	0+	N^{14}	1+	5568 y	0.155			
Ar^{39}	$\frac{7}{2}-$	K^{39}	$\frac{3}{2}+$	265 y	0.565	9.03		
Cl^{38}	2−	Ar^{38}	0+	37.3 m	4.91	8.15		
Na^{22}	3+	Ne^{22}	0+	2.6 y	2.40	11.9		
Be^{10}	0+	B^{10}	3+	2.5×10^6 y	0.56	12.08		
K^{40}	4−	Ca^{40}	0+	1.3×10^9 y	0.63	15.60		
In^{115}	$\frac{9}{2}+$	Sn^{115}	$\frac{1}{2}+$	6×10^{14} y	0.50	23.0		

The first few nuclei in the table, from the neutron to Cl^{34}, have allowed transitions. Moreover, the matrix elements may be computed on the basis of simple and reliable models.

C^{14} shows an allowed transition with an exceptionally small matrix element.

Ar^{39} and Cl^{38} with $\Delta I = 2$ and parity change are first forbidden transitions. Their spectrum departs from the simple Fermi form, and their ft value is high.

Na^{22} and Be^{10} with $\Delta I = 3$ and no change in parity are second forbidden transitions.

K^{40} has $\Delta I = 4$ and change in parity and is a third forbidden transition.

In^{115} has the largest known ft value.

Figure 9-17 Rapid method for calculating $\log_{10}(ft)$ values. [From S. A. Moszkowski, *Phys. Rev.*, **82,** 35 (1951).]

The following figures permit the rapid calculation of log (ft) for a given type of decay, given energy, half-life, etc. The notation is: E_0 for $\beta^{\pm}$ emission is the maximum kinetic energy of the particles in MeV; E_0 for K electron capture is the disintegration energy in MeV. When a β^{+} emission and K electron capture go from and to the same level, E_0 for K capture $= E_0$ for β^{+} emission $+ 1.02$ MeV. Z is the atomic number of the initial nuclei, t is the total half-life, and p is the percentage of decay occurring in the model under consideration. When no branching occurs, $p = 100$.

Procedures for obtaining log (ft):

1. First obtain log (f_0t), using part (a). E_0 is read off the left-hand side of the E_0 column for K electron capture, and off the right-hand side for $\beta^{\pm}$ emission. Put a straight edge over the given values of E_0 and t and note where it crosses the column of log (f_0t) values.
2. Then read off log (C) from part (b), (c), and (d) for β^{-}, β^{+}, and K electron capture, respectively.
3. Get Δ log (ft) from part (e) if $p < 100$. When $p = 100$, $\Delta \log(ft) = 0$.
4. Log $(ft) = \log(f_0t) + \log(C) + \Delta \log(ft)$.

For details concerning the construction, significance, and range of usefulness of these graphs, reference should be made to the original paper.

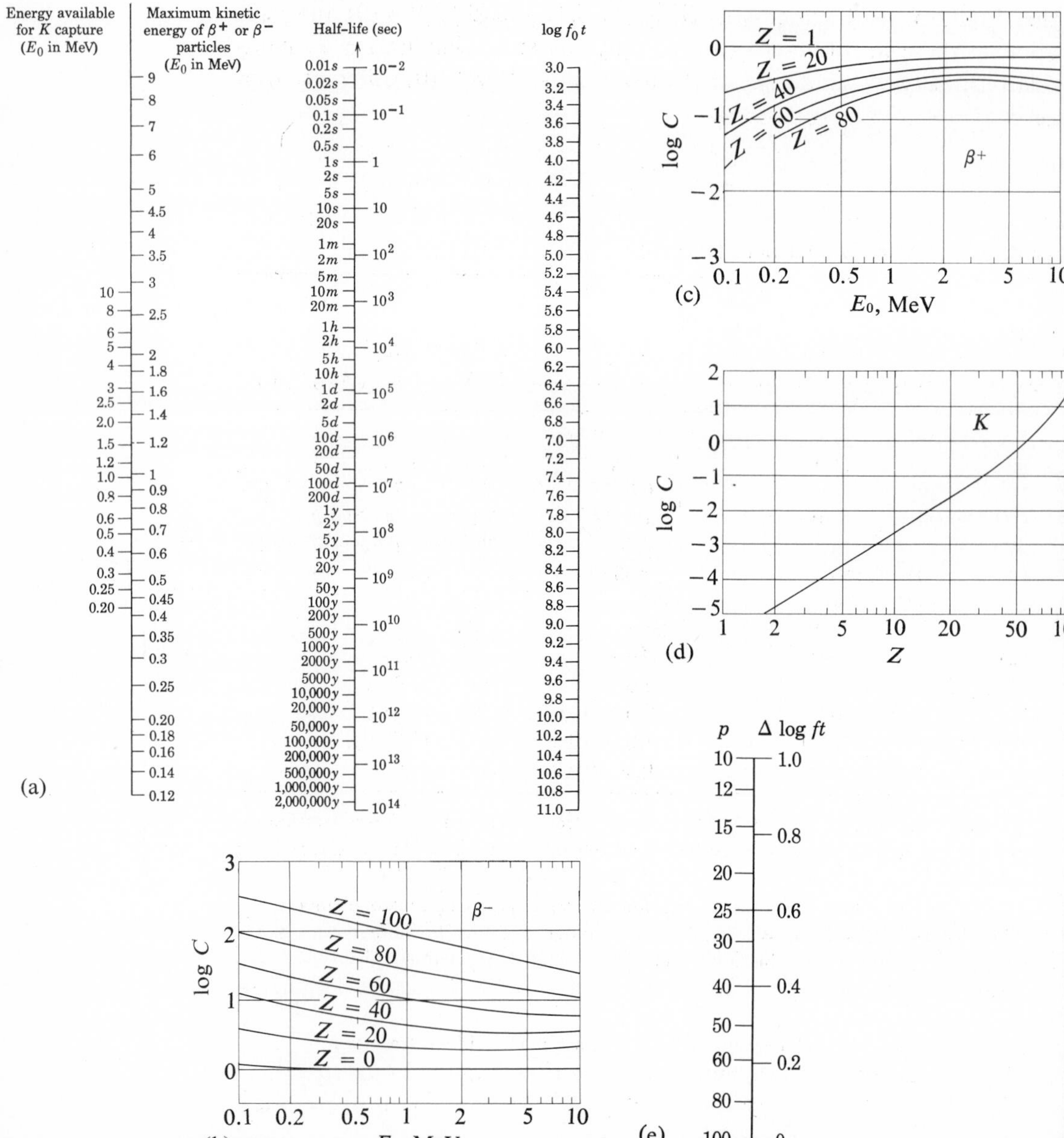

Relativistically l is no longer a good quantum number; however, j is, and it must have the value $\frac{1}{2}$ for both antineutrino and electron in order that $\psi(0) \neq 0$.

Since electron and antineutrino are emitted without orbital angular momentum coming from practically a point source ($R/\lambda \ll 1$, with R the nuclear radius and λ the de Broglie wavelength of the lepton), they carry away no total angular momentum if they are emitted with spins antiparallel (singlet states) or a total angular momentum of 1 if they are emitted with parallel spins (triplet states). In the first case, the spin of the nucleus cannot change at all in beta decay. We thus have the selection rule due to Fermi,

$$\Delta I = 0 \qquad \text{(F selection rule)} \tag{9-6.3}$$

In the second case, the *vector* difference between initial and final angular momentum must be 1; thus

$$\Delta I = \pm 1 \text{ or } 0, \text{ but no } 0 \to 0 \qquad \text{(GT selection rule)} \tag{9-6.4}$$

This selection rule is due to Gamow and Teller. In both F and GT cases, the nuclear eigenfunction must not change parity.

The interactions that give rise to F and GT selection rules are different. However, experiment shows that there are allowed transitions of the type

$$\Delta I = 1 \tag{9-6.5}$$

that obey GT selection rules but are forbidden by F selection rules. Such is the decay

$$He^6 \to Li^6 + e^- + \bar{\nu} \tag{9-6.6}$$

There are also allowed transitions of the 0–0 type that are allowed by F selection rules but forbidden by GT selection rules. For example,

$$O^{14} \to N^{14*} + e^+ + \nu \qquad \text{and} \qquad Al^{26} \to Mg^{*26} + e^+ + \nu \tag{9-6.7}$$

and

$$Cl^{34} \to S^{*34} + e^+ + \nu \tag{9-6.8}$$

Hence we must conclude that both types of interaction are operative. Of course, many transitions are allowed by both selection rules and are not mutually exclusive, for example, $n \to p + e^- + \bar{\nu}$.

Forbidden transitions occur because the finite extent of the nucleus requires us to consider not simply $\psi(0)$ but also the ψ of the electron and neutrino throughout the entire volume occupied by the nucleus. Thus p, d, and higher waves become evident. In other words, the higher terms in the plane wave development,

$$e^{i\mathbf{k}\cdot\mathbf{r}} = 1 + i\mathbf{k}\cdot\mathbf{r} - \frac{(\mathbf{k}\cdot\mathbf{r})^2}{2} + \cdots \tag{9-6.9}$$

are to be considered even though they are of order R/λ or smaller.

Another reason for the occurrence of forbidden transitions is the relativistic effects in the nuclear wave functions, which are of the order of $v/c \sim 0.1$. When the higher terms of the plane wave are considered, in forbidden transitions, they introduce powers of p_e and p_ν into the matrix element M_{if}. As a consequence the form of the beta spectrum changes, and the ordinary Kurie plot departs from a straight line. The plot can be reduced to a straight line by introducing the proper factor, which takes into account the dependence of M_{if} on p_e (Fig. 9-14). If the ordinary Kurie plot is not straight, the transition is not allowed; for possible and still uncertain exceptions consult the literature. The converse, however, is not always true, and special types of forbidden transitions may give rise to straight Kurie plots.

Selection rules for forbidden transitions depend on the term of the interaction producing the transition. For instance, if a transition is caused by the second term of Eq. (9-6.9), the leptons are emitted in a wave having $l = 1$ and changing parity. The Fermi selection rules then give as second approximation $\Delta I = \pm 1, 0$ (except $0 \rightarrow 0$); change of parity, yes. The Gamow–Teller rules, on the other hand, give $\Delta I = \pm 2, \pm 1, 0$ (except $0 \rightarrow 0$; $\frac{1}{2} \rightarrow \frac{1}{2}$; $0 \rightarrow 1$); change of parity, yes. It turns out that the inclusion of terms of the first order in v/c gives the same selection rules. Transitions forbidden by the selection rules (9-6.4) and (9-6.5) but allowed by the rules given above are first forbidden.

For more details on forbidden transitions we refer to the literature.

Some typical numerical examples are given in Table 9-1. Note that for forbidden transitions the evaluation of ft must take into account the proper form of the spectrum, which, as pointed out before, may be different from the normal Fermi spectrum.

Up to now we have accounted for two main results: the form of the beta spectrum and the relation between energy and lifetime (ft values). We shall now consider other, more refined experiments, most of which have been performed since 1956.

9-7 Further Experiments on the Beta Interaction

Further experiments relevant to the analysis of the beta interaction are those on:

1. The asymmetry of beta emission by polarized nuclei.
2. The measurement of the helicity of the neutrino.
3. The observation of $\boldsymbol{\sigma}_e \cdot \mathbf{p}_e$ (helicity of the electron).
4. The observation of the electron-neutrino angular correlation.
5. The observation of circular polarization of gamma rays which follow beta decay and are emitted in a certain direction with respect to the electron.
6. The simultaneous measurement of the angular correlation of neutron spin direction, electron momentum, and antineutrino momentum in neutron decay.

We shall limit ourselves to qualitative arguments and to the main points, without following the historical order. (1) The first experiment demonstrated the nonconservation of parity and has already been discussed. (2) We shall discuss an experiment that has established an important fact, namely, that the neutrino has helicity -1, or is left-handed (M. Goldhaber, Grodzins, and Sunyar, 1958). The experiment (Fig. 9-18) is as follows: Eu^{152m} undergoes K capture to become Sm^{152}. The K capture is followed by emission of a gamma ray of 961 keV. Eu^{152m} and the ground state of Sm^{152} have spin 0. The angular momentum carried off by the neutrino and by the gamma ray must therefore balance the angular momentum brought to the nucleus by the K capture, whose magnitude is $\frac{1}{2}$. Let the axis of quantization be the direction of motion of the gamma quantum, and m_γ, m_ν, and m_K represent the components (in this direction) of the angular momentum of the gamma ray, of the neutrino, and of the captured electron. Clearly, then,

$$m_\gamma = \pm 1 \qquad m_\nu = \pm \tfrac{1}{2} \qquad m_K = \pm \tfrac{1}{2} \tag{9-7.1}$$

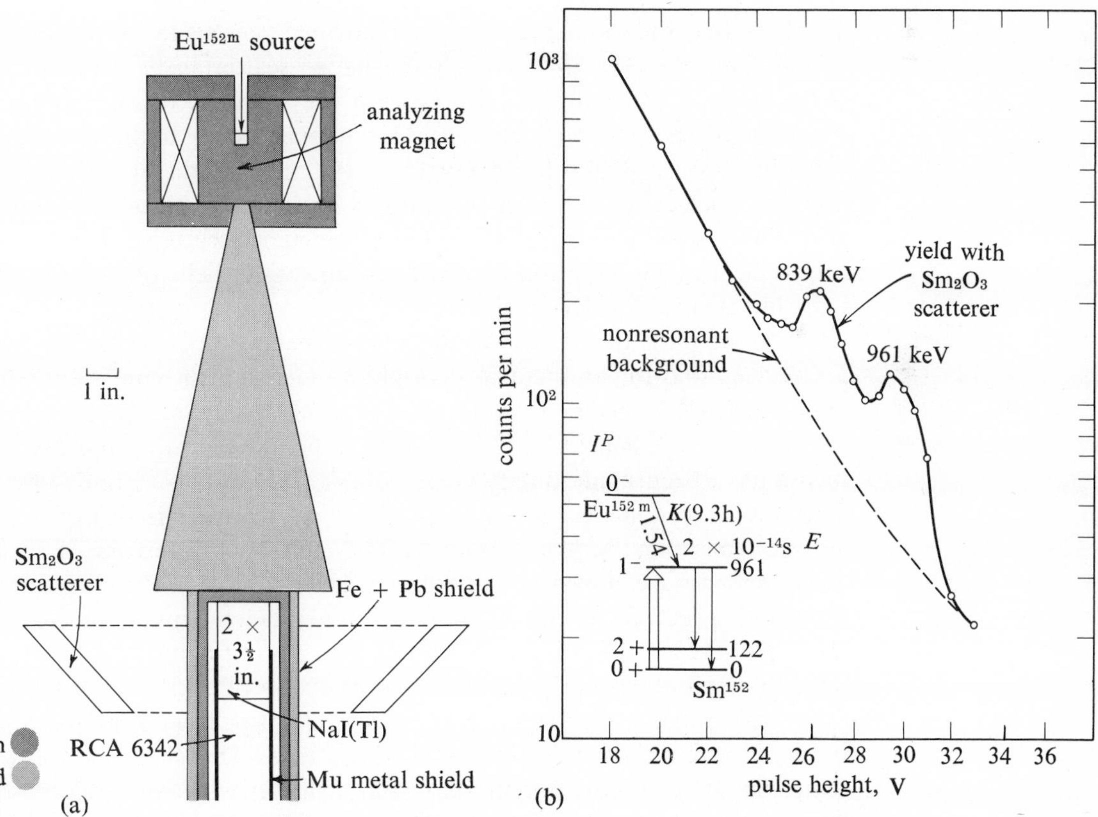

Figure 9-18 The Goldhaber–Grodzins–Sunyar experiment to determine the helicity of the neutrino. (a) The experimental arrangement. The analyzing magnets select a circular polarization of gamma rays. The Sm_2O_3 scatters preferentially nuclear fluorescence radiation into the sodium iodide detector. (b) Level schemes of samarium^{152}. The radiation following K capture excites the 961-keV state of Sm^{152} as indicated by the double arrow. This state decays emitting lines of 961 and 839 keV which are observed.

We also have

$$m_\gamma + m_\nu + m_K = 0 \tag{9-7.2}$$

and this leads to two possibilities:

$$m_\gamma = 1 \qquad m_\nu = -\tfrac{1}{2} \qquad m_K = -\tfrac{1}{2} \tag{9-7.3}$$

or

$$m_\gamma = -1 \qquad m_\nu = \tfrac{1}{2} \qquad m_K = \tfrac{1}{2} \tag{9-7.4}$$

Observation of the circular polarization of the downward, 960-keV gamma ray indicates that

$$m_\gamma = -1 \tag{9-7.5}$$

$$m_\nu = +\tfrac{1}{2} \qquad \text{or} \qquad 2\mathbf{m}_\nu \cdot \hat{\mathbf{p}}_\gamma = 1 \tag{9-7.6}$$

To determine the helicity of the neutrino, we still have to find its momentum. It will be shown shortly that momentum is opposite to that of the gamma ray. We conclude from this that the helicity of the neutrino is negative:

$$\mathscr{H} = 2\hat{\mathbf{p}}_\nu \cdot \mathbf{m}_\nu = -1 \tag{9-7.7}$$

To show that the momentum of the neutrino is opposite to that of the gamma ray, we note that nuclear resonance scattering of gamma rays occurs only if the source moves toward the scatterer (cf. Chap. 8) at the time of the gamma emission. This happens only if the preceding ejection of the neutrino has occurred in the opposite direction, because then the nuclear recoil moves the nucleus in the direction of the gamma ray. The use of gamma rays that are resonance-scattered by an Sm target ensures the condition mentioned above. A helicity -1 for the neutrino is thus directly proved.

On the basis of indirect arguments, we believe that the helicity of $\bar{\nu}$ is $+1$, i.e., that the antineutrino is right-handed. This is consistent with an intrinsic difference between ν and $\bar{\nu}$, as discussed in Sec. 9-2.

For point 3, helicity of the electrons in beta decay, several measurements have been made on P^{32}, Co^{60}, Na^{22}, $Ga^{66,68}$, Au^{198}, and others. The result is a value for the helicity of $+v/c$ for positrons and of $-v/c$ for electrons in all cases examined. The experimental errors of these measurements are, however, rather large. The principle of the most direct experiments [see, for example, Ullman, Frauenfelder, Lipkin, and Rossi, *Phys. Rev*, **122**, 536 (1961)] is to scatter beta rays of chosen momentum on a thin foil of magnetized iron. Two electrons of each iron atom are oriented parallel to the magnetizing field, which is parallel or antiparallel to the momentum of the impinging beta rays. The electron-electron scattering depends on the mutual spin orientation being greater for antiparallel than for parallel spin. The same is true for electron-positron collisions in the relativistic case (Fig. 9-19).

It is therefore possible by changing the direction of magnetization in the iron to determine the degree of longitudinal polarization of the beta rays. Experiments of type 5 support this result. We thus have the important results summarized in Table 9-2.

Table 9-2 Helicities

Particle	ν	$\bar{\nu}$	e^-	e^+
Helicity	-1	1	$-v/c$	v/c

These helicities are the maximum possible for ν and $\bar{\nu}$, and they are consistent with the two-component theory of the neutrino (see Sec. 9-8). Hence we can define the neutrino as a left-handed particle and the antineutrino as a right-handed particle.

Experiments of type 6 show that in beta decay electrons are generated together with antineutrinos and positrons are generated together with neutrinos. The relation of this fact to the angular correlation between positron and neutrino momentum may be seen in the case of a beta transition occurring without change of angular momentum. The neutrino and the positron, having helicities of opposite sign, must tend to move parallel in order not to carry away angular momentum; hence they will show an angular correlation. Similar qualitative arguments are valid in other cases.

9-8 Theory of the Beta Interaction

We now come to an important point of the theory of beta decay, which, of necessity, can be explained only by the use of fairly advanced quantum-mechanical methods. Rather than leave this argument untouched, we shall try to give some idea of the subject, referring for more complete treatment and proofs to the modern literature. A simple treatment of the quantum mechanics needed for this section is available in, for example (Ma 57), and a good review, with applications to beta decay is given by Konopinski and by Lipkin's papers listed in the bibliography of this chapter.

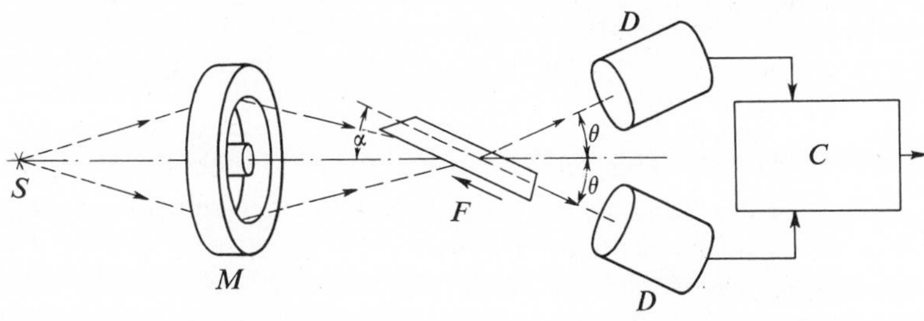

Figure 9-19 Basic arrangement for the measurement of electron and positron helicity by Møller and Bhabha scattering. *S*, source; *M*, monochromator; *F*, thin iron foil magnetized in the direction of arrow; *D*, detectors; *C*, coincidence. Electrons scattered by polarized electrons of the foil are detected, using the coincidences between the two electrons. The cross section depends on the mutual orientation of the spins. A change of the direction of magnetization in the foil thus affects the scattering cross section if the incident electrons are longitudinally polarized. [Frauenfelder et al.]

We have already pointed out that the matrix element of beta decay contains four wave functions *linearly*. Now the particles involved are all fermions of spin $\frac{1}{2}$, and their eigenfunctions should be four-component spinors in relativistic (Dirac) theory. This is certainly the case for the nucleons and the electron; the fact that the neutrino has a mass 0 and that the beta interaction is not parity-conserving makes possible a simpler description of that particle (with two components only). We shall touch on this description later. For the time being, if each particle is described by a spinor and we want the interaction hamiltonian to be a scalar, we must combine the four spinors two at a time in forms that may be a scalar, vector, tensor, axial vector, or pseudoscalar; then we combine two of these pairs of scalars, vectors, etc., in such a way as to form a scalar.

In his original work Fermi explicitly chose a form in which the beta radiation is generated proportionally to the leptonic current. This choice was suggested by the analogy with electromagnetic radiation, which is also generated in proportion to the electric current.

●The four-current producing the transition in Dirac's theory is written as

$$J_\mu = \bar{\psi}_p \gamma_\mu \psi_n \tag{9-8.1}$$

where the γ_μ are the 4 × 4 Dirac matrices defined by

$$\gamma_5^2 = \gamma_\mu^2 = 1 \qquad \gamma_\mu\gamma_\nu + \gamma_\nu\gamma_\mu = 2\delta_{\mu\nu} \qquad \mu,\nu = 1 \cdots 4$$
$$\gamma_5\gamma_\mu + \gamma_\mu\gamma_5 = 0 \tag{9-8.2}$$

or explicitly, for instance:

$$\gamma_k = \begin{vmatrix} 0 & -i\sigma_k \\ i\sigma_k & 0 \end{vmatrix} \quad k = 1,2,3 \qquad \gamma_4 = \begin{vmatrix} 1 & 0 \\ 0 & -1 \end{vmatrix} \qquad \gamma_5 = \begin{vmatrix} 0 & -1 \\ -1 & 0 \end{vmatrix} \tag{9-8.3}$$

where the σ_k are the 2 × 2 Pauli matrices and 1 is the 2 × 2 unit matrix. The ψ_p, ψ_n are the proton, neutron four-component Dirac wave functions, and $\bar{\psi}$ is $\psi^+\gamma_4$ where ψ^+ means the hermitian conjugate of ψ.

Fermi then assumed as the hamiltonian for the beta-decay interaction

$$H = g\,(\bar{\psi}_p\gamma_\mu\psi_n)(\bar{\psi}_e\gamma_\mu\psi_\nu) + \text{hermitian conj.} \equiv gV \tag{9-8.4}$$

The factors in this interaction are four-vectors; hence the name vector interaction. This form of interaction produces the F selection rules. Since there are allowed transitions obeying GT selection rules, we must have other terms in the interaction to produce them. One of the other possible choices is

$$H = g(\bar{\psi}_p\gamma_\mu\gamma_5\psi_n)(\bar{\psi}_e\gamma_\mu\gamma_5\psi_\nu) + \text{h.c.} \equiv gA \tag{9-8.5}$$

The factors in this interaction are axial vectors, hence the name axial-vector interaction.

A linear combination of these two is also admissible. There are other possible choices, e.g., scalar, giving rise to F selection rules, and tensor, giving rise to GT selection rules (see Fig. 9-20). But these choices predict a wrong angular correlation between the direction of the neutrino and the direction of the electron. Therefore we discard them. To see this point, at least qualitatively, consider the fact that in an F transition a right-handed antineutrino (helicity +1) must be accompanied by an electron of opposite spin, because together they carry off zero angular momentum. Electrons, according to Table 9-2, are generated with negative helicity; thus the momenta of electron and antineutrino must tend to be parallel, as predicted by calculations based on vector interaction. Calculations based on scalar interaction favor antiparallelism between the momenta and make the interaction unacceptable. ●

In GT transitions electrons and antineutrinos have parallel spin, because together they carry away one unit of angular momentum. The antineutrino has helicity +1, the electron is generated with negative helicity, and hence they must tend to have opposite momenta, as calculations based on axial-vector interaction predict. Calculations based on tensor interaction favor parallelism between the momenta and make the interaction unacceptable.

The situation is illustrated schematically in Fig. 9-20 and Table 9-3. Experimental verification is secured by measuring the electron momentum and the nuclear recoil. The neutrino momentum is then calculated on the principle of momentum conservation. When the electron and antineutrino tend to move parallel to each other, large values of the

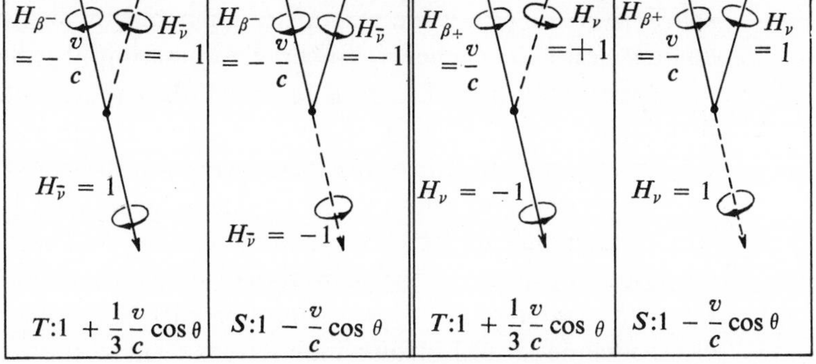

β^- decay		β^+ decay	
GT interaction $\Delta I = 1$	F interaction $I = 0 \to I = 0$	GT interaction $\Delta I = 1$	F interaction $I = 0 \to I = 0$
$A{:}1 - \frac{1}{3}\frac{v}{c}\cos\theta$	$V{:}1 + \frac{v}{c}\cos\theta$	$A{:}1 - \frac{1}{3}\frac{v}{c}\cos\theta$	$V{:}1 + \frac{v}{c}\cos\theta$
$H_{\beta^-} = -\frac{v}{c}$, $H_{\bar{\nu}} = -1$	$H_{\beta^-} = -\frac{v}{c}$, $H_{\bar{\nu}} = -1$	$H_{\beta^+} = \frac{v}{c}$, $H_{\nu} = +1$	$H_{\beta^+} = \frac{v}{c}$, $H_{\nu} = 1$
$H_{\bar{\nu}} = 1$	$H_{\bar{\nu}} = -1$	$H_{\nu} = -1$	$H_{\nu} = 1$
$T{:}1 + \frac{1}{3}\frac{v}{c}\cos\theta$	$S{:}1 - \frac{v}{c}\cos\theta$	$T{:}1 + \frac{1}{3}\frac{v}{c}\cos\theta$	$S{:}1 - \frac{v}{c}\cos\theta$

Figure 9-20 Correlations of neutrino helicities and beta interactions. The interactions and helicities realized in nature are framed in squares and represented by solid lines; other alternative interactions not realized in nature are unframed and represented by dashed lines. Angle θ is the angle between p_ν and p_e.

Table 9-3 Correlation between Momenta and Helicities

Momenta of $e^{\pm}$ and ν or $\bar{\nu}$	Parallel	Opposite
GT	Tensor	Axial vector
Fermi	Vector	Scalar

nuclear-recoil momentum are favored. When the electron and antineutrino tend to move in opposite directions, small nuclear recoils are favored.

Observing the recoil nucleus energy or momentum distribution in the pure GT transition occurring, for example, in He^6, and comparing it with the calculated one, we conclude that GT transitions are associated with the axial-vector interaction (see Fig. 9-4). From similar arguments and experiments for Ar^{35}, for example, we conclude that F transitions are due to the vector interactions.

A linear combination

$$g(C_A A + C_V V) \tag{9-8.6}$$

is also admissible.

Expression (9-8.6) for the hamiltonian, is not, however broad enough to describe beta decay, because the expression is parity-conserving. Lee and Yang have generalized Eq. (9-8.6), obtaining parity violation by writing

$$H = g \sum_{i=V,A} (\bar{\psi}_p O_i \psi_n)[\bar{\psi}_e O_i (C_i + C_i' \gamma_5)\psi_\nu] + \text{c.c.} \tag{9-8.7}$$

where O_V is the V operator of Eq. (9-8.4) and O_A is the A operator of Eq. (9-8.5). This hamiltonian brings about parity nonconservation by the simultaneous presence of the two terms in the square brackets. If either C or C' vanishes, the hamiltonian conserves parity.

Consider now the behavior of H when we perform the operation of space inversion (P), when we replace a particle by its antiparticle (charge conjugation C), or when we invert the direction of time (T).

Investigation of Eq. (9-8.7) shows that these operations leave its form unchanged except for the coefficients (complex numbers) C and C'. These are changed by the transformation indicated in Table 9-4.

There is an important theorem, due to Schwinger, Lüders, and Pauli, which states that under very broad conditions, and certainly for theories developed up to now, the hamiltonian is invariant under the operation CPT (the order of C, T, P is unimportant). This theorem is trivial for electromagnetic and strong interactions, where the hamiltonian is invariant for each operation, but becomes very important in weak interactions, where invariance for P is certainly violated. We shall postulate that in this case invariance under time reversal is preserved, and hence that invariance for the product CP is also preserved. Its meaning is easily

Table 9-4 Changes of Coefficient of C and C' under Different Transformations

Transformation	C	C'	Condition for invariance of Eq. (9-8.7)
Space inversion (P)	C	$-C'$	$C' = 0$ or $C = 0$
Charge conjugation (C)	C^*	$-C'^*$	C real, and C' imag. or C imag. and C' real
Time reversal (T)	C^*	C'^*	C, C' both real
TCP	C	C'	Automatically satisfied

illustrated with reference to Fig. 9-9. Part (b) of this figure *becomes correct* as drawn, provided cobalt is replaced by its charge conjugate, i.e., by a nucleus derived from ordinary cobalt by replacing each proton by an antiproton and each neutron by an antineutron. Although this experiment is at present practically unfeasible with nuclei, similar experiments with positive and negative mesons support *CP* invariance.

The decay of mesons is similar to beta decay and here two pairs of charge-conjugate particles are known: the positive and negative pion and the positive and negative muon (see Chaps. 13 and 14). For each pair the decay process of particle and antiparticle are mirror images of each other. Thus in these cases the *CP* transformation gives a result in agreement with experiment. This, together with the *CPT* theorem, proves the *T* invariance in these cases.

Because *T* invariance is very likely to be correct in general and because it simplifies further discussion appreciably, we shall make use of it. If it should be found experimentally that time-reversal invariance is violated, a more elaborate discussion would be needed. Such discussions are available in the literature.

Time-reversal invariance requires, as stated above, that coefficients C_A, C_A' and C_V, C_V' be real. Another important relation among the $C_{A,V}$ coefficients derives from the helicities given in Table 9-2. These values produce the relations

$$C_A = C_A' \qquad C_V = C_V' \tag{9-8.8}$$

which is equivalent to accepting a two-component theory of the neutrino in which the neutrino eigenfunctions are obtained by applying the projection operator $(\frac{1}{2})$ $(1 \pm \gamma_5)$ to the ordinary ψ_ν. One has then

$$\tfrac{1}{2}(1 \pm \gamma_5)\psi_\nu = \varphi^{\pm} \tag{9-8.9}$$

The upper sign gives left-handed, and the lower sign right-handed neutrinos. The experimental finding, that only left-handed neutrinos (right-handed antineutrinos) exist, indicates that only the upper sign in the operator $\frac{1}{2}(1 \pm \gamma_5)$ is realized in nature, and in turn this produces

$$C_A = +C_A' \qquad C_V = +C_V' \tag{9-8.10}$$

with the positive sign. The hamiltonian can thus be written as

$$H = g \sum_{i=A,V} C_i(\bar{\psi}_p O_i \psi_n)[\bar{\psi}_e O_i(1 + \gamma_5)\psi_\nu] + \text{c.c.} \qquad \textbf{(9-8.11)}$$

To complete the analysis we must next find the ratio C_A/C_V and the universal constant g. A study of the beta decay of the neutron and of some other especially suitable nuclei answers these questions.

9-9 Quantitative Study of Some Matrix Elements

To obtain numerical results, we first introduce a considerable simplification by treating the nuclear part of the matrix element in a nonrelativistic approximation. This is permissible because v_n/c is relatively small. We need to consider, then, only the two large components of the four-component nuclear eigenfunctions. The matrix elements corresponding to vector interaction in this approximation are simply

$$\int u_f{}^* u_i \, d\tau = M_{\text{F}} \qquad \textbf{(9-9.1)}$$

whereas those corresponding to axial-vector interaction are

$$\int u_f{}^* \boldsymbol{\sigma} u_i \, d\tau = M_{\text{GT}} \qquad \textbf{(9-9.2)}$$

where $\boldsymbol{\sigma}$ is an axial-vector operator whose components are the Pauli spin matrices.

Transitions of the first type, having nuclear matrix element M_{F}, are Fermi transitions; those of the second type are Gamow–Teller transitions. It is clear from the orthogonallity of the nuclear wavefunctions that M_{F} vanishes if initial and final states are different (e.g., have different I values) except for the transformation of a neutron into a proton and that M_{GT} requires also a spin flip in order not to vanish. In particular, the initial and final state (in each case) must have the same parity.

Here we see how the parity-nonconserving beta decay imposes a condition on the relative parity of the initial and final nuclear state.

We may go one step further and try to evaluate M_{F} and M_{GT} in specific cases. We note also that for practical purposes one needs an $\overline{M_{if}}$, where the bar indicates average over initial and sum over final z components of angular momentum.

The simplest cases are those in which a single neutron becomes a proton, or vice versa, without any other change in the eigenfunction. Examples are the decay of the free neutron without spin flip and the decay of O^{14} to an excited state of N^{14}, both having $I = 0$. For the first case $|M_{\text{F}}|^2 = 1$; for the second, $|M_{\text{F}}|^2 = 2$. For the decay of the free neutron with spin flip

$$\overline{|M_{\text{GT}}|^2} = 3 \qquad \textbf{(9-9.3)}$$

The evaluation of these matrix elements follows from Eqs. (9-9.1) and (9-9.2), but we shall not develop the relevant calculations. We have assumed that the interactions operative in beta decay are of the A and V type only. The first gives rise to GT selection rules, the second to F selection rules.

Under this assumption we can calculate $(gC_V)^2$ from a transition allowed only by F selection rules and for which $\overline{|M_F|^2}$ is calculable. Such is the decay of O^{14}. One then has

$$g^2C_V^2 = \frac{2\pi^3}{\overline{|M_F|^2}} \frac{\hbar^7}{m^5c^4} \frac{1}{ft} \qquad \textbf{(9-9.4)}$$

which gives with $\overline{|M_F|^2} = 2$ and with the observed ft of 3,071 sec (see Table 9-1)

$$gC_V = 1.41 \pm 0.01 \times 10^{-49} \text{ erg cm}^3 \qquad \textbf{(9-9.5)}$$

For the neutron we can write similarly

$$ft = \frac{1}{g^2} \frac{2\pi^3\hbar^7}{m^5c^4} \frac{1}{C_V^2\overline{|M_F|^2} + C_A^2\overline{|M_{GT}|^2}} \qquad \textbf{(9-9.6)}$$

with $|M_F|^2 = 1$, $|M_{GT}|^2 = 3$, and with an observed ft of 1,187 sec (see Table 9-1). The ratio between ft (neutron) and ft (O^{14}) then gives

$$\frac{2C_V^2}{C_V^2 + 3C_A^2} = 0.381 \qquad \textbf{(9-9.7)}$$

or

$$\frac{C_A^2}{C_V^2} = 1.42 \pm 0.08 \qquad \textbf{(9-9.8)}$$

The study of neutron beta decay also gives information as to the relative sign of C_V and C_A.

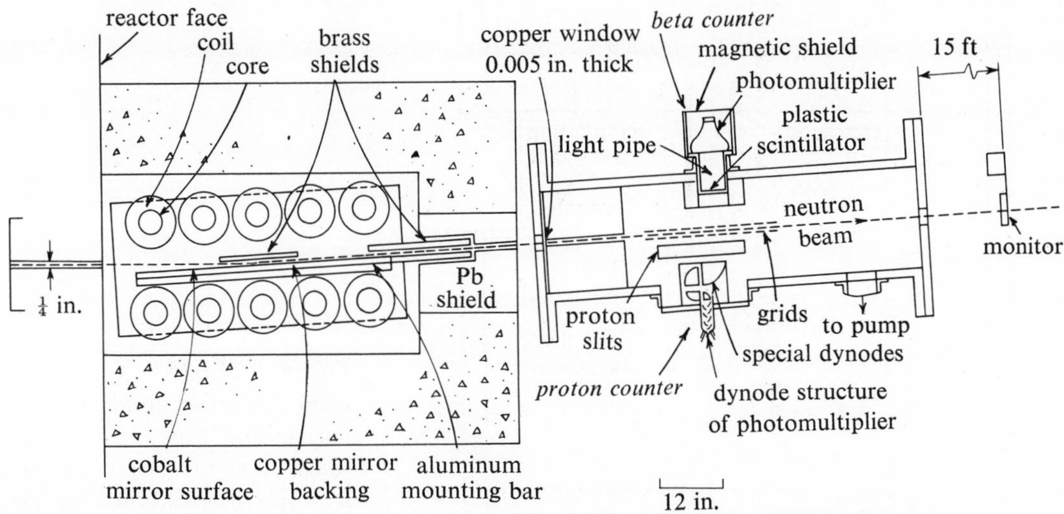

Figure 9-21 Horizontal section through the center of the apparatus used for studying the decay of polarized neutrons. [Burgy, Krohn, Novey, Ringo, and Telegdi, *Phys. Rev.*, **120,** 1829 (1960).]

It has been possible to measure experimentally the $\mathbf{p}_e$-$\mathbf{I}$ and $\mathbf{p}_\nu$-$\mathbf{I}$ angular correlation in neutron decay (Figs. 9-21 and 9-22). A beam of polarized neutrons (see Chaps. 10 and 12) passed into an evacuated tank, and both the electrons and the recoil protons coming from the decay in flight are observed. It is found that there is a very small negative angular correlation between $\mathbf{I}$ and $\mathbf{p}_e$ and a strong positive correlation between $\mathbf{I}$ and $\mathbf{p}_\nu$. This is evidence that the coefficients C_A and C_V have opposite sign, as indicated in Fig. 9-23. Their magnitude is not very different: one has

$$\frac{|C_A|}{|C_V|} = 1.19 \pm 0.02 \tag{9-9.9}$$

The g constant derived from the O^{14}, Al^{26}, and Cl^{34} ft parameter has the value

$$g = (1.41 \pm 0.01) \times 10^{-49} \text{ erg cm}^3 \tag{9-9.10}$$

We summarize in Table 9-5 some of the most important experiments relevant to beta decay, their immediate interpretation, and their theoretical consequences.

9-10 Conservation of Leptons

We assume that the reader knows the nomenclature and some of the relevant facts about muons and other particles discussed in Chaps. 13 and 14. In particular, recall that "leptons" are fermions, which are lighter than the nucleon (i.e., the neutrinos, electrons, and muons and their

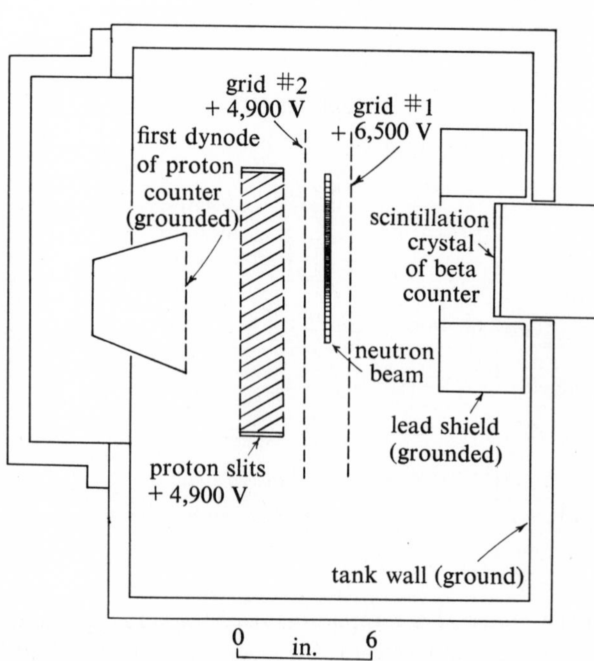

Figure 9-22 Detector arrangement for measurement of the correlation between the directions of neutron spin and antineutrino momentum. This is a cross section of the detector part of Fig. 9-21.

charge conjugates or antiparticles). For the time being, no distinction will be made between the two kinds of neutrinos (see Sec. 9-2). Each particle is assigned a leptonic number as follows:

$$\begin{aligned} l &= 1 \text{ for } e^-, \mu^-, \nu \equiv \nu_L \text{ (helicity } = -1) \\ l &= -1 \text{ for } e^+, \mu^+, \bar{\nu} \equiv \nu_R \text{ (helicity } = +1) \\ l &= 0 \text{ for all other particles} \end{aligned} \qquad \textbf{(9-10.1)}$$

Table 9-5 Main Features of Beta Decay

Experiment	Immediate consequence	Theory
Form of beta spectrum	Three-body decay	Neutrino mass, statistics, spin; general form of theory
Cobalt^{60} asymmetry	Nonconservation of parity and no charge conjugation invariance	
Inverse beta decay	Distinction between neutrino and antineutrino	
ft of O^{14*} $(0^+ \to 0^+)$ transition	F selection rules	Interaction V and/or S
ft of He^6 $(0^+ \to 1^+)$ transition	GT selection rules	Interaction T and/or A
ft of neutron $(\frac{1}{2}^+ \to \frac{1}{2}^+)$	Allowed by F and GT selection rules	$\lvert C_{GT}\rvert^2/\lvert C_F\rvert^2 = 1.42$
Recoil spectrum in F transition (Ar^{35})	Angular correlation $e\nu$ $(1 + a_F(v/c) \cos \theta_{e\nu})$ with $a_F = +1$	Interaction V
Recoil spectrum in GT transition (He^6)	Angular correlation $e\nu$ $(1 + a_{GT}(v/c) \cos \theta_{e\nu})$ with $a_{GT} = -\frac{1}{3}$	Interaction A
Recoil in K capture $Eu^{152} \to Sm^{152}$	Helicity of $\nu = -1$	
Electron polarization measurements: Co^{60}, Na^{22}, Cl^{34}, etc.	$P = +v/c$ for e^+; $P = -v/c$ for e	$C_S = -C_S'$; $C_V = C_V'$; $C_T = -C_T'$; $C_A = C_A'$
Decay of polarized neutrons[a]	Intensity $\sim 1 + a\hat{\mathbf{q}}\cdot\mathbf{v}/c + \mathbf{I}\cdot[A(\mathbf{v}/c) + B\mathbf{q} + D(\mathbf{v}/c) \times \hat{\mathbf{q}}]$	$D = 0$ time-reversal invariance
$A = -0.11 \pm 0.02$; $B = 0.88 \pm 0.15$; $D = -0.04 \pm 0.07$; $a = 0.09 \pm 0.11$		Values of A, B give $C_V = C_A$; other C_i and $C_i' = 0$; $a = 0$ gives $\lvert C_A\rvert^2 = \lvert C_V\rvert^2$
Spectra of B^{12} and N^{12}	Form of spectra	Conserved current theory

[a] $\mathbf{I}$ = neutron spin, $\hat{\mathbf{q}}$ = unit vector in the direction of neutrino velocity, $\mathbf{v}$ = electron velocity.

Writing the typical weak interaction reactions in the forms

$$
\begin{array}{ll}
n \to p + e^- + \bar{\nu} & p \to n + e^+ + \nu \\
\pi^+ \to \mu^+ + \nu & \pi^- \to \mu^- + \bar{\nu} \\
\mu^+ \to e^+ + \nu + \bar{\nu} & \mu^- \to e^- + \nu + \bar{\nu} \\
\mu^- + p \to n + \nu & \mu^+ + n \to p^+ + \bar{\nu} \\
K^+ \to \mu^+ + \nu & K^- \to \mu^- + \bar{\nu} \\
\pi^+ \to e^+ + \nu & \pi^- \to e^- + \bar{\nu} \\
e^+ + e^- \to 2\gamma &
\end{array}
\tag{9-10.2}
$$

it appears that the number of leptons on the right side of the equation is equal to that on the left. This equality is called the law of conservation of leptons. It is valid regardless of the interaction operative in the reaction.

The leptonic number of one particle, the e^-, say, is arbitrary. But once it is decided that l for e^- is $+1$, the conservation of leptons assigns to $\bar{\nu}$—defined by the first of Eqs. (9-10.2)—the leptonic number -1, and to ν defined by the second, the leptonic number $+1$, because e^+ according to the last equation (9-10.2) has $l = -1$. Similarly, other leptonic numbers are uniquely determined. Equations (9-10.2) have a physical content; e.g., the helicities of neutrino and antineutrino differ and the consequent angular correlations are sometimes observable.

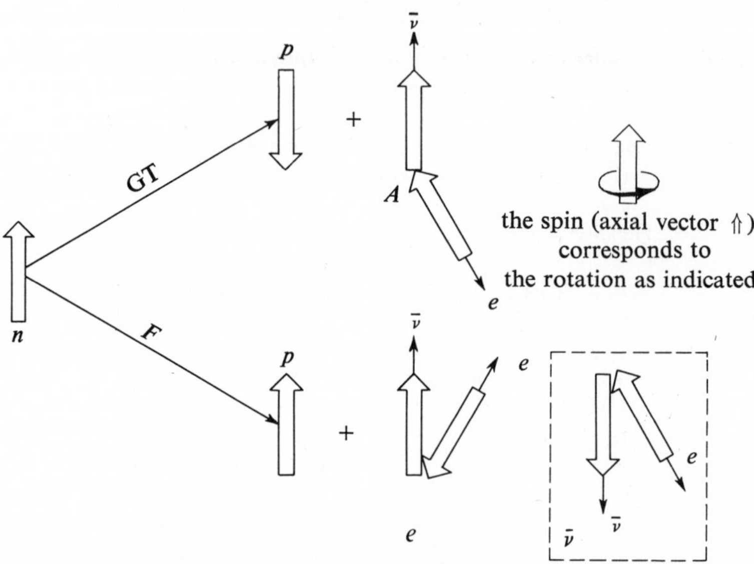

Figure 9-23 Angular correlations in neutron decay. ⇑, spin direction; ↑, momentum direction. The physical significance of the relative sign of V and A is indicated. The combination A-V shows no angular correlation $\mathbf{p}_e \cdot \mathbf{I}_n$ and a strong positive correlation $\mathbf{p}_{\bar{\nu}} \cdot \mathbf{I}_n$. In the combination $A + V$ (in dashed square) there would be strong negative $\mathbf{p}_e \cdot \mathbf{I}_n$ correlation and no $\mathbf{p}_{\bar{\nu}} \cdot \mathbf{I}_n$ correlation.

The origin of the law of conservation of leptons, as well as of the similar law of conservation of nucleons, is unknown. Although no exception to lepton conservation is known, one fails to observe certain reactions that one would expect if the assignments in Eqs. (9-10.2) were correct and complete. For instance, the reaction

$$\mu^- \to e^- + \gamma \tag{9-10.3}$$

would be obtained from

$$\mu^- \to e^- + \nu + \bar{\nu} \tag{9-10.4}$$

by the suppression of the neutrino-antineutrino pairs. In fact the branching ratio is less than 10^{-7}. This raised the suspicion that there might be more than one kind of neutrino. Direct experiment (see Sec. 9-2) has now shown that this is the case.

The discovery of two types of neutrinos, ν_e and ν_μ, complicates the classification of leptons because Eqs. (9-10.2) give ambiguous results unless, in addition to fixing the leptonic number of the electron, we make some further assumption. There are several competing schemes for assigning additional quantum numbers; and they are experimentally distinguishable, although the experiments are difficult. One of the simplest is to introduce, besides the leptonic number as defined in Eq. (9-10.1), a muonic number of $+1$ for μ^- and ν_μ, -1 for μ^+ and $\bar{\nu}_\mu$, and 0 for all other particles. If we assume that leptonic number and muonic number are separately conserved, some of the reactions in Eqs. (9-10.2) are written

$$\begin{array}{ll} \mu^- \to e^- + \bar{\nu}_e + \nu_\mu & \\ n \to p + e^- + \bar{\nu}_e & \mu^- + p \to n + \nu_\mu \end{array} \tag{9-10.5}$$

It is also apparent that the reaction $\mu^- \to e^- + \gamma$ is forbidden because the muonic number is not conserved.

9-11 Universal Fermi Interaction

It has been noted by many physicists that the phenomenon of the decay of the mu meson into an electron and a $\nu + \bar{\nu}$ pair is closely analogous to ordinary beta decay. For instance, the decay of the meson may be described in a manner very closely resembling the description of neutron decay if we replace

$$\begin{array}{llll} p & n & e^- & \bar{\nu}_e \end{array}$$

by

$$\begin{array}{llll} e^- & \mu^- & \bar{\nu}_e & \nu_\mu \end{array} \tag{9-11.1}$$

and use an interaction of the form

$$g(V - A) \tag{9-11.2}$$

The value of g in mu-meson decay differs no more than 3 per cent from the value derived from neutron decay, provided that we write the interaction for the neutron as

$$g\left(V - \frac{C_A}{C_V} A\right) \qquad \text{with } \frac{C_A}{C_V} = 1.19 \tag{9-11.3}$$

It is then very tempting to assume Eq. (9-8.11) as the fundamental law of beta decay. It is possible that there are enough subsidiary corrections in the beta decay of the neutron, due to mesonic effects, to account for the different coefficients of V and A appearing in Eq. (9-11.3).

Feynman and Gell-Mann have developed some theoretical arguments to explain why the coefficient of V is unaffected in passing from the system $pne\bar{\nu}$ to the system $\mu e\nu\bar{\nu}$, whereas the coefficient of A is modified. The change is attributed to pionic effects that cancel out exactly for the V part and affect only the A part.

The Feynman and Gell-Mann hypothesis, called the "conserved vector current" theory, gives an especially elegant formulation of the beta interaction, based on analogies with electromagnetism, and yields automatically the V-A form of the weak interaction. Important experimental support for this theory has come from recent experiments by Lee, Mo, and Wu (1963). They have shown that the beta-ray spectra in the decays of B^{12} and N^{12} to C^{12} take a form that can be accounted for quantitatively by the conserved vector current theory.

Other detailed information is obtained by studying the energy distribution of the electrons coming from muonic decay. This distribution is given by

$$N(\epsilon)\,d\epsilon = 4\epsilon^2[3(1-\epsilon) + \tfrac{2}{3}\rho(4\epsilon - 3)]\,d\epsilon \qquad \textbf{(9-11.4)}$$

where $\epsilon = E/E_{\max}$ and ρ is a parameter (Michel, 1949) having the value 0 if two identical neutrinos are emitted in the decay. If different neutrinos, or if a neutrino and an antineutrino, are emitted, ρ assumes the value $\frac{3}{4}$, close to the experimental values found, which range from 0.69 to 0.79. This evidence confirms the assignment of Eq. (9-10.4) in the case of muon decay.

The similarity between mu and neutron decay has suggested that four fermions, chosen according to the rule shown in Fig. 9-24, always interact with the V-A form of the Fermi interaction. Up to now calculations of known phenomena uphold this hypothesis, at least for the interactions considered in Puppi's triangle (Fig. 9-24). One side of the triangle indicates beta decay, in which the four fermions

$$n \to p + e^- + \bar{\nu}_e$$

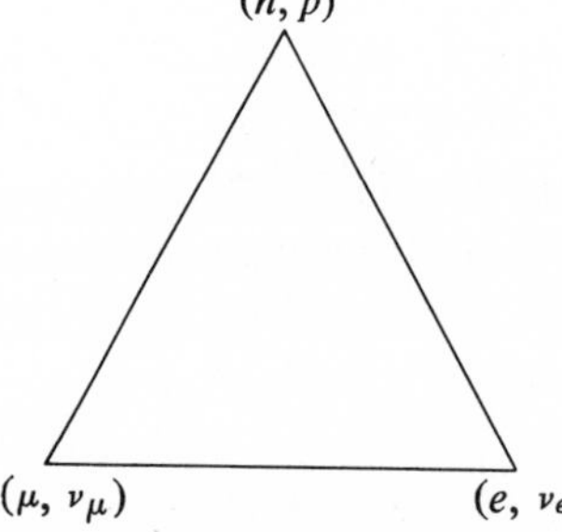

Figure 9-24 Puppi's triangle. Fermions at the vertices of the triangle interact with the universal Fermi interaction. The pairs $(\mu,\nu_\mu)(e,\nu_e)$ correspond to the mu decay, the pairs $(\mu,\nu_\mu)(n,p)$ correspond to the capture of a mu meson in a nucleus, the pairs $(e,\nu_e)(n,p)$ to the beta decay.

participate. The second side indicates muon decay, with $\mu^- \rightarrow e^- + \bar{\nu}_e + \nu_\mu$ involved. The third side, with $n \rightarrow p + \mu^- + \bar{\nu}_\mu$ involved, corresponds to the capture of a μ^- by a proton, which becomes a neutron, while a neutrino is emitted.

Every process mentioned has several variations depending on the electric charge of the particles involved: thus in beta decay we include positive- and negative-electron emission and orbital-electron capture, etc.

The decay of the pi meson according to the equation

$$\pi^- \rightarrow \mu^- + \bar{\nu}_\mu \tag{9-11.5}$$

may be thought of as a two-step process involving an intermediate virtual nucleon-antinucleon state

$$\pi^- \rightarrow n + \bar{p} \rightarrow \mu^- + \bar{\nu}_\mu \tag{9-11.6}$$

Particularly instructive is the comparison of the normal mode of decay, Eq. (9-11.5) with the rare mode of decay

$$\pi^- \rightarrow e^- + \bar{\nu}_e \tag{9-11.7}$$

which occurs about 10^{-4} as frequently as the normal decay (Fazzini, Fidecaro, et al., 1960). We may think of this process as being due to the two-step process

$$\pi^- \rightarrow n + \bar{p} \rightarrow e^- + \bar{\nu}_e \tag{9-11.8}$$

perfectly analogous to Eq. (9-11.6). In calculating the branching ratio between the decays in Eqs. (9-11.5) and (9-11.7) we first have to include a statistical factor depending on the momentum space available for the final state. This factor for a two-body decay is

$$\frac{dN}{dE} = \frac{4\pi p^2 \, dp}{(2\pi\hbar)^3 \, dE_0} = \frac{1}{2\pi^2\hbar^3 c} \frac{p^2}{1 + v/c} \tag{9-11.9}$$

and clearly favors the rare mode of decay. In fact considered alone it would give for the ratio of the decay constants λ_e/λ_μ:

$$\frac{p_e^2(1 + v/c)_\mu}{p_\mu^2(1 + v/c)_e} = \frac{(m_\pi^2 + m_e^2)\,(m_\pi^2 - m_e^2)^2}{(m_\pi^2 + m_\mu^2)\,(m_\pi^2 - m_\mu^2)^2} = 3.3 \tag{9-11.10}$$

The second-order matrix element is more complicated to compute; however, it contains essentially two factors: one corresponding to the first-step dissociation into the nucleon-antinucleon pair. This factor is common to both modes of decay and cancels out in the branching ratio. The second factor depends on the two legs of Puppi's triangle involved in the transitions, and for a *V-A* interaction it is proportional to $1 - (v/c)$. Expressing this factor through the masses of the particles involved, the branching ratio results:

$$\frac{\lambda_e}{\lambda_\mu} = \left(\frac{m_e}{m_\mu}\right)^2 \frac{(m_\pi^2 - m_e^2)^2}{(m_\pi^2 - m_\mu^2)^2} = 1.3 \times 10^{-4} \tag{9-11.11}$$

in excellent agreement with experiment.

The calculation of the absolute decay constant of the pion, which is beyond the scope of this book (see, for instance, Konopinski, 1959) confirms the universal Fermi interaction.

Another rare and particularly interesting mode of decay of the pion is

$$\pi^+ \to \pi^0 + e^+ + \nu_e$$

If we compare the particles involved to

$$n \to p + e^- + \bar{\nu}_e$$

the analogy with ordinary beta decay is apparent. This decay, which has been observed, has a branching ratio of the order of 10^{-8}, to be compared with the result of an exact calculation, based on the conserved-current hypothesis, giving 1.2×10^{-8}. The precise measurement would be important as a test of the conserved-current hypothesis.

The problem of whether or not all other weak interactions involving the so-called "strange particles" (see Chap. 15) can be fitted into this scheme or in a generalization of the Puppi triangle remains unsolved.

Bibliography

Allen, J. S., *The Neutrino*, Princeton University Press, Princeton, New Jersey, 1958.

Burgy, Krohn, Novey, Ringo, and Telegdi, "Measurements of Spatial Asymmetries in the Decay of Polarized Neutrons," *Phys. Rev.*, **120,** 1829 (1960).

Danby, Gaillard, Goulianos, Lederman, Mistry, Schwartz, and Steinberger, "Observation of High Energy Neutrino Reactions and the Existence of Two Kinds of Neutrinos," *Phys. Rev. Letters*, **9,** 36 (1962).

Davis, R., "The Attempt to Detect the Antineutrino from a Nuclear Reactor by the Cl^{37} ($\bar{\nu}$, e^-) A^{37} Reaction," *Phys. Rev.*, **97,** 766 (1955).

Dell'Antonio, G. F., and E. Fiorini, "Experiments and Theoretical Remarks on the Double β-decay," *Nuovo Cimento, Suppl.*, **17,** 132 (1961).

Deutsch, M., and O. Kofoed-Hansen, "Beta-Rays," in (Se 59), Vol. III.

Feinberg, G., and L. M. Lederman, "The Physics of Muons and Muon Neutrino," *Ann. Rev. Nucl. Sci.*, **13,** 431 (1963).

Feld, B. T., "Kinematics of β-Decay and Parity Non Conservation in Weak Interactions," *Phys. Rev.*, **107,** 797 (1957).

Fermi, E., "Tentativo d'una teoria dei raggi beta," *Nuovo Cimento*, **11,** 1 (1934).

Goldhaber, Grodzins, and Sunyar, "Helicity of Neutrinos," *Phys. Rev.*, **109,** 1015 (1958).

Inghram, M. G., and J. H. Reynolds, "Double Beta-Decay of Te^{130}," *Phys. Rev.*, **78,** 822 (1950).

Jackson, J. D. (Ja 58).

Konopinski, E. J., "The Experimental Clarification of the Laws of Beta-Radioactivity," *Ann. Rev. Nucl. Sci.*, **9,** 99 (1959).

Konopinski, E. J., and L. M. Langer, "The Experimental Clarification of the Theory of Beta Decay," *Ann. Rev. Nucl. Sci.*, **2,** 261 (1952).

Lee, T. D., and C. N. Yang, *Elementary Particles and Weak Interactions*, BNL 443, U.S. Department of Commerce, Office of Technical Services, Washington, D.C., October 1957.

Lipkin, H. J., *Beta Decay for Pedestrians*, Wiley-Interscience, New York, 1962.

Preston, M. A. (P 62).

Reines, F., "Neutrino Interactions," *Ann. Rev. Nucl. Sci.*, **10,** 1 (1960).

Reines, F., and C. L. Cowan, Jr., "Measurement of the Free Antineutrino Absorption Cross Section by Protons," *Phys. Rev.*, **113,** 273 (1959).

Siegbahn, K. (Si 55).

Telegdi, V., "The Experimental Status of the Weak Interactions of Non-Strange Particles," in *Proceedings of the Tenth Annual Rochester Conference on High Energy Physics*, Wiley-Interscience, New York, 1961, pp. 713–725.

Wick, G. C., "Invariance Principles of Nuclear Physics," *Ann. Rev. Nucl. Sci.*, **8,** 1 (1958).

Wu, C. S., "The Neutrino," in *Theoretical Physics in the Twentieth Century*, M. Fierz and V. F. Weisskopf (eds.), Wiley-Interscience, New York, 1960.

Wu, Ambler, Hayward, Hoppes, and Hudson, "Experimental Test of Parity Conservation in β-Decay," *Phys. Rev.*, **105,** 1413 (1957).

Wu, C. S., "The Universal Fermi Interaction and the Conserved Vector Current in Beta Decay," *Rev. Mod. Phys.*, **36,** 618 (1964).

Problems

9-1 Suppose that the cross section for the interaction of neutrinos with either protons or neutrons is 10^{-43} cm^2 per nucleon. Taking the mean density of the earth as 5 g cm^{-3} and the radius as 6×10^6 m, what is the probability that a neutrino will pass through the interior of the earth *without* interacting along the way?

9-2 The nucleus $_{30}Zn^{62}$ can decay either by positron emission or by K capture. The maximum kinetic energy for the positron is 0.66 MeV. (a) Calculate the maximum neutrino energy in positron decay. (b) Calculate the neutrino energy emitted in K capture. Neglect recoil and electron binding-energy corrections.

9-3 (a) A certain number of nuclei can decay by electron emission, by positron emission, and by electron capture. Give arguments to show that only odd Z, even A nuclei can have this property. (b) $_{29}Cu^{64}$ is such a nucleus. From the atomic masses given below, calculate (i) the maximum β^+ and β^- kinetic energies, (ii) the neutrino energy in electron capture, and (iii) the kinetic energy of the recoil nucleus in electron capture. Relevant atomic masses:

$_{29}Cu^{64}$	63.92976 amu
$_{28}Ni^{64}$	63.92796 amu
$_{30}Zn^{64}$	63.92914 amu

9-4 In what energy interval is L capture possible, K capture impossible? See whether you can find any example of this phenomenon.

9-5 Re^{187} decays by electron emission into Os^{187}. The energy of the decay is 2 keV. As a consequence, the interactions between the decay electron and the atomic electrons (negligible in ordinary cases) significantly affect the decay constant. Estimate the effects.

9-6 Calculate the allowed *energy* distribution of beta-decay electrons, assuming that the neutrino has a very small rest mass m_ν. Show that for energies near the upper limit, the shape of the distribution changes markedly from that obtained in the case of $m_\nu = 0$.

9-7 Estimate the difference between the decay constants of neutral Be^7 and twice-ionized Be^7, using even crudely approximate wave functions. Suppose that it were possible to produce Be^{7+++}. What would be its mean life?

9-8 Show that the muon and neutron decay give the same value of g.

9-9 Suppose we want to show that in beta decay only one neutrino is emitted (and not, say, two). Calculate the electron momentum distribution when two neutrinos are emitted. (*Note:* In this case, the momentum of the electron does not determine the momenta of the two neutrinos, and in the phase-space distribution both the electron momentum and one of the neutrino momenta enter as variables. To get the expected electron distribution, it is necessary to integrate over values of the neutrino momentum.)

9-10 Plot the form of a beta spectrum as a function of momentum or energy. How does one pass from the data obtained directly from a magnetic spectrometer to a Kurie plot?

9-11 Calculate the GT-matrix element for the neutron and show that it is 3.

9-12 Calculate the F-matrix element for the neutron and show that it is 1.

9-13 Show that from Fig. 9-12 one obtains the Kurie plot of Fig. 9-13.

CHAPTER X

The Two-Body Systems and Nuclear Forces

In this chapter we shall begin to deal with specific nuclear forces. The nature of these forces is still incompletely understood, and it is impossible to present them in a closed deductive form, as one can electromagnetic forces. We shall use instead a semiempirical approach, starting from the simplest facts. The scattering of neutrons on protons and the binding of the nuclei show immediately that nonelectromagnetic forces must be involved. Scattering experiments show also that these forces have short range; that is, their "sphere of influence" has a radius of the order of 10^{-13} cm. Their intensity over such short distances is large compared with that of electric forces, otherwise nuclei would disintegrate under the Coulomb repulsion of the protons.

The facts, summarized in the semiempirical mass formula of Chap. 6, also allow us to draw several other conclusions in regard to nuclear forces, most notably that the binding energy of a nucleus is proportional to the number of nucleons and that the density of nuclear matter is approximately constant. This leads us to conclude that nuclear forces have a "saturation property" similar to the one exhibited by the forces that act between molecules in solids and liquids.

The Yukawa theory postulates that nuclear forces are due to a field, the quanta of which are the pi mesons. From this point of view the first step in studying nuclear forces should be the investigation of the pion-nucleon interaction. One should then be able to derive the nucleon-nucleon interaction. This program has not been completed as yet, and it involves a number of complications.

To surmount the various difficulties one at a time, we shall start with phenomenologically the simplest problem: the interaction between two nucleons. The study of the neutron-proton system, in which there are no complications raised by electromagnetic forces (the purely magnetic spin-spin interaction is negligible) or by Pauli's principle, will be our first step. We shall at first neglect spin, although later we shall be forced to introduce it in order to account for the experimental facts. The comparison of the results for the neutron-proton system with those for the proton-proton system will lead us to introduce the concept of isotopic spin. Finally we shall consider the extension of the results obtained to systems containing more than two nucleons. The treatment will be essentially phenomenological. The connection with meson theory will be sketched in Chap. 14.

10-1 The Deuteron

The empirical facts about the deuteron are: binding energy, 2.22452 ± 0.00020 MeV; spin 1; magnetic moment, 0.85741 nuclear magnetons; electric quadrupole moment $+2.74 \times 10^{-27}$ cm². Moreover, we have extensive and precise data on the neutron-proton scattering cross section and on the photodisintegration of the deuteron over a large interval of energies.

The simplest possible model of a bound neutron-proton system (that is, of a deuteron) is obtained by considering an attractive force between them, having a square-well potential of radius r_0 and depth V_0. The binding energy makes necessary a relation between r_0 and V_0 (Fig. 10-1).

Because we shall find that the potential depends on the relative spin orientation, we shall indicate its depth by V_t for triplet states and by V_s for singlet states.

The value of the spin of the deuteron and the value of the magnetic moment, which is nearly the sum of the magnetic moments of the proton

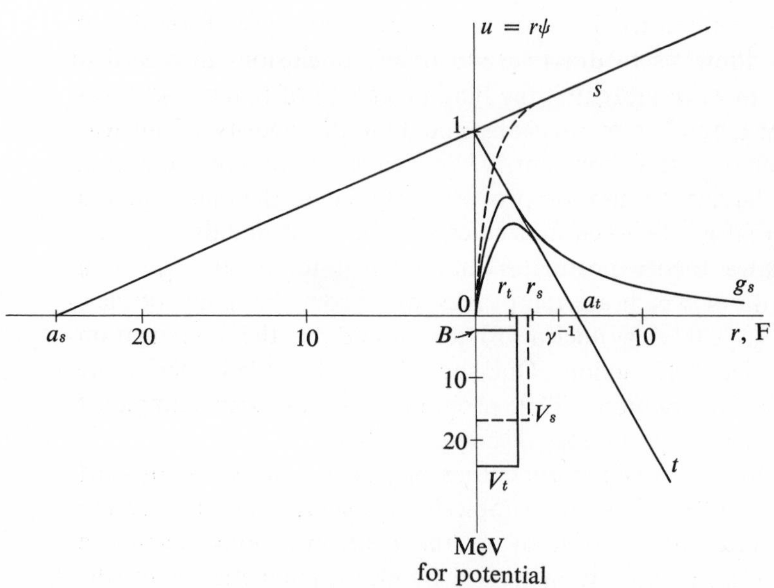

Figure 10-1 Potential well and eigenfunction for rectangular well. *s*, singlet-state eigenfunction, zero energy; *t*, triplet-state eigenfunction, zero energy normalized as indicated in text; g_s, ground-state eigenfunction (not normalized). $B = 2.226$ MeV.

radius of well $r_t = 2.04$ F $\quad V_t = -25.5$ MeV
radius of well $r_s = 2.37$ F $\quad V_s = -16.6$ MeV
$\gamma^{-1} = 4.32$ F

and neutron, show that the orbital motion in the ground state of the deuteron has angular momentum 0, and that the spins are parallel. Thus, we expect the deuteron ground state to be a $^3S_1$ state. However, this assumption cannot be strictly true, because it would rule out an electric quadrupole moment, the expectation value of

$$\langle {}^3S_1 | 3z^2 - r^2 | {}^3S_1 \rangle$$

being 0 for a spherically symmetric eigenfunction. We must conclude that our assumption is only approximately correct. In fact, the eigenfunction of the ground state of the deuteron assigns a probability of 0.07 to finding a $^3D_1$ state and a probability of 0.93 to finding a $^3S_1$ state.

There might also be a finite probability of finding a $^3P_1$ state of opposite parity, because weak interactions do not conserve parity, but quantitatively this effect is negligible.

The Schrödinger equation for the system in a $^3S_1$ state is then

$$\frac{d^2u}{dr^2} + \frac{2\mu}{\hbar^2}(E - V_t)u = 0 \tag{10-1.1}$$

where μ is the reduced mass $M_pM_n/(M_p + M_n) \simeq M/2$, $u = r\psi(r)$, and r is the distance between the nucleons. If E is negative, the state is bound and $-E$ is the binding energy. The solution of Eq. (10-1.1) for the square-well potential is

$$\begin{aligned} u &= A \sin k_t r \qquad & r \leqslant r_0 \qquad & k_t = \frac{1}{\hbar}[M(E - V_t)]^{1/2} \\ u &= Be^{-\gamma(r-r_0)} \qquad & r \geqslant r_0 \qquad & \gamma = \frac{1}{\hbar}(M|E|)^{1/2} \end{aligned} \tag{10-1.2}$$

and the continuity condition (which requires that u and u' are continuous) applied at $r = r_0$ gives

$$\frac{u'(r_0)}{u(r_0)} = k_t \cot k_t r_0 = -\gamma$$

and also

$$A = B\left(\frac{V_t}{E - V_t}\right)^{1/2} \tag{10-1.3}$$

The binding energy of the deuteron immediately gives [Eq. (10-1.2)]

$$\gamma = 2.32 \times 10^{12}\ \text{cm}^{-1}$$

The relation between the binding energy and r_0 and V_t gives V_t if r_0 is known. Experiments on neutron-proton collisions at an energy of several MeV give an approximate value of r_0 of the order of 10^{-13} cm $= 1$ F. Electron scattering experiments have given (see Chap. 6) a radius of the same order of magnitude. For the sake of definiteness we shall assume that $r_0 = 2.8$ F, which corresponds to twice the Compton wavelength $\hbar/m_\pi c$ of the pion. This is a reasonable value from the point of view of meson theory (see Chap. 14).

Insertion of this value in Eq. (10-1.3) gives

$$V_t = -21 \text{ MeV} \tag{10-1.4}$$

The normalized eigenfunction corresponding to somewhat better numerical values is plotted in Fig. 10-1. The normalization requires

$$4\pi A^2 \int_0^{r_0} \sin^2 kr\, dr + 4\pi B^2 \int_{r_0}^{\infty} e^{-2\gamma(r-r_0)}\, dr = 1 \tag{10-1.5}$$

With the values of r_0 and γ as given above, the second integral is about twice as large as the first. Hence, the nucleons in the deuteron spend only one-third of the time within the range of the nuclear force; two-thirds of the time they are at a distance larger than r_0. A crude but simple approximation to the normalized wave function is

$$u(r) = \left(\frac{\gamma}{2\pi}\right)^{1/2} e^{-\gamma r} \tag{10-1.6}$$

$1/\gamma$ can be called the "radius" of the deuteron (4.32 F). This calculation was made with a special form of the potential well. However, a good part of the results obtained are independent of this special form. An elegant mathematical development without unnecessary assumptions about the form of the potential well will be found in Appendix E.

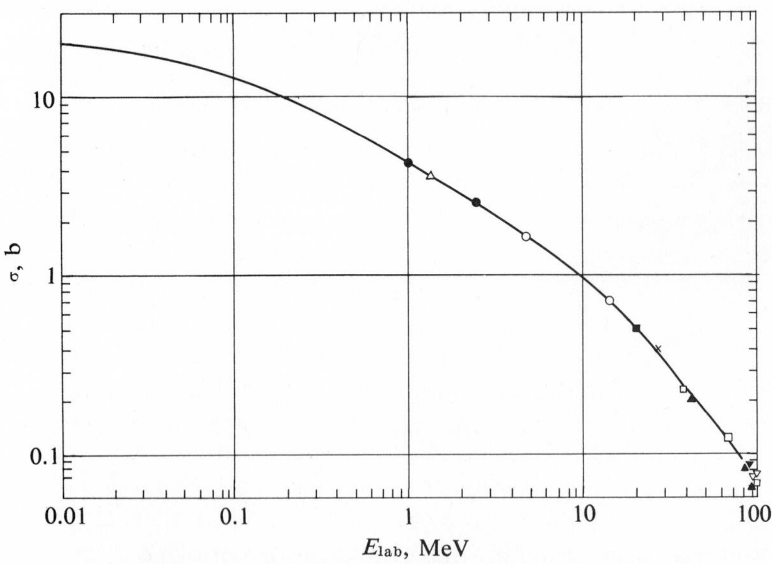

Figure 10-2 Total cross section of hydrogen atoms for neutron energies between 10^4 eV and 100 MeV. The total cross section in this energy interval is practically identical to the elastic cross section. At low energies the elastic cross section tends to 20.3 b and the capture cross section is 0.33 $[2{,}200/v_{(\text{m sec}^{-1})}]$ b, until one reaches energies comparable to the energy of the chemical bond of hydrogen (1 eV). Log-log plot. Energies and cross sections in the laboratory system.

We can use the value (obtained above) of the depth of the potential well to calculate neutron-proton scattering at low energy, i.e., under conditions such that only s waves are important ($\lambda\!\!\!^{-} \gg r_0$). Numerically $\lambda\!\!\!^{-}=9.10/E^{1/2}$, where $\lambda\!\!\!^{-}$ is in fermis and E is the laboratory kinetic energy in MeV.

Measurements of the total n-p cross section have been made at many energies because they are practically and theoretically important. Figure 10-2 gives the results. The substances employed are always hydrogenous compounds or liquid hydrogen: it is impractical to use atomic hydrogen. As it turns out, when the energy of the neutrons is smaller than or comparable to the energy of the chemical bond of the hydrogen atom, the molecule acts as a whole and the scattering cross section is increased, approximately by a factor of 4, over the value that would obtain for a free atom. The reason for the fourfold increase will be discussed in Chap. 12. To avoid complications due to the chemical bond, we shall compare cross sections at energies of several electron volts. In this region we have a value of 20.3 barns for $1 < E < 1{,}000$ eV, constant within 1 or 2 per cent. Here $\lambda\!\!\!^{-}$ is still very large compared with the range of nuclear forces, a condition which ensures that there is only s-wave ($l = 0$) scattering. The result of the comparison is that the experimental scattering cross section seems incompatible with the potential well given above for the ground state ($^3S_1$) of the deuteron. However, Wigner has pointed out that in n-p scattering the $^1S_0$ state is also important, and it is possible to reconcile the results of the scattering experiments with the deuteron binding energy if we give to the potential well in the $^1S_0$ state a depth of 11.5 MeV, instead of the 21 MeV found for the triplet state, assuming the same value of the well radius r_0. This means that the n-p force is strongly spin-dependent.

The following will justify the statements made above. Using a result of scattering theory (see Appendix D), we have

$$\sigma = 4\pi\lambda\!\!\!^{-2} \sin^2 \delta_0 \qquad \textbf{(10-2.1)}$$

where δ_0 is the s-wave phase shift. This can easily be calculated for a square well. If $E \ll V(r)$, we can approximate the wave function with two sine curves, one of which will correspond to the inside of the well and will have a wavelength much shorter than that of the exterior part of the wave function. In other words, inside the well ($r < r_0$) the wave function will be curved. Outside the well ($r > r_0$) it will become practically a straight line. The slope of the straight line at $r = r_0$ is obtained by writing the function u for $r < r_0$ where it obeys Eq. (10-1.1) for zero energy ($E \rightarrow 0$),

$$u'' - \frac{2\mu V_t}{\hbar^2} u = 0 \qquad -V_t = 21 \text{ MeV for } r < r_0 \qquad \textbf{(10-2.2)}$$

Its solution is

$$u = A \sin k_t r$$

with

$$k_t = \frac{(-2\mu V_t)^{1/2}}{\hbar} = \frac{(21)^{1/2}}{4.5 \times 10^{-13}} \text{ cm}^{-1} \simeq 10^{13} \text{ cm}^{-1} \qquad \textbf{(10-2.3)}$$

The index t on k and V reminds us that we are referring to the triplet state (ground state of the deuteron).

For $r > r_0$ the wave function in the limit of zero energy is $C(r - a_t)$; it thus intercepts the r axis at abscissa $r = a_t$. The quantity a_t is called the (triplet) "scattering length." (Some writers use a definition of scattering length differing in sign from this one. This is especially true of recent work in high-energy physics.) Joining the two functions at $r = r_0$, we have

$$\frac{u'(r_0)}{u(r_0)} = k_t \cot k_t r_0 = \frac{1}{r_0 - a_t} \qquad \textbf{(10-2.4)}$$

or

$$a_t = r_0 - \frac{1}{k_t} \tan k_t r_0 = r_0 \left(1 - \frac{1}{k_t r_0} \tan k_t r_0\right) \qquad \textbf{(10-2.5)}$$

Now consideration of Fig. 10-1 shows that the phase shift δ_0 is simply $-a_t/\lambda\!\!\!^{-}$. The straight line representing u is the limit for $\lambda\!\!\!^{-} \to \infty$ of a sine curve with wavelength $2\pi\lambda\!\!\!^{-}$; and this sine curve starts, not from the origin, but from a point of abscissa a_t. The sine function is thus

$$\sin\left(\frac{r}{\lambda\!\!\!^{-}} - \frac{a_t}{\lambda\!\!\!^{-}}\right) \qquad \textbf{(10-2.6)}$$

which means a phase shift

$$\delta_0 = \frac{-a_t}{\lambda\!\!\!^{-}} \qquad \textbf{(10-2.7)}$$

and hence a limiting value for $\lambda\!\!\!^{-} \to \infty$ of the cross section

$$\sigma_t = 4\pi\lambda\!\!\!^{-2} \sin^2 \delta_0 \to 4\pi a_t^2 \qquad \textbf{(10-2.8)}$$

Using the value of k_t corresponding to the potential derived from the binding energy of the deuteron ($V_t = 21$ MeV) and the usual $r_0 = 2.8$ F, we obtain $\sigma = 4.4$ barns, instead of the experimental value of 20.36 ± 0.05 barns. Reasonable variations of r_0 do not modify this result appreciably. We have, therefore, an apparent contradiction.

The way out was indicated by Wigner (1935), who noted that the scattering occurs not only in the triplet state, but in the singlet state as well. The binding energy of the deuteron gives information only about the triplet state; if the forces are spin-dependent, the singlet potential may be different from the triplet one. We use then the observed cross section to determine the singlet potential.

In collisions where the statistical weights determine the relative probability of singlet and triplet states (that is, for unpolarized beams on unpolarized targets), the singlet and triplet states are represented in the ratio of 1:3, as shown in Sec. 6-4. The cross section will then be

$$\sigma = \tfrac{1}{4}\,\sigma_s + \tfrac{3}{4}\,\sigma_t \qquad \textbf{(10-2.9)}$$

where σ_s and σ_t indicate the cross section in singlet and triplet states. We can use the calculated value $\sigma_t = 4.4$ barns and the experimental information on σ to calculate σ_s, and hence V_s. To fit the experimental data, we must have (in barns)

$$20.36 = \tfrac{3}{4}\,(4.4) + \tfrac{1}{4}\,\sigma_s \qquad \textbf{(10-2.10)}$$

from which $\sigma_s = 4\pi a_s^2 = 68$ barns and $|a_s| = 23.6$ F. This value of a_s can be inserted in Eq. (10-2.5) or better, in its equivalent for a_s, to find

$$k_s = \frac{(2\mu|V_s|)^{1/2}}{\hbar} = 5.28 \times 10^{12}\ \text{cm}^{-1} \qquad \text{and} \qquad V_s = -11.5\ \text{MeV} \tag{10-2.11}$$

The sign of a_s is not determined by the simple measurement of the cross section, which gives only a_s^2. To obtain the sign, one uses interference effects appearing in scattering from ortho- and parahydrogen, and one finds that a_s is negative, whereas the sign of a_t is positive (see Chap. 12).

The scattering-length concept can be extended to energies other than 0 by defining the scattering length through the relation

$$-ka(k) = \tan\delta_0 \tag{10-2.12}$$

which for $k \to 0$ agrees with Eq. (10-2.7). With this definition of $a(k)$, Eq. (10-2.8) gives

$$\sigma = \frac{4\pi}{k^2}\frac{1}{1+\cot^2\delta_0} = \frac{4\pi}{k^2 + a^{-2}(k)} \tag{10-2.13}$$

Equation (10-2.13) is convenient and shows that the knowledge of $a(k)$ is sufficient to determine completely the s-wave scattering.

In general $a(k)$ can be approximated by a simple and important formula that is the generalization for $k \neq 0$ of Eq. (10-2.7).

$$\frac{1}{a(k)} = -k\cot\delta_0 = \frac{1}{a(0)} - \frac{1}{2}r_0k^2 + \cdots \tag{10-2.14}$$

where r_0 is called the "effective range" of the potential (see Appendix E). Equation (10-2.14) is only approximate, but its next term would be in $k^4r_0^3$ with a small coefficient (~ 0.10). The physical meaning of the effective range corresponds to the mean distance of interaction between neutron and proton. The effective range is not to be confused with the width of a rectangular well [r_0 of Eq. (10-2.5)] or the length parameter in other forms of the potential, although for a given potential the two quantities are related and often of nearly the same magnitude. It is noteworthy that in this excellent approximation the whole neutron-proton scattering at low energy is described by two parameters: scattering length and effective range. Low-energy measurements cannot provide more than these two numbers.

The effective range approximation has been generalized to extend to waves with $l \neq 0$ and to systems other than the nucleon-nucleon. It is a powerful way of describing many scattering phenomena. It can also be formally extended to the bound state of the deuteron, for which γ [Eq. (10-1.3)] corresponds to $1/a_t(k)$, as Fig. 10-1 shows. For the bound state k is imaginary and equal to $i|\gamma|$, and Eq. (10-2.14) becomes

$$\gamma = a^{-1} + \tfrac{1}{2}r_0\gamma^2 + \cdots \tag{10-2.15}$$

If the last term is negligible compared with the others, then the radiu of the deuteron is equal to the scattering length. This refers, of cours to the bound triplet state.

Detailed comparisons with experiments with all refinements on th approximations have given the following values for the a's and r (Engelke et al., 1963):

$$a_t = 5.400 \pm 0.011 \text{ F} \qquad r_{0,t} = 1.732 \pm 0.014 \text{ F}$$

$$a_s = -23.677 \pm 0.029 \text{ F} \qquad r_{0,s} = 2.46 \pm 0.12 \text{ F}$$

These values summarize all the information obtainable from low-energ (< 10 MeV) neutron-proton scattering. The value of $\gamma = 0.232 \times 10$ cm^{-1} is obtainable from these data and Eq. (10-2.15). Figure 10- shows the separate contributions of singlet and triplet scattering com puted from the above constants and the experimental total cross sectio

10-3 Proton-Proton System and Scattering

In passing from the neutron-proton to the proton-proton syste we find two main differences: (1) to the specific nuclear forces we mus add the Coulomb repulsion; (2) the identity of the protons entai some quantum-mechanical complication (Mott, 1930). We shall firs consider point 2.

A first important consequence of Pauli's principle for the proton proton system is that it can exist only in states of ^1S, ^3P, ^1D, etc. T prove this statement, consider the spherical-harmonic part of th eigenfunction. On exchange of the protons, or, which is the same, o changing θ into $\pi - \theta$, the spherical harmonic is multiplied by $(-1)^l$

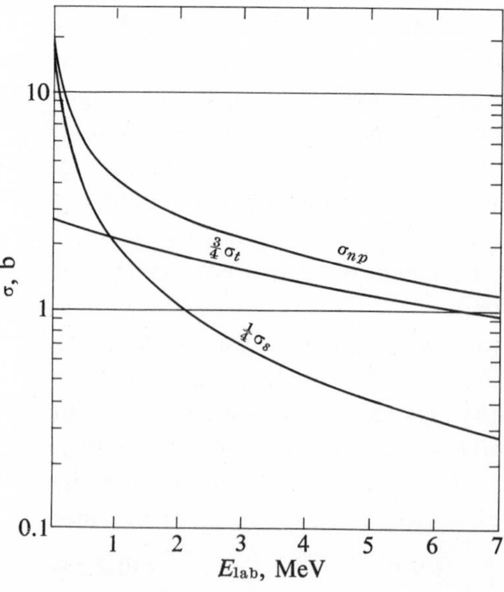

Figure 10-3 The neutron-proto scattering cross section σ_{np} ha two components: the single scattering ($\frac{1}{4}\sigma_s$) and the triple scattering ($\frac{3}{4}\sigma_t$). The two contri butions, as well as their sum, ar shown on the figure for the follow ing values of the parameters triplet state, $a_t = 5.40$ F, $r_{ot} =$ 1.73 F; singlet state, $a_s = -$ 23.7 F, $r_{os} = 2.5$ F. Ordinate i log scale. [From (BW 52).]

where l is the orbital angular momentum. As a consequence the spin eigenfunction must be singlet for l even or triplet for l odd so that the complete eigenfunction can change its sign as required by Pauli's principle.

Furthermore, we have seen that the scattering cross section is related to $f(\theta)$ of Appendix D by

$$\frac{d\sigma}{d\omega} = |f(\theta)|^2 \tag{10-3.1}$$

Consider now two *distinguishable* particles of the same mass. In the center-of-mass system, the probability that either will be scattered through an angle θ is

$$|f(\theta)|^2 + |f(\pi - \theta)|^2 \tag{10-3.2}$$

(see Fig. 10-4). However, if the particles are *identical*, their waves interfere; and instead of summing the squares of the amplitudes, we must first sum the amplitudes and then square them. Moreover, the eigenfunction must be symmetrical or antisymmetrical with respect to the exchange of the particles, according to whether they are bosons or fermions (see Chap. 6). The portion of the eigenfunctions containing only spatial coordinates, without spin, will then be

$$f(\theta) \pm f(\pi - \theta) \tag{10-3.3}$$

Exchange of the two proton coordinates means exchanging θ with $\pi - \theta$, as shown in Fig. 10-4. If the plus sign is used in Eq. (10-3.3), the expression is symmetrical with respect to the exchange of the coordinates; if the minus sign is used, the expression is antisymmetrical with respect to the same exchange. We have already seen that the spins give a symmetrical eigenfunction in the triplet state and an antisymmetrical eigenfunction in the singlet states [Eqs. (6-4.13) and (6-4.14)]. For protons

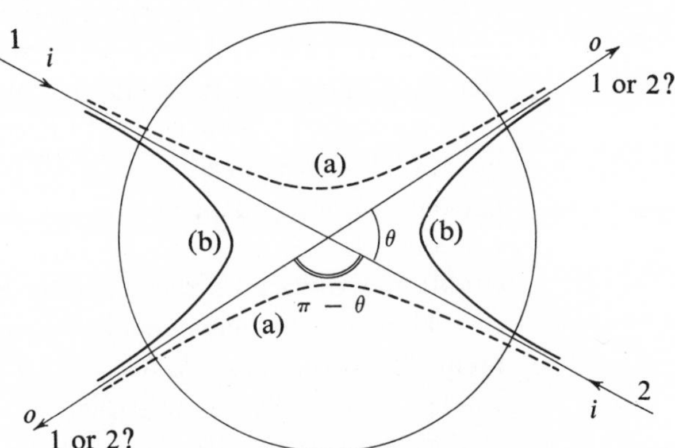

Figure 10-4 Scattering of identical particles. Incoming particles 1 and 2 move in directions marked i, outgoing in directions marked o. Classically one can follow the trajectories and distinguish case (a) corresponding to scattering by an angle θ from case (b) corresponding to scattering by an angle $\pi - \theta$. Quantum mechanically, trajectories are meaningless. One must consider wave functions symmetrical or antisymmetrical with respect to the exchange of the particles.

the total eigenfunction must be antisymmetrical; hence the triplet states will be associated with

$$f(\theta) - f(\pi - \theta) \tag{10-3.4}$$

and the singlet states will be associated with

$$f(\theta) + f(\pi - \theta) \tag{10-3.5}$$

The scattering cross section in triplet states is thus

$$\frac{d\sigma_t}{d\omega} = |f(\theta) - f(\pi - \theta)|^2 = |f(\theta)|^2 + |f(\pi - \theta)|^2 - 2\,\mathrm{Re}[f(\theta)\,f^*(\pi - \theta)] \tag{10-3.6}$$

and in singlet states it is

$$\frac{d\sigma_s}{d\omega} = |f(\theta) + f(\pi - \theta)|^2 = |f(\theta)|^2 + |f(\pi - \theta)|^2 + 2\,\mathrm{Re}[f(\theta)f^*(\pi - \theta)] \tag{10-3.7}$$

At very low energy the Coulomb repulsion is the most important force acting in the *p-p* system because the nucleons do not approach sufficiently to feel the nuclear forces. The scattering can then be calculated exactly, but the method of partial waves (Appendix D) is not applicable, because the potential does not decrease rapidly enough with *r*.

We shall present only the result of the calculation of $f(\theta)$:

$$f(\theta) = \frac{e^2}{Mv^2 \sin^2(\theta/2)} \exp\left(-\,i\eta \log \sin^2 \frac{\theta}{2}\right) \tag{10-3.8}$$

with $\eta = e^2/\hbar v$. M is the proton mass and v the relative velocity of the protons. Replacing Eq. (10-3.8) in Eq. (10-3.6), we obtain a σ_s and a σ_t. These must be added with the statistical weights $\frac{1}{4}$ and $\frac{3}{4}$, as in the *n-p* case. The final result, in the center-of-mass system, is

$$\left(\frac{d\sigma}{d\omega}\right)_c = \left(\frac{e^2}{Mv^2}\right)^2 \left[\frac{1}{\sin^4(\theta/2)} + \frac{1}{\cos^4(\theta/2)} - \frac{\cos[\eta \log \tan^2(\theta/2)]}{\cos^2(\theta/2)\sin^2(\theta/2)}\right] \tag{10-3.9}$$

The first two terms on the right represent the classical Rutherford scattering; the third term is a quantum-mechanical interference term. A similar term, but of opposite sign, occurs in the scattering of alpha particles in helium, as was demonstrated experimentally by Chadwick, Blackett, and Champion (1930). Note that the numerator of the third term is nearly 1 for protons of energy larger than 1 MeV and for angles not too close to 0 or 90°. A striking example of the effect of the identity between target and projectile is shown in Fig. 10-5. For nonidentical particles the third term of Eq. (10-3.9) would be missing and the equation would give the classical Rutherford scattering.

Thus far we have neglected specific nuclear forces. To include them, at low energy, we need consider only *s* waves or, more precisely, singlet *s* waves, since the triplet *s* state is ruled out by Pauli's principle. If they were the only ones present, without Coulomb force, the cross section would be given by an equation similar to Eq. (10-2.8). The amplitude $f(\theta)$ is then modified by the Coulomb force to

$$f(\theta) = \frac{e^2}{Mv^2} \frac{\exp[-i\eta \log \sin^2(\theta/2)]}{\sin^2(\theta/2)} + \frac{i}{2k}(e^{2i\delta_0} - 1)$$

From this we calculate the cross section, obtaining a term $(d\sigma/d\omega)_c$ as before, a term linear in $\sin 2\delta_0$ and a term containing $\sin^2 \delta_0$:

$$\left(\frac{d\sigma}{d\omega}\right) = \left(\frac{d\sigma}{d\omega}\right)_c + \left(\frac{e^2}{Mv^2}\right)^2 \left[\frac{2\hbar v}{e^2} \frac{\sin 2\delta_0}{2 \sin^2 \theta} + \left(\frac{2\hbar v}{e^2}\right)^2 \sin^2 \delta_0\right]$$

We have here assumed that the argument of the exponential is small ($E > 1$ MeV for $0.1 < \theta \ll \pi$). This can be compared with experiment to find δ_0.

The experimental data are analyzed further along lines similar to those used in neutron-proton scattering but are complicated considerably by the presence of the Coulomb force. A scattering length and an effective range for the $^1S_0$ state are derived, and then one asks the interesting question: What value would they have if it were possible to suppress the Coulomb interaction, leaving the specific nuclear force unchanged? The result would be

$$\begin{aligned} &\text{Scattering length: } -17.2 \pm 0.3 \text{ F} \\ &\text{Effective range: } 2.65 \pm 0.07 \text{ F} \end{aligned} \qquad \textbf{(10-3.10)}$$

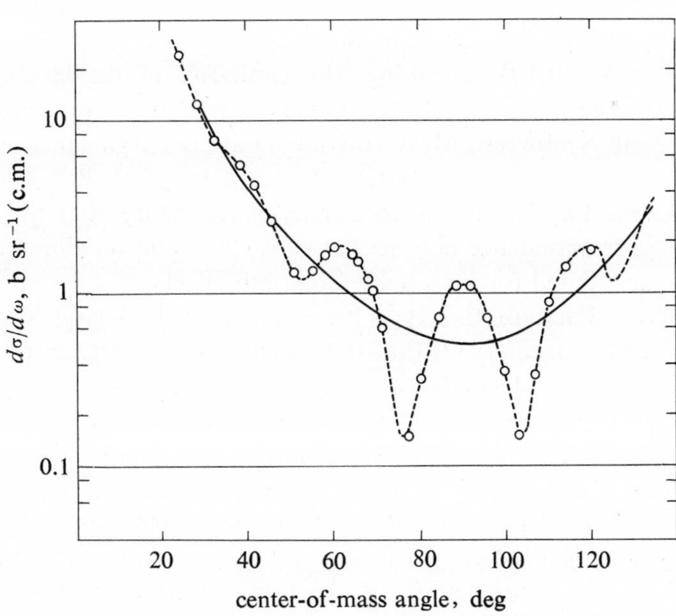

Figure 10-5 Carbon-carbon elastic scattering. Typical angular distributions for C^{12} elastically scattered from carbon at a c.m. energy of 5 MeV. The Rutherford and Mott scattering predictions (solid and dashed curves) differ only in that the latter includes the quantum-mechanical interference term arising from the identity of the incident and target nuclei. [From Bromley, Kuehner, and Almqvist, *Phys. Rev. Letters*, **4**, 365 (1960).]

These values are very close to the corresponding values for the *n-p* system. Indeed the similarities between *n-p* and *p-p* scattering were among the first indications (Breit, 1936) that the *n-p* and *p-p* nuclear forces might be identical.

It must be noted that the negative scattering length implies that even apart from the electrostatic repulsion, the $^1S_0$ state of the *p-p* system is unbound, as is the corresponding state of the *n-p* system. This conclusion extends to the *n-n* system if the *n-n* force, apart from the electrostatic repulsion, is the same as the *p-p* force.

10-4 Charge Independence of Nuclear Forces

The virtual identity of the *n-p* and *p-p* forces, shown in the low-energy scattering experiments mentioned above, manifests itself also in the properties of mirror nuclei, such as H^3 and He^3, Li^7, Be^7, etc., which are obtained one from the other by transforming all neutrons into protons, and vice versa. It is true that Coulomb forces are necessarily different in mirror nuclei, but apart from that, the nuclear levels show a remarkable similarity, as seen in Fig. 10-6. If we examine mirror nuclei of $N = Z \pm 1$, we find that, once correction is made for the electrostatic energy, the nuclei have the same mass. More precisely, we should expect, for the mass difference between two nuclei with $N = Z \pm 1$,

$$\Delta M = \frac{6e^2Z}{5R} = \frac{6e^2Z}{5r_0A^{1/3}} \tag{10-4.1}$$

where R is the nuclear radius. That this is indeed true is shown in Fig. 10-6. Strictly speaking, the similarity of the levels of mirror nuclei of the type $N = Z \pm 1$ tells us only that there is equality between *n-n* and *p-p* forces. More convincing are the arguments derived from nuclei with A even, such as He^6, Li^6, and Be^6; Li^8, Be^8, and B^8; or C^{10}, B^{10}, and Be^{10}; some of their energy levels are shown in Fig. 10-7. The correspondence between levels is clear, and the differences in energy are accounted for mainly by Coulomb effects.

Facts of this type have suggested to Heisenberg and to Condon and Cassen (1932) that the specific nuclear forces should be considered "charge-independent." The forces between *n-p*, *p-p*, and *n-n*, apart from electromagnetic effects, are assumed to be the same. This assumption is stronger than the assumption of charge symmetry, which postulates the equality of *n-n* and *p-p* forces but says nothing concerning *n-p* forces. There are many other phenomena supporting the charge-independence hypothesis and extending it to pi-meson physics as well. On the other hand, we must remember that charge independence is only approximate, because it obviously does not take into account electromagnetic effects or the neutron-proton mass difference.

To exploit the hypothesis fully we treat it by the isotopic spin formalism, which is its appropriate mathematical formulation. A nucleon is endowed with another degree of freedom besides the ordinary ones of

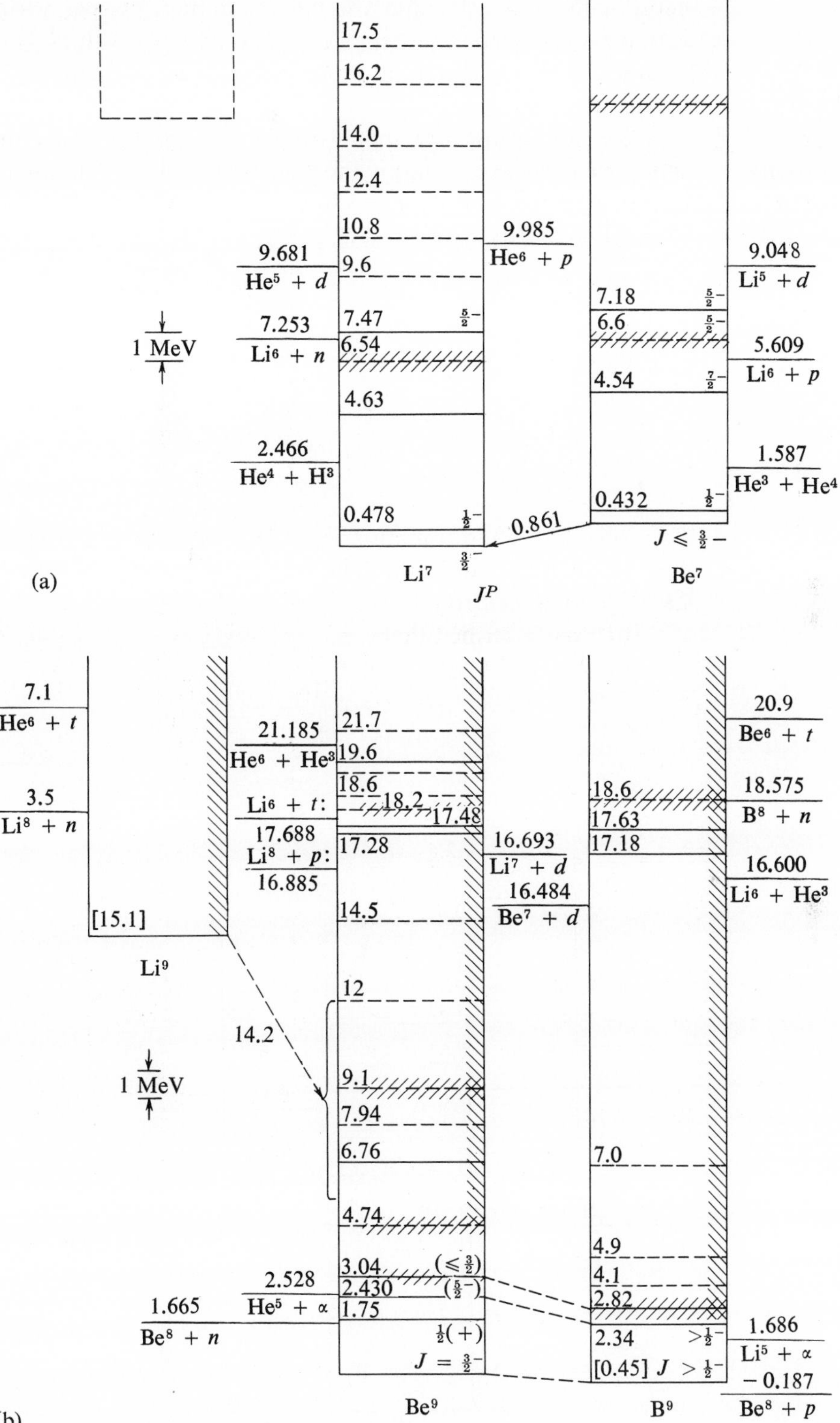

Figure 10-6 Mirror nuclei. Nuclear levels in mirror nuclei ($N = Z \pm 1$): Li^7, Be^7; Li^9, Be^9, B^9.

coordinates and spin, and the corresponding internal variable, called isotopic spin, isospin, or i spin, can take only two values, i.e., is "dichotomic." The nucleon is a proton or a neutron, depending upon its value.

We already have a model of dichotomic variables, the ordinary spin for a particle of spin $\frac{1}{2}$ in the Pauli treatment, which, we shall assume, is known to the reader. The i-spin function can take two values, which we shall write as

$$\begin{vmatrix} 1 \\ 0 \end{vmatrix} \equiv \pi \quad \text{or} \quad \begin{vmatrix} 0 \\ 1 \end{vmatrix} \equiv \nu \tag{10-4.2}$$

and the i-spin operators are

$$\tau_1 = \tfrac{1}{2}\begin{vmatrix} 0 & 1 \\ 1 & 0 \end{vmatrix} \qquad \tau_2 = \tfrac{1}{2}\begin{vmatrix} 0 & -i \\ +i & 0 \end{vmatrix} \qquad \tau_3 = \tfrac{1}{2}\begin{vmatrix} 1 & 0 \\ 0 & -1 \end{vmatrix} \qquad 1 = \begin{vmatrix} 1 & 0 \\ 0 & 1 \end{vmatrix} \tag{10-4.3}$$

They obey the same commutation relations and are a perfect analog to the spin matrices of Pauli. The state $\left|\begin{smallmatrix} 1 \\ 0 \end{smallmatrix}\right|$ corresponds to a proton, the state $\left|\begin{smallmatrix} 0 \\ 1 \end{smallmatrix}\right|$ to a neutron.

It is easily verified that

$$(\tau_1 - i\tau_2)\begin{vmatrix} 1 \\ 0 \end{vmatrix} = \tau_- \begin{vmatrix} 1 \\ 0 \end{vmatrix} = \begin{vmatrix} 0 \\ 1 \end{vmatrix} \tag{10-4.4}$$

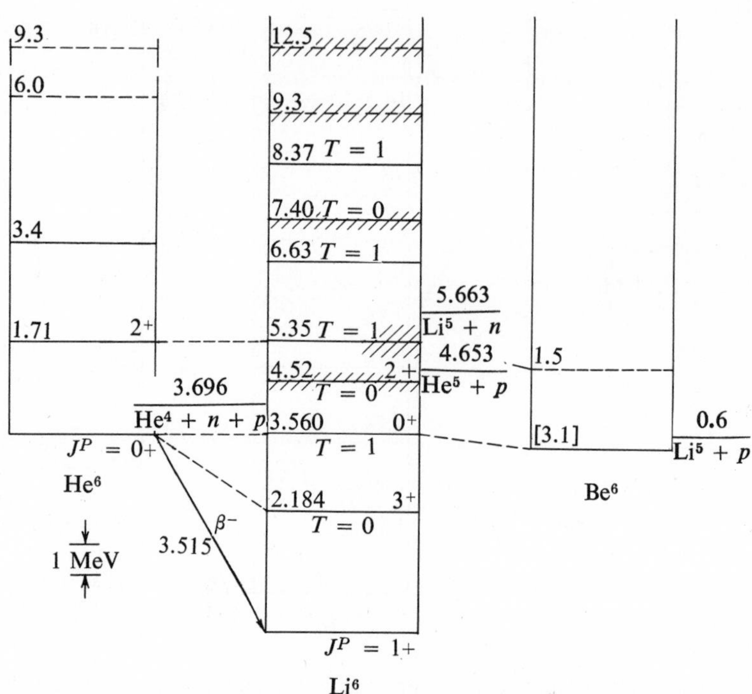

Figure 10-7 Nuclear levels in He^6, Li^6, and Be^6.

$$(\tau_1 + i\tau_2)\begin{vmatrix}1\\0\end{vmatrix} = \tau_+\begin{vmatrix}1\\0\end{vmatrix} = 0 \qquad (10\text{-}4.5)$$

$$\tau_3\begin{vmatrix}1\\0\end{vmatrix} = \tfrac{1}{2}\begin{vmatrix}1\\0\end{vmatrix} \qquad (10\text{-}4.6)$$

nd similar relations. The operator $\boldsymbol{\tau}_+$ transforms a neutron into a roton, and the operator $\boldsymbol{\tau}_-$ transforms a proton into a neutron. The hird component of the *i* spin has the value $+\frac{1}{2}$ for the proton, $-\frac{1}{2}$ for he neutron.

If we take two nucleons, the total *i* spin of the system is composed f the *i* spins of the individual nucleons, as it is for ordinary spin. We ave, therefore, a total *i* spin $\mathbf{T} = \boldsymbol{\tau}(1) + \boldsymbol{\tau}(2)$. The eigenvalues of $\mathbf{T}^2$ re $T(T+1)$, where $\tau(1) + \tau(2) \geqslant T \geqslant |\tau(1) - \tau(2)|$. In our case T is or 0, and $T^2 = 2$ or 0. Recalling the vector model, we shall refer to he two states as triplet, or $T = 1$, and singlet, or $T = 0$. Similarly for he third component of **T** we have $T_3 = \tau_3(1) + \tau_3(2)$, with eigenvalues , 0, -1.

The corresponding eigenfunctions of T^2 and T_3 are

$$\left.\begin{array}{l}\pi(1)\pi(2)\\ \dfrac{1}{\sqrt{2}}[\pi(1)\nu(2) + \pi(2)\nu(1)]\\ \nu(1)\nu(2)\end{array}\right\} \text{for } T^2 = 2 \qquad T_3\begin{cases} = 1\\ = 0\\ = -1\end{cases} \qquad (10\text{-}4.7)$$

$$\frac{1}{\sqrt{2}}[\pi(1)\nu(2) - \pi(2)\nu(1)] \qquad \text{for } T^2 = 0 \qquad T_3 = 0 \qquad (10\text{-}4.8)$$

The complete eigenfunction for the two-nucleon system is now ritten $f(\mathbf{r},\mathbf{s}_1,\mathbf{s}_2,\mathbf{t}_1,\mathbf{t}_2)$, with $\mathbf{r}$ the relative coordinates of the two nucleons, $\mathbf{s}_1$, $\mathbf{s}_2$ their spins, and $\mathbf{t}_1$, $\mathbf{t}_2$ their *i* spins. This expression can be factored s $f_r(r)f_\sigma(\mathbf{s}_1,\mathbf{s}_2)f_\tau(\mathbf{t}_1,\mathbf{t}_2)$ if we neglect, in the hamiltonian, interactions etween *i* spin and spin, spin and coordinates, etc., and in general between degrees of freedom of a different kind. The functions f_σ and f_τ ake the forms of Eqs. (6-4.13), (6-4.14), (10-4.7), and (10-4.8).

Pauli's principle may now be formulated by saying that the eigenunctions must be antisymmetric with respect to the exchange of *all* oordinates, including *i*-spin coordinates.

For a *p-p* or an *n-n* system the *i*-spin factor of the eigenfunction is $\pi(1)\pi(2)$ or $\nu(1)\nu(2)$, symmetric with respect to the exchange of 1 with 2. Hence the remainder of the eigenfunction must be antisymmetric with espect to the exchange of spatial and spin coordinates and we thus ave the usual requirement of Pauli's principle for identical particles.

As an application to the *n-p* system, note that, for the deuteron in he ${}^3S_1$ state, $f_r(r)f_\sigma(\mathbf{s}_1,\mathbf{s}_2)$ form a function symmetrical with respect to nterchange of nucleon 1 and 2. Hence f_τ has the form of Eq. (10-4.8) and s antisymmetrical. It belongs to the singlet state of *i* spin. It is easily hown in somewhat more general terms that for a two-nucleon system

$$l + S + T = \text{odd integer} \qquad (10\text{-}4.9)$$

where l is the orbital angular momentum, S the spin, and T the i spi of the system.

The total charge of a system of nucleons is related to the eigenvalu of T_3, T_3' by

$$\frac{Q}{e} = T_3' + \frac{A}{2} \qquad \textbf{(10-4.10)}$$

where A is the mass number or the number of nucleons.

The total isotopic spin has the remarkable property of being constant of the motion for specific nuclear forces, in the same way tha the total angular momentum is a constant of the motion for an isolate system. Although this conservation principle is only approximat (being violated, for instance, by electromagnetic interactions) it never theless proves to be most important, especially in pion physics. A present its foundation is empirical.

Coming back to nuclear forces we see that the collision experiment demonstrate that these forces are the same in the $^1S_0$ state for proton proton and neutron-proton systems, both of which correspond t $T = 1$, but each of which corresponds to different T_3. We postulate tha the forces depend on T but not on T_3.

This postulate is the mathematical formulation of the principle o charge independence of nuclear forces and can be generalized with use ful results. It is obviously an approximate principle, because electro magnetic forces are neglected and neutron and proton do not hav identical mass, but it is valid, so far as present knowledge extends, fo specific nuclear forces. In nuclear physics proper the postulate give rise to approximate selection rules that forbid transitions between state of different i spin under the action of nuclear forces. A remarkabl example is afforded by comparing the results of deuteron and proto bombardment in the light nuclei. In deuteron bombardment the isotopi spin cannot change, because the deuteron has an i spin of 0. In proto bombardment the i spin can change by $\frac{1}{2}$. If we bombard N^{14} [in it ground state ($T = 0$)] with protons or deuterons, it is possible to excit the state at 3.95 MeV, which has i spin 0. On the other hand, the stat at 2.35 MeV, which has i spin 1, can be excited by proton bombardmen (initial i spin $\frac{1}{2}$, final i spin $1 \pm \frac{1}{2}$) but not by deuteron bombardmen (initial i spin 0, final i spin 1).

Similarly it is impossible to form B^{10} in a state at 1.74 MeV whicl has $T = 1$ by bombarding C^{12} with deuterons, but the same state ca be reached by bombarding C^{13} with protons. In the first case the i spi of C^{12} and deuteron is 0, in the second the i spin of proton and C^{13} is 1

Even in gamma transitions the i spin gives rise to special selectio rules, which have been experimentally verified. Thus for $E1$ transition we have the selection rule

$$\Delta T = \pm 1, 0 \qquad \textbf{(10-4.11)}$$

and in the case of self-conjugate nuclei (i.e., nuclei that are unchange by transforming all neutrons into protons, and vice versa, such as He^4, C^{12}, etc.)

$$\Delta T = \pm 1 \qquad \textbf{(10-4.12)}$$

Transitions are found in O^{16} which are strongly inhibited by this specific selection rule.

As another nuclear example, consider *n-p* scattering as shown in Fig. 10-8, where θ is the angle of scattering of the neutron in the center-of-mass system. The *i*-spin eigenstates are given by Eqs. (10-4.7) and (10-4.8). The physical situation of the initial state $\nu(1)\pi(2)$ is thus a superposition of two eigenstates corresponding to $T = 1$ and 0,

$$\nu(1)\pi(2) = \frac{2^{1/2}}{2}\left[\frac{\nu(1)\pi(2) + \pi(1)\nu(2)}{2^{1/2}} + \frac{\nu(1)\pi(2) - \pi(1)\nu(2)}{2^{1/2}}\right] \qquad \textbf{(10-4.13)}$$

This scatters into a final state having the same *i*-spin part of the wave function. If the scattering amplitudes for $T = 1$ and $T = 0$ are $f_t(\theta)$ and $f_s(\theta)$, respectively, the scattering amplitude derived from Eq. (10-4.13) is

$$\tfrac{1}{2}(f_t + f_s) \qquad \textbf{(10-4.14)}$$

and the corresponding differential scattering cross section is

$$\sigma(\theta) = \tfrac{1}{4}\,|f_t(\theta) + f_s(\theta)|^2 \qquad \textbf{(10-4.15)}$$

For scattering through an angle $\pi - \theta$ the final state can be obtained from Eqs. (10-4.13) and (10-4.15) by interchanging *n* and *p*. We then have the relation

$$\sigma(\pi - \theta) = \tfrac{1}{4}|f_t(\theta) - f_s(\theta)|^2 \qquad \textbf{(10-4.16)}$$

Equations such as (10-4.15) and (10-4.16) give rise to important inequalities. For instance, from Fig. 10-9 we derive

$$\begin{gathered}[\sigma_{np}(\pi - \theta)]^{1/2} + [\sigma_{np}(\theta)]^{1/2} \geqslant [\sigma_{pp}(\theta)]^{1/2} \\ 4\sigma_{np}\,(90°) \geqslant \sigma_{pp}\,(90°)\end{gathered} \qquad \textbf{(10-4.17)}$$

Another very interesting type of application of the *i*-spin concept is indicated in Figs. 10-6 and 10-7. It will be noted that a level with a certain value of T occurs in $2T + 1$ isobars, corresponding to the possible values of T_3. For example, the ground level of Li^6 has $T = 0$ and occurs only in this nucleus, but the excited level at 3.56 MeV has

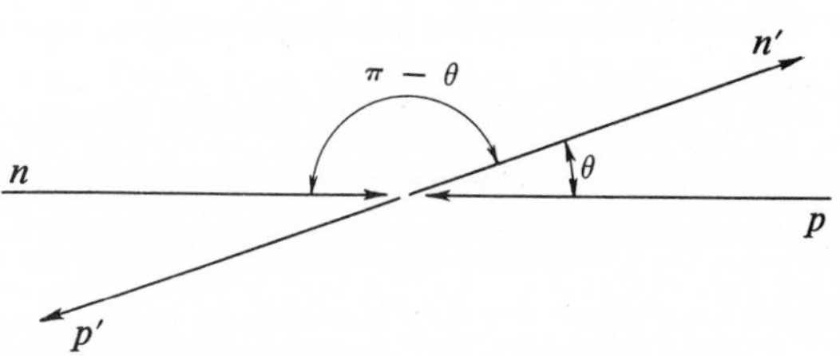

Figure 10-8 Neutron-proton collision in center-of-mass system. Definition of angles. *n*, *p*, direction of motion of neutron and proton before the collision; *n′*, *p′* same after the collision. θ = scattering angle.

$T = 1$ and occurs in three nuclei corresponding to the ground level of He^6 and Be^6. All corresponding levels with the same T have also the same I and parity, irrespective of T_3, as is to be expected from the hypothesis of charge independence of nuclear forces. An extensive classification of the low levels of light nuclei in "supermultiplets," based on the concept of i spin, was among the first applications (Wigner, 1940) of i spin. However, we cannot discuss this very important topic here.

There are many other examples of i-spin applications in nuclear physics proper. However, the concept of i spin finds even more useful application in meson physics, where it helps to clarify a great number of quantitative relations (see Chap. 14).

10-5 Spin-Dependent and Tensor Forces

Thus far, forces between two nucleons have been assumed to admit a potential function of the distance between the nucleons. This gives rise to central forces. We have seen that the forces are spin-dependent. This is best expressed mathematically with the help of the Pauli matrices $\boldsymbol{\sigma} = 2\mathbf{s}$ and by using the operator $\boldsymbol{\sigma}_1 \cdot \boldsymbol{\sigma}_2$, which we shall meet on several occasions. It is interesting to note its effect on the singlet or triplet eigenfunctions. The eigenfunctions of $(\boldsymbol{\sigma}_1 + \boldsymbol{\sigma}_2)^2$ and $\sigma_{1z} + \sigma_{2z}$ are also eigenfunctions of $\boldsymbol{\sigma}_1 \cdot \boldsymbol{\sigma}_2$, with eigenvalues -3 and 1. In fact, considering that $\sigma_x^2 = \sigma_y^2 = \sigma_z^2 = 1$, we have

$$(\boldsymbol{\sigma}_1 + \boldsymbol{\sigma}_2)^2 = \boldsymbol{\sigma}_1^2 + \boldsymbol{\sigma}_2^2 + 2\boldsymbol{\sigma}_1 \cdot \boldsymbol{\sigma}_2 = 6 + 2\boldsymbol{\sigma}_1 \cdot \boldsymbol{\sigma}_2$$

Now the eigenvalue of $(\boldsymbol{\sigma}_1 + \boldsymbol{\sigma}_2)^2$ for triplet states is 8. For singlet states the eigenvalue of $(\boldsymbol{\sigma}_1 + \boldsymbol{\sigma}_2)^2$ is 0. Hence

$$8 = 6 + 2\boldsymbol{\sigma}_1 \cdot \boldsymbol{\sigma}_2 \qquad \boldsymbol{\sigma}_1 \cdot \boldsymbol{\sigma}_2 = 1 \text{ for triplet states}$$
$$0 = 6 + 2\boldsymbol{\sigma}_1 \cdot \boldsymbol{\sigma}_2 \qquad \boldsymbol{\sigma}_1 \cdot \boldsymbol{\sigma}_2 = -3 \text{ for singlet states}$$

For an immediate application of this result we write the most general central force potential as

$$V_1(r) + V_2(r)\, \boldsymbol{\sigma}_1 \cdot \boldsymbol{\sigma}_2 \qquad \textbf{(10-5.1)}$$

where $V_{1,2}(r)$ are functions of the distance between the nucleons and $\sigma_{1,2}$ are the spins.

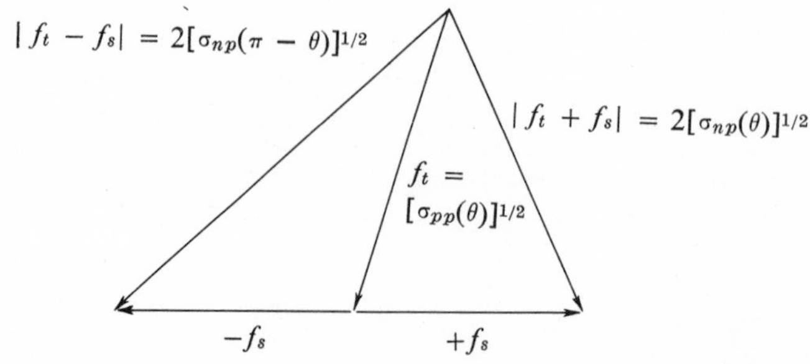

Figure 10-9 Triangular inequality. Graphical representation of the relations given in Eqs. (10-4.15), (10-4.16), and (10-4.17).

It follows then that the potential for singlet or triplet states are given by

$$V_s = V_1 - 3V_2$$

and

$$V_t = V_1 + V_2$$

respectively.

In 1941 Wigner and Eisenbud showed that the most general nucleon-nucleon potential (under the restrictions that the potential depends only on the distance r between the nucleons, and on their spins, so that the total momentum, angular momentum, and parity are constants of the motion) has the form

$$V_1(r) + V_2(r)\boldsymbol{\sigma}_1 \cdot \boldsymbol{\sigma}_2 + V_3(r)S_{12} \tag{10-5.2}$$

with

$$V_3(r)S_{12} \equiv V_3(r)\left[\frac{3(\boldsymbol{\sigma}_1 \cdot \mathbf{r})(\boldsymbol{\sigma}_2 \cdot \mathbf{r})}{r^2} - \boldsymbol{\sigma}_1 \cdot \boldsymbol{\sigma}_2\right] \tag{10-5.3}$$

The third term is identical in structure to the term that would represent the interaction between two magnetic dipoles at distance **r**. Naturally it depends on the orientation of the two spins with respect to **r**.

The actual presence of the third term [Eq. (10-5.3)] is demonstrated by the finite quadrupole moment of the deuteron. The argument runs as follows: If the eigenfunction of the deuteron were exactly a $^3S_1$ state, i.e., spherically symmetrical, the electric quadrupole moment would be 0. With a potential such as Eq. (10-5.1) for two nucleons, parity, $I^2 = (\mathbf{L} + \mathbf{S})^2$, I_z, L^2, L_z, S^2, S_z are constants of the motion, as can be directly verified. Thus, a $^3S_1$ state would not mix with any other state, and the electric quadrupole moment of the deuteron would be 0. The term $V_3(r)S_{12}$ leaves only parity, I^2, I_z, and S^2, but not L^2 and L_z, as exact constants of the motion. [(For proofs of these statements see (El 59).] This has the consequence that the ground state of the deuteron will have as its eigenfunction a mixture of $^3S_1$ and $^3D_1$, the latter being the only state with the same parity and I as $^3S_1$. The average value of the electric quadrupole moment is not 0, because of the terms

$$\langle \psi_{^3S_1} | 3z^2 - r^2 | \psi_{^3D_1} \rangle \tag{10-5.4}$$

which appear in its computation with the complete eigenfunction.

The admixture of the $^3D_1$ state also influences the magnetic moment of the deuteron. An analysis of all the data leads to the conclusion that the eigenfunction must have approximately the form

$$0.96\psi_{^3S_1} + 0.26\psi_{^3D_1} \tag{10-5.5}$$

with considerable uncertainty about the value of the admixture. This means that the deuteron in the ground state spends about 7 per cent of the time in a $^3D_1$ state.

There is no a priori reason why the forces acting between nucleons may not be velocity-dependent. In fact, there is good experimental evidence for a potential

$$V_l(r)\mathbf{l} \cdot \mathbf{S} \qquad \text{with} \qquad \mathbf{l} = \mathbf{r} \times \mathbf{p}, \qquad \mathbf{S} = \boldsymbol{\sigma}_1 + \boldsymbol{\sigma}_2 \tag{10-5.6}$$

between a nucleon and a nucleus, where the velocity appears through th momentum p. There are no other possible terms, linear in p, whic satisfy the usual conservation laws.

10-6 Nucleon-Nucleon Forces. Exchange Forces

It is highly desirable to be able to account for the main properti of the nuclei, as embodied, for instance, in the mass formula, by derivin them from the nucleon-nucleon interaction. This program has been th object of very extensive and difficult investigations (Brueckner, 1955 which up to now have been only partially successful. The difficulti are twofold: our imperfect knowledge of the nucleon-nucleon force, an the mathematical complexity of the multibody problem.

However, we can see at once that simple attractive potentia between nucleons are inadequate for the explanation of nuclear bindin Consider a nucleus of mass number A. The total energy of this nucle would be $T + U$, where T is the kinetic energy of all nucleons and their potential energy. Under our hypothesis of attractive potentia between each nucleon pair, the potential energy would be equal to th number of nucleon pairs, which is $A(A - 1)/2$ – times a function of th average distance between nucleons. On the other hand, the kineti energy is dominated by the exclusion principle. If we enclose a gas c fermions in a sphere of radius R, the particles in their lowest quantu state will occupy the lowest levels, one per level, according to th exclusion principle. For each level there is a kinetic energy, and th whole assembly will therefore have total kinetic energy, which is easil calculated and which we find to be proportional to $A^{5/3}R^{-2}$ (see Chap 11).

In the ground state $T + U$ will be minimum, and we determine th only parameter available, the nuclear radius R, by this condition. Fo large A the potential energy is proportional to A^2, and the kinetic energ is proportional to $A^{5/3}$. If we choose R so as to minimize the potenti energy, on varying R the corresponding increase of kinetic energy wi be insufficient to counterbalance the increase of potential energy, an the binding will be maximum near the value of R that minimizes th potential energy (i.e., for R equal to the range of nuclear forces, irres pective of A). In other words, the terms proportional to A^2 preva over those proportional to $A^{5/3}$, and it is enough to minimize the poten tial energy in order to obtain the ground state. All nuclei would hav the same radius, approximately equal to the range of nuclear force This is contrary to experiment, because we know that the nuclear rad are proportional to $A^{1/3}$ and not constant for large A. Moreover, th total binding energy for large A is proportional to A, and not to A as one would conclude from the arguments given above.

Nuclear forces must have a property (similar to that of the chemical valence forces), which brings about "saturation." Such a force woul attract a small number of nucleons but become repulsive for a large ımber. This type of interaction can be achieved in the simplest way , assuming a force which is strongly repulsive at a very short distance epulsive core) and attractive at a suitable range of distances. There good evidence for the existence of such forces, with the repulsive core ıving a radius of about 0.4 F. This core is in fact chiefly responsible r the constant density of nuclear matter.

However, in addition to the repulsive core, there are other mecha-sms which produce saturation. Chemical forces show very clear amples of saturation: two hydrogen atoms combine to form a hydro-n molecule, but a third atom is not bound by such a molecule. The ıantum-mechanical reason for this effect is well known. In the hydro-n molecule the two electrons overlap, or better, are in the same spatial bit, although with opposite spin. A third electron cannot occupy this bit, as it is prevented by Pauli's principle.

This situation suggests some analogies to the case of nuclei. The rong binding (28.11 MeV) of the alpha particle gives important ıalitative indications on this point. Consider, hypothetically, that ch nucleon has bonds qualitatively similar to chemical-valence bonds. the case of D, H^3, and He^4, we have, respectively, two particles and ıe shared bond, three particles and three shared bonds, and four ırticles and six shared bonds. From the mass defects we find the energy sociated with each bond to be 2.20, 2.78, and 4.69 MeV. A fifth par-le is not bound at all, both He^5 and Li^5 being unstable. The fact at saturation is reached for a structure of four nucleons, two neutrons, ıd two protons can be interpreted as indicating a strong interaction hen the nucleons have the same and hence overlapping eigenfunction far as space coordinates are concerned, irrespective of spin, because ıuli's principle allows two, and only two, protons, two, and only o, neutrons, each with the same space eigenfunction but with opposite in.

The strong binding of alpha particles was also used by Wigner show the short range of nuclear forces. His argument was that) having three bonds per nucleon, the nucleons come closer together an in the other light nuclei and (2) being closer together and the ıclear forces having a short range, the nucleons interact more strongly.

"Exchange forces" can produce saturation. They are typically ıantum mechanical in nature, and they occur as follows: The eigen-nction of a neutron and a proton can be written

$$\psi(r_1 s_1, r_2 s_2) = \psi(1,2) \tag{10-6.1}$$

here r_1, s_1 are the coordinate and spin of the neutron and r_2, s_2 are e coordinate and spin of the proton. The expectation value of the ›tential is obtained by the usual rule,

$$\langle U \rangle = \int \psi(1,2)^* U(1,2) \psi(1,2) \, d\tau_1 \, d\tau_2 \tag{10-6.2}$$

here the possible spin dependence of the potential is taken into account cause $U(1,2) \equiv U(r_1 s_1, r_2 s_2)$. However, one may also replace the potential U by more general operators which exchange the two particles. The expectation value of the potential energy will then be, not

$$\langle U \rangle = \int \psi(1,2)^* U(1,2) \psi(1,2)\, d\tau_1\, d\tau_2 \quad \textbf{(10-6.3)}$$

as for ordinary forces, but

$$\int \psi(2,1)^* U(1,2) \psi(1,2)\, d\tau_1\, d\tau_2 \quad \textbf{(10-6.4)}$$

The ordinary function U is replaced by the operator UP_H, where P_H exchanges the particles, or, formally, the coordinate *and* spin variable of the first and second particles. For the case of a neutron and proton this can be naively interpreted, in the meson theory of nuclear forces as the exchange of a charged pion. This pion in turn is the quantum o the field of nuclear forces (see Chap. 14).

One can still think of the possibility of operators that exchange, no both spin and coordinate of the particles, but only the coordinate an not the spin or only the spin and not the coordinate. These operator give the following explicit results:

$$P_H\psi(r_1s_1, r_2s_2) = \psi(r_2s_2, r_1s_1) \qquad \text{Heisenberg} \quad \textbf{(10-6.5)}$$

$$P_M\psi(r_1s_1, r_2s_2) = \psi(r_2s_1, r_1s_2) \qquad \text{Majorana} \quad \textbf{(10-6.6)}$$

$$P_B\psi(r_1s_1, r_2s_2) = \psi(r_1s_2, r_2s_1) \qquad \text{Bartlett} \quad \textbf{(10-6.7)}$$

named after the physicists who first suggested them. Ordinary force are generally called Wigner forces.

It is possible to show that some exchange forces can give rise to saturation. More specifically, of the three types of exchange force mentioned above, the Heisenberg forces would give special stability to the deuteron, and the Majorana forces to the alpha particles; the Bartlet forces do not give saturation. We conclude that exchange forces, a least in part of the Majorana type, must be present.

The existence of exchange forces can be shown directly by high energy neutron-proton scattering, as was pointed out by Wick (1933). Experiments on *n-p* scattering at 90 MeV showed that neutrons impinging on protons give rise, preferentially in the forward direction to protons (Figs. 10-10 and 10-11).

Calculating classically, with an ordinary force, we estimate th maximum momentum transfer in a collision between two particles o the same mass to be (average force) × (duration of collision). If th radius of action of the potential of depth U is r, the duration of th collision is r/v (where v is the relative velocity of the particles) and th average force is U/r. The momentum transfer is of the order of $\Delta p = U/v$. If the neutron stops and the proton escapes forward, $\Delta p \simeq 2p$ where p is the momentum of the impinging neutron. However, $U/v \ll p$, if we assume that $U = 20$ MeV, $Mv^2 \sim 500$ MeV as in the experimental conditions. This contradiction is removed by the hypothesis tha during the collision the particles exchange their charge and that the rea momentum transfer for the protons escaping forward is very small.

● The same result is obtained in quantum mechanics by considerin he collision in Born approximation. Here the scattered wave has the orm $f(\theta)(e^{ikr}/r)$, with

$$f(\theta) = \frac{m}{2\pi\hbar^2}\int e^{-i\mathbf{k}_f\cdot\mathbf{r}}U(r)\,e^{i\mathbf{k}_i\cdot\mathbf{r}}\,d\tau \tag{10-6.8}$$

here m is the reduced mass $\mathbf{r} = \mathbf{r}_1 - \mathbf{r}_2$ and θ, $\mathbf{k}_i$, $\mathbf{k}_f$ are in the center-f-mass system.

The integral for a short-range $U(r)$ is appreciable only if $\mathbf{k}_i - \mathbf{k}_f \simeq$, because otherwise the function exp $[i(\mathbf{k}_i - \mathbf{k}_f)\mathbf{r}]$ oscillates so rapidly ver the region for which $U(r)$ is appreciable that the result averages to 0. Now $\mathbf{k}_i - \mathbf{k}_f = 0$ indicates forward scattering. We thus find again hat the impinging neutrons are scattered forward, contrary to experi-nent. Upon introducing an exchange force, instead, the potential $U(r)$ s replaced by $U(r)P_M$, which gives, in place of Eq. (10-6.8),

$$f_e(\theta) = \frac{m}{2\pi\hbar^2}\int e^{+i\mathbf{k}_f\cdot\mathbf{r}}\,U(r)e^{i\mathbf{k}_i\cdot\mathbf{r}}\,d\tau \tag{10-6.9}$$

ecause the P_M operator changes particles 1 and 2 and hence transforms into $-\mathbf{r}$.

The $f_e(\theta)$ due to exchange forces is thus large when

$$\mathbf{k}_f + \mathbf{k}_i = 0 \tag{10-6.10}$$

e., when the neutron is scattered backward and the proton forward. he experimental result of Fig. 10-10 demonstrates clearly two maxima

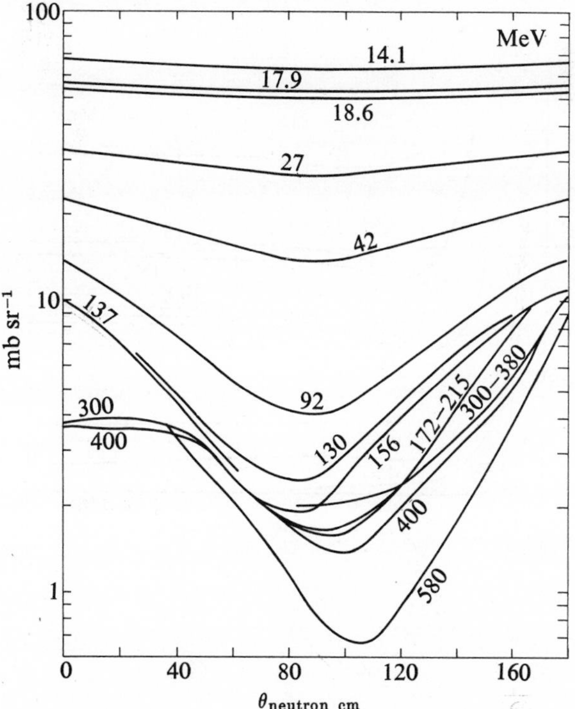

igure 10-10 Experimental alues of the differential neu-ron-proton cross section at vari-us energies. Cross sections and ngles refer to the center-of-nass system, energies to the aboratory system.

in the forward and backward directions at high energies. We must conclude that both normal and exchange forces are present and that they are of comparable intensities.

Exchange forces have the interesting feature of changing sign according to the value of the angular momentum of the two nucleons. To see this, consider the eigenfunction of the two nucleons in the center-of-mass system (neglecting spin and noncentral forces),

$$\psi(r,\theta,l) = f(r)\, Y_l^m(\theta,\varphi) \tag{10-6.11}$$

The operator P_M changes $\mathbf{r}$ into $-\mathbf{r}$, which is the same as leaving r unchanged, but changing θ into $\pi - \theta$ and φ into $\varphi + \pi$. This has the result of multiplying $Y_l^m(\theta,\varphi)$ by $(-1)^l$; hence

$$P_M\psi = (-1)^l\psi \tag{10-6.12}$$

and the result of any calculation involving $U(r)P_M$ is the same as that obtainable from $(-1)^l U(r)$, where l is the angular momentum of the operand on which $U(r)P_M$ operates.

Taking into account the spin, we must distinguish the operators P_M, P_H, and P_B. They give the following potentials:

$$UP_M = (-1)^l U \tag{10-6.13}$$

$$UP_H = (-1)^{l+S+1} U \tag{10-6.14}$$

$$UP_B = (-1)^{S+1} U \tag{10-6.15}$$

where S is the resultant spin of the two nucleons. ●

The operators $P_i (i = M, H, B)$ can also be written explicitly, using the operators σ and τ relative to spin and i spin. For instance,

$$P_B = \tfrac{1}{2}(1 + \boldsymbol{\sigma}_1 \cdot \boldsymbol{\sigma}_2) \qquad P_H = -\tfrac{1}{2}(1 + \tau_1 \cdot \tau_2) = -P_\tau \tag{10-6.16}$$

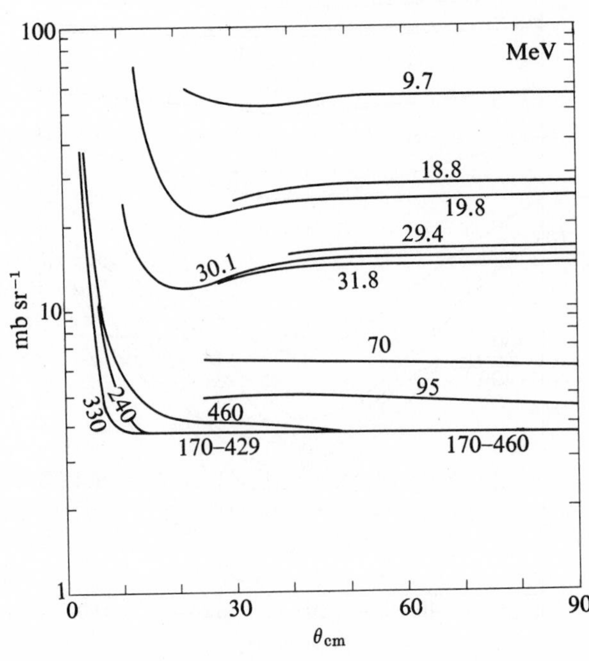

Figure 10-11 Experimental values of the differential proton-proton cross section at various energies up to 460 MeV. Cross sections and angles refer to the center-of-mass system, energies to the laboratory system.

where P_τ is the operator exchanging i spins. Assuming charge independence and remembering that parity i spin and S^2 are always constants of the motion, we can classify the velocity-independent forces. Consider separately, ordinary and tensor. Each type has its own dependence on r according to the even or odd parity of the state and to the total spin and i spin of the state. However, tensor forces do not exist for singlet spin states, because the operator S_{12} applied to a singlet eigenfunction gives identically zero. We thus have six functions of r to be determined. If we include also $\mathbf{l}\cdot\mathbf{S}$ forces (operating only in triplet states), we have eight functions.

These have been determined, at least approximately, by fitting a large number of empirical data such as the properties of the deuteron and the results of measurements on nucleon-nucleon scattering including polarization (see the next section). When possible, meson theory has also been used, mainly to determine the outer fringes of the potentials by the so-called one-pion exchange theory, or OPEP (Gammel, Thaler; Signell, Marshak; Breit and Yale group). The results are illustrated by the example in Fig. 10-12. These potentials do not yet give results in perfect agreement with experiment nor are they based on an exact theory; nevertheless, they reproduce fairly well the experimental collision data up to 200 MeV. Their qualitative features are important for explaining nuclear models in terms of nucleon-nucleon forces. An important characteristic of these forces is the strong dependence of the forces on the parity of states involved. The force is stronger in even states than it is in odd states. The spin dependence of the central force is relatively weak. Both central and tensor forces have a central repulsive core of about 0.4 F in radius and an outside attractive region of 1 to 2 F in radius. The spin-orbit potential has a much shorter radius.

Figure 10-12 (*see overleaf*) Yale nucleon-nucleon potentials. A potential (Yale) that reproduces the scattering experiments and phase shifts in nucleon-nucleon scattering. The form used is

$$V = V_C + V_T S_{12} + V_{LS}(\mathbf{L}\cdot\mathbf{S}) + V_q[(\mathbf{L}\cdot\mathbf{S})^2 + \mathbf{L}\cdot\mathbf{S} - \mathbf{L}^2]$$

The last term is omitted in the figures. V_c is different for even and odd states and depends also on S. We thus have four curves for V_C. V_T and V_{LS} are different from zero only for triplet states and also give four curves, depending on the parity of the states. (a) The singlet even-parity potential ${}^1V_c{}^+$, as a function of $x = rm_\pi c/\hbar$. The short vertical line is at the hard-core radius corresponding to $x_C = 0.35$. The potential is $+\infty$ for $x < x_C$. Different scales are used for $x < 1.0$ and $x > 1.0$. (b) The singlet odd-parity potential ${}^1V_c{}^-$, as a function of x. Other conventions as in (a). (c) The triplet even-parity central potential ${}^3V_c{}^+$, as a function of x. Other conventions as in (a). (d) The triplet even-parity potential function of x, ${}^3V_T{}^+$, which multiplies the tensor operator S_{12}. Other conventions as in (a). (e) The triplet even-parity potential function of x, ${}^3V_{LS}{}^+$, which multiplies the spin-orbit operator $\mathbf{L}\cdot\mathbf{S}$. Other conventions as in (a). (f) The triplet odd-parity central potential ${}^3V_c{}^-$, as a function of x. Other conventions as in (a). (g) The triplet odd-parity potential function of x, ${}^3V_T{}^-$, which multiplies the tensor operator S_{12}. Other conventions as in (a). (h) The triplet odd-parity potential function of x, ${}^3V_{LS}{}^-$, which multiplies the spin-orbit operator $\mathbf{L}\cdot\mathbf{S}$. Other conventions as in (a). [Courtesy of G. Breit.]

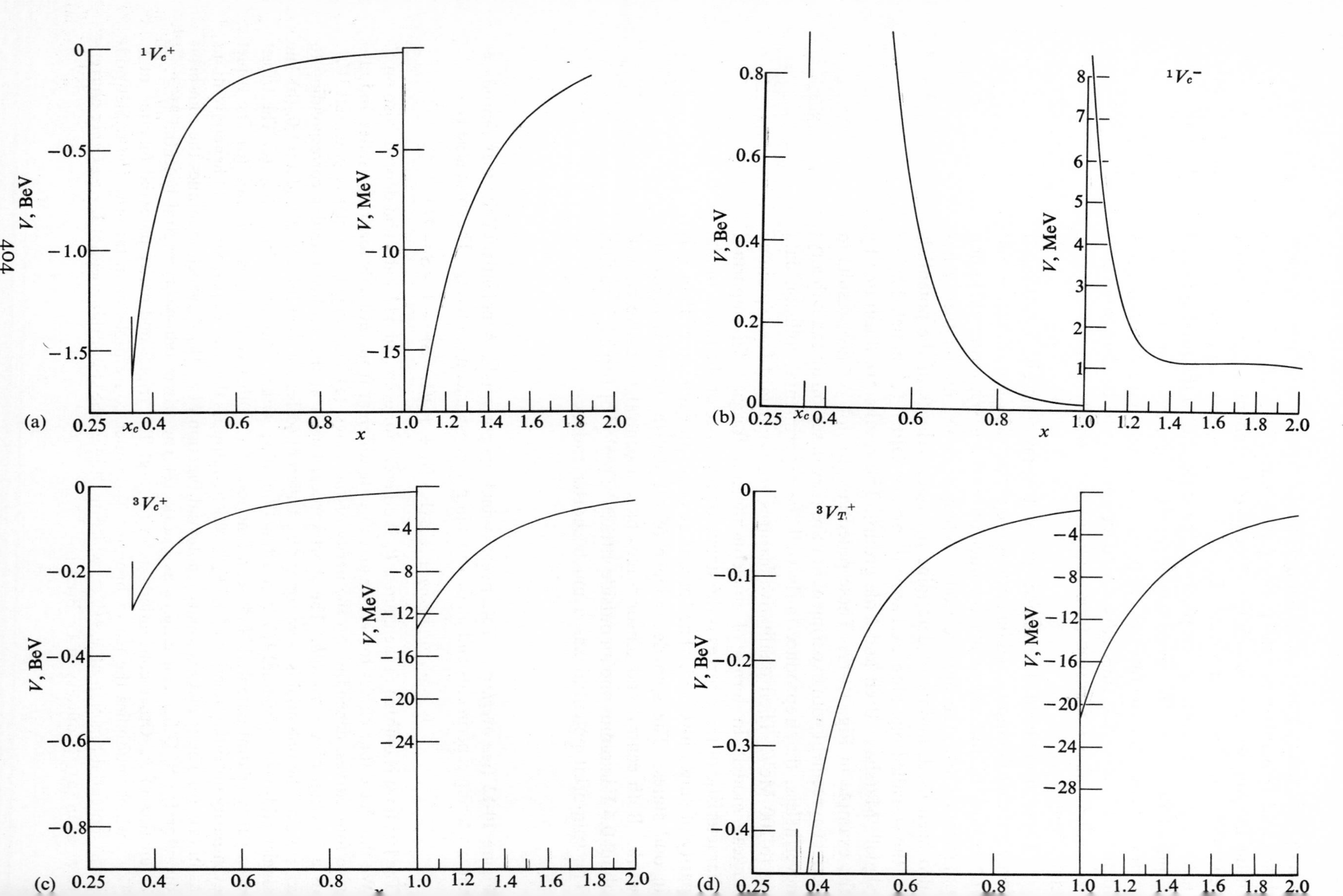
(a)
$^1V_c^+$
V, BeV
0
−0.5
−1.0
−1.5
V, MeV
−5
−10
−15
0.25
x_c 0.4
0.6
0.8
1.0 1.2 1.4 1.6 1.8 2.0
x
(b)
$^1V_c^-$
V, BeV
0.8
0.6
0.4
0.2
0
V, MeV
8
7
6
5
4
3
2
1
0.25
x_c 0.4
0.6
0.8
1.0 1.2 1.4 1.6 1.8 2.0
x
(c)
$^3V_c^+$
V, BeV
0
−0.2
−0.4
−0.6
−0.8
V, MeV
−4
−8
−12
−16
−20
−24
0.25 0.4 0.6 0.8 1.0 1.2 1.4 1.6 1.8 2.0
(d)
$^3V_T^+$
V, BeV
0
−0.1
−0.2
−0.3
−0.4
V, MeV
−4
−8
−12
−16
−20
−24
−28
0.25 0.4 0.6 0.8 1.0 1.2 1.4 1.6 1.8 2.0

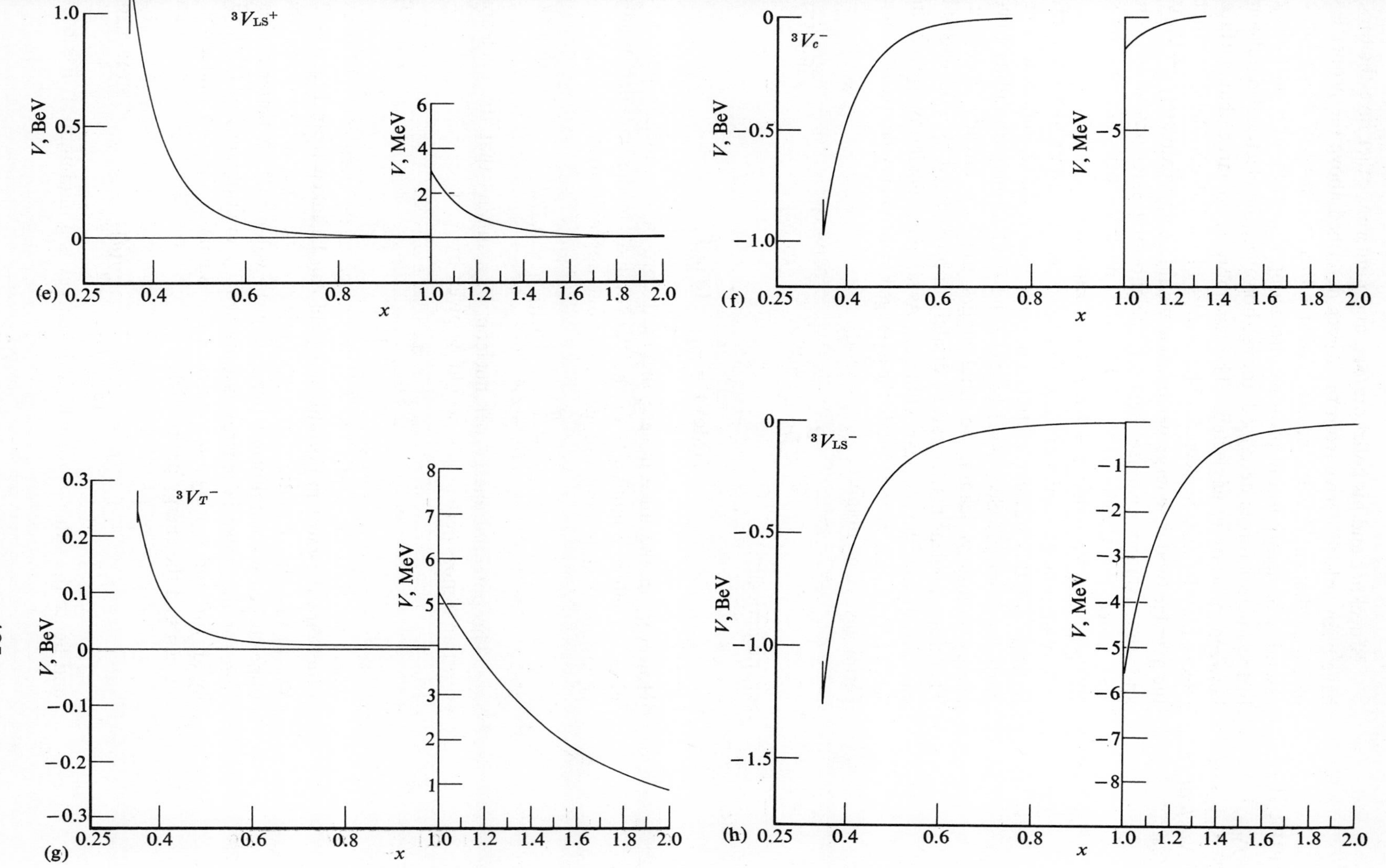

(e)
$^3V_{LS}^+$
V, BeV
1.0
0.5
0
V, MeV
6
4
2
0.25
0.4
0.6
0.8
1.0
1.2
1.4
1.6
1.8
2.0
x
(f)
$^3V_c^-$
V, BeV
0
−0.5
−1.0
V, MeV
−5
0.25
0.4
0.6
0.8
1.0
1.2
1.4
1.6
1.8
2.0
x
(g)
$^3V_T^-$
V, BeV
0.3
0.2
0.1
0
−0.1
−0.2
−0.3
V, MeV
8
7
6
5
3
2
1
0.25
0.4
0.6
0.8
1.0
1.2
1.4
1.6
1.8
2.0
x
(h)
$^3V_{LS}^-$
V, BeV
0
−0.5
−1.0
−1.5
V, MeV
−1
−2
−3
−4
−5
−6
−7
−8
0.25
0.4
0.6
0.8
1.0
1.2
1.4
1.6
1.8
2.0
x

Brueckner and his collaborators, and numerous other investigators, have been able to derive from the forces described above the properties of a hypothetical nuclear matter. Assume this to consist of a very large assembly of neutrons and protons interacting with each other according to the nuclear forces described above; however, the electrical repulsion between protons is neglected. The assembly is so large that surface effects may be also neglected. The results of the calculation show that the average binding energy per particle would be approximately 15 MeV and the average distance between neighboring nucleons $d = 1.8$ F and hence the density $d^{-3} = 0.17 \times 10^{39}$ nucleons per cm^3, or 2.85×10^{14} g cm^{-3}. Note that $d = 1.61 r_0$ (r_0 of Eq. 6-3.1).

A simplified account of the arguments used, according to Weisskopf, follows. In this nuclear matter, nucleons would move almost as free particles (compare Sec. 6-12) because the Pauli principle inhibits low-energy collisions leading to final stages that are already occupied. Therefore, nuclear matter can be crudely approximated by a degenerate gas occupying the nuclear volume. A simple calculation (given in Sec. 11-9) enables us to evaluate the average kinetic energy per particle in a Fermi gas. One obtains

$$T = \frac{B}{d^2} \qquad \text{with } B = \frac{3^{5/3}\pi^{4/3}\hbar^2}{2^{2/3}10m} \tag{10-6.17}$$

or, numerically,

$$T(\text{MeV}) = \frac{75}{d^2} \qquad (d \text{ in F})$$

However, in the nuclear case the hard core of the nuclear potential gives an effect reminiscent of the "covolume" in the van der Waals equation of state, and one gets in closer approximation

$$T = \frac{B}{(d - c)^2} \qquad \text{with } c \simeq 0.22d \tag{10-6.18}$$

The potential energy per nucleon U, assuming that the nucleons form an almost perfect gas, would be given by

$$-U = \frac{4\pi}{3}\frac{Vb^3}{d^3} \tag{10-6.19}$$

where the V is the depth and b is the range of the even central forces, which are the most important ones and can be taken from Fig. 10-12. We justify this equation by considering V as a perturbation on the unperturbed wave uniformly occupying the volume d^3. A better expression for the potential energy is obtained by multiplying Eq. (10-6.19) by an $f(d)$ and writing $-U = Cf(d)/d^3$. Summing the two expressions we can find the energy per particle:

$$E = \frac{B}{(d - c)^2} - \frac{C}{d^3}f(d) \tag{10-6.20}$$

and hence the value d_0 for which the energy is a minimum. It has been pointed out by Weisskopf that, near $d = d_0$, $f(d)$ is approximately $\frac{1}{2}(d/d_0)$. From Eq. (10-6.20) we find, by setting to zero the derivative with respect to d, the equilibrium d_0 and the average binding energy per nucleon (15 MeV).

Equation (10-6.20) also allows us to calculate the compressibility $\frac{1}{2}d^2\,(\partial^2\epsilon/\partial d^2)$ of nuclear matter and the "symmetry energy":

$$\frac{1}{2}\frac{\partial^2\epsilon}{\partial y^2} \qquad \text{with } y = \frac{N - Z}{N + Z}$$

The compressibility is about 100 MeV and the symmetry energy 30 MeV. These calculations are important because they connect the nucleon-nucleon force to observable properties of nuclear matter; however, they are not precise and they depend on the potential chosen, which is not uniquely determined.

10-7 Polarization. High-Energy Nuclear Scattering

High-energy nuclear scattering, for a laboratory kinetic energy above 50 MeV, involves, besides s waves, increasingly higher order waves, with $l = 1, 2, 3$, etc. The angular distribution is no longer spherically symmetrical, and analysis of the experimental data becomes increasingly complicated. It is possible to obtain a description of the scattering through phase shifts (see Appendix D). However, to obtain the phase shifts it is not enough to measure angular distributions of the scattering only: it is necessary to consider the polarization of the beams as well. A complete treatment of this subject is beyond the scope of this book, and we shall limit ourselves to the simplest ideas and facts.

We treat first the scattering of a nucleon on a spinless center, which is much simpler than nucleon-nucleon scattering and provides an experimental tool for many polarization experiments. Nucleons may be polarized, or polarized beams analyzed, by elastic scattering on a spinless center provided that the interaction producing the scattering is spin-dependent, as when it contains a term $\mathbf{l}\cdot\boldsymbol{\sigma}$, where $\mathbf{l}$ is the orbital angular momentum and $\frac{1}{2}\boldsymbol{\sigma}$ the spin. To polarize a beam of protons, we may scatter it on a target (which for simplicity we shall assume to be spinless and very heavy compared to the proton) and select the beam scattered under angle θ_1. By scattering this beam a second time on a target, under an angle θ_2, we find that the scattered intensity depends not only on θ_2 but also on angle φ, between the two planes of scattering, and that it has the form

$$I = +A(\theta_2) + B(\theta_2)\cos\varphi \tag{10-7.1}$$

The quantity B vanishes, unless the beam incident on the second target is polarized. To define φ precisely, consider the vector momenta of the incident and scattered particle in each scattering and call

$$\mathbf{n}_1 = \frac{\mathbf{p}_i \times \mathbf{p}_s}{|\mathbf{p}_i \times \mathbf{p}_s|} \tag{10-7.2}$$

where the index 1, 2 means first, second scattering, and i and s incoming and scattered. We have then

$$\mathbf{n}_1 \cdot \mathbf{n}_2 = \cos \varphi \tag{10-7.3}$$

We define the beam polarization as the ratio

$$P = \frac{N^+ - N^-}{N^+ + N^-} \tag{10-7.4}$$

where N^+ means the number of particles with spin up and N^- the number of particles with spin down. The direction up-down is here assumed to be perpendicular to the direction of the plane of scattering. This definition is equivalent to saying that P is the expectation value of the component of $\boldsymbol{\sigma}$ in the direction $\mathbf{n}$. If we scatter an unpolarized beam on a spinless target, the beam scattered under an angle θ acquires, generally speaking, a polarization P that is a function of θ, of the energy of the beam, and of the particles involved. This polarization is often called the polarizing power. In other words, P is the polarization after scattering, of an initially unpolarized beam.

Let us indicate by $p(+L+)$ the probability that an incident particle with spin up will be scattered to the left with spin up and by $p(+L-)$ the probability that the same particle will be scattered to the left with spin down. We have eight similar probabilities altogether. These, however are not independent, as we can see by observing that rotation by 180° around the incident-beam direction brings $p(+L+)$ into $p(-R-)$, and hence the two quantities must be equal.

Also, in the specific case of a particle of spin $\frac{1}{2}$ scattering on a spinless center, the spin component normal to the scattering plane cannot flip, or $p(+L-) = 0$.

As a consequence we can write for our case

$$\begin{aligned} p(+L+) &= p(-R-) = \tfrac{1}{2}(1 + P) \\ p(-L+) &= p(+R-) = 0 \\ p(+L-) &= p(-R+) = 0 \\ p(-L-) &= p(+R+) = \tfrac{1}{2}(1 - P) \end{aligned}$$

To measure the polarization of a beam, consider first the scattering of an unpolarized beam on a spinless center (Fig. 10-13). The number of particles scattered left and right with spin up or down is given in Table 10-1

The intensity left or right, after the first scattering, will be the same but the polarization of the beam scattered to the left will be

$$\frac{(1 + P_1) - (1 - P_1)}{(1 + P_1) + (1 - P_1)} = P_1 \tag{10-7.5}$$

On a second scattering of the "left" beam, the intensity of scattering to the left and right will be different. If in first and second scattering energy and θ are the same ($P_1 = P_2 = P$), we shall have an intensity to the left proportional to

$$L = (1 + P)^2 + (1 - P)^2 = 2(1 + P^2) \tag{10-7.6}$$

Table 10-1 Beam Intensities in Simple and Double Scattering

Beam	Spin	Intensity[a]
Incident	Up +	$\frac{1}{2}$
	Down −	$\frac{1}{2}$
Scattered once left (L)	+	$\frac{1}{2} p_1 (1 + P_1)$
	−	$\frac{1}{2} p_1 (1 - P_1)$
Scattered once right (R)	+	$\frac{1}{2} p_1 (1 - P_1)$
	−	$\frac{1}{2} p_1 (1 + P_1)$
Scattered twice left (LL)	+	$\frac{1}{2} p_1 p_2 (1 + P_1)(1 + P_2)$
	−	$\frac{1}{2} p_1 p_2 (1 - P_1)(1 - P_2)$
Scattered twice—first left,	+	$\frac{1}{2} p_1 p_2 (1 + P_1)(1 - P_2)$
then right (LR)	−	$\frac{1}{2} p_1 p_2 (1 - P_1)(1 + P_2)$

[a] p and P are functions of energy and θ (see Fig. 10-13).

and on the right an intensity proportional to

$$R = 2(1 + P)(1 - P) = 2(1 - P^2) \tag{10-7.7}$$

Hence

$$\epsilon = \frac{L - R}{L + R} = \frac{2 + 2P^2 - 2 + 2P^2}{2 + 2P^2 + 2 - 2P^2} = P^2 \tag{10-7.8}$$

The quantity ϵ is called the asymmetry. This ratio $(L - R)/(L + R)$ is directly measurable, and therefore we may obtain $|P|$ from it, although not the sign of P. The sign may be determined by studying the interference of nuclear scattering with Coulomb scattering, or by slowing down the polarized beam and using some processes of low-energy nuclear

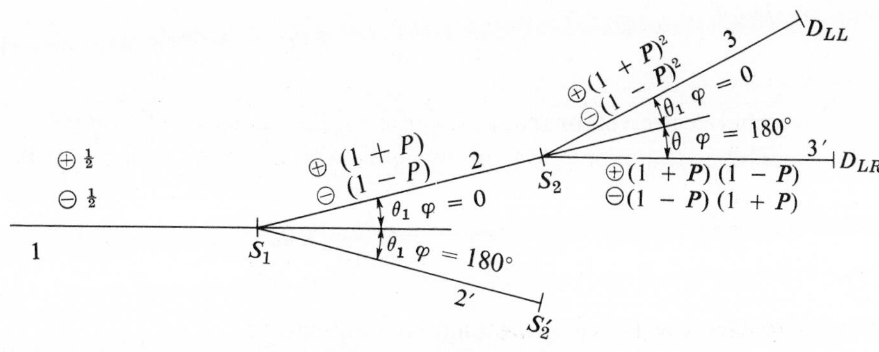

Figure 10-13 Scattering of spin $\frac{1}{2}$ particles by spinless center. The unpolarized beam 1 is scattered by scatterer S_1. The intensities scattered in directions 2 and 2′ are identical, but the scattered beams are polarized. Beam 2 scattered at S_2 now has different intensities in beams 3 and 3′. The number of particles with spin up or down in the different beams are proportional to the quantities indicated by ⊕ and ⊖. It has been assumed for simplicity that $P_1 = P_2 = P$ and factors $\frac{1}{2} p_1$ and $\frac{1}{2} p_1 p_2$ have been omitted.

physics in which the sign of the polarization is predictable (Marshall, 1955).

The quantity P is by definition the expectation value of the component of $\boldsymbol{\sigma}$ in the direction z perpendicular to the scattering plane. If parity is conserved in the scattering of an unpolarized beam on a spinless target, the direction of $\boldsymbol{\sigma}$ must be defined by the two momenta $\mathbf{p}_i$ and $\mathbf{p}_s$, which are polar vectors. However, $\boldsymbol{\sigma}$ is an axial vector, and the only way of forming an axial vector with two polar vectors is to set

$$\boldsymbol{\sigma} \propto \mathbf{p}_i \times \mathbf{p}_s$$

which shows that $\boldsymbol{\sigma}$ must be perpendicular to the plane of scattering. We conclude that in the case under consideration

$$P = \langle \sigma_z \rangle = \langle \sigma \rangle$$

However, one may have a beam with $\langle \boldsymbol{\sigma} \rangle$ in an arbitrary direction. If we want a complete measurement of $\langle \boldsymbol{\sigma} \rangle$, we must measure its three components. Taking the x axis in the direction of the beam, y and z perpendicular to it, scattering experiments in the xy and xz planes give $\langle \sigma_z \rangle$ and $\langle \sigma_y \rangle$. To obtain $\langle \sigma_x \rangle$ we deflect the beam magnetically or electrically so that the spin rotates (see Sec. 2-13). In the deflected beam the original $\langle \sigma_x \rangle$ has transversal components, which can be measured by a scattering experiment. In this way one determines the vector $\langle \boldsymbol{\sigma} \rangle$.

To understand the left-right asymmetry produced by nuclear scattering of polarized protons, consider the density distribution ρ of nuclear matter and a nucleon traveling through it. Nuclear forces are short-range, and the net force acting on a nucleon within the nucleus is 0. Near the surface, however, the nucleon is subject to a net force, because it has nuclear matter only on one side. In this region the energy (scalar) may depend only on $\boldsymbol{\sigma}$, $\mathbf{p}$, and $\nabla\rho$ through the scalar that can be formed with the axial vector $\boldsymbol{\sigma}$ and the two polar vectors $\mathbf{p}$ and $\nabla\rho$. This scalar is proportional to

$$\boldsymbol{\sigma} \cdot (\nabla\rho \times \mathbf{p}) \tag{10-7.9}$$

Here

$$\nabla\rho = \frac{\mathbf{r}\, d\rho}{r\, dr} \tag{10-7.10}$$

where $\mathbf{r}$ is a vector from the center of the nucleus to the point considered. This is the expression for the spin-orbit coupling energy. It may be rewritten as

$$V = \text{const.}\ \frac{1}{r}\frac{d\rho}{dr}\, \boldsymbol{\sigma} \cdot \mathbf{l} \tag{10-7.11}$$

where $\mathbf{l} = \mathbf{r} \times \mathbf{p}$ is the angular momentum.

According to the shell model of the nucleus, the sign of the coefficient of the spin-orbit coupling should be negative (Figs. 10-14 and 10-15).

Now let us use an optical model (see Chap. 11), adding the spin-orbit coupling to the complex potential $(U_1 + iU_2)$. For a first approximation use Born's method, which makes the scattering amplitude from each point of the scatterer proportional to the local value of the potential. If the incident wave has the equation $e^{i\mathbf{k}\cdot\mathbf{r}}$ and contains only particles with spin up, the wave scattered through a certain small angle θ has different amplitudes when scattered from the right and left side of the nucleus; for on one side the spin-orbit coupling V increases the scattering potential and on the other side decreases it.

The scattering from the two sides of the nucleus also has a phase difference of $\pm kR\theta$ from the scattering produced by the center of the nucleus. As a result, the wave scattered through a small angle θ has an amplitude

$$(U_1 + iU_2) \exp (ikr) - D \exp [ik (r - R\theta)] + D \exp [ik (r + R\theta)] = (U_1 + iU_2 + 2iD \sin k\theta R) \exp (ikr) \quad \textbf{(10-7.12)}$$

where D is the volume of the potential depression and rise near the nuclear edge, relative to the total nuclear volume, multiplied by the potential prevailing at the nuclear edge. This potential may be considered real, since for waves originating near the nuclear surface the absorption path is very small. R is the nuclear radius. In this expression we have taken into account the phase differences and the amplitude of the wavelets originating in the scattering nucleus. The intensity of the scattered beam, obtained from the modulus square of Eq. (10-7.12) is proportional to

$$U_1^2 + U_2^2 + 4D^2 \sin^2 k\theta R + 4U_2 D \sin k\theta R \quad \textbf{(10-7.13)}$$

It is the last term that generates a left-right asymmetry in the scattering intensity. Note that in order to produce an effect, U_2 must be different from zero (i.e., there must be nuclear absorption), and that the sign of D determines whether particles are scattered more often to the right or left. At small angles, particles with spin up go to the left if the sign of the spin-orbit coupling is the one required by the shell model.

The considerations given here to show the mechanism by which the asymmetry arises are mainly qualitative. A more refined theory is beyond the scope of this book. However, Appendix F gives methods for treating

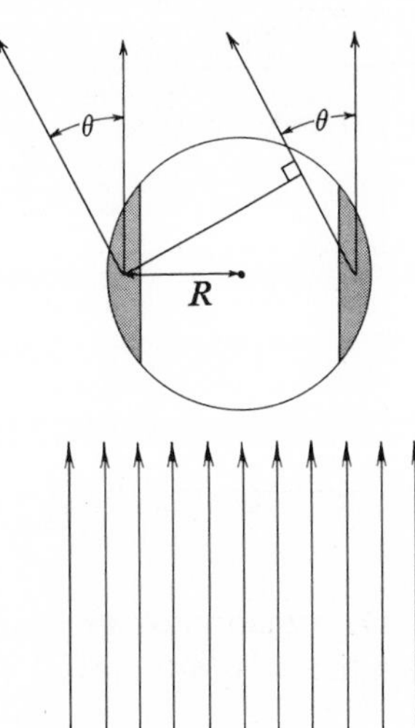

Figure 10-14 Beam of polarized protons (spin up) impinging on nucleus. The shaded area represents the region where the nuclear potential is distorted by the spin-orbit coupling. The figure is purely schematic.

polarized beams with a greater detail than that discussed above. It is shown there that the scattering of a spin $\frac{1}{2}$ particle on a spinless center is described by three numbers, each a function of energy and scattering angle. One could take as three such numbers, for instance, the differential scattering cross section, a number $\langle\sigma\rangle$ measuring the degree of polarization a scattered beam when the incident beam is unpolarized,and one of the Wolfenstein parameters shown in Fig. 10-16. These require in practice a triple scattering experiment: the first scattering polarizes the beam, the second is the scattering to be studied, and the third analyzes the final beam. In Fig. 10-16 the first and last scattering are omitted because they are not necessary in principle.

● Nucleon-nucleon scattering experiments, involving two particles of spin $\frac{1}{2}$, are much more complicated to analyze than the scattering of a nucleon on a spinless center. To completely describe the scattering, one requires in general eleven parameters that are functions of energy and angle, instead of the previous three. The number is reduced to nine if the nucleons are identical, or if one assumes charge independence. To obtain them one has to perform a number of experiments to determine the scattering cross section, polarization, Wolfenstein parameters, and, possibly, the correlation coefficients. Correlation coefficients may be obtained by starting with an unpolarized beam and unpolarized target and determining the expectation values of quantities such as $\langle\sigma_{1i}\sigma_{2k}\rangle = C_{ik}$, where

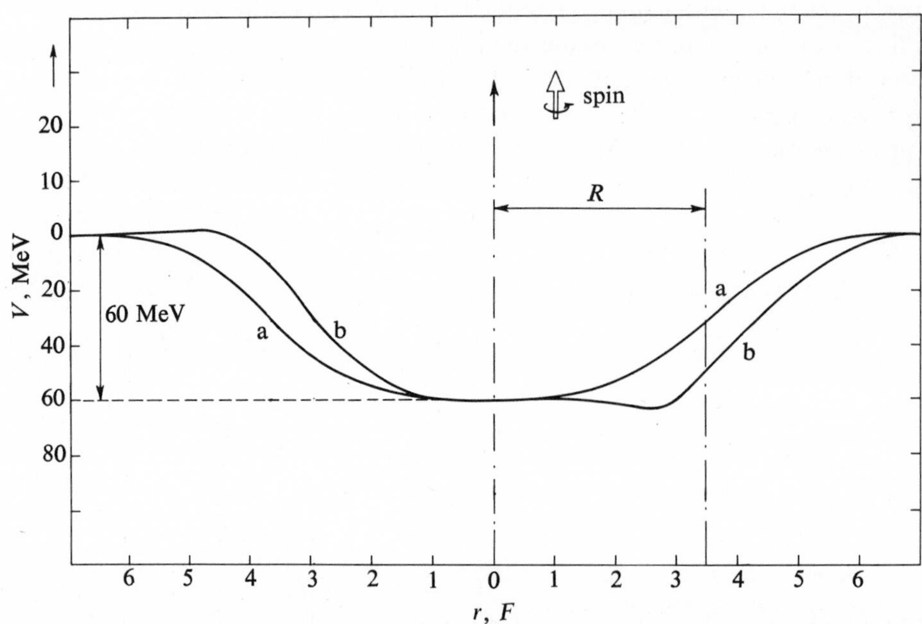

Figure 10-15 Deformation of the nuclear potential due to spin-orbit coupling for a spin-up particle directed perpendicularly into the drawing: (a) without spin-orbit coupling, (b) with spin-orbit coupling.

1 and 2 refer to the incident and scattered particles, i and k, to the direction in which the polarizations are observed (see Fig. 10-17). For instance, C_{pn} gives the expectation value that the projectile is polarized in the p direction and the recoil in the n direction. The quantities C_{ik} form a tensor that also determines the cross section when a beam polarized in direction i impinges on a target polarized in direction k. To completely determine the nine parameters mentioned above, it is possible to choose different sets of measurements: for an unpolarized beam on an unpolarized target a theoretically possible set is: $d\sigma/d\omega$, P, D, R, A, A'; C_{nn},

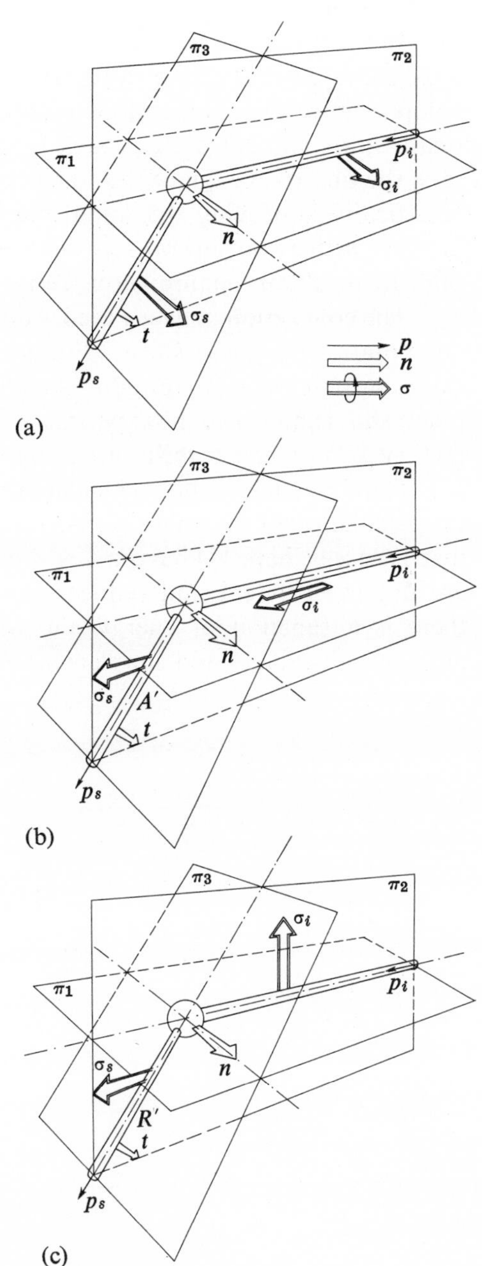

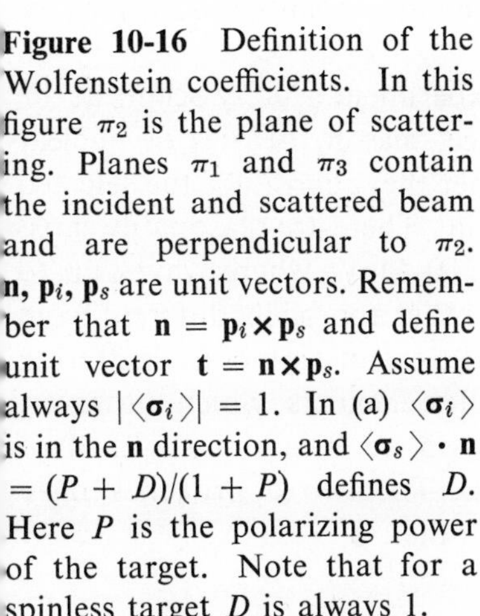
Figure 10-16 Definition of the Wolfenstein coefficients. In this figure π_2 is the plane of scattering. Planes π_1 and π_3 contain the incident and scattered beam and are perpendicular to π_2. $\mathbf{n}$, $\mathbf{p}_i$, $\mathbf{p}_s$ are unit vectors. Remember that $\mathbf{n} = \mathbf{p}_i \times \mathbf{p}_s$ and define unit vector $\mathbf{t} = \mathbf{n} \times \mathbf{p}_s$. Assume always $|\langle \boldsymbol{\sigma}_i \rangle| = 1$. In (a) $\langle \boldsymbol{\sigma}_i \rangle$ is in the $\mathbf{n}$ direction, and $\langle \boldsymbol{\sigma}_s \rangle \cdot \mathbf{n} = (P + D)/(1 + P)$ defines D. Here P is the polarizing power of the target. Note that for a spinless target D is always 1.

In (b) $\langle \boldsymbol{\sigma}_i \rangle$ is in the direction of $\mathbf{p}_i$. A is defined by $\langle \sigma_s \rangle \cdot \mathbf{t} = A$. One can also measure A' defined by $\langle \boldsymbol{\sigma}_s \rangle \cdot \mathbf{p}_s = A'$.

In (c) $\langle \boldsymbol{\sigma}_i \rangle$ is in the direction of $\mathbf{p}_i \times \mathbf{n}$. R is defined by $\langle \sigma_s \rangle \cdot \mathbf{t} = R$. One can also measure R' defined by $\langle \boldsymbol{\sigma}_s \rangle \cdot \mathbf{p}_s = R'$.

To observe quantities such as $\langle \boldsymbol{\sigma}_s \rangle \cdot \mathbf{t}$ one must perform a scattering in a plane containing $\mathbf{p}_s$ and perpendicular to $\mathbf{t}$. To observe components of $\langle \boldsymbol{\sigma}_s \rangle$ parallel to $\mathbf{p}_s$ one must first turn $\boldsymbol{\sigma}_s$ (for instance, by magnetic deflection; see Sec. 2-13), so that they become transversal to $\mathbf{p}_s$.

C_{qp}, C_{pp}, C_{qq}. With a polarized beam and an unpolarized target, or an unpolarized beam and a polarized target, it suffices to measure fewer quantities, and still fewer with a polarized beam and a polarized target. (For a detailed discussion see Bethe and Schumacher.)

To give an idea of the type of experimental data obtainable, Figs. 10-10 and 10-11 show the differential scattering cross section as a function of θ for neutron-proton and proton-proton. Figure 10-18 gives the total (elastic + inelastic) cross section as a function of energy for the same systems. Figure 10-19 shows typical polarization curves in proton-proton scattering. Figures 10-20 and 10-21 show results of measurements of A and R.

In analyzing nucleon-nucleon scattering, all available data are used to compute a set of phase shifts, as functions of energy, for the different component waves. This is done usually by starting from a random set of phase shifts and calculating back from them (using high-speed computers) the observable quantities, then changing some phase shifts and systematically improving the initial set in each trial. Such studies often produce at the end several sets of acceptable phase shifts and it may be difficult to obtain unambiguous results.

The connection between theory and experiment usually occurs at the computation of phase shifts. For instance, meson theories of nuclear forces or potentials are tested to see whether they reproduce the selected phase shifts and hence the experimental data. There are reasonably satisfactory sets of phase shifts up to about 300 MeV, where waves up to $L = 5$ and $J = 6$ have been calculated. Another approach, different from the calculation of the phase shifts, entails the calculation of a "scattering matrix" (see Chap. 11) having 4×4 complex elements, which, however, are not independent and reduce, as we said, to 9 numbers. Each of them is a function of energy and angle. The two approaches have different advantages and supplement each other. ●

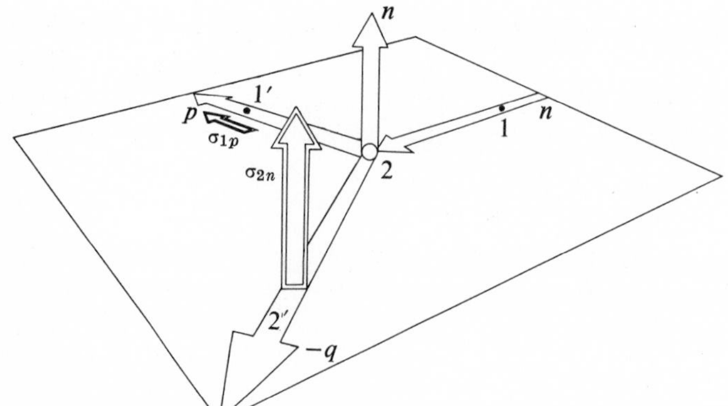

Figure 10-17 Unpolarized beam of nucleons (1) hits unpolarized target (2) and escapes with momentum **p**. The target recoils with momentum −**q**. C_{pq} is defined as the value of $\langle \sigma_{1p}\sigma_{2n} \rangle$, where σ_{1p} is the component of the spin of the scattered nucleon (1) in the **p** direction and σ_{2n} is the component of the recoiling target nucleon (2) in the **n** direction. The figure is drawn for the laboratory system.

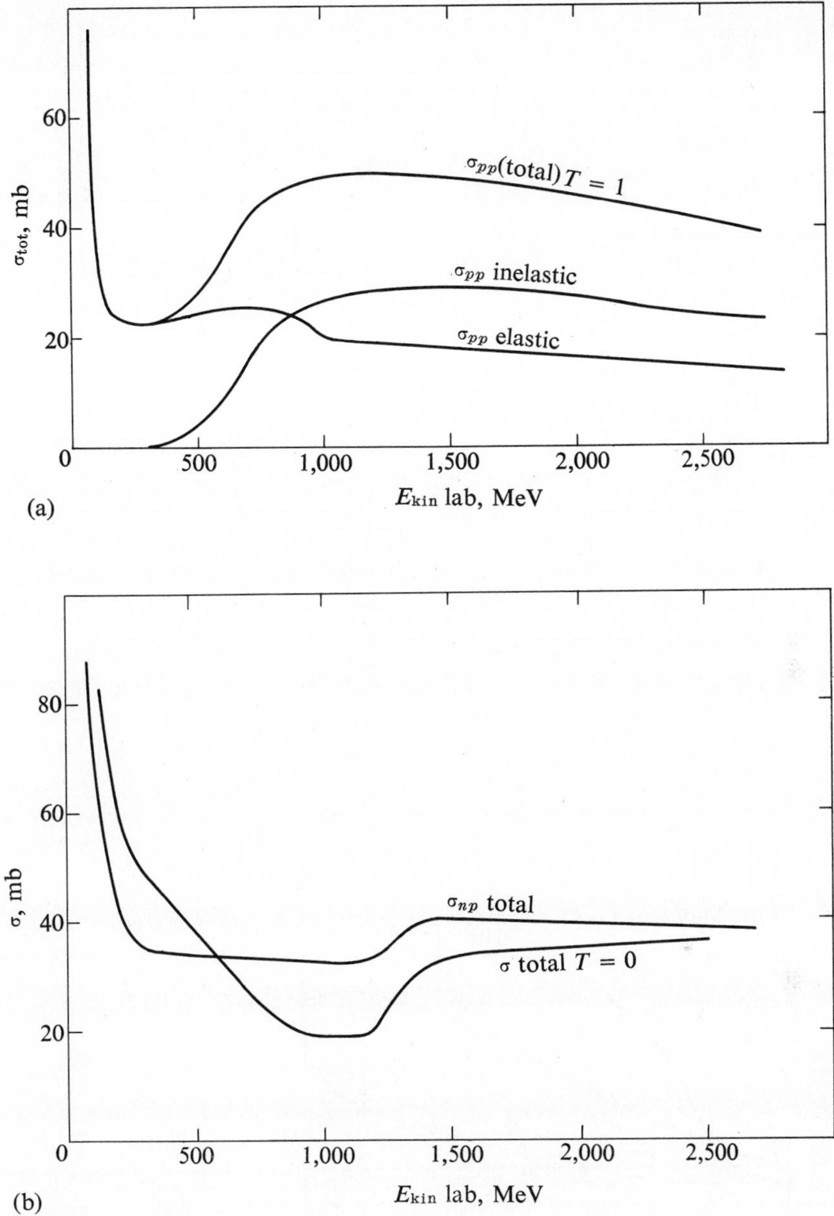

Figure 10-18 The neutron-proton total and the proton-proton total, elastic, and inelastic cross sections as a function of energy. All curves shown are empirical. The inelastic-cross-section curve has been obtained by subtraction of the elastic-cross-section curve from the total cross-section curve. The curves for pure *i*-spin states $T = 1$ and $T = 0$ are shown also. How is the $T = 0$ curve obtained?

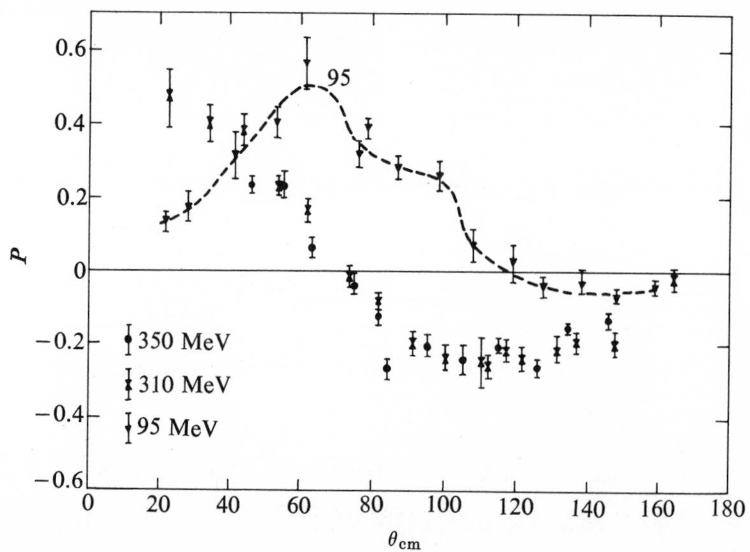

Figure 10-19 Neutron-proton measurements of $P(\theta)$ at different energies. [From McGregor, Moravcsik, and Stapp, compilation in *Ann. Rev. Nucl. Sci.*, **10**, 291 (1960).]

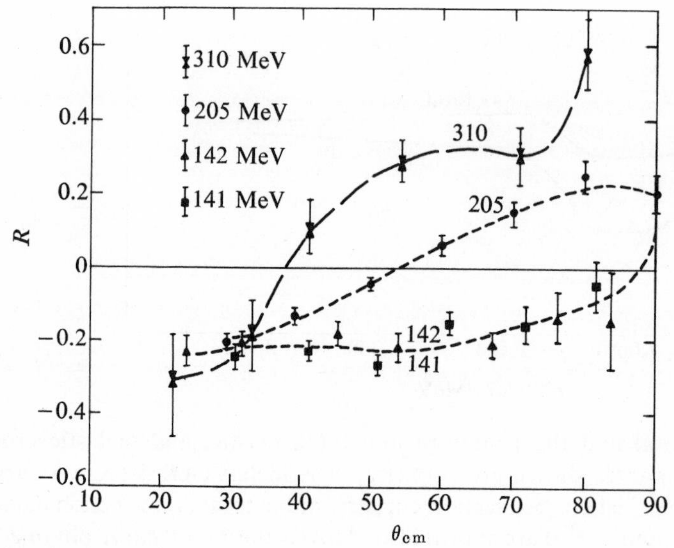

Figure 10-20 Proton-proton measurements of $R(\theta)$ at different energies.

Among the two-body problems that can be treated with good, imple approximations are the capture of slow neutrons by hydrogen and he reverse reaction, the photodisintegration of the deuteron, at least at low energies. They are interesting not only for their significance as wo-body problems, but also as examples of electromagnetic nuclear phenomena. The reactions treated are

$$n + p \rightleftharpoons d + \hbar\omega \tag{10-8.1}$$

Read from left to right one has the photodisintegration, from right to left, neutron capture. When slow neutrons are captured the energy of the gamma ray $\hbar\omega$ is 2.224 MeV.

In the capture reaction we must reach the only bound state of the deuteron, which is almost entirely $^3S_1$, starting from an *s* state of the continuum. Only *s* states are to be considered, because we limit ourselves to slow-neutron capture. The $^1S_0$ state of the continuum can pass to a $^3S_1$ state by magnetic dipole radiation according to the selection rules of Chap. 8. The $^3S_1$ states of the continuum do not give rise to radiative capture, as we shall see shortly.

The following is a classical model of the physical mechanism of the capture: The magnetic moment of the deuteron is not pointed in the same direction as the sum of the spins, because the two spins carry different magnetic moments (see Fig. 10-22). Hence, in an *n*-*p* system in the $^3S_1$ state, there is a resulting magnetic moment which precesses around the fixed total angular momentum and can, therefore, radiate. The radiation by a magnetic dipole (cf. Chap. 8) is completely analogous to that of an electric dipole moment, and the transition probability per unit time is

$$\lambda = \frac{4}{3}\frac{\omega^3}{\hbar c^3}|\mu_{fi}|^2 \tag{10-8.2}$$

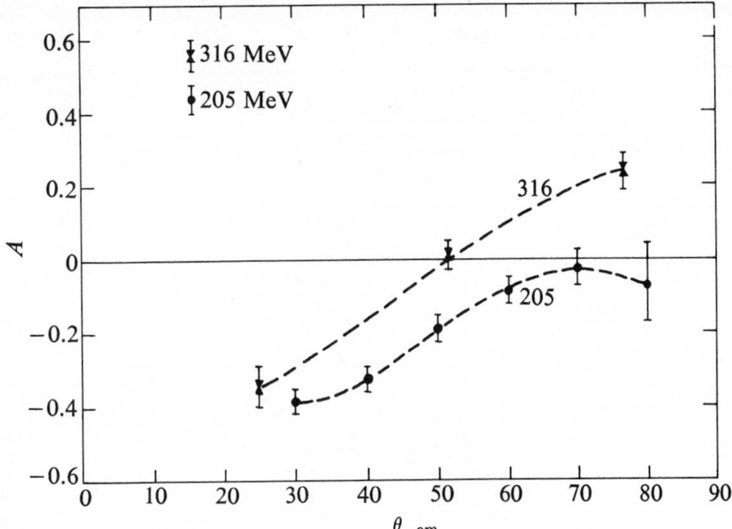

Figure 10-21 Proton-proton measurements of $A(\theta)$ at different energies.

where μ_{fi} is the matrix element of the magnetic moment between the initial and final states. The energy of the transition is 2.224 MeV, the kinetic energy of the neutron being neglected.

The final state has three eigenfunctions corresponding to the three possible values of the z component of the spin,

$$\psi_f = \frac{u(r)}{r}\begin{cases} \alpha(n)\alpha(p) & S_z = \ \ 1 \\ \dfrac{1}{\sqrt{2}}[\alpha(n)\beta(p) + \alpha(p)\beta(n)] & S_z = \ \ 0 \\ \beta(n)\beta(p) & S_z = -1 \end{cases} \tag{10-8.3}$$

where $\alpha(n)$ means neutron spin up, $\beta(n)$ means neutron spin down, etc., and, approximately [see Eq. (10-1.6)],

$$u(r) = \left(\frac{\gamma}{2\pi}\right)^{1/2} e^{-\gamma r} \tag{10-8.4}$$

with

$$\gamma = (1/\hbar)\,(M|E|)^{1/2}$$

(where $-E$ is the binding energy of the deuteron and M is the mass of the nucleon), as discussed in Sec. 10-1.

The eigenfunction of the initial state is asymptotically, for large r,

$$\psi_i \underset{r\to\infty}{\rightarrow} \frac{j(r)}{r}\frac{1}{\sqrt{2}}[\alpha(n)\beta(p) - \alpha(p)\beta(n)] \tag{10-8.5}$$

$$j(r) \rightarrow \frac{1}{k}\sin(kr + \delta_0) \tag{10-8.6}$$

where δ_0 is the phase shift for the s wave, produced by the singlet potential (see Appendix D).

This expression is valid for $r \gg$ radius of potential well. The normalization of ψ_i is such that in the incident wave there is one particle per unit volume ($\rho = 1$). The matrix element is then

$$\boldsymbol{\mu}_{if} = \int \psi^*_f \boldsymbol{\mu} \psi_i \, d\tau \tag{10-8.7}$$

where the magnetic-moment operator $\boldsymbol{\mu}$ is

$$\boldsymbol{\mu} = \mu_p \boldsymbol{\sigma}_p + \mu_n \boldsymbol{\sigma}_n = \tfrac{1}{2}(\mu_n + \mu_p)(\boldsymbol{\sigma}_n + \boldsymbol{\sigma}_p) + \tfrac{1}{2}(\mu_n - \mu_p)(\boldsymbol{\sigma}_n - \boldsymbol{\sigma}_p) \tag{10-8.8}$$

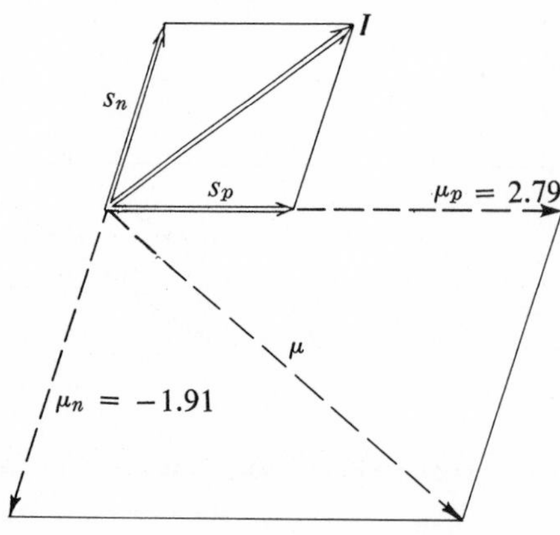

Figure 10-22 Angular momenta and magnetic moments in the neutron-proton capture. The whole figure rotates around the I axis.

ith μ_p and μ_n the magnetic moments of proton and neutron and $\boldsymbol{\sigma}$ the auli spin operator. Clearly $\boldsymbol{\mu}$ operates only on the spin-dependent part f the eigenfunction. Note that the term containing the factor $\mu_n + \mu_p$ anishes in a singlet state because there

$$\boldsymbol{\sigma}_n + \boldsymbol{\sigma}_p = 0 \tag{10-8.9}$$

he second term also would vanish if μ_n were equal to μ_p, as we should xpect according to the simple physical picture given above. As an xample we now calculate the z component of $\boldsymbol{\mu}$. We have

$$\sigma_n^{(z)}\alpha(n) = \alpha(n) \qquad \sigma_n^{(z)}\beta(n) = -\beta(n) \qquad \text{etc.} \tag{10-8.10}$$

Hence

$$\begin{aligned}(\sigma_n^{(z)} - \sigma_p^{(z)})\frac{1}{\sqrt{2}}[\alpha(n)\beta(p) - \alpha(p)\beta(n)] &= \frac{1}{\sqrt{2}}[\alpha(n)\beta(p) + \alpha(p)\beta(n) + \alpha(n)\beta(p) + \alpha(p)\beta(n)] \\ &= \frac{2}{\sqrt{2}}[\alpha(n)\beta(p) + \alpha(p)\beta(n)]\end{aligned} \tag{10-8.11}$$

n words, $\sigma_n^{(z)} - \sigma_p^{(z)}$ applied to the spin part of the singlet eigenfunction ives twice the eigenfunction for ${}^3S_1$, $S_z = 0$ and is orthogonal to those with $S_z = \pm 1$.

The matrix element is, therefore,

$$\mu_{if}^{(z)} = (\mu_n - \mu_p)\int_0^\infty \frac{u^*(r)\,j(r)}{r^2}\,4\pi r^2\,dr \tag{10-8.12}$$

Note that $u^*(r)$ is calculated with the triplet potential prevailing in the round state and $j(r)$ with the singlet potential for the continuum. Thus hey are not orthogonal. If the state in the continuum were a triplet state, $j(r)$ would be orthogonal to $u^*(r)$ and the matrix element would vanish, s we stated at the beginning of this section. The calculation of μ_x and μ_y n the case of unpolarized neutrons and unpolarized target gives the same esult as that of μ_z.

Using the relation between λ and the cross section ($\sigma\rho v = \lambda$) and he normalization $\rho = 1$, we obtain from Eqs. (10-8.2) and (10-8.12)

$$\sigma = \frac{16\pi^2}{v}\frac{\omega^3}{\hbar c^3}(\mu_p - \mu_n)^2 I^2 \tag{10-8.13}$$

where I is given by Eq. (10-8.14) below.

Here we have introduced the factor $\frac{1}{4}$ because only one-fourth the nitial n-p systems are in the singlet state, three-fourths being in the triplet tate. Another factor 3 derives from the fact that

$$\langle(\boldsymbol{\mu}_p - \boldsymbol{\mu}_n)_x\rangle^2 = \langle(\boldsymbol{\mu}_p - \boldsymbol{\mu}_n)_y\rangle^2 = \langle(\boldsymbol{\mu}_p - \boldsymbol{\mu}_n)_z\rangle^2$$

and that the transition probabilities add to each other, without interference terms.

We must still evaluate the integral

$$I = \int_0^\infty u^*(r) j(r) \, dr \tag{10-8.14}$$

Replacing the expressions for $u(r)$, $j(r)$, we have

$$\begin{aligned} I &= \frac{1}{k}\left(\frac{\gamma}{2\pi}\right)^{1/2} \int_0^\infty e^{-\gamma r} \sin(kr + \delta_0) \, dr \\ &= \frac{1}{k}\left(\frac{\gamma}{2\pi}\right)^{1/2} \frac{k \cos \delta_0 + \gamma \sin \delta_0}{k^2 + \gamma^2} \end{aligned} \tag{10-8.15}$$

To obtain a formula directly comparable to experiment, it is convenient to introduce the singlet scattering length a_s, which is related to the phase shift δ_0 by

$$k \cot \delta_0 = -\frac{1}{a_s} \tag{10-8.16}$$

[see Eq. (10-2.14)]. Expressing $\sin \delta_0$ and $\cos \delta_0$ through $\cot \delta_0$, we obtain

$$I = \left(\frac{\gamma}{2\pi}\right)^{1/2} \frac{1 - \gamma a_s}{(\gamma^2 + k^2)(1 + k^2 a_s^2)^{1/2}} \tag{10-8.17}$$

For orientation remember the numerical values

$$\begin{aligned} k &= \frac{Mv}{\hbar} = 2.20 \times 10^9 (E_{eV})^{1/2} \text{ cm}^{-1} \\ \gamma &= 0.232 \times 10^{13} \text{ cm}^{-1} \\ a_s &= -23.7 \text{ F} \\ \gamma a_s &= -5.5 \text{ F} \end{aligned} \tag{10-8.18}$$

Up to a few keV, $k \ll \gamma$, $ka_s \ll 1$; therefore, approximately

$$I = \left(\frac{\gamma}{2\pi}\right)^{1/2} \frac{1 - \gamma a_s}{\gamma^2} \tag{10-8.19}$$

Substituting this expression in Eq. (10-8.13) and measuring the magnetic moments in units $e\hbar/2Mc$, we obtain the approximate formula

$$\sigma = \frac{(4\pi)^2}{v} \frac{\omega^3}{c^3 \hbar} \left(\frac{e\hbar}{2Mc}\right)^2 (\mu_p - \mu_n)^2 \frac{\gamma}{2\pi} \frac{(1 - \gamma a_s)^2}{\gamma^4} \tag{10-8.20}$$

Note that $\hbar\omega$, the center-of-mass energy of the photon, is related to the laboratory velocity of the neutron captured by a proton at rest by

$$\hbar\omega\left(1 + \frac{\hbar\omega}{4Mc^2}\right) = \frac{M}{4} v^2 + |E| \tag{10-8.21}$$

where $|E| = 2.224$ MeV is the binding energy of the deuteron. It is clear that, for low-energy neutrons,

$$\hbar\omega \simeq |E| + \frac{\hbar^2 k^2}{M} \simeq |E| \tag{10-8.22}$$

Remembering also that $\gamma = (M|E|)^{1/2}/\hbar$ we obtain from Eq. (10-8.20) the expression

$$\sigma = \frac{6.2 \times 10^4 \text{ b}}{v(\text{cm sec}^{-1})} \tag{10-8.23}$$

which agrees very well with experiments at low energy.

10-9 Photodisintegration of the Deuteron

In the process

$$\hbar\omega + d \rightarrow n + p \tag{10-9.1}$$

at low energy, we have transitions from the bound $^3S_1$ state to the state of $^1S_0$ of the continuum. These are inverse transitions from those considered in Sec. 10-8. They are especially important at very low energies (up to a few tenths of an MeV above threshold) because the p states of the continuum require too high a relative velocity to be attained near the threshold. As the energy of the gamma ray increases, the electric-dipole transitions from $^3S_1$ to $^3P_{0,1,2}$ become predominant. The simple considerations to be developed here are valid only for energies up to about 10 MeV. At higher energies there are further effects difficult to evaluate.

The photodisintegration due to magnetic dipole radiation is obtained from Eq. (10-8.23) by applying the rule (see Chap. 11) relating inverse reactions

$$\frac{\sigma(1 \rightarrow 2)}{g_2 p_2^2} = \frac{\sigma(2 \rightarrow 1)}{g_1 p_1^2} \tag{10-9.2}$$

where g and p are the statistical weight and momentum of the final state for the cross section in the numerator of Eq. (10-9.2).

In our case, for capture, the final state has photons of momentum $\hbar\omega/c$; for photodisintegration the final state has nucleons of momentum $\hbar k$. Thus we have

$$\frac{c^2\sigma_c}{g_{p\hbar+d}(\hbar\omega)^2} = \frac{\sigma_{\text{dis}}}{g_{n+p}\hbar^2 k^2} \tag{10-9.3}$$

Now we express σ_c through Eqs. (10-8.13) and (10-8.15), taking the exact value of I given in Eq. (10-8.14), and we obtain

$$\sigma_{\text{dis}} = \frac{2\pi}{3}\frac{e^2}{\hbar c}\left(\frac{\hbar}{Mc}\right)^2(\mu_n - \mu_p)^2 \frac{k\gamma(1 - \gamma a_s)^2}{[(k^2 + \gamma^2)(1 + k^2 a_s^2)]^2} \tag{10-9.4}$$

and

$$\sigma_{\text{dis}} = \frac{2\pi}{3}\frac{e^2\hbar}{M^2c^3}(\mu_p - \mu_n)^2 \frac{(\omega_0)^{1/2}(\omega - \omega_0)^{1/2}[(\hbar\omega_0)^{1/2} + W_0^{1/2}]^2}{\omega[\hbar(\omega - \omega_0) + W_0]} \tag{10-9.5}$$

where W_0 is defined by

$$|a_s| = \frac{\hbar}{(MW_0)^{1/2}}$$

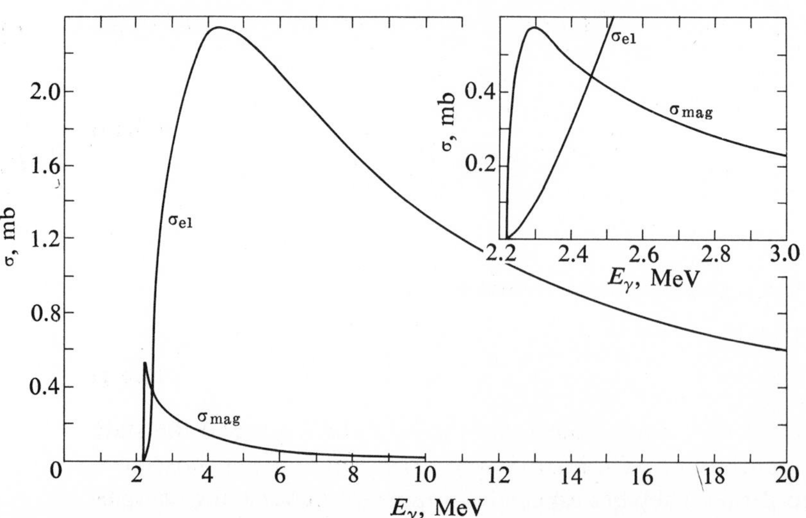

Figure 10-23 Photoelectric and photomagnetic cross sections of the deuteron. The inset shows th region near threshold energy much magnified.

just as $1/\gamma = \hbar/(m|E|)^{1/2}$ and $\hbar\omega_0 = |E|$. The electric-dipole part require the consideration of S—P transitions. We omit the calculation, limitin ourselves to the final result,

$$\sigma(E1) = \frac{8\pi}{3}\frac{e^2}{\hbar c}\frac{k^3\gamma}{(k^2 + \gamma^2)^3} \qquad \textbf{(10-9.6}$$

or

$$\sigma(E1) = \frac{8\pi}{3}\frac{e^2}{Mc\omega_0}\left[\frac{\omega_0(\omega - \omega_0)}{\omega^2}\right]^{3/2} \qquad \textbf{(10-9.7}$$

These cross sections are illustrated in Fig. 10-23.

Bibliography

Bethe, H. A., "Nuclear Many-Body Problem," *Phys. Rev.*, **103,** 1353 (1956).

Breit, Condon, and Present, "Theory of Scattering of Protons by Protons," *Phys. Rev.*, **50,** 825 (1936).

Faissner, H., "Polarisierte nucleonen," *Ergeb. Exakt. Naturw.*, **32,** 180 (1959

Gammel, J. L., and R. M. Thaler, "Phenomenology of the Nucleon-Nucleo Interaction," *Progr. Elem. Particle Cosmic Ray Phys.*, **5,** 9 (1960).

Gomes, Walecka, and Weisskopf, "Properties of Nuclear Matter," *Ann. Phys.*, **3,** 241 (1958).

Heisenberg, W., "Uber den Bau der Atomkerne. I," *Z. Physik*, **77,** 1 (1932

Hess, W. N., "Summary of High-Energy Nucleon-Nucleon Cross-Sectio Data," *Rev. Mod. Phys.*, **30,** 368 (1958).

Hull, M. H., Jr., "Coulomb Wave Functions," in (Fl E), Vol. 39.

Hulthen, L., "The Two-Nucleon Problem," in (Fl E), Vol. 39.

Kasarinov, J. M., and I. N. Silin, "Graphs on Nucleon-Nucleon Scattering from 40 to 310 MeV," in (RoC 62).

Majorana, E., "Uber die Kerntheorie," *Z. Physik*, **82,** 137 (1932).

McMaster, W. H., "Matrix Representation of Polarization," *Rev. Mod. Phys.*, **33,** 8 (1961).

Moravcsik, M. J., *The Two-Nucleon Interaction*, Oxford University Press, New York, 1964.

Nigam, B. P., "The Two-Nucleon Interaction," *Rev. Mod. Phys.*, **35,** 117 (1963).

Preston, M. A. (P 62).

Schumacher, C. R., and H. A. Bethe, "Usefulness of Polarized Targets in Reconstruction of Nucleon-Nucleon Scattering Matrix," *Phys. Rev.*, **121,** 1534 (1961).

Schwinger, J., and E. Teller, "The Scattering of Neutrons by Ortho- and Parahydrogen," *Phys. Rev.*, **52,** 286 (1937).

Stapp, MacGregor, and Moravcsik, "Nucleon-Nucleon Scattering Experiments and Their Phenomenological Analysis," *Ann. Rev. Nucl. Sci.*, **10,** 291 (1960).

Wigner, E., "On the Consequences of the Symmetry of the Nuclear Hamiltonian on the Spectroscopy of Nuclei," *Phys. Rev.*, **51,** 106 (1937).

Wigner, E., "Isotopic Spin-A Quantum Number for Nuclei," *Proc. Robert A. Welch Found. Conf. Chem. Res.*, 1*st*, *Houston* 1957 (publ. 1958), p. 67.

Wilson, R., *The Nucleon-Nucleon Interaction*, Wiley-Interscience, New York, 1963.

Wolfenstein, L., "Polarization of Fast Nucleons," *Ann. Rev. Nucl. Sci.*, **6,** 43 (1956).

Problems

10-1 Show that if deuterons are scattered by protons the maximum scattering angles in the center-of-mass and laboratory systems are 120° and 30°, respectively, but that if protons are scattered by deuterons, the maximum angle is 180° in both systems.

10-2 Plot $u = r\psi$ for the neutron-proton system at the positive energy of 1 eV in the triplet state. Indicate in the same figure the eigenfunction of the ground state of the deuteron and the corresponding rectangular potential.

10-3 Verify that for a potential in the neutron-proton system

$$V_1(r) + V_2(r)\,\boldsymbol{\sigma}_1\cdot\boldsymbol{\sigma}_2$$

$\mathbf{J}^2$, parity, $\mathbf{L}^2$, and $\mathbf{S}^2$ are constants of the motion.

10-4 Show that the expectation value of the electric quadrupole moment for a neutron-proton system in the state $^3S_1$ is zero.

10-5 If neutron and proton were bound in the deuteron in the $^1P_1$ or $^3P_1$ state, what would be the magnetic moment of the deuteron?

10-6 Calculate the effective range r_0 for a rectangular well of depth V_0 and width a.

10-7 Starting from the equation $k_t \cot k_t r_0 = -\gamma$, and assuming $E \ll V_0$, show that

$$\cot k_t r_0 \simeq -(|E|/V_t)^{1/2}$$

and

$$V_t r_0^2 \approx \frac{\pi^2 \hbar^2}{4M}$$

10-8 Assuming *n-p* and *n-n* forces to be identical, what would be the *n-n* scattering cross section at low energy (0 to 1,000 eV)?

10-9 Show that for $\lambda\!\!\!^{-} \gg r_0$ (range of forces)

$$\sigma = \frac{4\pi}{\gamma^2 + k^2} \qquad k = \frac{1}{\lambda\!\!\!^{-}}$$

10-10 Show that for $E = 10$ MeV this value agrees with experiment, but that for $E = 1$ eV there is no agreement. Explain why.

10-11 By what factor would the neutron capture cross section of hydrogen change if the singlet scattering length were positive (i.e., the singlet state were bound)?

10-12 Calculate the phase shift δ_0 for an impenetrable sphere of radius R. Compare its cross section to its geometrical area.

10-13 Neutrons of 100-eV energy, polarized with spin in the z direction, move along the x axis hitting protons having spin in a direction $\boldsymbol{\sigma}$. Find the total collision cross section.

10-14 For a proton-proton system there exist only the states ^1S, ^3P, ^1D, etc. Prove this statement and give the *i* spin of each state. Do the same thing for a neutron-proton system.

10-15 List the states with $J = 4$ for the proton-proton and neutron-proton system and classify them according to spin and parity. Indicate states that can mix with each other.

10-16 Prove Jacobson's inequality [Eq. (10-4.17)].

10-17 Show that the energy of two magnetic dipoles of moments $\boldsymbol{\mu}_1$, $\boldsymbol{\mu}_2$ is

$$V = \left[\frac{3(\boldsymbol{\mu}_1 \cdot \mathbf{r})(\boldsymbol{\mu}_2 \cdot \mathbf{r})}{r^2} - \boldsymbol{\mu}_1 \cdot \boldsymbol{\mu}_2\right]\frac{1}{r^3}$$

where $\mathbf{r}$ is the distance between the two dipoles. Calculate V for the *n-p* system and show by an order-of-magnitude estimate that it cannot account for the experimentally measured mixing of s and d states.

10-18 Show that if S_{12} is the tensor operator, then

$$S_{12} f(r)\alpha(1)\alpha(2) = f(r)\{a\, Y_2^0\alpha(1)\alpha(2) + b\, Y_2^1[\alpha(1)\beta(2) + \beta(1)\alpha(2)] + c\, Y_2^2\beta(1)\beta(2)$$

where $Y_l^m(\theta,\varphi)$ are spherical harmonics and determine the coefficients a, b, c.

10-19 Using Born's approximation, calculate the scattering cross section of protons for 100-MeV neutrons. Also give the total cross section and the cross section as a function of angle.

10-20 Show that

$$P_B = \tfrac{1}{2}(1 + \boldsymbol{\sigma}_1 \cdot \boldsymbol{\sigma}_2)$$

and that

$$P_H = -P_\tau = -\tfrac{1}{2}(1 + \boldsymbol{\tau}_1 \cdot \boldsymbol{\tau}_2)$$

where P_τ is an operator that exchanges only *i* spin between the nuclei [Eq. (10-6.16)].

10-21 The potential (Serber, 1949)

$$V = -g^2 \frac{e^{-kr}}{r} \tfrac{1}{2}(1 + P_M)$$

with $g^2/\hbar c = 0.405$ and 0.280 and $k^{-1} = 1.2$ F, has been extensively used. Show that it gives no force in odd states.

10-22 Show that for a spin $\frac{1}{2}$ particle scattering on a spinless center the spin component normal to the scattering plane cannot change. (Consider simultaneous conservation of parity and angular momentum.)

10-23 Show that in a time-reversible scattering of a spin $\frac{1}{2}$ particle on a spinless center,

$$p(-L+) = p(+L-)$$

10-24 Show that $D = 1$ for a nucleon on a spinless target. Show that $-1 + 2|P| \leqslant D \leqslant 1$.

10-25 Show that $R/R' = -\cot(\delta - \theta)$ and $A/A' = \tan(\gamma - \theta)$; θ is the scattering angle. Angles δ and γ should be found from Fig. 10-16.

10-26 Draw diagrams illustrating complete experiments to measure C_{pq} and C_{qp}.

10-27 Show that $C_{np} = C_{nq} = 0$.

10-28 Consider scattering between protons. Define suitably C_{ik} coefficients and show that $C_{pq} = -C_{qp}$.

10-29 Calculate the mean life of slow neutrons in water, assuming that they are absorbed only by radiative capture by the free protons.

10-30 Show the equivalence of Eqs. (10-9.4), (10-9.5), (10-9.6), and (10-9.7).

CHAPTER XI

Nuclear Reactions

THE STUDY OF NUCLEAR REACTIONS is one of the largest areas of nuclear and subnuclear physics. The threshold for forming pions is a suitable energy boundary between the two fields. Below this threshold we deal only with nuclear reactions in the strict sense of the word, above this threshold mesic and particle phenomena become increasingly important until in the multi-BeV region, nuclear features become of secondary importance and the interplay between pions, single nucleons, and other particles such as K mesons are the most prominent features, while the nuclear composition of targets becomes of secondary importance.

11-1 Introduction

At any energy, the conservation of energy and momentum imposes certain restrictions, improperly called "kinematic" restrictions, on the reactions. Although this part of the study is simply an application of mechanics, it is very important. It is considered in part in this section and also in Appendix G.

There are general formalisms, such as the phase-shift analysis, the scattering-matrix theory, and the Breit–Wigner theory of resonance, which are broad enough to accommodate nuclear and subnuclear phenomena. These general methods and their nuclear applications are described in this chapter, whereas the nonnuclear applications are reserved for Chaps. 14 and 15. Actually, the general methods find application even in fields apparently remote from nuclear physics (for instance, electrical engineering), thus demonstrating the deep formal interrelations between different areas of physics.

From the experimental point of view it is possible to generate beams of neutrons, protons, deuterons, helium ions, and ions of light nuclei such as C^{12} ranging over a tremendous energy interval. In the case of neutrons we go from less than 10^{-2} to 10^{10} eV. Charged particles cannot effectively react unless they have an energy comparable to the Coulomb barrier $zZe^2/R \simeq zZ/A^{1/3}$ (in MeV) of the target which sets the lower limit of usable energy. The upper energy attainable with accelerators is of the order of 10^{10} eV, but cosmic rays in rare cases give particles having as much as 10^{20} eV. Laboratory beams can be polarized and even polarized targets have been developed. These techniques give a hint of the variety of problems presented by the study of nuclear reactions.

In particle physics a severe limitation in the use of beams comes from the short life of many particles; nevertheless, there are available beams of muons, pions, K mesons, etc. Very often the most interesting target is liquid hydrogen.

The information obtainable from reactions is applicable to many kinds of questions. For instance, in nuclear-physics proper a few of the subjects treated are the assignment of quantum numbers to specific levels, nuclear models, and reaction mechanisms. Almost all the information in subnuclear physics comes from reactions. The answers to the most basic questions, such as mass determinations and the assignment of quantum numbers to particles, are derived almost exclusively from reactions studies, involving reaction kinematics, angular distributions, cross sections, polarization, etc.

Nuclear reactions at low energy are mostly of the type

$$A + a \rightarrow B + b + Q \tag{11-1.1}$$

where A is a target nucleus, a the impinging particle, and B and b the products; b is usually a light nucleus or a gamma ray. The reaction represented in Eq. (11-1.1) is often described in a very convenient notation devised by Bothe:

$$A(a,b)B$$

where the first letter is the target and the last letter the residual nucleus, those in parentheses are, first, the projectile and, second, the lighter escaping particle or particles. In this notation elastic proton scattering is represented by $A(p,p)A$, neutron capture followed by gamma-ray emission by $A(n,\gamma)B$, and so on.

The Q of the reaction is the rest-mass difference multiplied by c^2 of the left side minus the right side of the equation. If Q is positive, the reaction is exothermic; if Q is negative, the reaction is endothermic. In this case $|Q|$ is the minimum energy we must impart to the two particles at the left, in their center-of-mass system, if the reaction is to occur.

In a bombardment represented by Eq. (11-1.1), with A at rest in the laboratory, we must impart to the incident particle a an energy larger than $|Q|$ in order to obtain the reaction, because not all the kinetic energy of a is available inasmuch as the momentum of the center of mass is conserved.

Nonrelativistically, in the center-of-mass system, the velocities of a and A are related by

$$m_a v_a + m_A v_A = 0 \tag{11-1.2}$$

and for the minimum kinetic energy at which an endothermic reaction ($Q < 0$) occurs we have

$$\tfrac{1}{2}(m_a v_a^2 + m_A v_A^2) = |Q| \tag{11-1.3}$$

In the laboratory system (primed quantities)

$$v_A' = 0 \tag{11-1.4}$$

and the minimum velocity v_a' at which the reaction occurs is obviously

$$v_a' = v_a - v_A \qquad \textbf{(11-1.5)}$$

Equations (11-1.2) to (11-1.5) give for the kinetic energy of a in the laboratory system

$$\tfrac{1}{2}m_a v_a'^2 = \tfrac{1}{2}m_a v_a^2 \left(1 + \frac{m_a}{m_A}\right)^2 = |Q| \frac{m_A + m_a}{m_A} \qquad \textbf{(11-1.6)}$$

The threshold is thus obtained for a velocity v_a' such that

$$\frac{1}{2}\frac{m_a m_A}{m_A + m_a} v_a'^2 = |Q| \qquad \textbf{(11-1.7)}$$

The particle must have a velocity v_a' such that a particle having the reduced mass $\mu = m_a m_A/(m_a + m_A)$ and traveling with velocity v_a' has kinetic energy $|Q|$.

In much work on nuclear reactions, kinematic considerations are of paramount importance. In low-energy nuclear physics the non-relativistic approximation is usually adequate. In high-energy nuclear physics, on the other hand, exact relativistic formulas are needed in almost every case (see Appendix G).

The experimental study of nuclear reactions constitutes in itself a large part of experimental nuclear physics. To give a general idea of the methods, we shall mention some of the experimental approaches, without entering into technical details.

By bombarding a nucleus, say, for example, Al^{27}, with protons, we may produce a nuclear reaction, and the product may be radioactive. In our example the reaction (p,γ) would give the stable nucleus Si^{28}; the reaction (p,n) would give the positron emitter Si^{27}; the reaction (p,d) would give the positron emitter Al^{26}. A chemical or mass spectrographic separation of the products will show the type and yield of the reactions. Using a proton beam of known intensity and a known target thickness, and measuring the yields, one obtains a reaction cross section from the relation

$$\varphi\sigma\mathcal{N} = N \qquad \textbf{(11-1.8)}$$

where φ is the number of projectiles crossing the target, $\mathcal{N}$ is the number of target nuclei per unit area, σ is the cross section for the reaction considered, and N is the number of nuclei produced. This relation is valid for a target absorbing only a negligible fraction of the beam.

In our example φ could be measured by collecting the protons in a Faraday cage and thus obtaining the number of protons from their charge; $\mathcal{N}$ would be obtained from the thickness of the aluminum foil and N from the radioactivity accumulated in the target, corrected for decay. By stacking a pile of foils and considering the energy loss of the protons, we may obtain σ as a function of energy, or "excitation function." The aluminum foils may also be coated (e.g., by evaporation) with a different substance, and comparison between the activity induced in the aluminum and in the substance gives the excitation function of the substance, once that of aluminum is known. Figure 11-1 shows such an arrangement and a typical excitation function obtained by a stacked-foil experiment is given in Fig. 11-27.

To observe a scattering cross section, we could detect the scattered protons with a counter, as in Fig. 11-2. We might want to measure the number scattered per unit solid angle as a function of θ, thus obtaining the differential cross section $d\sigma/d\omega$. We may further measure the proton energy, in order to check whether the scattering is elastic or not. The energy may be obtained by measuring the range of the protons entering the counter, for instance, by putting over the counter a series of windows of increasing thickness. We thus obtain a differential cross section $d^2\sigma/d\omega\, dE$.

If we are interested in the polarization of the scattered protons, we must scatter them once more and look for a possible left-right asymmetry (Fig. 10-13). Similar measurements can be made for incident neutrons or other particles, and the flux is then measured by an integrating neutron counter such as the one described in Chap. 3 or by other suitable methods.

In the case of neutrons we are often interested in the total cross section, which is determined by a measurement of the attenuation of the primary beam. If I is the intensity of the incident beam and $I - \Delta I$ the transmitted intensity, we have, for $\Delta I/I$ small,

$$\frac{\Delta I}{I} = \sigma \mathcal{N} \tag{11-1.9}$$

However, normal neutron beams contain neutrons of different velocities. Often the velocity dependence of the cross section is of paramount interest. The primary beam must then be passed through a velocity selector, which may consist of two shutters, separated by a known distance d, opening in succession at a time interval t. The neutrons threading the two shutters must then perforce have the velocity d/t.

11-2 General Features of Cross Sections

The following considerations apply in general only to cases not involving resonances, i.e., where there is no single special nuclear level

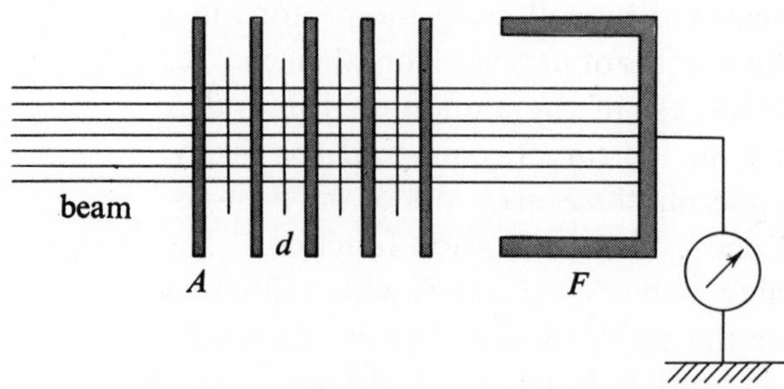

Figure 11-1 Schematic diagram of an experimental arrangement for an activation cross-section measurement. A, absorbers; d, detector foils; F, Faraday cage.

which plays a prominent role. Later we shall consider a treatment based on a generalization of the method of partial waves for collision processes (Appendix D). Here we shall be able to account for important characteristic features of some types of reactions by very simple considerations based on golden rule No. 2 (see Appendix A). This rule is derived from perturbation theory; however, many of the results we shall obtain are exact. This may be proved by more advanced methods than are available here. In particular, to obtain a rigorous formula the matrix element used in Eq. (11-2.1) must be defined somewhat differently from the way it is here.

In the reaction described in Eq. (11-1.1) we start from a definite state, specified by the initial particles, momentum, angular momentum, and polarization. On the other hand, the final accessible states form a continuum, because the conservation theorems do not suffice to single out one accessible state only. A similar situation occurs, in atomic physics, in the emission of a photon by an excited atom: the photon may escape in any direction, and this alone gives a continuum of final states.

Transitions of this type are best analyzed by using golden rule No. 2,

$$w = \frac{2\pi}{\hbar} \langle |H_{if}|^2 \rangle \frac{dn}{dE} \tag{11-2.1}$$

where w is the transition probability per unit time, dn/dE the density of the accessible final states, and $\langle |H_{if}|^2 \rangle$ an average value of the square of the matrix element connecting the initial and final states. We shall assume here that $|H_{if}|^2$ does not vary widely for the different accessible states. The density of the final states for a continuum is infinite, and at first sight Eq. (11-2.1) seems to give a divergent result. This is not the case, as can be verified by a limiting process. Enclose the system in a box of finite volume Ω. Then the levels of a free particle b, corresponding to the final state, do not form a continuum so long as Ω is finite; but we may still speak of a density of states, which is known to be (see Appendix B)

$$\frac{dn}{dE} = \frac{4\pi\Omega}{(2\pi\hbar)^3} p_b^2 \frac{dp_b}{dE} \tag{11-2.2}$$

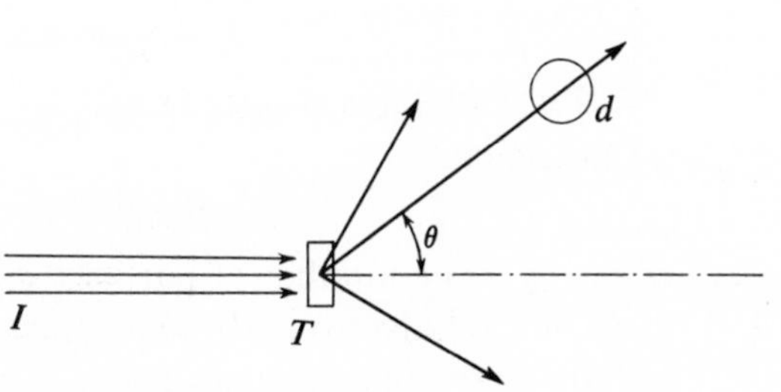

Figure 11-2 Measurement of the differential scattering cross section by the detection of scattered neutrons. The principle is based on the assumption that the sample is thin, and hence does not attenuate the incident beam appreciably. I, incident beam, T, target; θ, scattering angle; d, detector.

The matrix element H_{if} is

$$H_{if} = \int \psi_f^* U \psi_i \, d\tau \tag{11-2.3}$$

where U is the interaction energy, which will be appreciable only in the region occupied by the nucleus. However, we shall need at present only some very simple qualitative features of H_{if}, which are obtainable by general considerations.

Although in general it is not possible to calculate H_{if} explicitly, since it depends on the nuclear structure, we may say something about its form. The wave functions ψ_f^*, ψ_i are normalized in the volume Ω. In the center-of-mass system and for the relative distance $r \gg$ range of nuclear forces (neglecting for a moment Coulomb forces) we can think of ψ_i as a product of a function $e^{ikr}/\Omega^{1/2}$ describing the relative motion of a and A and two functions, one representing the internal coordinates of a and the other the internal coordinates of A. A similar expression holds for ψ_f^*. The matrix element H_{if} is thus proportional to $1/\Omega$ and H_{if} of Eq. (11-2.1) goes to 0 as $1/\Omega$. The contributions to H_{if} come only from the small region occupied by the nucleus. The remainder of the volume Ω does not contribute to the integral, because initial and final states are orthogonal. We can thus estimate H_{if} as

$$H_{if} \simeq \frac{1}{\Omega} \int \varphi_f^* U \varphi_i \, d\tau \tag{11-2.4}$$

where the integral is extended over the nucleus and the φ are functions only of the internal coordinates. Approximately,

$$H_{if} \simeq \frac{\langle U \rangle \times \text{(volume of the nucleus)}}{\Omega}$$

where $\langle U \rangle$ is an average over the nuclear volume.

For the case of charged particles, ψ, at the nucleus, is reduced by the Coulomb repulsion. Thus, if particle a is positively charged, there will be in ψ_i a factor e^{-G_a}, where

$$G_a = \frac{1}{\hbar} \int_{R_1}^{R_2} [2m_a(V_a - E_a)]^{1/2} \, dr \simeq \frac{\pi Z_A Z_a e^2}{\hbar v_a} \tag{11-2.5}$$

(see Chap. 7). This will give a factor e^{-2G_a} in $\langle |H_{if}|^2 \rangle$. Similarly, if particle b is charged, we shall have a reduction by a factor e^{-G_b} in ψ_f^*. We thus have, for charged particles,

$$H_{if} \simeq \frac{\langle U \rangle \times \text{(vol. nucleus)}}{\Omega} \exp(-G_a - G_b) \tag{11-2.6}$$

To calculate a reaction cross section starting from w of Eq. (11.2-1) we note that

$$v_{aA} n_a \sigma_{A \to B} = w \tag{11-2.7}$$

where n_a is the number of particles a per unit volume and v_{aA} is the velocity of a relative to A. In fact, $v_{aA} n_a$ represents the number of particles of type a crossing a unit surface per unit time, or, in short, the flux of a.

'his quantity multiplied by the cross section $\sigma_{A\to B}$ for the reaction of Eq. (11-1.1) gives by definition the number of transitions per unit time ·. With the normalization of one particle a in Ω, n_a is $1/\Omega$, and Eqs. 11-2.7), (11.2-1), and (11-2.2) give

$$\frac{1}{\Omega} v_{aA}\sigma_{A\to B} = \frac{2\pi}{\hbar} \langle |H_{if}|^2 \rangle \frac{4\pi}{(2\pi\hbar)^3} \Omega p_b{}^2 \frac{dp_b}{dE} \qquad \textbf{(11-2.8)}$$

As it should, the volume Ω disappears from this formula if we remember hat H_{if} is inversely proportional to Ω.

Next we replace dE by $v_b\, dp_b$, where for brevity v_{aA} and v_{bB} are lesignated v_a and v_b, respectively. Measuring p_b in the center-of-nass system and using the matrix element $\mathscr{H}_{if} = \Omega H_{if}$, which is inde-endent of the normalization volume Ω, we obtain

$$\sigma_{A\to B} = \frac{1}{\pi\hbar^4} \langle |\mathscr{H}_{if}|^2 \rangle \frac{p_b{}^2}{v_a v_b} \qquad \textbf{(11-2.9)}$$

In practice one ordinarily wants the cross section averaged over all nitial states of polarization and summed over all final states of polari-zation, such as would be found by starting with an unpolarized beam and observing outgoing particles with a detector insensitive to their polari-zation.

Equation (11-2.9) must then be slightly modified to take into account the statistical weights of initial and final states if the particles involved have spin. In our definition $\langle \mathscr{H}_{if} \rangle$ is an average of states that are not degenerate. If we take into account the spin degeneracy only, the aver-aging as far as spin is concerned means

$$\langle |\mathscr{H}_{if}|^2 \rangle = \frac{1}{g_i g_f} \sum_{if} |\mathscr{H}_{if}|^2 \qquad \textbf{(11-2.10)}$$

where the sum is extended over all possible combinations of i and f generated by spin orientation. The statistical weights g_i, g_f are, respec-tively, $(2I_A + 1)(2I_a + 1) = g_i$ and $(2I_B + 1)(2I_b + 1) = g_f$.

Experimentally the initial system is a uniform assembly of different spin states, but it is so normalized as to have weight 1. In the final state, however, we do not discriminate different spin orientations and thus we must multiply $\langle |\mathscr{H}_{if}|^2 \rangle$ by g_f. We thus have

$$\sigma'_{A\to B} = \frac{1}{\pi\hbar^4} \langle |\mathscr{H}_{if}|^2 \rangle \frac{p_b{}^2}{v_a v_b} (2I_B + 1)(2I_b + 1) \qquad \textbf{(11-2.11)}$$

where the prime specifies the particular type of cross section measured. Ordinarily we shall omit the prime, and unless otherwise specified σ indicates the cross section for an unpolarized beam on an unpolarized target.

Equation (11-2.11) permits several simple and interesting applica-tions to specific cases, giving general features of the cross-section versus energy curves for some types of reactions:

1. *Elastic scattering* (n,n) (both particles uncharged). $v_a = v_b$, therefore, $p_b^2/v_a v_b = (M_{\text{neutron}})^2$, a constant. At low energy $|\mathcal{H}_{if}|^2$ is approximately constant; therefore $\sigma \simeq$ constant at low energy (Fig. 11-3a).

2. *Exothermic reaction.* Low-energy *uncharged* bombarding particle as in (n,α), (n,p), (n,γ), (n,f) (neutron-induced fission) reactions. Q is usually positive and of the order of millions of electron volts, while neutron energy is $\simeq$ electron volts; therefore, $v_b \simeq$ constant, and $p_b^2/v_a v_b \propto 1/v_a$. Now $|\mathcal{H}_{if}|^2 \propto e^{-2(G_n+G_b)}$. However, G_n is 0 for a neutral particle and e^{-G_b} is $\simeq$ constant, since it depends on the almost constant energy of the outgoing particle. Therefore, $\sigma \sim 1/v_n$. The famous "$1/v$" law obtains (Fig. 11-3b).

3. *Exothermic reaction—charged incoming particle*, as in (p,n), (α,n), (α,γ), (p,γ) reactions. For incident energies $\ll Q$, the factor $p_b^2/v_a v_b \propto 1/v_a$ and the barrier factor e^{-G_a} are operative and $\sigma \propto (1/v_a)e^{-2G_a}$ (Fig. 11-3c).

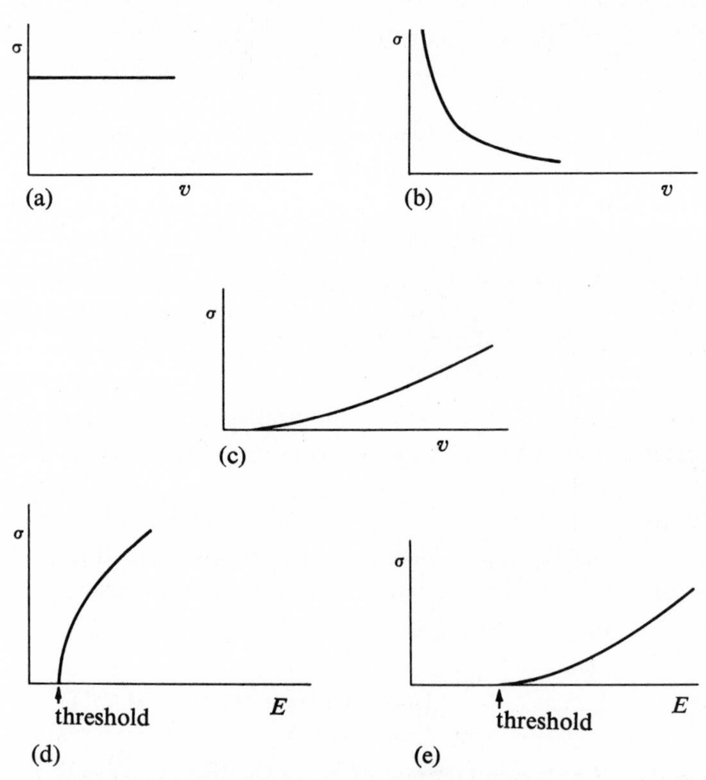

Figure 11-3 Behavior of cross sections at low energy as a function of the velocity v or energy E of the incident particle. (a) Neutron elastic scattering (n,n): $\sigma =$ constant. (b) Exothermic reactions, for example, (n,α), (n,γ): $\sigma \propto 1/v$. (c) Exothermic reaction with Coulomb barrier for projectile, for instance, (p,n), (α,n), (p,γ), (α,γ): $\sigma \propto (1/v) \exp[-2G\text{ (incident)}]$. (d) Behavior of cross sections near threshold. Endothermic inelastic scattering, for instance, (n,n'): $\sigma \propto (E - E_{\text{threshold}})^{1/2}$. (e) Behavior of cross sections near threshold. Endothermic reaction with Coulomb barrier for outgoing particle, for example, (n,α),(n,p): $\sigma \propto (E - E_{\text{threshold}})^{1/2} \exp[-2G\text{(outgoing)}]$.

4. *Inelastic scattering;* (n,n') reaction. The nucleus is left in an excited state. The process is endothermic. Q is negative and $-Q$ is the excitation energy of the nucleus. For incident neutron energies slightly above the threshold, $v_n \simeq$ constant, since the fractional change in incident energy is small. But $v_{n'}$ changes are great in this region: $v_{n'} \propto$ (excess of energy above threshold)$^{1/2}$. Therefore, $p_{n'}^2/v_n v_{n'} \propto$ (energy excess)$^{1/2}$. Hence near the threshold $\sigma \propto$ (energy excess)$^{1/2}$ (Fig. 11-3d).

5. *Endothermic reaction; charged outgoing particles* as in (n,α), (n,p) reactions. The reaction is exactly like that in case 4, except that the factor e^{-G_b} operates and is dominant. $\sigma \propto$ (energy excess)$^{1/2} \times e^{-2G_b}$ (Fig. 11-3e).

In all these reactions, no account has been taken of possible variations of $\mathscr{H}_{if}$ as shown, for instance, in resonance phenomena.

11-3 Inverse Reaction—Detailed Balance

Equation (11-2.11) allows us to establish a very important relation between the cross sections of reaction Eq. (11-1.1) when it proceeds to the right or to the left. Let us call the first cross section $\sigma_{A\to B}$ and the second $\sigma_{B\to A}$. Under very general assumptions H_{if} is hermitian, which means that

$$H_{if} = H_{fi}^* \tag{11-3.1}$$

and hence

$$\langle |H_{if}|^2 \rangle = \langle |H_{fi}|^2 \rangle \tag{11-3.2}$$

Here the two matrix elements are obviously evaluated at the same energy in the center-of-mass system. We can then write, using Eq. (11-2.11),

$$\frac{\sigma_{A\to B}}{\sigma_{B\to A}} = \frac{p_b^2\,(2I_B+1)\,(2I_b+1)}{p_a^2\,(2I_A+1)\,(2I_a+1)} \tag{11-3.3}$$

The two reactions are considered in the center-of-mass system, and the velocities and momenta are measured in that system. Relation (11-3.3) is the principle of detailed balance.

The principle of detailed balance may appear to be related to perturbation theory. Actually it is valid rigorously, provided that the two processes $A \to B$, $B \to A$ are related by time reversal. We must pay special attention to this condition when we deal with particles with spin.

The result of Eq. (11-3.3) may be obtained from statistical mechanics. Consider a box containing a mixture of A, a; B, b at equilibrium, the total energy of the system E being given. States of the system are described by giving the position and momenta of all particles and stating whether they are A, a or B, b. It is postulated that all states in the small energy interval ΔE near E have equal probability of being occupied. The justification of this postulate is one of the objectives of statistical mechanics and will not be considered here. Now divide the states into the Aa and Bb types. Our postulate asserts that the probability of an

Aa-type state being occupied is the same as that of a *Bb*-type state being occupied; hence the ratio

$$\frac{\text{No. of } Aa \text{ states occupied}}{\text{No. of } Bb \text{ states occupied}} = \frac{\text{No. of possible } Aa \text{ states in } \Delta E}{\text{No. of possible } Bb \text{ states in } \Delta E} \tag{11-3.4}$$

Now the number of possible *Aa* states in the energy interval ΔE is equal to the maximum number $\mathcal{N}$ of *Aa* pairs (obtainable from the number of particles) multiplied by the number of possible states for one pair. This last quantity is the volume of phase space available to *Aa* pairs divided by $(2\pi\hbar)^3$, that is,

$$\frac{4\pi\Omega p_a^2}{(2\pi\hbar)^3}\frac{dp_a}{dE}\Delta E$$

Thus the number of possible *Aa* states in ΔE is

$$\frac{\mathcal{N}4\pi\Omega}{(2\pi\hbar)^3}\frac{p_a^2}{v_a}\Delta E \qquad \text{because } \frac{dp_a}{dE} = \frac{1}{v_a} \tag{11-3.5}$$

Similarly the number of possible *Bb* states in ΔE is

$$\mathcal{N}\frac{4\pi\Omega}{(2\pi\hbar)^3}\frac{p_b^2}{v_b}\Delta E \tag{11-3.6}$$

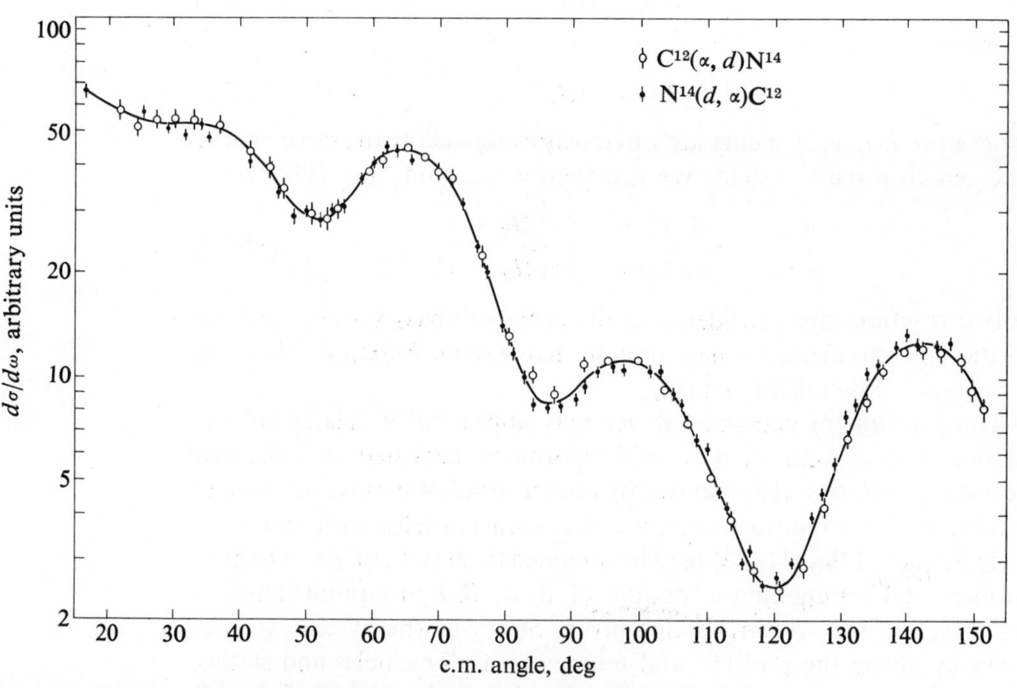

Figure 11-4 Angular distribution (center of mass) for the inverse reactions $C^{12} + \alpha \rightleftharpoons N^{14} + d$ at matched energies: $E_\alpha = 41.7$ MeV, $E_d = 20.0$ MeV (lab). Probable errors on experimental points include statistical errors and estimated uncertainties in the subtraction of small background contributions to the measured counting rates. [From Bodansky, Eccles, Farwell, Rickey, and Robinson, *Phys. Rev. Letters*, **2**, 101 (1959).]

At equilibrium the number of transitions $A \to B$ per unit time must be equal to the number of $B \to A$ transitions per unit time. The first number is equal to the number of A states occupied times the transition probability for an A state, and similarly for a B state. Equations (11-2.7), (11-3.5), and (11-3.6) give

$$v_a \frac{p_a^2}{v_a} \sigma_{A\to B} = v_b \frac{p_b^2}{v_b} \sigma_{B\to A} \qquad \text{or} \qquad \frac{\sigma_{A\to B}}{\sigma_{B\to A}} = \frac{p_b^2}{p_a^2} \tag{11-3.7}$$

We have omitted statistical weights. If we take them into account, we obtain Eq. (11-3.3) again. This equation is also valid for the differential cross section $d\sigma/d\omega$ (Fig. 11-4). To make it valid we need essentially only invariance under time reversal. The transition $A \to B$ must be the reversed of $B \to A$.

We have applied the relation between direct and inverse reactions to the photodisintegration of the deuteron and to neutron capture by protons (Sec. 10-9).

Another important application is the determination of the spin of the pion by the reactions

$$p + p \rightleftharpoons \pi^+ + D - 137 \text{ MeV} \tag{11-3.8}$$

The statistical weight on the left side would be 4 if the protons were not identical, but Pauli's principle eliminates half the states and thus we put 2 as the statistical weight. On the right side the statistical weight is $3(2I_\pi + 1)$. Thus in the center-of-mass system we have

$$\frac{\sigma_{pp \to \pi D}}{\sigma_{\pi D \to pp}} = \frac{3(2I_\pi + 1)}{2} \frac{p_\pi^2}{p_p^2} \tag{11-3.9}$$

The result from the measurements of the cross section is $I_{\pi^+} = 0$ (see Chap. 14).

Equation (11-3.4) applies if the beams involved are unpolarized. Otherwise more complicated relations must be used.

11-4 Reaction Mechanisms. The Compound Nucleus (Qualitative)

There are formal, rigorous theories based on quantum mechanics that are in principle adequate to describe nuclear reactions under very general assumptions (Kapur, Peierls, Wigner, and others). However, they are complicated and beyond the scope of this book.

Since the great variety of phenomena occurring in nuclear reactions precludes a unified treatment simple enough to be of practical use, it is necessary to use different models and approximations according to the nature and energy of the projectile and of the target.

Table 11-1 gives a survey of the most common reactions for intermediate ($25 \leqslant A < 80$) and heavy ($A \geqslant 80$) nuclei. Light nuclei have somewhat different reactions.

Following Weisskopf (Fig. 11-5) we shall try to give first an intuitive picture of a nuclear reaction, later describing in more detail special aspects of the phenomenon. We may consider the target nucleus as seen from an incoming particle as a region with a potential and an absorption coefficient. However, we must remember that this potential is due to the single nucleons composing the target nucleus. When the incoming particle hits the target it may be diffracted by the potential without losing any energy (elastic scattering). If the energy of the impinging particle is high and the absorption of the nucleus is such that it appears as a black sphere, we have the typical diffraction pattern exemplified in Fig. 11-6. If the energy of the incoming particle is low and can form standing waves in the target because it is absorbed only slightly, we shall find large scattering cross sections for the values of the nuclear radius (and correspondingly of A) that match the wavelength permitting the particle to form standing waves in the nucleus.

If the incoming particle enters the nucleus it may hit one nucleon

Table 11-1 Table of Nuclear Reactions

	Intermediate nuclei ($30 > A > 90$)				Heavy nuclei ($A > 90$)			
	Incident particle							
Energy of incident particle	n	p	α	d	n	p	α	d
Low, 0–1 keV	n(el.) γ (res.)	No appreciable reaction	No appreciable reaction	No appreciable reaction	γ n(el.) (res.)	No appreciable reaction	No appreciable reaction	No appreciable reaction
Intermediate, 1–500 keV	n(el.) γ (res.)	n γ α (res.)	n γ p (res.)	p n	n(el.) γ (res.)	Very small reaction cross section	Very small reaction cross section	Very small reaction cross section
High, 0.5–10 MeV	n(el.) n(inel.) p α (res. for lower energies)	n p(inel.) α (res. for lower energies)	n p α(inel.) (res. for lower energies)	p n pn $2n$	n(el.) n(inel.) p γ	n p(inel.) γ	n p γ	p n pn $2n$
Very high, 10–50 MeV	$2n$ n(inel.) n(el.) p np $2p$ α Three or more particles	$2n$ n p(inel.) np $2p$ α Three or more particles	$2n$ n p np $2p$ α(inel.) Three or more particles	p $2n$ pn $3n$ d(inel.) tritons Three or more particles	$2n$ n(inel.) n(el.) p pn $2p$ α Three or more particles	$2n$ n p(inel.) np $2p$ α Three or more particles	$2n$ n p np $2p$ α(inel.) Three or more particles	p $2n$ np $3n$ d(inel.) tritons Three or more particles

and lift it to a higher energy state or even to an unbound state and still preserve enough energy to leave the nucleus. This process is called "direct interaction." A typical example is given by collisions of high-energy protons in Li, where two protons emerge preferentially at 90° from each other and with energies roughly corresponding to those of a free proton-proton collision (Fig. 11-7).

The incident particle may lose so much energy that it cannot escape the struck nucleus. If this energy is transferred to a nucleon leaving it, however, bound, we have the case of formation of a compound nucleus. No nucleon can leave the nucleus until by further collisions the energy reconcentrates in one nucleon. The compound nucleus gives rise to a typical energy spectrum for the emitted particles having nearly a Maxwell distribution of velocities and a practically isotropic angular distribution. In contrast, the direct-interaction mechanism gives strong angular dependences, and characteristic maxima of the cross section as a function of energy (see Fig. 11-30).

Diffraction scattering and direct interactions are expected to occur in periods of the order of 10^{-20} sec. The compound nucleus, on the other hand, is expected to decompose in periods of the order of 10^{-16} or 10^{-17} sec. Present-day techniques do not permit the measurement of such short time intervals.

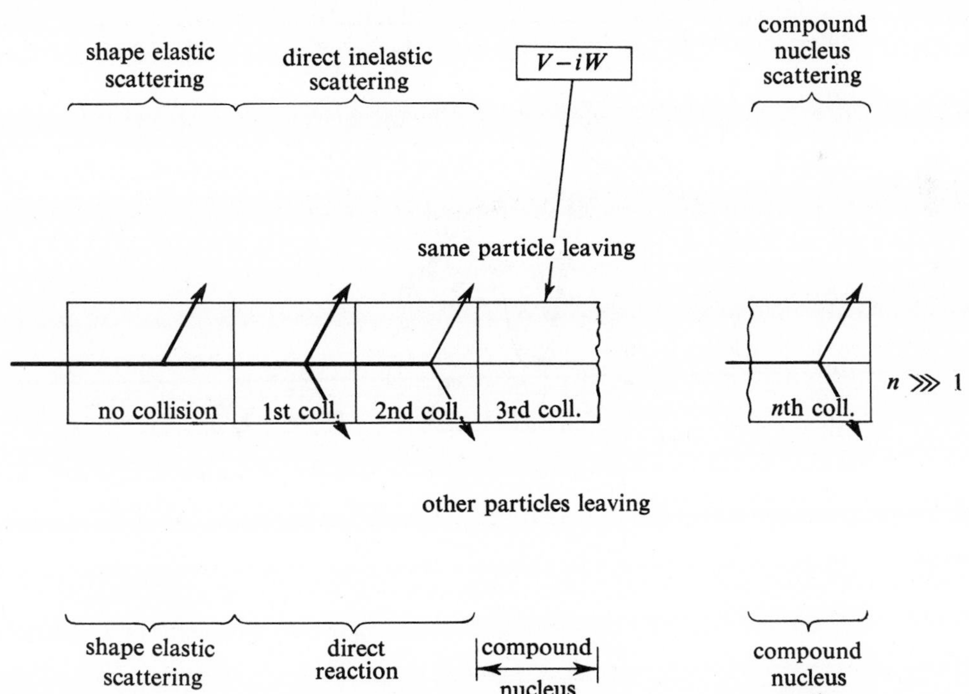

Figure 11-5 Graphic representation of the course of a nuclear reaction. As long as no collision takes place, only shape elastic scattering is possible. A first collision may produce direct reactions; later on, after many collisions, a compound nucleus is formed. [After Weisskopf.]

Some general results were obtained in Sec. 11-2 by a simplification of Eq. (11-2.1) on the hypothesis that $|\mathcal{H}_{if}|^2$ was approximately constant in the energy interval considered. However, this is not always the case. Thus, for the (n,γ) reaction produced by slow neutrons there are very important cross-section oscillations called resonances, as shown, for instance, in Fig. 11-8.

The fact that the cross section is so large only in small energy intervals suggests that there may be a sort of quantum state of the system in which the reaction occurs. This quantum state is not truly stationary. Actually, the fact that the energy region in which the cross section is anomalously large has the width ΔE suggests, according to the uncertainty principle, a mean life τ for the state, given by

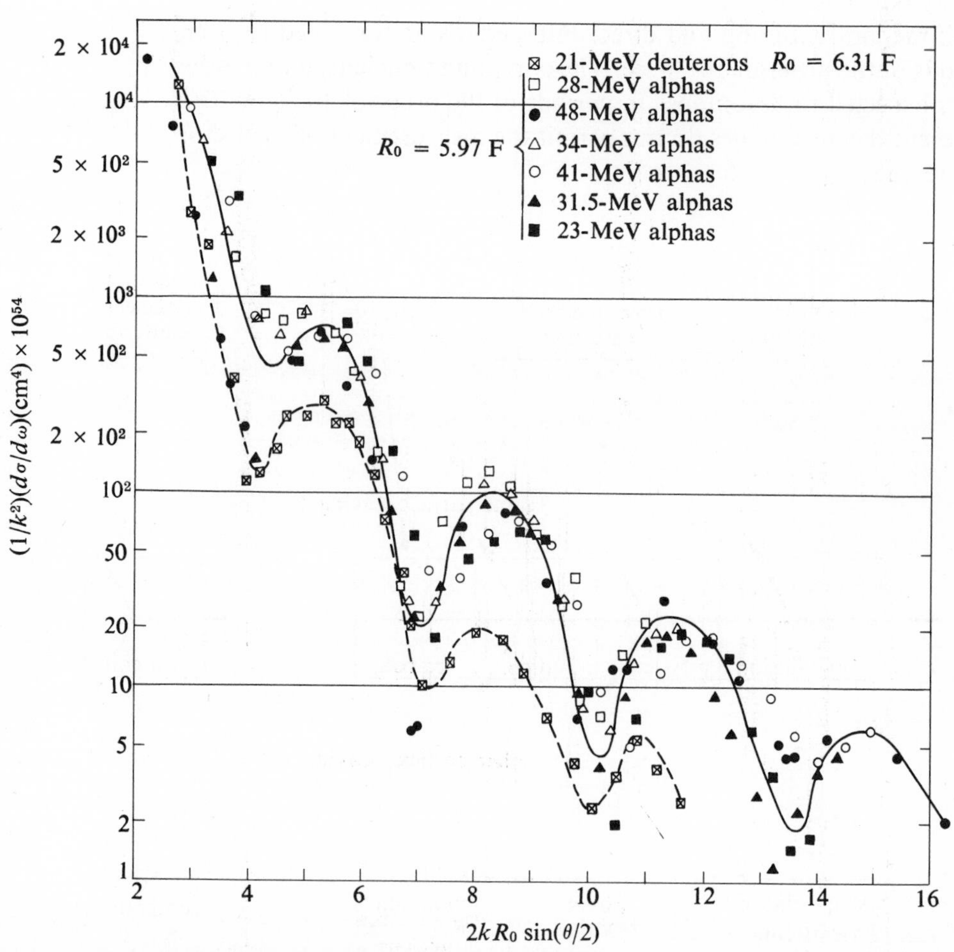

Figure 11-6 The observed elastic scattering cross section for alpha particles on magnesium divided by k^2, plotted as a function of $x = 2kR_0 \sin(\theta/2)$. k is the reciprocal de Broglie wavelength and R_0 the nuclear radius. For a black disk $d\sigma/d\omega = (kR_0^2)^2\ [J_1(x)/x]^2$ [cf. Eq. (6-3.3)]. All data refer to center-of-mass system. [From Blair, Farwell, and McDaniel, *Nucl. Phys.*, **17**, 641 (1960).]

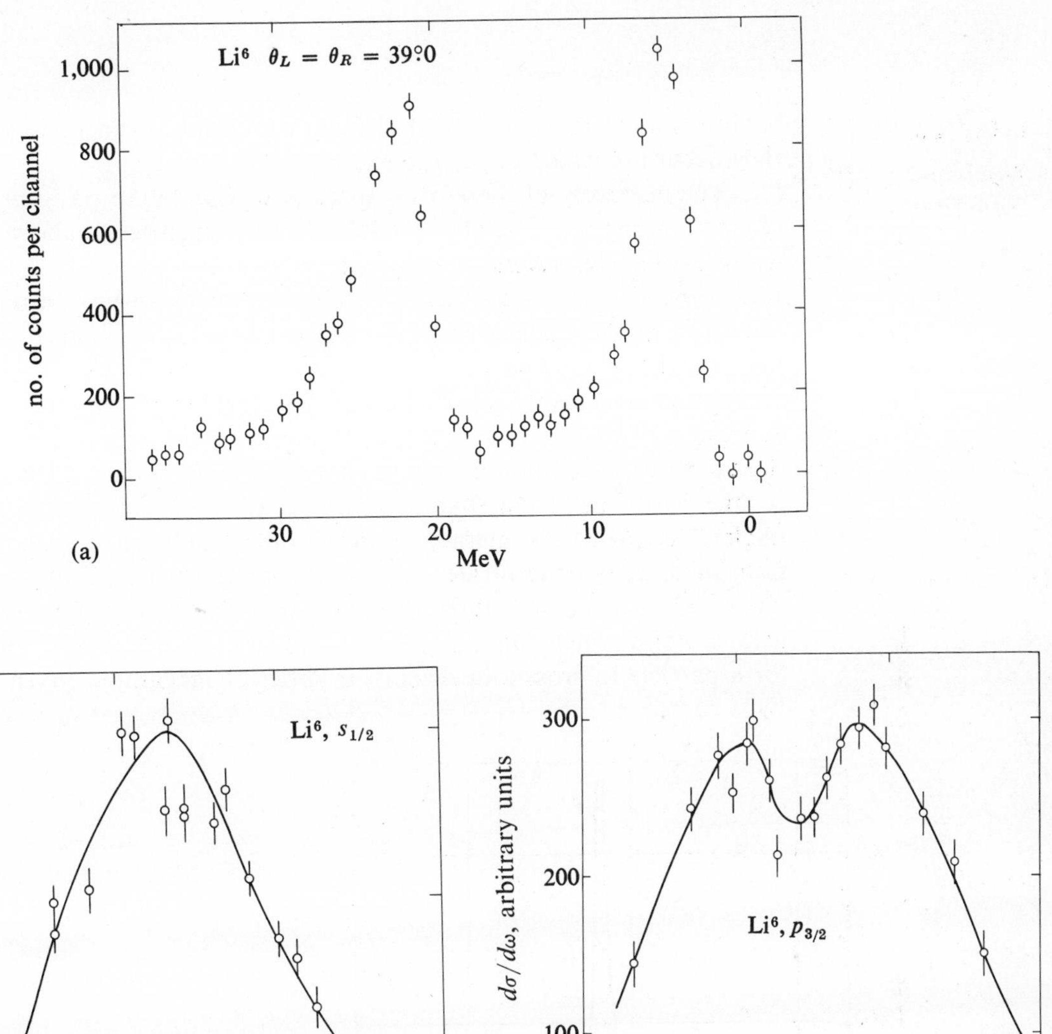

Figure 11-7 The energy carried away by each of two coincidence protons from (p, pp) reactions in Li^6 bombarded by 450-MeV protons has been measured. To the extent that the collision is quasi-elastic, the difference between the sum of these energies and the incident energy gives the binding energy of the struck proton in the nucleus. In part (a) the abscissa gives the difference between the sum of the energies of the escaping protons and the incoming proton. The two peaks correspond to the ejection of an $s_{1/2}$ and a $p_{3/2}$ proton bound with 22.3 and 5.2 MeV, respectively. (b) and (c) show the angular correlation between the escaping protons. $\theta_L = \theta_R$ are deflections left and right. For protons at rest the curve would be a delta function at 45°. The broadening is due to the momentum of the struck proton. Note the difference between collisions with s and p protons and the minimum in the center of distribution for $p_{3/2}$ protons. [Courtesy Tyren, Kullander, and Ramachandran.]

$$\frac{\hbar}{\tau} = \Delta E \equiv \Gamma \tag{11-4.1}$$

Such unstable states are called virtual states, and the energies at which they occur are called resonance energies.

The discovery of these resonances gave rise to the physical model of the "compound nucleus" (Bohr, 1936) mentioned above. Bohr assumed that the nuclear reaction proceeds in two steps: (1) the formation from $A + a$ of a compound nucleus C, which survives a relatively long time and (2) later decomposes into $B + b$. It is assumed that the motions in the intermediate state C are very complicated and that the compound nucleus "forgets" how it was formed, except for its total energy, parity, and angular momentum. The main reason for the long duration of the compound state is that the energy initially concentrated in one particle is soon shared by many other particles of the struck nucleus, because they interact with each other. Only when, by a fluctuation, the energy concentrates again on another particle, does the latter one escape. In the meantime the energy may also be lost by emission of gamma rays, which thus "compete" with the other process. The time for a particle to cross a nucleus is, in order of magnitude, given by the

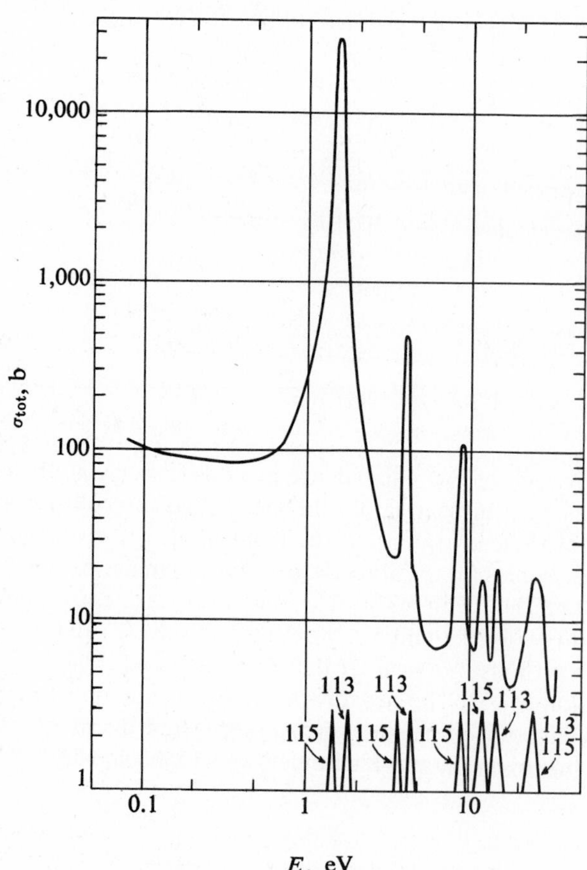

Figure 11-8 The total cross section of indium for neutrons, showing prominent resonances. The peaks are assigned to In^{113} (4.23 per cent) and In^{115} (95.77 per cent) by the triangles on the abscissa, which indicate also the resolution of the instrument. [V. L. Sailor and L. B. Borst, *Phys. Rev.*, **87**, 161 (1952).]

nuclear radius divided by the velocity of the particle, which is approximately $0.1c \sim 10^9$ cm sec^{-1}. This interval is $\sim 10^{-22}$ sec, and is called the "characteristic nuclear time." The time for emission of gamma rays is typically of the order 10^{-13} sec; to account for competition then, it becomes necessary to explain why a particle may stay in a nucleus 10^{10} characteristic times. The sharing of the energy by many nucleons provides such a reason.

With this simple picture we may split the collision into a first-phase formation of the compound nucleus for which we have a certain cross section σ_c, followed by a decomposition of the compound nucleus, with emission of the different particles n, p, γ, α, etc. Calling the probability of emission of each of them Γ_i, we may formally write the cross section for different processes as

$$\sigma_i = \sigma_c \frac{\Gamma_i}{\sum_i \Gamma_i} \qquad \textbf{(11-4.2)}$$

The program implicit in this formula must be implemented by the evaluation of σ_c and of Γ_i, which is a difficult problem. However, in its great simplicity, the formula gives a useful insight.

As an immediate application of the general ideas involved we shall first give an example in which compound-nucleus formation and decay seem to be directly verified. Consider the bombardment $p + Cu^{63}$ or $\alpha + Ni^{60}$. The same compound nucleus Zn^{64} is formed in both cases, and if the proton and the α have suitable energies, the compound nucleus also will have the same excitation energy. Its further "destiny" must be independent of the mode of formation according to the compound-nucleus hypothesis, and hence the ratio between the cross sections for emission of one neutron, one neutron and one proton, etc., must be constant (Fig. 11-9).

For the formation cross section σ_c (if the virtual states are separated by energy intervals large compared with their width), Breit and Wigner (1936), on the basis of a theoretical calculation stressing the analogy with light absorption, suggested the following form:

$$\sigma_c = \frac{A/v}{(E - E_0)^2 + \Gamma^2/4} \qquad \textbf{(11-4.3)}$$

where v is the velocity of the incident particle, E its energy, E_0 the resonance energy, Γ the level width, and A a constant depending on the specific reaction. This formula will be further discussed in Sec. 11-10.

In the case of light nuclei the levels of the compound nucleus are often widely separated, and their quantum numbers are known. The investigation of light nuclei is now well developed, and there are important summaries of this work (see the Bibliography).

We shall briefly review Be^8 as an example of an unstable light nucleus and its levels (Fig. 11-10). This nucleus may decay from its ground state, whose energy we shall assume to be 0, into two alpha particle according to

$$Be^8 = He^4 + He^4 + 94 \text{ keV}$$

The mean life for such a decay is very short because, although the reaction is barely exothermic, the Coulomb barrier is low. Calculation and indirect measurements put the mean life in the range of 10^{-15} to 10^{-16} sec^{-1}, corresponding to a width of 0.66 to 6.6 eV.

Information on the excited levels is obtained from reactions such as

$$Li^7 + H^1 \rightarrow Be^8 \rightarrow 2He^4$$
$$Li^7 + H^1 \rightarrow Be^7 + n$$

and from alpha-alpha scattering. For the last process the cross section should show a resonance at 2 × 94 keV (laboratory system), but this has thus far been unobservable because it is very narrow. A second resonance is seen at 2.90 MeV (in the center-of-mass system). It is broad

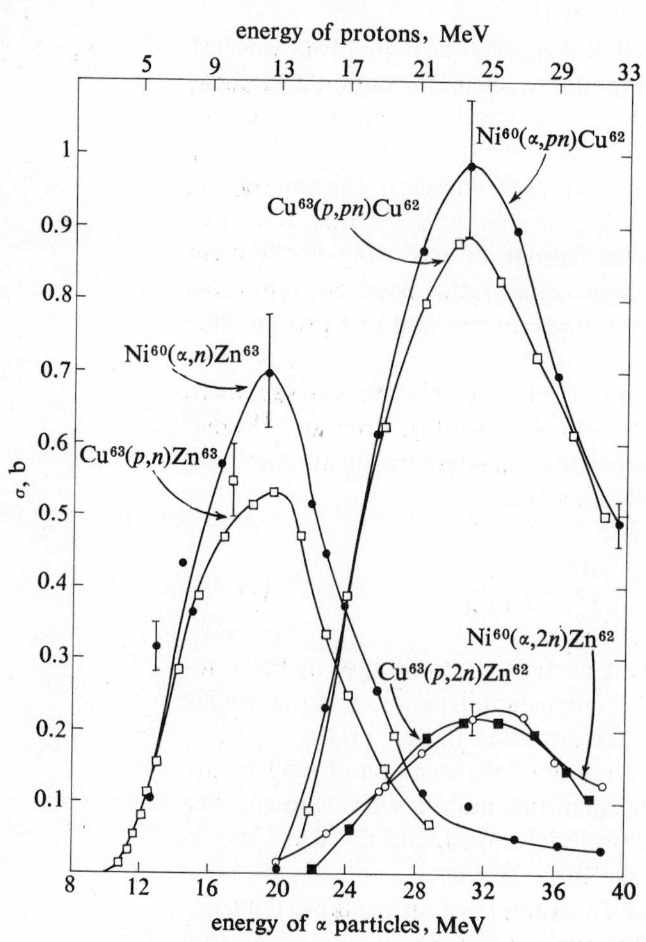

Figure 11-9 Yields of the decay products of the compound nucleus Zn^{64} according to Ghoshal. The proton energy scale has been shifted 7 MeV to the right. [S. N. Ghoshal, *Phys. Rev.*, **80**, 939 (1950).]

(1.2 MeV), corresponding to the short life of the excited state before it decomposes into two He^4 nuclei.

Another level corresponding to an alpha-alpha state in Be^8 is to be found at about 11.4 MeV (center of mass). It is several MeV wide. There are, however, levels in Be^8 that are stable with respect to disintegration

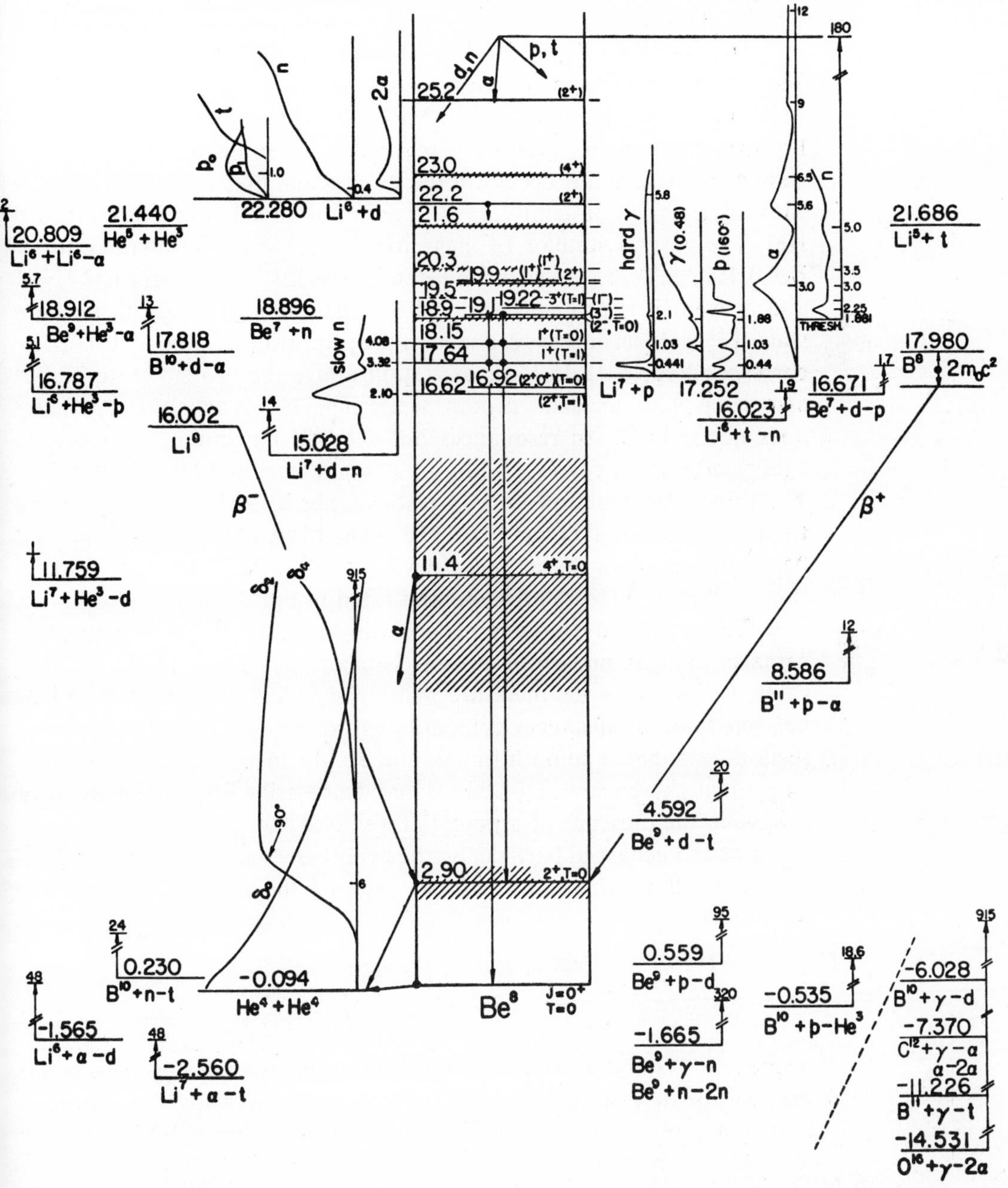

Figure 11-10 Energy levels of Be^8 with nuclear reactions leading to their formation. [From NRC-NAS Nuclear Data Sheets.]

into two He^4. This is best understood by noting that, for a system of two identical particles, interchange of the particles is equivalent to reflection about the center of the line joining the particles. Alpha particles are bosons; hence interchange must leave the wave function unaltered. The corresponding states must thus be of even parity and have $I = 0, 2, 4, 6, 8$, etc. We conclude that only even-parity states of Be^8, with I even, can decay into two He^4. Odd-I states of Be^8 can decay into even or odd-I states of Be^8 by gamma emission, according to the type of radiation: $E1$, $E2$, $M1$, etc.

The reaction $Li^7(p,\gamma)Be^8$ has a prominent narrow resonance at 441 keV proton energy, giving rise to a narrow line of gamma rays of 17.64 MeV and a broad one of $\sim$14.7 MeV. The lines correspond to transitions from a state at 17.64 MeV, reached by proton capture in Li^7. This state has $I = 1$, and it decays to the ground and first excited state of 2.9 MeV by emission of gamma rays. It does not directly break up into two He^4. The ground state of Li^7 has character $p_{3/2}$; the resonant state of Be^8 0.441 MeV above the ground state of the Li^7 + H system has $I = 1$ and is even: it is probably reached by absorption of a proton in the p state. Li^7 + H has other resonances, too; for instance, one at 1.03 MeV corresponding to 18.15 MeV excitation above the ground state of Be^8 associated with inelastic proton scattering. The reaction $Li^7(p,\alpha)He^4$ does not show sharp resonances but a broad maximum for a proton energy of 3 MeV, corresponding to a broad level at 19.9 MeV for Be^8. The $Li^7(p,n)Be^7$ reaction shows a resonance at 2.25 MeV, corresponding to an odd I state of Be^8 at 19.2 MeV. The $Li^6(d,\alpha)He^4$ reaction shows a peak corresponding to an even I level of Be^8 at 22.5 MeV. Other reactions and their interpretation are indicated in Fig. 11-10.

Well-separated energy levels occur in heavy nuclei for slow neutron capture, in light nuclei for proton bombardment, and in many other cases. Often, however, there are many resonances close to each other, i.e., separated by distances comparable to or smaller than Γ. The cross section σ_c is then a smooth function of E. For instance, at high energy, where many levels are involved, σ_c may be described by the behavior of a wave in the presence of a potential well (see Sec. 11-7).

For an uncharged particle, on the hypothesis that an ingoing neutron does not scatter elastically without entering the nucleus, one obtains for s waves

$$\sigma_c = \pi\lambda\!\!\!^{-2} \frac{4kK}{(k + K)^2} \tag{11-4.4}$$

where $k = 1/\lambda\!\!\!^{-}$ and K is the wave number inside the nucleus. This equation will be derived later [see Eq. (11-6.32)]. Numerically, for nucleons impinging on heavy targets, $\pi\lambda\!\!\!^{-2} = 0.65 \times 10^{-18} E^{-1}$ (eV) cm^2 and $K = 2.2 \times 10^9\,[E(\text{eV})]^{1/2}$ cm^{-1}.

In the case of a uniform potential well of depth V_0 we have

$$k^2 + K_0^2 = K^2 \tag{11-4.5}$$

where

$$\frac{\hbar^2 K_0^2}{2M} = V_0$$

Equation (11-4.4) gives for $K_0 \gg k$ (slow particles)

$$\sigma_c = \frac{4\pi\lambda\!\!\!^{-}}{K_0} \propto \frac{1}{v} \qquad \textbf{(11-4.6)}$$

Equation (11-4.6) for high energy gives $\sigma_c \to 0$, but we must remember that this refers only to the s wave and not to the total cross section for the formation of a compound nucleus (Fig. 11-11).

For charged particles Eq. (11-4.4) must be completed in order to take into account the Coulomb repulsion. This is obtained by multiplying the right side by a transmission factor $T \simeq e^{-G}$, where G is the Gamow barrier factor. Detailed numerical calculations for this are given by Blatt and Weisskopf (see also Fig. 11-12).

At still higher energies, when the de Broglie wavelength of the incident particle a is small compared with the nuclear radius, the cross section for the formation of the compound nucleus by neutral particles may be considered classically as the geometrical cross section

$$\sigma_c = \pi R^2 \qquad \textbf{(11-4.7)}$$

For charged particles, the projectile, in order to touch the nucleus, must have (1) enough energy to overcome the potential barrier, and (2) a suitable impact parameter. We obtain by an elementary consideration

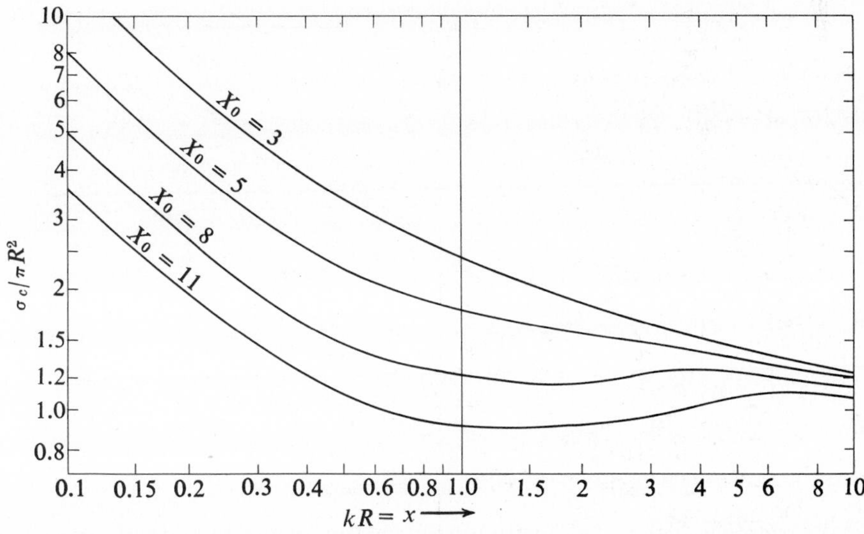

Figure 11-11 Cross section for the formation of the compound nucleus by neutrons. The abscissa is $x = kR = 0.218E^{1/2}$ if E is given in MeV and R in fermis. $X_0 = K_0R$ and is roughly equal to the nuclear radius in fermis. [(BW 52).]

$$\sigma_c = \pi R^2 \left(1 - \frac{V}{E}\right) \quad \text{for } E > V$$
$$= 0 \quad \text{for } E < V \tag{11-4.8}$$

where $V = Zze^2/R$ is the Coulomb barrier and E is the kinetic energy of the projectile (in the center-of-mass system).

For further evaluation of Eq. (11-4.2) we note that in some cases the qualitative behavior of Γ_i may be easily understood. For instance for a heavy nucleus and an incoming slow neutron of a few electron volts energy, it is clear that Γ_γ will not depend on the energy of the bombarding neutron. In fact, on capture there are several MeV of excitation, owing to the neutron binding energy, and the effect of the kinetic energy of the incoming neutron is negligible. On the other hand, for neutron remission Γ_n is proportional to v, as can be seen by an application of Eq. (11-2.1), keeping in mind that under the circumstances $dN/dE \propto v_n$. Moreover in this physical situation $\Gamma_\gamma \gg \Gamma_n$.

The combination of Eq. (11-4.2) and Eq. (11-4.3) for σ_c and the evaluations given above provide a qualitative justification of the Breit–Wigner formulas,

$$\sigma(n,\gamma) = \frac{A/v}{(E - E_0)^2 + \Gamma^2/4} \tag{11-4.9}$$

$$\sigma(n,n') = \frac{A}{(E - E_0)^2 + \Gamma^2/4} \tag{11-4.10}$$

which will be discussed more thoroughly later on.

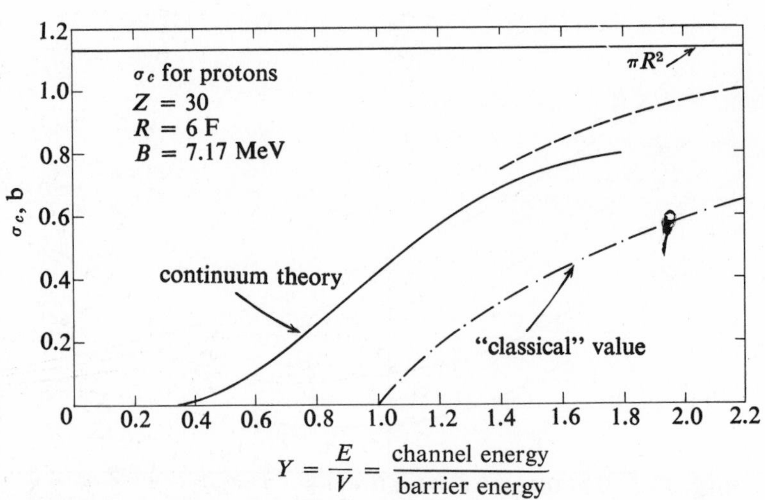

Figure 11-12 An example of the cross section for formation of the compound nucleus by protons. The solid curve represents the best theoretical value, the broken curve represents the approximation $\sigma_c \simeq \pi(R + \lambda\!\!\!^-)^2 \{1 - [V(R + \lambda\!\!\!^-)/E]\}$, and the dotted-and-dashed curve represents the classical value [Eq. (11-4.8)]. The asymptotic value, πR^2, is also shown. [(BW 52).]

However, there are conflicts between some experimental facts and the compound-nucleus picture. In proton bombardment, (p,p) reactions are often favored over (p,n) reactions, even when the opposite should be true, because of the barrier effect on the outgoing particle. In inelastic scattering, small energy losses are favored. Angular distributions favor the forward direction in reactions such as (p,α), etc. These facts point to the existence, already mentioned at the beginning of this section, of reaction mechanisms different from compound-nucleus formation.

11-5 Formal Developments—Scattering Matrix

To give a slightly more formal description of a large number of complex phenomena in a unified way, let us return to the theory of scattering of a spinless particle by a center of force (Appendix D) and generalize it so as to encompass the case where the impinging particle reacts with the scattering center.

Now we introduce the "channel" concept (Wigner), which is useful in considering nuclear reactions. Suppose that we have a particle a impinging on nucleus A, the whole system being specified completely from the quantum-mechanical point of view (i.e., in a definite quantum state). After this collision we may find the same particle and nucleus in a different quantum state, or even a different particle and a residual nucleus. The initial state is called the "entrance channel," and any pair of possible residual nucleus and emerging particle, each in a definite quantum state, is called a "reaction channel." A special channel is that of the elastic collision.

To generalize collision theory to the nonelastic case, consider again an incident plane wave, which may be expressed asymptotically as

$$e^{ikz} \rightarrow \frac{1}{2kr} \sum_l (2l + 1)i^{l+1}\left\{\exp\left[-i\left(kr - \frac{\pi}{2}l\right)\right] - \exp\left[i\left(kr - \frac{\pi l}{2}\right)\right]\right\} P_l(\cos\theta) \qquad \textbf{(11-5.1)}$$

where k represents $1/\lambda\!\!\!^{-} = Mv/\hbar = p/\hbar$, M being the reduced mass of the system and v the relative velocity of projectile and target, and where $z = r\cos\theta$.

The nuclear reaction changes expression [Eq. (11-5.1)] by acting on the outgoing wave only (i.e., on the coefficient of e^{ikr}/r). The asymptotic expression for the wave function is thus

$$\psi(r) = \frac{1}{2kr} \sum_l (2l + 1)i^{l+1}\left\{\exp\left[-i\left(kr - \frac{\pi l}{2}\right)\right] - \eta_l \exp\left[i\left(kr - \frac{\pi l}{2}\right)\right]\right\} P_l(\cos\theta) \qquad \textbf{(11-5.2)}$$

The scattered wave is obtained by observing that

$$\psi(r) = e^{ikz} + \psi_{\text{scattered}} \qquad \textbf{(11-5.3)}$$

and thus subtracting from Eq. (11-5.2) Eq. (11-5.1) we have

$$\psi_{sc} = \frac{1}{2kr} \sum_l (2l + 1) i^{(l+1)} (1 - \eta_l) e^{i(kr - \pi l/2)} P_l (\cos \theta) \qquad \textbf{(11-5.4)}$$

which can also be written

$$\psi_{sc} = \frac{e^{ikr}}{r} \sum_l \left(\frac{2l + 1}{2k}\right) i(1 - \eta_l) P_l(\cos \theta) \qquad \textbf{(11-5.5)}$$

In the case of purely elastic scattering $\eta_l = e^{2i\delta_l}$, where δ_l is the usual real phase shift and hence $|\eta_l| = 1$. In the case of nonelastic scattering, $|\eta_l| < 1$, because some of the particles from the entrance channel are diverted to different channels. Then Eq. (11-5.5) is not a solution of a Schrödinger equation for a stationary state in the ordinary sense, implying the conservation of particles, because it describes only part of the phenomenon, namely, elastic scattering. We can easily find from Eq. (11-5.5) the elastic-scattering cross section, but we shall also find that the flux removed by the target from the impinging wave is greater than the flux corresponding to the particles scattered elastically. The difference is due to particles that have disappeared following inelastic collisions, nuclear reactions, and, in general, diversion from the elastic-scattering channel.

The scattering cross section is obtained by dividing the flux corresponding to ψ by the flux incident on the unit surface, which for the plane wave e^{ikz} is v.

The flux corresponding to ψ_{sc} through a sphere of radius r_0 is, according to the rules of quantum mechanics,

$$\frac{\hbar r_0^2}{2iM} \int \left(\frac{\partial \psi_{sc}}{\partial r} \psi_{sc}^* - \frac{\partial \psi_{sc}^*}{\partial r} \psi_{sc} \right) d\omega \qquad \textbf{(11-5.6)}$$

By taking into account the relation

$$\int P_l P_{l'} \, d\omega = \frac{4\pi}{2l + 1} \delta_{ll'} \qquad \textbf{(11-5.7)}$$

Eqs. (11-5.5) to (11-5.7) yield, for the partial elastic-scattering cross section of angular momentum l,

$$\sigma_{sc}{}^l = \pi\lambda\!\!\!^{-2}(2l + 1)|1 - \eta_l|^2 \qquad \textbf{(11-5.8)}$$

The total flux entering a large sphere of radius r_0 may be computed from Eq. (11-5.6) now, by using $\psi(r)$, not ψ_{sc}. We obtain a formula similar to Eq. (11-5.6), and on evaluation we find, for the wave of angular momentum l, a net ingoing flux of

$$\pi\lambda\!\!\!^{-2} v(2l + 1)(1 - |\eta_l|^2) \qquad \textbf{(11-5.9)}$$

particles per second. These are lost to the incident beam and do not reappear in the scattered beam. They have "reacted" with the target, and the corresponding reaction cross section is

$$\sigma_r{}^l = \pi\lambda\!\!\!^{-2}(2l + 1)(1 - |\eta_l|^2) \qquad \textbf{(11-5.10)}$$

Note that if $|\eta_l| = 1$, this cross section vanishes, because the scattering is purely elastic. Obviously $|\eta_l|^2 \leqslant 1$; otherwise there would be a negative reaction cross section or creation of particles.

The total cross section is the sum of $\sigma_r{}^l$ and $\sigma_{sc}{}^l$ and is given by

$$\sigma_t{}^l = 2\pi\lambda\!\!\!^{-2}(2l+1)\,[1 - \mathrm{Re}(\eta_l)] \tag{11-5.11}$$

These expressions give rise to interesting and important limiting cases (Figs. 11-13 and 11-14). For instance, to maximize the total cross section we must have $\eta_l = -1$; the cross section is then entirely due to elastic scattering and becomes

$$\sigma_{sc}{}^l \max = 4\pi\lambda\!\!\!^{-2}(2l+1) \tag{11-5.12}$$

For *s* waves

$$\sigma_{sc}{}^0 \max = 4\pi\lambda\!\!\!^{-2} \tag{11-5.13}$$

Equation (11-5.10) admits of a semiclassical interpretation. For angular momentum between l and $l+1$, particles in the incident beam must have an impact parameter between $b_l = l\hbar/p$ and $b_{l+1} = (l+1)\hbar/p$. The area between the two circles of radii b_l and b_{l+1} is

$$\pi\frac{\hbar^2(2l+1)}{p^2} = \pi\lambda\!\!\!^{-2}(2l+1) \tag{11-5.14}$$

Complete removal of all the impinging particles from this ring gives the maximum reaction cross section for the partial wave and is obtained for $\eta_l = 0$. In fact, according to Eq. (11-5.10), $\eta_l = 0$ means that the nucleus absorbs the partial wave completely; in other words, it acts as a black disk. However, even in this case there is scattering. Equations (11-5.8) and (11-5.10) show that the elastic cross section is then equal to the reaction cross section.

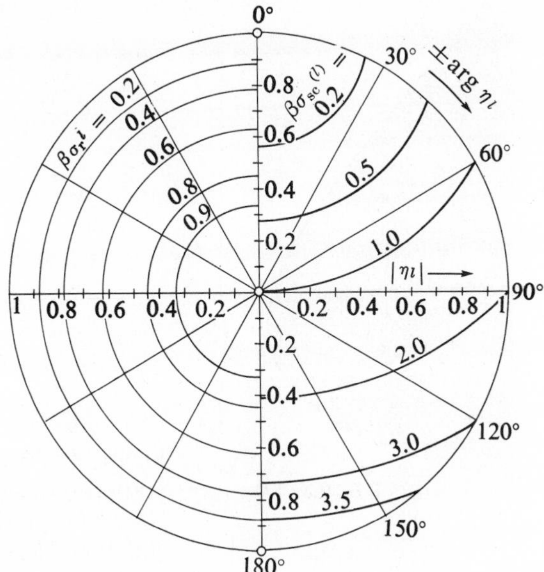

Figure 11-13 Values of $\sigma_{sc}{}^{(l)}$ and $\sigma_r{}^{(l)}$ as functions of $|\eta_l|$ and of arg η_l. The coefficient β is $k^2/\pi(2l+1)$. [(CO 58).

If a nucleus acts as a black disk of radius R (that is, for all particles of impact parameter $b \leqslant R$), the partial waves for which $R \leqslant \hbar l/p = \lambda_{l\max}$ will give $\eta_l = 0$ and Eq. (11-5.11) gives

$$\sigma_t = 2\pi\lambda\!\!\!^{-2} \sum_{l=0}^{l_{\max}=R/\lambda} (2l + 1) = 2\pi\lambda\!\!\!^{-2}(l_{\max} + 1)^2 \simeq 2\pi\lambda\!\!\!^{-2} \frac{R^2}{\lambda\!\!\!^{-2}} = 2\pi R^2 \tag{11-5.15}$$

which is twice the geometrical cross section. At first one would expect, thinking macroscopically, that a reaction cross section equal to πR^2 should not be accompanied by elastic scattering. However, from a wave point of view, in order to suppress completely the incoming wave behind the obstacle, we must place on it a source of the same amplitude, but opposite phase, uniformly spread over the obstacle. This source gives a beam, in a cone of angular aperture $\sim\lambda\!\!\!^{-}/R$, of intensity approximately equal to that intercepted by the obstacle. Hence, the true absorption giving rise to a cross section πR^2 is accompanied by a "diffraction scattering" corresponding to about the same cross section. The detectability of diffraction scattering depends clearly on the relative values of R and $\lambda\!\!\!^{-}$. It is observable when R is a few times $\lambda\!\!\!^{-}$, as in neutrons of a few MeV (Fig. 11-15). On the other hand, for macroscopic objects in the optical case, $\lambda\!\!\!^{-}/R$ is so small that the diffraction scattering is hardly observable.

At very high energies the wavelength of the projectile becomes small compared with R, and collisions occur with single nucleons in the nucleus. Between these two limiting cases, nuclei show a relative transparency for nucleons; they act as gray obstacles.

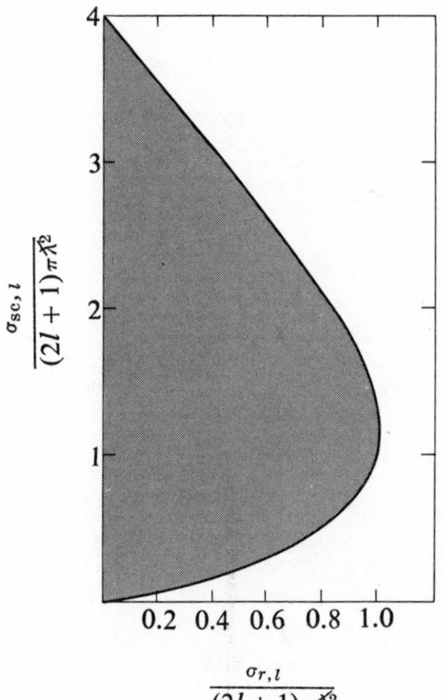

Figure 11-14 Upper and lower limit of the elastic scattering cross section for a given reaction cross section. Values inside the shaded region are possible; those outside the shaded region are impossible. [(BW 52).]

SECTION 11-5

Formal Developments —Scattering Matrix

• There are some formal features in the scattering problem which allow us to draw general conclusions. These are important for their wide range of applicability, including atomic, nuclear, and subnuclear phenomena. We shall discuss here the barest principles of this approach, which is presently being developed very actively.

For the sake of simplicity we shall treat only s waves and spinless particles. Consider a system of sufficiently high energy so that it can decompose according to several channels α, β, γ, etc.; for simplicity also, we shall assume two particles in each channel. In a given channel, for instance, α, the wave function will be

$$\psi_\alpha = \psi(r_a)\chi_\alpha \quad \textbf{(11-5.16)}$$

The first factor is the relative coordinate of the particles in channel α, and X_α is a function describing the internal coordinates of the particles.

For distances r_α large compared with the range of nuclear forces, $\psi(r_\alpha)$ has the form

$$\psi(r_\alpha) = [A_\alpha \exp(-ik_\alpha r_\alpha) + A'_\alpha \exp(+ik_\alpha r_\alpha)]r_\alpha^{-1}(4\pi v_\alpha)^{-1/2} \quad \textbf{(11-5.17)}$$

where the first term represents an outgoing wave and the second an

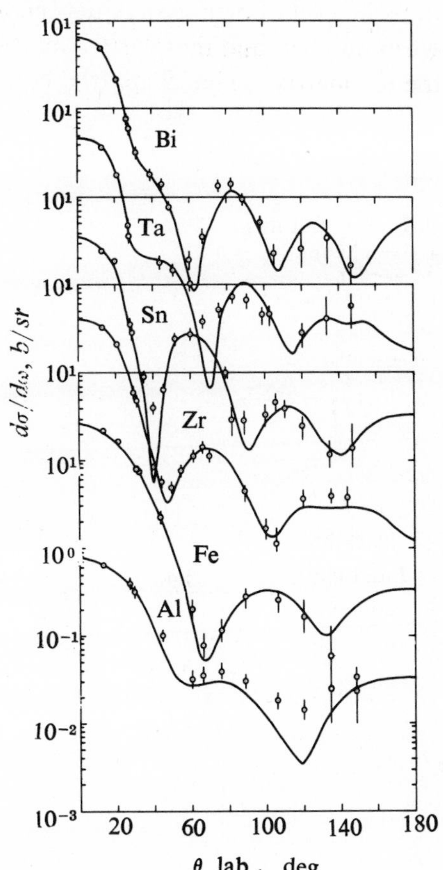

Figure 11-15 Experimental and theoretical differential elastic scattering cross sections for 7-MeV neutrons. The qualitative behavior is that of a diffraction curve from a sphere of radius $R = 1.4A^{1/3}$ F, but to obtain the detailed fit the sphere has been assumed not to be completely opaque and to have a fuzzy edge. [From S. Fernbach, *Rev. Mod. Phys.*, **30**, 414 (1958).]

incoming wave. The wave numbers k_α and the relative velocity v_α depend on the total energy of the system and on the state α. For a given total energy they will thus be different in different channels. The last factor of Eq. (11-5.17) has the purpose of normalizing the wave to flux one when A_α, A'_α are one.

Consider a wave function containing an incoming wave only in channel α, not in the others (Fig. 11-16). It will have outgoing waves not only in channel α, but also in other channels. The outgoing wave in channel α corresponds to elastic scattering; the waves in other channels correspond to inelastic scattering and include reactions. The asymptotic behavior of the waves corresponding to reactions is obtainable by looking at ψ_α in the region of configuration space near channel β, γ, etc., and of course for relative distances r_β, r_γ, etc., large compared with nuclear dimensions; there

$$\psi_\alpha = \psi_{\alpha\beta}(r_\beta)\chi_\beta \tag{11-5.18}$$

with

$$\psi_{\alpha\beta}(r_\beta) = -S_{\alpha\beta}\exp(ik_\beta r_\beta)(4\pi v_\beta)^{-1/2}r_\beta^{-1} \tag{11-5.19}$$

where $S_{\alpha\beta}$ is a complex number function of the energy.

At a given energy one may form as many ψ_α as there are entrance channels: call this number N. There are thus $N\ \psi_\alpha$, which may be assumed to form a set of orthogonal, degenerate functions. The quantities $S_{\alpha\beta}$ are N^2 in number, and they form a matrix, called the S matrix (or sometimes the U matrix). The S matrix completely determines the asymptotic

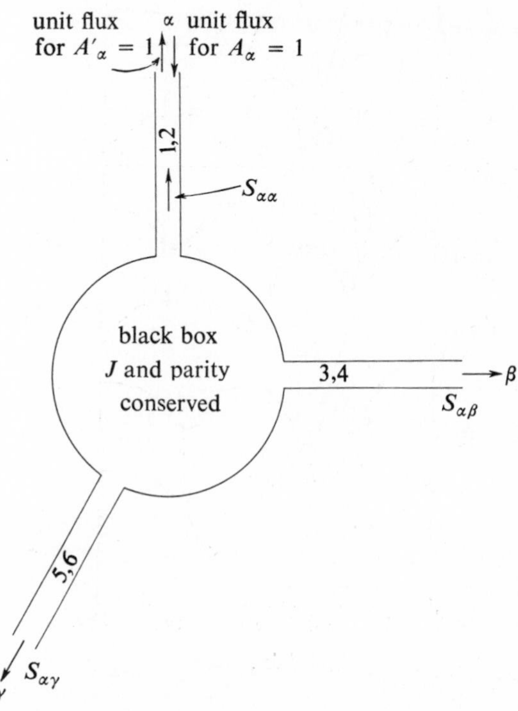

Figure 11-16 Symbolic figure and notations relative to scattering matrix. In channel α, particles 1 and 2; r_α their distance; $\chi(\alpha)$ their internal coordinates. In channel β, particles 3, 4; in channel γ, particles 5, 6.

behavior of the wave function. In this sense it represents the total information on the collision: the processes occurring at distances small compared with nuclear dimensions may, for instance, even in principle be unobservable, owing to the existence of a "fundamental length," but the results of experiments are always observed at distances from the collision site large compared with nuclear dimensions, and the S matrix would predict the observations.

Effective calculation of the scattering matrix is in practice impossible. However, it has some very important properties which can be derived from general principles. Although we cannot go into their derivation, the most important properties are as follows:

Unitarity is expressed by the relation

$$\sum_{\gamma} S^*_{\alpha\gamma} S_{\beta\gamma} = \delta_{\alpha\beta} \tag{11-5.20}$$

(note the order of the subscripts). In particular the relation

$$\sum_{\gamma} |S_{\alpha\gamma}|^2 = 1 \tag{11-5.21}$$

means that the sum of probabilities of ending in some channel is 1. In other words, when the incoming flux is one, the sum of the outgoing fluxes must also be one.

Time reversal. Consider in a process the incoming wave $\exp(-ik_\alpha r_\alpha)/(4\pi v_\alpha)^{1/2}$ and the outgoing wave $S_{\alpha\beta}\exp(+ik_\beta r_\beta)/(4\pi v_\beta)^{1/2}$. In the time-reversed situation consider the normalized incoming wave $\exp(-ik_\beta r_\beta)/(4\pi v_\beta)^{1/2}$ and the outgoing wave $S_{\beta\alpha}\exp(ik_\alpha r_\alpha)/(4\pi v_\alpha)^{1/2}$. If time reversal is permissible and there is no spin, the relation

$$S_{\alpha\beta} = S_{\beta\alpha} \tag{11-5.22}$$

obtains. If there are spins, one must be more careful in considering a situation and its time reversal. Without spin all we have to do to invert the direction of time is to invert all momenta. In the presence of spins, if we think of them as due to rotations, we must also invert the sense of rotations (i.e., the direction of the spin). If we define the channel $-\alpha$ $-\beta$ by inverting all momenta and also all spin directions, one has

$$S_{\alpha\beta} = S_{-\alpha-\beta} \tag{11-5.23}$$

The time-reversal relations are similar, but not identical, to the detailed balance conditions.

The conditions of unitarity and time-reversal invariance impose restrictions on the $2N^2$ real numbers entering into the scattering matrix. Other limitations come from information on the analytical properties of the $S_{\alpha\beta}$ considered as a function of energy.

The diagonal elements of the scattering matrix are the $\eta = S_{\alpha\alpha}$ of this section. By arguments similar to those already used for η, one can show that the cross sections are given by

$$\sigma_{\alpha\beta} = \pi\lambda\!\!\!^{-}{}_\alpha^2|\delta_{\alpha\beta} - S_{\alpha\beta}|^2 \tag{11-5.24}$$

For $\alpha = \beta$ we have the elastic cross section. The reaction cross section is obtained by summing over all $\beta \neq \alpha$,

$$\sigma_{sl} = \pi \lambda_\alpha^2 |1 - S_{\alpha\alpha}|^2 \quad \textbf{(11-5.25)}$$

$$\sigma_r = \pi \lambda_\alpha^2 \sum_{\beta \neq \alpha} |S_{\alpha\beta}|^2 \quad \textbf{(11-5.26)}$$

or, using the unitarity relation,

$$\sigma_r = \pi \lambda_\alpha^2 (1 - |S_{\alpha\alpha}|^2) \quad \textbf{(11-5.27)}$$

identical to Eq. (11-5.10).

The "optical theorem" (Appendix D) can also be derived by use of the scattering matrix. The theorem relates the imaginary part of the forward-scattering amplitude $f(0)$ to the total cross section

$$\sigma_{\text{tot}} = \frac{4\pi}{k} \operatorname{Im} f(0) \quad \textbf{(11-5.28)}$$

where k is the wave number of the incident particle. ●

11-6 Resonances

To maintain a reasonable simplicity of treatment, we shall consider only s waves. This restriction does not affect the very extensive and important case of slow neutrons, where only the s waves are important. We shall also neglect spin effects. For a more general treatment we must refer to the book by Blatt and Weisskopf or to the original literature. (From this point on, the subscript for the s partial wave will be omitted.) It is obvious that Eq. (11-5.8) for $l = 0$ and $\eta = e^{2i\delta}$ becomes

$$\sigma_{sc} = \pi \lambda^2 |1 - \eta|^2 = 4\pi \lambda^2 \sin^2 \delta \quad \textbf{(11-6.1)}$$

which is the equation used in treating low-energy neutron-proton scattering. Similarly,

$$\sigma_r = \pi \lambda^2 (1 - |\eta|^2) \quad \textbf{(11-6.2)}$$

and

$$\sigma_t = 2\pi \lambda^2 (1 - \operatorname{Re} \eta) \quad \textbf{(11-6.3)}$$

We see from these formulas that a knowledge of η is all that is required to find the three cross sections. However, a detailed knowledge of what happens inside the nucleus is not necessary in order to determine η. Assuming that the nucleus has a well-defined surface, η is determined by the value of

$$\left(\frac{u'}{u}\right)_{r=R} R = f \quad \textbf{(11-6.4)}$$

at the surface of the nucleus. Here $u = r\psi$, and R is the nuclear radius.

The wave function outside the nucleus, limited to s waves only, is

$$\psi_{\text{outside}} = \frac{i}{2kr}(e^{-ikr} - \eta e^{ikr}) \quad \textbf{(11-6.5)}$$

and the logarithmic derivative of u must be continuous everywhere, including R.

Everything happening inside the nucleus is transmitted to the outside by this logarithmic derivative u'/u. From Eqs. (11-6.4) and (11-6.5) we have

$$\left(\frac{u'}{u}\right)_{r=R} = \frac{f}{R} = \frac{-ike^{-ikR} - \eta ike^{ikR}}{e^{-ikR} - \eta e^{ikR}} = \frac{-ik(1 + \eta e^{2ikR})}{1 - \eta e^{2ikR}} \qquad \textbf{(11-6.6a)}$$

or

$$\eta = \frac{f + ikR}{f - ikR} e^{-2ikR} \qquad \textbf{(11-6.6b)}$$

We recall that kR for nucleons impinging on heavy nuclei is $3.2 \times 10^{-4} A^{1/3}[E(\text{eV})]^{1/2}$.

● If f is real, $|\eta| = 1$ and there is no reaction. In general f will be complex, and we indicate its real and imaginary parts by f_r and f_i,

$$f = f_r + if_i \qquad \textbf{(11-6.7)}$$

Note that, to have $|\eta| < 1$, f_i must be negative.

After some reductions, substitution of Eq. (11-6.6) in Eqs. (11-6.1) to (11-6.3) gives

$$\sigma_r = \pi\lambda\!\!\!^{-2} \left[\frac{-4f_i kR}{f_r^2 + (kR - f_i)^2}\right] \qquad \textbf{(11-6.8)}$$

and

$$\sigma_s = 4\pi\lambda\!\!\!^{-2} \left| e^{ikR} \sin kR + \frac{kR}{i(kR - f_i) - f_r} \right|^2 \qquad \textbf{(11-6.9)}$$

We see again that for f real $\sigma_r = 0$ and σ_s takes a form that may be easily interpreted if sin kR is very large or very small compared with $kR/|(ikR - fr)|$.

In the first case

$$\sigma_s = 4\pi\lambda\!\!\!^{-2} \sin^2 kR$$

and, if also $kR \ll 1$, **(11-6.10)**

$$\sigma_s = 4\pi R^2$$

which is four times the geometrical cross section. This type of scattering is called potential scattering.

In the second case

$$\sigma_s = 4\pi\lambda\!\!\!^{-2} \frac{(kR)^2}{f_r^2 + k^2R^2} \qquad \textbf{(11-6.11)}$$

This scattering cross section has a maximum value $4\pi\lambda\!\!\!^{-2}$ when $f_r = 0$ (resonance) and depends critically on f_r. Assume that, for a certain value E_0 of the energy of the incident particle, $f_r = 0$ and call f_r' the value of the derivative of f_r at $E = E_0$. We may then write

$$f_r(E) = (E - E_0)f_r' \qquad \textbf{(11-6.12)}$$

It can be proved that f_r' is always negative. Inserting in Eq. (11-6.11) we have

$$\sigma_s = 4\pi\lambda\!\!\!^{-2} \frac{(kR)^2}{(E - E_0)^2 f_r'^2 + (kR)^2} \tag{11-6.13}$$

or calling

$$\Gamma_s = -\frac{2kR}{f_r'} \tag{11-6.14}$$

where the subscript s on Γ_s indicates "scattering," we obtain

$$\sigma_s = \pi\lambda\!\!\!^{-2} \frac{\Gamma_s^2}{(E - E_0)^2 + \Gamma_s^2/4} \tag{11-6.15}$$

This equation shows again that the maximum possible cross section is

$$\sigma_s \max = 4\pi\lambda\!\!\!^{-2}$$

In a region near the energy E_0, the scattering cross section shows the typical resonance shape common to many phenomena, notably the refractive index of a medium near an absorption line. The physical meaning of Γ_s is the full energy width of the resonance peak at half its maximum value. More fundamentally, Γ_s is connected with the duration τ of the scattering process by $\hbar/\Gamma_s \sim \tau$, which, being finite, introduces an uncertainty in the resonance energy E_0. It is convenient to introduce Γ_s in the form of Eq. (11-6.14) in order to obtain Eq. (11-6.15) in the typical resonance form. Note that since f_r', is constant, Γ_s is proportional to k or to the velocity of the impinging neutrons. ●

A more refined treatment of scattering takes into account the full Eq. (11-6.9), which contains scattering coherent with the incident wave, caused by the nuclear surface. This coherent scattering is given by the term $e^{ikR} \sin kR$ of Eq. (11-6.9). The result is that the amplitudes of the scattered wave add, and Eq. (11-6.13) is replaced by

$$\sigma_s = 4\pi\lambda\!\!\!^{-2} \left| \frac{\Gamma_s/2}{(E - E_0) + i\Gamma_s/2} + R/\lambda \right|^2 \tag{11-6.16}$$

when $R/\lambda \ll 1$. In the vicinity of the resonance, Eq. (11-6.16) reduces to Eq. (11-6.15), while at greater distances from the resonance, potential scattering prevails. We note that the potential and resonance scattering can interfere and give rise to characteristic dips in the cross section for energies just below resonance, as is shown in Fig. 11-17.

We must now extend our treatment to f complex in order to encompass the case where there are reactions besides elastic scattering. As pointed out earlier, we are no longer dealing with the ordinary stationary states of Schrödinger's equation. Left to itself, the nucleus decays showing in the time dependence of the square of the modulus of its wave function the factor $e^{-\lambda t}$, where λ is the decay constant. In order to produce this time dependence, we formally introduce a complex value for the energy,

$$E = \epsilon - \frac{i\Gamma_r}{2} \tag{11-6.17}$$

where the subscript r on Γ reminds us that Γ_r refers to "reaction." The time-dependent factor of ψ, $e^{(-iE/\hbar)t}$, then becomes $\exp-[(i\epsilon t/\hbar) - (\Gamma_r t/2\hbar)]$, and the exponential decay of $\psi\psi^*$ follows the correct law if

$$\frac{\Gamma_r}{\hbar} = \lambda \tag{11-6.18}$$

We have, numerically, for the lifetime (in seconds)

$$\tau = \frac{1}{\lambda} = \frac{6.6 \times 10^{-16}}{\Gamma_r(\text{eV})} \tag{11-6.19}$$

This complex energy is analogous to the complex refractive index of optics, in which the imaginary part is connected with the absorption by the medium.

Thus we have a complex f which is a function of a complex variable E.

Assume that we have determined f by using a Schrödinger equation with real eigenvalues and that we have found

$$f_r(E_0) = 0$$

When we use a complex eigenvalue, as required by the physical situation, we must introduce a complex f.

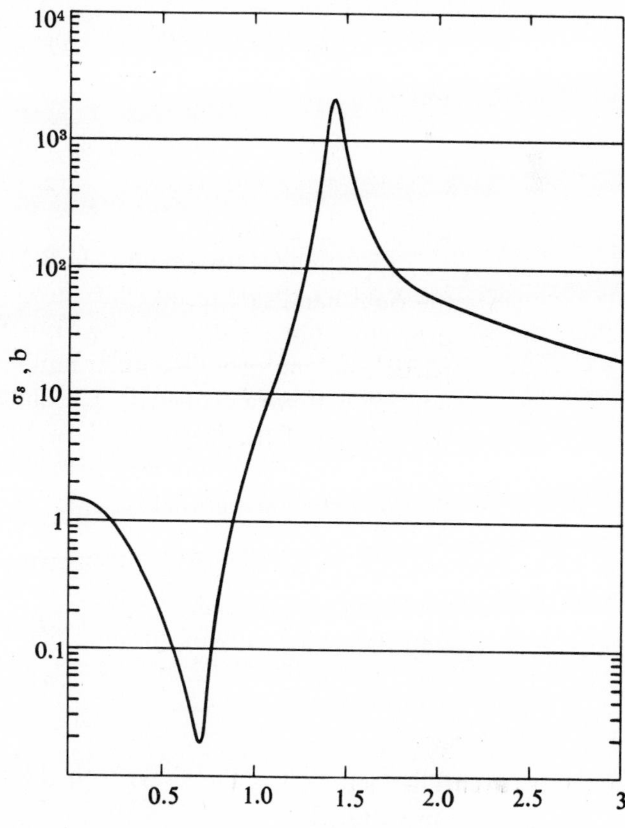

Figure 11-17 The scattering cross section for In^{115}, an isotope with a resonance near thermal energy; the dip in cross section below the resonance corresponds to interference between the negative resonance amplitude and the positive potential amplitude. Compare also Fig. 11-8. Ordinate logarithmic scale.

There will be a value of the complex variable near E_0 for which f will be zero. We call this value $E_r - \frac{1}{2}i\Gamma_r$ and we assume that both $(E_r - E_0)/E_0$ and $\Gamma_r/2E_0$ are $\ll 1$. The suffix r in E_r and Γ_r stands for "resonance." It is desired now to have f in the vicinity of its zero and for real values of the energy E. Expanding f in a power series and taking the first term only, we have, since $f(E_r - \frac{1}{2}i\Gamma_r) = 0$, $f(E) = (E - E_r + \frac{1}{2}i\Gamma_r)\, f'(E_r - \frac{1}{2}i\Gamma_r)$. The imaginary part of $f'(E_r - \frac{1}{2}i\Gamma_r)$ is small compared with the real part, as can be ascertained by using the definition Eq. (11-6.4), and in sufficient approximation $f'(E_r - \frac{1}{2}i\Gamma_r)$ can be replaced by $\text{Re}\, f'(E_r)$, which we indicate by $f_r'(E_r)$. Our expansion thus gives

$$f(E) = \left(E - E_r + \frac{i\Gamma_r}{2}\right) f_r' \tag{11-6.20}$$

where f_r' is calculated for $E = E_r$ and is real.

Using Eq. (11-6.14) we have for the real and imaginary parts

$$f_r(E) = -(E - E_r)\frac{2kR}{\Gamma_s} \tag{11-6.21}$$

$$f_i(E) = \frac{-kR\Gamma_r}{\Gamma_s} \tag{11-6.22}$$

Inserting these values in Eqs. (11-6.8) and (11-6.9) we obtain in the vicinity of a resonance

$$\sigma_{sc} = \pi\lambda\!\!\!^{-2}\frac{\Gamma_s^2}{(E - E_r)^2 + \Gamma^2/4} \tag{11-6.23}$$

and

$$\sigma_r = \pi\lambda\!\!\!^{-2}\frac{\Gamma_r\Gamma_s}{(E - E_r)^2 + \Gamma^2/4} \tag{11-6.24}$$

where $E_r \simeq E_0$ and $\Gamma = \Gamma_r + \Gamma_s$.

Equations (11-6.23) and (11-6.24) should also contain a factor g on the right-hand side to take into account the spin of the target and of the projectile. For instance, in the case of slow neutrons, where the incident particle has no orbital angular momentum but has spin $\frac{1}{2}$, the compound nucleus will have $2(I_A + \frac{1}{2}) + 1$ states if the neutron spin is parallel to the spin I_A of the target nucleus, and $2(I_A - \frac{1}{2}) + 1$ states if it is antiparallel. The total number of states is thus $4I_A + 2$. The probability of finding the spins parallel is

$$\frac{2(I_A + \frac{1}{2}) + 1}{4I_A + 2} = \frac{I_A + 1}{2I_A + 1} = g_+ \tag{11-6.25}$$

and the probability of finding them antiparallel is

$$\frac{2(I_A - \frac{1}{2}) + 1}{4I_A + 2} = \frac{I_A}{2I_A + 1} = g_- \tag{11-6.26}$$

The factor g has the value g_+ if the spins are parallel and g_- if they are antiparallel.

In the case of slow neutrons Eqs. (11-6.23) and (11-6.24) may be pecified further by noting that (with few exceptions, notably B and Li nd fissionable nuclei) Γ_r corresponds to the emission of a gamma ray nd can thus be called Γ_γ. It is essentially independent of the energy of he incoming slow neutron (Fig. 11-18). Γ_s corresponds to the remission f a neutron and is proportional to the velocity of the impinging neutron, nd we write for it Γ_n.

The fact that Γ_n is proportional to the velocity of the neutron uggests the introduction of a *reduced width* $\Gamma_n^{(0)}$ corresponding to a pecific velocity of the neutron. Usually the reduced neutron width is de-ined as the neutron width when the neutron has an energy of 1 eV,[1] or $\Gamma_n^{(0)} = \Gamma_n^{(r)}/[E_r(\text{eV})]^{1/2}$. Dimensionally $\Gamma_n^{(0)}$ is an energy, as is Γ_n. Also, $\Gamma_n \lambda\!\!\!^{-} = \Gamma_n^{(r)} \lambda\!\!\!^{-}_r$, where $\Gamma_n^{(r)}$ denotes Γ_n at the resonance energy E_r, and λ_r is the corresponding de Broglie wavelength.

Consideration of Eqs. (11-6.23) and (11-6.24) and the foregoing emarks give the famous Breit–Wigner formulas, which are of great mportance in neutron work.

[1] Other definitions of neutron widths are also used. For example, Wigner alls reduced width the quantity γ defined by $\Gamma = 2k\gamma^2 = 4.4 \times 10^9\,[E(\text{eV})]^{1/2}\gamma^2$ and Veisskopf the quantity γ defined by $\Gamma = 2kR\gamma = 6.4 \times 10^{-4}\,A^{1/3}\,[E(\text{eV})]^{1/2}\gamma$.

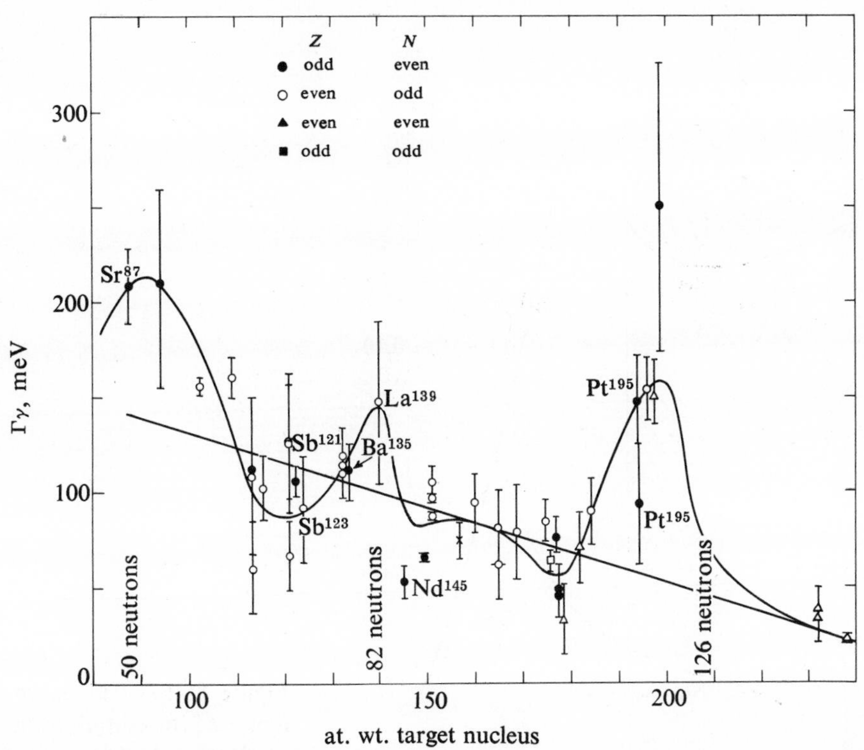

igure 11-18 Measured radiation widths plotted against atomic weight, revealing the slow decrease f radiation width with atomic weight, as well as a sharp discontinuity at the closed nuclear shells ear $A = 200$. [From D. J. Hughes, *Neutron Cross Sections*, Pergamon, London, 1957.]

$$\sigma(n,n) = \pi\lambda\!\!\!^{-}{}_r^2 \frac{\Gamma_n^{(r)2}}{\Gamma^2/4 + (E - E_r)^2} g \qquad \textbf{(11-6.27)}$$

$$\sigma(n,\gamma) = \pi\lambda\!\!\!^{-}\lambda\!\!\!^{-}{}_r \frac{\Gamma_\gamma \Gamma_n^{(r)}}{\Gamma^2/4 + (E - E_r)^2} g \qquad \textbf{(11-6.28)}$$

Classical examples of the (n,γ) resonance are illustrated in Figs. 11-8, 11-17, 11-19, 11-20, 11-21, and 11-49. If there are several resonating levels near each other, the cross section takes a more complex form. Many examples of neutron cross sections are to be found in the atlas of Hughes.

Equation (11-6.28) contains a $1/v$ factor, implicit in $\lambda\!\!\!^{-}$, multiplying a curve having the typical resonance shape. If the resonance is very broad with respect to the difference $E - E_r$, that is, if $\Gamma^2/4 \gg (E - E_r)^2$, or if $E_r \gg E$, so that variations of E do not affect the denominator, the resonance factor is almost constant and $\sigma(n,\gamma)$ obeys the famous $1/v$ law. This happens for instance in the reaction B^{10} (n,α), which is governed by a relation similar to Eq. (11-6.28), in which Γ_γ is replaced by Γ_α. Boron (normal isotopic composition 19.8 per cent B^{10}) shows a neutron absorption cross section given by

$$\sigma(v) = \frac{\sigma(v_0)v_0}{v} = \frac{(755 \pm 2)(2{,}200)}{v} b$$

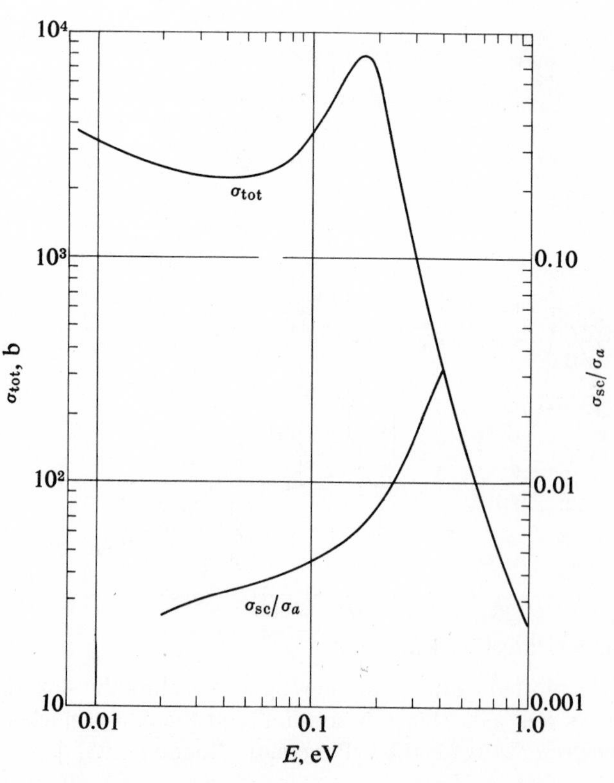

Figure 11-19 The energy dependence of the cadmium total cross section and the ratio between scattering and absorption cross sections for neutrons below 1 eV. Log-log scale.

where v is expressed in meters per second. This relation is valid for energies ranging from 10^{-3} to at least 10^2 eV. The absorption in boron is a good way of measuring the energy of neutrons.

As we have seen, the quantities η or f in Eqs. (11-5.8) to (11-5.11) and (11-6.6) completely describe scattering and reaction cross sections. One of the main problems in the study of nuclear reactions, therefore, is to calculate η from a model. At present any attempt to analyze the nuclear dynamics in detail (and thus obtain η) is hopeless. However, it is possible to devise some extreme conditions under which η should behave in a simple, predictable fashion.

We shall consider two examples. Suppose first that the particle entering the nucleus moves inside it with a kinetic energy much larger than it had outside, and that it is subject to strong interactions inside the nucleus so that it exchanges energy rapidly with the other nucleons. Under these assumptions an entering particle would have a very small probability of leaving the nucleus once it penetrated its surface. The wave function inside the nucleus would have approximately the form

$$u_i \propto e^{-iKr} \qquad \text{for } r < R \tag{11-6.29}$$

without an outgoing wave, and with K the reciprocal wavelength inside the nucleus. From this expression we obtain immediately

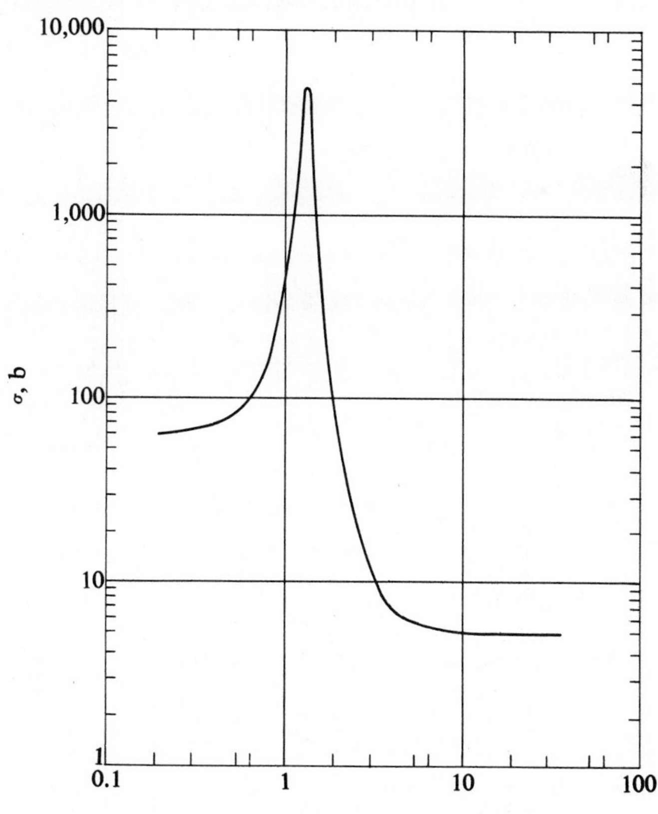

Figure 11-20 Total neutron cross section of Rh as a function of energy. Log-log scale.

$$f = -iKR \tag{11-6.30}$$

and from Eqs. (11-6.6) and (11-6.2) we obtain

$$\eta = \frac{K - k}{K + k} e^{-2ikR} \tag{11-6.31}$$

and

$$\sigma_r = \pi \lambda\!\!\!^{-2} \frac{4kK}{(K + k)^2} \tag{11-6.32}$$

We may consider this expression as the product of the cross section $\pi \lambda\!\!\!^{-2}$ and $4kK/(K + k)^2$, which has the meaning of a transmission factor varying between 0 and 1. We have already seen Eq. (11-4.5) that (roughly)

$$\frac{\hbar^2 K^2}{2M} = \frac{\hbar^2 k^2}{2M} + V_0 \tag{11-6.33}$$

where the last term corresponds to an energy of about 30 MeV.

The analysis for $l > 0$ and for charged particles is more complicated and will not be discussed here. The situation described above applies to neutrons with energies of several hundred keV up to some MeV.

In our second example the energy of the incident particle (e.g., slow neutron) is such that no other channel except the entrance channel is open; the compound nucleus can reemit only the incident particle with the incident energy. The wave function inside the nuclear surface is thus

$$u_{in} \sim e^{-iKr} + e^{i(Kr+2\xi)}. \tag{11-6.34}$$

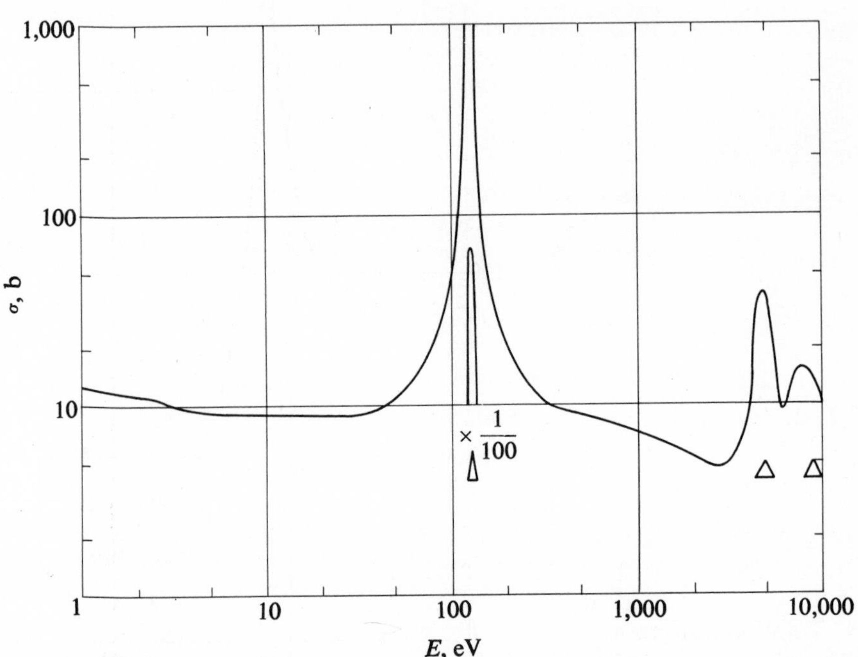

Figure 11-21 Total neutron cross section of cobalt as a function of energy. Log-log scale.

ith incoming and outgoing waves of the same amplitude but generally ifted in phase. We then have

$$f = -KR \tan (KR + \xi) \tag{11-6.35}$$

e phase ξ depending on the energy ϵ of the incident particle. At the lues of ϵ for which f becomes 0, there is a sharp maximum for the scatring cross section. In the vicinity of this maximum the scattering oss section shows a resonance shape, and its width is

$$\Gamma = -\frac{2kR}{df/d\epsilon} \tag{11-6.36}$$

Actually the zeros of f correspond to virtual energy levels. The resonce levels occur according to Eq. (11-6.35) whenever

$$KR + \xi = Z(\epsilon) = n\pi \tag{11-6.37}$$

ith n integral. If $dZ/d\epsilon$ were constant, the levels would be separated by energy interval D^* such that

$$\frac{dZ}{d\epsilon} D^* = \pi \tag{11-6.38}$$

he true average distance between levels D is of the same order of magnide as D^*, and from Eq. (11-6.36), observing that at resonance

$$-\frac{df}{d\epsilon} = \frac{KR\,dZ}{d\epsilon} \tag{11-6.39}$$

e obtain the interesting relation

$$\Gamma = \frac{4k}{K}\frac{D^*}{2\pi} \tag{11-6.40}$$

hich shows that the width of the levels is small compared with their stance as long as $k/K \ll 1$.

We can give a physical interpretation of Eq. (11-6.40) by noting at $\Gamma/\hbar$ is the reciprocal of the mean life of a level. Now our compound cleus, in order to decay, must return to a suitable configuration, an ent that occurs approximately periodically (period T). The probability decay from this configuration is the transparency or transmission coficient of the surface given by Eq. (11-6.32).

The periodic time T may be estimated, according to Weisskopf, om the following argument: Let us attempt to describe the motion of a rticle semiclassically. For this purpose we shall construct a wave cket, and this can be done only by superimposing a number of states, y, N. The energy of the states will not be too far from E_0, and for the ke of argument we shall assume it to be

$$E_n = E_0 + nD \tag{11-6.41}$$

here n is an integral number and D is the distance between neighboring ergy levels. The levels are thus assumed to be equally spaced, although is assumption is not essential.

The ψ of the system is then

$$\psi(t) = \sum_{0}^{N} a_n \varphi_n e^{-i(E_n t/\hbar)} = e^{-i(E_0 t/\hbar)} \sum_{n=0}^{N} a_n \varphi_n e^{-i(nDt/\hbar)} \qquad \textbf{(11-6.42)}$$

and $|\psi|^2$ has a period

$$T = \frac{2\pi\hbar}{D}$$

as can be verified immediately from Eq. (11-6.42).

The transparency is given by Eq. (11-6.32), which for $k/K \ll 1$ can be written $4k/K$, and hence

$$\frac{\Gamma}{\hbar} = \text{transparency} \times \frac{1}{T} = \frac{D}{2\pi\hbar}\frac{4k}{K} \qquad \textbf{(11-6.43)}$$

Introducing for convenience the reduced neutron width $\Gamma_n^{(0)}$, we rewrite Eq. (11-6.43) as

$$\Gamma_n^{(0)} = \frac{2}{\pi} D \left(\frac{E_n}{V_0}\right)^{1/2} \qquad \textbf{(11-6.44)}$$

where V_0 is the depth of the effective potential well for a neutron inside the nucleus, which amounts to about 30 MeV, and E_n the neutron energy outside is 1 eV. Thus, very roughly,

$$\frac{\Gamma_n^{(0)}}{D} = 1.1 \times 10^{-4}$$

Resonance scattering governed by the considerations developed above is observed in light nuclei and at relatively low energies up to 1 MeV according to the A of the target or for very low energy neutrons incident on intermediate nuclei. An example of the latter case is shown in Fig. 11-21, giving the resonance of cobalt at 132 eV. For this we have

$$\Gamma_\gamma \ll 1 \text{ eV} \quad \Gamma_n \simeq 4.9 \text{ eV}$$

Finally we have very important cases of resonance when radiative capture or fission competes successfully with the re-emission of a slow neutron, that is, $\Gamma_\gamma \gg \Gamma_n$ or $\Gamma_f \gg \Gamma_n$.

11-7 Optical Model

A further step in developing nuclear models based on simple hypotheses consists in applying the same basic idea involved in the shell model to nuclear reactions. The impinging particle enters a potential well similar to the well used in the shell model. Because the projectile dissipates its energy we must add to the real part of the potential an imaginary one. We thereby obtain the "optical model" (Bethe, 1940; Feshbach, Porter, and Weisskopf, 1954). For example, for neutrons between 0 and 41 MeV, one can take

$$V_0 = f(r)(1 + i\xi) \qquad \textbf{(11-7.1)}$$

where $f(r)$ is assumed to be a rectangular well of the form

$$f(r) = V_0 = -40 \text{ MeV} \quad r < R$$
$$f(r) = 0 \quad r > R$$

$$R = 1.45A^{1/3} \times 10^{-13} \text{ cm}$$
$$\xi = 0.03$$

For more refined calculations a form (Woods and Saxon, 1954) often used is

$$f(r) = \frac{V_0}{1 + e^{+(r-R)/a}} \qquad \textbf{(11-7.2)}$$

with

$$V_0 = -42 \text{ MeV}$$
$$\xi = 0.7 - 0.13$$
$$a = 0.6 \times 10^{-13} \text{ cm}$$
$$R = 1.35A^{1/3} \times 10^{-13} \text{ cm}$$

The parameters given above are to be considered only as typical examples. The constants of the model vary according to the nature and energy of the incoming particles.

The main feature of Eq. (11-7.2) is that it introduces a continuously changing potential, with a zone of rapid variation of thickness a at the nuclear surface ($r = R$). The imaginary part $\xi f(r)$ gives the absorption of the medium. This model has been called the "cloudy crystal ball." Formal solution of the Schrödinger equation with the complex potential allows the evaluation of the logarithmic derivative of the wave function at the nuclear surface and hence the determination of the scattering and reaction cross sections.

The results of this model can be expected to give only the average behavior of the nucleus over many resonances; consequently the results do not reproduce the region of separate resonances. However, at higher energies where individual resonances are not resolved, the model gives good agreement with the experimental findings for total and elastic nuclear cross sections up to an energy of a few MeV (as shown in Fig. 11-22). Waves with $l \leqslant 5$ must be considered, and in Fig. 11-22 waves with $l \leqslant 5$ have been included. The calculations practically require the use of high-speed computers.

Above 4 MeV the parameters given for Eq. (11-7.2) yield cross sections with an accuracy of 10 to 20 per cent up to about 10 MeV. The model may also be used to calculate angular distributions in neutron-nucleus scattering and it provides a good insight into more basic nuclear properties, such as the ratio Γ_n/D. We have previously seen that Γ_n/D is approximately constant, but with the optical model we can take a further step and calculate it as a function of A and E_n (Fig. 11-23).

Above about 50 MeV the optical model can be used again in a simple fashion by considering Fraunhofer diffraction from the cloudy

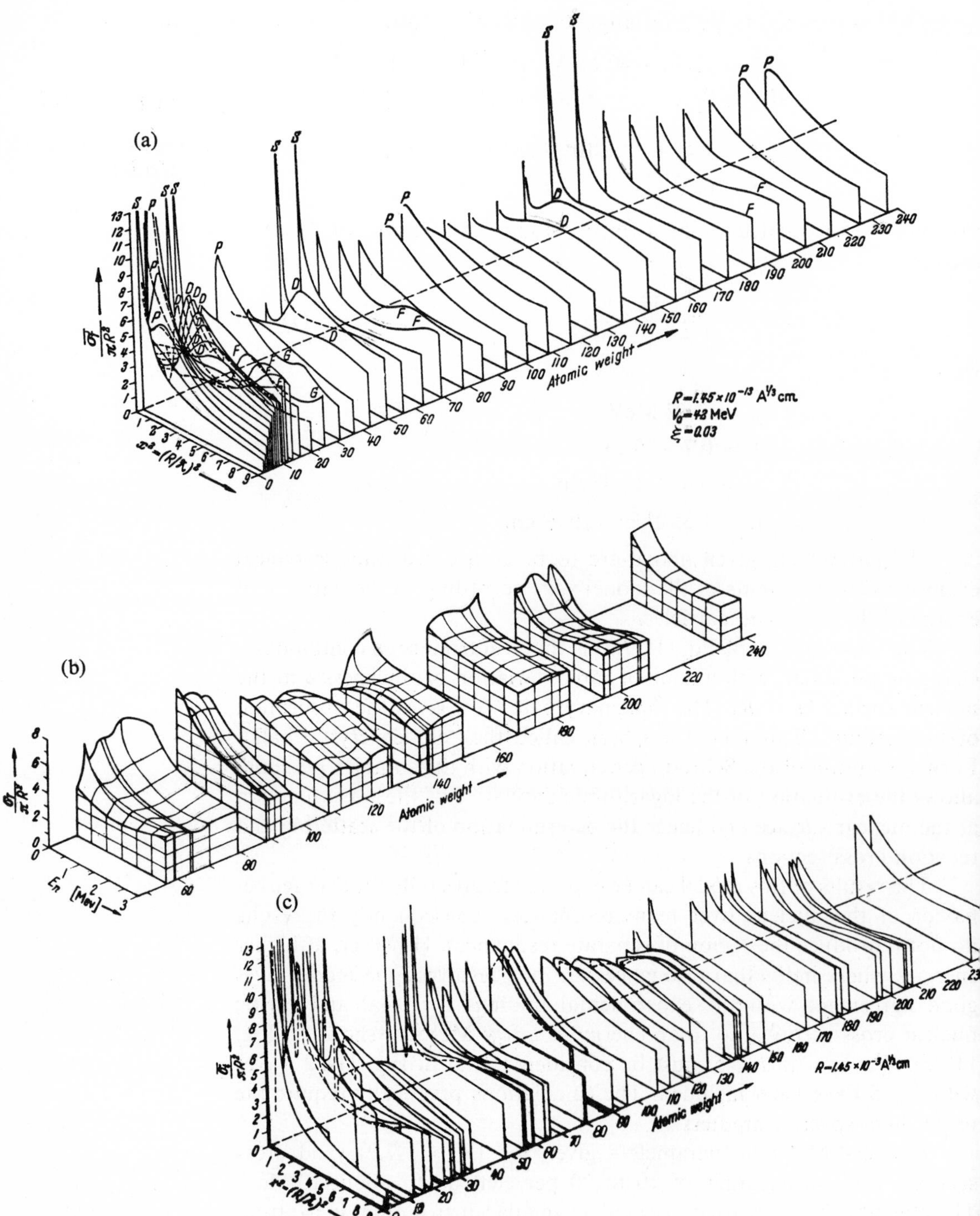

Figure 11-22 (a) Total neutron cross sections (calculated from the optical model) vs. $x^2 = (R/\lambda\!\!\!^{-})^2$ and A for different choices of the imaginary part of the potential. (b) Measured total neutron cross sections, averaged over resonances vs. E and A. (c) A similar plot using $x^2 = (R/\lambda\!\!\!^{-})^2$ in place of E. [Feshbach, Porter, and Weisskopf, *Phys. Rev.*, **96**, 448 (1954)].

rystal ball (Fernbach, Serber, and Taylor, 1949), although the constants f the well are somewhat different from those of Eq. (11-7.2), with V_0 decreasing and ξ increasing with energy.

The optical model can be extended to charged particles, but we shall mit this complication. The usefulness of the optical model can be seen n many other studies of nuclear reactions, such as pion collisions and ntiproton-nucleus collisions. Once the potential is supplemented with term proportional to $\boldsymbol{\sigma}\cdot\mathbf{l}$ (angular momentum and spin of the incident article), it also gives a satisfactory explanation of the polarization phenomena observed in proton-nucleus scattering (cf. Chap. 10).

The cloudy crystal ball model can be related to the shell model by rguments of the following type, which, however, are not unambiguous.

If the imaginary part of the potential were absent, we should have an

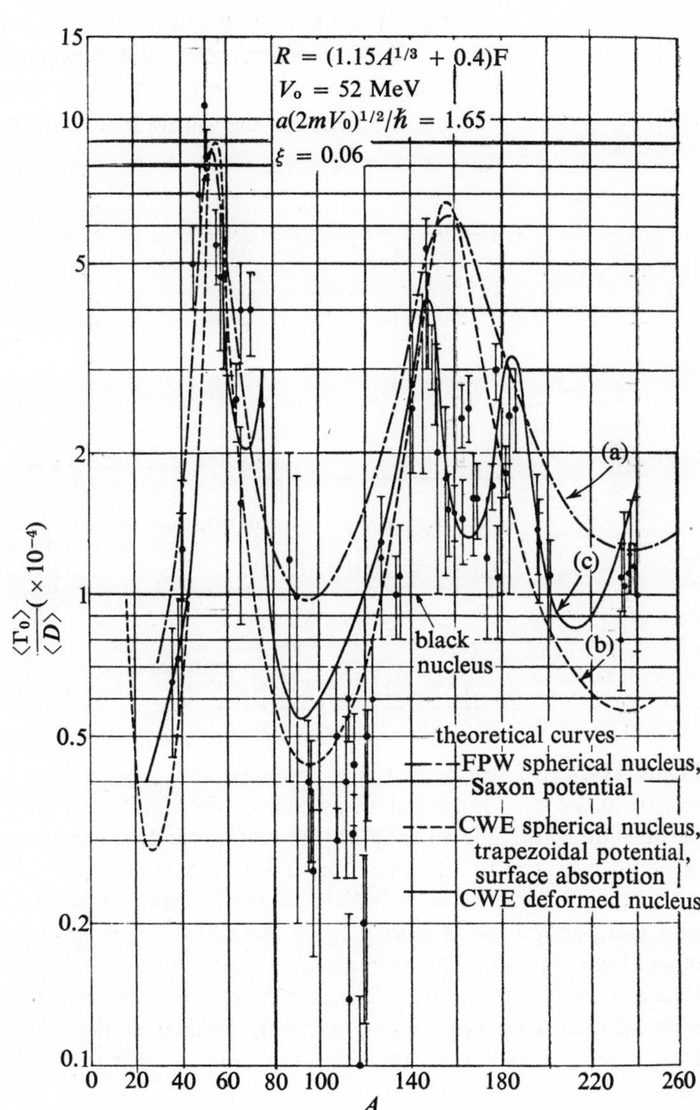

Figure 11-23 Neutron strength function at zero energy as a function of the mass number. Theoretical curve (a) corresponds to optical model with Saxon potential and constants indicated in the figure (FPW). Curve (b) corresponds to a spherical nucleus with trapezoidal potential and surface absorption (CWE). Curve (c) corresponds to a spheroidal nucleus according to Chase, Wilets, and Edmonds. [After J. A. Harvey, *Proc. Intern. Conf. Nucl. Structure*, Kingston, 1960.]

ordinary Schrödinger equation and corresponding stationary orbits. The shell model shows that such an approximation has considerable merit. One would then expect resonance levels of a compound nucleus to be determined by the characteristics of the well. With any of the well parameters ordinarily used, such resonances would be widely separated. Moreover, considering the levels available as a function of A, we should expect to find (for a given energy) a resonance for a narrow region of A values, because the energy considered is a resonance energy for the nuclear radius corresponding to a particular A. Suppose that we wanted to calculate V_0 from the shell model. We could observe that a certain level (e.g., the 3s level) is barely bound for a certain A; in this case $A \simeq 150$. This means that for $k = (2mV_0)^{1/2}$ the 3s wave function at $r = R = r_0A^{1/3}$ is 0, or that $kR = 2.64\pi$, this being the third zero of the Bessel function $J_{1/2}(x)$. From this, given R, we could find V_0. The agreement between V_0 calculated in this fashion and the value derived from scattering experiments is good if realistic forms of wells are used.

The resonance effects are indeed observed, however, not on single levels, but rather on groups of levels, clustering around certain energy regions because the single level obtainable from the shell model is highly

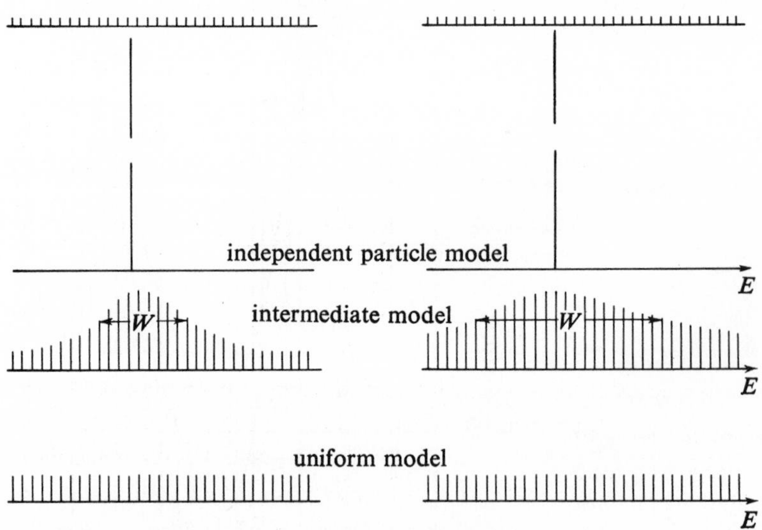

Figure 11-24 Figure from Lane, Thomas, and Wigner illustrating how the intermediate model is related to the strict independent-particle model, and to the uniform model. On the strict independent-particle model there is no coupling between individual particle states, so that the only resonances seen in neutron scattering are those for a single particle in a spherical potential well. In the uniform model the coupling between individual particle states is so strong that all configurations of the same spin and parity have, a priori, equal strengths for neutron-induced processes. In the intermediate model the coupling of many nuclear excited states to the incoming channel single nuclear excited state is such that the average strength function for nuclear levels of proper spin and parity displays a broad resonance behavior of width W peaked at the energy of the single-nucleon excited-state energy. Sum rules act to maintain the summed contribution of the strength function at a common value for all models.

degenerate. The main factor determining the position of the level is the well, but other interactions split the one level into many. Experimentally, either the energy-resolving power of the instrument used to observe scattering is insufficient to resolve the single resonances or the levels actually overlap. The groups of resonances are then observed as relatively slow variations of the cross section as a function of energy. This is called the "giant resonance" phenomenon (Fig. 11-24).

A more fundamental problem is how to relate the optical-model potential to the nucleon-nucleon interaction. This is a complicated subject. Suffice it to say that a connection between the forward-scattering amplitude in the nucleon-nucleon system and the constants of the optical model has been found (Riesenfeld and Watson, 1956).

11-8 Compound Nucleus—Level Density

The density of nuclear levels depends strongly on the energy of excitation and on A. Near the ground state of light nuclei the levels may be about 1 MeV apart, and in heavy nuclei about 50 keV apart (except for the magic numbers of neutrons or protons). This may be observed in scattering experiments.

At an energy corresponding to the binding energy of the neutron (8 MeV), slow-neutron resonances for a medium-heavy element are a few eV apart. The density of nuclear levels, or more precisely of nuclear levels of spin $I \pm \frac{1}{2}$, has thus increased by a factor of the order 10^5. This has been explained in simple fashion by Bohr. Suppose that the nucleus resembles a collection of oscillators with the proper frequencies $\omega_1, \omega_2, \ldots, \omega_N$. The energy levels are

$$E = \sum_{i=1}^{N} \hbar n_i \omega_i \qquad \textbf{(11-8.1)}$$

with n_i integral and $\hbar\omega_i \sim 10^5$ eV. The various ω_i are also different from each other.

At the lowest energies the levels are about $\hbar\omega_i$ apart from each other, because only very few n_i are $\neq 0$ and in any case the n_i have small values. However, to obtain an excitation energy of several MeV, many oscillators must be excited, and the n_i are also large. One may thus obtain many values of E in a small energy interval. This qualitative explanation of the rapid increase of the level density with energy can be refined, as we shall see later.

The region corresponding to slow-neutron capture is among the best explored. The level density increases with A in passing from light elements to $A \sim 100$. For higher A the binding energy of the neutron decreases from 8 MeV to ~ 5 MeV, and hence the compound nucleus is less excited than lighter nuclei. This effect tends to increase the level spacing and to compensate for the effect of increasing A, which has the opposite action. Nucleons bound following the closure of a shell have levels especially wide spaced, because their binding energy is small. This is reflected in small cross sections.

11-9 The Nucleus as Fermi Gas

The results discussed above in qualitative terms may also be obtained from another point of view, which introduces into nuclear physics some of the concepts of statistical mechanics and thermodynamics, mainly temperature. The nuclear system, when A is not too small, is complicated enough to warrant the use of these ideas, provided one keeps in mind that under ordinary circumstances the ensembles of fermions considered are in a state of extreme degeneracy and thus need to be treated by Fermi statistics. Consider a nucleus as a collection of free neutrons and protons enclosed in a sphere of radius R or volume Ω. The neutrons and protons are fermions and thus two identical particles must be in different quantum states according to the exclusion principle. The number of states corresponding to a momentum smaller than P_F for protons or for neutrons is

$$n = \frac{2}{(2\pi\hbar)^3}\frac{4}{3}\pi\Omega P_F{}^3 \tag{11-9.1}$$

which is obtained by dividing the phase space into cells of volume $(2\pi\hbar)^3$ and assigning two particles to a cell, in order to take into account the statistical weight of states of particles of spin $\frac{1}{2}$. At complete degeneracy (i.e., for the ground state), we have

$$P_F{}^{\text{proton}} = (3\pi^2)^{1/3}\hbar\left(\frac{Z}{\Omega}\right)^{1/3} \tag{11-9.2}$$

$$P_F{}^{\text{neutron}} = (3\pi^2)^{1/3}\hbar\left(\frac{A-Z}{\Omega}\right)^{1/3} \tag{11-9.3}$$

In crude approximation $Z = N = A/2$; furthermore if one puts $\Omega = (4/3)\pi R^3$, with $R = r_0A^{1/3}$, one has $\Omega = 4.18r_0^3$, and expressing r_0 in fermis one finds

$$P_F = \frac{1.59 \times 10^{-14}}{r_0}\text{ cgs} = \frac{297}{r_0}\text{ MeV/c} \tag{11-9.4}$$

independent of A. The corresponding kinetic energy ($P_F{}^2/2M = E_F$) is called the "Fermi energy." For $r_0 = 1.3$ F, E_F is 28 MeV. This is the maximum kinetic energy of a neutron bound in the nucleus. If the binding energy of the last nucleons is 8 MeV, the potential energy must then be 36 MeV (Fig. 11-25).

For protons the situation is similar except for the potential barrier. However, a nucleus contains fewer protons than neutrons and hence the maximum kinetic energy of the protons is less than that of the neutrons. The total energies for neutron or proton are the same; otherwise the nucleus would transform a neutron into a proton, or vice versa, by a beta process. We must thus conclude that the potential energy for protons is smaller than that for neutrons, an effect in part due to Coulomb repulsion.

The expression of the kinetic energy of all protons in a nucleus, onsidered as a degenerate gas at the absolute zero, is

$$E_0^{\text{protons}} = \frac{2\Omega}{(2\pi\hbar)^3}\int_0^{P_F}\frac{p^2}{2m}4\pi p^2\,dp = \frac{\pi^{4/3}3^{5/3}}{10}\left(\frac{Z}{\Omega}\right)^{2/3}Z\frac{\hbar^2}{m} = \frac{3}{5}E_F Z$$

ith a similar formula for neutrons.

If we excite a nucleus, the gas heats up and we may connect its xcitation energy to a "temperature" of the gas, using the formulas valid or a perfect gas of fermions in the case of high degeneracy.[1] For neutrons e have

$$(E_T - E_0)^{\text{neutrons}} = \frac{\pi^2}{4}(A - Z)\frac{(kT)^2}{E_F} \tag{11-9.5}$$

y using Eq. (11-9.3) for P_F, Eq. (11-9.5) becomes

$$(E_T - E_0)^{\text{neutrons}} = \left(\frac{\pi^2}{72}\right)^{1/3}\frac{\Omega M}{\hbar^2}\left(\frac{A - Z}{\Omega}\right)^{1/3}(kT)^2 \tag{11-9.6}$$

nd, similarly,

$$(E_T - E_0)^{\text{protons}} = \left(\frac{\pi^2}{72}\right)^{1/3}\frac{\Omega M}{\hbar^2}\left(\frac{Z}{\Omega}\right)^{1/3}(kT)^2 \tag{11-9.7}$$

The total energy of the nucleus is obtained by summing the two:

$$E_T - E_0 = 0.08A^{2/3}\,[Z^{1/3} + (A - Z)^{1/3}](kT)^2 = a(kT)^2 \tag{11-9.8}$$

here E_T, E_0, and kT are in MeV. If $A = 100$ and $Z = 44$, $E_T = 11(kT)^2$. hen $kT = 1$ MeV corresponds to $E_T - E_0 = 11$ MeV. If the gas were ot degenerate, each degree of freedom kinetic energy would have an

[1] See, for example, P. M. Morse, *Thermal Physics*, rev. ed., Benjamin, New York, 964, as a reference in statistical mechanics.

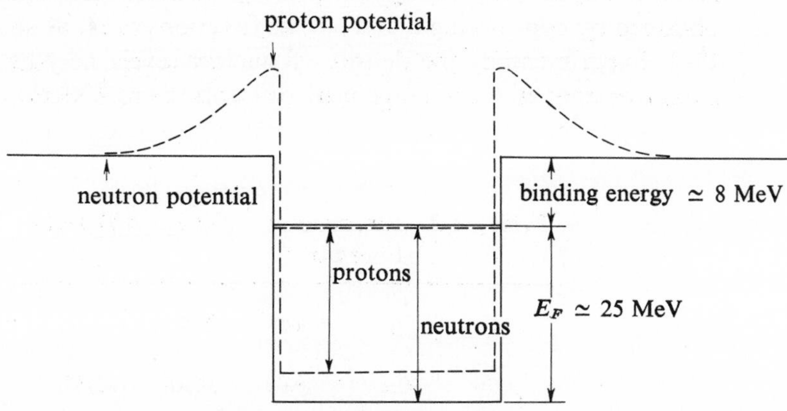

igure 11-25 Potential well for neutrons and protons in a heavy nucleus, showing the Fermi level. Note the difference between neutron and proton wells.

energy $\frac{1}{2}kT$. In our case $A = 100$ would give $3A = 300$ degrees o freedom, and $kT = 1$ MeV would correspond to $E_T - E_0 = 300$ MeV Note that the total energy of a degenerate gas depends quadraticall on the absolute temperature, in contrast to the total energy of a norma gas, which is notoriously proportional to the absolute temperature.

The density of nuclear states at a certain energy, $\rho(E) = 1/D(E)$, i related to the nuclear entropy S by

$$S = k \log \frac{\rho(E)}{\rho(0)} \qquad \text{or} \qquad \rho(E) = \rho(0)e^{S/k} \tag{11-9.9}$$

In fact, the statistical definition of entropy is $S(T) = k \log [\omega(T)/\omega(0)]$ where $\omega(T)$ is the number of quantum states available to the system a the specified temperature, and this number is proportional to $\rho(E)$. The thermodynamical definition of entropy,

$$S(T) = \int_0^T \frac{dE}{T} \tag{11-9.10}$$

in the specific case of a nucleus gives

$$S = 2ak^2 \int_0^T \frac{T\,dT}{T} = 2ak^2T = 2\,(ak^2E)^{1/2} \tag{11-9.11}$$

and we obtain from Eqs. (11-9.9) and (11-9.11)

$$\rho(E) = \rho(0)\, e^{2(aE)^{1/2}} \tag{11-9.12}$$

For $A = 100$ and $Z = 44$, $a = 11\ \text{MeV}^{-1}$, as seen above. To test thi equation, consider slow-neutron capture. Here $E \sim 8$ MeV, and Ec (11-9.12) gives

$$\rho(E) \sim \rho(0)\, e^{19} = \rho(0)10^8 \tag{11-9.13}$$

Assuming that $\rho(0) \sim 10^{-5}\ (\text{eV})^{-1}$, we obtain $\rho(8\ \text{MeV}) \sim 10^3\ (\text{eV})^{-1}$, or distance between levels of 1 meV. This is too small, even if we take int account the fact that experimentally only a small fraction of the level is observed, namely those with spin $I \pm \frac{1}{2}$. Better estimates of $\rho(E)$ ar obtained by considering a and $\rho(0)$ as functions of A, as shown in Tabl 11-2. Experimentally the density of nuclear levels may be obtained b measurements of the average neutron-capture cross section in a certai

Table 11-2 Parameters for the Level Density Formula

A	40	120	230	
$\rho(0)$	0.4	0.02	0.005	$(\text{MeV})^{-1}$
a	1	8	12	$(\text{MeV})^{-1}$

energy interval. The Breit–Wigner formula Eq. (11-6.28) integrated in an energy interval containing one resonance only gives

$$\int \sigma_r(E)\, dE = \pi g \int \frac{\lambda\!\!\!^{-2}\Gamma_n\Gamma_\gamma\, dE}{(E - E_r)^2 + \Gamma^2/4} \simeq 2\pi^2 g \lambda\!\!\!^{-2}{}_r \frac{\Gamma_n\Gamma_\gamma}{\Gamma} \tag{11-9.14}$$

To derive this formula, we have considered the isolated resonance as a sort of δ function having an area π and located at $E = E_r$. Consider now a neutron beam with an energy spread covering many resonances. We have, for the average capture cross section $\langle\sigma_r\rangle$ over a certain energy interval ΔE, the value given by Eq. (11-9.14) multiplied by the number of levels in the interval $\Delta E/D$ divided by the interval; that is,

$$\langle\sigma_r\rangle = 2\pi^2\lambda\!\!\!^{-2}\langle g\rangle \frac{\langle\Gamma_n\rangle\langle\Gamma_\gamma\rangle}{\langle\Gamma\rangle D} = 2\pi^2\lambda\!\!\!^{-}_0\lambda\!\!\!^{-} \frac{\langle\Gamma_n^{(0)}\rangle\langle\Gamma_\gamma\rangle}{\langle\Gamma\rangle D}\langle g\rangle \tag{11-9.15}$$

For heavy elements at low energy $\langle\Gamma_\gamma\rangle \gg \langle\Gamma_n\rangle$, and

$$\langle\sigma_r\rangle = 2\pi^2\lambda\!\!\!^{-2}\langle g\rangle \frac{\langle\Gamma_n\rangle}{D} \propto \frac{1}{v} \tag{11-9.16}$$

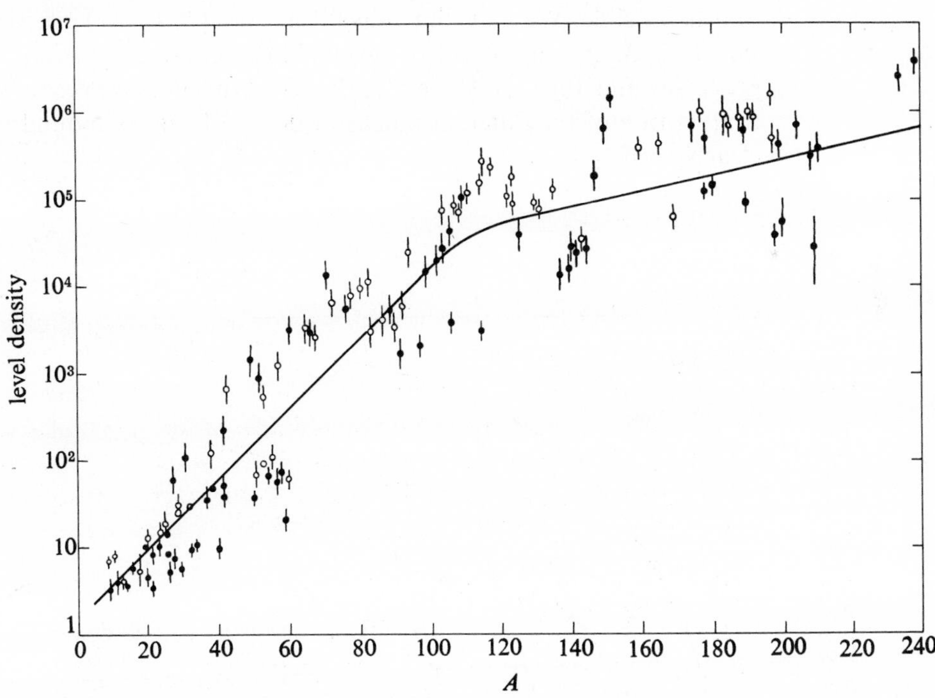

Figure 11-26 The observed level densities (number of levels per MeV) extrapolated to 7 MeV versus atomic number. The data are obtained from: the total level density of light nuclei ($A \leqslant 60$) the spacings of slow-neutron resonances ($A \geqslant 60$), and from the 1-MeV neutron cross sections, ● even-odd, odd-even, or even-even compound nuclei, ○ odd-odd compound nuclei. The full line in the density of levels at 7 MeV is given by Eq. (11-9.12). The errors are derived either from the number of levels used in determining the density or from errors involved in cross-section measurements. [From E. Vogt, BNL 331.]

For higher energy, up to about 1 MeV, where $\Gamma_\gamma < \Gamma_n$,

$$\langle \sigma_r \rangle = 2\pi^2 \lambda^2 \langle g \rangle \frac{\langle \Gamma \rangle}{D} \propto \frac{1}{E} \tag{11-9.17}$$

Γ_γ depends little on energy and can be measured directly ($\Gamma_\gamma \sim 0.1$ eV). It is then possible to obtain D from Eq. (11-9.17) (see Fig. 11-26).

The thermodynamic approach can be extended by considering the emission of neutrons or of other particles by the excited compound nucleus as an evaporation process. The evaporated neutrons have an energy distribution corresponding to a Maxwellian distribution at the temperature of the residual nucleus. This has been demonstrated, at least qualitatively, by experiment (Gugelot, 1949). In the case of charged particles the Coulomb barrier prevents the evaporation of low-energy particles; it thus changes the energy distribution by multiplying the Maxwell distribution by the Coulomb barrier penetration factor.

If the initial excitation energy of the compound nucleus is sufficient, the evaporation of one particle leaves enough energy in the residual nucleus to permit the evaporation of a second particle, and so on, until the nucleus is left with so little excitation energy that only gamma emission is possible. We may thus have, for example (α, xn) reactions, with $x = 1, 2, 3$, etc., up to six or seven. The excitation functions for these processes and Figs. 11-27 and 11-28 give typical examples in which the competition of the different modes of decay of the compound nucleus is clearly seen.

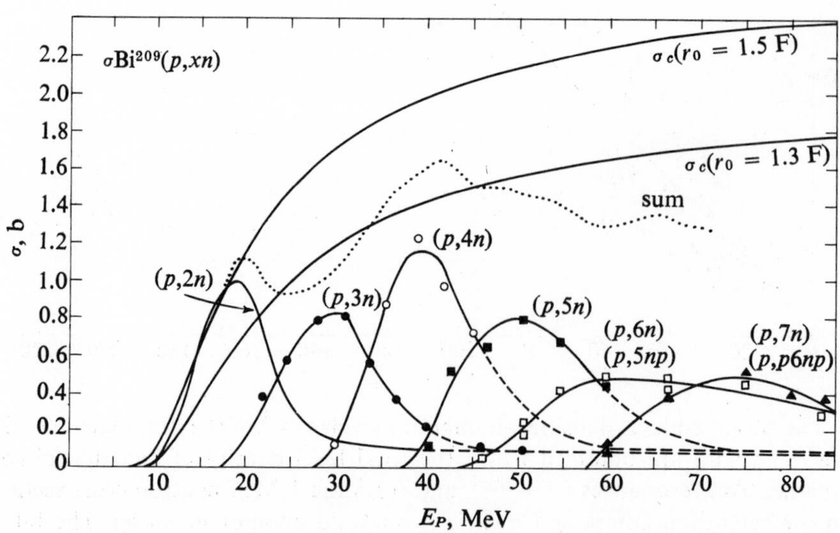

Figure 11-27 Excitation functions for the proton bombardment of bismuth, showing a statistical behavior of competing reactions. The calculated cross section for formation of the compound nucleus is indicated by σ_c. [R. E. Bell and H. M. Skarsgard, *Can. J. Phys.*, **34,** 745 (1956).]

In the qualitative description of nuclear reactions we have briefly mentioned direct interactions. An incoming particle hits a specific nucleon in the target and the remainder of the nucleus acts as a "spectator." If the nucleon is excited, the collision is inelastic. Such are, for instance, (p,p'), (n,n'), and (α,α') reactions. Characteristic for all of them, as opposed to compound nucleus formation, is the anisotropic angular distribution and the energy distribution.

The analysis of the angular distribution of the inelastically scattered particles gives important information about the quantum numbers of the initial and final states of the scattering nucleus. To see this qualitatively, write the vector angular momenta and spins of the particles and of the target. Referring to Fig. 11-29 representing an inelastic collision, for instance (p,p'), we write

$$\mathbf{I}_i + \mathbf{l}_i + \mathbf{s}_i = \mathbf{I}_f + \mathbf{l}_f + \mathbf{s}_f \tag{11-10.1}$$

where $\mathbf{l}$ and $\mathbf{s}$ are the orbital and spin angular momentum of the proton and $\mathbf{I}$ is the total angular momentum of the target, in the initial and final states, measured in units $\hbar$.

From this we get, by constructing the extreme cases of orientation of the vectors,

$$I_i + I_f + 1 \geqslant |\mathbf{l}_f - \mathbf{l}_i| \geqslant |\mathbf{I}_f - \mathbf{I}_i - \mathbf{s}_i + \mathbf{s}_f|_{\min} \tag{11-10.2}$$

Moreover, $l_f - l_i \equiv \Delta l$ must be odd if initial and final states of the target have opposite parity or even if they have the same parity.

Now Δl is caused by the change of angular momentum of the impinging proton. If we can localize the collision, for instance by assuming

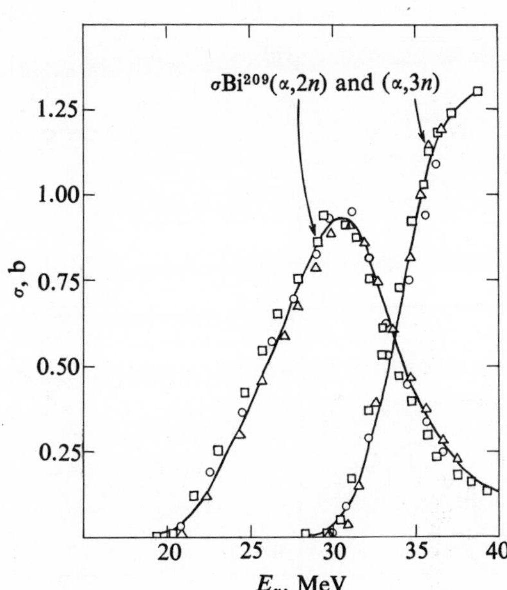

Figure 11-28 Excitation functions for alpha particle bombardment of bismuth [E. Kelly.]

it occurs at the nuclear surface at a distance R_0 from the center of mass of the system, we have

$$\Delta l = | \mathbf{k}_f - \mathbf{k}_i | R_0 \quad \textbf{(11-10.3)}$$

where $\hbar\mathbf{k}_i$, $\hbar\mathbf{k}_f$ are the initial and final linear momenta of the proton. Calling $\hbar\mathbf{k}$ the momentum transfer $\hbar\,|\mathbf{k}_i - \mathbf{k}_f|$ we have for Δl

$$\Delta l = kR_0 \quad \textbf{(11-10.4)}$$

Now from the cosine rule we have also

$$k^2 = k_i^2 + k_f^2 - 2k_ik_f \cos\theta \quad \textbf{(11-10.5)}$$

If Δl must have one or few values determined by the conditions of Eq. (11-10.2) there are only a few corresponding scattering angles θ that are preferred. For these the differential scattering cross section will show maxima. This qualitative semiclassical argument can be made into a theory, of varying degrees of accuracy. The following is a simplified treatment of a special example to give an idea of the procedures used.

● We shall treat the case of inelastic alpha scattering in Born plane-waves approximation (see Tobocman).

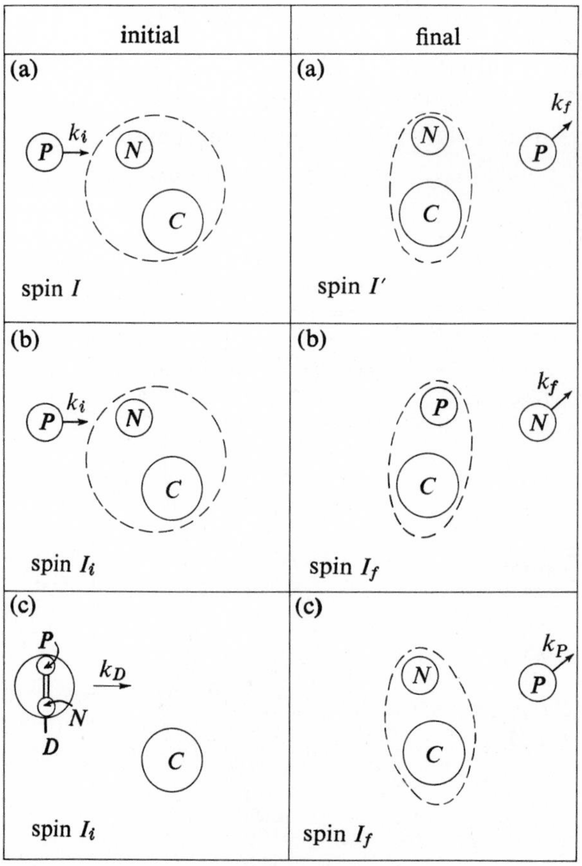

Figure 11-29 Schematic diagram for notations used in direct-interactions calculation. The nucleus NC has total angular momentum I or I' and its components N and C have orbital angular momentum l or l'. (a) Inelastic scattering, (b) knock-on reaction, (c) deuteron stripping.

The differential cross section is given by (see Appendix B)

$$\frac{d\sigma}{d\Omega} = \frac{M_\alpha^2}{(2\pi\hbar^2)^2}\frac{k_f}{k_i}|A_{if}|^2 \tag{11-10.6}$$

With reference to Fig. 11-29a, in which we now label the incident nucleus P with the symbol α and N is also an alpha particle,we find that the matrix element A_{if} is the sum of two integrals originating from the αN and αC interactions. We assume that these interactions are spherically symmetrical and represent them by the functions $V_{\alpha N}(r_{\alpha N})$ and $V_{\alpha C}(r_{\alpha C})$, respectively. Here $r_{\alpha C}$ means the distance between the center of mass of the α particle and of body C, and a similar notation is used for other r's.

To treat a simple case we shall assume that the initial target nucleus of eigenfunction $\varphi_0(r_{NC})$ has orbital angular momentum $l = 0$ and total spin I. The final nucleus has an orbital angular momentum l' and a total angular momentum I'. Its eigenfunction is $\varphi_{I'}(r_{NC})$. The function $\varphi_0(r_{NC})$ is thus spherically symmetrical; the function $\varphi_{I'}(r_{NC})$ has an angular dependence given by a linear combination of spherical harmonics $Y_{l'}^m\ (\theta,\varphi)$, with $m = l',\ l' - 1 \cdots - l'$. The part of the matrix element due to $V_{\alpha N}(r_{\alpha N})$ is written

$$A_{\alpha\alpha'}(V_{\alpha N}) = \int \varphi_{I'}{}^*(r_{NC}) \exp(-i\mathbf{k}_f \cdot \mathbf{r}_{\alpha I}) V_{\alpha N}(r_{\alpha N}) \exp(+i\mathbf{k}_i \cdot \mathbf{r}_{\alpha I}) \times \varphi_0(r_{NC})\, d\mathbf{r}_{\alpha I}\, d\mathbf{r}_{NC} \tag{11-10.7}$$

The integral Eq. (11-10.7) is simplified by a change of variables that permits us to decompose it into the product of two integrals. Replacing $r_{\alpha I}$ by its expression

$$\mathbf{r}_{\alpha I} = \mathbf{r}_{\alpha N} + \frac{M_C}{M_N + M_C}\mathbf{r}_{NC} \tag{11-10.8}$$

we have

$$A_{\alpha\alpha'}(V_{\alpha N}) = \int d\mathbf{r}_{\alpha N} \exp(-i\mathbf{k} \cdot \mathbf{r}_{\alpha N}) V_{\alpha N}(r_{\alpha N}) \int d\mathbf{r}_{NC} \exp(-i\mathbf{k}' \cdot \mathbf{r}_{NC}) \times \varphi_0(r_{NC})\varphi_{I'}{}^*(r_{NC}) \tag{11-10.9}$$

where

$$\mathbf{k} = \mathbf{k}_f - \mathbf{k}_i \tag{11-10.10}$$

and

$$\mathbf{k}' = \mathbf{k}\frac{M_C}{M_N + M_C} \tag{11-10.11}$$

Now the calculation of each factor can be carried further. Consider first the integral in $d\mathbf{r}_{NC}$. Assume as the z axis the direction of $\mathbf{k}'$ and expand the plane wave in spherical harmonics according to the known relation (Appendix D)

$$e^{ikz} = \sum_L 4\pi(2L + 1)i^L j_L(kr)\, Y_L^0\,(\cos\theta)$$

where $j_L(x)$ is the so-called *spherical Bessel function.*

The integration over angles gives zero unless $L = l'$ and $m = 0$, because of the orthogonality of the spherical harmonics, and the integral in $d\mathbf{r}_{NC}$ is proportional to

$$\int j_{l'}(k'r)\varphi_0(r)\varphi_{I'}^*(r)r^2\,dr \tag{11-10.12}$$

where $k' = |\mathbf{k}'|$ and by $\varphi_{I'}^*(r)$ we mean here only the radial part of the nuclear eigenfunction. Both $\varphi_0(r)$ and $\varphi_{I'}(r)$ decrease very rapidly beyond the nuclear surface corresponding to $r = R_I$. We may thus assume that the chief contribution to the integral comes to the region near the nuclear surface where the integrand is largest and conclude that the integral is proportional to $j_{l'}(k'R_I)$, which will thus appear as a factor in the final expression of $A_{\alpha N}$.

The evaluation of the other factor in the integral, Eq. (11-10.9), containing $V_{\alpha N}$, requires knowledge of this last function. One can give it different semiempirical forms—for instance, the Yukawa form $V_{\alpha N}{}^0\, e^{-r_{\alpha N}/\rho}/r$—and compute it. In view of the short range of the nuclear forces, we shall assume $V_{\alpha N} = V_{\alpha N}{}^0\delta(r_{\alpha N})$, where $\delta(r)$ is the tridimensional Dirac delta function. It follows immediately that the integral reduces to $V_{\alpha N}{}^0$.

The integral corresponding to $V_{\alpha C}$ can now be written in analogy to Eq. (11-10.9) using the expression

$$\mathbf{r}_{\alpha I} = \mathbf{r}_{\alpha C} - \frac{M_N}{M_N + M_C}\mathbf{r}_{NC} \tag{11-10.13}$$

However, when we write the expression corresponding to the second factor of Eq. (11-10.9) we find

$$\int d\mathbf{r}_{NC} \exp\{-i[M_N/(M_N + M_C)]\mathbf{k}\cdot\mathbf{r}_{NC}\}\varphi_0(r_{NC})\varphi_{I'}^*(r_{NC}) \tag{11-10.14}$$

Now the exponentional is nearly constant whenever $M_N \ll M_C$ (as we shall assume), and because of the orthogonality of φ_0 to $\varphi_{I'}$, the integral vanishes. For this reason we have neglected it.

In conclusion, we find that the matrix element A_{if} depends on θ only because k' appears in the Bessel function of Eq. (11-10.12). In fact we have

$$k^2 = k_i^2 + k_f^2 - 2k_ik_f\cos\theta = \left(\frac{M_N + M_C}{M_C}\right)^2 k'^2 \tag{11-10.15}$$

where θ is the angle of scattering. The spherical Bessel functions are shown in Fig. D-1 of Appendix D. They resemble damped oscillations and this behavior determines the oscillations in the cross section.

It is apparent that if l had been different from zero there could have been many more terms in the matrix element, namely, those for which $|l - l'| \leqslant L \leqslant l + l'$, and correspondingly more Bessel functions. The formulas thus become complicated, but they preserve the structure.

$$A_{PP'}(V_{NP}) \approx \delta_{mm'} \sum_L B_{NP}(Ll'lm)j_L\left(\frac{M_C}{M_I}\,kR_I\right) \tag{11-10.16}$$

with

$$\mathbf{k} = \mathbf{k}_i - \mathbf{k}_f \tag{11-10.17}$$

The values of L over which the sum is to be taken are restricted by the conditions

$$|l - l'| \leqslant L \leqslant l + l' \tag{11-10.18}$$

$$|I - I'| \leqslant L \leqslant I + I' \tag{11-10.19}$$

$$\text{parity of } L = \text{parity of } l + l' \tag{11-10.20}$$

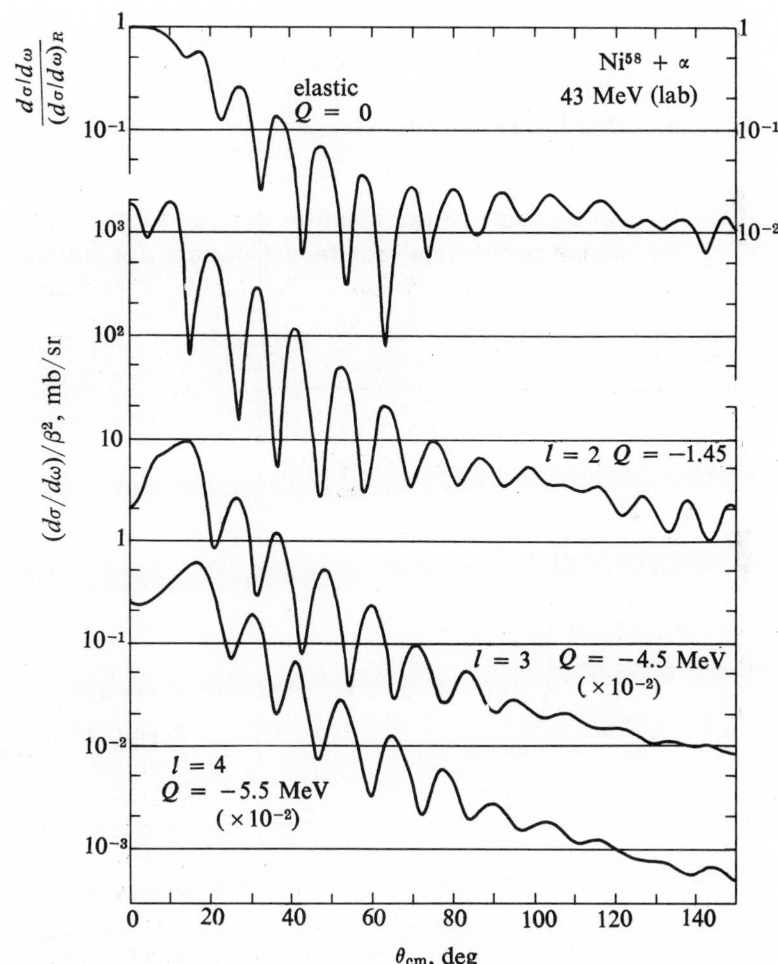

Figure 11-30 Theoretical elastic and inelastic scattering of alpha particles on Ni^{58}. The angular distribution is calculated by direct-interaction theory and shows the influence of the angular momentum of the levels excited. Upper curve (elastic) gives the ratio of the differential scattering cross section to the Rutherford value. Lower curves correspond to excitations of rotational levels. For meaning of β^2, a nuclear deformation parameter, and parameters used in calculation, see original paper. Existing experimental data ($\theta < 60°$) agree well with theory. [Bassel, Satchler, Drisko, and Rost, *Phys. Rev.*, **128**, 2693 (1963).]

These are often sufficient to leave in the sum only one or very few values of L (Fig. 11-30). For the case $l = 0$ explicitly treated, we have seen in fact only one value of L appearing in the sum. From the angular distribution of inelastic scattered particles we may thus extract information concerning the spin and the parity of the final state.

Similar to inelastic scattering are knock-on reactions, in which the incoming particle hits a particle of another kind and ejects it without forming a compound nucleus; for example, (α,p) (n,p) may go through this process (see Fig. 11-29). An evaluation of the cross section in Born approximation similar to that given above for inelastic scattering leads to a formula of the same structure as Eq. (11-10.16) and to the same selection rules, except that k in the Bessel function now means the magnitude of

$$\mathbf{k} = \mathbf{k}_i - \frac{M_I}{M_F}\mathbf{k}_f \tag{11-10.21}$$

and that Eq. (11-10.19) is replaced by

$$L \leqslant I_P + I_N + I_i + I_f \qquad \bullet \tag{11-10.22}$$

As an example we mention here an elegant application of direct interaction to the (p,n) reaction. Consider, for instance, the bombardment of V^{51} in the reaction V^{51} (p,n) Cr^{51}. V^{51} contains 23 protons and

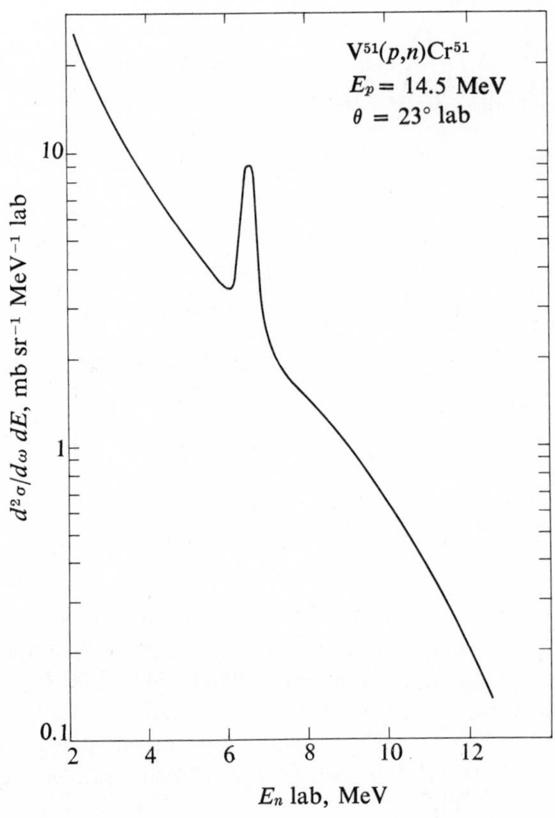

Figure 11-31 The proton-neutron reaction V^{51} (p,n) Cr^{51}. The neutrons show an evaporation spectrum and superimposed on it a peak at energy 6.4 MeV. The energy left in the nucleus (14.5 − 8.1) MeV represents the energy difference between a neutron and a proton in the same type of orbit and corresponds to the energy difference between the two bottoms of the wells of Fig. 11-25; it is all of coulombic origin. [Courtesy Anderson, Wong, and McClure.]

28 neutrons. Outside the 20 neutron-20 proton core are 3 protons and 8 neutrons in $f_{7/2}$ orbits. In the final state there are 4 protons and 7 neutrons in the $f_{7/2}$ orbit of Cr^{51}. The collision can be represented as changing a neutron into a proton without any change of orbits. The Q of the reaction must then be equal to the difference in Coulomb energy between V^{51} and Cr^{51}. In the spectrum of neutrons in this reaction one finds in fact a distinct peak corresponding to the incident proton energy minus the difference of the Coulomb energies (8.2 MeV calculated independently), and which emerges above the background of evaporation neutrons (see Fig. 11-31 and compare also with Fig. 11-25). In Fig. 11-25 the neutron or proton orbits, with the same quantum numbers, have the same energy measured from the bottom of their respective wells. This is a consequence of the charge independence of nuclear forces. The energy difference between a proton and a neutron orbit is then the same as the difference between the bottoms of the two wells.

Reactions initiated by deuterons show some interesting features attributable to surface effects and to the loose structure of the deuteron (see Chap. 10). These reactions often pass, not through an initial compound

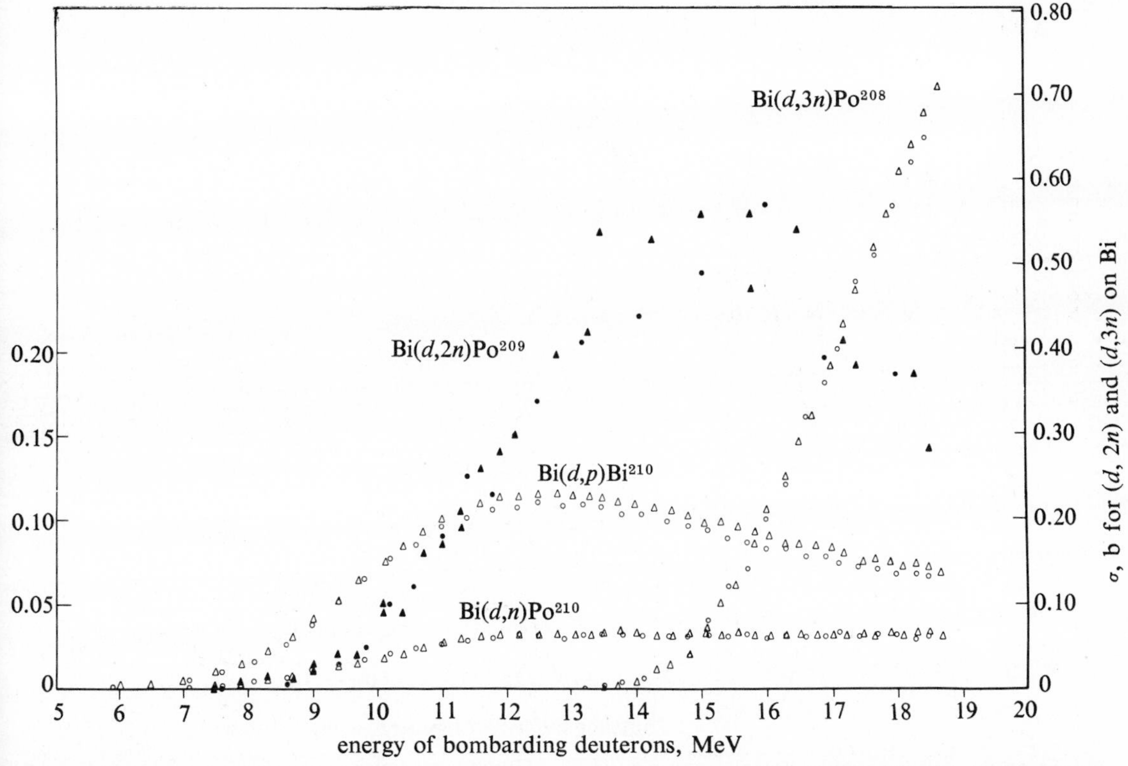

Figure 11-32 Excitation functions for the reactions Bi(d,2n) Po^{209}, Bi(d,3n)Po^{208}, Bi(d,p)Bi^{210}, and Bi(d,n)Po^{210}. [E. Kelly.]

state in which the whole deuteron would be absorbed, but through a "stripping mechanism," where the reaction may proceed at energies considerably below the Coulomb barrier (Oppenheimer and Phillips, 1936). The deuteron, without entering the target, is stripped of one of the nucleons (at very low energy, preferentially the neutron) and the other nucleon continues more or less along its initial trajectory. This process is predominant in the excitation function (d,p) of Fig. 11-32; a comparison of Figs. 11-31 and 11-32 shows the difference between the deuteron-initiated reaction and a reaction passing through the compound-nucleus process.

At low energy, but above the region in which Coulomb effects are important (3 to 14 MeV depending on Z of the target), (d,p), and (d,n) reactions behave quite similarly. Consider first (d,p) reactions, where the escaping protons show characteristic angular distributions, which can be explained by attributing them to deuterons that lose their neutron (stripping) without the proton entering the field of the nucleus. The analysis of the angular distribution of these protons provides information about the angular momentum of the captured neutron and on the

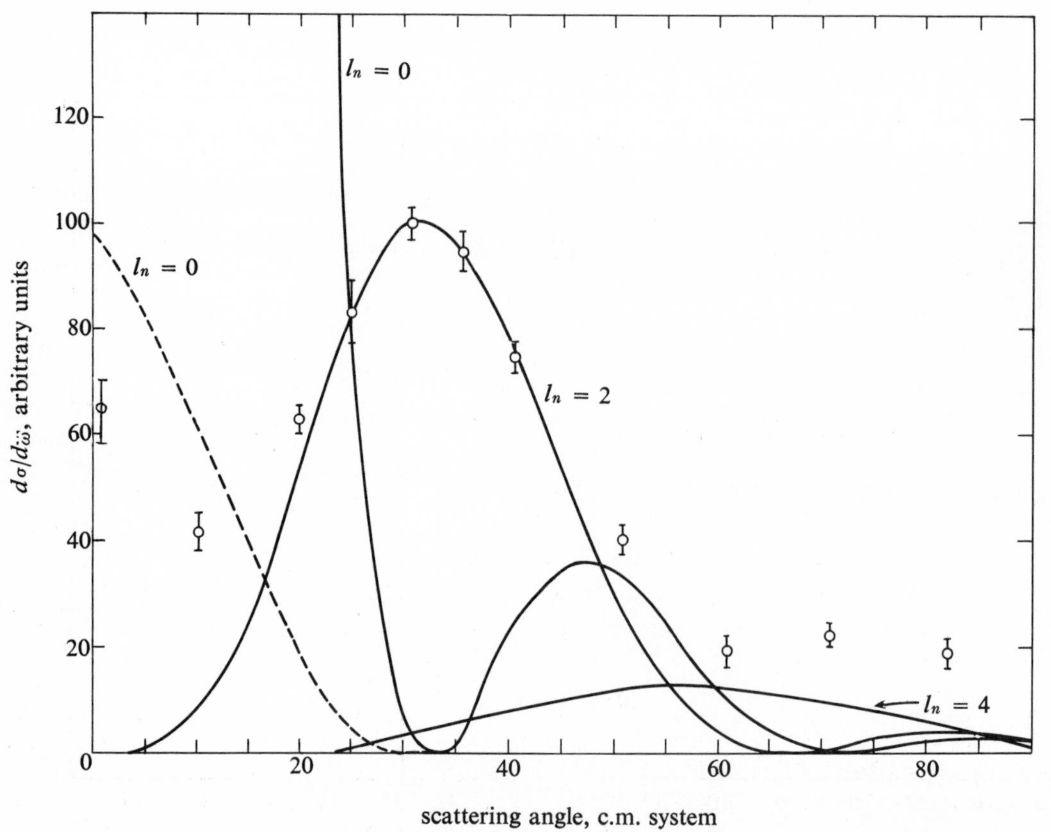

Figure 11-33 Angular distribution of protons from Cl^{35} (d,p) Cl^{36}. Curves are Butler curves for $l = 0$ and $l = 2$. The broken line is the curve for $l = 0$ reduced in scale by a factor 20.

spin and parity of the final nucleus (Butler, 1951) (Fig. 11-33). The following qualitative argument is very similar to the argument given above for the (p,p') reaction.

In the stripping reaction at low energies, up to a few MeV, we must consider the initial and final states of the nucleus with angular momenta $\mathbf{I}_i$, $\mathbf{I}_f$, the orbital angular momentum of the deuteron with respect to the target nucleus $\mathbf{l}_d$ and the deuteron spin $\mathbf{s}_d$.

In the collision the neutron is captured, with orbital angular momentum $\mathbf{l}_n$, and the proton escapes at an angle θ with respect to the initial direction of motion of the deuteron. There is an interesting relation between $\mathbf{l}_n$ and the angle θ. To see this, we first note that

$$\mathbf{I}_f = \mathbf{I}_i + \mathbf{l}_d + \mathbf{s}_d - \mathbf{l}_p - \mathbf{s}_p = \mathbf{I}_i + \mathbf{l}_n + \mathbf{s}_n \qquad \textbf{(11-10.23)}$$

which simply expresses the conservation of angular momentum. The orbital angular momentum of the captured neutron $\mathbf{l}_n$ is thus restricted by the inequality

$$I_f + I_i + \tfrac{1}{2} \geqslant l_n \geqslant \left| |I_i - I_f| - \tfrac{1}{2} \right| \qquad \textbf{(11-10.24)}$$

and also by the fact that, since the parity of the initial and final states are given, l_n must in some cases be even and in some cases odd, in order to satisfy parity conservation. For instance, starting from the ground state of C^{12}, $I_i = 0$ (even), if we want to land in the ground state of C^{13}, $I_f = \frac{1}{2}$(odd), l_n must be $\leqslant 1$ and odd; that is, $l_n = 1$.

The linear momentum associated with the neutron and delivered to the capturing nucleus is

$$\hbar\,(\mathbf{k}_d - \mathbf{k}_p) = \hbar\mathbf{k}_n \qquad \textbf{(11-10.25)}$$

and this momentum gives rise to $\mathbf{l}_n$. Since the capture must occur at a radius not greater than the nuclear radius R, we have

$$|(\mathbf{k}_d - \mathbf{k}_p) \times \mathbf{R}\,| = |\mathbf{k}_n \times \mathbf{R}| \geqslant l_n \qquad \textbf{(11-10.26a)}$$

or

$$(\mathbf{k}_d - \mathbf{k}_p)^2 \geqslant \frac{l_n^2}{R^2} \qquad \textbf{(11-10.26b)}$$

or, squaring and rearranging,

$$2k_pk_d \cos\theta \leqslant k_p^2 + k_d^2 - \frac{l_n^2}{R^2} \qquad \textbf{(11-10.27)}$$

In a given transition k_p^2 and k_d^2 are constants, determined by the conservation of energy, and Eq. (11-10.27) shows that the preferred angle of scattering θ will increase with increasing l_n. Actually, this semiclassical argument is vastly oversimplified.

The calculation of stripping in Born approximation may be done on lines similar to the calculation for inelastic scattering; however, this is appreciably more complicated, because it is not possible to factor the integrals in the matrix element by simple changes of variables and because the large size of the deuteron prevents the use of a zero-range potential.

The final result, however, is again very similar to that for the inelastic and knock-on reaction, but even simpler because the sum of Eq. (11-10.16) contains only one term. One finds

$$A_{DP}(V_{NP}) \approx \delta_{m0} D_{NP}(l) j_l(kR) \qquad \textbf{(11-10.28)}$$

with

$$\mathbf{k} = \mathbf{k}_d - \frac{M_C}{M_F}\mathbf{k}_p \qquad \textbf{(11-10.29)}$$

Here l is the orbital angular momentum of the final bound state. The inequality of Eq. (11-10.24) also obtains.

Stripping processes occur not only with deuterons but also with H^3 and He^3. The (t,d) or (he^3,d) reactions show many analogies with deuteron stripping. Stripping reactions are eminently suitable for determination of l and parity of nuclear levels from the angular distribution of the reaction products. In many cases, the results can be simply interpreted by the shell model. A different type of information concerning nuclear structure comes from the absolute value of the cross section.

At very high energies the stripping phenomenon may be described semiclassically (Serber, 1947) by considering one of the nucleons (e.g., the proton in the deuteron) as absorbed by a nucleus and the other as continuing along its trajectory almost unperturbed, with the initial velocity of the deuteron and, hence, half its energy. In this way, the extremely nonadiabatic collision gives rise to neutrons with an energy and angular distribution obtainable from the addition of the internal momentum of the deuteron to half the momentum of its center of mass. The energy spread and the angular spread of the neutron beam are

$$\Delta E = 1.5(\epsilon_d E_d)^{1/2} \qquad \textbf{(11-10.30)}$$

$$\Delta\theta = 1.6\left(\frac{\epsilon_d}{E_d}\right)^{1/2} \qquad \textbf{(11-10.31)}$$

where ϵ_d is the binding energy of the deuteron and E_d its kinetic energy.

The converse of the stripping process is the "pick up" (n,d), (p,d) process in which, for example, a neutron entering a nucleus finds a proton with the right momentum and distance to form a deuteron, and the pair escapes as a bound deuteron. These reactions have been frequently observed and their cross sections are connected by detailed balancing with the stripping cross sections.

11-11 The Fission Process

Among nuclear processes fission is very spectacular and of the greatest practical importance. A heavy nucleus such as uranium, under bombardment by a number of projectiles, splits into two large fragments such as Ba^{139} and Kr^{97}, which fly apart with an average energy of 170 MeV. The phenomenon is called fission (Hahn and Strassmann, 1939), and since it is accompanied by evaporation of neutrons, which can stimulate further fission, it offers the possibility of a chain reaction.

Occasionally, heavy nuclei undergo fission spontaneously, without outside stimulation (spontaneous fission; Flerov and Petrjak, 1940). Actually this mode of decay, which is negligible compared with alpha decay in nuclei having $Z \simeq 92$, such as uranium, already shows for Cf^{252} a branching of approximately 0.03 and for Cf^{254} it becomes the main decay channel.

We shall now discuss the fission process without reference to whether it is spontaneous or stimulated. Consider first the mass formula of Chap. 6 or a table of masses. Let us inquire whether a nucleus of mass number A and atomic number Z, $M(A,Z)$, is stable with respect to its splitting into two equal parts of mass $M(A/2, Z/2)$. We have

$$M(A,Z) - 2M(A/2,Z/2) = 17.2\,A^{2/3}(1-2^{1/3}) + 0.70 \times \frac{Z^2}{A^{1/3}}(1-2^{-2/3}) \quad \text{MeV} \tag{11-11.1}$$

This is positive for heavy nuclei and gives an energy of about 169 MeV for U^{236}. However, the original nucleus of mass $M(A,Z)$ is stable for small deformations from a spherical shape, as can be determined by the type of considerations used to establish the mass formula. In order to see this, assume that we slightly deform the spherical nucleus into an ellipsoidal one. If the potential energy increases, the spherical shape is stable. There are two contributions to the potential energy affected by the deformation: the surface energy E_s and the electrostatic energy E_c. We consider deformation at constant volume, assuming that nuclear matter is incompressible. We merely change the nuclear spherical shape into an ellipsoid of semiaxes a and b. To ensure the constancy of the volume we take the major semiaxis a as

$$a = R(1 + \epsilon) \tag{11-11.2}$$

and the minor semiaxes b as

$$b = R(1 + \epsilon)^{-1/2} \tag{11-11.3}$$

The volume $V = \frac{4}{3}\pi ab^2$ is thus constant. Now E_s, the surface energy, is proportional to the surface area of the ellipsoid, which is given by

$$S = 2\pi b^2 + 2\pi \frac{ab}{e} \sin^{-1} e \tag{11-11.4}$$

where $e = (1 - b^2/a^2)^{1/2}$. Approximately, up to terms in ϵ^2, one has

$$S = 4\pi R^2(1 + \tfrac{2}{5}\epsilon^2 + \cdots) \tag{11-11.5}$$

Using Eq. (6-3.1) we have

$$E_s = 17.5A^{2/3}(1 + \tfrac{2}{5}\epsilon^2 + \cdots) \tag{11-11.6}$$

The electrostatic energy is given by $\frac{1}{2}\rho^2 \int (dv_1\, dv_2/r_{12})$, where dv_1, dv_2 are volume elements, r_{12} is the distance between them, and ρ is the charge density. For a sphere this integral gives the main term of Eq. (11-11.7). Its correction for an elongated ellipsoid may be calculated as

$$\frac{3}{10}\frac{Z^2e^2}{(a^2 - b^2)^{1/2}} \log \frac{a + (a^2 - b^2)^{1/2}}{a - (a^2 - b^2)^{1/2}}$$

which for small elongation reduces to the term in ϵ^2 of Eq. (11-11.7):

$$E_c = \frac{3}{5}\frac{e^2Z^2}{R}\left(1 - \frac{\epsilon^2}{5} + \cdots\right) \tag{11-11.7}$$

The total change of energy in MeV is then

$$\Delta E = \Delta E_s + \Delta E_c = \epsilon^2\,[(2/5)\,17.5A^{2/3} - (1/5)\,0.71Z^2A^{-1/3}] \tag{11-11.8}$$

with the constants suggested by Green (see Sec. 6-5) and where ΔE_s and ΔE_c are the differences between the surface and Coulomb energies for the ellipsoid and for the sphere. If ΔE is positive, the spherical configuration is stable. From Eq. (11-11.8) it is clear that $\Delta E > 0$, for $Z^2/A < 49$. This is a criterion for stability.

The curve of the potential energy versus nuclear distance for two nuclei thus has the qualitative aspect of Fig. 11-34. The point for $\epsilon = 0$ is given by the nuclear mass; the region from $r = R_1 + R_2$ to infinity ($R_1 = R_2$ = sum of the radii of the fragments) is a hyperbola of equation

$$V = \frac{Z_1Z_2e^2}{r} \tag{11-11.9}$$

as required by Coulomb's law. The region between 0 and $r = R_1 + R_2$ is unknown, but the difference between the energy at $r = 0$ and $r = \infty$ is obtainable from a table of masses, because it is the difference between the mass of the original nucleus and that of the two fragments. It is thus possible to trace the energy curve except for the region mentioned above. The difference between the energy at $r = 0$ and at $r = R_1 + R_2$ is the energy that must be supplied to the nucleus to provoke its fission, that is, the activation energy for the fission reaction.

The tunnel effect of quantum mechanics has the consequence that there can be a small probability of fission even below the activation energy, owing to the zero-point energy of the nuclear motions. This is

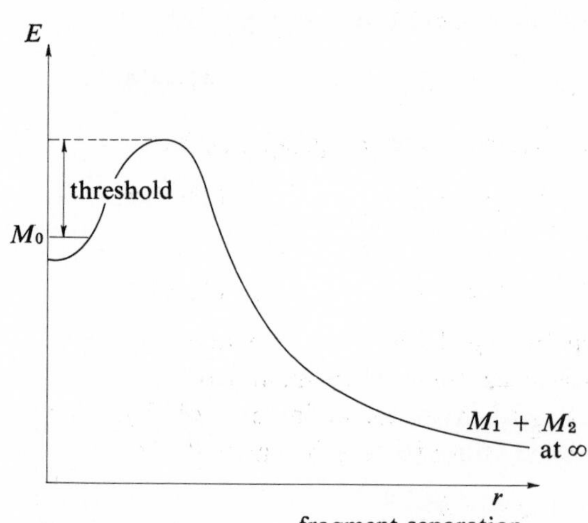

Figure 11-34 Energy of a fissioning nucleus as a function of the distance of the fragments.

the reason for spontaneous fission. In Fig. 11-35 we have plotted the spontaneous-fission probability for heavy elements as a function of Z^2/A, which according to Eq. (11-11.8) is the parameter that determines stability under small deformations. The zero-point energy of collective motions of the nucleus produces a deformation that has a definite probability of leading to fission by the tunnel effect. This probability is greater the closer Z^2/A is to the critical value.

Fission is a probable process ($\tau \sim 10^{-14}$ sec) for a nucleus excited above the activation energy. However, its probability decreases very rapidly with decreasing energy. One thus has an apparent threshold for fission, as shown in Fig. 11-36, and one commonly speaks of fission thresholds. The binding energy of a neutron to a nucleus having an odd number of neutrons is greater by about 2 MeV than it is to a nucleus having an even number of neutrons (see Chap. 6). Hence a slow neutron captured by a nucleus with N odd, such as U^{235} or Pu^{239}, gives rise to a compound nucleus that is more excited by about 2 MeV than the nuclei obtainable by slow-neutron capture in U^{238} or other even

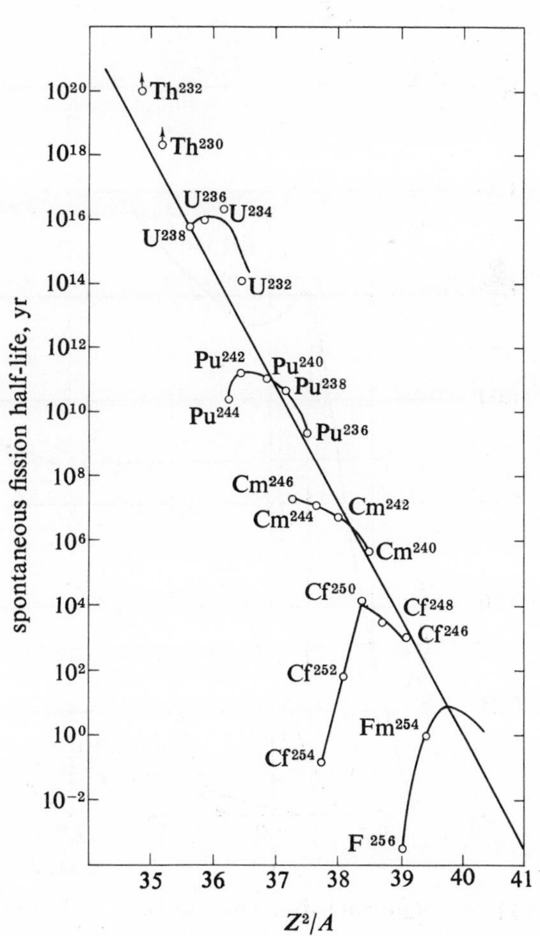

Figure 11-35 The probability of spontaneous fission per unit time is $0.69/T$, where T is the "half-life" for spontaneous fission. The figure gives T as a function of Z^2/A on a semilog scale.

Table 11-3 Neutron Fission Thresholds

Target nucleus	Th^{232}	U^{233}	U^{234}	U^{235}	U^{236}	U^{238}	Np^{237}	Pu^{239}
Compound nucleus	Th^{233}	U^{234}	U^{235}	U^{236}	U^{237}	U^{239}	Np^{238}	Pu^{240}
n-Fission threshold, MeV	1.3	<0	0.4	<0	0.8	1.2	0.4	<0

nuclei. The excitation of about 7 MeV obtainable on capture of a slow neutron by an even-odd nucleus is sufficient to produce fission. Table 11-3 gives the threshold for neutron-induced fission in a number of elements, and confirms the influence of the even or odd number of neutrons.

The fission fragments produced by slow-neutron fission in U^{235} show a yield as a function of A, given in Fig. 11-37. It is most remarkable that fission tends to occur with unequal fragments. The fragments that clearly have an excess of neutrons revert to stability by a succession of beta decays, forming chains of isobars decaying into each other. As an

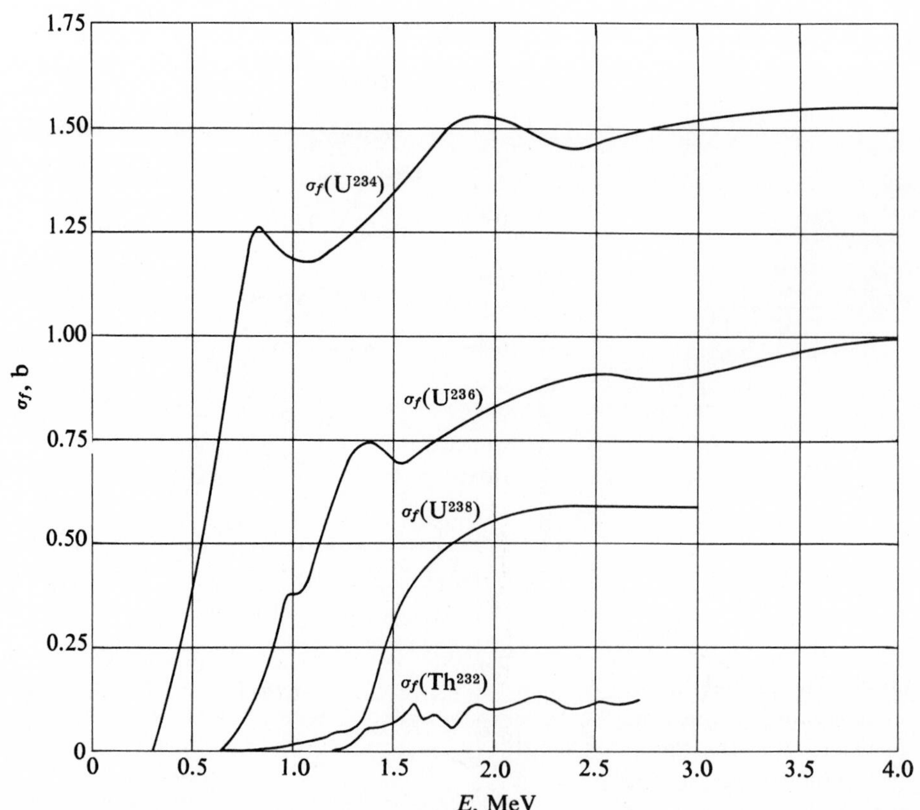

Figure 11-36 Neutron fission cross sections of Th^{232}, U^{234}, U^{236}, and U^{238}. [(WW 59).]

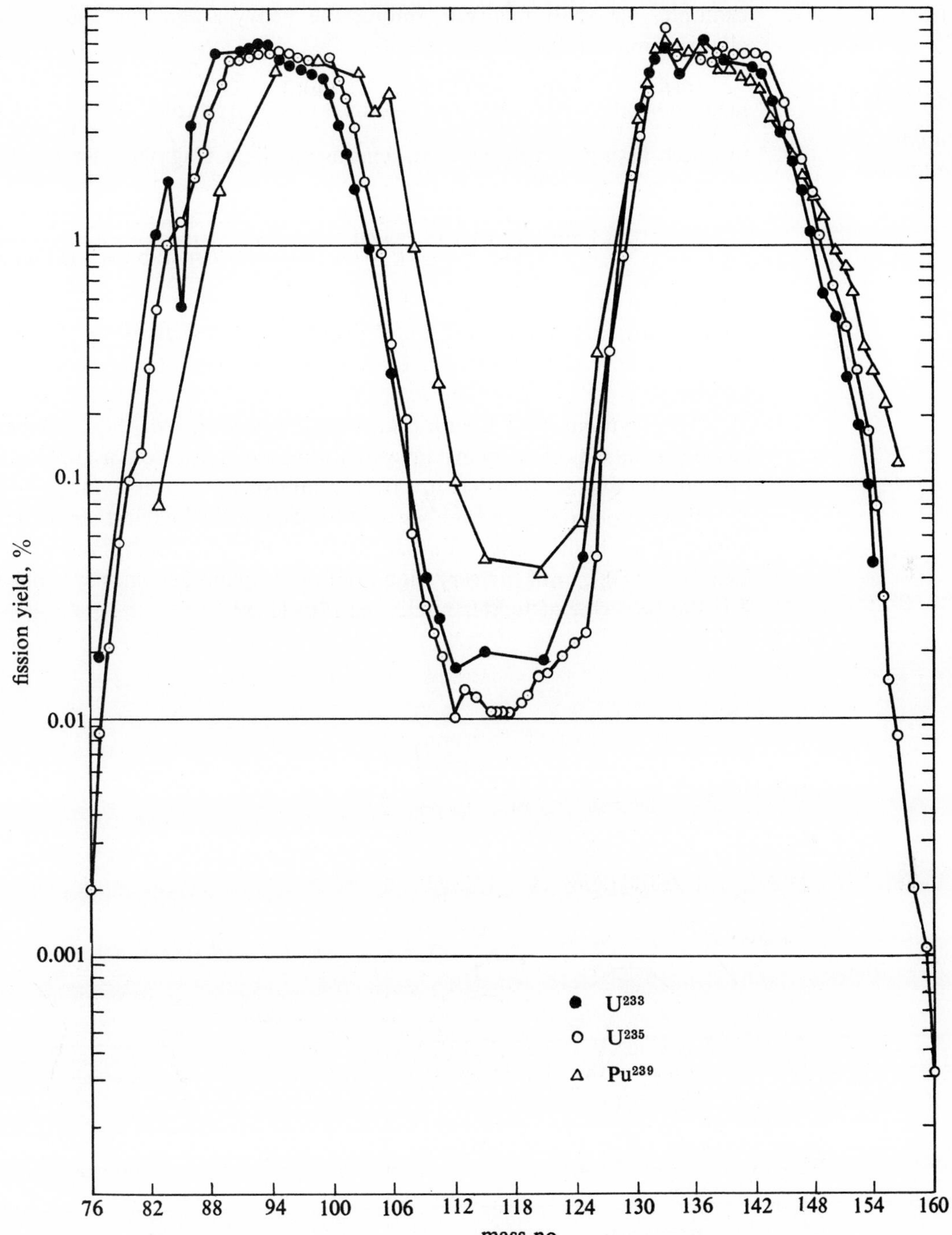

Figure 11-37 Abundance of different mass numbers in slow-neutron fission of U^{233}, U^{235}, and Pu^{239}. [(WW 59).]

example, we shall mention among the heavy fragments the famous chain of mass 140,

$$_{54}\text{Xe} \xrightarrow{(16\text{s})} {_{55}\text{Cs}} \xrightarrow{(66\text{s})} {_{56}\text{Ba}} \xrightarrow{(12.8\text{d})} {_{57}\text{La}} \xrightarrow{(40\text{h})} {_{58}\text{Ce}}\ (\text{stable}) \qquad \textbf{(11-11.10)}$$

in which fission was discovered. Among the light fragments we mention the chain of mass 99,

$$_{40}\text{Zr} \xrightarrow{(30\text{s})} {_{41}\text{Nb}} \xrightarrow{(3.8\text{m})} {_{42}\text{Mo}} \xrightarrow{(67\text{h})} {_{43}\text{Tc}} \xrightarrow{(2.12 \times 10^5\text{y})} {_{44}\text{Ru}}\ (\text{stable}) \qquad \textbf{(11-11.11)}$$

which is an important source of the artificial element technetium. Both these chains are among the most probable modes of fission for U^{235} bombarded by slow neutrons. Each occurs in about 6 per cent of the fissions.

The asymmetry of fission (i.e., the difference in A of the fragments) has been the object of many investigations, but until now a completely satisfactory explanation has not been established.

Fission occurring in highly excited nuclei of the heaviest elements as obtained by high-energy bombardment shows decreasing asymmetry (see Fig. 11-38), until for very high excitation fission becomes symmetric. For the behavior of lighter nuclei see Fig. 11-39.

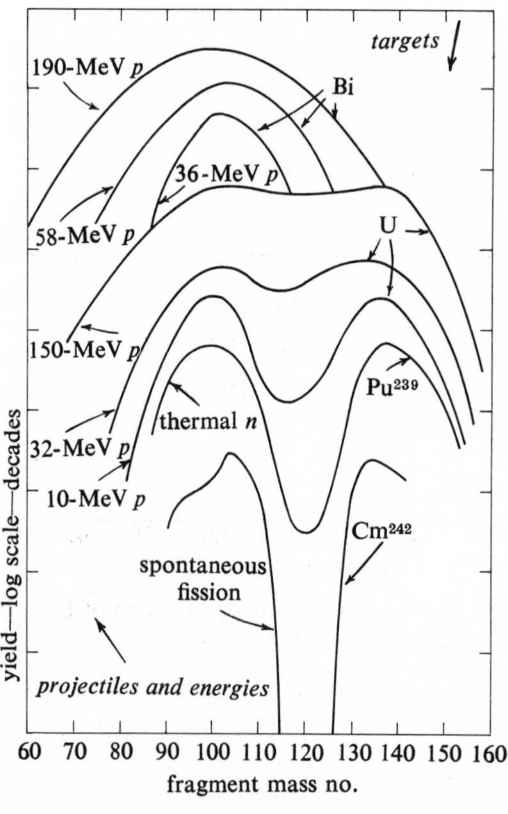

Figure 11-38 Shapes of mass distributions to show their dependence on the nature of the fissioning species and on the energy of the projectiles. [From I. Halpern, *Ann. Rev. Nucl. Sci.*, **9,** 245 (1959).]

	Fission probability	Shape of mass yield curve: Near threshold	Exc. energy 10–40 MeV	Exc. energy > 40 MeV
Highly fissile elements (thorium and heavier elements)	Asymmetric fission threshold lies lower. Γ_f/Γ_n moderate to high. σ_f approaches σ_{tot}. Not strongly dependent on excitation energy.	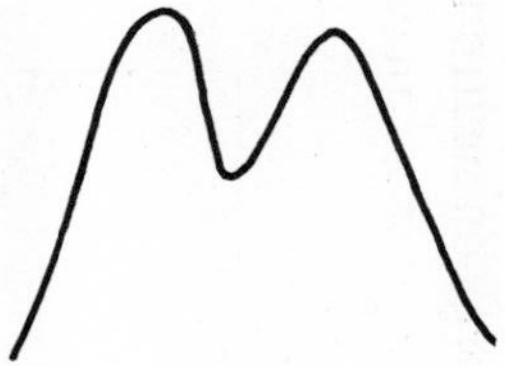	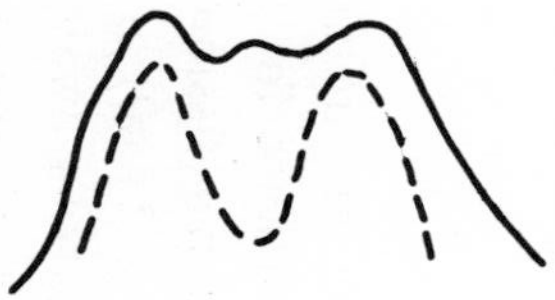	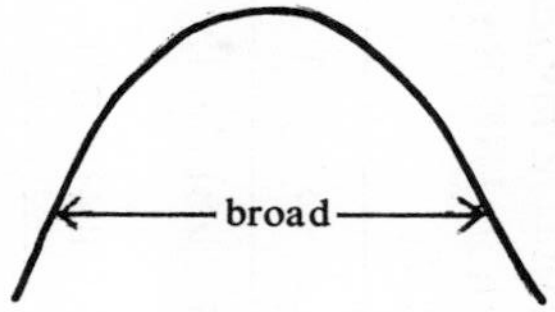 broad
Intermediate elements (actinium, radium, etc.)	Symmetric and asymmetric fission thresholds about equal. Γ_f/Γ_n low. Asymmetric fission does not increase with excitation. Symmetric fission increases rapidly and soon washes out asymmetric fission.	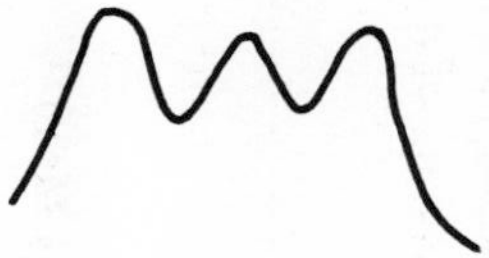	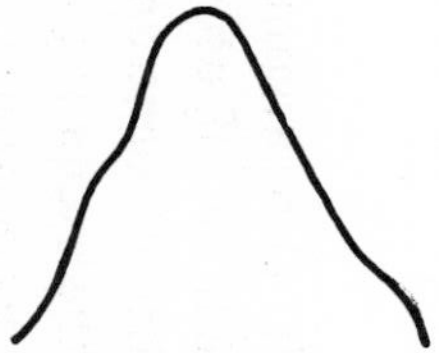	
Slightly fissile elements (lead-bismuth)	Symmetric fission threshold lies lower. Γ_f/Γ_n very low but increases markedly with energy; but σ_{fiss} never approaches σ_{tot}. Symmetric fission predominates. Γ_f/Γ_n levels off at high excitation.	 very narrow		

Figure 11-39 Schematic summary of fission properties. [From E. Hyde, UCRL 9036 (rev.).]

Table 11-4 Probabilities for the Emission of n Neutrons per Fission in U^{235} Bombarded by Neutrons of Energy E

E	0	1	2	3	4	5	ν
80 keV	0.02	0.17	0.36	0.31	0.12	0.03	2.45
1.25 MeV	0.02	0.11	0.30	0.41	0.10	0.06	2.65

Data from R. B. Leachman, *Phys. Rev.*, **101,** 1005 (1956); B. C. Diven, H. C. Martin, R. F. Taschek, and J. Terrell, *Phys. Rev.*, **101,** 1012 (1956). (WW 58.)

Fission is also accompanied by an instantaneous emission of neutrons, which are of decisive importance for a chain reaction. The average number of neutrons emitted per fission is called ν. It varies according to the excitation energy (Fig. 11-40) of the fissioning nucleus because each evaporation neutron carries away a certain amount of energy and enough must be left to permit the evaporation of the next neutron. The apparent dependence of ν on the fissioning nucleus is primarily caused by its excitation energy on neutron capture. The probabilities for emission of n neutrons are given as an example in Table 11-4

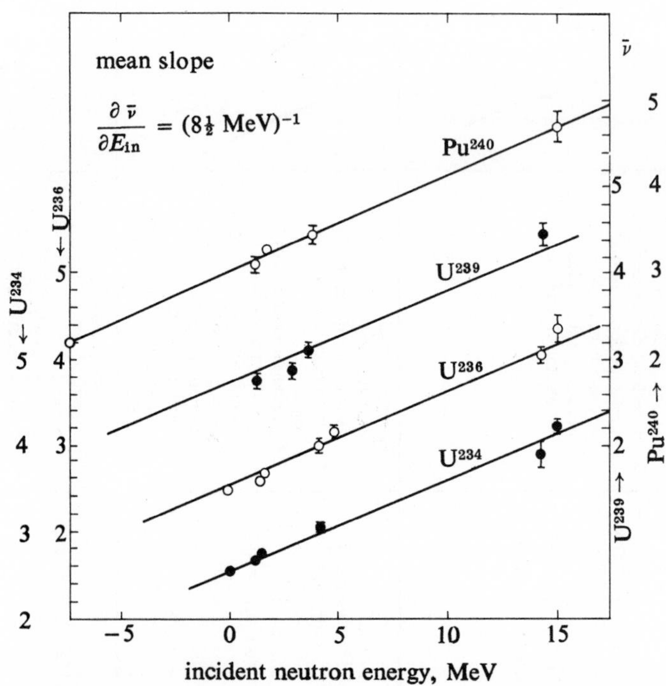

Figure 11-40 The average number of neutrons emitted per fission in neutron-induced fission plotted as a function of the bombarding energy. Each curve is labeled according to the compound nucleus formed. The point at the left for Pu^{240} refers to spontaneous fission. [From R. B. Leachman, *Proc. Intern. Conf. Peaceful Uses Atomic Energy*, Geneva, 1958.]

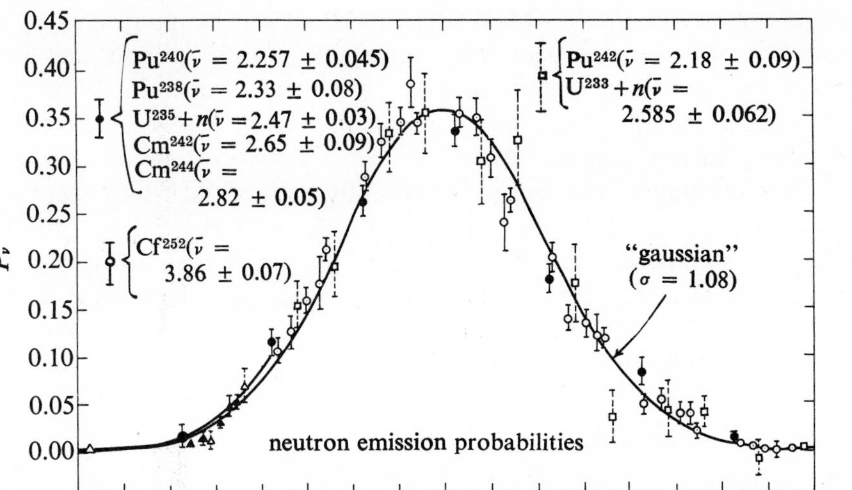

Figure 11-41 Experimental number of neutrons emitted per fission plotted to show the probability of emission of ν neutrons versus $\nu - \langle\nu\rangle$. [From J. Terrell, *Phys. Rev.*, **108,** 783 (1957).]

and in Fig. 11-41. The energy spectrum of fission neutrons is represented by the semiempirical equation

$$f(E) = 2 \times 0.775 \left(\frac{0.775E}{\pi}\right)^{1/2} e^{-0.775E} \qquad \textbf{(11-11.12)}$$

where $f(E)\,dE$ is the probability that a neutron has its energy in interval

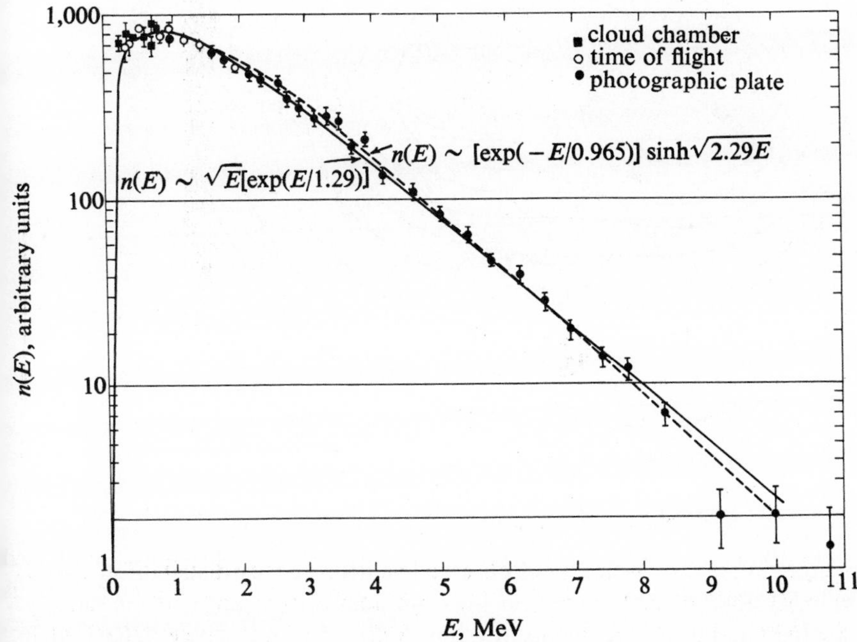

Figure 11-42 Fission neutron spectra from U^{235}. [(WW 59), after Leachman.]

dE and E is measured in MeV (Fig. 11-42). It can be interpreted as an evaporation spectrum from the moving fragments, an interpretation confirmed by the study of the angular correlation of direction of motion of the neutrons and of the fission fragments, at least for fission produced by slow neutrons (Fig. 11-43).

In addition to the neutrons promptly emitted in fission there are delayed neutrons associated only indirectly with the fission process. They are mentioned here only for completeness. A fission fragment of atomic number Z, with a large neutron excess, may beta-decay to an excited state of an isobar of atomic number $Z + 1$. This state may be above the binding energy of the neutron and hence susceptible to emitting a neutron instantaneously. However, the emission of the neutron follows

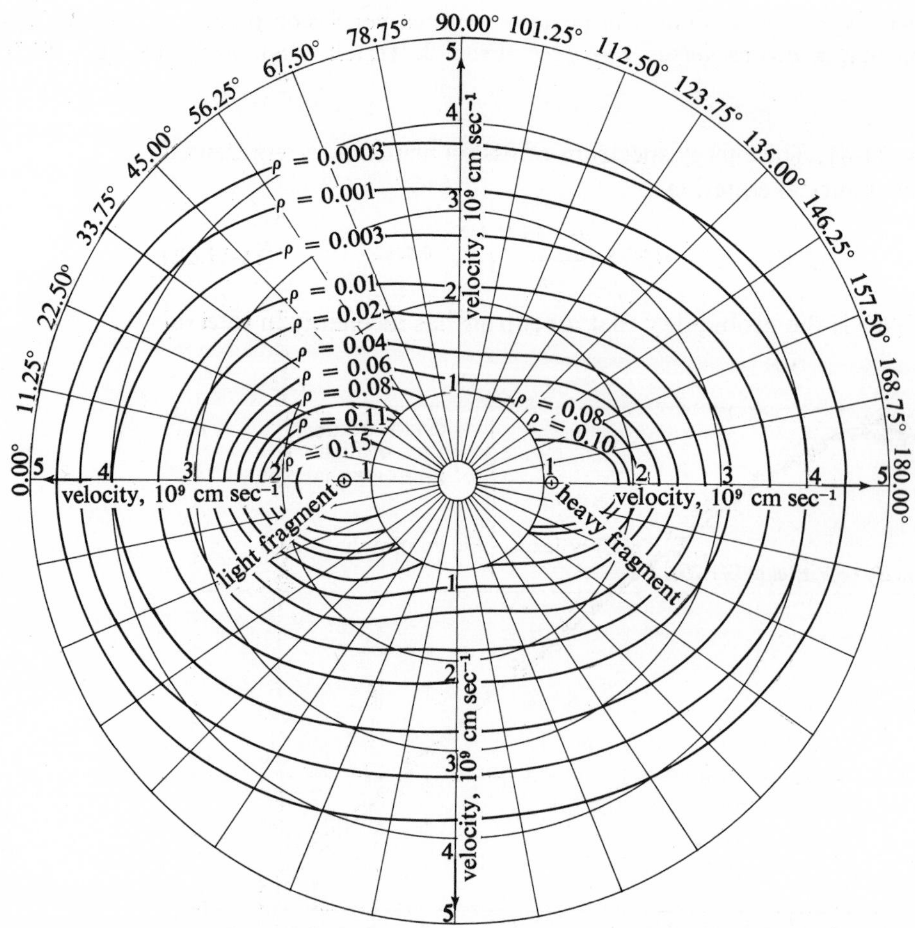

Figure 11-43 Contour diagram in polar coordinates of observed neutron density distribution $\sigma(v, \theta)$ as a function of neutron velocity and angle. The contour lines are lines of constant neutron density. The average velocities of the light and heavy fragments are shown also. [From E. Hyde, UCRL 9036 (rev.).]

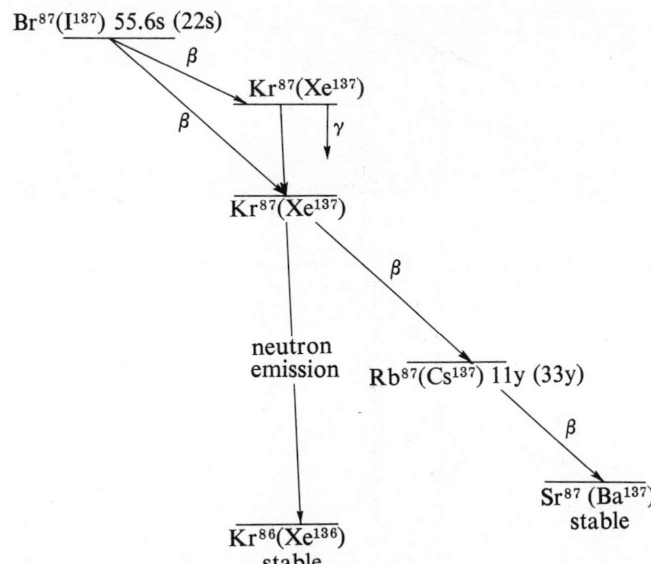

Figure 11-44 Origin of delayed neutrons in the fission chains of mass 87 and 137.

the beta decay of the preceding nucleus. For this reason neutrons appear to be emitted according to an exponential decay law with a decay constant corresponding to the beta decay of the preceding nucleus. Delayed neutrons are associated with the fission fragments and have the abundance indicated in Table 11-5. Outside the fission fragments the same mechanism of emission of delayed neutrons is operative in N^{17}, which decays by beta emission into an excited O^{17*}. This last nucleus transforms instantaneously into O^{16} by losing a neutron. A level scheme showing the situation in two cases is reproduced in Fig. 11-44. A similar mechanism in the case of neutron deficient isotopes leads to the emission of

Table 11-5 Delayed Neutrons

Half-life, sec	Decay constant, sec^{-1}	Energy, MeV	Number per 100 fission neutrons				
			Th^{232}	U^{233}	U^{235}	U^{238}	Pu^{239}
54 (Br^{87})	0.0128	0.25	0.085	0.020	0.03	0.015	0.01
22 (I^{137})	0.0315	0.56	0.35	0.075	0.18	0.17	0.06
5.6 (Br^{89-91})	0.125	0.43	0.45	0.105	0.22	0.28	0.045
2.12	0.325	0.62	1.20	0.075	0.23	0.71	0.085
0.45	1.55	0.42	0.45	0.025	0.07	0.42	0.03
0.15	4.5		0.09		0.02	0.15	
			2.6	0.30	0.75	1.75	0.23
Number of delayed neutrons per 100 fissions			6.3	0.78	1.80	4.4	0.67

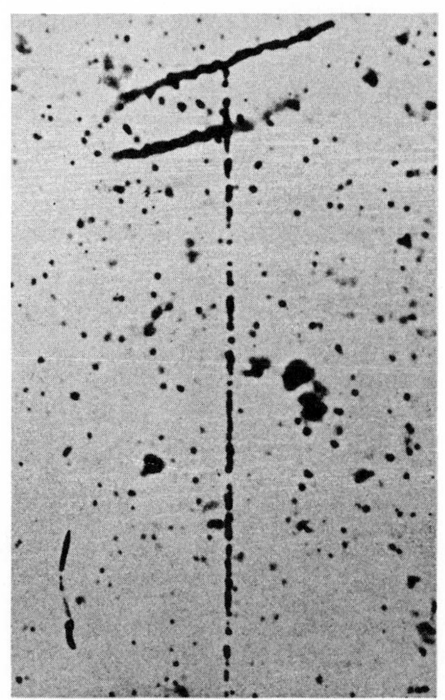

Figure 11-45 Fission tracks with a secondary alpha particle. [K. T. Titterton.]

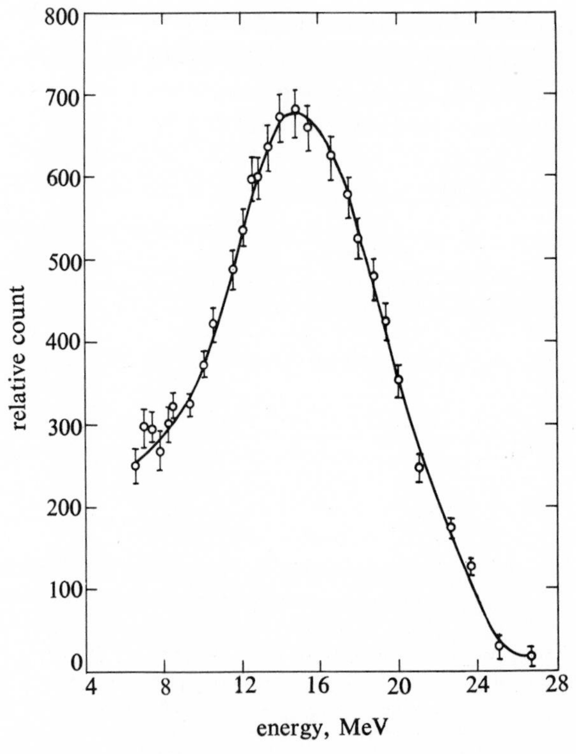

Figure 11-46 Energy distribution of long-range alpha particles from pile neutron fissions of U^{235}. [After C. B. Fulmer and B. L. Cohen, *Phys. Rev.*, **108,** 370 (1957).]

elayed protons. Thus, for instance, Si^{25} by positron decay goes to an xcited state of Al^{25} which emits protons.

Occasionally fission is accompanied by the emission of long-range lpha particles (up to 20 MeV). In U^{235} this occurs about once for every 00 fissions. The alpha particles show a definite tendency to escape in a irection perpendicular to that of the fragments (Fig. 11-45). Their nergy spectrum is a continuum (Fig. 11-46).

Finally an emission of "prompt" gamma rays occurs at the moment f fission, within the resolving time of experiments. It is to be assumed hat the prompt gamma rays are emitted within 10^{-11} sec of fission, and hus mostly after neutron emission, as in all nuclear reactions. The amma rays show a continuous spectrum (Fig. 11-47) with an average nergy of 1 MeV; their total energy is about 6 MeV per fission.

We may thus establish the energy balance for an average fission roduced by a slow neutron in U^{235} (Table 11-6). The fluctuation around he average for the first item is demonstrated in Fig. 11-48, which is

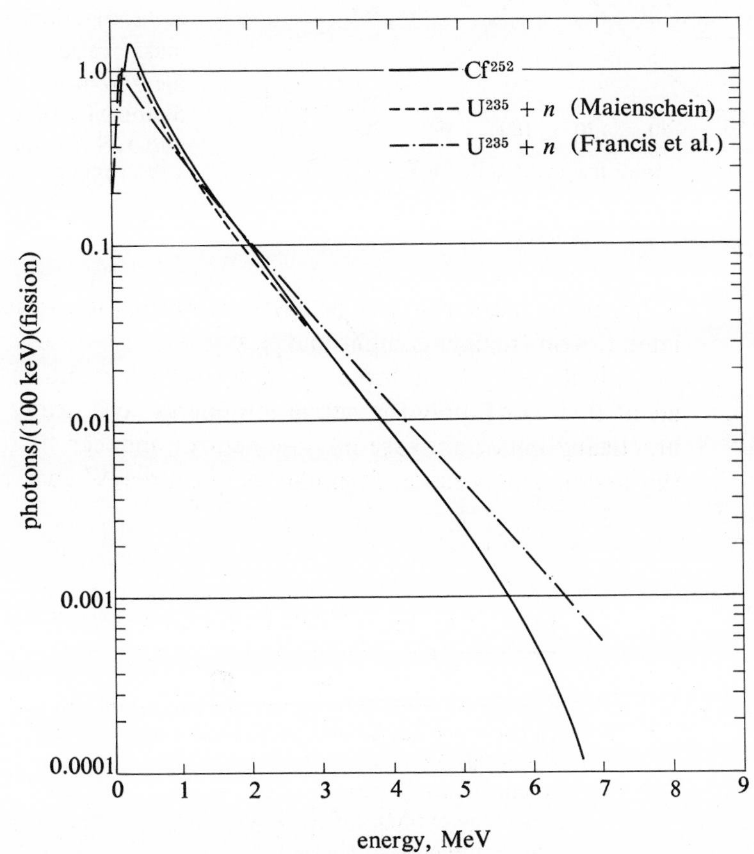

Figure 11-47 Spectra of prompt fission photons. The spectrum obtained in the thermal fission of U^{235} is apparently similar to that in the spontaneous fission of Cf^{252}. [From E. Hyde, UCRL 9036 (rev.).]

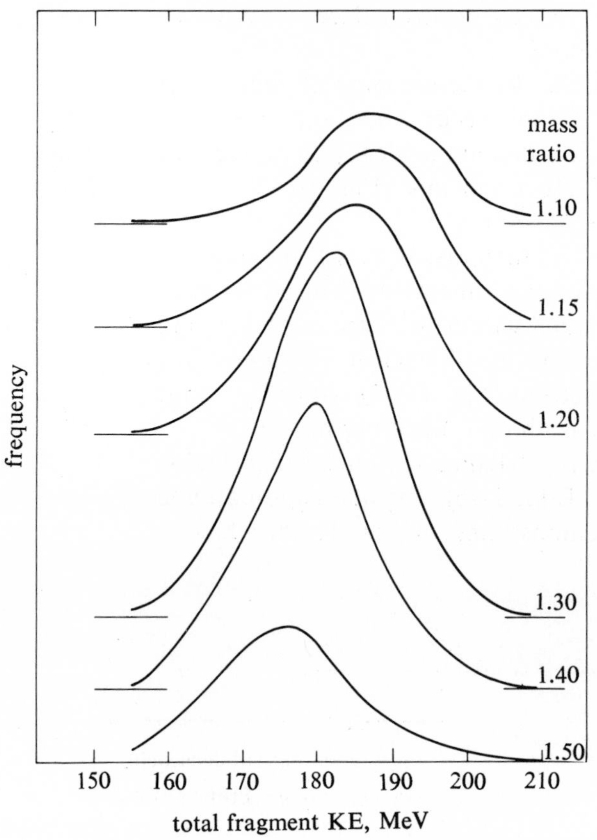

Figure 11-48 The distribution of total fragment kinetic energies as a function of the fragment mass ratio according to the measurements for spontaneous fission of Cf^{252}. [J. C. D. Milton and J. S. Fraser, *Phys. Rev.*, **111**, 877 (1958).]

obtained by measuring the energy lost through ionization by the correlated fission fragments, light and heavy.

Fission may be induced by many particles, and in general by any agent that can supply the activation energy to a heavy nucleus. In the practically important case of slow neutron-induced fission, we have for the fission cross-section formulas of the Breit-Wigner type:

Table 11-6 Energy Balance for an Average Fission

	MeV
Kinetic energy of fission fragments (2 nuclei: $A \simeq 95, A \simeq 140$)	165 ± 5
Prompt γ rays (5 γ rays)	6 ± 1
Beta decay of fragments (7 β rays)	8 ± 1.5
Neutrinos related to above	12 ± 2.5
Gamma rays related to above (7 γ rays)	6 ± 1
Kinetic energy of neutrons (2 to 3 neutrons)	5
	204 ± 7

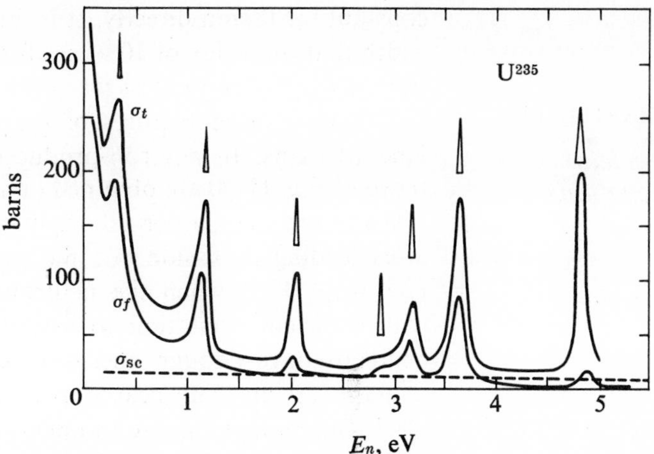

Figure 11-49 Observed total fission and scattering cross sections of U^{235} from 1.0 to 5 eV. The fission cross section was normalized to 500 at 0.0253 eV. [From F. J. Shore and V. L. Sailor, *Proc. Intern. Conf. Peaceful Uses Atomic Energy*, Geneva, 1958.]

$$\sigma_f = \pi\lambda\!\!\!^{-2} \frac{\Gamma_f \Gamma_n}{(E - E_r)^2 + \Gamma^2/4} \tag{11-11.13}$$

where Γ_f is the partial width for fission and $\Gamma = \Gamma_\gamma + \Gamma_f + \Gamma_n$. By direct measurement of the capture and fission cross sections, it is possible to obtain the practically important quantity,

$$\alpha = \frac{\sigma(n,\gamma)}{\sigma(n,f)} \tag{11-11.14}$$

In the immediate vicinity of a resonance this is the same as Γ_γ/Γ_f. Different resonances have different Γ_f, Γ_γ, and Γ_n; as an example, we give some data relative to U^{235} in Fig. 11-49. The great complexity of the overlapping resonances is apparent. The value of Γ_f gives the decay

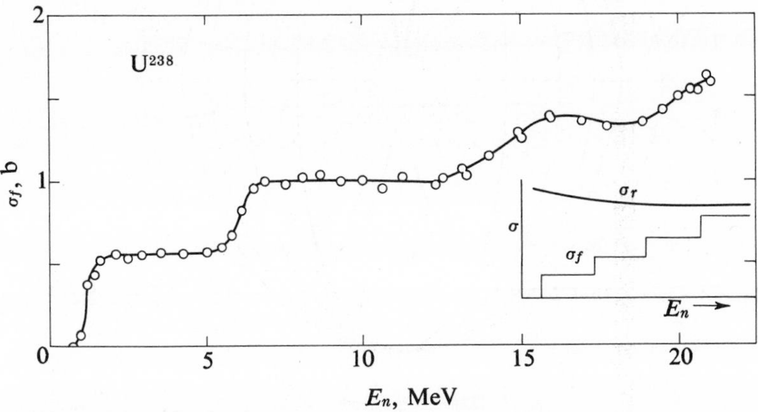

Figure 11-50 The fast-neutron fission cross section in U^{238} according to Smith, Henkel, and Nobles. The inset is an idealization to show how the fission cross section σ_f increases suddenly at definite thresholds. By comparing σ_f to the total reaction cross section σ_r one can, in principle, determine how fissionability varies with excitation energy. [From I. Halpern, *Ann. Rev. Nucl. Sci.*, **9**, 245 (1959).]

constant for fission directly. It is through the measurement of the fission width that the value of 10^{-14} sec for the order of magnitude of the duration of the fission process was obtained.

Among other features of fissions we shall mention a few miscellaneous items. In neutron-produced fission, excitation curves such as those of Fig. 11-50 are obtained on increasing the energy of the neutrons. The striking steps observed originate at the energies at which new processes leading to fission become possible. Thus the first step is due to U^{238} (n,γ), U^{239} when the neutrons have enough energy to leave U^{239} with sufficient excitation to fission. The second step occurs when the neutrons have enough energy to excite U^{238} by an (n,n') reaction to undergo fission. The next step occurs when the $(n,2n)$ reaction leaves U^{237} with enough energy to undergo fission, and so on.

With projectiles of sufficiently high energy it is possible to fission nuclei as light as Cu. Fission then competes with the process of spallation, the disintegration of the nucleus into a large number of free nucleons or very small fragments such as alpha particles, deuterons, etc. (see Fig. 11-39).

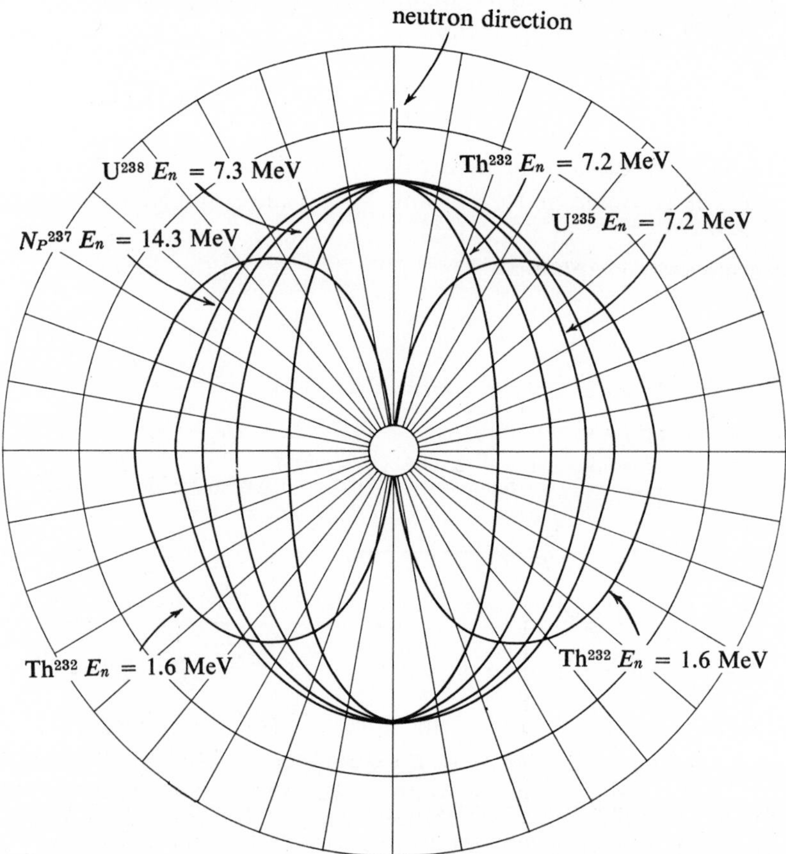

Figure 11-51 Angular distribution of fission fragments. [Data from Henkel and Brolley, from E. Hyde, UCRL 9065.]

When fission is induced by neutrons there are correlations between direction of motion of the projectile and of the fission fragments (see Fig. 11-51) depending on the energy of the neutrons. For fission produced by gamma rays the directions of the gamma ray and of the fission fragments tend to be perpendicular. A graphic summary of the time sequence in the fission process is given in Fig. 11-52.

The total activity of all fission products is of interest in many practical problems. There are empirical formulas that give the beta-decay activity and the gamma activity of all fission products. If fission has occurred at time 0, the energy emitted as beta and gamma rays is given respectively by $B(t) = 1.26\, t^{-1.2}$ MeV sec^{-1} and $\Gamma(t) = 1.40\, t^{-1.2}$ MeV sec^{-1}, where $10^5 > t > 1$ sec (Fig. 11-53).

11-12 Heavy-Ion Nuclear Reactions

In recent years machines have been developed which accelerate ions of Li, C, N, etc., up to Ne, to energies of approximately 10 MeV per nucleon contained in the ion. These ions show a variety of interesting phenomena, and the study of their behavior in nuclear collisions forms a small but interesting chapter of nuclear physics.

At sufficiently low energy the ions undergo Coulomb repulsion and thus only show Rutherford scattering. If, however, they touch the target nuclei, they react. Now, calling b the impact parameter and p the relative momentum, we have, by conservation of angular momentum,

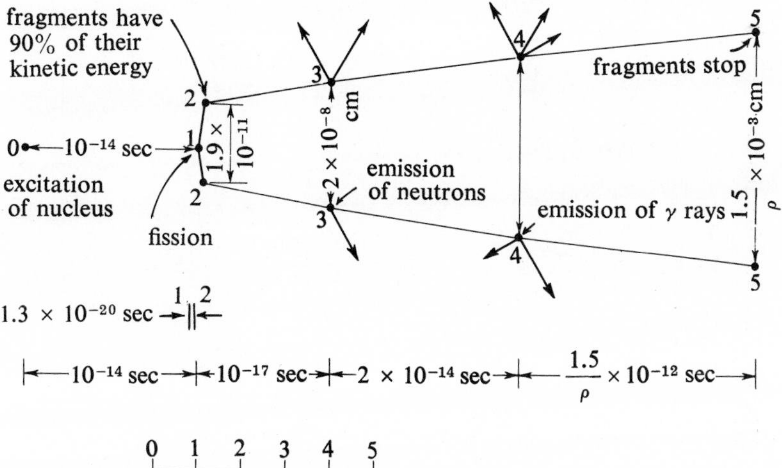

Figure 11-52 Graphic representation of the fission process. The events are: 0, excitation of nucleus; 1, fission; 2, fragments acquire 90 per cent of their kinetic energy; 3, emission of neutrons; 4, emission of gamma rays; 5, fragments stop. The horizontal scale indicates the duration of the process: two events separated by the time t are $20 + \log_{10} t$ units apart horizontally. The vertical scale indicates the distance of the fragments from each other: a distance r is indicated by $13 + \log_{10} r$ units; ρ is the density of the material in which the fragments travel, and the diagram is drawn for $\rho = 1$. [From (WW 59).]

$$pb = l\hbar = p'X \tag{11-12.1}$$

where $l\hbar$ is the angular momentum, X the minimum distance between the ions, and p' their relative momentum at that distance. We have also, by conservation of energy,

$$\frac{p^2}{2m} - E_B \frac{R}{X} = \frac{p'^2}{2m} \tag{11-12.2}$$

where m is the reduced mass and $E_B = Zze^2/R$ is the potential energy when the nuclei are in contact. From Eqs. (11-12.1) and (11-12.2), calling $p^2/2m = E$, we have as the condition for contact of the nuclei

$$2mR^2(E - E_B) \geq l_c^2\hbar^2 \tag{11-12.3}$$

The elastic scattering has been calculated (Blair, 1954) by taking the Coulomb scattering amplitude and subtracting from it all the partial waves with $l < l_c$, assuming that these are absorbed in the collision. The only parameter available in this calculation is R, written in the form

$$R = r_0(A_1^{1/3} + A_2^{1/3}) \tag{11-12.4}$$

where A_1,A_2 are the mass numbers of the two nuclei. Such a simple semiclassical method gives good results, as can be seen from Fig. 11-54. The value of r_0 thus obtained is near 1.45 F. Note the high values of l_c. This calculation can be improved by taking into account the nuclear surface.

In distant collisions, where nuclear forces do not play a role, one often obtains nuclear excitation by the electromagnetic interaction (Coulomb excitation; cf. Sec. 8-7). In the case of heavy ions the Weizsäcker–Williams method gives a good picture of the phenomenon. A

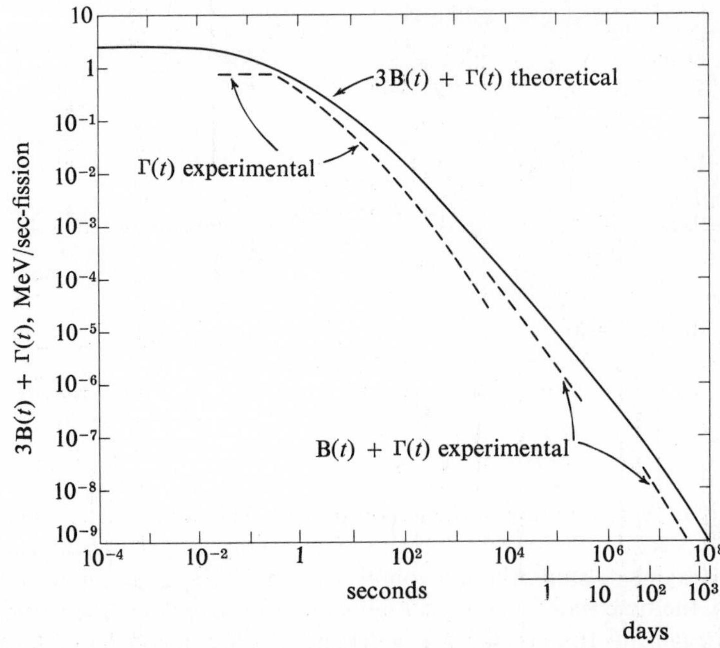

Figure 11-53 Energy release from fission products. The neutrino energy is assumed to be twice the beta energy. $B(t)$ and $\Gamma(t)$ energy released as beta and gamma radiation, respectively. [(WW 59).]

characteristic effect occurring among the heavy ions is the excitation of high rotational levels. In even-even heavy nuclei, such as U^{238}, highly developed rotational bands have been found, with only even levels $I = 0, 2, 4, 6, \ldots, 12$ (Fig. 6-42). All these have been excited by Coulomb interaction. The excitation process is multiple. The nucleus is excited by quadrupole transitions in successive jumps produced by the electromagnetic field of the *same* projectile.

What happens when the colliding nuclei touch each other? There are

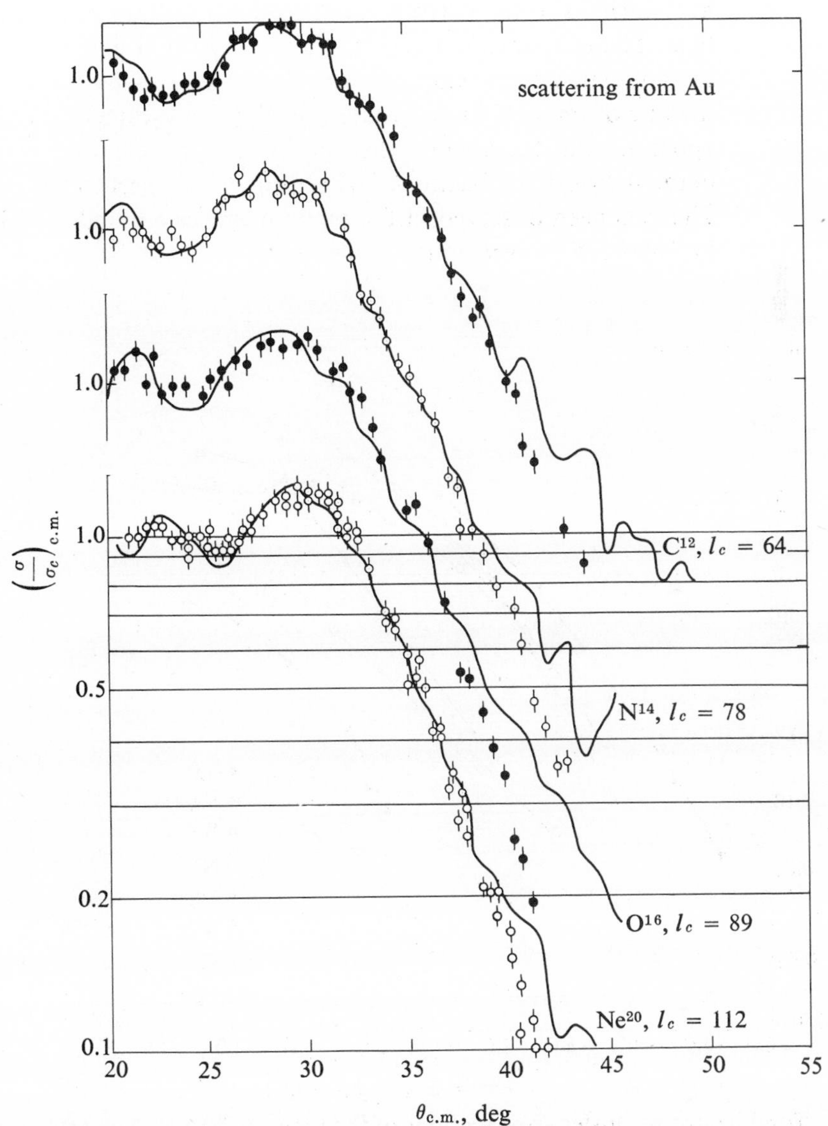

Figure 11-54 The ratio of the elastic to the Coulomb scattering cross section for C^{12}, N^{14}, O^{16}, and Ne^{20} scattered from gold at an energy of about 10 MeV per nucleon. The solid lines are the sharp cutoff calculations with the appropriate l_c indicated in the figure. [Data of Reynolds, Goldberg, and Kerlee, from A. Zucker, *Ann. Rev. Nucl. Sci.*, **10**, 27 (1960).]

frequent simple reactions corresponding to the transfer of one nucleon, for instance

$$Mg^{26}(N^{14}N^{13})Mg^{27} \qquad \textbf{(11-12.5)}$$

Such reactions occur in peripheral collisions without formation of a compound nucleus, with cross sections up to approximately 50 mb (Fig. 11-55).

At higher energies there occur more complicated reactions, corresponding to the formation of a compound nucleus. Here a peculiar effect is observed in the angular distribution of the evaporation particles. The compound nucleus frequently has very high angular momentum ($> 50\hbar$), necessarily directed perpendicular to the trajectory of the incoming particle. The evaporating particles then escape in a plane perpendicular to the angular momentum and, with equal probability, at an angle θ with the line of impact. As we rotate this plane of escape of the particles, it is apparent that the angular distribution will have a $1/\sin\theta$ shape peaked in the forward and backward direction with respect to the line of impact. This has been observed in the alpha particles emitted by Ni bombarded by 160-MeV oxygen ions.

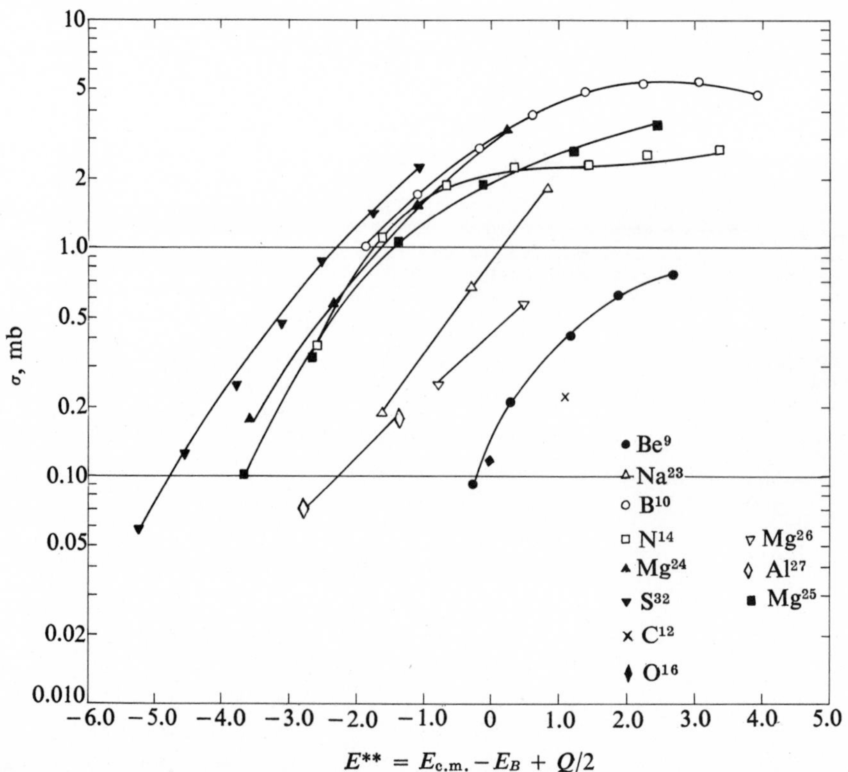

Figure 11-55 Total neutron-transfer cross sections of the type Mg^{26} (N^{14}, N^{13}) Mg^{27} for eleven light elements plotted as a function of $E^{**} = E_{c.m.} - E_B + Q/2$, where $E_{c.m.}$ is the incident kinetic energy in the center-of-mass system, E_B is the barrier energy, and Q is the reaction energy. Note that $E^{**} + Q/2$ is the energy available to the two nuclei at the moment immediately after the transfer has occurred. [From Fisher, Zucker, and Gropp, *Phys. Rev.*, **113,** 542 (1959).]

Similar effects appear in fission, where the fission fragments tend to escape in the line of collision for fission induced in Au^{197} by 100-MeV C^{12} ions (Fig. 11-56).

Another remarkable type of reaction has been observed in C^{12}-C^{12} collisions at 90° (Bromley, Kühner, and Almquist, 1960). The cross section shows rapid fluctuations as a function of energy, and this has been attributed to the formation of a C^{12}-C^{12} (Mg^{24}) nucleus, strongly elongated and having rotational levels like a diatomic molecule (Fig. 11-57).

11-13 Photonuclear Reactions

Many reactions initiated by gamma rays are known to occur, for example, (γ,n), (γ,p), (γ,f), (γ,α), etc. They are observed by directing a beam of gamma rays at the target and detecting the emitted particles or the radioactivity of the product nucleus. Monochromatic sources of gamma rays are available from the rays emitted in some disintegrations, for instance, ThC′, Na^{24}, and Co^{60}, which however, are in the 1-3MeV energy region. The p + Li reaction gives a gamma ray of 17 MeV, which has been used extensively. Electron accelerators give a continuum of gamma rays from the bremsstrahlung (see Chap. 2). The upper limit of

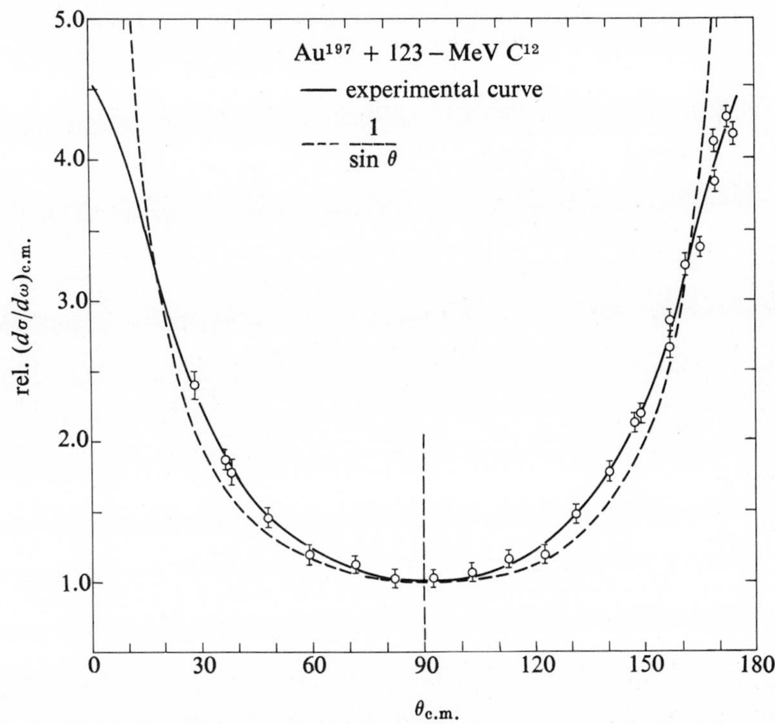

Figure 11-56 Angular distribution of fission fragments in the center-of-mass system for fission of Au^{197} induced by C^{12} ions of 123-MeV energy. [Gordon, Larsh, and Sikkeland, from E. Hyde, UCRL 9065.]

the continuum is well determined, and it is possible to measure cross sections for photoreactions as a function of energy by using a bremsstrahlung spectrum and varying the energy of the electrons that produce it. However, this procedure is difficult and laborious. Effects similar to those produced by gamma rays also result from electron bombardments, not through the bremsstrahlung generated by the electrons, but by a direct electron-nuclear interaction of electromagnetic nature. The effect of this interaction, as an order of magnitude, is $e^2/\hbar c = \alpha$ times that of a gamma ray of the same energy as the electrons. The cross sections for electron interaction are thus about 100 times smaller than those for photon interaction.

The photodisintegration of the deuteron is the simplest photonuclear reaction. It has been treated in Chap. 10 for the relatively low energy region, for which a simple theory is adequate. Figure 11-58 shows an over-all view of the photon absorption of an idealized nucleus.

A remarkable phenomenon in photonuclear absorption is the maximum shown by the cross section at energies around 20 MeV (Figs. 11-59 and 11-60). The shape of the curves and the positions of the maximum depend on A. A simple model accounting for this "giant resonance" has been proposed by Goldhaber and Teller. They consider a collective motion of all protons with respect to all neutrons in a nucleus. This

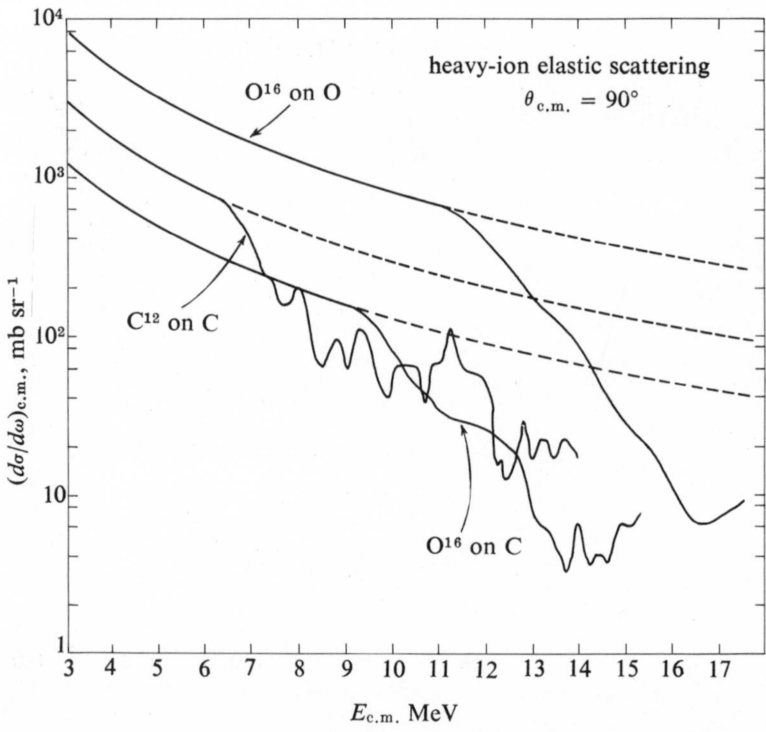

Figure 11-57 Differential cross sections at 90° cm for the elastic scattering of O^{16} from oxygen, C^{12} from carbon, and O^{16} from carbon as a function of energy. The dashed lines are Rutherford scattering cross sections. [Bromley, Kuehner, and Almqvist, *Phys. Rev. Letters*, **4,** 365 (1960).]

motion gives rise to an electric-dipole moment, which should account for the absorption. The frequency of the motion has been estimated by Jensen and others by means of a model in which neutrons and protons move in a fixed sphere in such a way that nuclear matter changes its composition from point to point, although the density of nucleons remains constant. The change of composition causes an increase in potential energy that is estimated from the nuclear-mass formula [Eq. (6-5.8)]. This energy produces a restoring force, and the consequent vibrations may be calculated hydrodynamically, yielding approximately the right frequency for light nuclei.

A theorem that is valid in the absence of exchange forces gives for the integrated dipole photoabsorption cross section the sum rule:

$$\int_0^\infty \sigma_{\text{abs}}(E_\gamma)\, dE_\gamma = 2\pi^2 e^2 \frac{\hbar}{mc}\frac{NZ}{A} = 0.058\frac{NZ}{A} \text{ MeV b} \qquad \textbf{(11-13.1)}$$

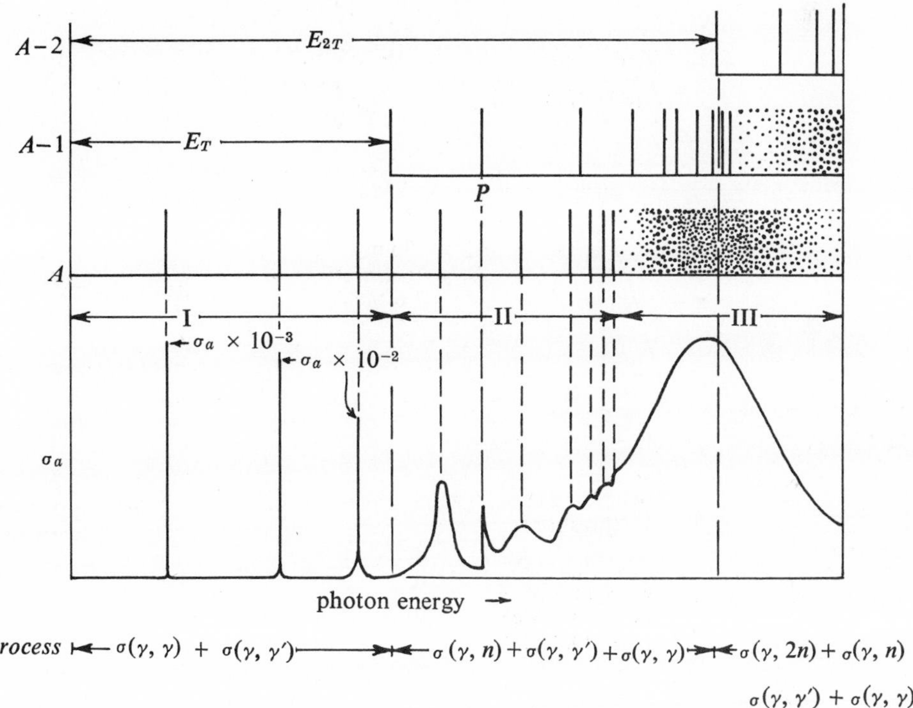

Figure 11-58 The photon absorption cross section for an idealized nucleus. Region I is that part of the energy scale below the particle thresholds where the absorption is into discrete energy levels. Region II is the energy range above the binding energy where structure may still exist in the absorption cross section. In region III the absorption cross section is smooth. The processes that can take place are indicated along the abscissa; $\sigma(\gamma, n)$ here stands for the cross section for nucleon emission. The energy levels in the nucleus A, A-1, and A-2 are illustrated at the top of the diagram. The binding energies for one and two particles are designated by E_T and E_{2T}. The level P_1 in A-1 represents a parent of the ground state of nucleus A. [From E. G. Fuller and E. Hayward, in (En 62).]

where N, Z, and A are the number of neutrons, the number of protons, and the mass number of the nucleus. M is the mass of a nucleon. The giant resonance accounts for most of the integral, the high-energy cross section contributing little to it. The sum rule expressed by Eq. (11-13.1) will now be proved from general principles.

In the case of $E1$ radiation ($\lambda\!\!\!^{-}$ of the radiation $\gg$ dimensions of the nuclear system), the transition probability from the ground level i to a level f induced by an electric field $\mathscr{E}$ cos ωt directed in the z direction is

$$\int_{\text{line}} |a_f(t)|^2 \, d\omega = \mathscr{E}^2 e^2 \frac{\pi}{2\hbar^2} |z_{if}|^2 t \tag{11-13.2}$$

where z_{if} is the matrix element of the coordinate z and $|a_f(t)|^2$ is the probability of finding the nucleus in state f at time t. This relation may be obtained by time-dependent perturbation theory (Appendix A).

The cross section for the photon absorption is by definition the transition probability per unit time divided by the photon flux per unit surface, $\mathscr{E}^2 c/8\pi\hbar\omega$. That is, limiting ourselves to a small frequency interval $\Delta\omega$ containing the absorption line of frequency.

$$E_f - E_i = \hbar\omega_{fi} \tag{11-13.3}$$

$$\frac{(\mathscr{E}^2 e^2 \pi/2\hbar^2)|z_{if}|^2 \Delta\omega}{(\mathscr{E}^2 c/8\pi)\,(1/\hbar\omega)} = \frac{4\pi^2 e^2}{\hbar c}\,\omega_{fi}\,|z_{if}|^2\,\Delta\omega = \langle\sigma\rangle\,\Delta\omega \tag{11-13.4}$$

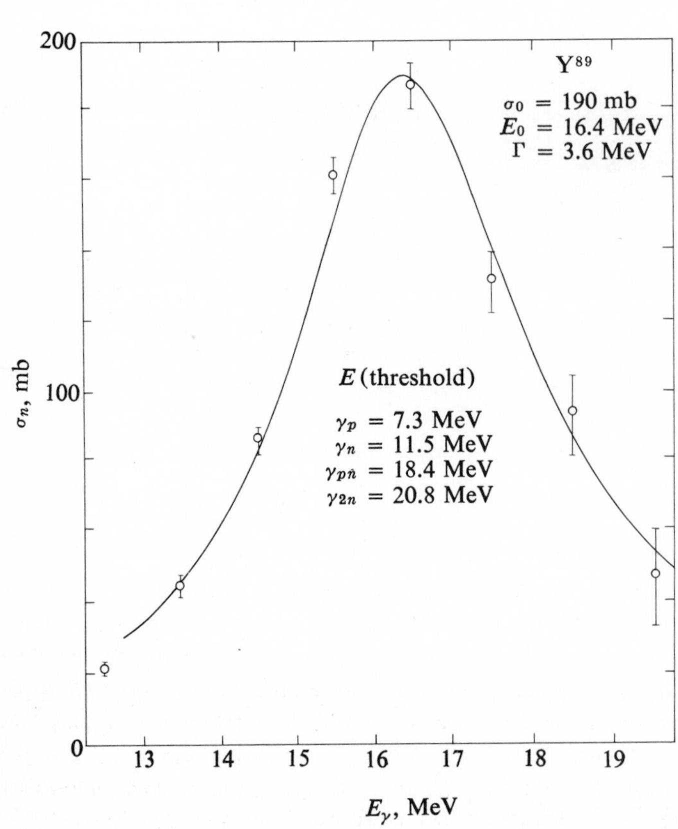

Figure 11-59 Cross sections for photo-neutron production in Y^{89} showing giant resonance. [P. F. Yergin and B. P. Fabricand, *Phys. Rev.*, **104**, 1334 (1956).]

Introducing the dimensionless quantity

$$f_{if} = \frac{2m}{\hbar}\,\omega_{fi}\,|z_{if}|^2 \qquad \textbf{(11-13.5)}$$

called oscillator strength, we may rewrite Eq. (11-13.4) as

$$\sigma\,\Delta\omega = \frac{2\pi e^2}{mc} f_{if} \qquad \textbf{(11-13.6)}$$

If we want the total absorption of our system, we shall integrate Eq. (11-13.6) on the left side and sum over all final states on the right:

$$\int \sigma\,d\omega = \frac{2\pi^2 e^2}{mc} \sum_f f_{if} \qquad \textbf{(11-13.7)}$$

A remarkable theorem states that the

$$\sum_l f_{il}$$

of all oscillator strengths starting from one state i and ending in all other states is 1. Note that oscillator strengths may be positive or negative according to whether

$$E_i > E_l \qquad \text{or} \qquad E_i < E_l$$

This theorem is proved by starting from the fundamental commutation relation for conjugate variables,

$$pq - qp = \frac{\hbar}{i} \qquad \textbf{(11-13.8)}$$

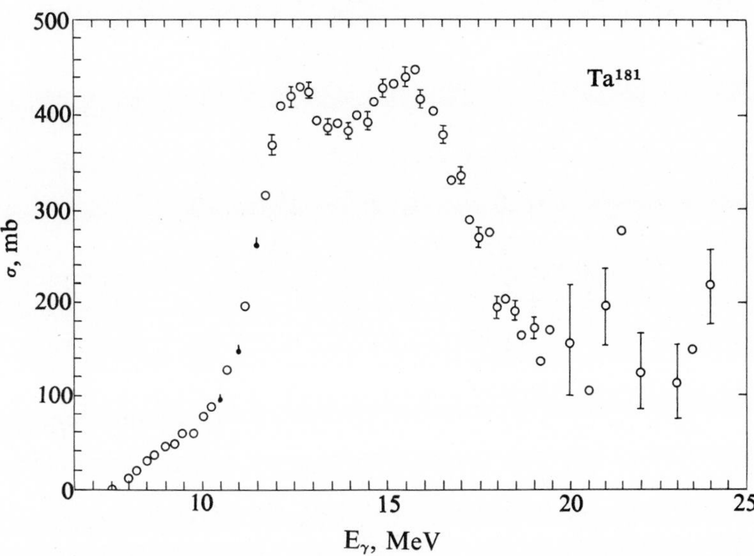

Figure 11-60 Giant dipole resonance for tantalum, a strongly deformed nucleus, showing two peaks. The separation of the two peaks reflects the quadrupole deformation of Ta ($Q_0 = 6.3$ b), while the relative integrated peak strengths yield a factor close to 2 in favor of the higher energy peak which is associated with the smaller nuclear dimension, pointing to prolate deformation; axial symmetry is favored by the absence of a third peak. [E. G. Fuller and M. S. Weiss, *Phys. Rev.*, **112,** 560 (1958).]

Writing this in matrix form for the z coordinate and its conjugate momentum $p_z = m\dot{z}$, we obtain

$$m \sum_l (\dot{z}_{jl} z_{lj} - z_{jl} \dot{z}_{lj}) = \frac{\hbar}{i} \tag{11-13.9}$$

Now, if we use a representation in which the energy is diagonal,

$$\dot{z}_{jl} = -\frac{i}{\hbar}(E_j - E_l)\, z_{jl} = i\omega_{lj} z_{jl} \tag{11-13.10}$$

Remembering that $z_{jl} = z_{lj}^*$ and substituting Eq. (11-13.10) into Eq. (11-13.9) we have

$$\sum_l \omega_{jl} |z_{jl}|^2 = \frac{\hbar}{2m} \tag{11-13.11}$$

Inserting Eq. (11-13.11) into the definition of f_{jl} [Eq. (11-13.5)] gives immediately

$$\sum_l f_{jl} = 1 \tag{11-13.12}$$

Equation (11-13.12) is the famous sum rule of Thomas and Kuhn (1924), which had great importance in the early development of quantum mechanics. In the present form this rule gives

$$\int \sigma\, d\omega = \frac{2\pi^2 e^2}{mc} \tag{11-13.13}$$

In order to apply this result to a nuclear system containing many nucleons, we must replace ez by

$$\sum_1^A e_i z_i$$

where e_i is the proton charge for the protons (i varying from 1 to Z) and 0 for the neutrons (i from $Z + 1$ to A). We write this sum as

$$\sum_1^A e_i z_i = e\left\{\sum_1^Z z_i + \frac{Z}{A}\sum_{Z+1}^A z_i - \frac{Z}{A}\sum_{Z+1}^A z_i\right\}$$

$$= e\left\{\frac{Z}{A}\sum_1^Z z_i + \frac{N}{A}\sum_1^Z z_i + \frac{Z}{A}\sum_{Z+1}^A z_i - \frac{Z}{A}\sum_{Z+1}^A z_i\right\} \tag{11-13.14}$$

The sum of the first and third term on the right is the z of the center of mass of the system, $\langle z \rangle$, times the atomic number. We can thus write

$$\sum_1^A e_i z_i = e_p' \sum_1^Z z_i + e_n' \sum_{Z+1}^A z_i + eZ\langle z \rangle \tag{11-13.15}$$

where $e_p' = eN/A$, $e_n' = -eZ/A$ are called effective charges of the protons and neutrons, respectively.

Under the action of the external field the charges will move, and we may consider the motion as the sum of the motion of the center of mass, combined with a motion relative to the center of mass. It is this second motion that is important for nuclear reactions. The first motion gives rise to Thomson scattering of the nucleus as a whole. Applying the sum rule to the internal motion only, we have

$$\int \sigma\, d\omega = \frac{2\pi^2}{c}\frac{1}{m}(Ze_p'^2 + Ne_n'^2) = \frac{2\pi^2 e^2}{mc}\frac{ZN}{A} \qquad \textbf{(11-13.16)}$$

which is Eq. (11-13.1).

Exchange forces increase the value of the integral. More refined sum rules have been developed, and they are useful in analyzing reactions started by photons. Equation (11-13.16), when compared with the experimental results, shows that the observed cross section in the giant resonance exhausts the integral. There is also some evidence from the angular distribution of the photoneutrons and photoprotons showing that the transitions involved in the giant resonance are indeed electric-dipole transitions (Figs. 11-58 and 11-59).

11-14 High-Energy Reactions

We shall arbitrarily and conventionally set our limit for "high energy" reactions at the pion formation threshold (140 MeV c.m.).

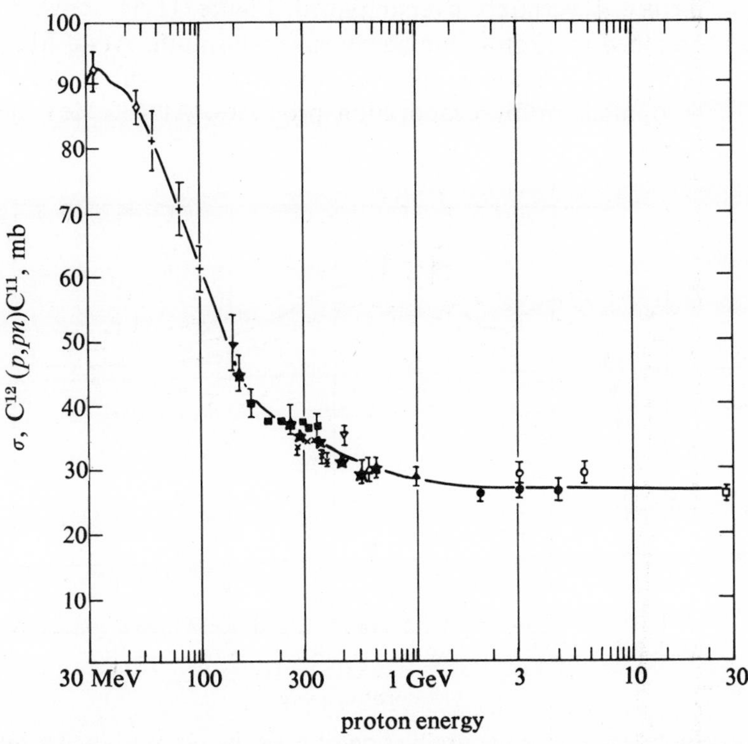

Figure 11-61 Excitation function for the reaction C^{12} (*p,pn*)C^{11}. The smooth curve is used as a basis for calculating cross sections. [From J. B. Cumming, *Ann. Rev. Nucl. Sci.*, **13,** 261 (1963).]

In the study of these reactions one of the first important technical problems is the calibration of the intensity of proton beams generated by accelerators. The cross section of the C^{12} (*p,pn*) C^{11} reaction has been measured and is given in Fig. 11-61; this together with the cross section given in Fig. 11-62 may be used as a standard. These curves already show a form that is hardly reconcilable with compound-nucleus formation and there are many other signs pointing to direct interactions. For example, many more charged particles escape that can be accounted for by compound-nucleus formation.

Surface phenomena also occur; for example, the abundant high-energy inelastically scattered nucleons. These are attributable to peripheral collisions in which the incident particle chips off nucleons from the nuclear surface without compound-nucleus formation. The direct-reaction interpretation is corroborated by a study of the angular distribution of the inelastically scattered particles. Those of high energy are mostly scattered forward, as expected in a direct collision. Those of low energy are isotropically scattered, as expected in an evaporation process.

In a very high energy collision ($E \simeq 400$ MeV) a good picture is obtained by following the collisions of the impinging nucleus (nucleonic cascade). This has been done by the Monte Carlo method (Fig. 11-63), and part of the observed effects are thus accounted for. The struck nucleus after the nucleonic cascade is finished may be left in an excited state, from which an evaporation process takes place. However, this picture is certainly oversimplified. Figure 11-64 shows the mass yield obtained by proton bombardment of bismuth. At 40 MeV the reaction products have a mass number close to that of the target and are mainly accounted for by evaporation processes. At 480 MeV the yield curve

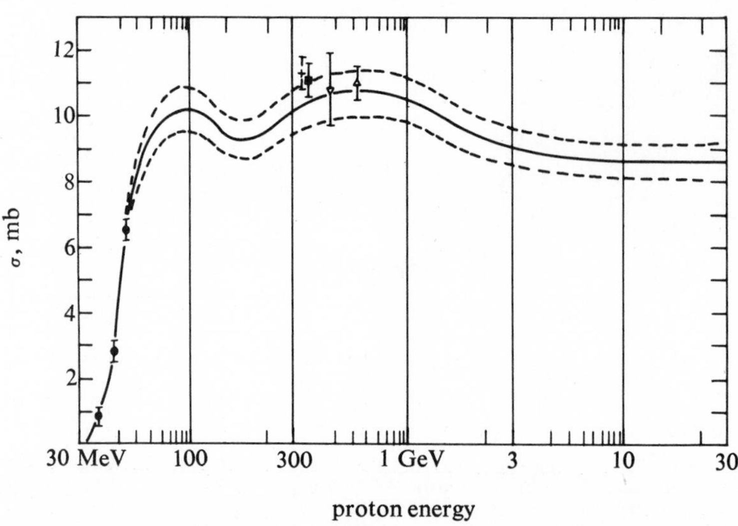

Figure 11-62 Excitation functions for the production of Na^{24}, by proton bombardment of Al. The dashed curves indicate the estimated ($\pm$ 6.5 per cent) standard deviation of the solid curve. [From J. B. Cumming, *Ann. Rev. Nucl. Sci.*, **13,** 261 (1963).]

shows two peaks. The peak around $A = 190$ is due to the primary process, which knocks off many nucleons or small aggregates of nucleons (d, He^4, etc.). This process is called "spallation." It ends by leaving a variety of excited nuclei, some of which may have enough energy to undergo fission into two fragments having mass near 100; this is the origin of the second peak. At still higher energies of 3,000 MeV, the yield curve changes character. Products with $6 < A < 30$ appear, which at lower energies are absent. These light nuclei are probably formed in the primary process (fragmentation).

At 10 to 20 BeV one sees a diffraction scattering of the nucleus as a whole and, superimposed on it, interactions with single nucleons. It is remarkable, for instance, that using protons in beryllium one finds a narrow peak due to the single nucleons (Fig. 11-65). Moreover, the energy dependence of the total cross section for protons, pions, etc., parallels the energy dependence of the *nucleon* cross sections for the same projectiles.

Even at an energy of 30 BeV, pick-up reactions are manifest, as demonstrated in bombardment of beryllium (Fig. 11-66).

At still higher energies, in the hundred BeV region, the phenomenon of jet formation appears. An impinging particle produces a narrow beam of secondaries in the forward direction (laboratory). The secondaries are mostly pions; sometimes the struck nucleus also evaporates nucleons of small fragments.

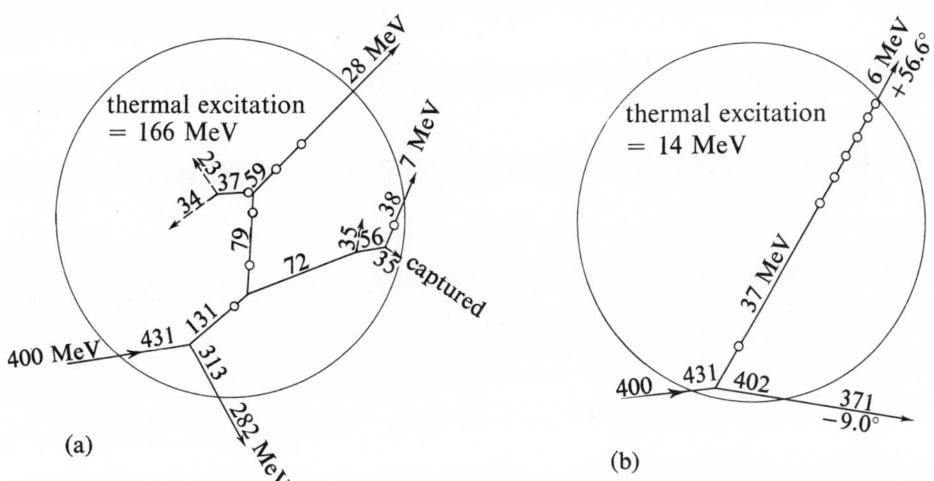

Figure 11-63 (a) A two-dimensional diagram of the Monte Carlo method, showing the development of a cascade. The entering nucleon has 400 MeV of kinetic energy; the numbers indicate the energy of the nucleons involved. The path of each nucleon is shown until it leaves the nucleus or until its energy becomes less than 35 MeV, indicated by a broken line and arrow. An open circle indicates the position at which a collision would have occurred but was forbidden by the Pauli exclusion principle. In this collision three cascade particles emerge in the forward hemisphere and the nucleus is left with a thermal excitation of 66 MeV. (b) A two-dimensional diagram for the Monte Carlo method, which illustrates a case where a quasi-elastic scattering interaction developed. [From Bernardini, Booth, and Lindenbaum, *Phys. Rev.*, **88**, 1017 (1952).]

Cosmic rays are the only available source at present for energies greater than 30 BeV and they extend to 10^{19} to 10^{20} eV. The detecting technique most widely used is the photographic emulsion (Figs. 11-67 to 69). The tracks emerging from a star are usually divided into two types:

1. Shower particles which give a grain density < 1.4, the minimum grain density; these are relativistic particles, pions for the most part. Their number is indicated by n_s.

2. Heavy ionizing particles with a grain density > 1.4 minimum; these are subdivided into black tracks, with an ionization > 10 times minimum, and gray tracks, with a density of ionization between 1.4 and 10 times minimum. A proton of 25 MeV is about at the limit of the black tracks. The number of black tracks is indicated by N_b, the number of gray tracks by N_g. The star is represented by

$$(N_b + N_g) + n_s(p) \tag{11-14.1}$$

where (p) means the primary. Thus the star in Fig. 11-68a would be indicated by $4 + 50\alpha$, meaning that it has four heavy ionizing particles, fifty shower particles, and a primary alpha particle.

It is obviously of great interest to determine the energy of the primary particle. An approximate method is based on the observation of the secondaries. Call γ_c and β_c the γ and β of the primary in the center-of-mass system and γ_p, β_p the corresponding quantities in the laboratory. Assume the primary to be a nucleon of mass M, colliding with a particle of mass N. One has

$$\gamma_c = \left[\frac{(M\gamma_p + N)^2}{(M^2 + N^2 + 2MN\gamma_p)}\right]^{1/2} \simeq \left(\frac{M\gamma_p}{2N}\right)^{1/2} \tag{11-14.2}$$

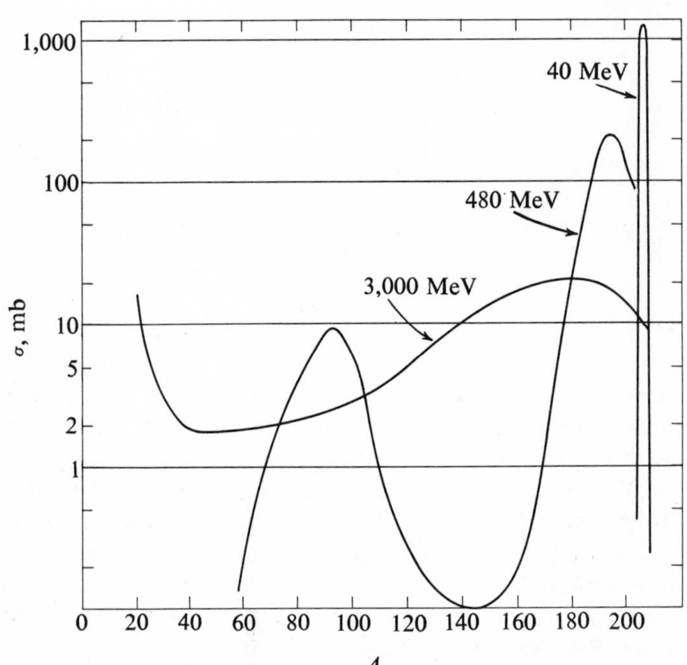

Figure 11-64 Mass-yield curves for the proton bombardment of bismuth. [From J. M. Miller and J. Hudis, *Ann. Rev. Nucl. Sci.*, **10**, 159 (1960).]

where the approximation is for $\gamma_p \gg 1$. If one knows the nature of the target particle and γ_c, one then finds the total energy of the projectile $M\gamma_p$.

A determination of γ_c may be attempted by assuming that in the center-of-mass system the secondaries are emitted at angles $\bar{\theta}$ broadly distributed around the collision axis in the center of mass. Call $\bar{\gamma}_s$, $\bar{\beta}_s$, and $\bar{\theta}_s$ the quantities relative to a secondary and referred to the center-of-mass system. One has

$$\tan\theta = \frac{\sin\bar{\theta}}{\gamma_c(\cos\bar{\theta} + \beta_c/\bar{\beta}_s)} \tag{11-14.3}$$

If two secondaries 1 and 2 are emitted at angles $\bar{\theta}$ and $\pi - \bar{\theta}$ and with equal momenta, one has for the tracks in the laboratory

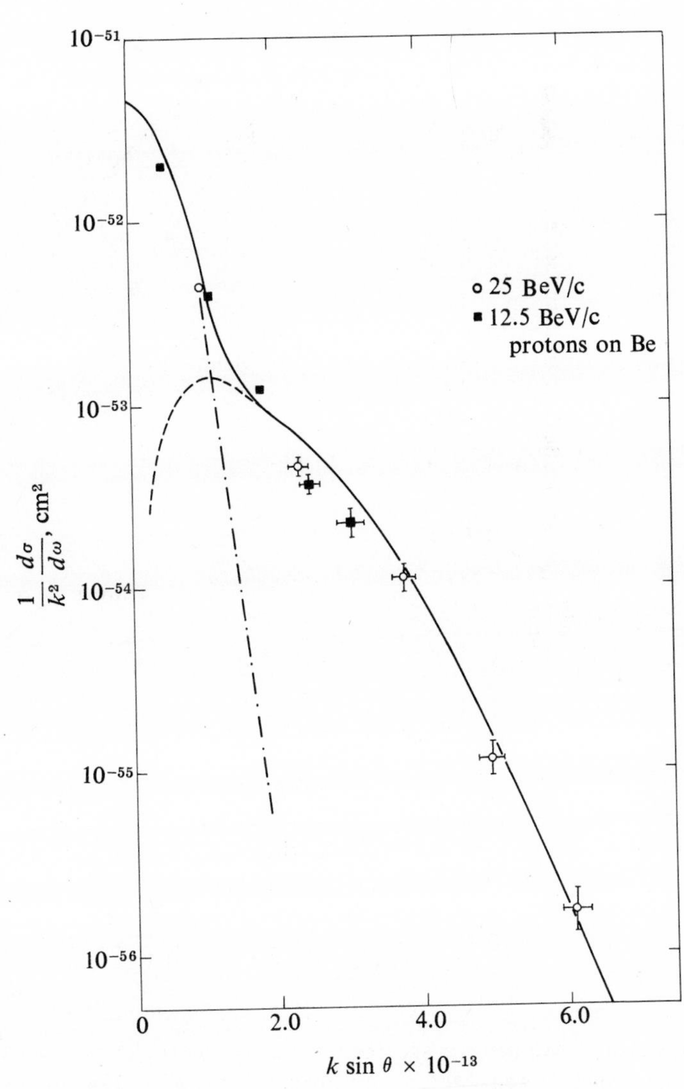

Figure 11-65 Angular distribution of protons produced by the collision of high-energy protons with Be nuclei. [N. R. Steenberg, *Nucl. Phys.*, **32**, 381 (1962).]

$$\tan\theta_2 \times \tan\theta_1 = \frac{\sin^2\bar{\theta}}{\gamma_c^2\,[-\cos^2\bar{\theta} + (\beta_c/\bar{\beta}_s)^2]} \tag{11-14.4}$$

Given many secondaries distributed in such a way that, for each θ_1, there is its corresponding θ_2, we have, since $\beta_c \approx \bar{\beta}_s \approx 1$,

$$\langle \tan\theta_1 \tan\theta_2 \rangle = \frac{1}{\gamma_c^2} \tag{11-14.5}$$

or

$$\log \gamma_c = -\frac{1}{n}\sum \log \tan\theta \tag{11-14.6}$$

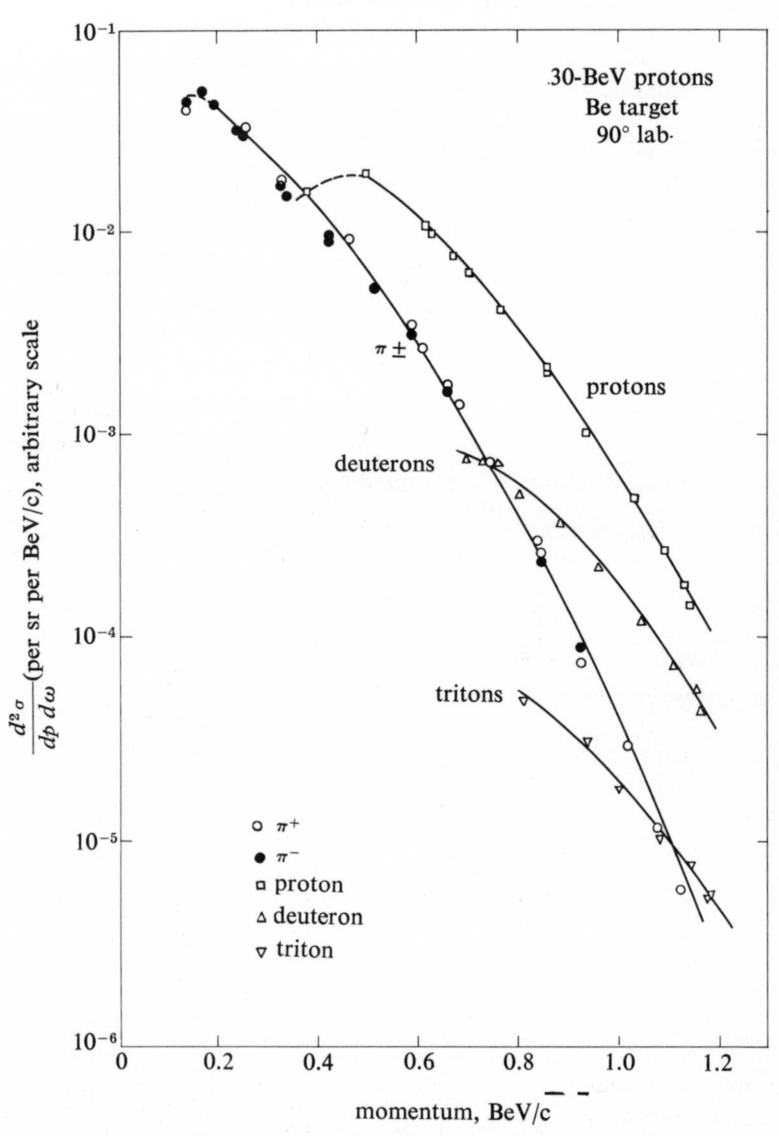

Figure 11-66 Momentum spectrum of various particles produced at 90° by 30-BeV protons incident on a Be target. [Fitch, Meyer, and Piroué, *Phys. Rev.*, **126**, 1849 (1962).]

If we remember that γ_c is large and θ correspondingly small, Eq. (11-14.6) may be approximated by

$$\gamma_c \simeq \frac{1}{\langle \theta \rangle} \qquad \textbf{(11-14.7)}$$

where $\langle \theta \rangle$ is an average value of θ for the particles in the jet.

Another important parameter of a collision is its inelasticity K, defined in a nucleon-nucleon collision as the fraction of the initially available energy radiated as newly created particles (pions, nucleon-

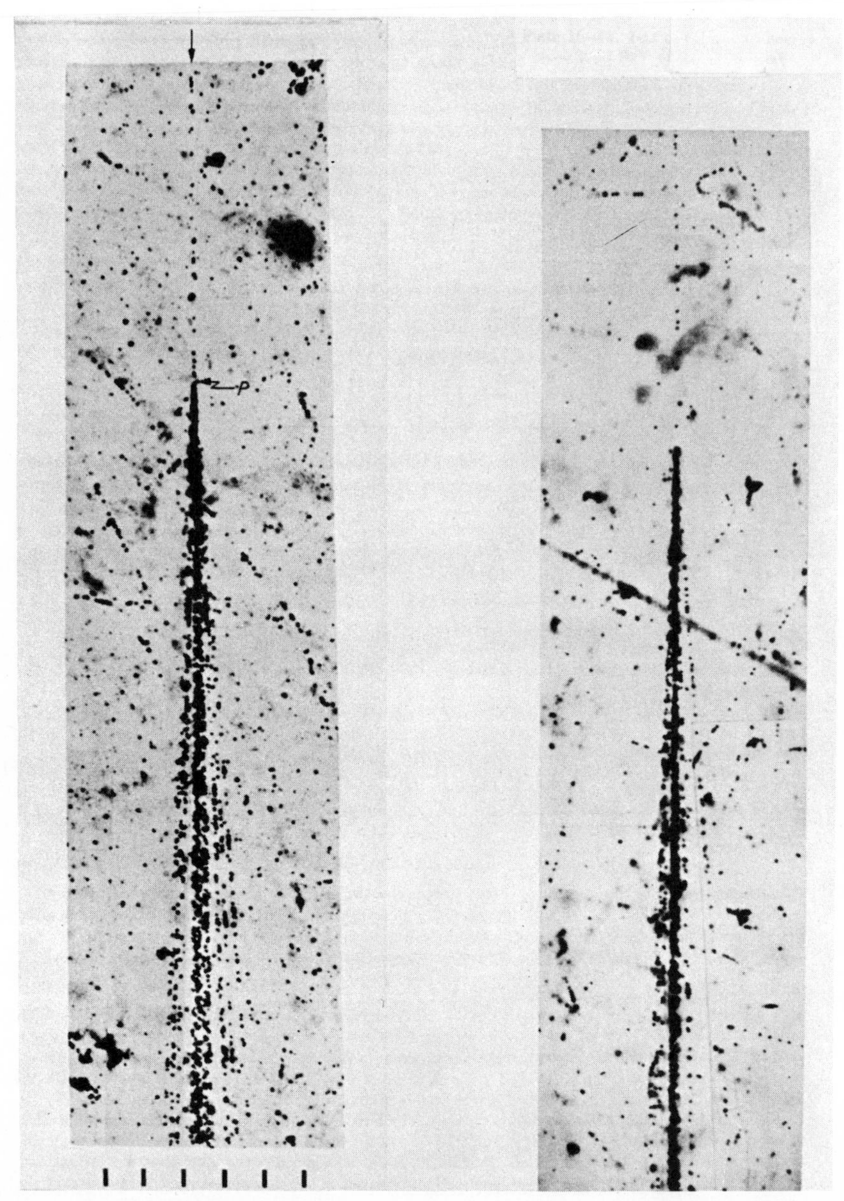

Figure 11-67 Jets of mesons of energy = 3,000 BeV and = 9,000 BeV. (a) is $0 + 28p$, (b) is $0 + 32p$. For an analysis see (PFP 59), p. 552.

antinucleon pairs). The inelasticity may be determined from photographic-emulsion experiments. For extremely high energies it proves to be small (0.20). Thus an incident particle of many thousands of BeV energy preserves about 80 per cent of its energy after a collision.

The highest-energy phenomena observed are colossal showers formed in air by incoming cosmic rays. These showers may contain as many as 10^9 particles and may cover areas of some square kilometers. The total energy has been found to reach 10^{19} eV. The jets noted in photographic emulsions may be the initial phase of such high-energy interactions, but the full development occurs outside the stack. The observations are made by covering an extended area with counters and measuring the location and time of arrival of the particles (Rossi, 1959).

11-15 Statistical Theory of High-Energy Nuclear Collisions

Fermi proposed a model for treating high-energy collisions which, although extremely crude, is also extremely simple and brings out some of the features that must of necessity be present in nuclear collisions. The idea is that when two nucleons collide, they suddenly release all their kinetic energy in a small volume of the order of magnitude of the cube of the range of nuclear forces. In spite of the small duration of the collision, it is assumed that the strong interactions are so strong as to allow the establishment of a statistical equilibrium in this small volume. The subsequent course of the reaction is then dominated by phase-space factors for the final states.

It is at once apparent that this type of consideration excludes all processes slower than those determined by strong interactions. For example, the very existence of electromagnetic radiation is ignored. On the other hand, the only parameter involved in the model is the volume Ω, in which equilibrium is established.

The distance at which nucleons interact is approximately the Compton wavelength of the pion $\hbar/m_\pi c$ (see Chap. 14); therefore the volume in which equilibrium is established must be reasonably near to

$$\Omega = \frac{4}{3}\pi\left(\frac{\hbar}{m_\pi c}\right)^3 \tag{11-15.1}$$

or relativistically to

$$\Omega = \frac{4}{3}\pi\left(\frac{\hbar}{m_\pi c}\right)^3 \frac{2m_p c^2}{W} \tag{11-15.2}$$

The last factor, valid in the case of nucleon-nucleon collisions in their center-of-mass reference system, represents the Lorentz contraction of the volume in which equilibrium is established. W is the total energy in the center-of-mass system.

The model is especially suited to the treatment of multiple production of strongly interacting particles such as pions. An increase of Ω tends to increase the multiplicity in production phenomena.

The conservation laws that are valid for strong interactions must be satisfied, and this condition puts additional constraints on the statistical equilibrium. In practice, conservation of energy and momentum are always taken into account. However, in many calculations some of the other conservation laws have been omitted for the sake of simplicity.

Statistical equilibrium means that all single states are equally probable. Hence the probability of obtaining a certain physical result is proportional to the number of single states (statistical weight) corresponding to it. For example, the statistical weight $S(n)$ of n independent spinless particles, with momenta $p_1 \cdots p_n$ and total energy W, in a volume Ω inside a large box of volume V, is computed as follows: Designate $Q(W)$ as the volume in momentum space inside the surface of constant energy W_0. Then the number of states per unit energy interval is

$$\frac{dN}{dW} = \frac{dQ}{dW} V^n \frac{1}{(2\pi\hbar)^{3n}} \tag{11-15.3}$$

The first factor comes from the momentum space; the second comes from the normalization volume V; the third is the volume of the unit cell in phase space.

The probability of n independent particles being all in volume Ω is $(\Omega/V)^n$, and the statistical weight of the state where all n particles are in Ω with the specified momenta is

$$S(n) = \frac{\Omega^n}{(2\pi\hbar)^{3n}} \frac{dQ(W)}{dW} \tag{11-15.4}$$

However, the conservation of momentum effectively reduces the number of degrees of freedom of the system. The momentum space is $3(n-1)$-dimensional, hence the exponent n is replaced by $n - 1$ in Eq. (11-15.4).

Other factors in $S(n)$ may come from the spin of the particles and from the identity of some of the particles. The isotopic spin conservation may also affect the number of accessible states. Finally the conservation of angular momentum should be taken into account. This last condition introduces considerable complications in the calculations but usually affects the results by relatively small numerical factors and is largely neglected.

Once the $S(n)$ are computed, the cross sections for different processes are obtained by multiplying a geometrical cross section

$$\sigma_{\text{tot}} = \pi R^2 = \pi\left(\frac{\hbar}{m_\pi c}\right)^2 \simeq 6 \times 10^{-26}\ \text{cm}^2 \text{ by } \frac{S(n)}{\sum S(n)} \tag{11-15.5}$$

● As a very simple example, let us consider (following Fermi) a nucleon-nucleon collision slightly above the threshold for pion production. The competing processes are elastic collision, with a statistical weight $S(2)$, and pion production, with statistical weight $S(3)$. In order to compute $S(2)$, consider the two nucleons to be nonrelativistic; one finds

$$S(2) = \frac{\Omega p^2}{2\pi^2\hbar^3(v_1 + v_2)} = \frac{\Omega m_N p}{4\pi^2\hbar^3} \tag{11-15.6}$$

where p is the momentum of one nucleon in the center-of-mass system and v_1, v_2 are the magnitudes of the velocity of the nucleons. Calling $T + m_\pi c^2$ the kinetic energy of the two nucleons in the center-of-mass system, we have in the case of elastic collision

$$m_\pi c^2 + T = \frac{p^2}{m_N} \tag{11-15.7}$$

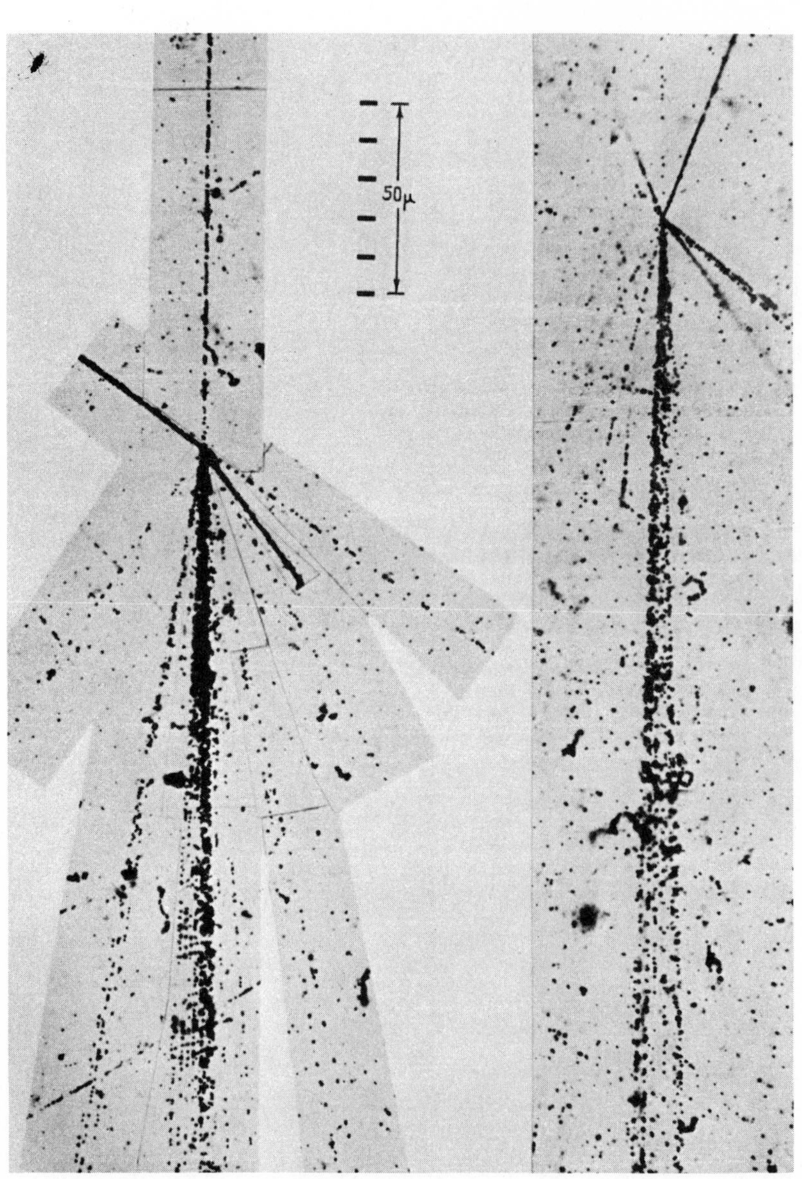

Figure 11-68 "Jets" from high-energy nuclear collisions. (a) is $4 + 50\alpha$ and has an energy of $\sim$ 3,000 BeV. (b) has an energy of $\sim$ 600 BeV. For an analysis see (PFP 59), p. 526.

and, from Eq. (11-15.6),

$$S(2) = \frac{\Omega m_N^{3/2}}{4\pi^2\hbar^3}(m_\pi c^2 + T)^{1/2} \tag{11-15.8}$$

The statistical weight for three particles $S(3)$ in the nonrelativistic approximation is

$$S(3) = \frac{\Omega^2}{16\pi^3\hbar^6}\left(\frac{m_1 m_2 m_3}{m_1 + m_2 + m_3}\right)^{3/2} T^2 = \frac{\Omega^2}{16\pi^3\hbar^6}\left(\frac{m_N^2 m_\pi}{2m_N + m_\pi}\right)^{3/2} T^2 \tag{11-15.9}$$

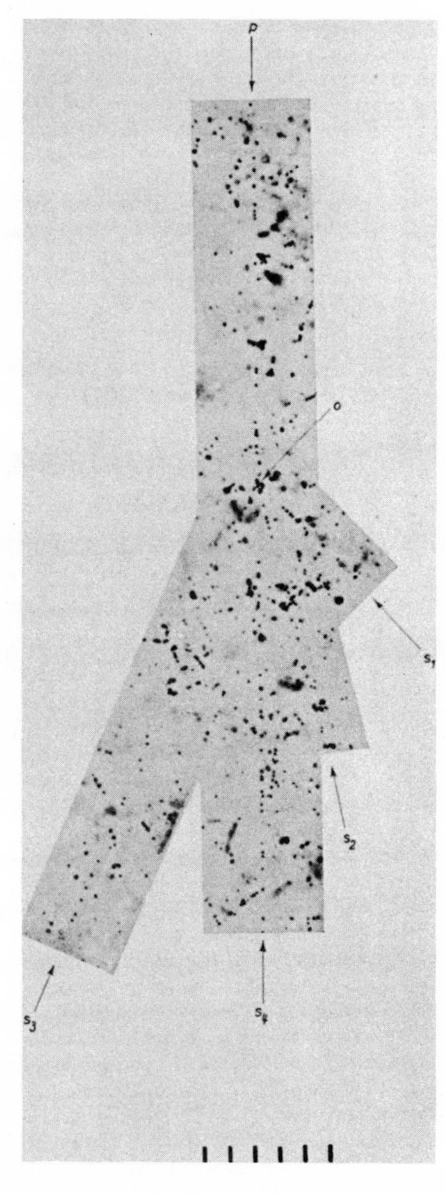

Figure 11-69 Nuclear interaction of a proton of energy ~ 40,000 BeV. For secondaries and analysis see (PFP 59), p. 559.

where m_1, m_2, m_3 are the masses of the particles and T is the total kinetic energy in the center-of-mass system.

Near the threshold for pion production,

$$S(3) \ll S(2) \quad \textbf{(11-15.10)}$$

Moreover, $T \ll m_\pi c^2$ in Eq. (11-15.7) and we neglect m_π versus $2m_N$ in the denominator of Eq. (11-15.9), obtaining

$$\frac{S(2)}{S(3)} = \frac{1}{6\sqrt{2}}\left(\frac{T}{m_\pi c^2}\right)^2 \quad \textbf{(11-15.11)}$$

The cross section for pion production then becomes

$$\sigma = \pi\left(\frac{\hbar}{m_\pi c}\right)^2 \frac{1}{6\sqrt{2}}\left(\frac{T}{m_\pi c^2}\right)^2 \quad \textbf{(11-15.12)}$$

where the first factors represent the geometrical area determined by the range of nuclear forces and the last factor represents the ratio given in Eq. (11-15.5). ●

It is noteworthy that Eq. (11-15.12) gives even an approximately correct answer, because it does not contain any constant characteristics of the strong interactions except the pion mass.

The model can be extended and simplified at extremely high energy when the volume Ω can be treated as a small volume heated at a temperature τ. This volume in very relativistic cases closely resembles the black body of radiation theory, except that the light quanta are replaced by pions or nucleon-antinucleon pairs. The particles formed must also be extremely relativistic. These conditions obtain for energies $> 10^{12}$ eV.

An extensive statistical study at the laboratory energy of 25 BeV, as in the CERN accelerator in Geneva, has been performed by Hagedorn and Cerulus (1960). They have also tried to take into account some further experimental results not contained in the fundamental statistical hypotheses. For instance in *p-p* collisions at 6.2 BeV cm, they consider the $T = 3/2$, $J = 3/2$ resonance of the pion-nucleon system in the final state, the nucleon-antinucleon annihilation. Moreover, they have also varied the interaction volume for heavier mesons. The results agree well with the experimental data available thus far and are very useful, at least in providing orientation for planning experiments.

Bibliography

Ajzenberg-Selove, F. (ed.), *Nuclear Spectroscopy*, Academic Press, New York, 1960.

Barber, W. C., "Inelastic Electron Scattering," *Ann. Rev. Nucl. Sci.*, **12,** 1 (1962).

Bishop, G. R., and R. Wilson, "The Nuclear Photoeffect," in (Fl E), Vol. 42.

Blatt, J. M., and V. Weisskopf (BW 52).

Bodansky, D., "Compound Statistical Features in Nuclear Reactions," *Ann. Rev. Nucl. Sci.*, **12,** 79 (1962).

Burcham, W. E., "Nuclear Reactions, Levels, and Spectra of Light Nuclei," in (Fl E), Vol. 40.

Butler, S. T., and O. H. Hittmar, *Nuclear Stripping Reactions*, Wiley, New York, 1957.

Clementel, E., and C. Villi, *Conference on Direct Interactions and Nuclear Reaction Mechanisms, Padua, 1962*, Gordon and Breach, New York, 1963.

Cohen, Fulmer, McCarthy, and Mukherjee, "Location of Neutron Single-Particle Levels from Stripping Reactions," *Rev. Mod. Phys.*, **35,** 332 (1963).

Cumming, J. B., "Monitor Reactions for High Energy Proton Beams," *Ann. Rev. Nucl. Sci.*, **13,** 261 (1963).

Eisberg, R. M., and C. E. Porter, "Scattering of Alpha Particles," *Rev. Mod. Phys.*, **33,** 190 (1961).

Endt, P. M., M. Demeur, and P. B. Smith (ed.), *Nuclear Reactions*, Wiley-Interscience, New York, 1959–1962.

Glendenning, N. K., "Nuclear Stripping Reactions," *Ann. Rev. Nucl. Sci.*, **13,** 191 (1963).

Gol'danskii, V., and A. M. Baldin, *Kinematics of Nuclear Reactions*, Pergamon, London, 1961.

Halpern, I., "Nuclear Fission," *Ann. Rev. Nucl. Sci.*, **9,** 245 (1959).

Hayward, E., "Photodisintegration of Light Nuclei," *Rev. Mod. Phys.*, **35,** 324 (1963).

Hendricks, C. D., and J. M. Schneider, "Stability of a Conducting Droplet under the Influence of Surface Tension and Electrostatic Forces," *Am. J. Phys.*, **31,** 450 (1963).

Hughes, D. J., et al., *Neutron Cross Sections*, Brookhaven National Laboratory, Upton, New York, 1958–1960.

Hyde, E. K., "A Review of Nuclear Fission," UCRL 9036 and 9065, Lawrence Radiation Laboratory, Berkeley, California, 1960–1963.

Kinsey, B. B., "Nuclear Reactions, Levels, and Spectra of Heavy Nuclei," in (Fl E), Vol. 40.

Kretzschmar, M., "Statistical Methods in High Energy Physics," *Ann. Rev. Nucl. Sci.*, **11,** 1 (1961).

Lane, A. M., "Reduced Width of Individual Nuclear Energy Levels," *Rev. Mod. Phys.*, **32,** 519 (1960).

Levinger, J. S., *Nuclear Photodisintegration*, Oxford University Press, New York, 1960.

Macfarlane, M. H., and J. B. French, "Stripping Reactions and the Structure of Light and Intermediate Nuciei," *Rev. Mod. Phys.*, **32,** 567 (1960).

Miller, J. M., and J. Hudis, "High Energy Nuclear Reactions," *Ann. Rev. Nucl. Sci.*, **9,** 159–202 (1959).

Perkins, D. H., "Observations on Cosmic-Ray 'Jet' Interactions in Nuclear Emulsions," *Progr. Elem. Particle Cosmic Ray Phys.*, **5,** 259 (1962).

Preston, M. A. (P 62).

Rainwater, J., "Resonance Processes by Neutrons," in (Fl E), Vol. 40.

Riesenfeld, W. B., and K. M. Watson, "Optical-Model Potential for Nucleons Scattered by Nuclei," *Phys. Rev.*, **102,** 1157 (1956).

Talmi, I., and I. Unna, "Theoretical Interpretation of the Energy Levels of Light Nuclei," *Ann. Rev. Nucl. Sci.*, **10,** 353 (1960).

Tobocman, W., *Theory of Direct Nuclear Reactions*, Oxford University Press, New York, 1961.

Wattenberg, A., "Nuclear Reactions at High Energies," in (Fl E), Vol. 40.

Wilkinson, D. H., "Nuclear Photodisintegration," *Ann. Rev. Nucl. Sci.*, **9,** 1 (1959).

Wolfenstein, L., "Polarization of Fast Nucleons," *Ann. Rev. Nucl. Sci.*, **6,** 43–76 (1956).

Zucker, A., "Nuclear Interactions of Heavy Ions," *Ann. Rev. Nucl. Sci.*, **10,** 27–62 (1960).

Problems

11-1 Find the threshold (lab) for the reaction

$$Na^{23}\,(p,n)\,Mg^{23}$$

given that the upper limit of the positron spectrum emitted by Mg^{23} is 3.0 MeV.

11-2 Fifty grams of copper containing a gold impurity bombarded with a thermal neutron flux of 10^8 n sec^{-1} for 7 hours gives 100 counts per second due to Au^{198} in a certain apparatus. What is the percentage of gold in the sample, by weight? σ_{th} of Au = 96 b, $T_{1/2}$ = 2.7 days. Plan the details of the experiment including calibrations and possible chemical operations required.

11-3 The reaction N^{14} (d,α) C^{12} has been studied in order to verify detailed balance [Bodansky, Eccles, Farwell, Rickey, and Robinson, *Phys. Rev. Letters*, **2,** 101 (1959)]. The deuterons used had 20 MeV of energy (lab), what was the corresponding lab energy of the helium ions? If in the direct experiment one observed helium ions escaping at 20° in the lab, at what angle did the corresponding deuterons in the inverse reaction escape? (See Fig. 11-4.)

11-4 The reaction

$$He^3\,(n,p)\,H^3$$

has a cross section in barns of 5,000 × (2,000/v) (v in m sec^{-1}). Calculate the cross section for the inverse reaction and specify the energy of the incoming proton (neglect Coulomb barriers).

11-5 Prove classically that for a charged particle

$$\begin{aligned} \sigma_c &= \pi R^2(1 - V/E) \qquad &\text{for } E > V \\ &= 0 &\text{for } E < V \end{aligned}$$

where $V = Zze^2/R$ (R = nuclear radius).

11-6 If only elastic scattering is possible, the scattering matrix contains only one element, $S_{\alpha\alpha}$. Relate it to η.

11-7 Using Breit–Wigner formulas show that the corresponding scattering matrix is for two channels (elastic scattering and reaction):

$$T = \frac{1}{\epsilon - i}\begin{pmatrix} x & [x(1-x)]^{1/2} \\ [x(1-x)]^{1/2} & 1 - x \end{pmatrix}$$

where $x = \Gamma_s/\Gamma$ and $\epsilon = (2/\Gamma)(E_r - E)$. Show that all complex matrix elements are represented as a function of energy by vectors from the origin to a point of a circle passing through the origin and having its center on the imaginary axis.

Problems

11-8 Plot in Fig. 11-14 lines of constant δ and variable η. In particular, discuss the cases $\delta = 0$ and $\delta = 90°$ and interpret them physically.

11-9 The reflection factor η_l may be averaged over a certain energy interval, giving $\bar{\eta}_l$. Show that the corresponding average elastic and total cross sections are

$$\bar{\sigma}_{el}^{(l)} = \pi ƛ^2(2l + 1)\{|1 - \bar{\eta}_l|^2 - |\bar{\eta}_l|^2 + \overline{|\eta_l|^2}\}$$

$$\bar{\sigma}_t^{(l)} = \pi ƛ^2(2l + 1)\{|1 - \bar{\eta}_l|^2 + 1 - |\bar{\eta}_l|^2\}$$

[Feschbach, Porter, and Weisskopf, *Phys. Rev.*, **96,** 448 (1954).]

11-10 Prove that $(r\psi)'/r\psi$ must be a continuous function of r.

11-11 Cd^{113} has a capture cross section (n,γ) given in the following table:

E(eV)	0.01	0.02	0.03	0.05	0.08	0.10	0.15	0.20	0.30	0.40	0.50	0.70	1.00
$\sigma_{(n,\gamma)}$	3,500	2,700	2,500	2,500	2,800	3,600	7,000	7,000	1,500	300	150	50	22

Find the constants for expressing it through a single resonance Breit–Wigner formula.

11-12 Find the constants of the Breit–Wigner formula for slow-neutron absorption of In from the experimental data plotted in Fig. 11-8.

11-13 Using the following data referring to Xe^{135}, plot its slow-neutron absorption cross section versus energy in the energy interval 10^{-2} to 1 eV. Use the Breit–Wigner formula with one resonance at

$$I = 3/2 \qquad E_0 = 0.082 \text{ eV} \qquad \Gamma_n^{(r)} = 24 \text{ meV} \qquad \Gamma_\gamma = 86 \text{ meV}$$

11-14 Show that the maximum possible scattering cross section due to a resonance is

$$\sigma_{sc} \max = 4g \frac{0.65 \times 10^6}{E_r(\text{eV})} \text{ (barns)}$$

What relation is required between Γ_γ and Γ_n?

11-15 Show that the maximum possible slow-neutron reaction cross section according to the Breit–Wigner formula is

$$\sigma_r \max = g \frac{0.65 \times 10^6}{E_r(\text{eV})} \text{ (barns)}$$

What relation is required between Γ_γ and Γ_n? Apply this to Xe^{135} ($I = 3/2$).

11-16 Show how one can find Γ_n/Γ_r by a measurement of σ_r at a resonance.

11-17 Calculate σ_s in the case $f = -iKR$.

11-18 Verify that if $f = -KR \tan(KR + \xi)$ the scattering cross section has a resonance shape in the vicinity of its maximum and calculate Γ.

11-19 Show that from Eq. (11-9.7) one obtains the numerical relation

$$\langle \sigma_r(E) \rangle = \frac{1.8 \times 10^{16} f}{E^{1/2}} \frac{\Gamma_r}{\Gamma_r + 0.44 \times 10^{10} f D E^{1/2}} \text{ in } 10^{-24} \text{ cm}^2$$

E in eV, and $f = (ƛ/2)(\Gamma_n/\bar{D})$ in cm [(WW 59), p. 57].

11-20 The Breit–Wigner formulas may also be derived by a second-order perturbation calculation [see (Fe 50)].

11-21 Find the threshold energy for forming a π meson by bombarding proton with proton, carbon with proton, and carbon with helium. For the last two cases take the Fermi energy into account.

11-22 Show that in a degenerate gas the average kinetic energy per particle is $\frac{3}{5}$ of the Fermi energy.

11-23 Plot the probable number of neutrons that a nucleus will emit as a function of excitation energy [see (Fe 50)].

11-24 Prove that for high-energy deuteron stripping the energy E of the escaping neutrons (lab) is $E_d/2$ with a spread

$$\Delta E = 1.5\,(\epsilon E_d)^{1/2}$$

and that they escape with an angular spread

$$\Delta\theta = 1.6\,(\epsilon/E_d)^{1/2}$$

where ϵ is the binding energy of the deuteron.

11-25 Estimate how much Tc^{99} is produced in a natural uranium pile for every kilogram of Pu^{239} produced.

CHAPTER XII

Neutrons

THE NEUTRON affords an interesting example of a major scientific discovery. Its existence had been hypothesized by Rutherford as early as 1920. His arguments, however, were purely speculative, and until 1932 no experimental evidence supporting them was available. In 1930, Bothe and Becker bombarded beryllium with alpha particles and

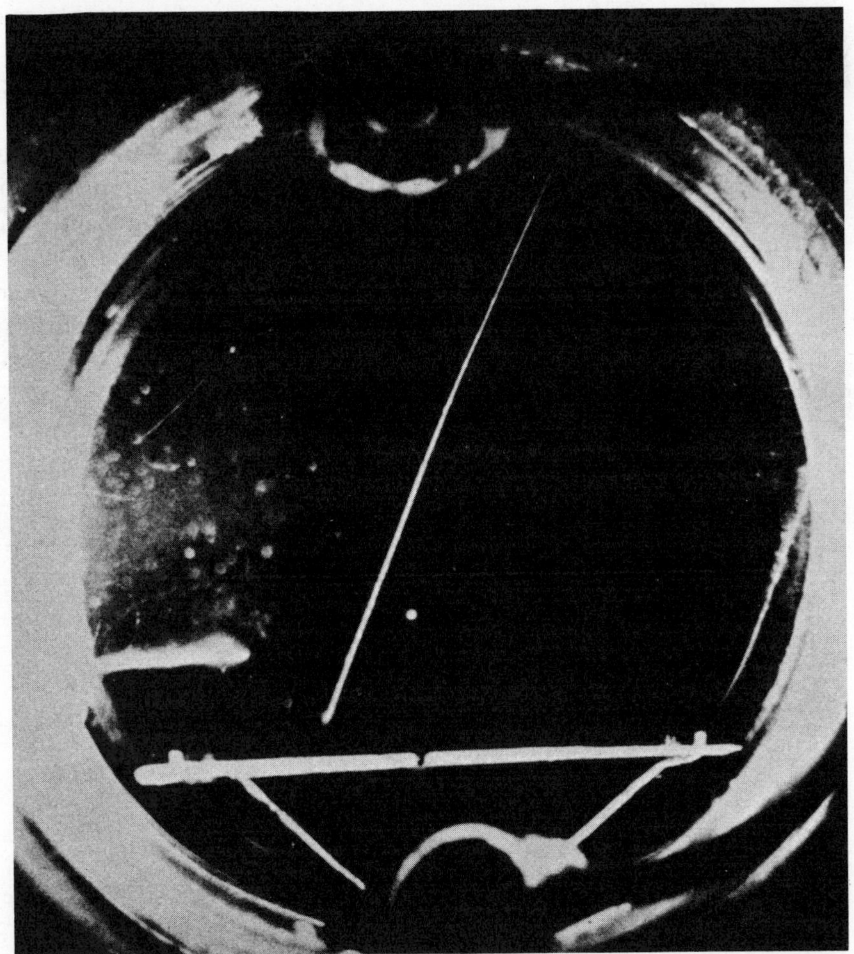

Figure 12-1 Recoil proton observed by Curie and Joliot before the discovery of the neutron. [I. Curie and F. Joliot, *Compt. Rend.*, **194**, 867 (1932).]

observed a very penetrating radiation; they then showed that the penetrating radiation was composed of gamma rays. Further study by I. Curie and F. Joliot gave the surprising result (1932) that this "gamma radiation" also had a component that was capable of imparting energies of several MeV to protons in a cloud chamber (Fig. 12-1). At first Curie and Joliot interpreted the observed energy transfer as a Compton effect on protons. The correct explanation, however, was soon provided by Chadwick, who showed that the recoil protons observed by Curie and Joliot had been hit by a neutral particle of approximately protonic mass, which he called the neutron. Chadwick bombarded with neutrons not only hydrogen but other light nuclei as well, and measured the range of the recoil particles. From the conservation of energy and momentum and range-energy relations he was able to determine the mass of the new particle "as very nearly the same as the mass of the proton."

12-1 Neutron Sources

The simplest neutron source is a mixture of a suitable radioactive substance and a light element such as beryllium or boron. Neutrons are generated by the (α,n) or (γ,n) process. These sources are weak compared with other types, but they are small and constant (Table 12-1).

Reactions produced by accelerators give rise to neutrons, and here we find large intensities. Moreover, it is possible, by using a thin target and by selecting the neutrons emitted in a given direction, to obtain a fairly monochromatic beam of neutrons. For example, the reaction $Li^7 + H^1 \rightarrow Be^7 + n - 1.647$ MeV (endothermic) can produce neutrons with energies a few keV and up, as shown in Fig. 12-2. The reactions $H^3 + H^2 = He^4 + n + 17.6$ MeV, $H^2 + H^2 = He^3 + n + 3.27$ MeV can

Table 12-1 Yields of (α,n) Neutron Sources

Source	Measured yield, neutrons per 10^6 α particles	Calculated yield, neutrons per 10^6 α particles
Po – α – Li	2.4	2.6
	4.7	2.5
Po – α – Be	73	70
Po – α – B	20	24
Po – α – BF_3	13.5	15.4
Po – α – F	10.4	12
Pu – α – Be	42	35
Ra – α – Be[a]	1.4×10^7 neutrons per sec per g Ra	1.35×10^7 neutrons per sec per g Ra

[a] This yield is for a source containing 4.5 g of Be and 1 g of Ra.

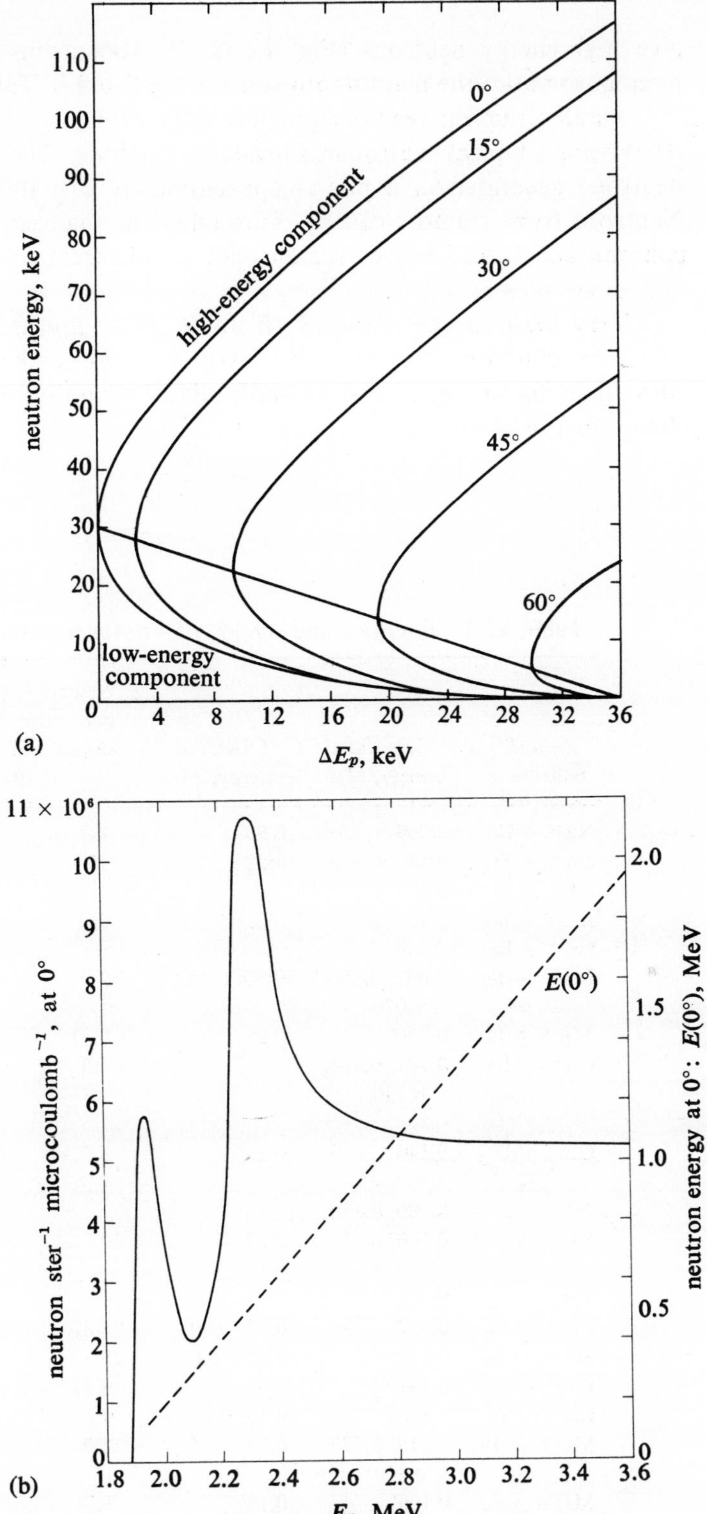

Figure 12-2 (a) Neutron energies from a thin lithium target as a function of the difference ΔE_p between the energy of the bombarding proton and the threshold energy, for various angles of emission in the laboratory system. (b) Yield of neutrons at 0° from the Li(p,n) reaction as a function of the proton energy. Target thickness 40 keV. [Hanson, Taschek, and Williams, *Rev. Mod. Phys.*, **21**, 635 (1949).]

give high-energy neutrons (Fig. 12-3). Photoneutrons are also fairly monochromatic; the main photo sources are listed in Table 12-2.

Finally, nuclear reactors generate high neutron fluxes, 10^{14} n cm^{-2} sec^{-1} being a typical neutron flux in a large machine. The total number of neutrons generated in a pile is approximately 6×10^{13} n (sec kw)$^{-1}$. Neutrons from reactors can be thoroughly thermalized with a thermal column, and special energy regions can be selected by crystal reflection and other means.

Very high energy neutrons (from 50 MeV upward) are best obtained by deuteron stripping or by charge-exchange collisions of protons with light nuclei. A typical example of the resulting energy spread is shown in Fig. 12-4.

Table 12-2 Energies and Yields of Photoneutrons

(γ,n) Sources	Calculated energy, MeV	Observed energy, MeV	Neutrons per sec per curie (1 g of target at 1 cm) $\times 10^{-4}$
Na^{24} + Be	0.966	0.83	14
Na^{24} + D	0.261	0.22	27
Al^{28} + Be	0.103		
Al^{28} + Be	0.103		
Cl^{38} + Be	0.430		
Mn^{56} + Be	0.092, 0.350, 1.076	0.15, 0.30	2.9
Mn^{56} + D	0.320	0.22	0.31
Ga^{72} + Be	0.181, 0.484, 0.750		5.9
Ga^{72} + D	0.140	0.13	6.9
			4.6
As^{76} + Be	0.089, 0.350		
Y^{88} + Be	0.166, 0.972	0.22 0.16	10
Y^{88} + D	0.265		0.3
In^{116} + Be	0.377	0.15, 0.30	0.82
Sb^{124} + Be	0.031	0.025, 0.035	19
La^{140} + Be	0.747	0.62	0.31
La^{140} + D	0.140	0.13, 0.15	0.8
MsTh + Be	0.119, 0.475, 0.848	0.83	3.5
MsTh + D	0.196	0.197	9.5
Ra + Be	0.021, 0.084, 0.137, 0.377, 0.475, 0.670		1.2
Ra + D	0.096	0.12	0.1

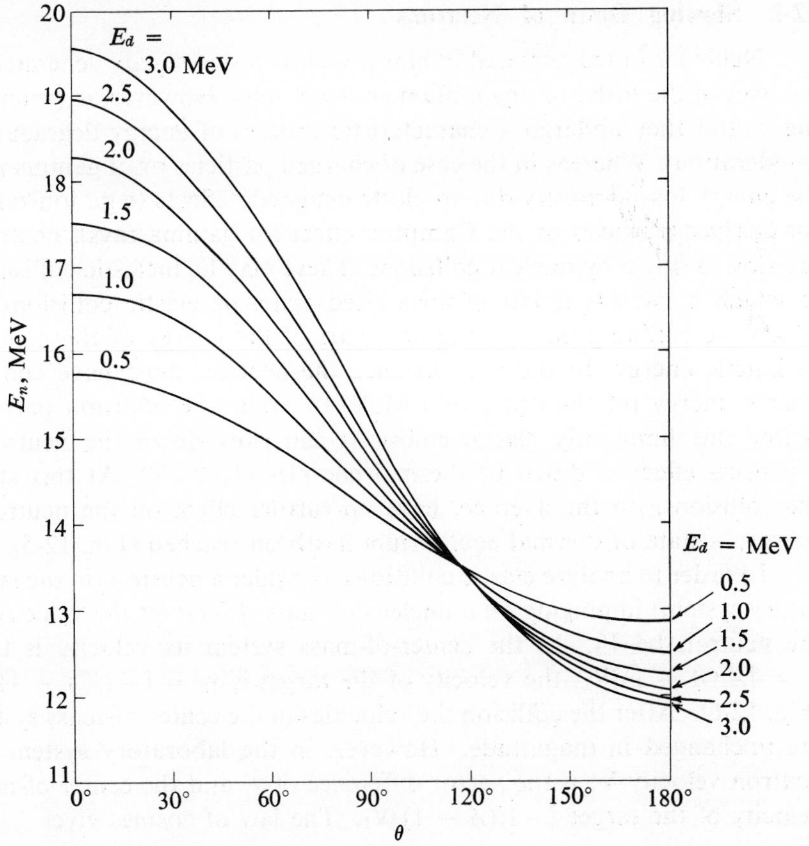

Figure 12-3 The energies of the neutrons emitted from the $H^3(d,n)$ He^4 reaction for various values of E_d as a function of the angles of emission in the laboratory system. [Hanson, Taschek, and Williams, *Rev. Mod. Phys.*, **21**, 635 (1949).]

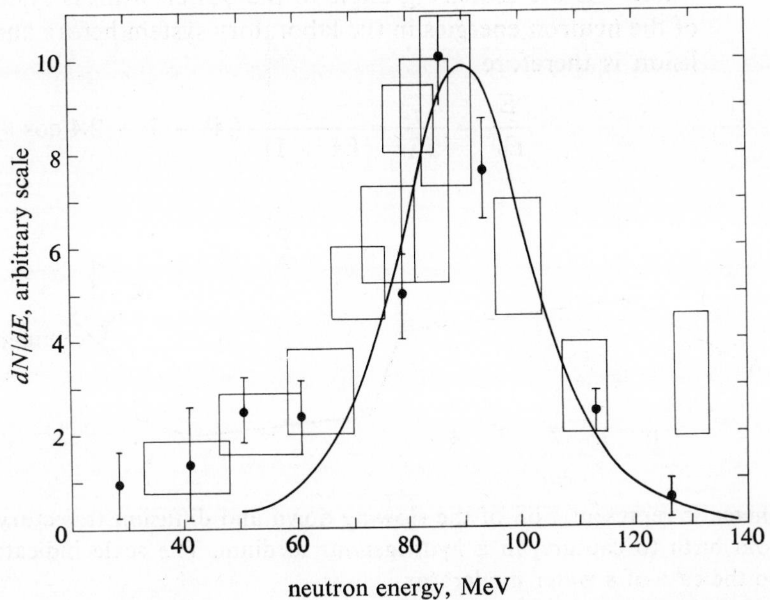

Figure 12-4 Energy distribution of neutrons obtained by stripping a 190-MeV deuteron on a 1.27-cm-thick beryllium target. The curve is from the stripping approximation.

12-2 Slowing Down of Neutrons

Neutrons in reactors and in many nuclear processes are generated at energies of the order of one million electron volts. However, in penetrating matter they undergo a characteristic process of energy degradation (moderation). Whereas in the case of charged particles or of gamma rays the energy loss is mostly due to electromagnetic effects (e.g., ionization for charged particles or the Compton effect for gamma rays), neutrons are slowed down by nuclear collisions. These may be inelastic collisions, in which a nucleus is left in an excited state, or elastic collisions, in which the colliding nucleus acquires part of the energy of the neutron as kinetic energy. In the first instance the neutron must have enough kinetic energy (of the order of 1 MeV) to excite the collision partner. Below this limit only elastic collisions can slow down the neutrons, a process effective down to thermal energies (1/40 eV). At this stage the collisions, on the average, have no further effect on the neutron's energy: a state of thermal equilibrium has been reached (Fig. 12-5).

In order to analyze elastic collisions, consider a neutron (in the laboratory system) impinging on a nucleus of mass A, and let the velocity of the neutron be V_1. In the center-of-mass system its velocity is then $\mathbf{v}_1 = [A/(A + 1)]\mathbf{V}_1$; the velocity of the target is $\mathbf{v}_2 = [-1/(A + 1)]\mathbf{V}_1$ (Fig. 12-6). After the collision the velocities in the center-of-mass system are unchanged in magnitude. However, in the laboratory system the neutron velocity $\mathbf{V}_1'$ is the vector difference of $\mathbf{v}_1'$ and the center-of-mass velocity of the target $[-1/(A + 1)]\mathbf{V}_1$. The law of cosines gives

$$V_1'^2 = \left(\frac{A}{A+1}V_1\right)^2 + \left(\frac{1}{A+1}V_1\right)^2 - 2V_1^2A\left(\frac{1}{A+1}\right)^2 \cos(\pi - \theta) = \frac{V_1^2}{(A+1)^2}(A^2 + 1 + 2A\cos\theta) \qquad \text{(12-2.1)}$$

where θ is the scattering angle in the center-of-mass system. The ratio of the neutron energies in the laboratory system before and after the collision is therefore

$$\frac{E}{E_0} = \frac{V_1'^2}{V_1^2} = \frac{1}{(A+1)^2}(A^2 + 1 + 2A\cos\theta) \qquad \text{(12-2.2)}$$

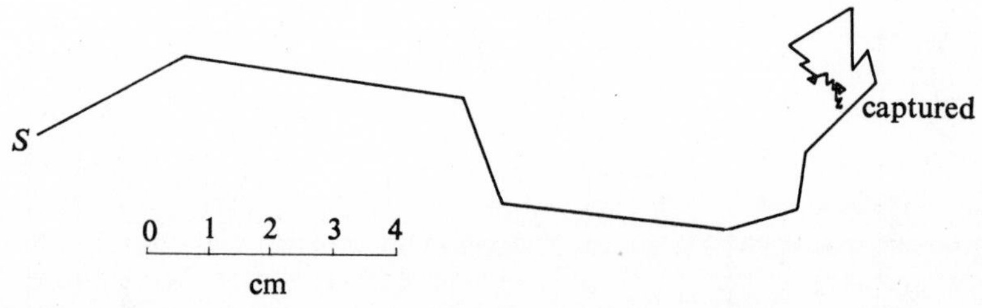

Figure 12-5 Schematic representation of the slowing down and diffusion trajectory of an initially fast neutron, from birth to capture, in a hydrogenous medium. The scale indicated corresponds approximately to the case of a water moderator.

which yields immediately the interesting inequality

$$\left(\frac{A-1}{A+1}\right)^2 \leqslant \frac{E}{E_0} \leqslant 1 \tag{12-2.3}$$

We can also calculate for future reference the relation between θ and θ_L, the laboratory scattering angle. We obtain from Fig. 12-6

$$V_1^2\left(\frac{A}{A+1}\right)^2 = V_1'^2 + \frac{1}{(A+1)^2}V_1^2 - 2V_1V_1'\cos\theta_L$$

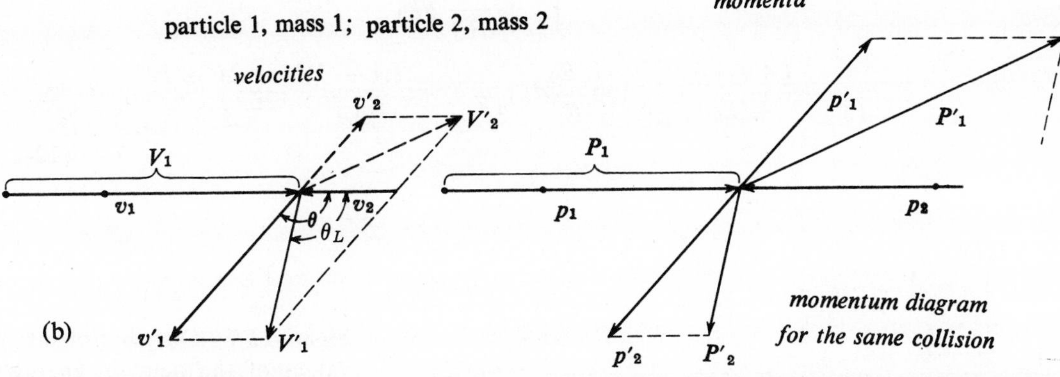

Figure 12-6 (a) Collision between particles of equal mass. At left, center of mass; at right, laboratory system (velocities and momentum). (b) Collision between particles of mass 1 and 2. At left a velocity diagram (in laboratory V_i, in center of mass v_i); at right, momentum diagram (in laboratory P_i, in center of mass p_i). Unprimed quantities are before the collision; primed quantities are after the collision.

which gives, when combined with Eq. (12-2.2),

$$\cos \theta_L = \frac{A \cos \theta + 1}{(A^2 + 1 + 2A \cos \theta)^{1/2}} \tag{12-2.4}$$

For neutrons up to at least a few hundred keV energy, scattering is due only to the s wave and hence is spherically symmetrical in the center-of-mass system. The probability dW that the scattering occurs within a solid angle $d\omega$ is thus proportional to $d\omega$, that is,

$$dW = \frac{d\omega}{4\pi} = \frac{\sin \theta \, d\theta}{2} = -\frac{d(\cos \theta)}{2} \tag{12-2.5}$$

Hence, after collision, we have equal probabilities of reaching equal intervals of $\cos \theta$ independently of θ. Differentiation of Eq. (12-2.2) gives

$$\frac{dE}{E_0} = \frac{2A}{(A + 1)^2} d(\cos \theta) \tag{12-2.6}$$

which shows that equal intervals of $\cos \theta$ correspond to equal energy intervals. We conclude that after one collision the probability of reaching equal energy intervals anywhere between E_0 and $[(A - 1)/(A + 1)]^2 E_0 = \alpha E_0$ is the same (see Fig. 12-7). For $A = 1$, that is, collisions with hydrogen, any energy between E_0 and 0 is equally probable.

One can determine the average energy after n collisions, which in the case of hydrogen is $\langle E_n \rangle = (1/2^n) E_0$. However, this average arises from a distribution in which high energies are very rare. The median and the most probable energy are well below $\langle E_n \rangle$ (Fig. 12-8).

In treating the slowing down of neutrons it is convenient to operate with the quantity $u = \log (E_0/E)$, where $E_0 = 10$ MeV, called the "lethargy." This definition gives a different scale for measuring the energy (Fig. 12-9). We calculate first the average value of $\log (E_0/E_1)$ after one collision, a quantity which we shall call ξ. We have

$$\xi = \left\langle \log \frac{E_0}{E_1} \right\rangle = \frac{\int_{\alpha E_0}^{E_0} \log \frac{E_0}{E_1} \frac{dW_1}{dE_1} dE_1}{\int_{\alpha E_0}^{E_0} \frac{dW_1}{dE_1} dE_1}$$

$$= \frac{(A + 1)^2}{4AE_0} \int_{\alpha E_0}^{E_0} \log \frac{E_0}{E_1} dE_1 = 1 + \frac{(A - 1)^2}{2A} \log \frac{A - 1}{A + 1} \tag{12-2.7}$$

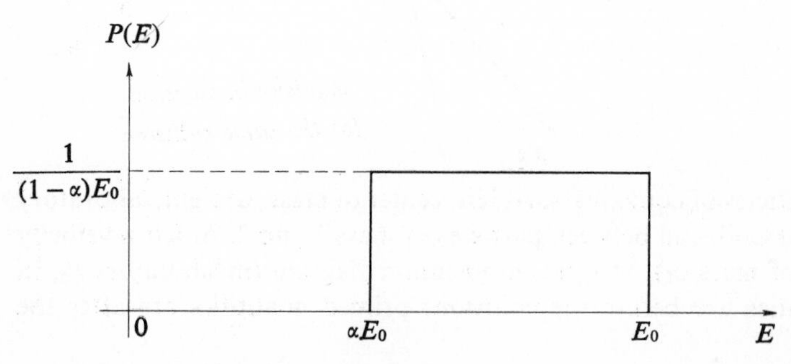

Figure 12-7 Distribution of the values of the neutron energy E after one collision in the case of isotropic scattering in the center-of-mass system for a neutron of initial energy E_0. The quantity $\alpha = (A - 1)^2/(A + 1)^2$.

Table 12-3 Average Value of the Decrease of log E per Collision (ξ)

$A = 1$	2	12	14	Large A
$\xi = 1$	0.725	0.158	0.153	$2/(A + 2/3)$

Each collision decreases the average value of log E by ξ, and hence, after n collisions we have

$$\langle \log E_n \rangle = \log E_0 - n\xi \tag{12-2.8}$$

The quantity ξ as a function of A has the values given in Table 12-3.

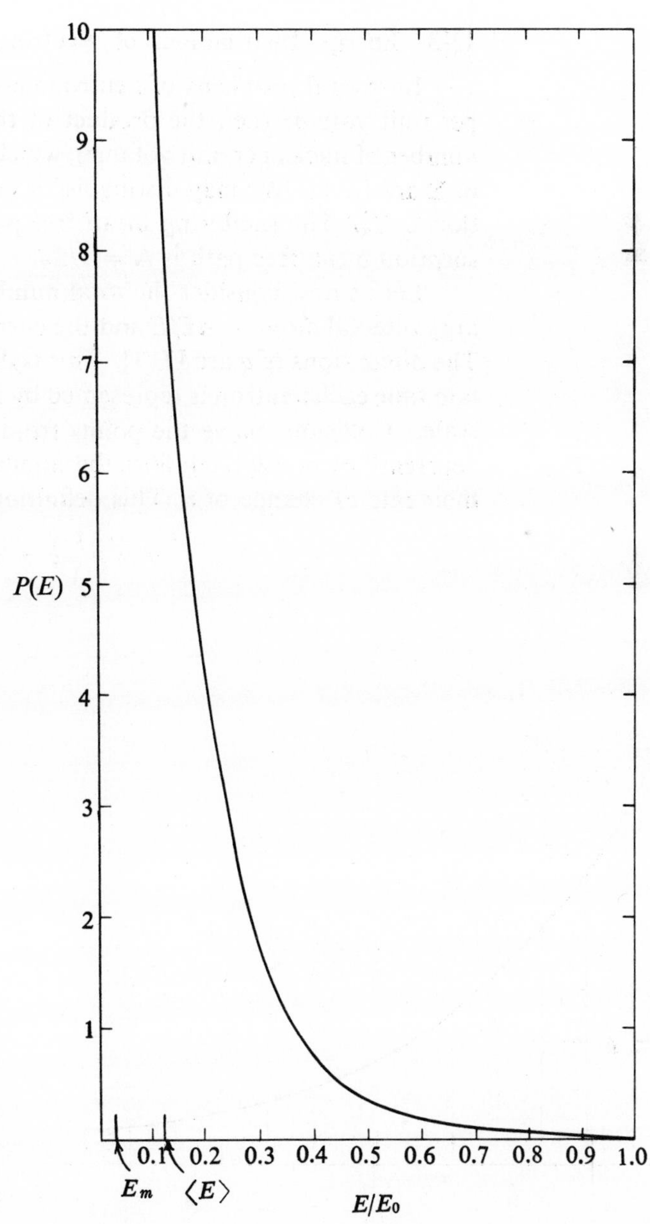

Figure 12-8 Energy distribution of neutrons of initial energy E_0 after four collisions with protons. Note the average energy $\langle E \rangle$ and the median energy E_m.

Equation (12-2.8) can be used to calculate the number of collisions needed to thermalize neutrons of a given energy. For example, for $E_0 =$ 1 MeV the number required to reach thermal energy (1/40 eV) is 17.6 collisions in hydrogen or 110 collisions in carbon. Actually Eq. (12-2.8) breaks down for values of E_n near thermal energies because there, since the energy of the scattering nuclei is comparable to that of the neutrons, the collision may impart energy to the neutron instead of subtracting it. Moreover, for a molecular or crystalline moderating medium, when an energy comparable to that of the chemical bond is reached, the collision partner is no longer a free atom but a larger unit (molecule, lattice, etc.), and the laws governing energy loss become quite complicated.

12-3 Energy Distributions of Neutrons from a Monoenergetic Source

In several problems of neutronology we shall use the cross sections per unit volume (i.e., the product of the nuclear cross section and the number of nuclei per unit volume), which we shall call Σ. The dimensions of Σ are $[L^{-1}]$. We may distinguish a scattering Σ or Σ_s and an absorption Σ, Σ_a. The scattering mean free path λ is clearly $1/\Sigma_s$, and the absorption mean free path is $\Lambda = 1/\Sigma_a$.

Let us now consider the total number of neutrons in a certain lethargy interval $du = -dE/E$ and the current of neutrons q along a u axis. The dimensions of q are $[T^{-1}]$. This is illustrated in Fig. 12-10. At a certain time each neutron is represented by a point on the logarithmic energy scale. Collisions move the points from left to right, and we obtain the "current" by multiplying $n(u)$, the number of neutrons per unit u, times their rate of change of u. This definition of q at once gives the relation

$$q = n\frac{v}{\lambda}\xi = nv\Sigma_s\xi \tag{12-3.1}$$

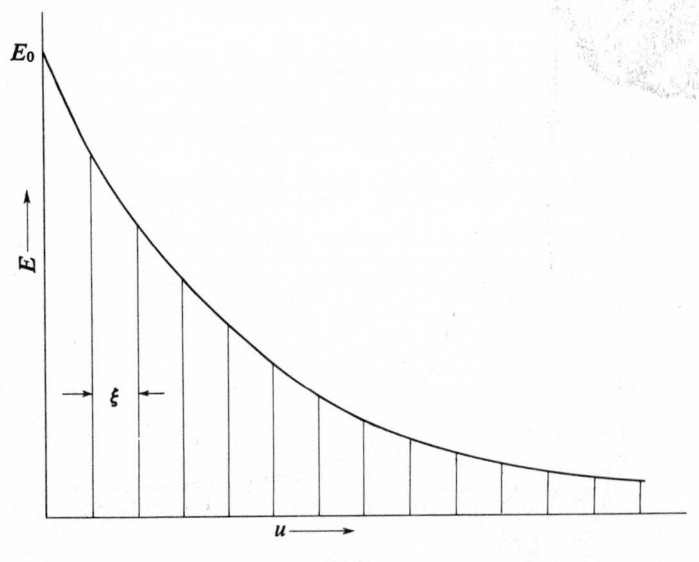

Figure 12-9 Relationship between energy and lethargy.

because v/λ is the number of collisions undergone by a neutron per unit time and ξ is the increase in lethargy per collision.

We now ask the question: What is the number of neutrons in a given energy interval in a neutron-moderating medium? We consider a steady-state situation. Let Q be the production rate of neutrons at the source; Q has the dimensions $[T^{-1}]$. We shall treat first the simpler case of no absorption. In a steady state, then, Q neutrons per second must pass any given lethargy, or

$$q(u) = Q = n\frac{v}{\lambda}\xi \tag{12-3.2}$$

and

$$n(u)\,du = -Q\frac{\lambda}{v\xi}\frac{dE}{E} \sim E^{-3/2}\,dE \tag{12-3.3}$$

if λ is energy-independent.

In most practical cases one is interested in the neutron flux nv in a certain lethargy interval, rather than the neutron density n in the same lethargy interval. Using Eq. (12-3.3) we can write

$$-nv\,du = \frac{Q\lambda}{\xi}\frac{dE}{E} \tag{12-3.4}$$

which is the total neutron flux along the u axis of neutrons in the lethargy range du. This is, for example, approximately the energy distribution of epithermal neutrons in a reactor. Epithermal refers here to energy greater than 1/40 eV and less than the first resonance of the moderator.

If absorption takes place, $q(u)$ is not constant, because neutrons disappear by absorption, and for an increase in the lethargy du the current q decreases according to

$$-\,dq(u) = \frac{nv}{\Lambda}\,du \tag{12-3.5}$$

Remembering Eq. (12-3.2), which defines q, we may write

$$-\,\xi d(nv\Sigma_s) = n\frac{v}{\Lambda}\,du = nv\Sigma_a\,du \tag{12-3.6}$$

or

$$-\,\xi\frac{d(nv\Sigma_s)}{nv\Sigma_s} = \frac{\Sigma_a}{\Sigma_s}\,du \tag{12-3.7}$$

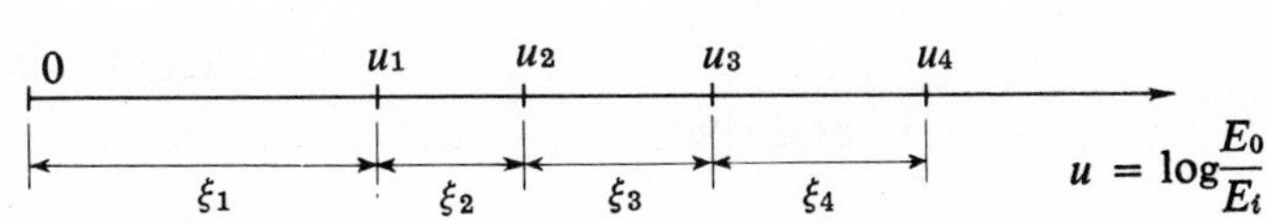

Figure 12-10 Representation of the slowing down of a neutron in a logarithmic scale (lethargy). ξ_i is $\log(E_{i-1}/E_i)$.

This equation can be integrated between the initial lethargy and an arbitrary lethargy value,

$$-\xi \log (nv\Sigma_s)\Big]_u^{u_0} = \int_u^{u_0} \frac{\Sigma_a}{\Sigma_s}\, du \tag{12-3.8}$$

and, by Eq. (12-3.2),

$$-\xi \log \left(\frac{Q}{\xi}\right) + \xi \log (nv\,\Sigma_s) = \int_u^{u_0} \frac{\Sigma_a}{\Sigma_s} du \tag{12-3.9}$$

from which

$$nv = \frac{Q}{\xi\Sigma_s} \exp \left(-\frac{1}{\xi}\int_{u_0}^{u} \frac{\Sigma_a}{\Sigma_s}\, du\right) \tag{12-3.10}$$

Implicit in Eq. (12-3.10) is the necessary hypothesis that Σ_a varies slowly with energy, or, better, $\Delta\Sigma_a/\Sigma_a \ll 1$ if $\Delta E \simeq \xi E$.

12-4 Mean Distance from a Point Source vs. Energy

In this section we shall calculate $\langle R^2(\mathrm{E})\rangle$, the mean-square distance between a monoenergetic point source and all the neutrons of energy E generated by slowing down the neutrons from that source. If the mean free path were energy-independent and the scattering one-dimensional, either left or right, we should argue as follows: In order to go from energy E_0 to energy E, we need N collisions, where

$$N = \frac{1}{\xi} \log \frac{E_0}{E} \tag{12-4.1}$$

We then have N steps of a random walk, each step of length λ. Hence

$$\langle R^2\rangle = N\lambda^2 = \frac{\lambda^2}{\xi} \log \frac{E_0}{E} \tag{12-4.2}$$

In order to prove the last relation, that is, $\langle R^2\rangle = N\lambda^2$ for random walk in one dimension, consider the end points after $N = N_1 + N_2$ steps, where N_1 is the number of steps to the right and N_2 the number of steps to the left. The displacement to the right of the origin of the walk is

$$X_N = \lambda(N_1 - N_2) = \lambda(N - 2N_2) \tag{12-4.3}$$

Since the probability of a step to the right is equal to that of a step to the left, or $\langle N_1\rangle = \langle N_2\rangle = \frac{1}{2}N$, we have $\langle X_N\rangle = 0$. For N large, the end points of any samples will have a gaussian density distribution around $\langle X_N\rangle = 0$, with a square of the standard deviation

$$\sigma^2 = \langle (X_N - \langle X_N\rangle)^2\rangle = N\lambda^2 \tag{12-4.4}$$

as can be seen by noting that in Eq. (12-4.3) X_N gives rise to a standard deviation

$$\sigma^2(X_N) = \lambda^2\sigma^2(2N_2) \tag{12-4.5}$$

and that

$$\sigma^2(2N_2) = \langle 2N_2\rangle = N \tag{12-4.6}$$

In three dimensions the displacement in the X direction is

$$X = \lambda \sum_{1}^{N}{}_{i} \cos \alpha_i \qquad (12\text{-}4.7)$$

and

$$\langle (X - \langle X \rangle)^2 \rangle = \lambda^2 \sum_{1}^{N}{}_{ik} \cos \alpha_i \cos \alpha_k = \lambda^2 \frac{N}{3} \qquad (12\text{-}4.8)$$

where α_i is the angle between the X axis and the direction of the ith step. The last step of Eq. (12-4.8) depends on the fact that $\Sigma_{i \neq k} \cos \alpha_i \cos \alpha_k$ averages to 0 and that the average value of $\cos^2 \alpha_i$ (on a sphere) is $\frac{1}{3}$. The same reasoning also applies to the Y and Z components of the displacement; and, since they are independent and lie in orthogonal directions, we have

$$\langle R^2 \rangle = \langle (X - \langle X \rangle) \rangle^2 + \langle (Y - \langle Y \rangle) \rangle^2 + \langle (Z - \langle Z \rangle) \rangle^2 = \langle \lambda^2 \rangle N \qquad (12\text{-}4.9)$$

In Eq. (12-4.9) we have replaced λ^2 by $\langle \lambda^2 \rangle$ in order to take into account the variability of the free path between collisions.

We now compute $\langle \lambda^2 \rangle$ from λ. The probability of a free path of length between x and $x + dx$ is the probability of no collision between the origin and x, which is $e^{-x/\lambda}$, times the probability of a collision in dx, dx/λ. The average of the square of the mean free path is, therefore,

$$\int_0^\infty x^2 e^{-x/\lambda} \frac{dx}{\lambda} \Big/ \int_0^\infty e^{-x/\lambda} \frac{dx}{\lambda} = 2\lambda^2 = \langle \lambda^2 \rangle \qquad (12\text{-}4.10)$$

We thus have from Eqs. (12-4.9) and (12-4.10)

$$\langle R^2 \rangle = \frac{2\lambda^2}{\xi} \log \frac{E_0}{E} \qquad (12\text{-}4.11)$$

This equation must be corrected to take into account the persistence of velocity (i.e., the fact that in the laboratory frame neutrons tend to continue to travel in their original direction after a collision). The persistence of velocity is inferred by averaging $\cos \theta_L$ as given by Eqs. (12-2.1) and (12-2.3). We have

$$\langle \cos \theta_L \rangle = \frac{1}{2} \int_{-1}^{+1} d(\cos \theta) \frac{A \cos \theta + 1}{(A^2 + 2A \cos \theta + 1)^{1/2}} = \frac{2}{3A} \qquad (12\text{-}4.12)$$

and not 0, as would be the case if there were no persistence of velocity. The effect increases $\langle R^2 \rangle$. Moreover, the mean free path is a function of energy, and Eq. (12-4.11) therefore is modified to

$$\langle R^2 \rangle = \frac{2}{[1 - (2/3A)]\xi} \int_E^{E_0} \lambda^2(E) \frac{dE}{E} \qquad (12\text{-}4.13)$$

Even Eq. (12-4.13) is only approximate, but it is useful in many cases and is simple to interpret.

An interesting application of Eq. (12-4.13) is the experimental determination of $\langle R^2 \rangle$ as a function of energy. A detector containing a thin indium foil sandwiched between two cadmium foils is very sensitive to neutrons of 1.44 eV energy, because indium has a sharp resonance at this energy and cadmium absorbs all neutrons of lower energy. When the detector is immersed in a tank of water at a distance R from a neutron source, it acquires a radioactivity by the (n, γ) reaction, proportional to the density of the 1.44-eV neutrons, and one obtains the curve of Fig. 12-11, from which one computes $\langle R^2 \rangle$ by graphical integration. Using a substance I with a different resonance energy one obtains a different curve from that in Fig. 12-11. If λ does not vary with energy, as is the case for water and energies between 1 and 100 eV, we can write, from Eq. (12-4.13),

$$\langle R^2{}_{In} \rangle - \langle R^2{}_I \rangle = 6\lambda^2 \log \frac{E_{\text{res}}(In)}{E_{\text{res}}(I)} \tag{12-4.14}$$

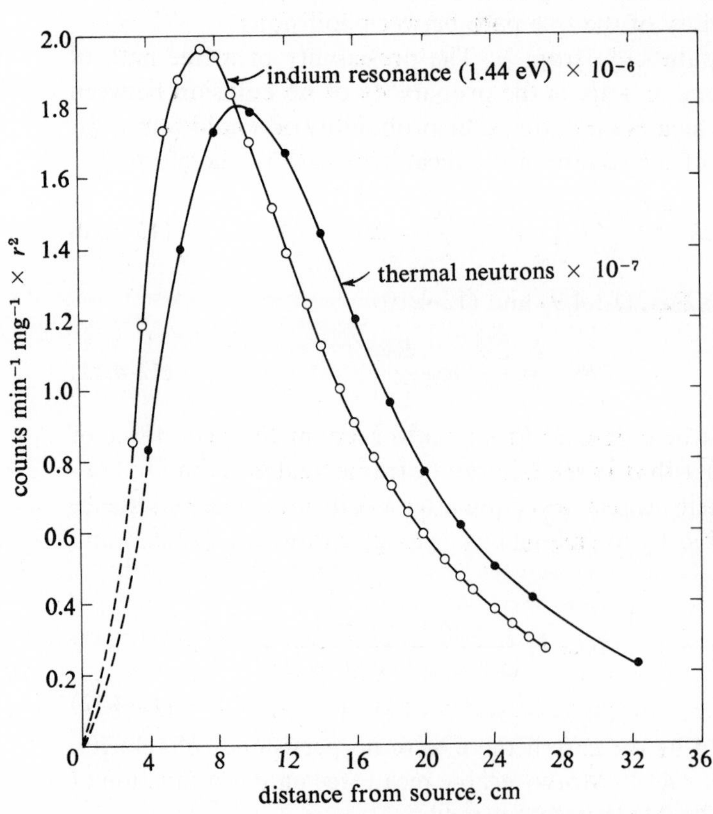

Figure 12-11 Distribution of slow neutrons from a Ra–α–Be source in water. The ordinate is the activity $\times\ r^2$ of a thin indium foil. The curve labeled "indium resonance" represents the activity of a cadmium-covered foil; the curve labeled "thermal neutrons" represents the activity of a bare foil minus 1.07 times the activity of cadmium covered foil. The source intensity was 13.2×10^6 neutrons per second. The ordinate scale can be converted to a scale of thermal neutron flux $(nv) \times r^2$ by multiplying by 1.6×10^6. [From (Se 59).]

Such experiments were among the earliest performed by Fermi (1936) in order to determine resonance energies.

12-5 Diffusion Theory—Introduction

We shall now treat the slowing down and diffusion of neutrons in an infinite medium (moderator). The process involves two steps. First the neutrons change their average energy and diffuse, until they reach thermal energy. The density of the neutrons is thus a function of the coordinates and the energy. In a second phase the thermal neutrons diffuse without changing their average energy; the density is a function of the coordinates only. We shall consider steady-state problems, and the sources or sinks of neutrons will appear as boundary conditions. The elementary theory for the first phase is most applicable when $\xi \ll 1$, that is, when many collisions are needed to slow down the neutrons, and when the mean free path does not vary too much with energy. For these reasons the theory is a much better approximation for a graphite moderator than for a water moderator. In a water moderator 17 collisions only will slow a 1-MeV neutron to thermal energies, and the mean free path changes from about 4 cm to 0.4 cm. Note that this last value of the mean free path does not correspond to collisions with free protons, but is affected by the chemical bond of the hydrogen in the molecule.

12-6 The Age Equation

We shall now derive the neutron diffusion equation for energies above thermal. This procedure is known as the *Fermi age method.*

Let $n(\mathbf{r},u)$ be the number of neutrons per unit volume per unit u. This is the same as the previous $n(u)$ except for the addition of "per unit volume." The dimensions of $n(\mathbf{r},u)$ are $[L^{-3}]$. Let $q(\mathbf{r},u)$ be the current density along the u axis. This is the previous $q(u)$ per unit volume. It is called the "slowing-down density" and is related to $n(\mathbf{r},u)$ by

$$q(\mathbf{r},u) = n(\mathbf{r},u)\frac{v}{\lambda}\xi \tag{12-6.1}$$

Its dimensions are $[L^{-3}T^{-1}]$.

Consider now a volume element of the medium and the neutrons with lethargy between u and $u + du$ contained in it. This number can vary for two reasons: (1) Neutrons of this lethargy diffuse into the volume element considered; changes due to this cause are indicated by ∂'. (2) Neutrons of lower lethargy reach the lethargy under consideration by collisions; changes due to this cause are indicated by ∂''.

For the first mechanism the fundamental diffusion relation

$$\mathbf{j} = -D \operatorname{grad} n \tag{12-6.2}$$

(where $\mathbf{j}$ is the current density of neutrons and D the diffusion coefficient) gives, by a well-known argument,[1]

[1] See, for example, Sir James Jeans, *Introduction to the Kinetic Theory of Gases*, Cambridge University Press, New York, 1940, or P. M. Morse, *Thermal Physics*, rev. ed., Benjamin, New York, 1964.

$$\frac{\partial' n(\mathbf{r},u)}{\partial t} = D\nabla^2 n(\mathbf{r},u) \tag{12-6.3}$$

The diffusion coefficient D is defined by Eq. (12-6.2) and is related to λ and v, as kinetic theory shows, by

$$D = \frac{\lambda v}{3[1 - (2/3A)]} \tag{12-6.4}$$

the quantity in brackets in the denominator originating from the persistence of velocity.

The second mechanism mentioned above gives another reason for a time change of n. Actually $q(u)$ neutrons enter the lethargy interval in question, but $q(u + du) = q(u) + (\partial q/\partial u)\, du$ leave it per unit time and per unit volume. Hence,

$$-\frac{\partial'' n}{\partial t} = \frac{\partial q}{\partial u} \tag{12-6.5}$$

In the stationary state $\partial' n/\partial t + \partial'' n/\partial t = 0$ and therefore

$$-\frac{\partial q}{\partial u} + D\nabla^2 n = 0 \tag{12-6.6}$$

It is now advantageous to introduce a new variable, called "Fermi age," defined by the relation

$$\tau \equiv \int_{u_0}^{u} \frac{\lambda^2(u)}{3\xi[1 - (2/3A)]}\, du = \int_{t_0}^{t} D\, dt \tag{12-6.7}$$

the last equality deriving from Eq. (12-6.4) and $du = \xi(v/\lambda)\, dt$. For λ constant, Eq. (12-4.13) shows that

$$\tau = \frac{\lambda^2}{3\xi[1 - (2/3A)]}(u - u_0) = \tfrac{1}{6}\langle R^2 \rangle \tag{12-6.8}$$

where $\langle R^2 \rangle$ is the mean-square distance between the neutron and its source in passing from lethargy u_0 to lethargy u. From this relation it is clear that the dimensions of τ are $[L^2]$. Its physical significance is also evident—one-sixth the mean-square distance from the source. Introducing the new variable τ, we can write

$$\frac{\partial q}{\partial u} = \frac{\partial q}{\partial \tau}\frac{\partial \tau}{\partial u} = \frac{\partial q}{\partial \tau}\frac{\lambda^2}{3\xi[1 - (2/3A)]} \tag{12-6.9}$$

and Eq. (12-6.6) becomes

$$\frac{\lambda v}{3[1 - (2/3A)]}\nabla^2 n - \frac{\lambda^2}{3\xi[1 - (2/3A)]}\frac{\partial q}{\partial \tau} = 0 \tag{12-6.10}$$

which by remembering Eq. (12-6.1) yields immediately the age equation,

$$\nabla^2 q = \frac{\partial q}{\partial \tau} \tag{12-6.11}$$

Mathematically this is the same as Fourier's heat-conduction equation,

$$\frac{k}{\rho c} \nabla^2 T = \frac{\partial T}{\partial t} \tag{12-6.12}$$

All the mathematical techniques developed for this equation are applicable to the age equation.

In particular a point source at the origin of the coordinates, emitting Q neutrons per second of energy E_0 corresponding to $\tau = 0$ in an infinite medium, gives as a solution to Eq. (12-6.11),

$$q(r,\tau) = \frac{Q}{(4\pi\tau)^{3/2}} e^{-r^2/4\tau} \tag{12-6.13}$$

Equation (12-6.11) being linear, a sum of solutions is still a solution, and hence it is possible to construct a general solution of Eq. (12-6.11) by superposition of solutions of the type of Eq. (12-6.13). From the singular solution [Eq. (12-6.13)] we obtain the mean-square distance reached by neutrons of age τ,

$$\langle R^2 \rangle = \frac{\int_0^\infty r^2 e^{-r^2/4\tau} 4\pi r^2 \, dr}{\int_0^\infty e^{-r^2/4\tau} 4\pi r^2 \, dr} = 6\tau \tag{12-6.14}$$

which agrees with the result of Eq. (12-4.13).

Equation (12-6.11) can be solved by the classical methods of mathematical physics. As an example of practical importance we shall consider briefly a monoenergetic source at the center of the base of a square prism of base side b and indefinite length z. The variables in the age equation are first separated by putting

$$q = Q(\mathbf{r})\, T(\tau) \tag{12-6.15}$$

and obtaining

$$\frac{\nabla^2 Q}{Q} = \frac{1}{T} \frac{dT}{d\tau} = -k^2 \tag{12-6.16}$$

The boundary conditions for q are that it is 0 on the lateral faces of the prism, that it has a singularity at $x = y = b/2$, $z = 0$, and that it vanishes for $z \to \infty$. The conditions on the faces can be fulfilled only for a discrete set of numbers k^2, the eigenvalues of the problem. We have the general solution as a series of functions

$$q = \sum a_n Q_n(\mathbf{r}) T_n(\tau) \tag{12-6.17}$$

the constant coefficients a_n to be determined by the initial conditions, i.e., by putting

$$\sum a_n Q_n(\mathbf{r}) T_n(0) = F(\mathbf{r}) \tag{12-6.18}$$

where $F(\mathbf{r})$ is the q of the source of neutrons at age 0. The development of this calculation is to be found in standard texts on heat conduction, the final result being

Table 12-4 Fermi Age of Neutrons of 1.4 eV and Thermal in Various Moderators

	$\tau(1.4\text{ eV})$	τ_{th}
H_2O	31 cm²	33 cm²
D_2O	109	120
Beryllium	80	98
Graphite	311	350

$$q(\mathbf{r},\tau) = \frac{2Q}{b^2(\pi\tau)^{1/2}} e^{-z^2/4\tau} \sum_{m,n \text{ odd}} -(-1)^{(m+n)/2} \times \sin\frac{m\pi x}{b} \sin\frac{n\pi y}{b} \exp\left[-\frac{\pi^2}{b^2}(m^2+n^2)\tau\right] \tag{12-6.19}$$

where m, n are odd integral numbers and Q is the source strength. For a sufficiently large τ only the first harmonic corresponding to $m = n = 1$ is important.

The boundary condition assumed, $n(\mathbf{r},\tau) = 0$ at the boundary of the moderator, seems reasonable, because free space should act as a perfect sink inasmuch as no neutron will ever be reflected by it. A more refined consideration, however, shows that the neutron density near the surface varies linearly with depth and that for a medium filling the half-space $x > 0$ it would vanish at $x = -\frac{2}{3}\lambda$ (Fig. 12-12) or, better, at $x = -0.71\lambda$. The correct boundary condition, therefore, is that n vanishes at a distance of 0.71λ outside the moderator.

The particular example treated here was very important in the so-called sigma experiments that were used in testing materials for the first nuclear reactor. By using an indium sandwich detector to measure $q(0,0,z,u_{\text{res}})$ one obtained $\tau(u_0,u_{\text{res}})$ for the source and medium under

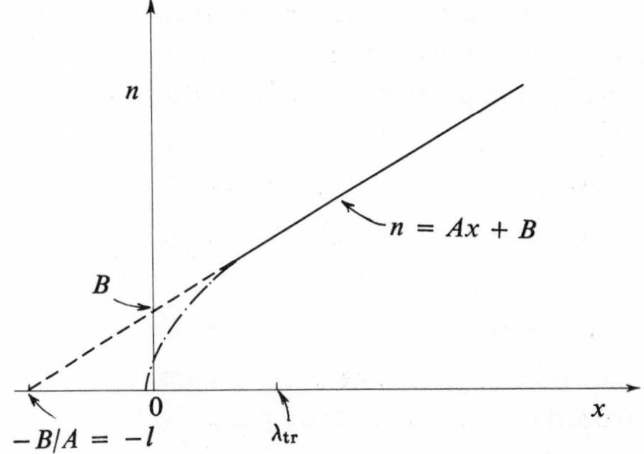

Figure 12-12 Schematic representation of the neutron density in the vicinity of the medium-air boundary ($x = 0$). The solid line is the solution of the elementary diffusion equation; the broken line is its extrapolation. The dash-dotted line represents the actual neutron density in the region $x \leqslant \lambda_{\text{tr}}$.

investigation. If the source is not monoenergetic, it may be considered as the sum of several monoenergetic sources (multigroup methods).

In the important case of fission neutrons the values of τ(1.4 eV) and of τ(thermal) for several moderators are given in Table 12-4. These numbers are obtained by averaging over the fission neutron energy spectrum.

The diffusion theory gives a neutron density depending on r as $e^{-r^2/4\tau}$ for large r. However, neutrons arrive occasionally at large distances from the source without a collision, the probability of this event being $e^{-r/\lambda}$. It is clear that when $e^{-r/\lambda} \gg e^{-r^2/4\tau}$ there will be more neutrons than calculated by diffusion theory.

In these developments we have neglected absorption. In fact, absorption may be important, especially for moderators mixed with fissionable material showing strong resonances, as we shall see later.

12-7 Diffusion of Thermal Neutrons

Let $n(\mathbf{r})$ be the density of thermal neutrons, let

$$D = \frac{\lambda v}{3} \tag{12-7.1}$$

be their diffusion coefficient, and let Λ be their absorption mean free path, $1/\Sigma_a$. The mean life of a thermal neutron, T, is Λ/v. If Σ_a is proportional to $1/v$, as is often the case, T is independent of velocity. Thermal neutrons are generated in a medium when higher-energy neutrons are thermalized by a collision. Call $q_{\text{th}}(\mathbf{r})$ the number of neutrons per cm³ becoming thermal per unit time. The quantity $q_{\text{th}}(\mathbf{r})$ is the slowing-down density considered previously for τ = thermal age.

We shall now establish a steady-state condition. We have, per unit volume, an increase in neutron density caused by

Diffusion: $D\nabla^2 n$

Slowing down: q_τ

Absorption: $-\,n/T$

Summing these up, we have for the stationary state

$$\frac{\partial n}{\partial t} = 0 = D\nabla^2 n + q_\tau - \frac{n}{T} \tag{12-7.2}$$

or, using the expression of D [Eq. (12-7.1)],

$$\nabla^2 n - \frac{3}{\lambda\Lambda} n + \frac{3q_\tau}{\lambda v} = 0 \tag{12-7.3}$$

The quantity

$$L = \left(\frac{\lambda\Lambda}{3}\right)^{1/2} \tag{12-7.4}$$

is called the "diffusion length." Equation (12-7.3) must be solved with the boundary condition $n = 0$ on the surface of the moderator. The inhomogeneous term q_τ must be obtained by previously solving Eq. (12-6.11) with its sources and boundary conditions.

The mathematical formulation of the slowing-down and diffusion problems is thus complete in the approximation when diffusion theory is valid. Simultaneous solution of Eqs. (12-6.11) and (12-7.2) with the proper boundary conditions would give the complete answers. As an example of the solution of Eq. (12-7.2) we shall first give, as in the case of Eq. (12-6.11), the solution for a point source of thermal neutrons, located in the origin and emitting Q neutrons per second,

$$n(r) = \frac{Q}{4\pi Dr} e^{-r/L} \tag{12-7.5}$$

Note that this solution decreases less rapidly as a function of r than does the corresponding solution of Eq. (12-6.11).

As a second example we shall treat again the square column of side b in the x and y directions and of infinite height. With the boundary conditions $n = 0$ for $x = 0$ and $x = b$, $y = 0$ and $y = b$, the solution is

$$n(x,y,z) = \sum_{1=j,k}^{\infty} n_{jk}(z) \sin\frac{\pi jx}{b} \sin\frac{\pi ky}{b} \tag{12-7.6}$$

and

$$n_{jk}(z) = c \exp\left[-\left(\frac{1}{L^2} + \pi^2 \frac{j^2 + k^2}{b^2}\right)^{1/2} z\right] \tag{12-7.7}$$

with j, k integral numbers. The mode of slowest decay in the z direction is the one with $j = k = 1$, for which

$$n(x,y,z) = c \sin\frac{\pi x}{b} \sin\frac{\pi y}{b} \exp\left[-\left(\frac{1}{L^2} + \frac{2\pi^2}{b^2}\right)^{1/2} z\right] \tag{12-7.8}$$

Here the thermal neutron source is on the plane $z = 0$. The arrangement we are considering here, called the thermal column, can be realized in practice by putting a graphite column on a reactor. Essentially the same purpose is served by the sigma pile, in which a fast neutron source is located at the base of a graphite prism. Provided that one is far enough from the source ($z^2 \gg 4\tau_{\text{th}}$), the slow neutron density decays on the axis as

$$\exp\left[-\left(\frac{1}{L^2} + \frac{2\pi^2}{b^2}\right)^{1/2} z\right] \tag{12-7.9}$$

and thus measurement of the slow neutron density gives L, the diffusion length. Naturally the measurements are sensitive to L^2 only if

$$\frac{2\pi}{b^2} \ll \frac{1}{L^2} \qquad \text{or} \qquad L \ll \frac{b}{(2\pi)^{1/2}} \tag{12-7.10}$$

Such measurements are suitable for determining the absorption coefficients of the weakly absorbing materials used in nuclear reactors and

Table 12-5 Density, Diffusion Length, and Mean Free Path for Scattering and Absorption of Slow Neutrons in Important Materials

	ρ, g cm^{-3}	$L=(\lambda\Lambda/3)^{1/2}$, cm	λ, cm	Λ, cm
H_2O	1.00	2.70	0.43	51.8
D_2O	1.10	102	2.4	1.34×10^4
Be	1.84	22.2	2.1	705
Graphite	1.62	47.2	2.7	2480

were of great importance in the development of the first pile: Fermi called them exponential experiments.

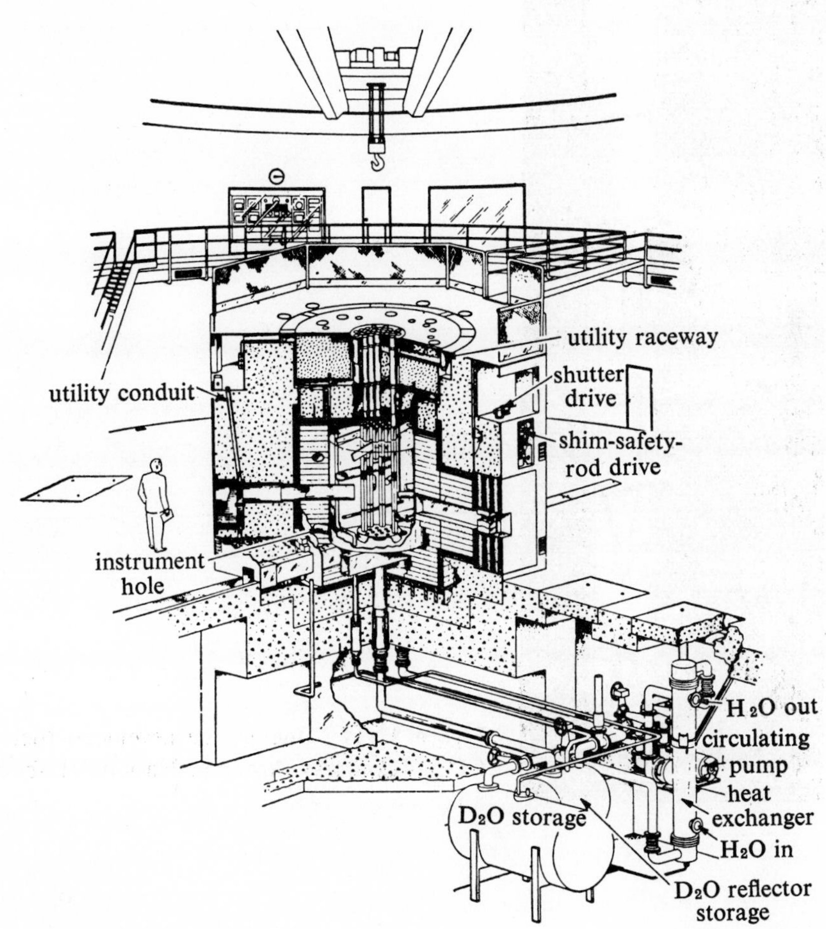

Figure 12-13 Pictorial assembly of Argonne National Laboratory research reactor (CP-5).

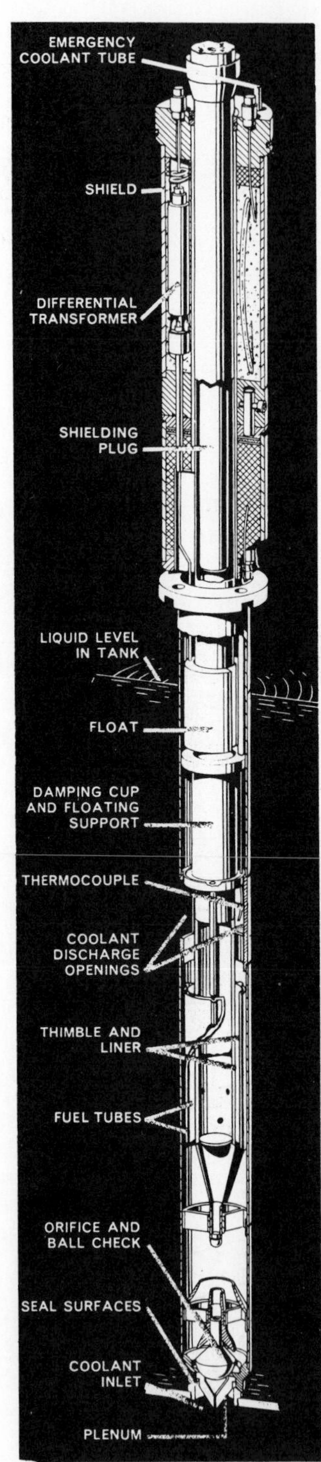

Figure 12-14 One of the seventeen fuel elements of CP-5. [Courtesy Argonne National Laboratory.]

Table 12-5 gives data for important materials obtained by the combination of exponential experiments and measurements of total cross sections.

12-8 Chain-Reacting Pile

In Secs. 12-5 to 12-7 we have studied the moderation and diffusion of neutrons in an inert medium. If we add to this medium a fissionable material, for example, U^{235}, neutrons are occasionally captured by it, fission results, and more neutrons are generated. The process may become divergent, giving rise to a chain reaction. A reactor is an apparatus in which fissionable material is accumulated (or piled, hence the name "pile") in such a way that a chain reaction develops (Figs. 12-13 and 12-14).

By a "generation" of neutrons we mean the processes from the production of a neutron to its final absorption. By "generation time" τ we mean the time required for this succession of processes. Naturally individual neutrons have different life histories. In a "generation" and "generation time" we consider suitable averages over all neutrons. We call k, the "multiplication constant," the number of neutrons produced by a single neutron in a generation in an infinite medium, or the ratio between the number of neutrons produced and the number of neutrons absorbed per unit time in an infinite medium. For a chain reaction to occur it is necessary that $k > 1$. The neutron density in the medium then grows according to the equation

$$\frac{dn}{dt} = \frac{n(k-1)}{\tau} \tag{12-8.1}$$

whose solution is

$$n(t) = n(0)\, e^{(k-1)t/\tau} \tag{12-8.2}$$

In a reactor of finite size, some neutrons are lost by escape through the walls. To attain criticality, we can compensate for the losses by using a medium with a k sufficiently larger than 1. It is useful to define a number k_{eff} = average number of neutrons produced in reactor per unit time $\div$ (average number of neutrons absorbed in reactor + average number of neutrons escaping from reactor per unit time). Clearly $k > k_{\text{eff}}$. The number k is a function of the medium only, and k_{eff} is a function of k and of the geometry of the reactor. The condition $k_{\text{eff}} > 1$ is the criticality condition for a finite reactor.

We shall first study k for a homogeneous mixture of uranium, possibly enriched in U^{235}, and a moderator (graphite). We define the following:

$\sigma_r(U)$ = absorption cross section for thermal neutrons by all processes, excluding fission; mostly (n,γ) reaction

$$\sigma_f = \text{fission cross section for thermal neutrons}$$
$$\sigma_f + \sigma_r = \sigma_a = \text{total absorption cross section}$$
$$N_C = \text{number of atoms of species } C \text{ per unit volume}$$
$$\sigma_r/\sigma_f = \alpha = (\sigma_a - \sigma_f)/\sigma_f$$

ν = average number of neutrons produced per fission, is a nuclear constant depending slightly on the energy of the neutrons producing fission. Unless otherwise specified, ν refers to fission produced by thermal neutrons

η = average number of neutrons emitted per thermal neutron absorbed in fissionable material (fuel)

We have by definition

$$\eta = \nu \frac{\sigma_f(U)}{\sigma_f(U) + \sigma_r(U)} \tag{12-8.3}$$

Table 12-6 gives numerical values for the quantities mentioned above.

The neutrons generated on fission are absorbed in part by the fuel, in part by the moderator. The fraction absorbed by the fuel will depend on the energy interval considered. For thermal neutrons it is called the "thermal utilization factor" and is indicated by the letter f. The quantity f is a function of the composition of the medium. Precisely, for a homogeneous medium

$$f = \frac{N_U \sigma(U)}{\sum_C N_C \sigma(C) + N_U \sigma(U)} \tag{12-8.4}$$

If we could neglect all phenomena occurring before thermalization, the result would be that one neutron has a probability f of being absorbed in the fuel and will, in such a case, generate η neutrons. Hence

$$k = \eta f \tag{12-8.5}$$

This relation would be approximately true in a reactor operating on a homogeneous mixture of U^{235} and a moderator.

Table 12-6 Values of Nuclear Constants Important for Chain Reactors[a]

(v = 2,200 m sec^{-1}, σ in 10^{-24} cm^2)

	U nat.	U^{233}	U^{235}	Pu^{239}
σ_a	7.68	588	694	1,025
σ_f	4.18	532	582	738
σ_{scat}	8.3		10	9.7
ν	2.47	2.52	2.47	2.91
η	1.34	2.28	2.07	2.09

[a] From (WW 59).

For natural or slightly enriched uranium we must consider the possibility of producing fission with fast-fission neutrons. By the "fast-fission factor" ϵ we mean the ratio of neutrons produced by fast and thermal fission to those produced by thermal fission only. In the case of lumped materials the number ϵ is appreciably different from 1. A fission neutron crossing the lump produces fission in about 1 per cent of the cases, giving typical values of ϵ between 1.02 and 1.04.

In natural uranium a neutron has an appreciable probability of being captured by U^{238} in the resonance region, before thermalization, without producing fission neutrons. We designate by p the probability that a neutron will escape resonance capture. Both ϵ and p depend on the composition and geometrical arrangement of the fuel and the moderator. The important invention of distributing the fuel on a lattice embedded in the moderator (lumping) has four effects: (1) It increases ϵ, which is advantageous. (2) U^{238} has strong resonance absorption, and it is therefore desirable to accomplish the moderation in a uranium-free region; the lumping of uranium acts in this advantageous direction. (3) Resonance capture in uranium occurs essentially at the surface of a lump. Neutrons in the uranium resonance-energy region have a very large σ_r and do not penetrate the uranium lumps; hence the uranium inside a lump does not tend to lower p. Consequently we want large lumps in which the surface-layer volume is small compared with the total volume. (4) On the other hand, large-volume lumps tend to lower f, because the neutron density in or near the lumps tends to be smaller than in the moderator, favoring neutron absorption in the moderator, which is detrimental. It is clear that the requirements for optimum values of f and p conflict with each other and must be resolved by compromise. Of the four effects mentioned above, the most important is (3).

When we take into account fast neutron fission and resonance capture, k becomes

$$k = \eta f \epsilon p \tag{12-8.6}$$

a famous formula called the "four-factors formula."

For the calculation of p and ϵ we must refer to the special literature. Only for a diluted homogeneous mixture can p be approximated by

$$p(E) = \exp\left[-\frac{N(U)}{\xi}\int_E^{E\text{ source}} \lambda(E)\sigma_U(E)\frac{dE}{E}\right] \tag{12-8.7}$$

where λ is the mean free path in the medium and $\sigma_U(E)$ is the capture cross section of the fissionable material. For very dilute natural uranium λ may be considered energy-independent and determined entirely by the moderator. It is thus convenient to evaluate p by using the "resonance integral"

$$I = \int_{0.3\text{ eV}}^{E_0} \sigma_U \frac{dE}{E} = 240 \times 10^{-24}\text{ cm}^2 \tag{12-8.8}$$

Then p is given by

$$p(0.3\text{ eV}) = \exp\left(-\frac{N\lambda}{\xi} I\right) \tag{12-8.9}$$

The effect of lumping drastically reduces the resonance capture. For instance, the resonance integral for lumps of natural uranium is given empirically by

$$I = \int_{\text{th}}^{E_0} \sigma_{\text{eff}} \frac{dE}{E} = 9.25 + 24.7 \frac{S}{M} (10^{-24}\ \text{cm}^2) \qquad \textbf{(12-8.10)}$$

where S is the surface of the lump in square centimeters and M its mass in grams. The term σ_{eff} indicates the cross section for the uranium atom, which gives a resonance integral, and this, when inserted in Eq. (12-8.9), gives the correct p.

We are now ready to consider a reactor of finite size, for which the effective multiplication factor k_{eff} may be written

$$k_{\text{eff}} = kP \qquad \textbf{(12-8.11)}$$

where P is the probability that a neutron will not leak out of the reactor.

Table 12-7 Neutron Economy for Homogeneous System of U^{235} and Diluent

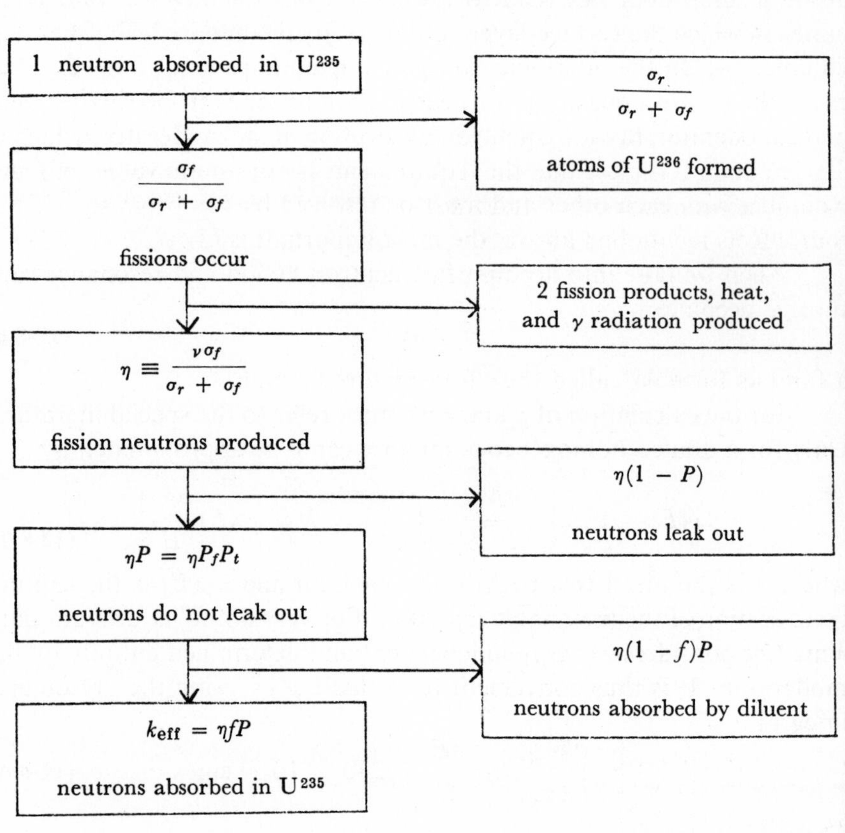

From (WW 59).

Tables 12-7 and 12-8 show diagrammatically the neutron economy in a finite reactor.

To determine the minimum critical dimensions for a reactor material of a given $k > 1$, and on the assumption (for the sake of simplicity) that the neutrons are thermal throughout their life, we return to Eq. (12-7.2) and consider the neutron balance, including multiplication. Equation (12-7.2) is then replaced by

$$D\,\nabla^2 n + \frac{(k-1)n}{T} + q_{\text{th}} = \frac{\partial n}{\partial t} \tag{12-8.12}$$

Table 12-8 Neutron Economy in Natural Uranium Chain Reactor

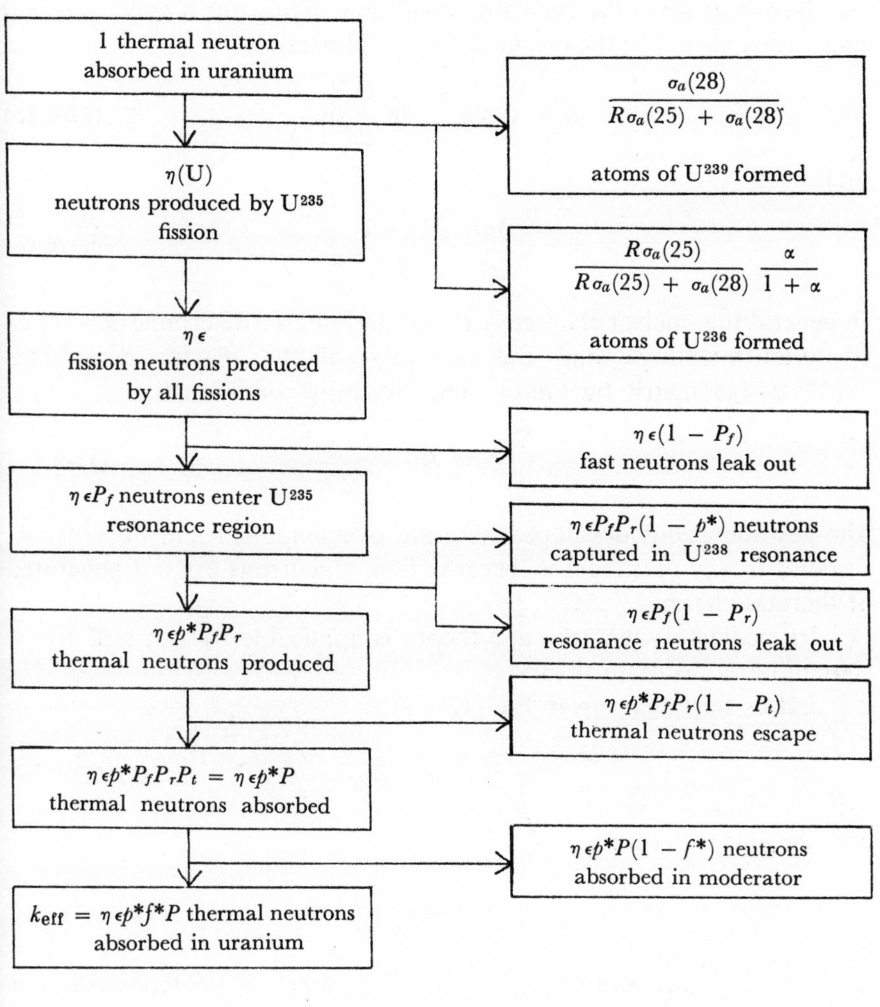

From (WW 59).

R is the atomic fraction of U^{235} in uranium. For natural uranium $R = 0.007205$

p^*, f^* take into account the influence on the resonance escape probability and on the thermal utilization factor of the geometry of the reactor. In practice, $p^* \gtrsim p, f^* \gtrsim f$

and the criticality condition is characterized by a $\partial n/\partial t = 0$, even in the absence of sources q, that is, by

$$D\nabla^2 n + \frac{k-1}{T} n = 0 \tag{12-8.13}$$

Introducing for D its value from Eq. (12-7.1) and remembering Eq. (12-7.4), we have

$$\nabla^2 n + \frac{k-1}{L^2} n = 0 \tag{12-8.14}$$

This equation is to be solved with the boundary condition $n = 0$ on the surface of the reactor.

Equation (12-8.14) gives rise to an eigenvalue problem, and the lowest eigenvalue gives the criticality condition. Thus, for a cube of side a and with a corner in the origin of the coordinates,

$$n = C \sin\frac{\pi x}{a} \sin\frac{\pi y}{a} \sin\frac{\pi z}{a} \tag{12-8.15}$$

and

$$\frac{3\pi^2}{a^2} = \frac{k-1}{L^2} \tag{12-8.16}$$

In general the nuclear characteristics of the material determine $(k - 1)/L^2$ (material buckling), and the geometry of the reactor determines $-(\nabla^2 n)/n$ (geometric buckling). The criticality condition is

$$-\frac{\nabla^2 n}{n} = B^2 = \frac{k-1}{L^2} \tag{12-8.17}$$

The considerations developed here are oversimplified and do not correspond to any real reactor, because fission neutrons are not generated at thermal energy.

In media to which the age theory is applicable we can still give a simple, fairly accurate theory.

Let us start again from Eq. (12-7.3):

$$\frac{\lambda v}{3} \nabla^2 n - \frac{v}{\Lambda} n + q_{\text{th}} = \frac{\partial n}{\partial t} \tag{12-7.3}$$

and the age equation

$$\nabla^2 q = \frac{\partial q}{\partial \tau} \tag{12-6.11}$$

We recall the meaning of q_{th} as the number of neutrons per unit time per unit volume becoming thermal at the position x, y, z. Appropriately, q is called the "density of nascent thermal neutrons." Assume, as before, a cubical pile of side a. The boundary conditions require that the functions n,q vanish on the surface of the pile. Moreover, we assume that the neutrons are generated at an energy E (average energy of fission neutrons). We develop n, q in Fourier series and limit ourselves to the first harmonic writing.

$$n = n' \sin \frac{\pi}{a} x \sin \frac{\pi}{a} y \sin \frac{\pi}{a} z \qquad \textbf{(12-8.18)}$$

$$q(x,y,z,\tau) = Q\Theta(\tau) \sin \frac{\pi}{a} x \sin \frac{\pi}{a} y \sin \frac{\pi}{a} z \qquad \textbf{(12-8.19)}$$

Note that the space dependence of q is the same as that of n, irrespective of age. By Q we mean a constant to be determined, such that for $\tau = 0$, q becomes the q corresponding to the fission neutrons generated in the pile.

From Eqs. (12-6.11) and (12-8.19) we have separating variables:

$$\frac{-3\pi^2}{a^2}\Theta = \frac{d\Theta}{d\tau} \qquad \textbf{(12-8.20)}$$

from which

$$\Theta(\tau) = \Theta(0)e^{-B^2\tau} \qquad \textbf{(12-8.21)}$$

with $-B^2 = -3\pi^2/a^2$ and $\Theta(0) = 1$, because for $\tau = 0$ the function q is $Q \sin(\pi/a)x \sin(\pi/a)y \sin(\pi/a)z$.

We obtain now from Eq. (12-7.3) by substitution

$$n\left(-\frac{\lambda v}{3}\frac{3\pi^2}{a^2} - \frac{v}{\Lambda} + \frac{Q}{n}e^{-B^2\tau_{\text{th}}}\right) = \frac{\partial n}{\partial t} \qquad \textbf{(12-8.22)}$$

However, the ratio of Q/n can be determined from the reproduction factor of the pile. In fact, if n is the density of slow neutrons, then nv/Λ neutrons per second and cubic centimeter are absorbed. Of these, the fraction f is absorbed in the fuel and each generates η fission neutrons. The fission neutrons are multiplied by ϵ in escaping from the lumps, but only the fraction p escapes resonance absorption.

In conclusion, remembering the four-factors formula [Eq. (12-8.6)], we find

$$\frac{knv}{\Lambda} = Q \qquad \textbf{(12-8.23)}$$

Substituting in Eq. (12-8.22) we have a criticality condition

$$-\frac{\lambda v}{3}\frac{3\pi^2}{a^2} - \frac{v}{\Lambda} + \frac{kv}{\Lambda}e^{-B^2\tau_{\text{th}}} = 0 \qquad \textbf{(12-8.24)}$$

or

$$-L^2B^2 - 1 + k\,e^{-B^2\tau_{\text{th}}} = 0 \qquad \textbf{(12-8.25)}$$

where

$$L^2 = \frac{\lambda\Lambda}{3} \qquad B^2 = \frac{3\pi^2}{a^2} = \text{geometrical buckling} \qquad \textbf{(12-8.26)}$$

Solving for k we find

$$k = (1 + L^2B^2)\, e^{B^2\tau_{\text{th}}} \tag{12-8.27}$$

which, as expected, for $\tau = 0$ gives the same result as Eq. (12-8.17). If, as usual, the exponential is near 1, we can write Eq. (12-8.27) as

$$k = 1 + \frac{3\pi^2}{a^2}(L^2 + \tau_{\text{th}}) \tag{12-8.28}$$

and, remembering Eq. (12-8.12),

$$-\frac{\nabla^2 n}{n} = \frac{k - 1}{\tau_{\text{th}} + L^2} \tag{12-8.29}$$

The similarity between Eqs. (12-8.29) and (12-8.17) is obvious: The diffusion length L has been replaced by the "migration length,"

$$(L^2 + \tau_{\text{th}})^{1/2} = M \tag{12-8.30}$$

For a finite pile one often uses the "effective multiplication constant" k_{eff} defined by

$$k_{\text{eff}} = \frac{ke^{-B^2\tau_{\text{th}}}}{1 + B^2L^2} \tag{12-8.31}$$

The criticality condition expressed through k_{eff} is then $k_{\text{eff}} > 1$. Table 12-9 gives typical figures for a low-enrichment thermal reactor and affords a quantitative idea of the relative importance of the effects considered thus far.

To show the effect of distributing fissionable material in lumps, we note that for a homogeneous natural uranium–graphite mixture the maximum obtainable k is 0.78 for a ratio of 400 carbon atoms to 1 atom of uranium. It is therefore impossible to render such a mixture critical. On the other hand, for a lattice of uranium bars 2.5 cm in diameter, placed at a distance of 11 cm from axis to axis, in a graphite matrix,

$$\epsilon = 1.028 \quad p = 0.905 \quad f = 0.888 \quad \eta = 1.308 \quad k = 1.0625$$
$$\tau_{\text{th}} = 300 \text{ cm}^2 \quad L^2 = 350 \text{ cm}^2$$

and a "bare" cube measuring 5.55 m on a side would be critical.

Table 12-9 Neutron Balance—Large, Low-Enrichment Thermal Reactors

Virgin fast neutrons from thermal fissions	+ 100.0
Fast neutrons lost by fast absorption	− 0 to 3
Fast neutrons gained by fast fission	+ 0 to 8
Fast neutrons lost in leakage	− 2 to 10
Resonance capture in fertile material	− 15 to 25
Thermal neutrons lost in leakage	− 1 to 5
Thermal neutrons captured in structural materials, moderator, reflector, coolant, control	− 5 to 15
Thermal neutrons absorbed by fission product	− 2 to 5
Thermal-neutron capture in fertile material	− 10 to 20
Thermal neutrons captured parasitically in fissionable material	− 6 to 8
Thermal-neutron fission captures	∸ 40

The reactors considered up to now are "bare." In practice most reactors are surrounded by a reflector. This is a layer of moderating material free of fissionable material. The reflector reduces the critical mass of the core, because neutrons that would escape from the bare core are reflected back into it by the surrounding material.

12-9 Pile Kinetics

Up to now we have considered the critical condition of a reactor without regard to the time dependence of the neutron flux. In practice a pile must be controlled; i.e., the operator must be able to vary its k_{eff}. "Control rods" usually serve this purpose. These are rods of a strongly neutron-absorbent material, such as cadmium or boron-containing steel, which can be introduced or removed from the pile structure. The introduction of the rod decreases k_{eff}, because neutrons are lost to the rod and also because the neutron distribution is altered, thereby affecting the leakage from the pile.

We must study now the behavior, with respect to time, of a pile when k is changed. For a neutron in a thermal pile most of the time is usually spent in diffusion after moderation; e.g., moderation may require a few microseconds and diffusion a few milliseconds. It is therefore clear that in 1 sec there would be hundreds of generations, and, considering Eq. (12-8.1), we recognize that control of a pile would require prohibitively fast action. The situation is greatly eased by the delayed neutrons, as we shall see shortly. At first, however, let us neglect their presence. Equation (12-8.12) gives, for the time dependence of the neutron density, and taking Eq. (12-8.30) into consideration as well,

$$D\nabla^2 n + \frac{D(k-1)}{M^2} n = \frac{\partial n}{\partial t} \tag{12-9.1}$$

which is valid if $M \ll$ pile dimensions. Note that, if k were 0, $M^2/D = \tau_0$ would represent the mean life for absorption of a neutron introduced in the pile [cf. Eq. (12-7.2)]. Separating the variables, we find from Eqs. (12-9.1) and (12-8.17) that

$$n = n(\mathbf{r})e^{t/T} \tag{12-9.2}$$

with

$$\frac{1}{T} = \frac{k - 1 - B^2M^2}{M^2/D} = \frac{k_{eff} - 1}{\tau_0} \tag{12-9.3}$$

where T is the pile "relaxation time" and B^2 is the geometric buckling for the fundamental mode. Actually a more accurate expression is obtained by using for τ_0 the expression

$$\tau_0 = \frac{L^2}{D_{th}} \tag{12-9.4}$$

In a graphite-moderated reactor τ_0 is of the order of 10^{-3} sec, and hence even $k_{\text{eff}} = 1.001$ already gives a doubling time for the reactor flux of only 1 sec (approximately), which is too short for comfortable operation.

The delayed neutrons, however, change the situation radically, and we shall now consider their effect, although our treatment is oversimplified. The number of delayed neutrons per fission in U^{235} amounts to about 0.016 neutron per fission. We shall call β the ratio of this number to ν; for U^{235} $\beta = 0.0064$. The half-life of the delayed neutrons in U^{235} range from 55.7 to 0.23 sec. Here we shall assume that they all have the same mean life τ_d.

It is clear that k may now be considered as the sum of a reproduction factor due to prompt neutrons only, k_p, and a reproduction factor due to delayed neutrons only, k_d. We thus write

$$k = k_p + k_d = k_p + \beta k \tag{12-9.5}$$

or

$$k_p = k(1 - \beta) \tag{12-9.6}$$

If the reactor is critical on the prompt neutrons only—i.e., if $k_{\text{eff}} > 1$ or $k_{p,\text{eff}} > 1/(1 - \beta)$—the kinetics is practically unaffected by the delayed neutrons. On the other hand, if the pile is subcritical on prompt neutrons only, but supercritical on prompt plus delayed neutrons, the time constant of the pile is obtainable as follows: First Eq. (12-8.12) is replaced by

$$D\nabla^2 n + \frac{k_p - 1}{\tau_0} n + \frac{C}{\tau_d} = \frac{\partial n}{\partial t} \tag{12-9.7}$$

in which $C(\mathbf{r})$ is the density of the "pregnant" nuclei, as the delayed neutron emitters are called. The quantity C is simply related to n by

$$\frac{\partial C}{\partial t} = \frac{k_d}{\tau_0} n - \frac{C}{\tau_d} \tag{12-9.8}$$

One then solves the two coupled equations [(12-9.7) and (12-9.8)] by assuming $n(\mathbf{r},t) = n_0 N(\mathbf{r}) e^{t/\tau}$ and $C(\mathbf{r},t) = C_0 N(\mathbf{r}) e^{t/\tau}$, with $N(\mathbf{r})$, a function of the coordinates only, and n_0, C_0 constants, to be eliminated. From the coupled equations one obtains the connection between the period of the pile T and the excess reactivity ρ,

$$\rho = \frac{k_{\text{eff}} - 1}{k} = \frac{\tau_0}{kT} + \sum_i \frac{\beta_i \tau_i}{T + \tau_i} \tag{12-9.9}$$

Equation (12-9.9) is called the "inhour" (inverse hour) equation. It relates the excess reactivity ρ to the parameters of the delayed neutron emitters and the period of the pile.

Substituting numerical values in Eq. (12-9.9) and defining as 1 inverse hour the amount of excess reactivity that would give rise to a period of 1 hr, we find

$$(k_{\text{eff}} - 1) \text{ for 1 inhour} = 2.6 \pm 0.2 \times 10^{-5}$$

The relation between the excess reactivity in inhours and the period of the pile in seconds, as set forth in Eq. (12-9.9), is shown in Fig. 12-15.

An interesting physical application of Eq. (12-9.9) is the measurement of small-neutron-absorption cross section. A sample of the absorber is introduced into a pile, and the control rods are moved so as to compensate for the change in T of the pile produced by the absorber. The effect of the rod's position on ρ can be calibrated with known absorbers such as boron ($\sigma_a = 755 \times 10^{-24}$ cm at 2,200 m/sec) and by using Eq. (12-9.9) to interpolate or extrapolate the experimental data.

12-10 Breeding and Converting

In a uranium pile part of the neutrons are absorbed by U^{238} and yield ultimately Pu^{239}. The pile thus "converts" some U^{235}, which is used to keep it going, into Pu^{239}. The ratio of the desired nuclei generated to fuel nuclei destroyed is called the "conversion ratio" and is indicated by the letter C; the conversion gain G, or breeding, is $C - 1 = G$.

Indicating by l the neutrons lost by leakage or absorption in all but fissionable material we have

$$C = \eta - 1 - l \qquad \textbf{(12-10.1)}$$

$$G = \eta - 2 - l \qquad \textbf{(12-10.2)}$$

At thermal energies η is only slightly greater than 2 for all known nuclei except U^{233}, and hence a thermal breeder is likely only with this substance. At higher energies conditions are more favorable, because η increases with energy, owing to the decrease of σ_a and to a lesser extent to the increase of ν. At 1 MeV η is estimated to reach 2.45 for U^{233}, 2.3 for U^{235}, and 2.7 for Pu^{239}.

12-11 Fusion Reactions

We have seen how heavy elements may liberate large amounts of

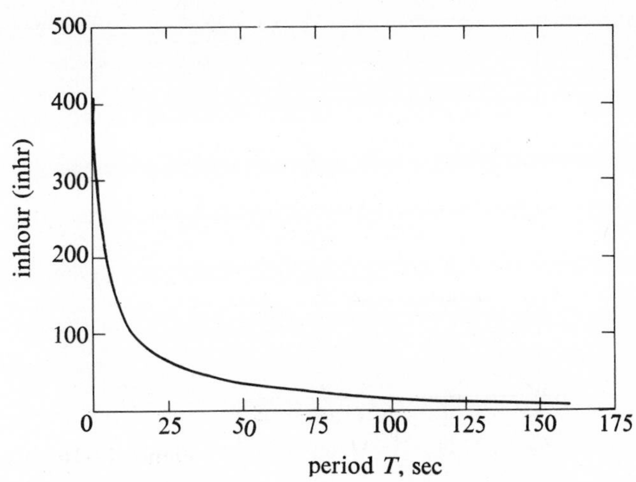

Figure 12-15 The inhour formula in graphical form. A measurement of the reactor period can be converted into an inhour of reactivity by referring to this graph.

energy on fission. Light elements can do the same on "fusion," i.e., by forming heavier nuclei through nuclear combinations of lighter ones. For example, if we could bind together two neutrons and two protons to form an alpha particle, we should set free 26 MeV.

Such fusion reactions are of colossal importance, because they are the source of solar energy. On the earth they occur in hydrogen bombs, and great effort is being devoted to produce them at a controlled rate.

We shall treat briefly some of the astrophysical reactions. Only binary reactions are of any practical importance; the collision of four particles cited above does not occur in actuality. However, the same result is achieved through a series of reactions which form a cycle, reconstituting some of the participating nuclei, which act only as catalysts.

There are two notable solar cycles. The first is

$$\begin{aligned}
&C^{12} + H^1 \rightarrow N^{13} + \gamma && 1.93\text{ MeV}\\
&N^{13} \rightarrow C^{13} + e^+ + \nu + \gamma && 1.20\text{ MeV}\\
&C^{13} + H^1 \rightarrow N^{14} + \gamma && 7.60\text{ MeV}\\
&N^{14} + H^1 \rightarrow O^{15} + \gamma && 7.39\text{ MeV}\\
&O^{15} \rightarrow N^{15} + e^+ + \nu + \gamma && 1.71\text{ MeV}\\
&N^{15} + H^1 \rightarrow C^{12} + He^4 && 4.99\text{ MeV}
\end{aligned} \tag{12-11.1}$$

This is called the "carbon cycle" (Fig. 12-16; Bethe, 1938), and its net effect is to combine four protons to form He^4, gamma rays, and neutrinos (the two excess positrons will ultimately annihilate) and to liberate about 26 MeV of thermal energy, the neutrinos escaping. Note that the carbon is not destroyed in the process but acts only as a catalyst. The other cycle is

$$\begin{aligned}
&H^1 + H^1 \rightarrow H^2 + e^+ + \nu && 0.41\text{ MeV}\\
&H^2 + H^1 \rightarrow He^3 + \gamma && 5.51\text{ MeV}\\
&He^3 + He^3 \rightarrow He^4 + 2H^1 + \gamma && 12.98\text{ MeV}
\end{aligned} \tag{12-11.2}$$

which also ultimately combines four protons to make an alpha particle.

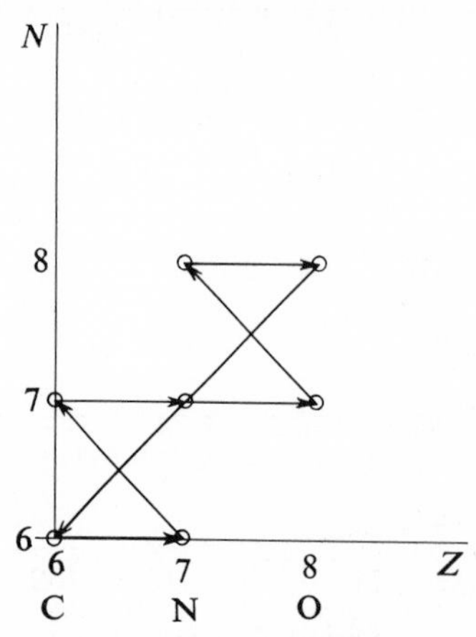

Figure 12-16 Carbon cycle on a Z–N diagram.

Temperatures at the interior of the stars are in the range 10 to 20 million degrees centigrade, and the nuclear kinetic energies are of the order of 1 keV. All atoms are ionized, and there are no free neutrons.

The cross sections for the nuclear reactions between the charged particles involved show, at low energies, a very strong energy dependence on the Gamow factor (Fig. 12-17). Thus, in a gaseous mixture at a certain temperature T, the fastest particles in the Maxwellian distribution will react preferentially. The number of particles in a given energy interval, however, is a strongly decreasing function of energy, and the result is that the reactions will occur in a rather narrow energy interval around an optimum energy. More precisely, the Maxwellian distribution of velocities introduces into the reaction rate a factor $e^{-E/kT}$, and the effect of the Coulomb barrier gives the factor $e^{-Z_1Z_2e^2/\hbar v}$, where Z_1Z_2 are the atomic numbers of the nuclei colliding with relative velocity v. After integrating over all velocities, the reaction rate is approximately proportional to

$$\tau^2 e^{-\tau} \tag{12-11.3}$$

with $\tau = 3(\pi^2 m e^4 Z_1^2 Z_2^2 / 2\hbar kT)^{1/3}$, where m is the reduced mass. The main contribution to this integral comes from the region where the function has a maximum which, under stellar conditions, corresponds to E between 3 and 50 keV (Fig. 12-18). The absolute rates in Table 12-10 are reported from a paper by Salpeter.

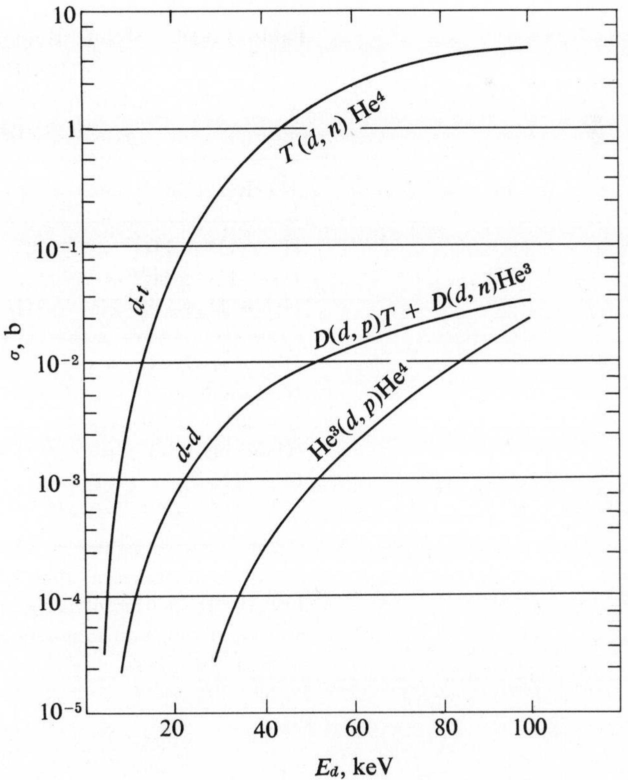

Figure 12-17 Nuclear-fusion reaction cross sections as a function of relative particle energy.

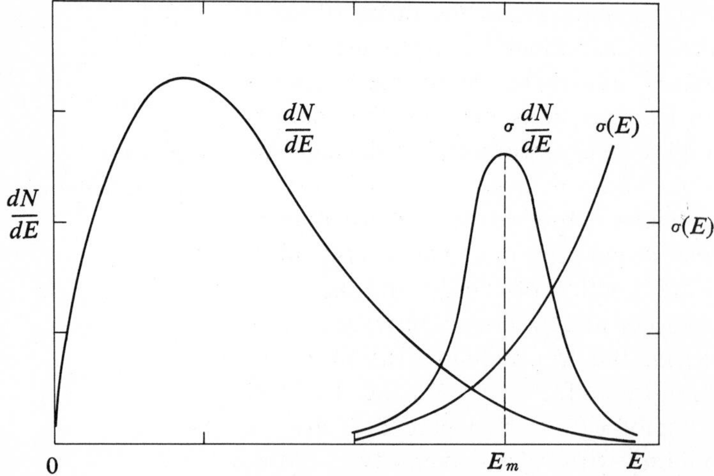

Figure 12-18 Effect of Maxwellian energy distribution on nuclear reaction rate. $\sigma(E)$, cross section; dN/dE, number of particles having relative energy E; the reaction rate is $\sigma dN/dE$.

12-12 Effect of Chemical Binding of Hydrogen Scatterer

In the remainder of this chapter we shall discuss some properties of slow neutrons and some typical problems that have been investigated by slow neutron techniques. The chain-reacting pile has been the preferred neutron source for the investigations we shall report here.

Table 12-10 Mean Reaction Times in Proton-Proton Chain and Carbon-Nitrogen Cycle for Typical Stellar Conditions[a]

Reaction	t_r
$H^1 + H^1 \rightarrow H^2 + e^+ + \nu$	7×10^9 years
$H^2 + H^1 \rightarrow He^3 + \gamma$	4 sec
$He^3 + H + e^3 \rightarrow He^4 + 2H^1$	4×10^5 years
$C^{12} + H^1 \rightarrow N^{13} + \gamma$	10^6 years
$N^{13} \rightarrow C^{13} + e^+ + \nu$	10 min
$C^{13} + H^1 \rightarrow N^{14} + \gamma$	2×10^5 years
$N^{14} + H^1 \rightarrow O^{15} + \gamma$	$< 3 \times 10^7$ years
$O^{15} \rightarrow N^{15} + e^+ + \nu$	2 min
$N^{15} + H^1 \rightarrow C^{12} + He^4$	10^4 years

[a] Mean reaction time t_r for a temperature T of 15×10^{6}°K, density of 125 g cm^{-3}, hydrogen concentration x_H of 0.8, and total concentration x_{CN} of C and N of 0.01 (by mass).

When a neutron of energy much greater than the molecular binding energy strikes a hydrogen nucleus in a molecule, it knocks this proton out of the molecule; and it loses, on the average, one-half its energy to the proton (assuming elastic *s*-wave scattering). However, if the energy of the neutron is less than the $\hbar\omega$ of the molecular vibration, it cannot lose any energy to vibration or to freeing of the hydrogen. Consequently the proton acts as if it had the mass of the whole molecule. This makes it hard for the slow neutron to lose energy. Thus, as the thermal region is approached, neutrons find it increasingly difficult to lose energy. For these reasons, at energies below $\hbar\omega$ the reduced mass of a neutron and proton approaches $\mu = M$ rather than $\mu = M/2$. As a consequence the scattering cross section increases by a factor of 4 in passing from large energies to energies small compared with that of the chemical bond.

By the Born approximation (see Appendix B), the differential scattering cross section is

$$\sigma(\theta) = \frac{\mu^2}{4\pi^2\hbar^4}\left|\int \psi_f^* U \psi_i \, d\tau\right|^2 \tag{12-12.1}$$

where ψ_f and ψ_i are plane waves normalized for unit volume. Thus, in Eq. (12-12.1) $\sigma_{\text{bound}} = 4\sigma_{\text{free}}$, because μ_{bound} is twice as large as μ_{free}. Although the ordinary criterion for the applicability of the Born approximation is not satisfied for thermal energies, it can be shown that Eq. (12-12.1) is still valid.

The fact that the total cross section for a bound proton is four times larger than for a free proton may also be proved by a simple argument developed by Blatt and Weisskopf. The incident slow neutron has a wavelength λ large compared with the dimensions of the molecule in which the proton is bound, and hence we have spherical symmetrical scattering (*s* wave only) in the center-of-mass system, which practically coincides with the system in which the molecule is at rest,

$$\frac{d\sigma}{d\Omega} = c \tag{12-12.2}$$

In scattering by a free proton, the scattering is also spherically symmetrical in the center-of-mass system, which, however, moves with half the velocity of the neutron with respect to the laboratory. If we call a the *n-p* incoherent scattering length [$a = (\frac{3}{4}a_t^2 + \frac{1}{4}a_s^2)^{1/2}$; see Sec. 10-3], we know from Eq. (10-2.8) that in the center-of-mass system

$$\frac{d\sigma}{d\omega} = a^2 \tag{12-12.3}$$

where $d\omega$ is the center-of-mass solid angle. In the laboratory with Θ the scattering angle, this gives

$$\frac{d\sigma}{d\Omega} = \frac{d\sigma}{d\omega}\frac{d\omega}{d\Omega} = a^2\frac{d\cos 2\Theta}{d\cos\Theta} = 4a^2\cos\Theta \tag{12-12.4}$$

In the forward direction ($\cos\Theta = 1$) the two cross sections must be equal, because the collision does not impart any momentum to the proton and thus cannot be affected by the proton being free or bound. Hence

$$c = 4a^2 \tag{12-12.5}$$

and the total cross section

$$\sigma_{\text{tot bound}} = 4\pi c = 16\pi a^2 \tag{12-12.6}$$

is four times as large as

$$\sigma_{\text{tot free}} = 4\pi a^2 \tag{12-12.7}$$

To estimate the energy at which the cross section increases because of the chemical bond, note that for the carbon-hydrogen bond in paraffin the longitudinal vibration is 3,000 cm^{-1}, or 1/3 eV. The transverse vibration is 600 cm^{-1}, or 1/15 eV. Samples of the scattering-cross-section curve are shown in Fig. 12-19.

This type of argument can be extended from molecules to crystal lattices, and the results are closely related to the recoilless processes of gamma emission and absorption (Sec. 8-8; Lamb, 1939).

12-13 Low-Energy Scattering from Complex Nuclei

Let us first consider the scattering of a slow neutron from a free isolated nucleus. Only s-wave scattering will be important, because the de Broglie wavelength of the neutron is very large compared with the range of nuclear forces. The asymptotic expression of the wave function of the system (see Sec. 11-5) is

$$\psi \sim e^{ikz} + C_0 \frac{e^{ikr}}{r} \tag{12-13.1}$$

and

$$k = \frac{1}{\lambdabar} = \frac{p}{\hbar} \tag{12-13.2}$$

The constant C_0 is $(i/2k)(1 - \eta_0)$ of Eq. (11-5.5). It is related to the s-phase shift δ by

$$C_0 = \frac{\lambdabar}{2i}(e^{2i\delta} - 1) = \lambdabar e^{i\delta} \sin\delta \simeq \lambdabar\delta \text{ (for } \delta \text{ small)} \tag{12-13.3}$$

For pure elastic scattering, δ is real, and we have for the total scattering cross section

$$\sigma_s = 4\pi\lambdabar^2 \sin^2\delta \tag{12-13.4}$$

We now use the scattering length (see Sec. 10-2) defined by

$$\lambdabar \sin\delta = -a \tag{12-13.5}$$

The scattering length in the case of

$$\left|\frac{a}{\lambdabar}\right| = |\sin\delta| \ll 1 \tag{12-13.6}$$

represents the intercept of the tangent to $r\psi$ at $r = R$ (nuclear radius) with the r axis. The total elastic cross section is then

$$\sigma_{\text{el}} = 4\pi \mid a \mid^2 \tag{12-13.7}$$

The order of magnitude of a is usually 10^{-12} cm. If there is a reaction besides scattering, we can use a complex δ and a complex a defined by Eq. (12-13.5).

However, for slow neutrons the real part of a is large compared with the imaginary. On the assumption of a real, the scattered wave according

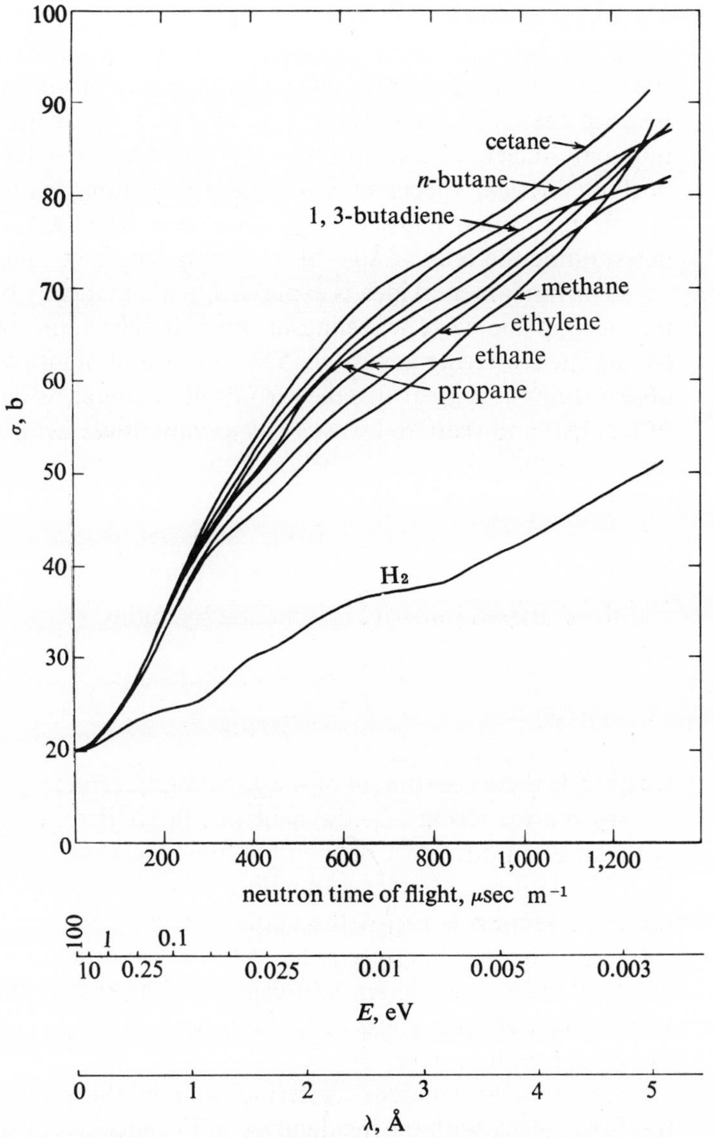

Figure 12-19 The slow neutron cross section of protons bound in various hydrocarbons and in H_2 gas. All corrections for the effect of thermal translational motion have been made. [From Amaldi in (Fl E).]

to Eqs. (12-13.1), (12-13.3), and (12-13.5) may be written $-ae^{ikr}/r$. It has no phase shift with respect to the incident wave if a is negative and a phase shift of π if a is positive. In most cases, a is positive, but there are a few exceptions, notably n-p scattering in the singlet state.

12-14 Determination of Scattering Lengths

Clearly the scattering length for slow neutrons is a function of the scatterer and of the mutual orientation of the neutron and scatterer spin if the latter is not 0.

Experimental determination of the scattering length rests on the scattering by material systems composed of many nuclei. The result of scattering by bulk matter depends not only on the scattering lengths of the nuclei involved but also on the arrangement of nuclei in the scatterer, because there are interference phenomena between waves scattered by different nuclei. These interference phenomena determine many important physical effects such as Bragg reflection, scattering from polyatomic molecules, index of refraction, etc. They are also essential for determining the relative sign of scattering length of different nuclei.

The fundamental idea is expressed mathematically by considering an incoming plane wave traveling in the z direction and scattering centers having the scattering length a_j. The distance of point j from the point of observation, at a great distance from the scatterer, is called r_j. The sum of incident and scattered waves has an amplitude, with multiple scattering neglected,

$$A = e^{ikz} - \sum \frac{a_j}{r_j} e^{ik(z_j+r_j)} \tag{12-14.1}$$

and the scattered intensity is obtained by taking

$$I = \left| \sum_j \frac{a_j}{r_j} e^{ik(z_j+r_j)} \right|^2 \tag{12-14.2}$$

where z_j is the z coordinate of the j scattering center.

In the scattering of slow neutrons (a similar situation occurs with X rays), often only part of the amplitudes scattered by different centers interfere with one another and with the incident wave. The corresponding cross section is called the "coherent cross section." The scattered waves that do not interfere either with one another or with the incident wave form the "incoherent scattering." Note that in the forward direction the scattering is always coherent, because $r_j + z_j$ in Eq. (12-14.1) is the same for all centers.

To visualize coherent scattering, we may think of centers set in vibration in phase with the incident wave. For incoherent scattering we may think of centers that frequently and suddenly change phase with respect to the incident wave.

In a gas the interference terms due to waves scattered from different molecules cancel out, and the scattered intensity is the sum of the intensities scattered by single molecules. Thus, in the case of a simple monoatomic monoisotopic gas the scattering is spherically symmetrical in the center-of-mass system, and the scattering cross section is

$$\sigma = 4\pi|a|^2 \tag{12-14.3}$$

Note that a simple scattering experiment is insufficient to determine the sign of a.

Even in this case we must apply a small correction depending on whether we want a for a free or a bound nucleus. In the first case the reduced mass is given by $1/\mu_f = 1 + (1/A)$. In the latter case the reduced mass for the target nucleus bound to a molecule of mass M is given by $1/\mu_b = 1 + (1/M)$, and using, for example, the Born approximation, we see that

$$\sigma_{\text{bound}} = \left[\frac{1 + (1/A)}{1 + (1/M)}\right]^2 \sigma_{\text{free}} \tag{12-14.4}$$

or

$$a_{\text{bound}} = \frac{M}{A}\left(\frac{A + 1}{M + 1}\right) a_{\text{free}} \tag{12-14.5}$$

A nucleus is to be regarded as bound when the energy transferred in the collision is small compared with the binding energy of the molecule. For nuclei bound in solids or liquids M tends to infinity.

Let us now consider a gas of diatomic molecules of a substance having two spinless isotopes and assume that λ of the neutron is very large compared with the interatomic distance in the molecule, so that for scattering purposes we may sum the amplitudes scattered by the two nuclei of each molecule. Let the relative abundance of the two nuclei be p_1, p_2 ($p_1 + p_2 = 1$), and their scattering lengths a_1 and a_2, respectively. In the gas there are molecules having both nuclei of species 1, both nuclei of species 2, or mixed nuclei. Their relative abundance is

$$p_1^2,\ p_2^2,\ 2p_1p_2$$

The average cross section for scattering per molecule of the gas is then given by

$$\begin{aligned}\sigma &= 4\pi\,[p_1^2(2a_1)^2 + p_2^2(2a_2)^2 + 2p_1p_2(a_1 + a_2)^2] \\ &= 4\pi\,[4(p_1a_1 + p_2a_2)^2 + 2p_1p_2(a_1 - a_2)^2]\end{aligned} \tag{12-14.6}$$

The scattering is thus the same as that produced by two equal nuclei scattering coherently, each with scattering length $a = p_1a_1 + p_2a_2$, and at the same time scattering incoherently, with a cross section

$$\sigma_{\text{inc}} = 4\pi p_1p_2(a_1 - a_2)^2 \tag{12-14.7}$$

If we define

$$\sigma_{\text{coh}} = 4\pi(p_1a_1 + p_2a_2)^2 \tag{12-14.8}$$

the scattering from the molecule takes the form

$$\sigma = 4\sigma_{\text{coh}} + 2\sigma_{\text{inc}} \tag{12-14.9}$$

the factors 4 and 2 pointing to the fact that for coherent scattering we have summed the amplitudes and for incoherent scattering the intensities. Note also that

$$\sigma_{\mathrm{coh}} + \sigma_{\mathrm{inc}} = 4\pi\,(p_1 a_1^2 + p_2 a_2^2) \qquad \textbf{(12-14.10)}$$

These results may be generalized. If we have N nuclides randomly mixed with relative abundance p, the scattering length

$$a = \sum p_j a_j \qquad \textbf{(12-14.11)}$$

determines the interference properties of the substance. In the absence of nuclear polarization one isotope with spin I acts as a mixture of two isotopes with relative abundance $(I + 1)/(2I + 1)$ and scattering length a_+, relative abundance $I/(2I + I)$ and scattering length a_-, respectively. Here a_+ and a_- are the scattering lengths for parallel or antiparallel neutron and nuclear spin and the I factors express the statistical probabilities of the corresponding spin orientations.

From what we have said we discover, at least in principle, methods for determining the relative sign of the scattering amplitude of two nuclear species. Measuring a phenomenon where the waves produced by the two scatterers interfere, we can measure $(a_1 + a_2)^2$. Measuring the scattering by the two species separately, we have a_1^2 and a_2^2. From this, one obtains the relative sign of a_1 and a_2.

A notable property of scattering is that when neutrons scatter flipping their spin, their waves cannot interfere; the spin-flip scattering is incoherent. To see this, note that if we scatter a neutron from a system of nuclei in such a way as to produce interference, we cannot specify on which nucleus the scattering has occurred. Interference can arise only when scattering occurs on more than one nucleus. On the other hand, if we have spin flip in the neutron, we can specify the scattering nucleus by observing which nucleus has changed its I_z. To treat this situation, we must generalize Eq. (12-14.1) in order to take into account the wave function of the scatterer as well.

To discuss this question in mathematical terms, consider an incident plane neutron wave with spin up, traveling in the z direction, and the scatterer's initial wave function φ. The system is then represented by

$$e^{ikz}\begin{pmatrix}1\\0\end{pmatrix}\varphi$$

Call φ_j the wave function of the scatterer when the j nucleus has flipped its spin and by a', a indicate the scattering length with or without spin flip. We look for an asymptotic solution of the form

$$e^{ikz}\begin{pmatrix}1\\0\end{pmatrix}\varphi - \sum_j \frac{a_i}{r_j} e^{ik(z_j+r_j)}\begin{pmatrix}1\\0\end{pmatrix}\varphi - \sum_j \frac{a_i'}{r_j} e^{ik(z_j+r_j)}\begin{pmatrix}0\\1\end{pmatrix}\varphi_j$$

The scattered intensity is obtained by taking the modulus square of the scattered part of the wave, integrated over the scatterer coordinates. By definition,

$$\int \varphi_i^* \varphi_k \, dq = \delta_{ik} \qquad (\delta_{ik} \text{ is the Dirac delta function}) \qquad \textbf{(12-14.12)}$$

and this eliminates all terms of the sum containing $\varphi\varphi_j^*$, leaving those with $|\varphi|^2$ and $|\varphi_j|^2$. The scattered intensity has the form

$$\left| \sum_j \frac{a_j}{r_j} e^{ik(r_j+z_j)} \right|^2 + \sum_j \frac{|a_j'|^2}{r_j^2}$$

The first term is the scattering without spin flip and shows interference between scattering from different centers. The second is spin-flip scattering and is incoherent.

12-15 Scattering in Ortho- and Parahydrogen

Scattering from ortho- and parahydrogen is another important example of the application of the ideas of Sec. 12-14. We shall consider only scattering at very low temperatures and for neutron wavelengths large compared with the internuclear distance (0.74 Å). We cannot apply the formulas of Sec. 12-14 directly, because at very low temperatures, in the presence of a catalyst, all hydrogen molecules are in the zero rotational state, which has antiparallel nuclear spins. The spins are thus not distributed at random. We shall calculate the scattering cross section for such a molecule and also for a molecule in which the spins of the two hydrogens are parallel (orthohydrogen).

To do this we write the neutron-proton scattering length formally as

$$a = a_s\pi_s + a_t\pi_t \tag{12-15.1}$$

where a_s and a_t are the ordinary singlet and triplet scattering length corrected for the mass effect

$$a_{s,t} = \tfrac{4}{3}\, a_{s,t\ \text{free}} \tag{12-15.2}$$

and π_s is an operator which has the values 1 for singlet states, 0 for triplet states. The operator π_t has instead values 0 for singlet states, 1 for triplet states. Such operators (projection operators) are, as we can derive immediately from the calculation at the beginning of Sec. 10-5

$$\pi_s = \tfrac{1}{4}\,(1 - \boldsymbol{\sigma}_n \cdot \boldsymbol{\sigma}_p) \tag{12-15.3}$$

and

$$\pi_t = \tfrac{1}{4}(3 + \boldsymbol{\sigma}_n \cdot \boldsymbol{\sigma}_p) \tag{12-15.4}$$

with $\boldsymbol{\sigma} \equiv$ Pauli spin operator. To compute the scattering from our molecule, we write the scattering length of each atom as a_1, a_2, using Eq. (12-15.1). The scattering length for the molecule is

$$\begin{aligned} a_1 + a_2 &= a_s\,\pi_{s1} + a_t\pi_{t1} + a_s\pi_{s2} + a_t\pi_{t2} \\ &= a_s[\tfrac{1}{2} - \tfrac{1}{4}\,\boldsymbol{\sigma}_n\cdot(\boldsymbol{\sigma}_{p1} + \boldsymbol{\sigma}_{p2})] + a_t \\ &\quad \times [\tfrac{3}{2} + \tfrac{1}{4}\,\boldsymbol{\sigma}_n\cdot(\boldsymbol{\sigma}_{p1} + \boldsymbol{\sigma}_{p2})] \end{aligned} \tag{12-15.5}$$

Now $\frac{1}{2}(\boldsymbol{\sigma}_{p1} + \boldsymbol{\sigma}_{p2})$ is the spin $\mathbf{S}$ of the two hydrogen nuclei; for orthohydrogen $S = 1$, and for parahydrogen $S = 0$. Substituting in Eq. (12-15.5) and rearranging, we have

$$a = (\tfrac{3}{2}\, a_t + \tfrac{1}{2}a_s) + (+\tfrac{1}{2}a_t - \tfrac{1}{2}a_s)\,(\boldsymbol{\sigma}_n \cdot \mathbf{S}) \tag{12-15.6}$$

For parahydrogen the scattering cross section is thus

$$\sigma_{\text{para}} = 4\pi\,(\tfrac{3}{2}a_t + \tfrac{1}{2}a_s)^2 \qquad \textbf{(12-15.7)}$$

For orthohydrogen Eq. (12-15.6) gives, on squaring, linear terms in $\boldsymbol{\sigma}_n \cdot \mathbf{S}$ which for unpolarized beams and target cancel. The term containing $(\boldsymbol{\sigma}_n \cdot \mathbf{S})^2$ averaged gives $S(S + 1) = 2$. We thus obtain

$$\sigma_{\text{ortho}} = 4\pi[(\tfrac{3}{2}a_t + \tfrac{1}{2}a_s)^2 + \tfrac{1}{2}(a_t - a_s)^2] \qquad \textbf{(12-15.8)}$$

The cross section of parahydrogen depends very strongly on the relative sign of a_s, a_t, as was pointed out by Teller (1937). According to experiment, $\sigma_{\text{ortho}} = 125$ b, $\sigma_{\text{para}} = 4$ b; this result is explainable only if a_s, a_t have opposite signs. The quantitative interpretation, i.e., derivation of the scattering lengths from the scattering by molecular hydrogen, requires numerous refinements that are beyond the scope of this book.

12-16 Interference Phenomena in Crystals

Since the slow-neutron de Broglie wavelength is

$$\lambda = 2.86 \times 10^{-9}/E^{1/2} \text{ cm } (E \text{ in eV}) \qquad \textbf{(12-16.1)}$$

it reaches 1.81×10^{-8} cm for thermal values. It is then comparable to the interatomic distances in solid lattices, and the neutrons will show

(a)

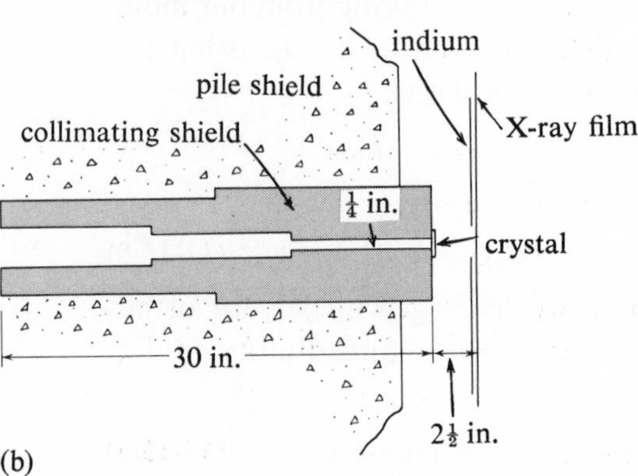

(b)

Figure 12-20 (a) Laue photograph showing neutron diffraction by an NaCl crystal. [From Wollan, Shull, and Marney, *Phys. Rev.*, **73,** 527 (1948).] (b) Schematic diagram of the Laue camera used to obtain the neutron diffraction pattern.

many of the phenomena characteristic of the interaction of X rays with crystals, such as Laue and Bragg diffraction, a small refractive index, and others.

The experimental techniques employed are similar, and crystal spectographs and similar instruments are used for both radiations. Figure 12-20 shows the similarity of the photographs obtained by diffraction with neutrons and X rays. Strong monochromatic neutron sources are usually obtained by a mechanical velocity selector (Fig. 12-21), by crystalline reflection, or by some other device. However, there are important differences between the two types of radiation. In many respects they supplement each other very usefully in solid-state investigations. For instance, hydrogen, which is most difficult to detect by X-ray diffraction, has a large a and is easily observable by means of neutrons. We shall treat briefly some of the most important topics of this aspect of neutron physics.

We shall begin with the scattering by a crystalline lattice, giving rise through interference phenomena to Bragg reflection. Consider a set of parallel planes having a distance d between successive planes and containing identical spinless scattering nuclei of scattering length a. The scattered neutrons originating at depth md will give rise to an amplitude (see Fig. 12-22).

$$A = \sum_{1}^{N}{}_{m} - a\, e^{2ikmd \cos\theta} \tag{12-16.2}$$

where N is the number of layers involved. Performing the sum, which is a geometric progression, we find

$$A = -a\left\{\frac{1 - e^{2ikNd\cos\theta}}{1 - e^{2ikd\cos\theta}}\right\} e^{2ikd\cos\theta} \tag{12-16.3}$$

The intensity is proportional to $|A|^2$, where

$$|A|^2 = |a|^2 \frac{\sin^2 (N\, kd \cos\theta)}{\sin^2 (kd \cos\theta)} \tag{12-16.4}$$

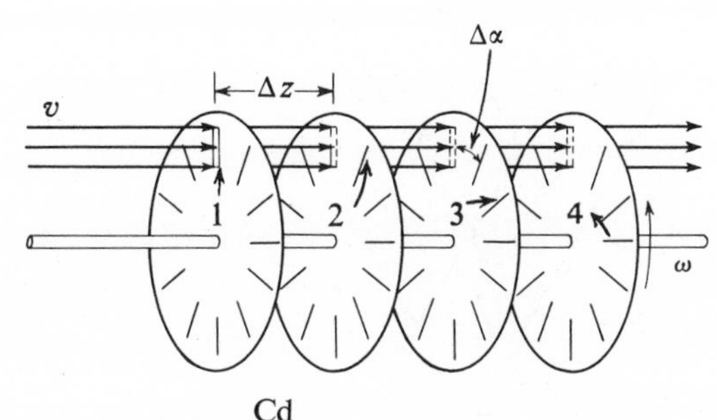

Figure 12-21 An example illustrating the principle of a mechanical monochromator for slow neutrons. The selector is transparent to neutrons of velocity $v = (\Delta z/\Delta\alpha)\omega$, where ω is the angular velocity of the selector, Δz the distance between the disks, and $\Delta\alpha$ is the angular shift of the window from one disk to the next. Neutrons of this velocity will thread, for instance, slots 1, 2, 3, 4.

is large for those values of θ for which the denominator vanishes, i.e., if

$$kd \cos \theta = n\pi$$

or

$$n\lambda = 2d \cos \theta$$

which is the famous Bragg relation (W. Bragg and L. Bragg, 1913). If the crystal contains several isotopes, we must use in Eq. (12-16.4) the weighted sum of the scattering lengths in order to determine the effective scattering length for coherent scattering. Naturally such a crystal is not a "perfect" crystal, because the isotopes are randomly distributed in the lattice and, in addition to the coherent scattering, incoherent scattering must be present.

Consider now the case of atoms of two kinds, as in NaCl. The (1,1,1) planes are equidistant and consist alternately of sodium and chlorine. In the first-order Bragg reflection the optical path for reflection from sodium planes differs by $\lambda/2$ from the path for reflection from chlorine planes. Consequently, if sodium and chlorine nuclei cause the same change in phase of the scattered neutron wave, their contributions will subtract and the order will have low intensity; the contrary will happen if they scatter with opposite phase change.

The situation for the second order is reversed. High intensity here is connected with scattering by sodium and chlorine, when both produce the same change in phase. On these effects is superimposed a continuous decrease of intensity from order to order, as in X rays.

In more complicated cases the intensity of the various orders is determined, as for X rays, by the form factor, defined as the effective coherent scattering amplitude per unit cell of the crystal,

$$F = \left| \sum a_j \exp\left(\frac{2\pi i n \delta_j}{d}\right) \right| \qquad \textbf{(12-16.5)}$$

where d is the spacing of the lattice planes, n is the order of the Bragg

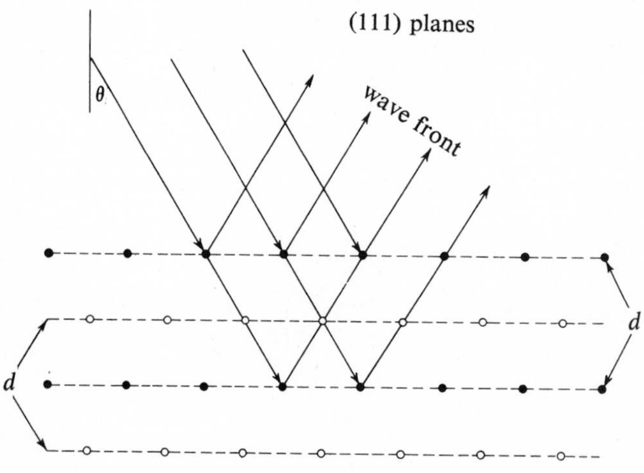

Figure 12-22 Neutron diffraction from the (1,1,1) planes of a cubic crystal.

reflection, and δ_j is the perpendicular distance of the jth nucleus to one of the planes of reflection assumed as reference. The sum is extended to all nuclei in the unit cell. It is clear that F depends strongly on the signs of a_j, and an analysis of the intensities for the different orders may lead to the determination (Fig. 12-22; NaCl) of the relative sign of the scattering lengths for the different nuclei of the lattice.

An interesting application of the Bragg condition is the preparation of beams of very slow neutrons. By passing a beam of neutrons of different velocities through a polycrystalline medium, the neutrons that satisfy the Bragg relation for some crystal are reflected out, and soon only those of $\lambda > 2d$, which can never satisfy the Bragg condition, are left in the beam. We have thus a cutoff at high neutron velocity. The intensity falls off at low neutron velocity because of the original velocity distribution in the beam (Fig. 12-23).

Bragg reflection can also be used to investigate the magnetic properties of a material. We shall see that the scattering length is affected by the orientation of a neutron with respect to the electronic magnetic moment of an atom. In a saturated ferromagnetic material there will be a strong dependence of the reflecting power on the neutron polarization, and thus Bragg reflection can be used to polarize neutrons.

In a different application the Laue patterns for neutrons, produced by ferromagnetic substances, depend on the magnetization of the scatterer. Finally, we have the interesting case of antiferromagnetic compounds. These are solids in which the spins of the atoms are aligned, but always in pairs with opposite directions, as in two saturated ferromagnetic lattices with equal and opposite magnetizations, superimposed on each other. These substances do not show macroscopic properties

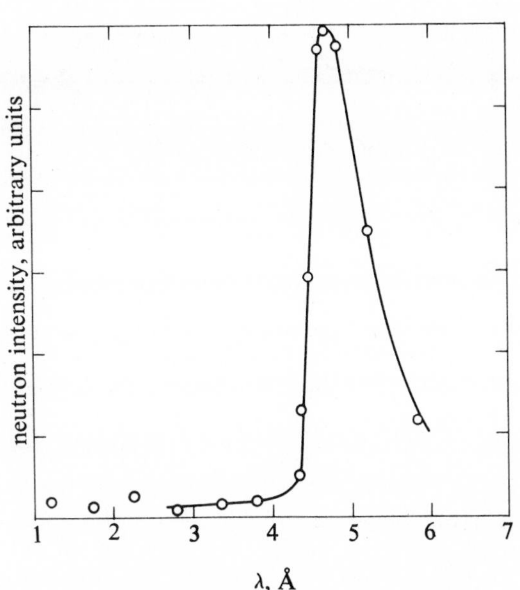

Figure 12-23 Spectral distribution of cold neutrons from a beryllium oxide filter (Fermi and Marshall).

such as ferromagnetism but reveal their structure in neutron diffraction analysis (Fig. 12-24).

Another interesting application of very slow neutrons has been in the investigation of properties of liquid helium II. This liquid at very low temperatures may be described by a system containing quanta (*excitons*) of a certain energy and momentum. The relation between energy and momentum of the excitons may be investigated experimentally by scattering very slow neutrons ($\lambda > 4\text{Å}$) in liquid He II. A neutron scatters, producing an exciton in the liquid, and the energy and momentum of the exciton must be equal, by the conservation of energy and momentum laws, to the loss of energy and momentum of the neutron. These losses are measurable, and thus one obtains the relation between E and p of the excitons. This function is of great importance for the theory of liquid He II. The applications of neutrons to molecular and solid-state problems are rapidly increasing. The examples cited should give the reader an idea of the possibilities of this most elegant tool of investigation.

12-17 Index of Refraction

Another application of the theory of coherent scattering is the atomic explanation of the refractive index. The forward scattering of

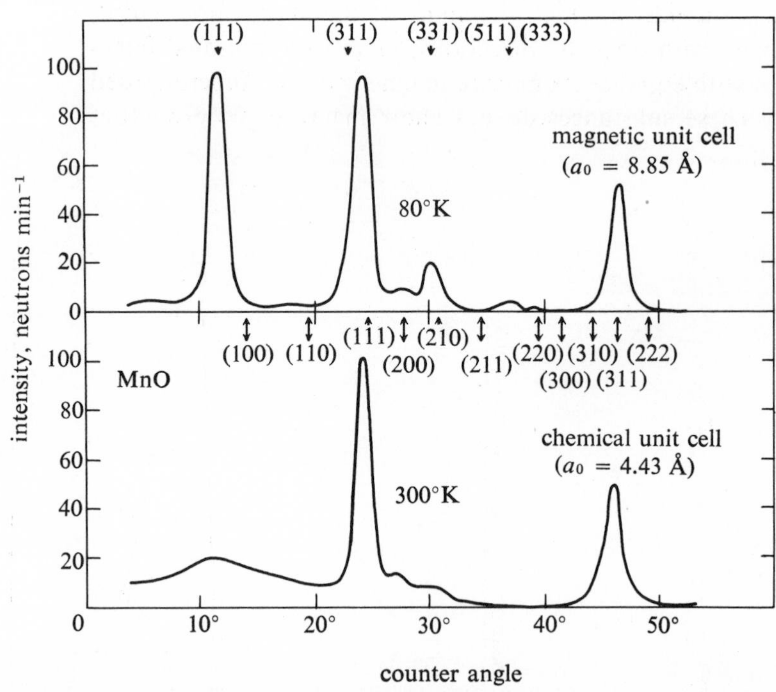

Figure 12-24 Powder diffraction patterns for crystalline manganese oxide at 80°K and at room temperature, due to Shull and Smart [*Phys. Rev.*, **76**, 1256 (1949)]. The additional peaks, in the low-temperature pattern, are characteristic of a magnetic unit cell of twice the dimensions of the chemical unit cell, clearly indicating the antiferromagnetic structure of manganese oxide.

neutrons, light, X rays, etc., is always coherent, and its interference with the incoming beam gives rise to the refractive index of the scattering material.

The connection between scattering length and refractive index is obtained by the following calculation: Assume for the sake of simplicity that the scattering is spherically symmetrical, and consider a thin slab of material of thickness T, containing N nuclei per unit volume. A plane wave $\psi_0 = e^{ikz}$ impinges normally on the slab, and we calculate the amplitude of the wave at the point P (Fig. 12-25),

$$\psi_P = e^{ikz} - 2\pi NT \int_0^\infty \frac{a}{r} e^{ikr} x\, dx \tag{12-17.1}$$

where we have neglected the absorption in the slab. Now $x^2 + z^2 = r^2$, whence $x\, dx = r\, dr$ and

$$\psi_P = e^{ikz} - 2\pi NTa \int_z^\infty e^{ikr}\, dr \tag{12-17.2}$$

The last integral can be evaluated either by using the artifice of the Fresnel zones or by adding a small positive imaginary part to k and passing to the limit for this small part vanishing, the result being that the value of the integral at the upper limit vanishes. We thus obtain

$$\psi_P = \left(1 - \frac{2\pi i\, NTa}{k}\right) e^{ikz} \tag{12-17.3}$$

Now consider the effect of attributing a refractive index n to the slab. The propagation vector in the material is nk versus k in vacuum; hence

$$\psi_P \approx e^{ik(z-T) + inkT} = e^{ikz} e^{ik(n-1)T} \tag{12-17.4}$$

and for $k(n - 1)\, T \ll 1$

$$\psi_P \approx e^{ikz}[1 + ik(n - 1)T] \tag{12-17.5}$$

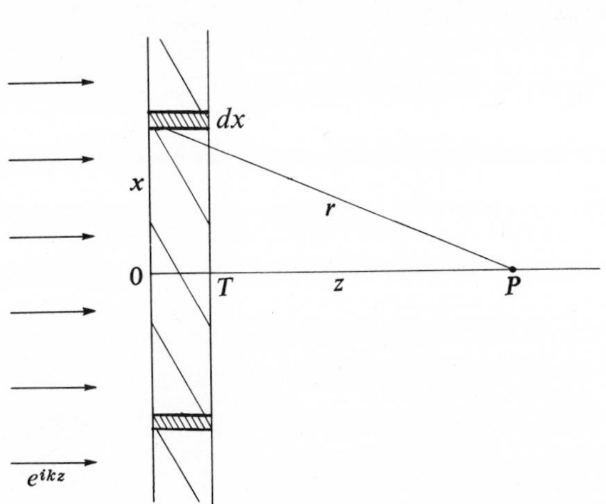

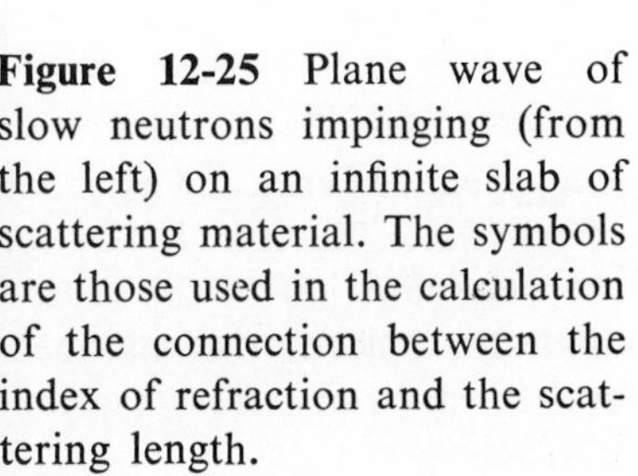

Figure 12-25 Plane wave of slow neutrons impinging (from the left) on an infinite slab of scattering material. The symbols are those used in the calculation of the connection between the index of refraction and the scattering length.

Comparison of Eqs. (12-17.3) and (12-17.5) gives

$$n = 1 - \frac{2\pi Na}{k^2} = 1 - \frac{\lambda^2}{2\pi} Na \tag{12-17.6}$$

For positive a the index of refraction is thus smaller than 1. Its value is very near 1 for slow neutrons; in fact, typical values would be, for example, $\lambda = 10^{-8}$ cm, $N = 10^{23}$ cm^{-3}, $a = 10^{-12}$ cm, $n - 1 = \pm 2 \times 10^{-6}$. In the case $n < 1$ total reflection from a surface is possible; it occurs whenever $\sin i_c \geqslant n$. Since $n \simeq 1$, $i_c \simeq 90°$, and calling $90° - i_c = \epsilon$, we have $\sin i_c = \cos \epsilon \cong 1 - (\epsilon^2/2)$, or

$$-\frac{\epsilon^2}{2} \geqslant n - 1 \tag{12-17.7}$$

Remembering Eq. (12-17.6) we thus have the limiting angle

$$\epsilon = \left(\frac{N\lambda^2}{\pi} a\right)^{1/2} = \lambda \left(\frac{N}{\pi}\right)^{1/2} \left(\frac{\sigma_{\text{tot}}}{4\pi}\right)^{1/4} \tag{12-17.8}$$

Clearly total reflection occurs at a given angle only for λ greater than a critical λ_c defined by Eq. (12-17.7). We therefore have a way of obtaining a neutron velocity selector (Fig. 12-26).

Even more interesting is the reflection on magnetized mirrors. It can be shown (see Sec. 12-18) that the refractive index of a neutron for a ferromagnetic substance depends on the relative orientation of the magnetization and the neutron spin. More precisely,

$$n_\pm = 1 - \frac{\lambda^2 Na}{2\pi} \mp \frac{\mu_n B}{2E_n} \tag{12-17.9}$$

where the $\pm$ refer to the orientation of the field with respect to the neutron spin, μ_n is the magnetic moment of the neutron, E_n its energy, B the

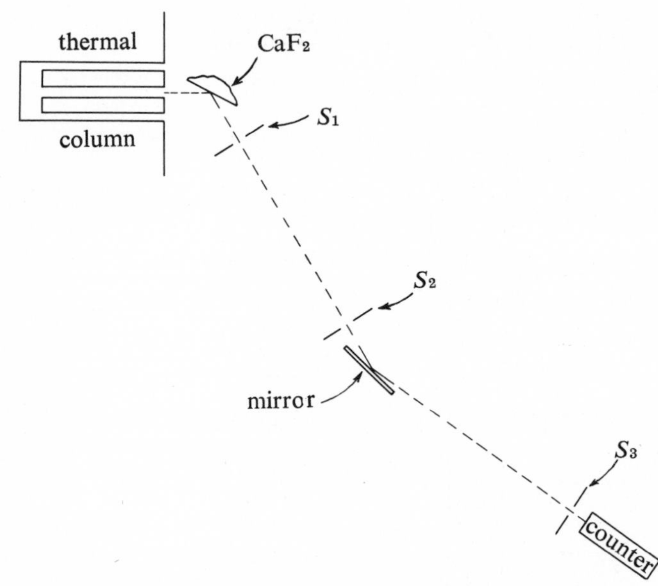

Figure 12-26 Experimental arrangement of Fermi and Marshall [*Phys. Rev.*, **71**, 666 (1947)] for the determination of the critical angle for reflection of monoenergetic neutrons from various mirrors.

magnetic flux density in the mirror in the direction of the mirror plane, and a the scattering length of the mirror material. Hence from Eq. (12-17.8) it can be seen that neutrons of opposite spin direction may have different limiting angles. Total reflection from a magnetized mirror then affords a method of polarizing neutrons.

Finally, total reflection from hydrocarbons of different C/H ratio provides an important means of measuring the ratio of the scattering amplitude of carbon to that of hydrogen, or, more precisely, to that of

$$\tfrac{3}{4}a_3 + \tfrac{1}{4}a_1 = a_H \qquad \textbf{(12-17.10)}$$

the weighted average of singlet and triplet scattering lengths (Hughes, Burgy, and Ringo, 1950). The carbon scattering length (practically monoisotopic, spinless C^{12}) can be measured directly from free-carbon cross-section measurements, and one obtains

$$a_C = -\,6.63 \pm 0.03 \times 10^{-13}\ \text{cm}$$

$$a_H = 3.78 \pm 0.02 \times 10^{-13}\ \text{cm}$$

This is probably the most reliable measurement of a_H. It is interesting to compare it with the value of

$$\tfrac{1}{4}|a_1|^2 + \tfrac{3}{4}|a_3|^2 = \frac{\sigma_{sc}}{4\pi} = \frac{20.4}{4\pi}\,10^{-24}\ \text{cm}^2 \qquad \textbf{(12-17.11)}$$

obtained from incoherent scattering on hydrogen. Equations (12-17.10) and (12-17.11) are compatible only if a_1 and a_3 have opposite signs, an important result that shows again that the singlet state of the deuteron is virtual (see Sec. 10-2).

12-18 Polarization of Slow-Neutron Beams

Since the scattering lengths a_+ and a_- are not generally equal, a crystal with all its nuclei oriented in the same direction will have different cross sections for the two directions of the spin of the incident neutrons. If $a_+ > a_-$, more of the neutrons with spin parallel to that of the scatterer (spin up) will be scattered away, leaving a transmitted beam which is predominantly "spin down." The polarization would approach 100 per cent if the path through the crystal were made sufficiently long. However, this method is not very practical, since one has to line up the nuclear spins, which is generally difficult.

In ferromagnetic materials, the *atomic* magnetic moments can be lined up. We shall now show how this can give different cross sections for the two possible neutron orientations, by considering the scattering using the Born approximation for the amplitude.

Let $U = b\delta(r) \pm \mu_N B_z$ represent the interaction potential between the neutron and the Fe atom in its lattice position. The upper sign obtains for the magnetic moment of the neutron parallel to B, the lower sign for the magnetic moment of the neutron antiparallel to B. (Remember that spin and magnetic moment in the neutron are antiparallel.) Using the Born approximation, one obtains

$$\sigma(\theta) = \frac{m^2}{4\pi^2\hbar^4}\left|\int U e^{i(\mathbf{k}'-\mathbf{k})\cdot\mathbf{r}}\, d\tau\right|^2$$

$$= \frac{m^2}{4\pi^2\hbar^4}\left| b \mp \mu_N \int B_z(r) e^{i(\mathbf{k}'-\mathbf{k})\cdot\mathbf{r}}\, d\tau\right|^2 \qquad \textbf{(12-18.1)}$$

where the region of integration is that part of the lattice belonging to one Fe atom. For slow neutrons λ is of the order of the lattice distance, and the exponential is $\simeq 1$ over the region of integration. Thus

$$\sigma(\theta) = \frac{m^2}{4\pi^2\hbar^4}\left| b \mp \mu_N \int B_z(r)\, d\tau\right|^2 \qquad \textbf{(12-18.2)}$$

where the integral is extended to the lattice volume occupied by an Fe atom. To give the reader an idea of the order of magnitude of the magnetic-field contribution, we shall take b as 0 in the following estimate. Let

$$b = 0$$

$$\lambda \gg \text{atomic dimensions}$$

$$B_z = 23{,}000 \text{ G (saturated Fe)}$$

$$\int B_z\, d\tau = 2.7 \times 10^{-19} \text{ G}\cdot\text{cm}^3$$

Then $\sigma = 4.9 \times 10^{-24}$.

The experimental result for thermal neutrons on magnetized iron is $\sigma = (12 + 3.15)$ b or $\sigma = (12 - 3.15)$ b; the first value, $\sigma = 15.15$ b, obtains for the neutron spin parallel to B; the second value, $\sigma = 8.85$ b, corresponds to spin antiparallel to B. Naturally, if we filter neutrons through magnetized iron we shall obtain a polarized beam with an orientation such that $\sigma = 8.85$ b, the opposite orientation being preferentially removed from the beam.

A disadvantage of this method is that it happens to be very sensitive to incomplete polarization of the iron. Iron is completely polarized in each domain, but in the small number of domains that are not properly oriented, the neutrons will precess about **B** and undo most of the work done by the previous "good" domains.

Let us call $\sigma_0 \pm \sigma_m$ the cross sections for neutrons with spin parallel or antiparallel to the magnetization, and let us assume complete saturation of the iron. If we pass a beam of incident unpolarized intensity I_0 through a slab of thickness d containing N atoms of iron per unit volume the emerging beam will have intensities I_+, polarized with spin parallel to the magnetization, and I_-, polarized antiparallel.

The following relations are immediately derived:

$$I_+ = \tfrac{1}{2} I_0\, e^{-(\sigma_0+\sigma_m)Nd} \qquad \textbf{(12-18.3)}$$

$$I_- = \tfrac{1}{2} I_0\, e^{-(\sigma_0-\sigma_m)Nd} \qquad \textbf{(12-18.4)}$$

$$P = \frac{I_+ - I_-}{I_+ + I_-} = -\tanh N\sigma_m d \simeq -N\sigma_m d \qquad \textbf{(12-18.5)}$$

A second slab of magnetized iron may then be used as an analyzer;

depending on the direction of its magnetization, we have, for the intensity passing through both slabs,

$$I = I_0 e^{-N\sigma_0(d_1+d_2)} \cosh N\sigma_m (d_1 \pm d_2) \qquad \textbf{(12-18.6)}$$

where the upper or lower sign refers to parallel or opposite magnetizations of the slabs.

Bibliography

Amaldi, E., "The Production and Slowing Down of Neutrons," in (Fl E), Vol. 38.2.

Bacon, G. E., *Neutron Diffraction*, Oxford University Press, New York, 1962.

Burbidge, G., "Nuclear Astrophysics," *Ann. Rev. Nucl. Sci.*, **12,** 507 (1962).

Blatt, J. M., and V. Weisskopf (BW 52).

Cole, T. E., and A. M. Weinberg, "Technology of Research Reactors," *Ann. Rev. Nucl. Sci.*, **12,** 221 (1962).

Etherington, H. (ed.), *Nuclear Engineering Handbook*, McGraw-Hill, New York, 1958.

Feld, B. T., "The Neutron," in (Se 59), Vol. II.

Fermi, E. (Fe 50).

Fermi, E., *Collected Papers of Enrico Fermi*, University of Chicago Press, Chicago, 1962.

Fermi, E., and L. Marshall, "Interference Phenonema of Slow Neutrons," *Phys. Rev.*, **71,** 666 (1947).

Glasstone, S., and M. C. Edlund (GE 52).

Glasstone, S., *Controlled Thermonuclear Reactions*, Van Nostrand, Princeton, N. J., 1960.

Goldberger, M., and F. Seitz, "Theory of the Refraction and the Diffraction of Neutrons by Crystals," *Phys. Rev.*, **71,** 294 (1947).

Hughes, D. J. (Hu 53).

Hughes, D. J., *Neutron Optics*, Wiley-Interscience, New York, 1954.

Hughes, D. J., "Reactor Techniques," in (Fl E), Vol. 44.

Marion, J. B., and J. L. Fowler (eds.), *Fast Neutron Physics*, Wiley-Interscience, New York, 1960-1963.

Post, R. F., "High Temperature Plasma Research and Controlled Fusion," *Ann. Rev. Nucl. Sci.*, **9,** 367 (1959).

Salpeter, E. E., "Energy Production in Stars," *Ann. Rev. Nucl. Sci.*, **2,** 41 (1952).

Schwinger, J., and E. Teller, "The Scattering of Neutrons by Ortho- and Parahydrogen," *Phys. Rev.*, **52,** 286 (1937).

Weinberg, A., and E. Wigner (WW 59).

Wilkinson, Wollan, and Koehler, "Neutron Diffraction," *Ann. Rev. Nucl. Sci.*, **11,** 303 (1961).

Problems

12-1 Devise methods for producing neutron beams within an energy range from 10^{-3} to 10^8 eV and for measuring their energy and intensity.

12-2 How many neutrons per second are emitted by 1 g of Ra enclosed in a Be sphere having an internal cavity of 0.75 cm radius and an external radius of 2.5 cm?

12-3 Prove that for large A the average lethargy increase per collision tends to $2/[A + (2/3)]$.

12-4 Find the number of collisions with D, He, Be, U necessary to reduce the energy of a neutron from 10^6 to 1 eV.

12-5 Show that the energy distribution of neutrons of initial energy E_0, after n collisions in hydrogen, is given by

$$P_n(E)\,dE = \frac{[\log (E/E_0)]^{n-1}}{(n-1)!}\frac{dE}{E_0}$$

12-6 A neutron of initial energy E_0 has reached by elastic collisions in hydrogen the energy E. Show that the probability p_n(E) of the number of collisions suffered being n is given by

$$p_n(E) = \frac{[\log (E_0/E)]^{n-1}}{(n-1)!}\frac{E}{E_0}$$

12-7 Give the physical interpretation and explanation of the different factors of Eqs. (12-4.1) and (12-4.2).

12-8 Show that the diffusion coefficient is given by

$$\frac{\lambda v}{3[1 - (2/3A)]}$$

12-9 Assuming λ constant, find the relationship between the "age" of the neutron and the period of time that has passed since its birth. The neutron diffuses and passes from an initial energy E_0 to an energy E.

12-10 High-energy neutrons are produced in the upper atmosphere. In the high-energy range they are slowed down by both elastic and inelastic scattering. Call Q the number crossing the 10^5–eV energy per second. How many reach thermal energy? Assume $\sigma_s = 11$ b for N, 4.2 b for O, and σ_r for N = 1.78 b × (2,200/v in m sec^{-1}). [See (Fe 50), p. 184.]

12-11 Develop Eq. (12-6.19). [See (Fe 50), p. 190.] The source is a δ function.

12-12 Calculate the diffusion length in graphite if $\sigma_s = 4.8$ b and $\sigma_a =$ 4.5 mb. Compare this with the actual distance traveled by a thermal neutron before capture.

12-13 An isotropic source of thermal neutrons is placed at the center of a beryllium sphere of 10 cm radius. Calculate the flux distribution if the source emits 100 neutrons per second, assuming the sphere is surrounded with cadmium so that all neutrons leaving the sphere are lost by radiative capture. What fraction of the source neutrons will be captured in the cadmium? Suppose that in the case of beryllium Σ_a were equal to zero. What fraction of the source neutrons would leak out under these conditions? Explain the difference.

12-14 How much fuel would be consumed by a nuclear-powered submarine traveling at an average power of 30 MW for 1 month?

12-15 Calculate the critical size of a sphere of pure U^{235}.

12-16 Calculate the critical thickness of a slab of material having a certain k. Repeat the calculation for the slab sandwiched between two layers of material having the diffusion coefficient D and thickness T.

12-17 Calculate the critical mass of a pile having a given k and a cylindrical form. Find the most favorable ratio between height and radius.

12-18 What is the minimum concentration of uranyl nitrate in heavy water which can go critical? Assume pure U^{235}.

12-19 A reaction of current interest in the application of thermonuclear processes to power production is the following:

$$D + D = He^3 + n$$

(*a*) If the deuterium nuclei interact at rest, calculate the total final kinetic energy of the neutron and of the helium nucleus (in MeV). (*b*) Calculate the momentum of each (in MeV/c). (*c*) If the deuterium nuclei must come within 10^{-11} cm of each other, what energy must be supplied to overcome the electrostatic repulsion? (*d*) If this energy is supplied by heating the deuterium to a very high temperature, what order of magnitude of temperature is required?

12-20 Show that if neutron scattering is due to the effect of a single Breit-Wigner resonance level then the scattering length is given by

$$-a = \frac{\lambda_R \Gamma_n}{E - E_R + i\Gamma}$$

where Γ_n and Γ are the neutron and the total half-width at half-maximum, and λ_R and E_R refer to the resonance.

12-21 Represent a heavy nucleus by a potential well of radius $R = 1.2 \times 10^{-13} A^{1/3}$ cm and a depth of 30 MeV. Thermal neutrons will have several waves of $r\psi$ inside the well. As a consequence (draw a figure) it is unlikely that the intercept of the tangent to $r\psi$ at R cuts the x axis on the negative side. Moreover, the scattering length is likely to be comparable to the nuclear radius.

12-22 Show that for a complex scattering length $a = a_r + ia_i$ with $a_r \gg a_i$ one has $a_r/a_i = \lambda(\sigma_s)^{1/2}/\pi^{1/2}\sigma_a$.

12-23 Show that the probability of spin flip per scattering is given by

$$Q = \frac{2}{3}\frac{\sigma_{\text{inc}}}{\sigma_s}$$

[G. C. Wick, *Phys. Z*, **38**, 403, 689 (1937).]

12-24 Find the probability that an *n-p* scattering is accompanied by spin flip.

12-25 Show that on the scattering of neutrons in liquid He II the energy and momentum of the exciton are given by

$$E = \frac{\hbar^2(\lambda\!\!\!^-{}_i^{-2} - \lambda\!\!\!^-{}_f^{-2})}{2m_N}$$

$$p^2 = \hbar^2 (\lambda\!\!\!^-{}_i^{-2} - \lambda\!\!\!^-{}_f^{-2} - 2\lambda\!\!\!^-{}_i^{-1}\lambda\!\!\!^-{}_f^{-1} \cos \varphi)$$

assuming $2\pi\lambda\!\!\!^-{}_i = 4$A and $E = vp$ ($v = 240$ m/sec). Plan an experiment to verify this relation [Yarwell and others, *Phys. Rev.*, **113**, 1379 (1959).]

12-26 For NaCl on (001) planes make a table of the wavelengths reflected in 1st and 2nd order at angles 1, 5, 10, 20, and 40°. What is the relative intensity of the first- and second-order beam assuming a distribution $\sim v^3 e^{-mv^2/2kT}$ for the neutrons?

12-27 Derive the relation between refractive index (complex) and scattering length for a complex.

12-28 Derive the relation between refractive index and scattering for a scattered wave amplitude $f(\theta)$.

12-29 Calculate the polarization of a slow-neutron beam from the intensities measured in a double absorption experiment in magnetized iron.

PART III

Subnuclear Particles

CHAPTER XIII

Muons

In this and the following two chapters we shall treat particle physics. The study of subnuclear entities, which we shall loosely call "particles," takes us one step beyond the nucleus in analyzing the structure of matter. The situation is similar in some respects to the step from atomic to nuclear physics. To study the atom it was sufficient to assume the validity of Coulomb's law and the existence of the nucleus and peripheral electrons. The structure of the nucleus could be neglected to a large extent. We needed to know its charge and its approximate size, but little else was necessary except for very detailed investigations. In the next step, the study of the nucleus, it was sufficient to know that its constituents are neutrons and protons and to have an idea of the range and strength of nuclear forces in order to derive a fairly complete picture. Beta decay introduces new problems and a new type of force: the so-called weak interaction or Fermi force. However, until one asks detailed questions about nuclear forces, it is sufficient in describing nuclear phenomena to consider only neutrons, protons, electrons, neutrinos, and gamma quanta.

From the theoretical point of view, a deeper study of nuclear forces was the starting point of the next development (Yukawa, 1935). A parallel development was the experimental discovery of numerous particles, many of them first detected in cosmic rays. The technical development of large accelerating machines made it possible to generate these particles in the laboratory and thus to study them in detail.

13-1 Introduction to Particle Physics

The whole concept of "elementary particle," including its definition, is not clearly settled. Attempts have been made to classify particles in various ways, attributing to some of them a more fundamental role than to others. There have also been attempts to put them all on equal footing, introducing a single field which should describe them all. This field obeys a nonlinear equation which contains a fundamental length as a parameter. The different particles and their properties should be derivable from this field (Heisenberg). Other approaches consider the observable collision phenomena in terms of a "scattering matrix." This matrix becomes the main object of the theory, and its study should provide the ultimate information. Until now, however, none of these ambitious theories has been able to make enough predictions to establish itself solidly.

We shall limit ourselves to a semiphenomenological approach, describing the experimental facts, their immediate consequences, and the theoretical interpretations which seem solidly established.

Many of the relevant concepts have already been introduced in previous chapters. For instance, spin and statistics are treated in Chap. 6 and *i* spin is treated in Chap. 10. The whole chapter on beta decay has many arguments in common with the following chapters. For the convenience of the reader we shall first give some general nomenclature and classification.

One may consider four families of particles in order of increasing rest mass: the first contains only one member, the *photon*, a boson of spin 1. The second family, *leptons*, contains fermions of spin $\frac{1}{2}$, lighter than the proton. Leptons are subject to electromagnetic and Fermi interactions only, not to the strong interactions. The third family, *mesons*, comprises bosons of spin 0. These are heavier than the leptons, lighter than the protons, and subject to all three types of interaction. The fourth family, *baryons*, comprises the proton and heavier fermions. Baryons are subject to all three types of interaction; those heavier than the neutron are called *hyperons*.

The discovery and classification of these particles is one of the major achievements of the decade 1950–1960. In its progress, it has given rise to a complicated nomenclature, which is now falling into disuse, just as the study of natural radioactivity left us with a complicated nomenclature for the natural radioactive substances. Table 13-1 lists the particles and their principal characteristics as they are known today, with the pertinent nomenclature, although there are strong indications that this nomenclature may not be the final one. We need note in this respect only that even in the recent literature both K and θ are used for the same mesons (called K here) and that the τ mesons of the literature are K mesons, decaying into three pions. Measurement of the mass of the different particles is made by observations of reactions in which they transform into other particles of known mass, as will be seen later. The assignment of spin is for the most part indirect; in the arguments used, in general high spins are ruled out a priori. From the decay modes of the particles we know with certainty whether they are fermions or bosons and hence whether they have integral or half integral spins.

The table comprises only particles that cannot decay by strong interaction and thus have mean lives long compared with the characteristic nuclear time 10^{-22} sec.

● Each particle has its own antiparticle. For the electron and for fermions of spin $\frac{1}{2}$ this derives from Dirac's equation. For an electron in an electromagnetic field:

$$\left(\frac{\partial}{\partial t} + \boldsymbol{\alpha}\cdot\boldsymbol{\nabla} + im\beta\right)\psi = ie\,(\boldsymbol{\alpha}\cdot\mathbf{A} - V)\psi \qquad \textbf{(13-1.1)}$$

where $\hbar = c = 1$, **A** and V are the vector and scalar electromagnetic potentials, and $\boldsymbol{\alpha}$ and β are Dirac's matrices, obeying the relations

$$\alpha_\mu \alpha_\nu + \alpha_\nu \alpha_\mu = 2\delta_{\mu\nu} \; (\mu,\nu = 1, 2, 3, m) \qquad \alpha_m \equiv \beta \tag{13-1.2}$$

It is possible to choose $\boldsymbol{\alpha}$ and β such that all the matrix elements of $\boldsymbol{\alpha}$ are real and those of β are purely imaginary. The ψ has four components.

Table 13-1 Masses and Mean Lives of Stable and Semistable Particles[a]

	Particle	Spin	Mass (errors represent standard deviation), MeV		Mass difference, MeV		Mean life, sec
Photon	γ	1	0	γ		γ	Stable
Leptons	ν_e	$\frac{1}{2}$	$< 2 \times 10^{-4}$ prob. 0	ν		ν	Stable
	ν_μ	$\frac{1}{2}$	< 4 prob. 0	ν		ν	Stable
	$e^\mp$	$\frac{1}{2}$	0.511006 ± 0.000002	$e^\mp$		$e^\mp$	Stable
	$\mu^\mp$	$\frac{1}{2}$	105.659 ± 0.002	$\mu^\mp$		$\mu^\mp$	$(2.2000 \pm 0.0015) \times 10^{-6}$
					-33.94 ± 0.05		
Mesons	π^+	0	139.60 ± 0.05	$\pi^\pm$		$\pi^\pm$	$(2.55 \pm 0.03) \times 10^{-8}$
					4.59 ± 0.01		
	π^0	0	135.01 ± 0.05	π^0		π^0	$(1.8 \pm 0.5) \times 10^{-16}$
	$K^\pm$	0	493.9 ± 0.2	K^+		K^+	$(1.230 \pm 0.008) \times 10^{-8}$
					-3.9 ± 0.6		
	K^0			K^0		K^0	50% K_1, 50% K_2
	K_1	0	497.8 ± 0.6	K_1		K_1	$(0.92 \pm 0.02) \times 10^{-10}$
					$(-0.47 \pm 0.2)\hbar/\tau(K_1)$		
	K_2			K_2		K_2	$(6.2 \pm 0.8) \times 10^{-8}$
	η		548 ± 1			η	$> 10^{-22}$ (prob. $\sim 10^{-17}$)
Baryons	p	$\frac{1}{2}$	938.256 ± 0.005	p		p	Stable
					-1.2939 ± 0.0004		
	n	$\frac{1}{2}$	939.550 ± 0.005	n		n	$(1.013 \pm 0.029) \times 10^3$
	Λ	$\frac{1}{2}$	1115.45 ± 0.13	Λ		Λ	$(2.62 \pm 0.09) \times 10^{-10}$
	Σ^+	$\frac{1}{2}$	1189.40 ± 0.15	Σ^+		Σ^+	$(0.79 \pm 0.03) \times 10^{-10}$
	Σ^-	$\frac{1}{2}$	1197.6 ± 0.5	Σ^-		Σ^-	$(1.58 \pm 0.05) \times 10^{-10}$
					4.45 ± 0.4		
	Σ^0	$\frac{1}{2}$	1193.2 ± 0.7	Σ^0		Σ^0	$< 10^{-14}$ (prob. 10^{-19})
	Ξ^-	?	1321.2 ± 0.3	Ξ^-		Ξ^-	$(1.74 \pm 0.05) \times 10^{-10}$
					6.8 ± 1.6		
	Ξ^0	?	1314.4 ± 1.6	Ξ^0		Ξ^0	$(3.0 \pm 0.3) \times 10^{-10}$
	Ω^-	?	1686 ± 12			Ω^-	0.7×10^{-10} (1 event)

[a]The antiparticles are assumed to have the same spins, masses, and mean lives as the particles listed.

If we take the complex conjugate on both sides of Eq. (13-1.1) we obtain

$$\left(\frac{\partial}{\partial t} + \boldsymbol{\alpha}\cdot\nabla + im\beta\right)\psi^* = -ie(\boldsymbol{\alpha}\cdot\mathbf{A} - V)\psi^* \qquad \textbf{(13-1.3)}$$

That is, ψ^* obeys the same equation as ψ except that the charge e has been changed into $-e$. If Eq. (13-1.1) has a positive energy solution $\psi \sim e^{-iEt}(E > 0)$, then Eq. (13-1.3) has a negative energy solution, and vice versa. ●

It is clear that the negative energy solutions of Eq. (13-1.3), whose meaning may seem at first sight questionable, correspond to positive energy solutions of Eq. (13-1.1), provided the sign of charge is reversed. They correspond to the motion of *positrons*.

Dirac interpreted the positrons as "holes" in a distribution, with almost all states of negative energy filled, but here Dirac's theory is formulated in a perfectly symmetrical form in which the electron and positron are treated on an equal footing. This is important because it shows that the symmetry between electron and positron is not related to their statistics, as one might think from the "hole" picture, in which the exclusion principle plays a fundamental role.

The concept of charge conjugation can be extended to bosons. One finds that for each charged particle an antiparticle exists that has the same mass and spin as the particle. Their electric charge and magnetic moment are equal in magnitude but opposite in sign.

For neutral particles, if they have electromagnetic properties (e.g. a magnetic moment, as in the case of the neutron) the same relations apply as for charged particles. Thus for instance a neutron and an antineutron with parallel spins have equal and opposite magnetic moment.

If they have no electromagnetic interactions, the particles may be self-conjugate like the π^0 or they may have distinct antiparticles like the neutrino. Whether one case or the other occurs can be decided by experiment; for instance, in the case of the neutrino, by observation of the inverse beta decay. The relations between particle and antiparticle are summarized in Table 13-2.

In the case of fermions, particle and antiparticle must be generated or annihilated in pairs. This can be looked upon as a consequence of the hole theory of Dirac and it has been experimentally verified in every case. It is also required by the principle of conservation of leptons and nucleons.

Annihilation occurs in a variety of forms. For electron-positron pairs annihilation is always electromagnetic, and light quanta are emitted. In the case of nucleons-antinucleons, pi mesons are the most frequent annihilation product (Fig. 13-1) but occasionally K mesons are also emitted. Electromagnetic annihilation into gamma rays or electron-positron pairs is expected to occur only seldom in comparison with pion-producing annihilation. Particle and antiparticle have the same i spin but opposite T_3.

As important as the acquaintance with particles and relative nomen-
ature is a knowledge and classification of the interactions to which they
re subject. Although this topic has been touched upon in other chapters
e shall again summarize its results.

The interactions between elementary particles can be classified in
our groups:

1. *Strong interactions.* This group comprises the Yukawa interaction and its derivatives, such as the nucleon-nucleon force. It is characterized by a coupling constant f, called g in Sec. 14-1. The dimensionless constant $f^2/\hbar c$ is found to be of the order of 1.
2. *Electromagnetic interactions.* These are characterized by the coupling constant $e^2/\hbar c = 1/137$.
3. *Weak interactions* such as the one causing beta decay or the decay of the K meson into three pions. Their coupling constant (see Chap. 9) may be expressed in a dimensionless form by the Fermi constant of beta decay g divided by the rest energy of the pion and the cube of its Compton wavelength. Its value is $G^2/\hbar c \simeq 5 \times 10^{-14} \simeq g^2(mc^2)^{-2}(\hbar/mc)^{-6}$.
4. *Gravitational interaction.* A dimensionless coupling constant is $Km^2/\hbar c \simeq 2 \times 10^{-39}$, where K ($K = 6.67 \times 10^{-8}$ dyne cm^2 g^{-2}) is Newton's constant and for m we take the mass of the proton. This interaction is much weaker than (3); it will not be considered here.

To understand the meaning of the numerical values of the dimen-
onless coupling constants, first consider the electromagnetic inter-
ctions. In estimating the cross section for a process, (e.g., Compton
attering), one finds orders of magnitude by taking a dimensionally
orrect natural unit and multiplying it by $e^2/\hbar c$ as many times as the

Table 13-2 Relation between Particle and Antiparticle

	Particle	Antiparticle	
Mass		Same	
Spin		Same	
Charge	$+q$		$-q$
Magnetic moment	μ		$-\mu$
Mean life (free decay)		Same	
Annihilation	In pairs	For fermions only	
Generation	In pairs	For fermions only	
i spin		Same	
Third comp. of i spin	T_3		$-T_3$
Intrinsic parity (see Sec. 14-4)		Same for bosons Opposite for fermions	

order of the process. Thus, in the case of Compton scattering one cou take $(\hbar/m_e c)^2\,(e^2/\hbar c)^2$. The last factor is squared because the photon absorbed and reemitted. In the electron-positron annihilation one wou take $(\hbar/m_e c^2)\,(e^2/\hbar c)^2$ as the mean life for two-quanta annihilation, et Naturally these crude estimates have to be taken with great caution an are valid only for allowed processes.

For the strong interactions the constant $f^2/\hbar c$ can be estimated fro the pion-nucleon cross section. If we take the cross section to be ($mc)^2(f^2/\hbar c)^2$, with m equal to the nucleon mass, we have $f^2/\hbar c \simeq 1$ However, this order of magnitude depends on the specific form of t interaction. The theory is often formulated in such a way that the fu damental coupling constant to be considered is $(f^2/\hbar c)(m_\pi/2m_p)^2 = 0.0$ The value 1 quoted above is a sort of compromise between the differe definitions. According to some modern ideas the strong interactio might even be "as strong as possible." By this it is meant that if one ha a complete theory considering all strong interactions between all particle the scattering matrix elements would be as large as permitted by t unitarity and other analytic properties of the matrix. According to the ideas no special constant may be attached to the strong interaction and the f here considered originates from our considering only a pa of the total scattering matrix. The constant f is an empirical paramet describing the neglected interactions. In a complete theory it wou vanish. However, $f^2/\hbar c$ is, in any reasonable definition, considerab larger than $e^2/\hbar c$.

The constant g of weak interactions is dimensionally different fro e and f. To derive a dimensionless constant from g one must introdu a characteristic length and energy. Using the pion Compton waveleng and rest energy, one obtains the value given above. However, even t proton gives a number small compared with $e^2/\hbar c$.

In conclusion: Although in establishing the numerical values of t coupling constants for the different types of interactions, there is a certai amount of arbitrariness, depending on the specific form given to t theory; nevertheless, the strengths of the interactions are so different th the classification is useful. A sharper and more precise criterion of class fication is given by the conservation laws of Table 13-3. Wheneve necessary we shall indicate strong interactions by $\Rightarrow$, electromagnet interactions by $\rightsquigarrow$, and weak interactions by $\rightarrow$.

Note that the electromagnetic interaction is strictly proportional t the charges. There are no electromagnetic interactions besides the usu ones between charges and currents. Anomalous magnetic moments an such phenomena are not to be attributed to special couplings but can b reduced to interactions produced by an electric current due to meson Gell-Mann expresses this by saying that there is a "minimal electroma netic interaction."

The conservation laws listed in Table 13-3 have all been verified em pirically. The conservation of energy, momentum, and angular mome tum are fundamentally related to the invariance properties of space-tim

The conservation of charge is related to the so-called gauge invariance of the electromagnetic field [see (Ja 62)]. Strangeness will be defined in Sec. 15-2. For other conservation properties we have no "theoretical" justification. This is especially true of the conservation of nucleons and of leptons. The experimental data, however, argue very strongly for their validity. For instance, the half-life for a hypothetical disintegration of the proton is greater than 10^{28} years; there must thus be a very powerful selection rule preventing it from transforming into lighter particles. This selection rule is the conservation of nucleons. The quantities conserved and the relative quantum numbers behave in two radically different ways when one considers a system formed by the combination of two other systems. For instance, the angular momentum of the whole is the sum of the angular momenta of the components. The corresponding quantum numbers are called "additive" quantum numbers. On the other hand, the parity of a compound system is the product of the parities of the components. The corresponding quantum numbers are called "multiplicative" quantum numbers. The last column of Table 13-3 indicates the character of the quantum numbers by A (additive) or M (multiplicative). The character of the conservation laws is ultimately an experimental question. For instance, we have listed among the conservation laws one for the number of leptons (additive). There are theoretical schemes in which the conservation of leptons is further subdivided, giving rise to a multiplicative or to an additive conservation law for muons; the question of which is valid is still undecided.

● We give here some additional selection rules for strong and electromagnetic interactions mainly as a summary of results. To be complete, the explanations given here, admittedly inadequate, would require theoretical knowledge beyond the level of this book. The relevant materials

Table 13-3 Conservation Laws and Their Validity

Conservation of	Strong	Electromagnetic	Weak	Character
Energy-momentum	Yes	Yes	Yes	
Angular momentum	Yes	Yes	Yes	A
Parity	Yes	Yes	No	M
i spin	Yes	No	No	A
Strangeness	Yes	Yes	No	A
Number of nucleons	Yes	Yes	Yes	A
Leptons	Yes	Yes	Yes	A
Electric charge	Yes	Yes	Yes	A
Invariance under charge conjugation	Yes	Yes	No	M
Invariance under time reversal	Yes	Yes	Probably yes	M

can be found in the article of Wick or in Marshak and Sudarshan (see Bibliography). However, the results can be understood to a certain extent without proofs and they are practically useful.

We shall sometimes use here, for convenience, the Dirac notation and indicate by $|K\rangle$ the eigenfunction corresponding to the quantum number K, in particular to a particle K. In ordinary notation ψ_K would be used for $|K\rangle$. The symbol $\langle K'|K\rangle$ means $\int \psi_{K'}^* \psi_K \, d\tau$. It is thus the Fourier coefficient of the development of ψ_K in $\psi_{K'}$ eigenfunctions. An operator $\mathcal{O}$ operating on $|K\rangle$ gives as a result the function $\mathcal{O}|K\rangle$.

For instance, the parity operator applied to a pion

$$P|\pi\rangle = -|\pi\rangle \tag{13-1.4}$$

because the pion has negative intrinsic parity. The parity operator applied to a wave function labeled according to orbital angular momentum gives

$$P|l\rangle = (-1)^l|l\rangle \tag{13-1.5}$$

The charge conjugation operator C gives

$$C|\pi^0\rangle = |\pi^0\rangle \tag{13-1.6}$$

indicating that the π^0 is self-conjugate and that $|\pi^0\rangle$ is an eigenstate of C with eigenvalue $+1$.

On the other hand, $|\pi^+\rangle$ and $|\pi^-\rangle$ are not eigenstates of C, because

$$C|\pi^{\mp}\rangle = |\pi^{\pm}\rangle \tag{13-1.7}$$

The result follows from the fact that C changes π^+ into π^-, and that $C^2 = 1$. The sign in front of $|\pi^{\mp}\rangle$ is to some extent arbitrary: we shall

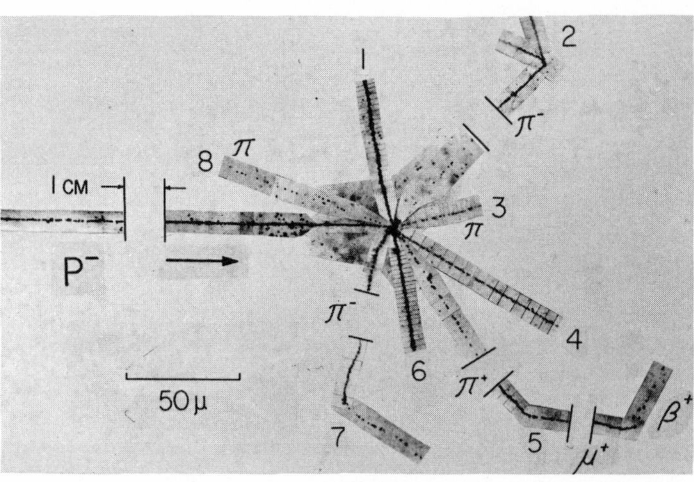

Figure 13-1 Proton-antiproton annihilation in a photographic emulsion. The annihilating proton is bound in a nucleus. The nucleus is disrupted and tracks 1, 4, and 6 are fragments of the nucleus. The other tracks are charged pions coming from the annihilation. Neutral pions are invisible. The total visible energy released is 1,300 MeV > 938 MeV (the mass of the incoming antiproton) proving that annihilation has taken place. A study of the primary antiproton track permits the determinations of the $\bar{p}$ mass with an accuracy of a few per cent.

assume $C|\pi^{\pm}\rangle = |\pi^{\mp}\rangle$. For one light quantum $C|\gamma\rangle = -|\gamma\rangle$, and for n quanta the eigenvalue of C is $(-1)^n$.

The operation of charge conjugation gives important results for systems containing equal number of particles and antiparticles plus any number of self-conjugate particles. These systems are eigenstates of C with the eigenvalue

$$(-1)^{l+S} \tag{13-1.8}$$

where S is the total spin and l the total orbital angular momentum. Thus, for positronium in the $^3S_1$ state ($l = 0$, $S = 1$) the eigenvalue of C is -1 and thus it cannot decay into two quanta whose eigenvalue for C is $+1$.

In strong interactions C and the total i spin $\mathbf{T}$ are constants of the motion. The two operators do not commute, however; therefore the simultaneous conservation of both gives interesting results. These are best found by investigating the effect of the operation: (charge conjugation) $\times$ (rotation by π around the 2-axis in i-spin space). The effect of the rotation operation above, indicated by $T_2(180°)$ for i spin $\frac{1}{2}$, is to transform

$$\begin{vmatrix} \psi_a \\ \psi_b \end{vmatrix} \quad \text{into} \quad \begin{vmatrix} \psi_b \\ -\psi_a \end{vmatrix}$$

Thus, for the nucleon $T_2(180°)|p\rangle \rightarrow -|n\rangle$ and $T_2(180°)|n\rangle \rightarrow |p\rangle$. For i spin 1 the same operation transforms

$$\begin{vmatrix} \psi_a \\ \psi_b \\ \psi_c \end{vmatrix} \quad \text{into} \quad - \begin{vmatrix} \psi_c \\ \psi_b \\ \psi_a \end{vmatrix}$$

or

$$T_2(180°)|\pi^+\rangle = -|\pi^-\rangle \qquad T_2(180°)|\pi^0\rangle = -|\pi^0\rangle$$
$$T_2(180°)|\pi^-\rangle = -|\pi^+\rangle$$

From these rules the product operator $C \cdot T_2(180°) = G$ has the property $CT_2(180°)|p\rangle = -|\bar{n}\rangle$; $CT_2(180°)|\pi^+\rangle = -|\pi^+\rangle$, etc. This shows that pions are eigenstates of the operator G, but nucleons are not, because a baryon is converted in an antibaryon. Systems composed of equal numbers of nucleons and antinucleons may be simultaneous eigenstates of G and T. The corresponding eigenvalue η_G is then

$$\eta_G = (-1)^{T+l+S} \tag{13-1.9}$$

Systems of pions have

$$\eta_G = (-1)^n \tag{13-1.10}$$

where n is the number of pions.

For instance, a proton-antineutron system in the $^3S_1$ state has $T = 1$, $l = 0$, $S = 1$, $\eta_G = +1$, and it cannot annihilate into three pions for which $\eta_G = -1$. The G quantum number is derived from charge conjugation and i-spin conservation and needs to be constant only in strong interactions.

For electromagnetic interactions, on the assumption of "minimality" (that is, that the electromagnetic field is proportional to the charges), one also finds a selection rule for *i* spin. The charge may be written as

$$q = T_3 + \frac{Y}{2} \tag{13-1.11}$$

It is therefore a linear function of the third component of the *i*-spin vector (see Chap. 15 for definition of Y). When vectors appear in an interaction one obtains the selection rule

$$\Delta T = \pm 1{,}0 \qquad \bullet \tag{13-1.12}$$

The remainder of this chapter is devoted to muons. These are the heaviest leptons; however, some of the topics, such as the determination of mass, provide examples applicable to the study of all particles. Other topics are peculiar to muons only. Chapter 14 is devoted mainly to pions. These are better known than other mesons and deserve a separate chapter. The new quantum number, *strangeness*, introduces an essentially new concept in particle physics. This justifies lumping together all the strange particles in a single chapter (Chap. 15).

13-2 Muon Production

Muons were first discovered in cosmic rays about 1936 by C. D. Anderson, S. H. Neddermeyer, and others. Previously, particles of approximately the muon mass had been postulated by Yukawa (1935) as quanta of the field responsible for nuclear forces. It turned out, however, that the particles of intermediate mass (mesons) first seen in cosmic rays were *not* the particles postulated by Yukawa; for, although they have about the right mass, they do not interact appreciably with nucleons (Conversi, Pancini, and Piccioni, 1947). These particles, now called muons, in many ways resemble heavy electrons. They belong to the lepton family comprising particles that are not subject to specific nuclear interactions, but only to electromagnetic and weak interactions. For historical reasons the muon is sometimes called, rather improperly, mu meson. The word meson should preferably be reserved for bosons.

Leptons resemble each other very closely except in the mass. Thus, they have the magnetic moment predicted by Dirac's theory (as later refined). It is one of the unsolved problems of particle physics to find the reason for the difference in mass between leptons, and which other quantum numbers, of an undiscovered nature, characterize them.

The charge of muons (positive and negative) is equal in magnitude to the charge of the electron. There are no neutral muons. As we shall see, muons are unstable. They are usually obtained as a decay product of the pion (see Chap. 14) according to the reactions

$$\pi^+ \to \mu^+ + \nu_\mu \tag{13-2.1}$$

$$\pi^- \to \mu^- + \bar{\nu}_\mu \tag{13-2.2}$$

It is noteworthy that the neutrino appearing in this reaction seems to be different from the neutrino of beta decay. This is demonstrated by bombarding nuclei with ν_μ. One occasionally gets muons ($\sigma \sim 10^{-38}$ cm^2 at 1 BeV) which are interpreted as the product of the reactions

$$\nu_\mu + n \rightarrow \mu^- + p \tag{13-2.3}$$

$$\bar{\nu}_\mu + p \rightarrow \mu^+ + n \tag{13-2.4}$$

However, the reactions

$$\nu_e + n \rightarrow e^- + p \tag{13-2.5}$$

$$\bar{\nu}_e + p \rightarrow e^+ + n \tag{13-2.6}$$

(the inverse of beta decay) are known; under the conditions of the bombardment one would also expect to produce electrons, provided the two kinds of neutrinos are identical. In fact, no electrons have been found, leading to the conclusion that there are two different kinds of neutrinos. By this, we do not mean neutrinos ν, and antineutrinos $\bar{\nu}$, but two totally different kinds of particles, which we have indicated by ν_e and ν_μ. Apart from this phenomenological distinction implied by the experiment described, we do not know what the difference between the two neutrinos is.

Although the most common source of muons is the pion decay, muons appear as branchings in other decays such as

$$\Sigma^\pm \rightarrow \mu^\pm + \nu + n \tag{13-2.7}$$

$$\Lambda \rightarrow \mu^- + \nu + p \tag{13-2.8}$$

$$K \rightarrow \mu + \nu, \text{ etc.} \tag{13-2.9}$$

Muons can also be generated in pairs by photoproduction. The cross section for this process is similar to that for electron pair production, except that the mass of the muon replaces the mass of the electron in the formula.

13-3 Mass of the Muons

The example of the muon will illustrate the methods available for the determination of the mass of particles. Many of the techniques and principles involved are well known; however, the instability of the muon and the conditions for its production bring about some peculiarities worth discussing.

The fundamental idea is always to measure two quantities on the same particle, such as energy and momentum and to derive the mass. This method was applied to the muons found in cosmic rays and gave a first measurement accurate to about 5 per cent of the muon mass. The quantities measured were momentum (from the curvature of a cloud-chamber track in a magnetic field) and the specific ionization (from the number of droplets condensed along the track) (see Fig. 13-2). In photographic emulsions one can count the number of grains from the end of the range, thereby obtaining the energy of the particle and the grain density obtaining the velocity. From these one finds the mass.

When particles are produced in the laboratory more precise methods become feasible. These methods measure the ratio of the mass of a particle to that of some standard, for example the proton. They are based on the observation that many quantities, for instance momentum, energy, range, total ionization, and others have the form

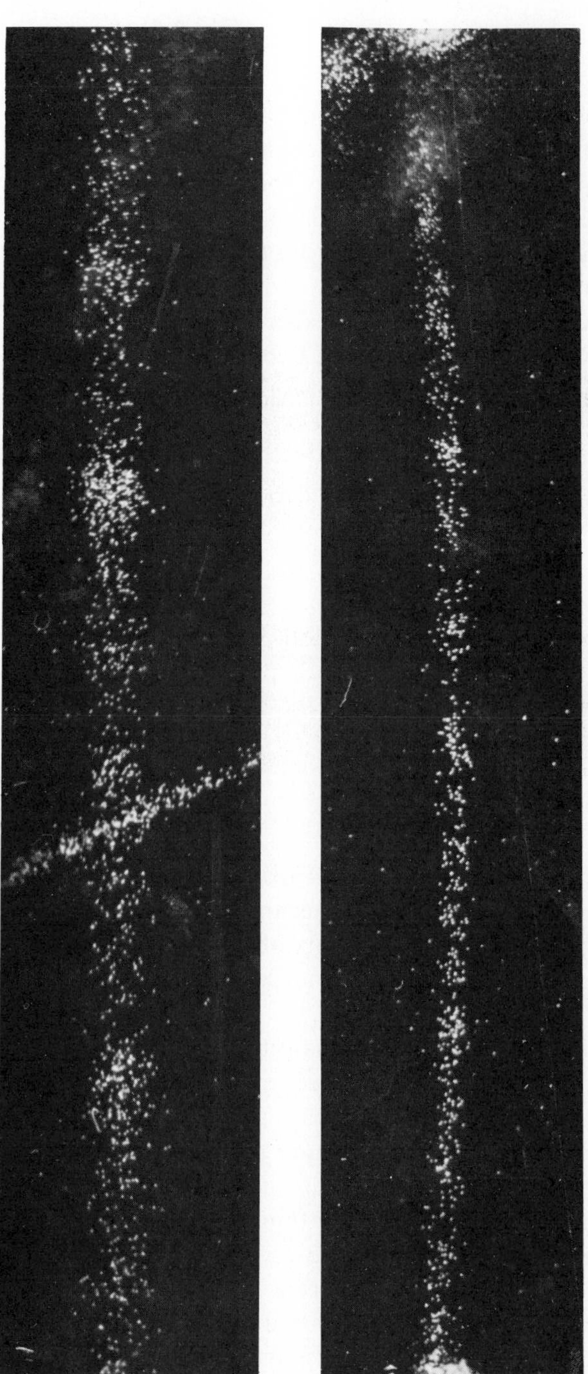

Figure 13-2 An early cloud-chamber picture showing the velocity (from the ionization, i.e., the number of droplets per unit path length) and momentum (from the curvature) of a meson. Pressure in cloud chamber 1.5 atm of N_2. Magnetic field 800 G. Expansion occurred 0.5 sec after particle had crossed the chamber to give time to the ions to diffuse and make droplets countable. [Courtesy R. B. Brode and D. R. Corson.]

$$p = m\pi(v) \qquad E = m\epsilon(v) \qquad R = m\rho(v)/z^2 \text{ etc.} \qquad \textbf{(13-3.1)}$$

where m is the rest mass of the particle, and π,ϵ,ρ are functions of the velocity only (cf. Sec. 2-3).

If two different kinds of particles 1, 2, *having the same velocity*, are stopped in a photographic emulsion, then the momenta are in the same ratio as their ranges and this common ratio is the ratio of masses. This relation derives from the equations

$$\frac{p_1}{p_2} = \frac{m_1}{m_2}\frac{\pi(v_1)}{\pi(v_2)}$$

$$\frac{R_1}{R_2} = \frac{m_1}{m_2}\frac{\rho(v_1)}{\rho(v_2)}$$

which are immediate consequences of Eq. (13-3.1).

Experimentally Barkas and co-workers (1956) measured the ratio of the pion-muon mass and of the pion-proton mass. The variables

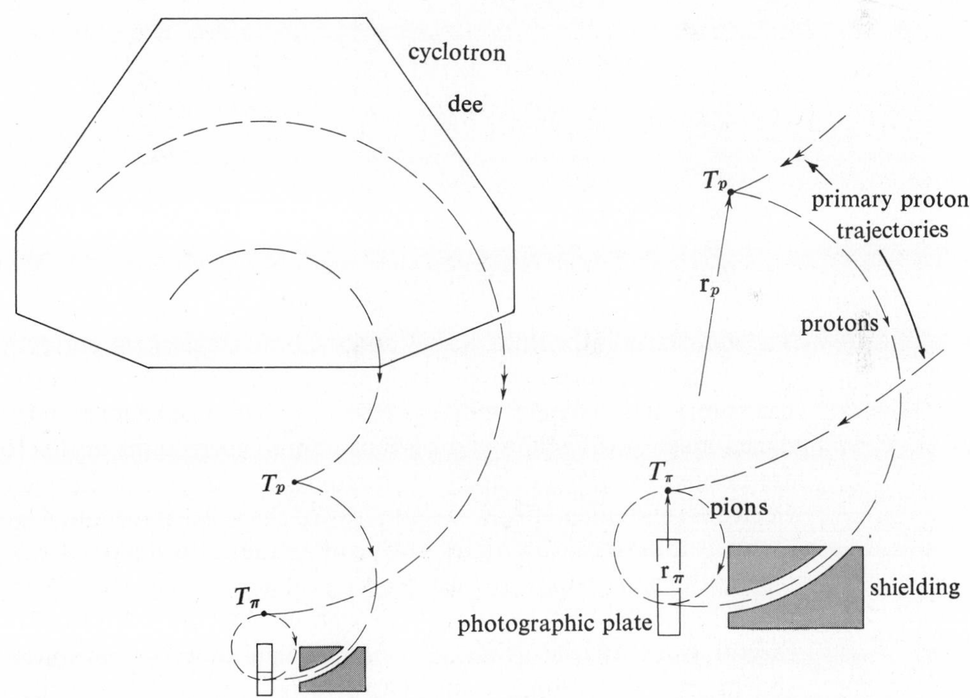

Figure 13-3 Determination of the masses of π^+ mesons by a method independent of the range-energy relation. The primary protons bombard the two targets, T_p and T_π, which serve as sources of protons and π mesons, respectively. The two types of particles, in certain intervals of momenta, enter the photographic plates, where their ranges can be compared. At any point in the plate, the ratio of $Hr \sim$ momentum for the two types of particles has a certain value which can be determined. At the same point, the ratio of the ranges can also be measured. The experiment consists in determining the point where $(Hr)_p/(Hr)_\pi$ and R_p/R_π have the same values. This common value is also equal to the ratio of the masses, m_p/m_π; it occurs at that point in the plate where the two types of particles enter with equal velocities. [Barkas, Birnbaum, and Smith, *Phys. Rev.*, **101,** 778 (1955).]

measured were the range (in emulsion) and momentum (see Fig. 13-3). These measurements give the masses with an accuracy of about one part in a thousand.

There are other, less direct ways of measuring the muon mass. When muons are generated according to the reaction $\pi \rightarrow \mu + \nu_\mu$ measurement of the momentum p_μ with which they are produced from pions at rest gives (provided the rest mass of ν_μ is zero)

$$m_\pi - m_\mu = \frac{2m_\pi/m_\mu}{(m_\pi/m_\mu) + 1} \frac{p_\mu}{c} \tag{13-3.2}$$

One measures p_μ directly and finds 29.80 ± 0.04 MeV/c or 4.12 MeV energy. By combining the measurement of the pion-muon mass difference with that of their mass ratio obtained from another experiment, we can determine the two masses.

A completely different way of obtaining the muon mass is offered by the study of radiative transitions in mu-mesic atoms. Mu-mesic atoms are systems of one nucleus and one negative muon, resembling a hydrogen atom. In first approximation the energy levels of such a mu-mesic atom are given by

$$E = \frac{1}{2} mc^2 \left(\frac{Z\alpha}{n}\right)^2 \left[1 + \left(\frac{Z\alpha}{n}\right)^2 \left(\frac{n}{|k|} - \frac{3}{4}\right)\right] \tag{13-3.3}$$

with Z = atomic number

$$\alpha = e^2/\hbar c$$

$$n = \text{integral}$$

$$|k| = \begin{cases} l + 1 & \text{for } j = l + \frac{1}{2} \\ l & \text{for } j = l - \frac{1}{2} \end{cases}$$

The main term is the Bohr energy and the bracket gives the correction due to spin in the Sommerfeld–Dirac approximation, assuming that the muon has spin $\frac{1}{2}$ and magnetic moment equal to $e\hbar/m_\mu c$. The mass m is the reduced mass of the muon and nucleus. Small corrections in this formula are needed to take into account the finite nuclear size, the screening by electrons, and other effects. The energy of the radiation emitted by mesic atoms is thus about 206 times greater than that of ordinary X rays emitted by the same atom. It has been possible to detect mesic X rays and measure their energy by critical absorption (see Chap. 2). In particular, careful work on the $3D_{3/2,5/2} - 2P_{3/2,1/2}$ multiplet in phosphorus has shown that the strongest line ($D_{5/2} - P_{3/2}$) has an energy of 88,000 ± 10 eV. This gives a precise value of m_μ/m_e = 206.77, accurate to a few parts in 10^4.

In this section we have assumed that the charge of the muon is exactly equal to that of the electron. This is hardly debatable, and direct experiments have confirmed the equality of charge to one part in 20,000 or better. Also, the zero rest mass for ν_e is reasonably certain. Although it is likely that ν_μ also has a zero rest mass, the upper limit obtained in direct experiment is 4 MeV.

Free muons decay into electrons and neutral particles. The electron spectrum is a continuum; thus more than one invisible neutral partner is required to conserve energy and momentum. The form of the spectrum agrees with the predictions of a reaction

$$\mu^- \rightarrow e^- + \nu_\mu + \bar{\nu}_e \qquad \textbf{(13-4.1)}$$

proceeding by weak interaction and completely similar to beta decay (see Sec. 9-10). Of the two neutrinos, one is believed to be of the kind found in beta decay, and the other of the kind found in pion decay. Direct experiment failed to reveal any sizable amount of gamma radiation associated with muon decay. The maximum momentum of the decay electrons is given by $m_\mu c^2 = (p_e^2 c^2 + m_e^2 c^4)^{1/2} + p_e c$ (p_e = 52 MeV/c).

The continuous energy spectrum of decay electrons has the form indicated in Fig. 13-4. The energy of the electrons is greatest when the two neutrinos escape in the same direction, opposite to that of the electron. The probability of this occurrence, in the case of identical neutrinos, is 0. The qualitative reason for this is related to Pauli's principle, which prevents two identical neutrinos from moving into the same quantum state. Thus, if the two neutrinos were identical, there would be no electrons with the maximum possible energy, and the energy spectrum would look like the line $\rho = 0$ in Fig. 13-4. We conclude, therefore, that in muon decay two different neutrinos are emitted. These were

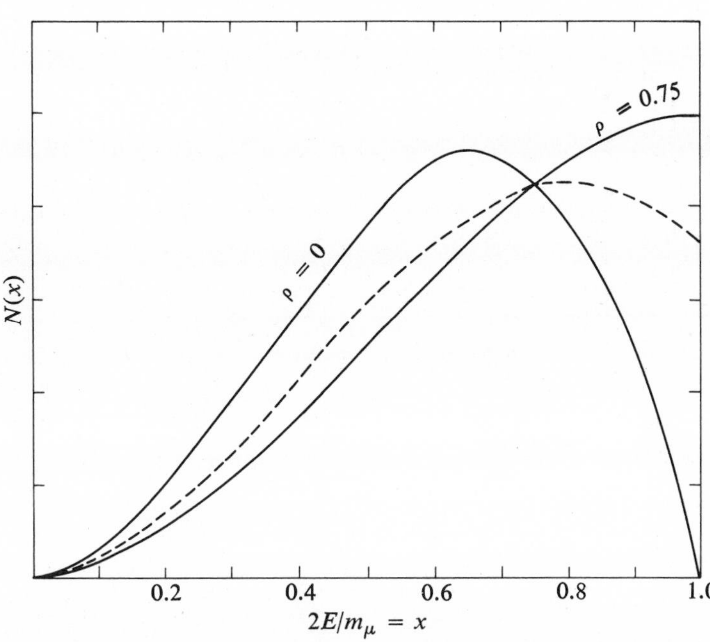

Figure 13-4 Energy spectrum of electrons emitted in the decay of the mu meson. Maximum energy is 52 MeV. The equation of the curve is $N(x) = 4x^2[3(1-x) + \frac{2}{3}\rho(4x - 3)]$. Curves for the Michel parameter $\rho = 0$ and $\rho = 0.75$ (see Chap. 9) are shown, as well as a dashed curve representing the statistical phase-space distribution. Experiments indicate a spectrum with $\rho = 0.76 \pm 0.02$.

Table 13-4 Table of Leptons

	e^-	e^+	μ^-	μ^+	ν_e	$\bar{\nu}_e$	ν_μ	$\bar{\nu}_\mu$
Leptonic number	1	-1	1	-1	1	-1	1	-1
Helicity	$(-\beta)$	$(+\beta)$	$(-\beta)$	$(+\beta)$	-1	$+1$	-1	$+1$
Muonic number	0	0	1	-1	0	0	1	-1

$\beta = v/c.$

once supposed to be particle and antiparticle. Now it is assumed that they belong to the two different species of neutrinos. This in turn gives two possibilities for the neutrino pair: it could consist of an electron antineutrino $\bar{\nu}_e$ and a muon neutrino ν_μ or of a ν_e and a $\bar{\nu}_\mu$; in any case their combined helicity is zero. The choice $\nu_e + \bar{\nu}_\mu$ is preferred because it associates the e^+ with the ν_e as in beta decay.

Consider now the component of the angular momentum in the direction of motion of the electron. For electrons having the maximum possible energy, the neutrino pair has zero angular momentum in that direction, and the electron must have the same angular momentum as the decaying muon. The angular momentum of the positron has actually been measured in the case of positive muons and found to be parallel to the direction of motion, which indicates that the spin of the muon itself is preferentially parallel to the direction of emission of the high-energy positrons (see Fig. 13-5).

The orientations of all spins are thus consistent with the assignments of decay,

$$\pi^- \to \mu^- + \bar{\nu}_\mu \qquad \pi^+ \to \mu^+ + \nu_\mu \tag{13-4.2}$$

$$\mu^- \to e^- + \bar{\nu}_e + \nu \qquad \mu^+ \to e^+ + \nu_e + \bar{\nu}_\mu \tag{13-4.3}$$

helicities in

$\pi \to \mu \to e$ decay

$\pi^+ \to \mu^+ + \nu_\mu$ $\qquad$ $\mu^+ \to e^+ + \nu_e + \bar{\nu}_\mu$

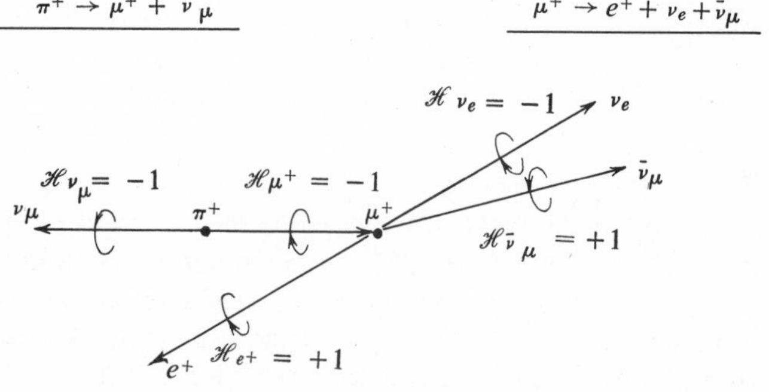

Figure 13-5 Schematic diagram of momenta and helicities in the decays $\pi^+ \to \mu^+ + \nu_\mu$ and $\mu^+ \to e^+ + \bar{\nu}_\mu + \nu_e$.

which in turn are equivalent to the conservation of leptons and of muonic number, provided that one defines e^- as a lepton and assigns the leptonic and muonic numbers as shown in Table 13-4 (cf. Sec. 9-10).

The mean life of the free muon is important for comparing the coupling constant of muon decay with that of beta decay. First consider positive muons. Their mean life was first inferred from their disappearance in cosmic rays traversing the atmosphere, but a direct measurement was performed by Rasetti (1940), who observed their arrival and stoppage in a carbon block and the subsequent emergence of a positron. This experiment has been repeated under improved conditions with machine-generated muons (see, for example, Fig. 13-6); the accepted value of the mean life, for positive muons, is

$$\tau_\mu = (2.200 \pm 0.0015) \times 10^{-6} \text{ sec}$$

It is noteworthy that calculation of τ_μ based on the beta-decay theory with a *V-A* interaction gives this mean life within 3 per cent, provided one assumes the same coupling constant for the μ decay and the beta decay. This is one strong argument for the universal Fermi interaction.

Free negative muons have the same decay constant as positive muons. The determination of this result, anticipated by the particle-antiparticle relation, has a precision of about one part in one thousand.

Negative muons stopped in matter may decay freely, but they may also interact with nuclei of the stopping substance and disappear by

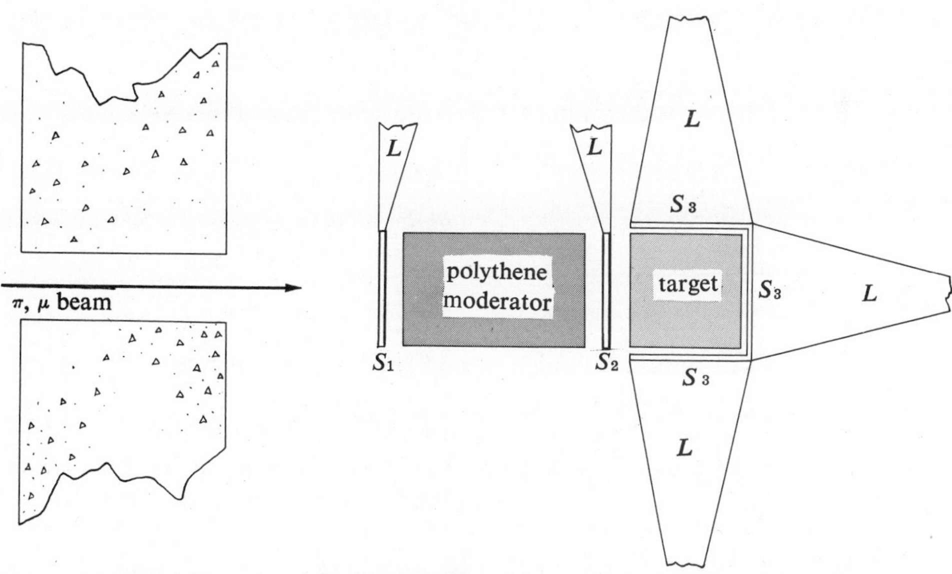

Figure 13-6 A typical apparatus used in measuring the μ^+ lifetime. A mixed beam of pions and muons enters the polythene moderator, which stops the pions. The arrival of a muon is signalled by a S_1,S_2 coincidence. The successive decay of a muon stopped in the target is detected by S_3. The average time interval between arrival and decay gives the mean life of the muon; *S*, scintillators; *L*, light guides. [After Astbury, Hattersley, Hussain, Kemp, and Muirhead (RoC 60).]

capture. In very light elements they show about the same mean life as positive muons. This important fact, discovered by Conversi, Pancini, and Piccioni in 1947, demonstrated that they interact only weakly with nuclei and laid the foundation for the distinction between pions and muons.

When negative muons are stopped in substances of a given Z, their mean life is

$$\frac{1}{\tau} = \frac{1}{\tau_\mu} + \frac{1}{\tau_c} \tag{13-4.4}$$

The first term on the right corresponds to the free decay and the second to the disappearance caused by interaction with the nucleus of the stopping medium.

For $Z = 11$ the two terms are almost equal. This fact throws an interesting light on the capture process. We try to estimate $1/\tau_c$, assuming an interaction that produces the process

$$p + \mu^- \rightarrow n + \nu$$

(cf. Chap. 9).

The matrix element for this interaction is simply a characteristic constant $g_{\mu N}$ divided by a normalization volume Ω. The rate for the process is calculated by golden rule No. 2 as

$$\text{rate} = \frac{2\pi}{\hbar}\left(\frac{g_{\mu N}}{\Omega}\right)^2 \rho \tag{13-4.5}$$

The density of final states ρ in this case is

$$\rho = \frac{\Omega p^2}{2\pi^2\hbar^3}\frac{1}{(c + v_N)} \tag{13-4.6}$$

where p is the momentum of the neutrino and v_N the velocity of the recoil neutron, which is given by

$$m_\mu c^2 = cp + \frac{p^2}{2M_N} \tag{13-4.7}$$

and

$$p = m_N v_N$$

For a muon bound to a nucleus, the normalization volume is replaced by the volume of the mesic atom. We may think of the muon as enclosed in a box of volume $\pi a^3/Z^3$, where a is the radius of the hydrogen Bohr orbit divided by m_μ/m_e. We multiply the result by Z, in order to take into account the fact that there are Z protons in the nucleus, obtaining

$$\frac{1}{\tau_c} = \frac{1}{\pi^2} g_{\mu N}{}^2 \frac{E_\nu{}^2 Z}{\hbar^4 c^2(c + v_N)}\left(\frac{Z}{a}\right)^3 \tag{13-4.8}$$

Equation (13-4.8) is not intended to be quantitative. An important correction is introduced by the exclusion principle, which rules out transitions in which the neutron would go into an occupied orbit. This correction is estimated to introduce a factor $\frac{1}{4}$. Moreover τ_μ of Eq. (13-4.4) is only approximately equal to the decay constant of the free muon, because at least three factors affect the decay constant of a bound meson: the energy available for the decay is decreased by the binding of the meson and this affects the density of final states; the wave function of the escaping electron is influenced by the nucleus; relativity has a kinematic effect on the mean life. It would, theoretically, be simpler to observe muon capture in hydrogen (Hildebrand, 1962) and calculate from this the coupling constant $g_{\mu N}$. However, the experimental difficulties are considerable (Fig. 13-7). One of the most informative studies on μ capture involves capture in He^3. Here the experimental difficulties are less than for capture in H, and theory is still manageable. One finds that the branching ratio between decay and capture corresponds to within about 1 per cent to the value predictable on the basis of a weak interaction having the form $g_{\mu N}(V\text{-}A)$, with the value of $g_{\mu N}$ very close to the Fermi constant of beta decay. A refined calculation comparing the best information available in beta decay and in muon decay establishes the equality of the constants to within a fraction of 1 per cent.

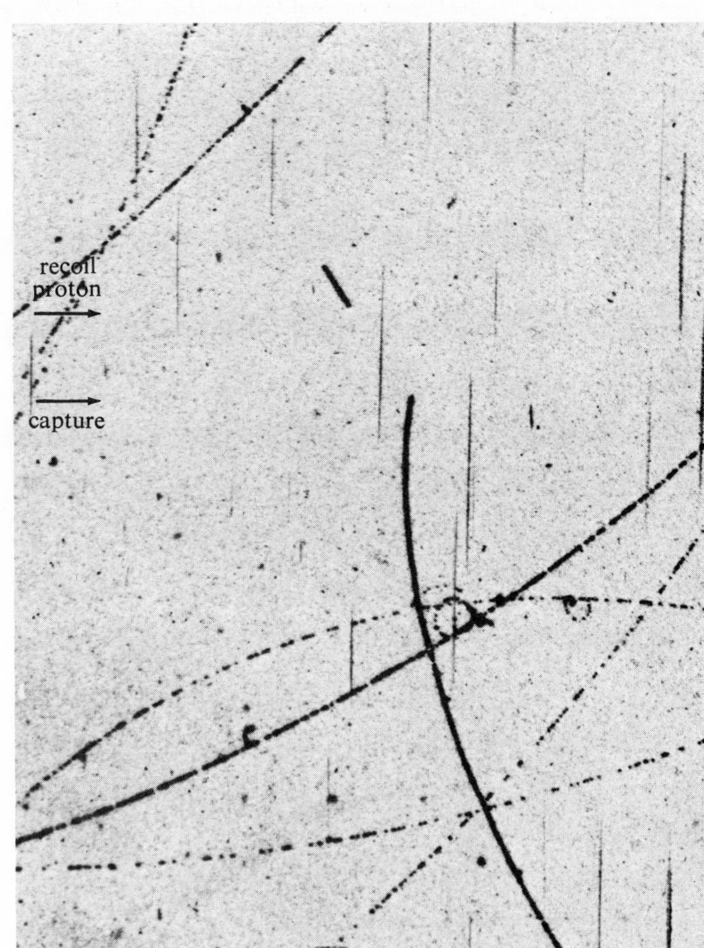

Figure 13-7 A muon is captured in liquid hydrogen according to the reaction $\mu^- + p \rightarrow n + \bar{\nu}$. The neutron recoils with an energy of 5.2 MeV and collides with a proton giving a track about 2.5 mm long (in the original). [Courtesy R. Hildebrand.]

There are several processes which are known not to occur, or at least one has very small upper limits for the branching ratio between the mode considered and the regular free decay. For example:

$$\mu^+ \to e^+ + e^+ + e^- \qquad \text{branching} < 1.5 \times 10^{-7}$$
$$\mu^+ + e^- \to 2\gamma \qquad \text{branching} < 5 \times 10^{-6}$$
$$\mu^\pm \to e^\pm + \gamma \qquad \text{branching} < 2 \times 10^{-8}$$

Their importance for establishing the existence of two types of neutrinos has been mentioned in Chap. 9.

13-5 Spin and Magnetic Moment of Muons

The spin of the muon is $\frac{1}{2}$. The proof came from experiments which also showed the nonconservation of parity in muon decay. Assume that a π^+ comes to rest and decays, emitting a neutrino and a μ^+ in opposite directions. The pion has no angular momentum, and hence the μ^+ has an angular momentum equal and opposite to that of the neutrino. If the neutrino is polarized with the spin antiparallel to the direction of motion, so is the muon. This has been verified by direct experiment (Hyams et al., 1961). The mu meson comes to rest in a very short time compared with its half-life; if the polarization is not destroyed in the moderation process, we have the emission of a positron and two particles of zero rest mass from a polarized source. This process shows a marked

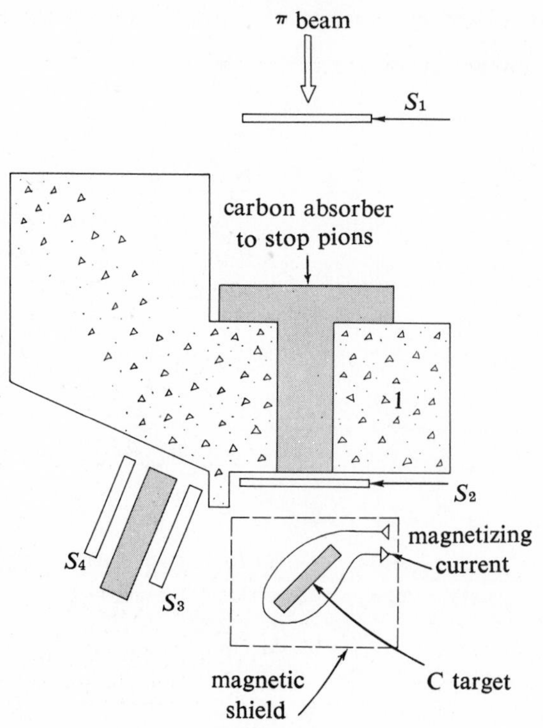

Figure 13-8 A beam of pions and muons passes scintillator S_1. The pions but not the muons are stopped before reaching scintillator S_2. Thus, 1 and 2 coincidences signal the arrival of a muon which will be stopped in the carbon target. The positrons from the muon decay are revealed by a coincidence between counters 3 and 4. The magnetic field perpendicular to the figure, acting in the target area, produces a precession of the muon spin. The correlation between spin direction and preferred direction for the positron emission is shown in Fig. 13-9. [After Garwin, Lederman, and Weinrich.]

asymmetry in the sense that the positrons tend to travel parallel to the spin direction (Figs. 13-8 and 13-9).

Suppose now that we apply a magnetic field to the muon at rest. The field produces a rotation of the direction of polarization with an angular velocity

$$\omega = g\frac{eH}{2m_\mu c} \tag{13-5.1}$$

where $g = \mu/I$ is the gyromagnetic ratio, that is, the magnetic moment in natural units $e\hbar/2m_\mu c$, divided by angular momentum in units $\hbar$. This rotation is observed as a change of the direction of preferential emission of the positrons. These phenomena were observed in experiments by Friedman and Telegdi and by Garwin, Lederman, and Weinrich, who found $g = 2 \times (1.0020 \pm 0.0005)$, very close to the g value of the electron. This result is a strong, if not binding, argument for a spin $\frac{1}{2}$ of the muon. Indeed, if this spin were $\frac{3}{2}$ or larger, the g value would be very odd indeed.

Another argument comes from mu-mesic atoms, whose spectra show structures consistent with the assignment of spin $\frac{1}{2}$ and $g \simeq 2$ for the muons.

A very direct proof comes from the study of muonium, a system composed of a positive muon and an electron, resembling a hydrogen atom. Muonium is obtained (Hughes et al., 1960) by stopping muons in argon. To reveal it, one observes the direction of emission of positrons coming from the decay of the muon. This direction, in a magnetic field,

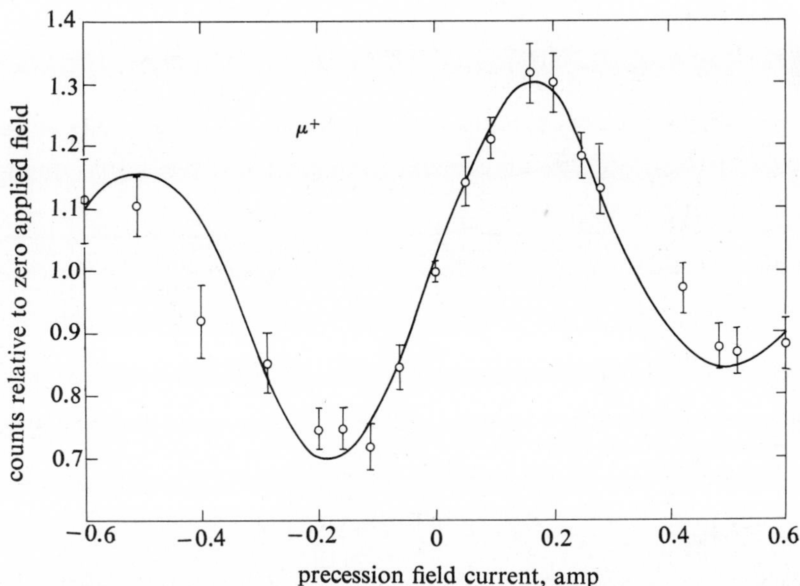

Figure 13-9 Variation of gated 3–4 counting rate with magnetizing current. The solid curve is computed from an assumed electron angular distribution $1 - \frac{1}{3}\cos\theta$, with counter and gate-width resolution folded in.

precesses with a characteristic frequency. Hughes et al. have observed the fine structure of the ground state of muonium (Figs. 13-10 and 13-11) and have measured spin and magnetic moment of the muon.

The experiments mentioned here are complemented by another experiment of considerable precision (CERN, 1961), giving the quantity $g - 2$. The principle of the method used is as follows (Fig. 13-12). A muon moves in a magnetic field that is constant in time but variable in space, and perpendicular to the initial velocity of the muon. The trajectory of the muon is plane and cycloidal. The velocity vector of the muon then rotates with an angular velocity:

$$\omega = \frac{eH}{m_\mu c\gamma} \qquad \gamma = \left(1 - \frac{v^2}{c^2}\right)^{-1/2} \tag{13-5.2}$$

Under these circumstances, the spin, supposed to be initially parallel to the velocity, rotates with an angular velocity:

$$\omega_s = \omega\left[\left(\frac{1}{2}g - 1\right)\gamma + 1\right] \tag{13-5.3}$$

After a certain t spin and velocity make an angle in the rest frame of the muon

$$\varphi = \frac{g-2}{2}\omega\gamma t \tag{13-5.4}$$

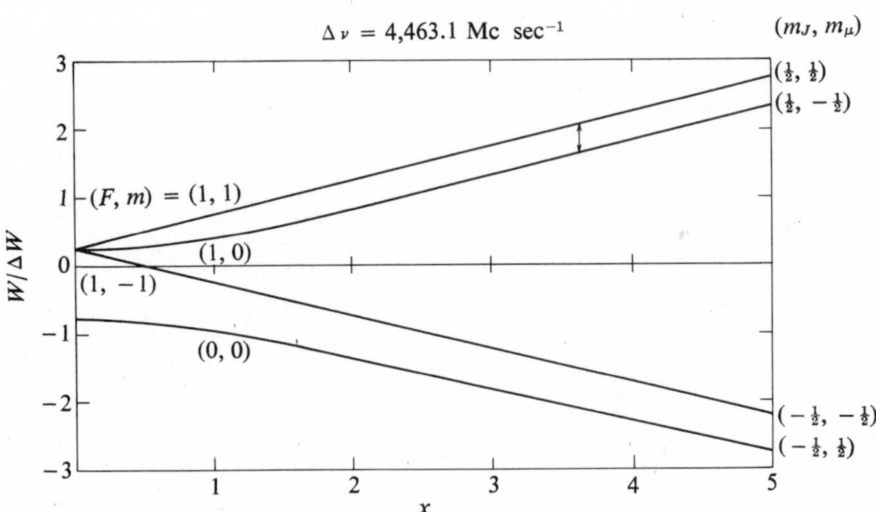

Figure 13-10 Energy-level diagram for the ground $1^2S^{1/2}$ state of muonium in a magnetic field H obtained from the Breit–Rabi equation:

$$W_{F=\frac{1}{2}\pm\frac{1}{2},\,m} = -\frac{\Delta W}{4} + \mu_0 g_\mu Hm \pm \frac{\Delta W}{2}(1 + 2mx + x^2)^{1/2}$$

ΔW is the zero-field hfs separation between the states $F = 1$ and $F = 0$, $x = (g_J - g_\mu)\mu_0 H/\Delta W$, g_J and g_μ are the electron and muon g values in units in which $g_J \simeq 2$, μ_0 = Bohr magneton, and $\Delta\nu = \Delta W/h$. The levels are designated by both their weak-field quantum numbers (F,m) and their strong-field quantum numbers (m_J,m_μ). The transition observed is indicated by the arrow at $x \cong 3.6$.

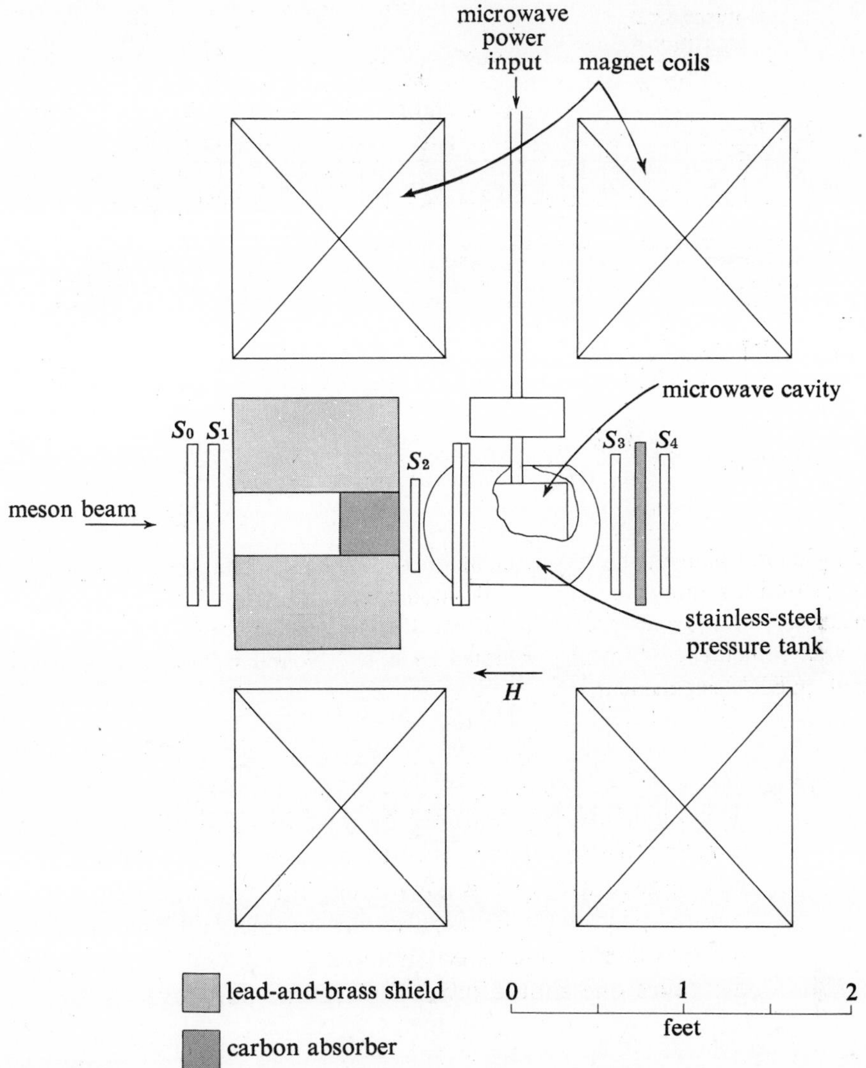

Figure 13-11 Apparatus used by Hughes for detection of muonium. A muon is stopped in purified argon at high pressure and is subject to microwave magnetic field. A stopped muon is indicated by a $12\bar{3}$ count; a decay positron is indicated by a $34\bar{2}$ count and recorded as an event if it occurs in the time interval between 0.1 μsec and 3.3 μsec after the $12\bar{3}$ count. The number of events and the number of $12\bar{3}$ counts are measured, with the microwave field off and with the microwave field on, as a function of the static magnetic field. The ratio R is then computed, where

$$R = \frac{(\text{events}/12\bar{3})_{\text{microwaves on}}}{(\text{events}/12\bar{3})_{\text{microwaves off}}}$$

At resonance the transition should be observed as an increase of R to a value greater than 1. [From V. W. Hughes (RoC 62).]

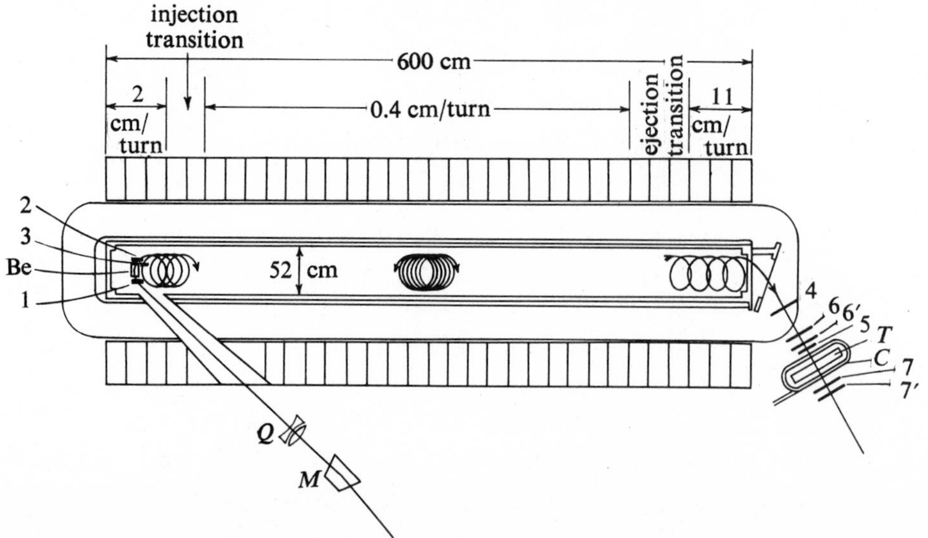

Figure 13-12 General plan of the six-meter magnet. M, bending magnet; Q, pair of quadrupoles; 1, Be, 2, 3: injection assembly consisting of Be-moderator and counters 1, 2, 3; T, methylene iodide target; counters 66′, 77′: "backward" and "forward" electron telescopes. A stored and ejected muon is registered as a coincidence 4, 5, 66′, $\bar{7}$, gated by a 1, 2, 3 and by either a forward or backward electron signal. [CERN experiment.]

This angle can be measured by injecting into the field muons with spin parallel to the velocity, and then observing the direction of preferred beta emission of the muons emerging from the field. The time t the muons spend in the field is also measurable, and from the combination of the two measurements one obtains $g - 2$. On the basis of pure electrodynamics one should have, for a Dirac particle,

$$\frac{g-2}{2} = \frac{\alpha}{2\pi} + \frac{0.74}{\pi^2}\alpha^2 + \cdots = 0.001165 \qquad \alpha = \frac{e^2}{\hbar c} \tag{13-5.5}$$

The experiment gives 0.001162 ± 0.000005. The result is notable in that it indicates that a muon obeys Dirac's equation very closely.

The absence of any "anomalous" part in the muon magnetic moment is an argument to indicate that the muon is subject only to weak and electromagnetic interactions. The "anomalous" magnetic moments of neutron and proton are in fact ascribed to the strong interactions to which they are subject (see Chap. 6).

Bibliography

Bargmann, Michel, and Telegdi, "Precession of the Polarization of Particles Moving in a Homogeneous Electromagnetic Field," *Phys. Rev. Letters*, **2,** 435 (1959).

Barkas, Birnbaum, and Smith, *Phys. Rev.*, **101,** 778 (1956).

Bethe, H., and F. de Hoffmann (BH 55).

Feinberg, G., and L. M. Lederman, "The Physics of Muons and Muonic Neutrinos," *Ann. Rev. Nucl. Sci.*, **13,** 431 (1963).

Fermi, E. (Fe 51).
Feynman, R. P., *The Theory of Fundamental Processes*, Benjamin, New York, 1961.
Jackson, J. D. (Ja 58).
Marshak, R. E., and E. C. G. Sudarshan, *Introduction to Elementary Particle Physics*, Wiley–Interscience, New York, 1961.
Nishijima, K., *Fundamental Particles*, Benjamin, New York, 1963.
Primakoff, H., "Theory of Muon Capture," *Rev. Mod. Phys.*, **31,** 802 (1959).
Rainwater, J., "Mu-Meson Physics," *Ann. Rev. Nucl. Sci.*, **7,** (1957).
Roman, P., *Theory of Elementary Particles*, 2nd ed., Wiley–Interscience, New York, 1961.
Segrè, E., "Antinucleons," *Ann. Rev. Nucl. Sci.*, **8,** 127 (1958).
Wick, G. C., "Invariance Principles of Nuclear Physics," *Ann. Rev. Nucl. Sci.*, **8,** 1 (1958).
Williams, S. C., *Introduction to Elementary Particles*, Academic, New York, 1962.

Problems

13-1 Of the following decay processes, state which are strictly forbidden, which are weak, which are electromagnetic, and which are strong; give the reasons for your decision.

(*a*) $p \to e^+ + \gamma$

(*b*) ${}_3\mathrm{Li}^8 \to {}_4\mathrm{Be}^8 + e^+ + \nu$

(*c*) $\pi^+ \to \mu^+ + \gamma$

(*d*) $\gamma \to e^+ + e^-$ (in vacuum)

(*e*) $p \to n + e^+ + \nu$ (for free proton)

(*f*) $K^+ \to \pi^+ + \gamma$

(*g*) $\Lambda^0 \to p^+ + e^- + \nu$

(*h*) $\Lambda^0 \to n + \gamma$

(*i*) $\Xi^- \to \Sigma^0 + K^-$

13-2 If the spin of the K^0 meson were 1, the decay mode $K^0 \to 2\pi^0$ would not be allowed. Why not?

13-3 Show by comparing the energy released in beta decay of the neutron and in muon decay on the one hand, and the mean life for the two processes on the other, that their coupling constants are of the same order of magnitude.

13-4 Estimate the mean life for annihilation of positronium and compare it with the experimental value. Try to do the same for muonium ($\mu^- + e^+$). Experiment shows that the mean life for annihilation is much larger than the mean life for spontaneous decay. Try to find an explanation.

13-5 Prove Eq. (13-1.8) for the case of $2\pi^0$.

13-6 Prove Eq. (13-1.8) for a $\pi^+\pi^-$ system.

13-7 Consider a system composed of a nucleon and its antinucleon in the $^1S_0$, $^3S_1$, $^1P_1$, $^3P_{0,1,2}$ states. Find their possible parity, *i* spin, *G*-quantum number, and charge-conjugation quantum number.

13-8 Try to prove as much as possible of Table 13P-1.

13-9 The conservation laws of Table 13-3 give rise to constants of the motions. These are quantized with discrete values, except energy and momentum. Why? Note that if the system is enclosed in a box, energy and momentum also have only discrete values.

13-10 Prove that a system of two π^0 cannot have an *i* spin of 1.

13-11 Prove that a two-pion system with $T = 1$ must have odd angular momentum and odd parity and that two pions with $T = 0$ must have even angular momentum and even parity.

13-12 Find the *i* spin of all 2π systems.

13-13 Show that a $\pi^+\pi^-$ system under the *CP* transformation is unchanged (eigenvalue of $CP = +1$).

13-14 Devise a method for measuring the pion mass solely from observation of photographic emulsions. (Protons have been stopped in the same emulsion.)

13-15 Molecular ions containing a deuteron and a proton bound by one muon, corresponding to the ordinary molecular ion HD^+, are occasionally formed by stopping μ^- in liquid hydrogen containing a small amount of deuterium. Estimate the internuclear distance in the ion and show that the nuclei may react to form He^3. In this case what happens to the muon? Discuss, in qualitative terms, possible life histories of muons in liquid hydrogen containing small amounts of deuterium in solution (see Feinberg and Lederman, 1963).

13-16 Calculate the energy of X rays emitted in mu-mesic transitions in O and S and plan an experiment to measure them. Consider especially any doublet due to the muon magnetic moment.

13-17 In muon capture there is emission not only of X rays but also of Auger electrons. Estimate the fluorescent yield in a specific case.

Table 13P-1 Strong-Interaction Decay Properties of N–$\bar{N}$ Combinations

N–$\bar{N}$ state	Spin and parity	T	C	G	Possible decays: 2π	3π	$\pi + \gamma$'s	$(n\gamma)_{\min}$	$K - \bar{K}$
$^1S_0$	$0-$	0	+	+	No (P)[a]	No (G)[a] also no 4π	$\pi^0 + 2\gamma$ $\pi^+ + \pi^- + \gamma$	2	No (P)
		1	+	−	No (P,G)	Yes $\left(\frac{\pi^\pm\pi^+\pi^-}{\pi^\pm 2\pi^0} = 4;\ \frac{\pi^+\pi^-\pi^0}{3\pi^0} = \frac{2}{3}\right)$	$\pi + 2\gamma$ $2\pi + \gamma$ (no $2\pi^0$)		No (P)
$^3S_1$	$1-$	0	−	−	No (G)	Yes (no $3\pi^0$)	$\pi^0 + \gamma$	3	Yes $\left(\frac{K^+ + K^-}{K^0 + \bar{K}^0} = 1\right)$
		1	−	+	Yes (no $2\pi^0$)	No (G)	$\pi + \gamma$		Yes $\left(\frac{K^+ + K^-}{K^0 + \bar{K}^0} = 1\right)$
$^1P_1$	$1+$	0	−	−	No (P,G)	Yes (no $3\pi^0$)	$\pi^0 + \nu$	3	No (P)
		1	−	+	No (P)	No (G)	$\pi + \gamma$		No (P)
$^3P_0$	$0+$	0	+	+	Yes $\left(\frac{\pi^+\pi^-}{2\pi^0} = 2\right)$	No (P,G)	$\pi^0 + 2\gamma$	2	Yes [no $K\bar{K} + \pi$] (P)
		1	+	−	No (G)	No (P)	$\pi + 2\gamma$ $2\pi + \gamma$		Yes [no $K\bar{K} + \pi$](P)
$^3P_1$	$1+$	0	+	+	No (P)	No (G)	$\pi^0 + 2\gamma$	4	No (P,G)
		1	+	−	No (P,G)	Yes (see $^1S_0$)	$\pi + 2\gamma$ $\pi^\pm + \gamma$ $2\pi + \gamma$ (no $2\pi^0$)		No (P,G)
$^3P_2$	$2+$	0	+	+	Yes (see $^3P_0$)	No (G)	$\pi^0 + 2\gamma$	2	Yes
		1	+	−	No (G)	Yes (see $^1S_0$)	$\pi^\pm + \gamma$ $\pi^0 + 2\gamma$ $\pi^+ + \pi^- + \gamma$		Yes

[a] (P), (G) means forbidden by parity or G-parity conservation.

CHAPTER XIV

Pions

THIS CHAPTER is devoted to pions and their interactions. We have discussed before how Yukawa postulated, as the quantum of nuclear forces, a particle with mass approximately $m = \hbar/rc$, where r is the range of nuclear forces, and how these particles were found in cosmic rays by Lattes, Occhialini, and Powell in 1947 (see Fig. 14-1). Soon thereafter, when the Berkeley cyclotron reached sufficient energy to produce pions (Lattes and Gardner, 1948), beams of charged pions became available in the laboratory. The neutral pion has such a short life that it is practically impossible to obtain neutral-pion beams. However, its decay into two gamma rays of about 70 MeV in the center-of-mass system is so characteristic that from this radiation it was possible to infer the existence of the π^0 and to determine several of its properties (Björklund, Crandall, Moyer, and York, 1950). The pions are bosons of spin zero.

14-1 Yukawa Interaction

In 1935 Yukawa tried to develop a theory of nuclear forces. The most important experimental feature of these forces is that they have a "range." That is, nuclear forces decrease extremely rapidly when the interacting particles are at a distance greater than about 10^{-13} cm. Experiment shows that in practice there is a critical length beyond which the interaction does not extend. In this it differs fundamentally from a $1/r^2$ force such as the electric force. We must thus expect that, if there is a nuclear potential, it will contain a parameter with the dimensions of a length. Actually such a potential was first proposed by Yukawa in the form

$$V(r) = g\frac{e^{-kr}}{r} \qquad \textbf{(14-1.1)}$$

where k is the reciprocal of the length which can be assumed to represent the range of nuclear forces.

Although field theory is definitely beyond the scope of this book, it is necessary at this point to introduce, at least qualitatively, several principles of field theory. The electromagnetic field is classically described by Maxwell's equations. Planck's constant does not appear in the equations and they do not describe any of the quantum phenomena. However, it is possible to subject the expressions of the fields or of the potentials to a process of quantization somewhat similar to that by which Schrödinger's equation is obtained from a classical hamiltonian. One finds that the energy of the field is quantized; i.e., it has the expression

$$E = \sum \hbar\omega_s(n_s + \tfrac{1}{2}) \qquad \textbf{(14-1.2)}$$

where the ω_s are the classical eigenfrequencies of the radiation field and the n_s are integral numbers $\geqslant 0$. This expression for the energy is interpreted as a manifestation of light quanta of energy

$$\epsilon_s = \hbar\omega_s \qquad \textbf{(14-1.3)}$$

The energy of the electromagnetic field is the sum of the energies of its quanta. A momentum is also associated with a light quantum, its direction being that of the propagation of the light and its magnitude being

$$p = \frac{\hbar\omega}{c} = \frac{\hbar}{\lambda\!\!\!^{-}} \qquad \textbf{(14-1.4)}$$

Any field in general shows quantum properties, and the process of quantization connects the wave with the corpuscular aspects.

When we try to apply this type of idea to nuclear forces, the first problem to arise, by analogy with the electromagnetic force, is that of finding the properties of the quanta of a field that is associated with the Yukawa potential of Eq. (14-1.1). Table 14-1 shows a very suggestive correspondence. In the first line we note that for the electromagnetic field the expression of the static potential does not contain any characteristic length, whereas the opposite is true in the case of nuclear forces.

Table 14-1 Comparison between Electromagnetic and Yukawa Fields

	Electromagnetic field	Nuclear field
Static potential	$V = \frac{g}{r}$	$V = g(e^{-kr}/r)$
Eq. of propagation for the potential	$\nabla^2 V - (1/c^2)\,(\partial^2 V/\partial t^2) = 0$	$\nabla^2 V - k^2 V - (1/c^2)\,(\partial^2 V/\partial t^2) = 0$
Plane-wave solution	$V = V_0 \exp\{-i[(z/\lambda\!\!\!^{-} - \omega t)]\}$	$V = V_0 \exp\{-i[(z/\lambda\!\!\!^{-} - \omega t)]\}$
Relation between $\lambda\!\!\!^{-}$ and ω	$\frac{-1}{\lambda\!\!\!^{-2}} + \frac{\omega^2}{c^2} = 0$	$\frac{-1}{\lambda\!\!\!^{-2}} + \frac{\omega^2}{c^2} - k^2 = 0$
Relation between p and E	$\frac{-p^2}{\hbar^2} + \frac{E^2}{\hbar^2 c^2} = 0$	$\frac{-p^2}{\hbar^2} + \frac{E^2}{\hbar^2 c^2} - k^2 = 0$
or	$E = cp$	$(c^2p^2 + k^2\hbar^2c^2)^{1/2} = E$

The second line gives the well-known wave-propagation equation in the case of electromagnetic field and for the nuclear forces the natural generalization (Klein–Gordon equation). The third line gives the relation of ω, $\lambda\!\!\!^{-}$, and k to one another in the plane-wave solution of the preceding equation.

Note that according to de Broglie we have the relation

$$\lambda\!\!\!^{-} = \frac{\hbar}{p} \tag{14-1.5}$$

between the momentum of a particle and the de Broglie wavelength of its associated wave. The relation $\hbar\omega = E$ is also valid. With the help of these expressions we write line 6. The relation

$$c^2p^2 + \hbar^2c^2k^2 = E^2 \tag{14-1.6}$$

immediately suggests a connection between $\hbar^2k^2c^2$ and a rest mass m^2 for the quantum of the nuclear force. In fact, if

$$k = \frac{mc}{\hbar} \tag{14-1.7}$$

the expression for the energy becomes

$$E = (m^2c^4 + c^2p^2)^{1/2} \tag{14-1.8}$$

the well-known expression for the total energy of a particle of rest mass m and momentum p.

We are thus led to expect a connection between the range of nuclear forces and the rest mass of its quanta. Numerically, if we assume that $k = 10^{13}\ \text{cm}^{-1}$, we find that $m = 0.3 \times 10^{-24}$ g, approximately 300 times the mass of the electron, in very good qualitative agreement with the pion mass ($273m_e$).

From a different point of view an argument due to Wick (1938) justifies Eq. (14-1.7). The interaction between two nucleons is transmitted by the field of nuclear forces and is accompanied by the emission and absorption of the corresponding quanta. If a nucleon emits a quantum of a certain rest mass m, the energy of the system is increased at least by mc^2; and if we could measure it between the time of emission of the quantum and its absorption by the other nucleon, we should find a creation of energy in the amount of at least mc^2. However, in order to perform this measurement, according to the uncertainty principle, we require a time

$$t \simeq \frac{\hbar}{E} = \frac{\hbar}{mc^2} \tag{14-1.9}$$

Unless the quantum lasts a time comparable to t, no violation of the conservation of energy can be ascertained. Now, during such a time, the quantum may travel a distance of up to

$$ct = r_0 = \frac{\hbar}{mc} \tag{14-1.10}$$

and thus interacting particles must be closer than r_0, which is then, by definition, the range of nuclear forces.

The existence of exchange forces for which the interaction brings about the transformation of a neutron into a proton, and vice versa (Chap. 10), leads to the expectation that quanta of nuclear force may carry an electric charge of magnitude e. On the other hand, there must also be neutral quanta in order to explain ordinary forces, and in fact there are pions of charge $\pm e$ and 0.

What we have said thus far brings us to a consideration of the process by which a nucleon (N) transforms into a nucleon plus a pion,

$$N \rightarrow N' + \pi \tag{14-1.11}$$

as the elementary step of the nuclear interaction, similar to that of the emission of a quantum by an electric charge; this is called the Yukawa process. Nuclear interactions come about by a succession of Yukawa processes in which a nucleon emits a pion, thereby changing its momentum; the pion is then absorbed by another nucleon. In the process there is over-all conservation of energy, momentum, and electric charge.

The nucleon-nucleon interaction is then a process of the second order according to the scheme

$$N + N \rightarrow N' + \pi + N \rightarrow N' + N'' \tag{14-1.12}$$

where the primes on the symbol indicate its charge and momentum.

The matrix element corresponding to the process of Eq. (14-1.11) can be established as an order of magnitude from simple considerations based on the elements of field theory [see (Fe 51)]. It is

$$g \frac{\hbar c}{(2\Omega w_s)^{1/2}} \tag{14-1.13}$$

where g is a constant characteristic of the Yukawa interaction. Its value must be derived from experiment; w_s indicates the total energy of the pion that has been created or destroyed in the Yukawa process. In this connection we note that the Yukawa process does not necessarily consider the creation or destruction of *real* pions. The process may be a "virtual" one, describable formally as a real process but with any value of w_s, even those incompatible, for the single step, with the conservation laws. Ω is a normalization volume which disappears from the final formulas.

The process represented by Eq. (14-1.12) is a second-order process, and the matrix elements corresponding to a transition between the initial and final state are calculable by second-order perturbation theory.

For a second-order perturbation the effective matrix element has the form

$$H'_{if} = \sum_m \frac{H_{im} H_{mf}}{W_i - W_m} \tag{14-1.14}$$

where the H_{im}, H_{mi} are the first-order matrix elements relating the initial state of energy W_i to an intermediate state of energy W_m. In the specific case of the Yukawa interaction, the intermediate state is the one in which a pion is created, and in which $W_i - W_m = -W = -(m_\pi^2c^4 + c^2p^2)^{1/2}$, at least approximately. Substituting the first-order matrix elements in Eq. (14-1.14), we obtain

$$H_{if} = \frac{1}{w}\left[\frac{g\hbar c}{(2\Omega w)^{1/2}}\right]^2 = -\frac{g^2\hbar^2c^2}{2\Omega(m_\pi^2c^4 + c^2p^2)} \qquad \textbf{(14-1.15)}$$

The momentum p is equal to the momentum of the pion emitted by the first nucleon m, because in the intermediate states momentum (not necessarily energy) is conserved. When the pion is absorbed by the second nucleon, this momentum is transferred to it.

Appendix B shows that the matrix element of the transition from a state of momentum p' to a state of momentum p'' is the Fourier transform of the potential $U(r)$. We must then have

$$-\frac{g^2\hbar^2c^2}{2\Omega(m_\pi^2c^4 + c^2p^2)} = \frac{1}{\Omega}\int U(\mathbf{r})e^{-i\mathbf{p}\cdot\mathbf{r}/\hbar}\,d\mathbf{r} \qquad \textbf{(14-1.16)}$$

where $\mathbf{p}$ is the momentum transfer. This equation can be solved to yield

$$U(\mathbf{r}) = \frac{-g^2}{16\pi^3\hbar}\int \frac{e^{i\mathbf{p}\cdot\mathbf{r}/\hbar}}{m_\pi^2c^2 + p^2}\,d\mathbf{p} = \frac{-g^2}{8\pi r}e^{-m_\pi cr/\hbar} \qquad \textbf{(14-1.17)}$$

This potential is then equivalent to the Yukawa interaction. Experimentally a collision process may be interpreted either as a transition produced by the Yukawa interaction or as a deflection resulting from a nucleon-nucleon potential. Thus we again find the relation among nuclear forces, their range, and the mass of the pion, from which we started.

All the considerations discussed in this section are qualitative only. Their quantitative development is mathematically complicated and not yet completed. In particular, since it is not legitimate to use perturbation theory for strong interactions, different approaches are being studied. Furthermore, the pions are not the only particles involved in the nucleon-nucleon force. Heavier particles, corresponding to shorter radii of action, enter the picture. For instance, in the case of the repulsive core of the nucleon, groups of pions especially associated to each other play a role (see Sec. 14-7).

14-2 Mass and Decay Modes of Pions

The mass of the charged pions is determined by the methods discussed in connection with muons (Sec. 13-3). The result is

$$M_{\pi}\pm = 273.33 \times m_e = 139.69 \pm 0.05 \text{ MeV} = 2.4898 \times 10^{-25}\text{ g}$$

The neutral pion decays spontaneously, by electromagnetic interaction, into two gamma rays. The observed reaction

$$\pi^- + p \rightarrow \underset{\substack{\downarrow \\ 2\gamma}}{\pi^0} + n \qquad \textbf{(14-2.1)}$$

is particularly important for the determination of the π^0 mass. Assume that the π^- is captured at rest. The π^0 and n acquire a relative kinetic energy equal to $(m_{\pi^-} + m_p - m_{\pi^0} - m_n)c^2$. This energy can be directly measured by the observation of the gamma spectrum of the decaying π^0. The two-decay gamma rays have equal and opposite momentum in the coordinate system in which the π^0 is at rest. In the laboratory system they appear at an angle to each other, and their frequency shows the Doppler shift due to the motion of the π^0. The spectral "line" of the decay radiation is transformed into a band with a maximum and minimum frequency (Fig. 14-1). The mass difference between π^- and π^0 is thus obtainable. The experiment was carried out by Panofsky, Steller, and Steinberger (1951). They stopped π^- in hydrogen and observed the spectrum of the gamma rays emitted, using a pair spectrometer. Two reactions occur,

$$\pi^- + p \rightarrow n + \pi^0 \tag{14-2.2}$$

$$\pi^- + p \rightarrow n + \gamma \tag{14-2.3}$$

The second gives rise to a monochromatic gamma ray and the first to a continuum from which one can derive the mass of π^0, as explained above. The probability of reaction (14-2.2) relative to reaction (14-2.3) is 1.56 ± 0.02 (Panofsky ratio).

More direct, but experimentally difficult, is the measurement of the neutron velocity in reaction (14-2.2) by a time-of-flight method. The result (Crowe, 1959) is

$$m_{\pi^0} - m_\pi = 4.59 \pm 0.01 \text{ MeV} \tag{14-2.4}$$

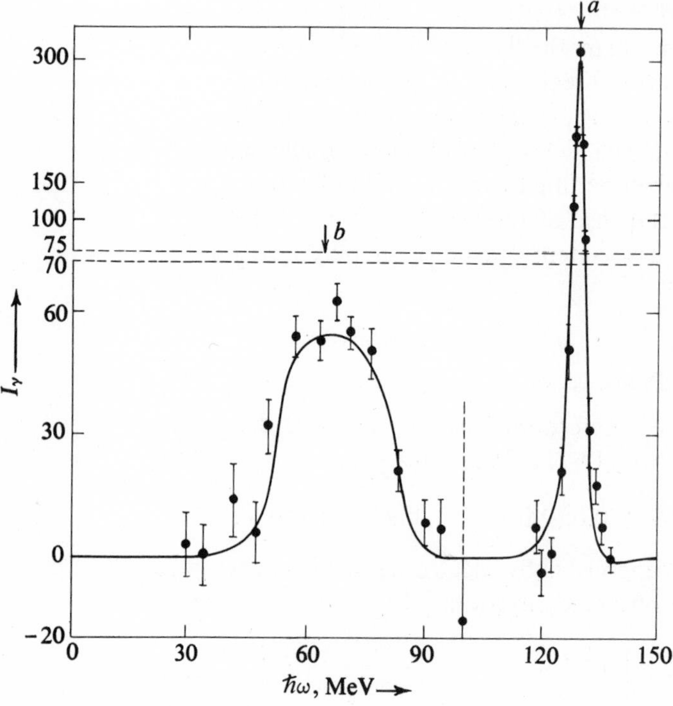

Figure 14-1 Gamma-ray spectrum resulting from the capture of negative π mesons in hydrogen. Note that the values of the intensity, for $\hbar\omega < 100$ MeV, have been increased fivefold to display the features of the distribution due to the reaction $\pi^- + p \rightarrow \pi^0 + n$. [K. M. Crowe and R. H. Phillips, *Phys. Rev.*, **96,** 470 (1954).]

From the evaluation of all experiments the value of the mass of the π^0 results,

$$m_{\pi^0} = 264.20 m_e = 135.0 \pm 0.05 \text{ MeV} \tag{14-2.5}$$

Charged pions decay spontaneously into muons and one particle of rest mass 0. This mode of decay is proved by the fact that the muons deriving from pions at rest always have the same energy, as shown for example, by their range. This decay is due to the weak interaction.

A careful search for gamma rays coincident with π–μ decay shows that the decay partner is not a gamma ray.

Pions may also decay according to the reaction

$$\pi^{\pm} \rightarrow e^{\pm} + \nu_e \tag{14-2.6}$$

This mode of decay is rare (Fazzini, Fidecaro, et al., 1958), occurring about 10^{-4} as frequently as the normal decay. Even rarer (10^{-8}) is the decay, perfectly analogous to beta decay,

$$\pi^{+} \rightarrow \pi^{0} + e^{+} + \nu_e \tag{14-2.7}$$

The significance of these modes for weak-interaction theory is discussed in Sec. 9-11.

We pass now to the discussion of the absolute decay constants of pions. The neutral pion decays with a mean life of about 2×10^{-16} sec into two gamma rays. The mean life is obtained from photographic-emulsion experiments. There are several methods. Occasionally, for instance, one of the decay gamma rays is replaced by a pair of electrons

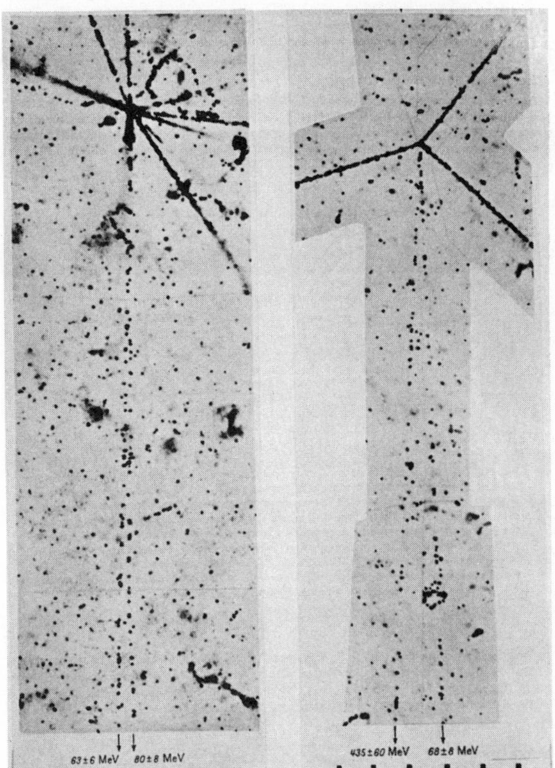

Figure 14-2 Electron pairs, apparently emerging directly from nuclear disintegrations attributed to the decay of the neutral π-meson into a Dalitz pair and an invisible gamma quantum. [From (PFP 59).]

of opposite sign (Dalitz pair, 1951; Fig. 14-2). The probability of this event occurring is approximately $e^2/\hbar c$. Suppose that a neutral pion emerges from a star in the photographic emulsion and decays into a Dalitz pair and an invisible gamma ray. It is possible to infer the time interval between emission and decay of the neutral pion from the distance between the star and the origin of the Dalitz pair and from the momentum of the decaying pion. This momentum is also derived from a study of the pair (see Fig. 14-3).

Application of detailed balance to the reaction

$$\pi^0 \rightleftharpoons \gamma + \gamma$$

also gives the mean life of π^0. The inverse reaction, or its equivalent, is obtained by using high-energy photons to produce π^0 in the electric field near the nucleus of a heavy element. The cross section for production is proportional to the decay constant of the pion, and experiment again gives a mean life of approximately 2×10^{-16} sec.

For positively charged pions the mean life is best obtained by electronic measurements of the following sequence of events: arrival and stoppage of a pion in a scintillator, emission of the muon, and, much later, decay of the muon into electron and neutrinos. The sequence of events is characteristic enough to enable one to recognize pions. The time interval between the arrival of the pion and its decay gives the mean

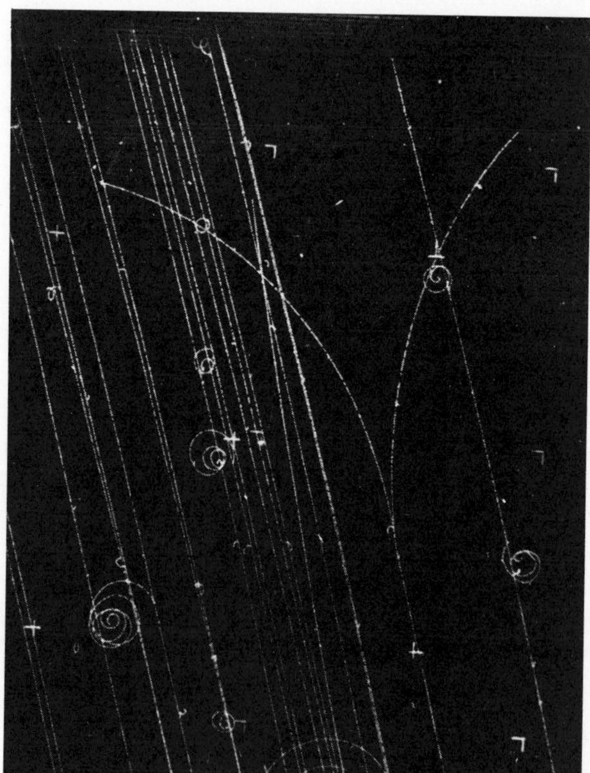

Figure 14-3 Dalitz pair seen in a hydrogen bubble chamber. A π^- makes a charge-exchange collision with a proton generating a π^0 which decays into an invisible gamma ray and a Dalitz pair. [Courtesy Lawrence Radiation Laboratory.]

life directly (Wiegand, 1951): the best value at present is $2.55 \pm 0.03 \times 10^{-8}$ sec (Fig. 14-4). This method is applicable to positive pions, which decay freely. Negative pions interact with nuclei, and their disappearance is dependent on other phenomena. However, it is assumed that their mean life in vacuum is identical to that of positive pions, because they are charge conjugates of each other.

The great difference in the decay constants of neutral and charged pions depends on the different interactions effective in the decay. Neutral pions decay electromagnetically, charged pions decay by weak interactions.

14-3 Spin of the Pions

The neutral pion decays into two gamma rays. This fact limits the possible spin values to integral multiples of $\hbar$ and establishes the π^0 as a boson.

More subtle arguments, based on transformation properties

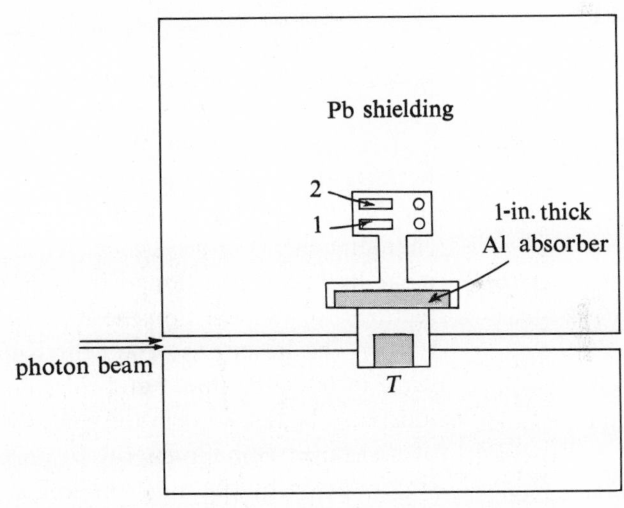

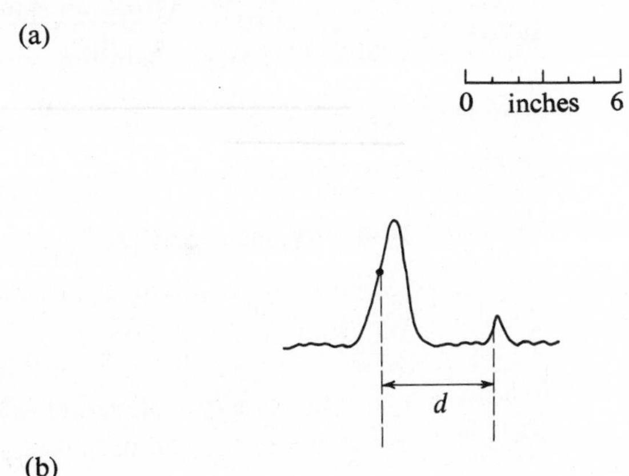

Figure 14-4 Measurement of the π^+ mean life. (a) The photon beam generates π^+ in the polyethylene target *T*. These mesons are stopped in target No. 2 after crossing 1; the resulting 1, 2 coincidence signal starts the sweep of the oscilloscope. This signal appears in (b) as the large pulse. The $\pi \rightarrow \mu$ decay gives the succeeding pulse. The average of time interval *d* is the mean life of the π^+. [From C. E. Wiegand, *Phys. Rev.*, **83**, 1085 (1951).].

under rotation and reflection of the wave function describing two gamma rays, rule out odd spins. Spins 2, 4, 6, etc., are not ruled out by gamma decay, but in view of a vast number of indirect arguments they appear to be extremely unlikely. We thus conclude by assigning spin 0 to the π^0 meson. As a consequence it must also have 0 magnetic moment.

For the π^+ meson there is direct experimental evidence for spin 0. Consider the reaction

$$p + p \rightleftharpoons \pi^+ + d \tag{14-3.1}$$

and its inverse. Going from the left to the right, the reaction is the production of π^+ and d in p-p collisions; proceeding in the opposite dirction, it is the absorption of π^+ in deuterium. We may apply the principle of detailed balance (see Sec. 11-3) to the two reactions and obtain the relation, valid for an unpolarized beam on an unpolarized target,

$$\frac{\underset{1\to 2}{\sigma(E_1)}}{\underset{2\to 1}{\sigma(E_2)}} = \frac{g_2}{g_1}\frac{p_\pi^{\,2}}{p_p^{\,2}} \tag{14-3.2}$$

where the cross sections and the momenta are measured in the center-of-mass system and g_2 and g_1 are the statistical weights of the final states

$$g_2 = (2I_\pi + 1)(2I_d + 1) = (2I_\pi + 1)3 \tag{14-3.3}$$

because the spin of the deuteron is 1. One the other hand,

$$g_1 = (\tfrac{1}{2})(2I_p + 1)^2 = 2 \tag{14-3.4}$$

because the spin of the proton is $\frac{1}{2}$. The factor $\frac{1}{2}$ in g_1 originates from the fact that we have identical protons; and the states obtained by interchanging them, in a classical sense, are not distinguishable. This argument has been mentioned in a different form in Sec. 11-3. The cross sections for the reactions of Eq. (14-3.1) may be either total or differential; in the latter case the center-of-mass scattering angle must be the same in both the direct and the inverse process. The energies E_1 and E_2 must also be the same in the center-of-mass system. Thus to the collision of a slow π^+ (kinetic energy 0) corresponds a kinetic energy in the p-p system given by the mass difference $\pi^+ + d - 2p = 138$ MeV.

Evaluation of the experimental results gives $I_{\pi^+} = 0$. The spin of the π^- is also 0. Although there is no direct evidence for this, the indirect evidence is overwhelming.

In conclusion, all pions have spin 0, are bosons, and have no magnetic moment.

14-4 Intrinsic Parity

A full treatment of intrinsic parity is beyond the scope of this book. We shall limit ourselves to the most elementary notions, which are however indispensable even for a first introduction to the subject.

The principle of conservation of parity may be stated crudely by saying that the mirror image of a natural phenomenon represents another possible physical phenomenon. We can rearrange our apparatus, substances, etc., in such a way as to realize exactly what we see in the mirror. Then, performing an experiment with the original apparatus or with the rearranged apparatus, we obtain as the result of our observations certain numbers, e.g., differential cross sections. If the numbers obtained are identical, we say that the phenomenon obeys the principle of conservation of parity, or that it is reflection-invariant. This invariance is true only if we limit ourselves to strong and electromagnetic interactions. For weak interactions, the invariance holds only if the reflection is accompanied by the simultaneous replacement of each particle by its own antiparticle (Fig. 14-5 and see Chap. 9).

Instead of the operation of mirroring, we may consider the operation of changing the sign of all coordinates, or the reflection on a point (Fig. 14-6). In both mirroring and reflection, the right hand changes into the left hand. Again the two physical situations must be equivalent as far as strong and electromagnetic interactions are concerned.

The requirement mentioned above has important physical consequences, such as selection rules forbidding certain reactions which, at first sight, would seem possible. For example, consider slow neutron capture in Be^7 according to the equation

$$Be^7 + n \rightarrow 2He^4 \qquad \textbf{(14-4.1)}$$

On the right hand the system of two identical bosons must have l even, and hence positive parity, because a spherical harmonic of even l does not change sign on reflection. On the left hand Be^7, according to the shell model, has an odd neutron in a p state. Hence, over-all parity of Be^7 in the ground state is the same as that of a neutron in a p state, i.e., negative. A slow neutron is necessarily in an s state. Therefore the total

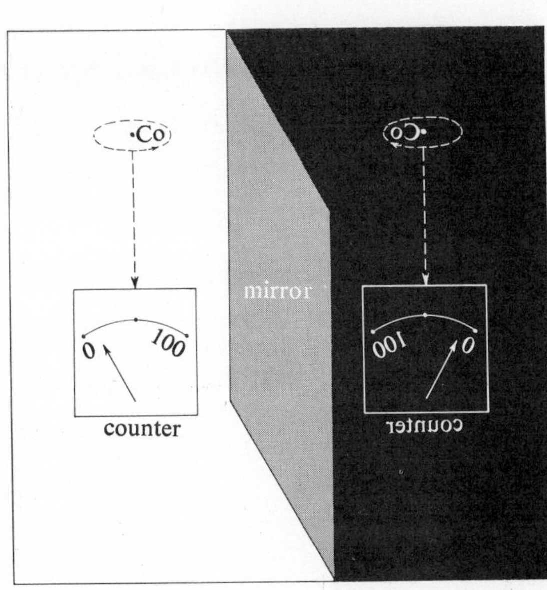

Figure 14-5 Symbolic drawing (C. N. Yang) of the beta decay of matter and antimatter. The operation of reflection and charge conjugation is illustrated by representing antimatter by white lines against a black background. In this figure the reading of the meter on the left is L, that of the meter on the right is R. Experiments show that these two readings are the same.

parity on the left hand is negative. We conclude that the reaction is forbidden by the conservation of parity, and indeed it has never been observed experimentally. Note the assumption that neutrons and protons in a state of orbital angular momentum l have a parity $(-1)^l$. The conservation of parity imposes many conditions on nuclear reactions. These conditions are always satisfied when the forces involved are nuclear or electromagnetic.

A special consideration is needed when we extend the rule to processes in which new particles are created.

When a particle is emitted or absorbed, e.g., when a nucleon emits a pion, we must study the influence of this absorption or emission on the parity of the system. For some particles such as pions we find that the parity of a system composed of a nucleon and a pion in an even orbital angular momentum state is the opposite of the nucleon parity; and we then say that the pion has negative, or odd, intrinsic parity. If the parity of a nucleon is not changed by emission of the particle in even angular momentum state, the emitted particle is said to have positive, or even,

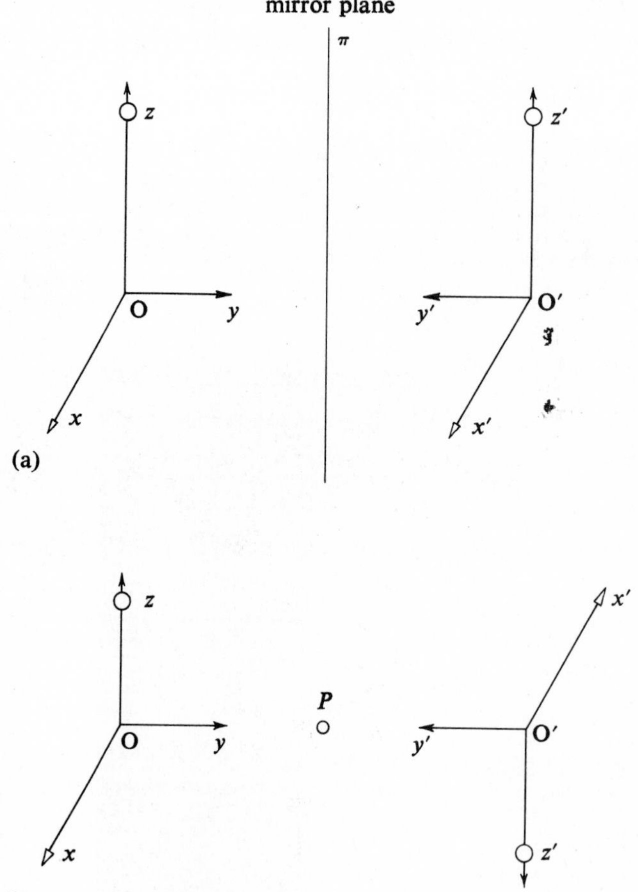

Figure 14-6 Reflection on a plane (a) and reflection on a point P (b). Part (b) (reflecting on a point) may be obtained by reflection on a plane as in part (a), followed by a rotation of 180° around the axis y.

intrinsic parity. In other words, in a reaction involving strong interactions, we postulate that parity is conserved. We check the parity on the two sides of the equation by measuring the usual orbital angular momentum, we assign positive parity, by definition, to nucleons, and if the final result seems to violate the conservation of parity, a case occurring only when new particles such as pions are created, we ascribe to the pion an "intrinsic parity," thereby reestablishing the conservation of parity rule. This procedure has a physical significance—it is not a play on words, as one might think. First of all, the result is always the same for a given particle, no matter which reaction is used. Furthermore it prevents the superposition of even and odd states by strong interactions and thus establishes special symmetries in angular distributions, gives selection rules, and so forth.

To take an example of determination of intrinsic parity consider the emission of a pion by colliding nucleons: Is the parity of the system changed when the pion is emitted in a state $l = 0, 2, 4$ or when it is emitted in a state $l = 1, 3, 5$, etc? The question is answered by considering the reverse process, the capture of π^- in deuterium. Here we have the reaction

$$\pi^- + d \to n + n \qquad \textbf{(14-4.2)}$$

The π^- slow down by ionization until they are practically at rest; an analysis of the capture process shows that it occurs from an s orbit ($l = 0$).

The total angular momentum on the left is thus given by the spin of the deuteron, because the pion is spinless. Hence, the total angular momentum has the value 1. On the right hand, the two neutrons can only be in states ${}^1S_0$, ${}^3P_{012}$, ${}^1D_2$, etc., other states being ruled out by the exclusion principle. The only allowed state of spin 1 is thus ${}^3P_1$, which has parity -1. We must conclude that a pion plus a deuteron in an s state has negative parity. This state of affairs is then expressed by saying that the pion has a negative intrinsic parity, assuming conventionally that a nucleon has a positive intrinsic parity.

The experimental evidence for reaction (14-4.2) is based on the branching ratio between the reactions

$$\pi^- + d \to 2n \qquad \textbf{(14-4.3)}$$

$$\pi^- + d \to 2n + \gamma \qquad \textbf{(14-4.4)}$$

$$\pi^- + d \to 2n + \pi^0 \qquad \textbf{(14-4.5)}$$

For pions at rest one finds

$$\frac{\text{probability of } \pi^- + d \to 2n}{\text{probability of } \pi^- + d \to 2n + \gamma} = 2.35 \pm 0.35 \qquad \textbf{(14-4.6)}$$

and no evidence for the third reaction $\pi^- + d \to 2n + \pi^0$. The absence of this reaction confirms capture in the s state. In fact, when capture occurs in the s state, J on the left side of (14-4.5) is 1. On the right side there is very little available energy and the orbital angular momentum of the two neutrons is bound to be zero, which means that the two neutrons are in the $^1S_0$ state. The pion also has insufficient energy to go into a state of angular momentum 1 in the center of mass of the system. Consequently there is no possibility of balancing angular momenta. The experiment is accomplished by observing the gamma rays emitted when the π^- are stopped in deuterium. Only gamma rays corresponding to reaction (14-4.4), i.e., with energy approximately equal to the rest energy of the π^-, are found. The two-neutron reaction is difficult to observe directly, and its intensity is measured indirectly by replacing deuterium with hydrogen in the experimental setup and comparing the results.

The qualitative fact of the high probability of reaction (14-4.3) is sufficient to prove that it is allowed and hence to establish the negative intrinsic parity of the π^-.

In the case of electromagnetic radiation, the parity of a system changes on emission of $E1$, $E3$, El(odd), etc., or $M2$, $M4$, Ml(even), etc., radiation. It does not change on emission of $E2$, $E4$, El(even), etc., or $M1$, $M3$, Ml(odd), etc., radiation. The angular momentum carried away is always l. We may summarize the results by saying that the parity of the radiation is

$$(-1)^l \Pi_{\text{int}}$$

where Π_{int} is 1 for all electric radiation, -1 for all magnetic radiation (cf. Sec. 8-2).

Some of these assignments, such as the intrinsic parity of $E1$ radiation and the intrinsic parity of the proton, have the character of convention. Other assignments of intrinsic parity then follow from experimental facts and the initial conventions. For instance, a system of spin 0, decaying into two gamma rays, gives rise to quanta with parallel polarization planes if the original system has even parity, or with perpendicular polarization planes if the original system has odd parity. In the case of positronium in an $^1S_0$ state, which annihilates into two quanta (cf. Chap. 2), experiment shows that the system has odd parity. We conclude that the electron and the positron have opposite intrinsic parities. For the case of the π^0 the experiment mentioned above has not been performed directly, but the decay into Dalitz pairs gives a direct determination of the intrinsic parity. If the planes of two Dalitz pairs originating from the same pion tend to be parallel, the intrinsic parity of the pion is positive; if they tend to be perpendicular, the intrinsic parity is negative. Enough cases of this rare type of decay have been observed to show that the intrinsic parity of π^0 is negative. In fact the intrinsic parity of all pions is negative.

Note an interesting consequence of this property for the Yukawa interaction:

$$N \to N + \pi \qquad \textbf{(14-4.7)}$$

This interaction conserves parity and angular momentum. On the left hand, the parity is even by definition, and the angular momentum is the pin $\frac{1}{2}$ of the nucleon. On the right hand, in order to have angular momentum $\frac{1}{2}$, we may consider only the state $l = 0$ or $l = 1$, where l is the orbital angular momentum in the center-of-mass system of the pion and nucleon. But only the state $l = 1$ is odd; hence in the Yukawa interaction the pion is emitted (virtually) in a p state.

A remarkable relation between the intrinsic parity of a particle and its antiparticle, provable in the same sense as the relation between spin and statistics, is that such parity is the same for bosons and opposite for fermions.

14-5 Isotopic Spin

We have already introduced the concept of the isotopic spin for the nucleon (Chap. 10). The same concept is extended to pions by assigning them a coordinate susceptible of three values only, similar to the z component of a spin-1 vector. We shall consider this new variable as the third component of a vector $\mathbf{t}$ in "isotopic spin space." The physical interpretation of t_3 is given by its relation to the charge q of the meson,

$$\frac{q}{e} = t_3 \tag{14-5.1}$$

The complete eigenfunction of a meson will thus be the product of a part depending on the space coordinates and of a part depending on i spin. The i spin obeys the same commutation relation as ordinary angular momentum and for spin 1 is easily represented by eigenfunctions having the properties of spherical harmonics of order 1.

These formal considerations are important because, as discussed in Chap. 10, nuclear forces are charge-independent or, more precisely, the behavior of nuclear forces is determined by the total i spin of the system, not by its third component. Moreover, strong interactions conserve i spin; i.e., the initial and final states of a system undergoing a transition produced by strong interactions have the same i spin. These statements are based on experimental facts, as we shall illustrate by examples. The conservation of i spin is formally similar to that of angular momentum for an isolated system, except that it is only approximate when there are interactions other than strong ones, because neither electromagnetic nor weak interactions conserve i spin. Hence, there can be transitions between states of different i spin, but their probability is in general much smaller than that of transitions due to interactions involving nuclear forces.

The eigenfunction of a particle will contain a factor depending on i spin. We shall indicate this part symbolically for a proton as p, and for a neutron as n with a similar notation for other light nuclei. This notation is analogous to the α,β notation for ordinary spin. For pions we use a superscript $+$, ^{0}, $-$, according to the charge of the pion. Thus, p^+ means proton and positive pion, dp means deuteron and proton, etc. For a system of two or more particles we define a total i spin

$$\mathbf{T} = \mathbf{t}^{(1)} + \mathbf{t}^{(2)} + \cdots \tag{14-5.2}$$

and

$$T_3 = t_3^{(1)} + t_3^{(2)} + \cdots \tag{14-5.3}$$

The eigenfunctions corresponding to a physical system such as p^0 are *not* always eigenfunctions of $\mathbf{T}^2$ and T_3. Generally we have to make linear combinations with appropriate coefficients (Clebsch–Gordan coefficients), in perfect analogy with the composition of angular momenta (Table 14-2) (and see Appendix I). Remember that one often calls, for brevity, an eigenfunction of $\mathbf{T}^2$ with eigenvalue $K(K+1)$ an eigenfunction corresponding to a state with $T = K$. We shall write, according to the usual conventions, the eigenfunctions of $\mathbf{T}^2$ and T_3 as $\chi_T^{T_3}$, where for brevity the subscript is twice the i spin and the superscript twice its third component. Thus

$$p^+ = \chi_3^{\,3} \tag{14-5.4}$$

meaning that the physical situation p^+ corresponds to an eigenstate of $\mathbf{T}^2$ and T_3 with eigenvalues $\frac{3}{2}(\frac{3}{2}+1)$ and $+\frac{3}{2}$.

Using a table of Clebsch–Gordan coefficients, we can write Table 14-2 for the nucleon-pion system. The relations can be solved by expressing the six functions p^+, p^0, p^-, n^+, n^0, and n^- through the χ's. Note that we can experimentally realize the pure $T = \frac{3}{2}$ state by bombarding protons with positive pions or, at least in principle, by bombarding neutrons with negative pions. The pure state $T = \frac{1}{2}$, however, cannot be realized in a nucleon-pion bombardment.

We list the following examples of experimental facts demonstrating the conservation of i spin.

1. The equality between pp and np interactions was discussed in Chap. 10.

2. Consider now the reaction

$$\begin{aligned} p + d &= \mathrm{He}^3 + \pi^0 \\ &= \mathrm{H}^3 + \pi^+ \end{aligned} \tag{14-5.5}$$

Table 14-2 Eigenfunctions for the Nucleon-Pion System

$T = 3/2$		$T = 1/2$	
T_3		T_3	
$\frac{3}{2}$	$\chi_3^{3} = p^+$		
$\frac{1}{2}$	$\chi_3^{1} = \sqrt{(\frac{2}{3})}p^0 + \sqrt{(\frac{1}{3})}n^+$	$\frac{1}{2}$	$\chi_1^{1} = -\sqrt{(\frac{1}{3})}p^0 + \sqrt{(\frac{2}{3})}n^+$
$-\frac{1}{2}$	$\chi_3^{-1} = \sqrt{(\frac{2}{3})}n^0 + \sqrt{(\frac{1}{3})}p^-$	$-\frac{1}{2}$	$\chi_1^{-1} = +\sqrt{(\frac{1}{3})}n^0 - \sqrt{(\frac{2}{3})}p^-$
$-\frac{3}{2}$	$\chi_3^{-3} = n^-$		

The left side of this equation has *i* spin $\frac{1}{2}$ and $T_3 = \frac{1}{2}$, because the *i* spin of the deuteron is 0 and that of the proton is $\frac{1}{2}$ with $T_3 = \frac{1}{2}$. The *i* spins of H^3 and He^3 are $\frac{1}{2}$, as can be seen by considering them as a deuteron plus a neutron or a proton. The third component of the *i* spin is $-\frac{1}{2}$ and $+\frac{1}{2}$ for H^3 and He^3, respectively. An eigenstate of T and T_3 with eigenvalues $\frac{1}{2}$ and $+\frac{1}{2}$, respectively, is obtained by combining the eigenfunctions of the π and of He^3 or H^3, respectively.

$$\chi_1{}^1 = -\sqrt{(\tfrac{1}{3})}he^0 + \sqrt{(\tfrac{2}{3})}h^+ \qquad \textbf{(14-5.6)}$$

as can be seen by analogy with the state $T = \frac{1}{2}$, $T_3 = \frac{1}{2}$ of Table 14-2. Here *he* and *h* replace *p* and *n*, respectively.

Now the *i*-spin part of the state *pd* is unchanged by collision and is $\chi_1{}^1$ (Table 14-2). The amplitudes with which he^0 and h^+ are represented in this state are in the ratio $1 : \sqrt{2}$. The probabilities of ending in the states h^+ and he^0 are proportional to the square of these amplitudes and hence the differential cross sections for reactions Eq. (14-5.5) must be in the ratio 1 : 2. This has been well verified (Fig. 14-7).

3. The conservation of *i* spin gives selection rules for photonuclear reactions, which are verified experimentally.

4. Light nuclei show energy levels that are well explained on the charge-independence hypothesis (cf. Chap. 10).

5. One of the most striking "instances" of charge independence is the nucleon-pion scattering, which we shall discuss in the next section.

14-6 Pion-Nucleon Scattering

There are the following observable scattering processes between nucleons and pions:

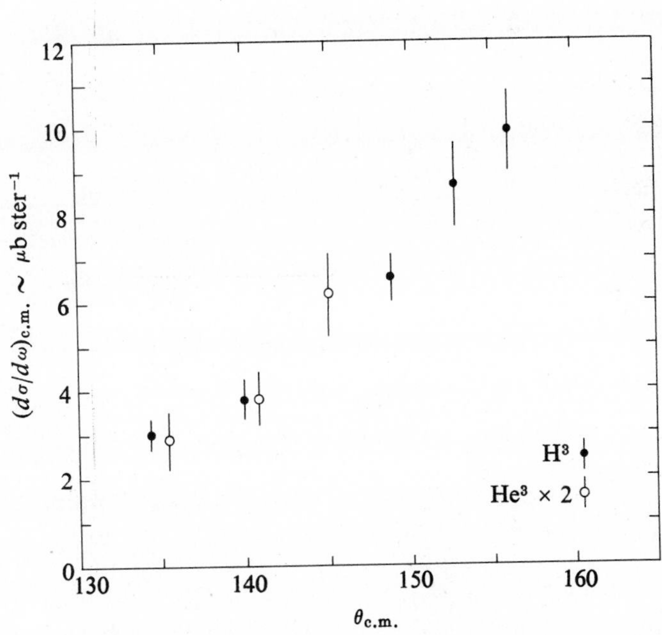

Figure 14-7 The differential cross sections for the reactions $p + d \to \pi^+ + H^3$ and $p + d \to \pi^0 + He^3$ with 450-MeV protons. The measured cross sections for the second reaction have been multiplied by a factor of two to facilitate a direct comparison. The cross sections are given in arbitrary units, which are, however, approximately microbarns per steradian. [From Crewe, Garwin, Ledley, Lillethun, March, and Marcowitz, *Phys. Rev. Letters*, **2**, 269 (1959).]

$$\begin{aligned}&(a)\ \pi^+ + p \to \pi^+ + p\\&(b)\ \pi^- + p \to \pi^- + p\\&(c)\ \pi^- + p \to \pi^0 + n\end{aligned} \qquad \textbf{(14-6.1)}$$

In addition there are the processes

$$\pi^0 + p \to \pi^0 + p \qquad \textbf{(14-6.2)}$$

and the processes obtained from Eqs. (14-6.1) by replacing the proton with a neutron and the π^+ with a π^-. These are difficult to observe and have not yet been studied experimentally.

The experiments on pion-nucleon scattering have been performed by using beams of mesons produced by the bombardment of targets with protons. Neutral pions are also generated at the target, but they

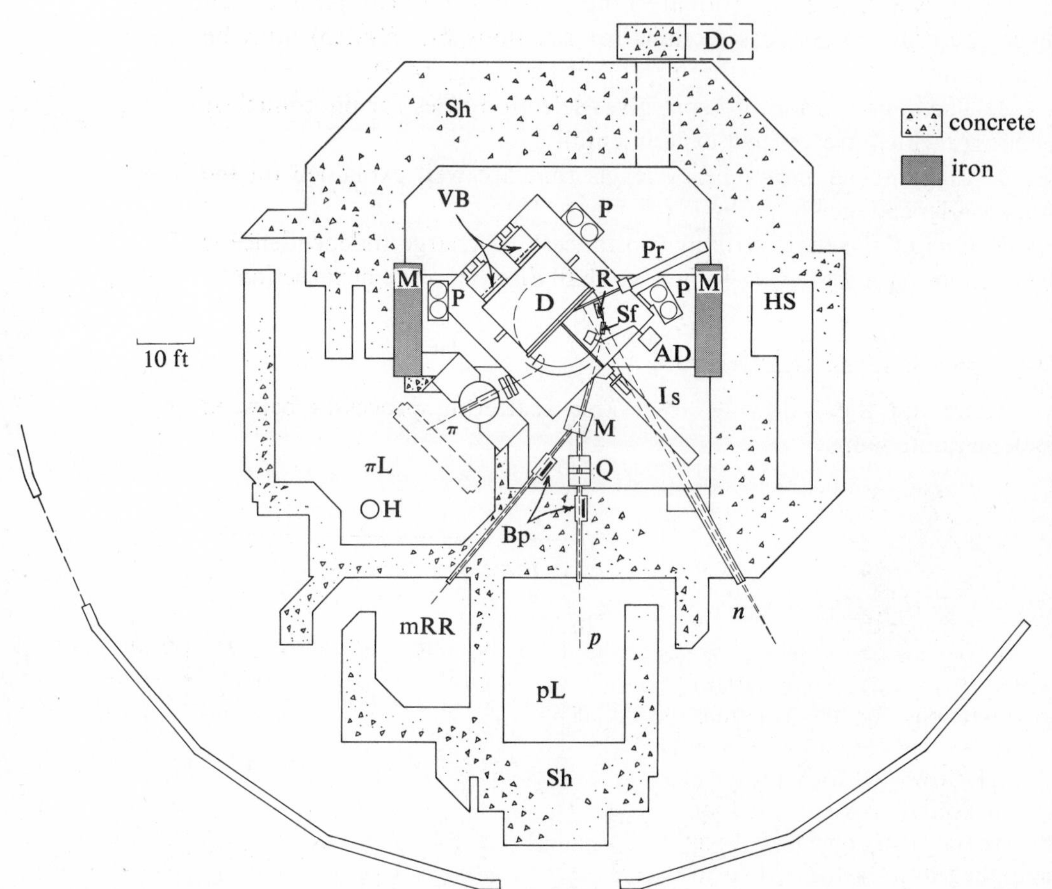

Figure 14-8 Cyclotron for producing many beams which are selected according to particles and momentum. Sh, concrete shielding; Do, door; P, pumps; Pr, probe; VB, vibrating blades condenser; D, dee; AD, auxiliary dee; Is, ion source; M, steering magnet; Q, quadrupole magnets; *p*, proton beam; *n*, neutron beam; H, hole (30 ft. deep); M, magnet leg; π, pion beam; pL, proton laboratory; πL, pion laboratory; mRR, medical research room; Bp, beam plugs; Sf, strong-focusing element for beam extraction; R, regenerator for beam extraction; HS, hot storage for radioactive samples. (184-in. cyclotron, Lawrence Radiation Laboratory, Berkeley, Calif.)

decay within less than 10^{-15} sec. Charged pions are collimated, deflected, and focused so as to permit the selection of a beam of particles of a single momentum (Fig. 14-8). A typical beam of positive pions with a momentum definition of 1 per cent at an energy of 300 MeV may have a flux of 5×10^4 cm^{-2} sec^{-1} over an area of 25 cm^2. The intensity of negative pions is about ten times smaller. Mu mesons coming from pion decay and electrons are also present in the beam. Sometimes they can be distinguished by their range. The targets used are Dewar vessels full of liquid hydrogen, and the detecting devices can be counters, photographic emulsions, cloud or bubble chambers, and spark chambers. The measurements give the differential scattering cross section for processes (14-6.1a, b). We assume that we are operating with unpolarized targets and are not observing the polarization of the scattered nucleons.

Let us now introduce the scattering amplitudes f_1, f_3 for the isotopic spin states $T = \frac{1}{2}, \frac{3}{2}$, respectively. An incoming plane wave described by

$$e^{ikz}\chi_1 \qquad \textbf{(14-6.3)}$$

gives rise to a scattered wave $f_1\chi_1$, and an incoming plane wave $e^{ikz}\chi_3$ gives rise to a scattered wave $f_3\chi_3$. In these statements we have expressed implicitly the *i*-spin conservation, because, according to the statements, scattering does not change χ_1 into χ_3, or vice versa. The scattering amplitudes f_1 and f_3 are functions of the energy and of θ, the scattering angle.

In the scattering of positive pions on protons, p^+, only the *i*-spin-$\frac{3}{2}$ state is involved, and hence the scattering amplitude is f_3. For the case of scattering of negative pions on protons, p^-, the initial state contains a mixture of $\chi_1{}^{-1}$ and $\chi_3{}^{-1}$, as can be seen immediately.

Solving the equations in Table 14-2, we have the physical state

$$p^- = \sqrt{(\tfrac{1}{3})}\chi_3{}^{-1} - \sqrt{(\tfrac{2}{3})}\chi_1{}^{-1} \qquad \textbf{(14-6.4)}$$

Similarly we have

$$n^0 = \sqrt{(\tfrac{2}{3})}\chi_3{}^{-1} + \sqrt{(\tfrac{1}{3})}\chi_1{}^{-1} \qquad \textbf{(14-6.5)}$$

The p^- scattering is thus described by

$$p^-e^{ikz} = \{\sqrt{(\tfrac{1}{3})}\chi_3{}^{-1} - \sqrt{(\tfrac{2}{3})}\chi_1{}^{-1}\}\, e^{ikz} \rightarrow \sqrt{(\tfrac{1}{3})}f_3\chi_3{}^{-1} - \sqrt{(\tfrac{2}{3})}f_1\chi_1{}^{-1} \qquad \textbf{(14-6.6)}$$

We now express $\chi_3{}^{-1}, \chi_1{}^{-1}$ through physical states n^0, p^- and obtain

$$\begin{aligned} p^-e^{ikz} &\rightarrow \sqrt{(\tfrac{1}{3})}[\sqrt{(\tfrac{2}{3})}n^0 + \sqrt{(\tfrac{1}{3})}p^-]f_3 + \sqrt{(\tfrac{2}{3})}[-\sqrt{(\tfrac{1}{3})}n^0 + \sqrt{(\tfrac{2}{3})}p^-]f_1 \\ &= n^0\sqrt{2}\,(f_3 - f_1)\,\tfrac{1}{3} + p^-\,(f_3 + 2f_1)\,\tfrac{1}{3} \qquad \textbf{(14-6.7)} \end{aligned}$$

We see that $(f_3 + 2f_1)/3$ is the amplitude for elastic scattering (p^- goes into p^-) and $\sqrt{2}(f_3 - f_1)/3$ is the amplitude for charge-exchange scattering (p^- goes into n^0).

The processes of Eq. (14-6.1) must have cross sections in the ratio of the squares of their amplitudes. It has been found that at energies up to about 200 MeV $f_3 \gg f_1$. Then, if we neglect f_1 compared with f_3, we have, for the ratios of the cross sections, total as well as differential, $p^+ \rightarrow p^+$: $p^- \rightarrow n^0$: $p^- \rightarrow p^- = 9:2:1$. In fact the measurement of these ratios led to the conclusion, theoretically predicted, that the important scattering amplitude for energies below 200 MeV corresponds to $T = \frac{3}{2}$ and verified in an impressive way *i*-spin conservation.

The measurements of cross section and angular distribution for the p^+, p^- scatterings [Eq. (14-6.1)] suggest a resonance process (Fig. 14-9), and the question arises as to what the total angular momentum of the wave involved in the resonance is. Several arguments indicate that it is $J = \frac{3}{2}$. First, the maximum value of the scattering cross section for a state of given J and l is

$$\sigma_{\max} = 2\pi\lambda\!\!\!^{-2}(2J + 1) \qquad \textbf{(14-6.8)}$$

where $2\pi\lambda\!\!\!^{-}$ is the de Broglie wavelength of the pion in the center-of-mass system. This formula is an extension of Eq. (11-5.12) to the case of particles with spin and is proved, for instance, in (BW 52). The value of $\sigma_{\max}$ for $J = \frac{1}{2}$ would definitely be smaller than the experimental cross section at 195 MeV (laboratory), which is 195×10^{-27} cm^2. This value is very close to $8\pi\lambda\!\!\!^{-2}$, which is the maximum obtainable, according to Eq. (14-6.8), for $J = \frac{3}{2}$. Moreover, the angular distribution in p^+ elastic scattering, $\sigma(\theta) \sim 1 + 3\cos^2\theta$ (Fig. 14-10) shows that the scattering occurs

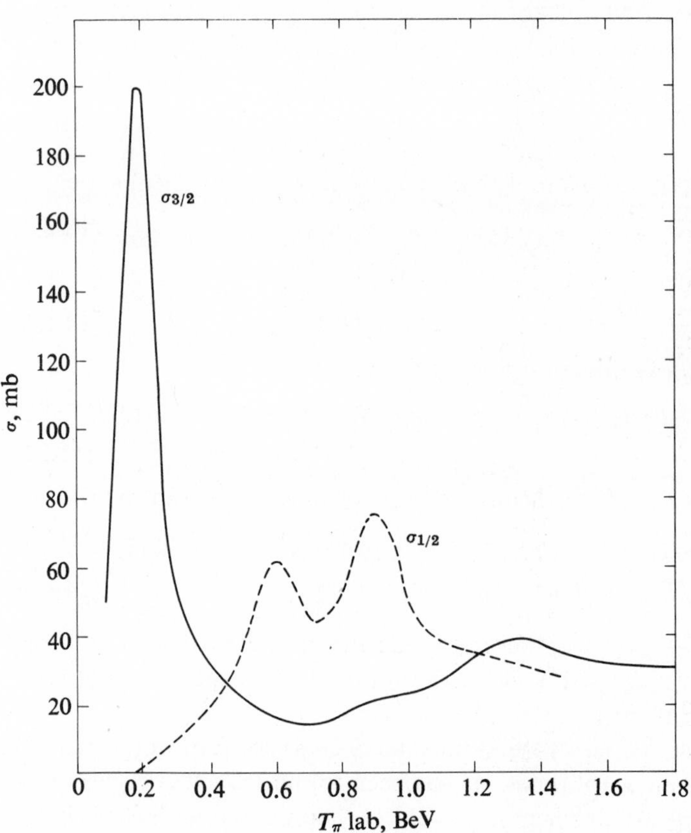

Figure 14-9 Total pion-proton and pion-neutron cross section analyzed according to isotopic spin: $\sigma_{3/2} = \sigma(\pi^+p)$; $\sigma_{1/2} = \frac{3}{2}\sigma(\pi^-p) - \frac{1}{2}\sigma(\pi^+p)$.

in a $J = \frac{3}{2}$ state, and in view of the energy this is a $p_{3/2}$ and not a $d_{3/2}$ state. Now $J = l \pm \frac{1}{2}$ for the pion-nucleon system, and we conclude that the resonance corresponds to a state with $T = \frac{3}{2}, l = 1, J = \frac{3}{2}$. Another experimental argument confirming this assignment is the energy dependence, at low energies, of the total cross section on the relative momentum, $\sigma_t \sim p^4$, a dependence characteristic of p-wave scattering.

The total scattering cross section for the $T = \frac{3}{2}$ state may be described very well by a single-level resonance formula (Brueckner, 1952).

$$\sigma = 2\pi \lambda\!\!\!^{-2} \frac{\Gamma^2}{(E - E_0)^2 + \Gamma^2/4} \tag{14-6.9}$$

where $E_0 = 159$ MeV (center-of-mass system) and Γ is given by

$$\Gamma = \frac{2(p/m_\pi c)^3\,(0.88)^3}{1 + (p/m_\pi c)^2\,(0.88)^2}\,\gamma^2 \tag{14-6.10}$$

Here $\gamma^2 = 58$ MeV, and m_π is the rest mass of the pion (Fig. 14-11).

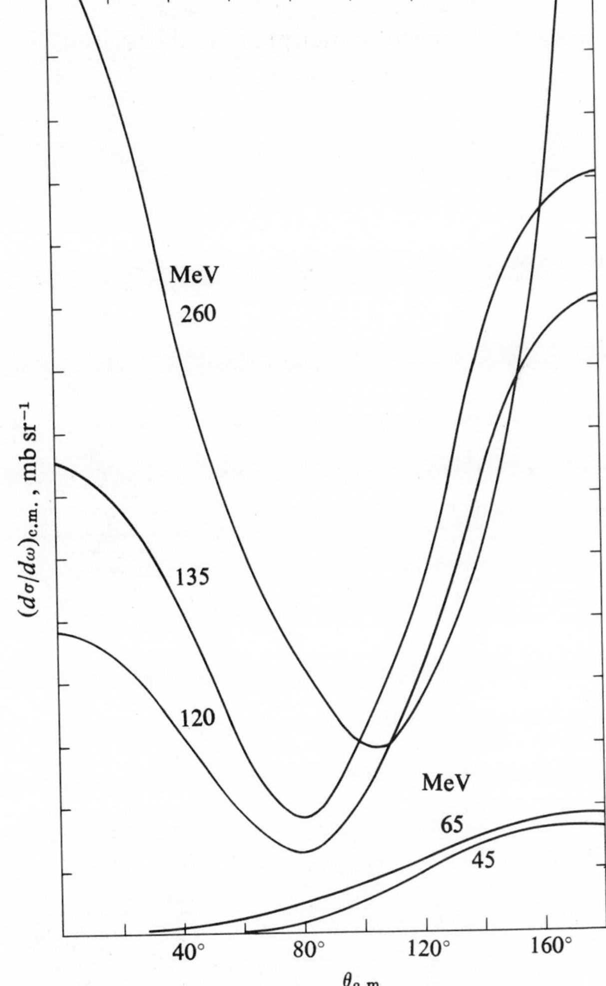

Figure 14-10 The angular distribution for the elastic π^+-proton scattering in the center-of-mass system. Differential cross section and scattering angle in the c.m. system. Curves are labeled according to the laboratory kinetic energy of the pion.

Table 14-3 Nomenclature of Phase Shifts

	$l = 0$	$l = 1$	
	$J = \frac{1}{2}$	$J = \frac{1}{2}$	$J = \frac{3}{2}$
$T_{1/2}$	δ_1	δ_{11}	δ_{13}
$T_{3/2}$	δ_3	δ_{31}	δ_{33}

A more refined analysis of the nucleon-pion interaction involves the measurement and calculation of the phase shifts of the scattered partial waves. Great effort has been spent on this important task. At low energy only *s* and *p* waves are important, the *p* waves dominating, as mentioned above. The states are now classified according to *T*, *J*, and *l*. The usual notation for the phase shifts, introduced by Fermi, is given in Table 14-3. The rule is: For *s* waves the subscript is $2T$. For *p* waves the first figure of the subscript is $2T$, the second $2J$.

The results of the analysis for energies below 100 MeV are

$$\delta_1 = 0.17\,\frac{p}{m_\pi c}$$

$$\delta_3 = -0.11\,\frac{p}{m_\pi c} \tag{14-6.11}$$

$$\delta_{33} = 0.235\left(\frac{p}{m_\pi c}\right)^3$$

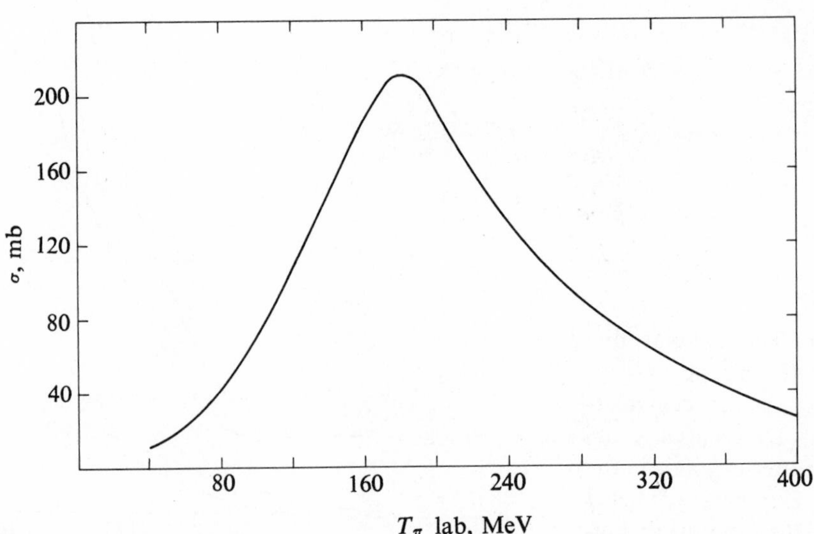

Figure 14-11 A one-level resonance formula for the $\pi^+ - p$ scattering.

Table 14-4 Pion-Nucleon Resonances

Total energy, MeV	T	State	Parity	Width, MeV	Q, MeV
1,238	$\frac{3}{2}$	$P_{3/2}$	+	90	160
1,512	$\frac{1}{2}$	$D_{3/2}$	− ?	150	434
1,688	$\frac{1}{2}$	$F_{5/2}(D_{3/2})$	+ ?	100	610
1,920	$\frac{3}{2}$	$F_{7/2}$	+	200	842

and δ_{11}, δ_{31}, δ_{13} are approximately 0. Above 100 MeV δ_{33} passes through $\pi/2$ (resonance) at about 195 MeV in the laboratory system.

Note that phase shifts near threshold depend on the $(2l + 1)$th power of momentum. This dependence is required by theory, if the interaction has a range small compared with the de Broglie wavelength of the pions.

The $T = \frac{3}{2}$, $J = \frac{3}{2}$ is the most prominent and best-studied resonance of the pion-nucleon system. However, there are other resonances, which have appeared at higher energies and which are under study (Fig. 14-12). Their characteristic quantum numbers are derived from angular distributions and, if necessary, by the study of the polarization of the recoil nucleon. The results available are summarized in Table 14-4. The

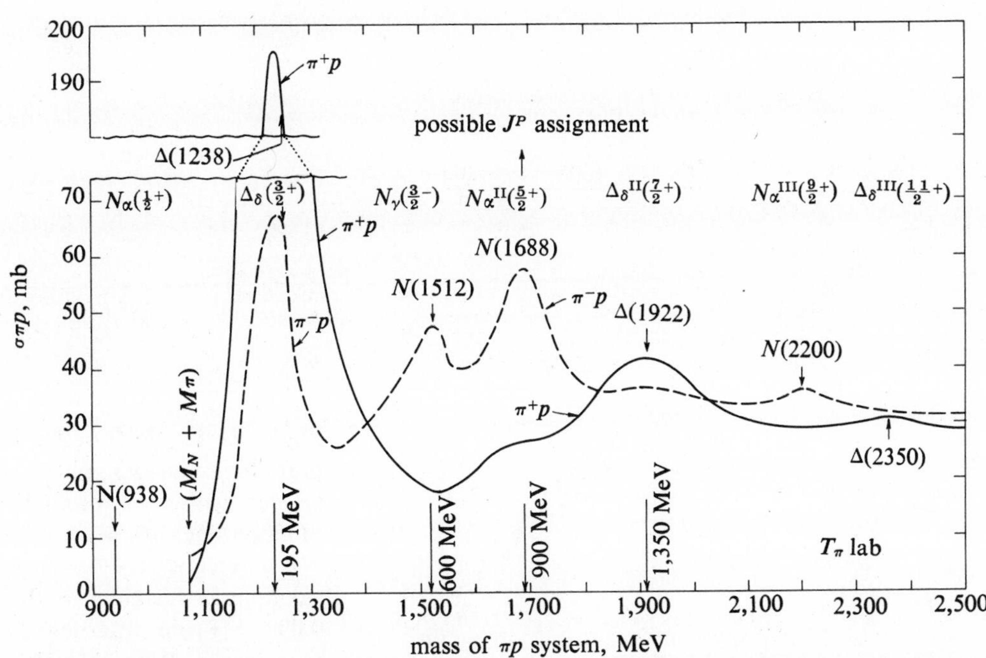

Figure 14-12 Pion-nucleon cross section showing resonances known to 1963. The symbols N_γ, N_α^{II}, etc., refer to a nomenclature proposed by Chew, Gell-Mann, and Rosenfeld. (See Sec. 15-7.)

higher resonances are not as prominent as the $\frac{3}{2}$, $\frac{3}{2}$ resonance, and the interpretation of the experimental data required mixtures of several states.

The phase shifts should be derivable from meson theory, provided that one knows the correct form of the meson-nucleon interaction and can solve the mathematical problem involved. Approximate forms of the interaction are known, and calculations of phase shifts based on them have been developed in close analogy with the effective range expressions in *n-p* scattering. For instance, for the δ_{33} phase shifts (Fig. 14-13) one has approximately

$$\frac{q^3 \cot \delta_{33}}{\omega^*} = \frac{3}{4f^2}(1 - \omega^* r_{33}) \tag{14-6.12}$$

where q and $\omega = \omega^* - (q^2/2M)$ (M of the proton) are the momentum and total energy of the pion in the center-of-mass system, in units $m_\pi c$ and $m_\pi c^2$, r_{33} is an "effective range" for the $N-\pi$ interaction in the $T = \frac{3}{2}$, $J = \frac{3}{2}$ state, in units $\hbar/m_\pi c$, and f^2 is the fundamental pion-nucleon coupling constant.

From an experimental plot of this formula one derives f^2 and r_{33}. The data of Fig. 14-13 give $f^2 = 0.088 \pm 0.002$; $r_{33} = 0.65$ F.

The same value of the constant f^2 is obtained from several other phenomena, e.g., pion photoproduction and nucleon-nucleon scattering.

Note that dimensionally $[f^2] = [e^2]$, where e is the electric charge. In the same units, $e^2 = 1/137 = 0.0073$.

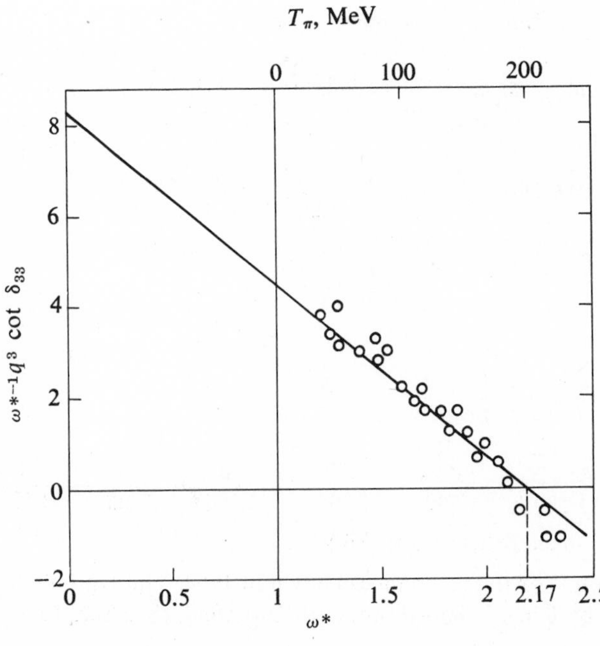

Figure 14-13 Effective range plot for the 3,3 phase shift. $(q^3 \cot \delta_{33})/\omega^*$ is plotted as a function of $\omega^* = \omega_q + q^2/2M$. The intercept at $\omega^* = 0$ implies a coupling constant $f^2 = 0.088 \pm 0.002$. [From Barnes, Rose, Giacomelli, Ring, Miyake, and Kinsey, *Phys. Rev.*, **117**, 226 (1960).]

Pions may be produced by nucleon-nucleon collisions. The simplest case is when only one pion is produced according to the reaction

$$N + N \rightarrow 2N + \pi \tag{14-7.1}$$

This reaction can assume many forms,

$$\begin{aligned} p + p &\rightarrow p + p + \pi^0 \\ &\rightarrow p + n + \pi^+ \\ n + p &\rightarrow p + p + \pi^- \\ &\rightarrow n + p + \pi^0 \\ &\rightarrow n + n + \pi^+ \end{aligned} \tag{14-7.2}$$

etc. Moreover, the neutron and proton at the right may escape as a bound deuteron. The conservation of i spin allows us to express all the cross sections of Eq. (14-7.2) as a function of only three of them (Rosenfeld, 1954). The experimental verification of these relations is another confirmation of the conservation of i spin. As a very simple example, consider the reactions

$$\begin{aligned} &\text{(a)}\ p + p \rightarrow d + \pi^+ \\ &\text{(b)}\ n + p \rightarrow d + \pi^0 \end{aligned} \tag{14-7.3}$$

In Eq. (14-7.3a) the i spin of $p + p$ is 1, the i spin of d is 0, and the i spin of the pion is 1. We have a pure state of i spin 1 on both sides. In reaction (14-7.3), on the right side, we have a pure state of i spin 1, but on the left side the np state is not an eigenstate of i spin. It can be expressed as

$$\frac{1}{\sqrt{2}}\left\{\frac{np + pn}{\sqrt{2}} + \frac{np - pn}{\sqrt{2}}\right\} \tag{14-7.4}$$

and hence the system has equal probabilities of having $T = 1$ or $T = 0$. Only in the first case can the reaction occur, and then with the amplitude corresponding to $T = 1$. We have thus

$$\sigma(pp \rightarrow d\pi^+) = 2\sigma(np \rightarrow d\pi^0) \tag{14-7.5}$$

Turning to pion photoproduction, processes such as

$$\begin{aligned} \gamma + p &\rightarrow p + \pi^0 \\ \gamma + p &\rightarrow n + \pi^+ \end{aligned} \tag{14-7.6}$$

have been observed.

The source of gamma rays is generally the bremsstrahlung of electrons accelerated by machines. The spectrum is thus continuous. However, determination of the momentum vector of the pion or nucleon in one of the reactions of Eq. (14-7.6) is sufficient to reconstruct completely the kinematics of the process and thus to determine a unique gamma-ray energy.

Near the threshold only the lowest angular momentum states are

Table 14-5 Classification of the Photoproduction of Pions

Type of radiation absorbed	Parity of final state	l of pion	J of final state	Momentum dependence of σ
$M1$	+	1	$\frac{1}{2}$	q^3
$M1$	+	1	$\frac{3}{2}$	q^3
$E1$	−	0	$\frac{1}{2}$	q
$E1$	−	2	$\frac{3}{2}$	q^5
$E2$	+	1	$\frac{3}{2}$	q^3
$E2$	+	3	$\frac{5}{2}$	q^7

involved, and we can analyze the reaction according to Table 14-5 (we must remember that the nucleon has $J = \frac{1}{2}$ and even parity and the pion has odd intrinsic parity; Fig. 14-14). The momentum dependence of the cross section at threshold is q^{2l+1}, and hence at low energy $E1$ is the dominating process when it occurs. When it does occur, photoproduction depends on the electric dipole moment of the nucleon-pion system, and we see from Fig. 14-15 that for the same distance the dipole moments for a nucleon and a pion are in the ratios

$$\text{dipole } 1 + \frac{m_\pi}{M} \quad : \quad 1 \quad : \quad \frac{m_\pi}{M} \quad : \quad 0$$

$$\text{for } \pi^- p; \qquad \pi^\pm n; \qquad \pi^0 p; \qquad \pi^0 n$$

Near threshold we expect the cross section for photoproduction to be

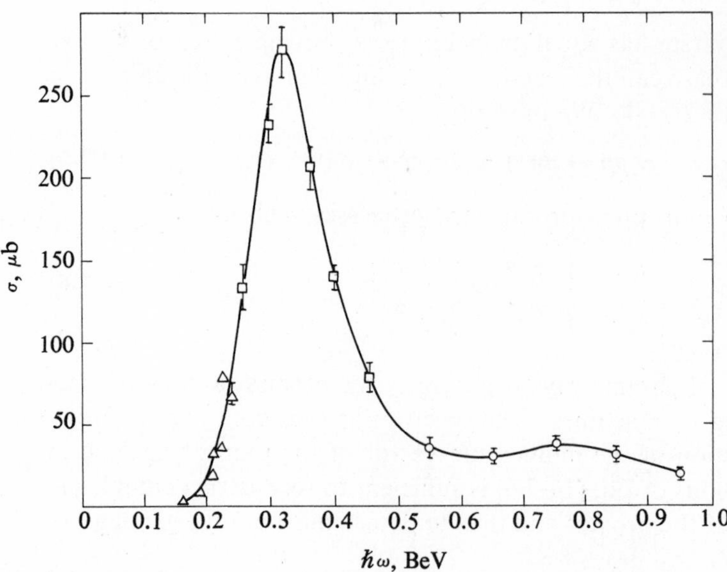

Figure 14-14 Reaction $\gamma + p \rightarrow \pi^0 + p$; total cross section as a function of energy.

in the same ratio as the square of the dipole moments, and this is approximately verified.

14-8 Pion-Pion Interaction

Collisions between free pions are practically unobservable, but several phenomena demonstrate, indirectly, a strong pion-pion interaction. The simplest and clearest of these is the occurrence of strong correlations between pions produced in proton-antiproton annihilation. Maglic, Alvarez, Rosenfeld, and Stevenson (1961) examined a great number of annihilation stars corresponding to a given number of pions, say, five. For each star they combined pions three at a time, and for each triple of pions they plotted the expression

$$Mc^2 = \left[\left(\sum_{1i}^{3} E_i\right)^2 - \left(\sum_{1i}^{3} cp_i\right)^2\right]^{\frac{1}{2}} \tag{14-8.1}$$

which is the total energy of the three pions in their center-of-mass system (see Appendix G). This energy may vary from a minimum of $3m_\pi c^2$ to a certain maximum. The relative probability of finding a certain value of the energy contains phase space for the final state as a factor. However, the experimental curve shows characteristic narrow spikes. These indicate sharp maxima for the transition matrix element, corresponding to given energies, or "states," of a system that decays into three pions. Sometimes such states are called "resonances" because the matrix element has a Breit–Wigner form (cf. Chap. 11) at a specific energy and most of the considerations developed for resonances are applicable to these cases.

We thus have a system lasting a long time, on a nuclear time scale, which decays and gives rise to three pions. The energy of the system is indicated by the position of the spike in Fig. 14-16; it is 787 MeV, corresponding to $5.74m_\pi$. The mean life is indicated by the width of the "line" in the same figure, according to the uncertainty relation,

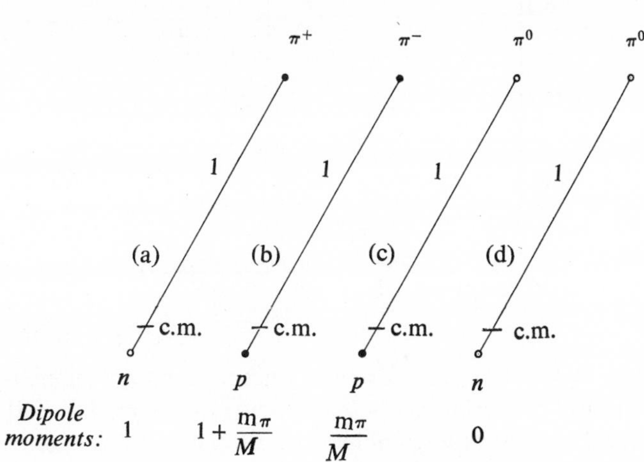

Figure 14-15 Electric dipole moments for a nucleon-pion system: (a) π^+n, (b) π^-p, (c) π^0p, (d) π^0n. The moments are in the ratios $1:1 + (m_\pi/M): m_\pi/M: 0$.

$$\tau = \frac{\hbar}{\Delta E} \tag{14-8.2}$$

These states have also a definite *i* spin *T*, total angular momentum *J*, and intrinsic parity. For these reasons they are also often called "particles."

The relevant quantum numbers may sometimes be found from relatively simple observations. For instance, a three-pion system may have *i* spin 3, 2, 1, 0. The peak, however, is observed only when the decaying system is neutral ($\pi^+\pi^-\pi^0$), although there is no constraint forcing this condition by charge conservation only. This rules out at once that the resonance has any *i* spin except 0. In order to determine the spin

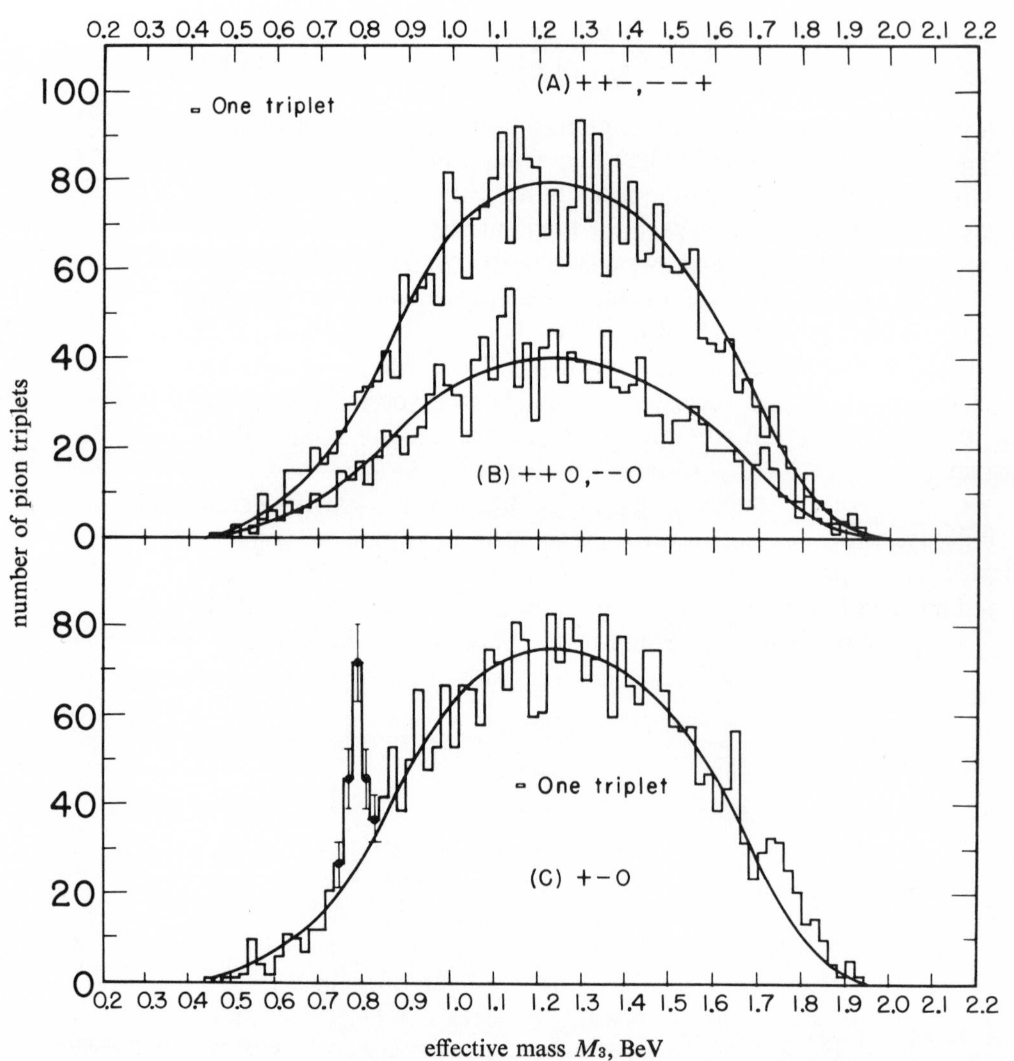

Figure 14-16 Evidence for the ω meson. Number of pion triplets versus effective mass (M_3) of the triplets for reaction $\bar{p} + p \rightarrow 2\pi^+ + 2\pi^- + \pi^0$. (*A*) is the distribution for the combinations of charge 1; (*B*) for the combinations of charge 2; and (*C*) for the neutral combinations. [Maglic, Alvarez, Rosenfeld, and Stevenson, *Phys. Rev. Letters*, 7, 178 (1961).]

and parity, one makes a Dalitz plot (see Chap. 15); the density distribution of its representative points gives $J = 1$ and negative parity. The annihilation reaction may then be interpreted, in the case considered here, as producing an intermediate step

$$p + \bar{p} \to \omega + 2\pi \quad (\omega \to 3\pi)$$

Thus the three-pion resonance is also called the ω meson.

Similarly, at least one two-pion system, called the ρ meson, has been identified in proton-antiproton annihilation. Its rest energy is 755 MeV, corresponding to $5.50m_\pi$. The width of the resonance is 110 MeV. It has $J = 1$, $T = 1$, and negative intrinsic parity.

Evidence for pion-pion interactions appears as well in so-called peripheral collisions similar to direct reactions of Chap. 11. Consider the reaction

$$\pi^- + p \to \pi^0 + \pi^- + p \tag{14-8.3}$$

in the limiting case in which the final nucleon receives a very small momentum. We may interpret this reaction as a collision of the initial π^- with a meson in the mesonic cloud around the proton, with the latter acting as a "spectator." If the spectator receives a very small momentum, the collision corresponds almost to that between free pions. Such collisions are said to be peripheral. The intuitive, qualitative argument given here can be made precise (Goebel; Chew and Low, 1959) and quantitative. Studies of reactions of the type of Eq. (14-8.3) gave the first experimental indications of resonances in the pion-pion system. (Anderson, Bang, Burke, Carmony, and Schmitz, at Berkeley). The method of peripheral collision was used to establish the ρ meson (Erwin, March, Walker, and West, at Wisconsin, 1961; Stonehill, Baltay, Courant, Fickinger, Fowler, Kraybill, Sandweiss, Sanford, and Taft, at Yale, 1961) in the reactions

$$\pi^- + p \to \rho^- + p \quad (\rho^- \to \pi^- + \pi^0) \tag{14-8.4}$$

$$\pi^- + p \to \rho^0 + n \quad (\rho^0 \to \pi^+ + \pi^-) \tag{14-8.5}$$

A recent illustration of this type of observation is demonstrated in Fig. 14-17. The i spin of the ρ, assigned from the branching ratio (1 : 2) between reactions [Eqs. (14-8.4) and (14-8.5)] is 1. The angular momentum must then be odd. The angular distribution of the line of flight of the two pions formed in decay, with respect to the line of flight of their center of mass, gives the value 1 for the angular momentum.

Indications of pion-pion interaction have been found in reactions other than those mentioned above. Abashian, Booth, and Crowe (1960) studied the reactions

$$\begin{aligned} p + d &\to 2\pi^0 + \mathrm{He}^3 \\ &\to \pi^+ + \pi^- + \mathrm{He}^3 \\ &\to \pi^+ + \pi^0 + \mathrm{H}^3 \end{aligned} \tag{14-8.6}$$

They found that in the first reaction the He^3 tends to recoil as if the two pions escaped in a bound state. This effect is prominent near the threshold for two-pion production. No similar effect is found in the second reaction. The authors concluded from this that the matrix element for two-pion production is unusually large near the threshold for $T = 0$ states. A possible interpretation is that the two-pion system in the $T = 0$, $J = 0$ state has a strong interaction that can be represented by a scattering length (see Chap. 10) of about $2\hbar/m_\pi c$. This is relatively large. The situation is in this respect similar to that of the *n-p* system in the singlet state.

Pion-pion interactions appear in still other phenomena. In fact the first indication of dipion states occurred in the analysis of nuclear form factors (Chap. 6). We can give only a qualitative idea of the line of argument. The form factors are interpreted as a consequence of the presence of a meson cloud around a central bare nucleon. The size of the cloud is directly measured by experiment and is related, according to the argument of Sec. 14-1, to the mass of the particles present in the cloud; the

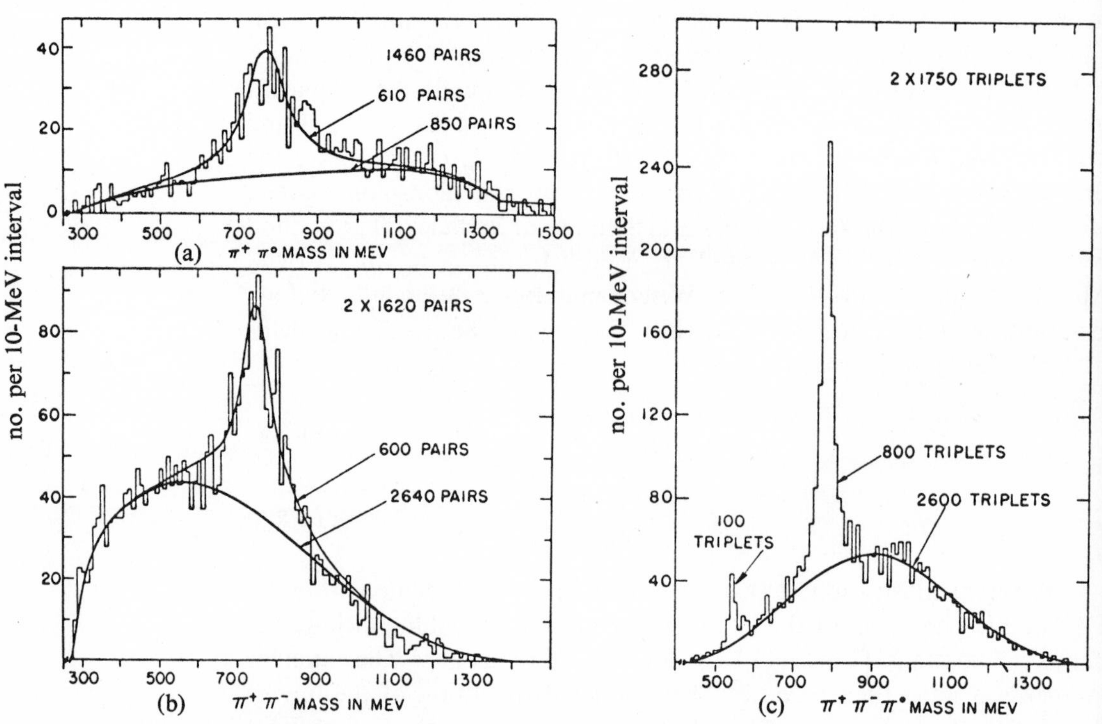

Figure 14-17 Evidence for the ρ mesons and ω mesons. Positive pions of momentum $\sim$ 2.9 BeV/c impinge on protons generating two, three, or four pions. The pions produced are often associated as ρ, η, or ω mesons. This is shown in (a), where the mass distribution (in their own center of mass) for $\pi^+\pi^0$ pairs from $\pi^+ + p \rightarrow \pi^+ + \pi^0 + p$ is given. The peak corresponds to ρ^+. In (b) the mass of $\pi^+\pi^-$ from the reaction $\pi^+ + p \rightarrow \pi^+ + \pi^+ + p + \pi^-$ is plotted. The peak corresponds to ρ^0. In (c) the mass of $\pi^+\pi^0\pi^-$ triplets originating from $\pi^+ + p \rightarrow p + \pi^+ + \pi^- + \pi^0$ is given. The peak corresponds to ω^0. The smooth curves correspond to phase space. [From Alff et al. (Columbia and Rutgers Universities), *Phys. Rev. Letters*, **9**, 322 (1962).]

Table 14-6 Strongly Decaying Particles

Particle	Quantum numbers[a] Established $T(J^{PG})$	Possible assignment $T(J^{PG})$	S	Y	Mass, MeV	Γ,[b] MeV	Mass², (BeV)²	Decay characteristics Mode	%
ω	$0(1^{--})$		0	0	783	9	0.697	$\pi^+\pi^-\pi^0$	88
								$\pi^+\pi^-$	<2
								$\pi^0\gamma$, $\pi^0\pi^0\gamma$	10
K_1K_1	$0(J^{++}_{\text{even}})$	$0(0^{++})$	0	0	1,020	?	1.08	$K\bar{K}$(K_1K_1 or K_2K_2 not K_1K_2)	
ϕ	$0(J^{--}_{\text{odd}})$	$0(1^{--})$	0	0	1,019	6	1.038	K_1K_2	25
								K^+K^-	61
								$\rho\pi$	8
								$\pi\pi$	6
f_0	$0(\geqslant 2^{++})$	$0(2^{++})$	0	0	1,250	75	1.109	2π	Large
								4π	8
								$K\bar{K}$ (not K_1K_2)	
$K\bar{K}\pi$	(?)	$0(1^{+-})$	0	0	1,410	60	1.99	$K\bar{K}\pi$	Large
ρ	$1(1^{-+})$		0	0	755	120	0.570	$\pi\pi$	100
B	1(?)	1(?)	0	0	1,220	100	1.49	$\omega\pi$	Large
								$\bar{K}K$	Small
								$\pi\pi$	?
A	$?(?^-)$	1(?)	0	0	1,200	350	1.44	$\pi^+\rho^0$	Large
								3π	
K^*	$\frac{1}{2}(1^{--})$		+1	+1	891	46	0.794	$K\pi$	~100
								$K\pi\pi$	<0.2
								$\kappa\pi$	<0.2
κ	1(?)	?	+1	+1	723	<12	0.523	$K\pi$	100
$N^*_{1/2}$ (1,512) (600 MeV πp)	$\frac{1}{2}(\frac{3}{2}\ -)$		0	+1	1,512	125	2.286	$N\pi$	79
								$N\pi\pi$	
$N^*_{1/2}$ (1,688) (900 MeV πp)	$\frac{1}{2}(\frac{5}{2})$	$\frac{1}{2}(\frac{5}{2}\ +)$	0	+1	1,688	170	2.849	$N\pi$	91
								$N\pi\pi$	
$N^*_{1/2}$ (2,190) (2.08 GeV πp)	$\frac{1}{2}(?)$	$\frac{1}{2}(\frac{9}{2}^+)$	0	+1	2,190	200	4.80	$N\pi$	30
								$N\pi\pi$	
								ΣK	?
$N_{3/2}^*$ (1,238) Isobar	$\frac{3}{2}(\frac{3}{2}^+)$		0	+1	1,238	125	1.533	$N\pi$	100

Table 14-6 *(continued)*

$N^*_{3/2}$ (1,920) 1.35 GeV πp	$\frac{3}{2}(\frac{7}{2}+)$		0	+1	1,920	~200	3.68	$N\pi$ ΣK	30 ?
$N^*_{3/2}$ (2,360) 2.51 GeV πp	$\frac{1}{2}$(?)	$\frac{3}{2}(\frac{11}{2}+)$	0	+1	2,360	200	5.57	$N\pi$ Others	{100
Y^*_0 (1,405)	0(?)	$0(\frac{1}{2}-)$	−1	0	1,405	50	1.97	$\Sigma\pi$	100
Y^*_0 (1,520)	$0(\frac{3}{2}-)$		−1	0	1,519.4	16.4	2.309	$\Sigma\pi$ $\bar{K}N$ $\Lambda\pi\pi$	54.6 29.3 16.2
Y^*_0 (1,815)	$0(J \geqslant \frac{5}{2})$	$0(\frac{5}{2}+)$	−1	0	1,815	120	3.29	$\bar{K}N$ $\Sigma\pi$ $\Lambda\pi\pi$	82 6 12
Y^*_1 (1,385)	$1(\frac{3}{2}+)$		−1	0	1,383.5	47	1.914	$\Lambda\pi$ $\Sigma\pi$	~96 ~4
Y^*_1 (1,660)	$1(\frac{3}{2})$	$1(\frac{3}{2}-)$	−1	0	1,660	40	2.76	$\bar{K}N$ $\Sigma\pi$ $\Lambda\pi$ $\Sigma\pi\pi$ $\Lambda\pi\pi$	9 27 32 18 14
Y^*_1 (1,765)	1(?)	?	−1	0	1,765	50	3.12	KN Others	~60 ~40
Ξ^* (1,530)	$\frac{1}{2}(\frac{3}{2}+)$		−2	−1	1,530	<7	2.34	$\Xi\pi$	100
Ξ^* (1,770)	$\frac{1}{2}$(?)	?	−2	−1	1,770	<80	3.13	$\Xi\pi$ $\Xi\pi\pi$	100

[a] In this column the numbers at the left and in the center are observational, the numbers at the right are theoretically assigned on the basis of SU_3 symmetry and Regge recurrences (see Sec. 15-7).

[b] Γ = empirical full width at half-maximum with background subtracted.

cloud is so large that these particles cannot be anything heavier than pions. The anomalous part of the magnetic moment of the nucleons has the same origin. From the measurement of the magnetic moment and charge form factors it has been possible to conclude that they are associated with the virtual emission or absorption of pion pairs. However, the probability of emission or absorption of virtual pions is calculable from the value of the constant f of Sec. 14-7, and it is insufficient to account for the experimental magnetic properties of the nucleons if we consider the pions as independent. To resolve this difficulty a strong pion-pion interaction was postulated and the energy and quantum numbers of a resonance of the $\pi\pi$ system were assigned, in fair agreement with those of the not yet discovered ρ meson.

The multipion states known up to April 1964 are summarized in Table 14-6 and in Fig. 15-5, which, however, also contain strange particles to be discussed in Chap. 15. The data come from compilations of Dr. A. H. Rosenfeld. For the nomenclature of the first column see Sec. 15-7.

Bibliography

Annual International Conference on High Energy Physics (RoC 60— . . .).

Ashkin, Cassels, Touschek, Puppi, Fubini, Cini, and Corinaldesi, "Lectures on Pion Physics," *Nuovo Cimento, Suppl.*, **14,** 215 (1959).

Barkas, Birnbaum, and Smith, "Mass Ratio Method Applied to the Measurement of L-mesons, Masses, and the Energy Balance in Pion Decay," *Phys. Rev.*, **101,** 778 (1956).

Bernardini, G., "Lectures on Photoproduction," *Nuovo Cimento, Suppl.*, **11,** 104 (1955).

Bethe, H. and F. de Hoffmann (BH 55).

Chew, G., *S-Matrix Theory of Strong Interactions*, Benjamin, New York, 1961.

Dalitz, R., "Meson Phenomena and the Meson Theory," *Progr. Nucl. Phys.*, **4,** 95 (1955).

Fermi, E. (Fe 51).

Fermi, E., "Lectures on Pions and Nucleons," *Nuovo Cimento, Suppl.*, **11,** 17 (1955).

Gell-Mann, M., and K. M. Watson, "The Interaction between π-mesons and Nucleons," *Ann. Rev. Nucl. Sci.*, **4,** 219 (1954).

Jackson, J. D. (Ja 58).

Lattes, Occhialini, and Powell, "Observations on the Tracks of Slow Mesons in Photographic Emulsions," *Nature*, **160,** 453 (1947).

Lock, W. O. (Lo 60).

Moyer, B. J., "$\pi^- - p$ Elastic Scattering in the Energy Region 500–1500 MeV," *Rev. Mod. Phys.*, **33,** 367 (1961).

Nishijima, K., *Fundamental Particles*, Benjamin, New York, 1963.

Omnès, R., and M. Froissart, *Mandelstam Theory and Regge Poles*, Benjamin, New York, 1964.

Puppi, G., "Pionic Resonances," *Ann. Rev. Nucl, Sci.*, **13,** 287 (1963).

Williams, S. C., *Introduction to Elementary Particles*, Academic Press, New York, 1962.

Yukawa, H., "Interaction of Elementary Particles," *Proc. Phys. Math. Soc. Japan*, **17,** 48 (1935).

Problems

14-1 Show by an argument of the type developed by Wick [*Nature*, **142,** 993 (1938)] that the quanta corresponding to Coulomb's law have zero mass.

14-2 Assume that a neutron and a proton have an interaction

$$V = \pm g^2 e^{-kr}/r$$

Using the Born approximation, calculate the total and differential scattering cross section. Do the same for a potential

$$V' = -(V/2)(1+P)$$

where P is the neutron-proton exchange operator.

14-3 (*a*) Calculate the maximum electron energy emitted in μ-meson decay. (*b*) Calculate the μ-meson energy in the decay $\pi^+ \to \mu^+ + \nu$ and the electron energy in the decay $\pi^+ \to e^+ + \nu$.

14-4 Calculate the threshold energy for the process

$$\gamma + p \to \pi^0 + p$$

14-5 Consider the reaction $\pi^- + p \to n + \pi^0$, where the initial π^- and proton are at rest. Calculate (*a*) the velocity of the emitted π^0; (*b*) the maximum and minimum energies of the gamma rays emitted in the π^0 decay; (*c*) the spectrum of the γ emitted.

14-6 Plan an experiment to determine the mean life of π^0, using the decay

$$K^+ \to \pi^+ + \pi^0$$

and the formation of Dalitz pairs from the π^0.

14-7 Calculate the energy for a π beam impinging on d which is to be used to study detailed balance in the reaction $p + p = d + \pi$ at $Tp = 450$ MeV (laboratory system).

14-8 Why does the reaction $\pi^- + d = 2n + \pi^0$ not occur for pions at rest?

14-9 Show that if capture occurs in an s state, the reaction $\pi^- + d \to 2n + \pi^0$ is forbidden.

14-10 The reaction $d + d = \text{He} + \pi^0$ has never been observed. Why?

14-11 Show that isospin invariance for nuclear forces is sufficient to ensure the equality of *np*, *nn*, and *np* interaction in all states antisymmetrical in spin and space.

14-12 Show that for pion-pion states symmetric in space, isospin invariance does not require that the interaction be the same in all states. Show that there are two independent interactions.

14-13 Show that the interaction of the electromagnetic field with a system of neutrons and protons can be written, nonrelativistically, as

$$H = \frac{e}{mc}\sum_i \tfrac{1}{2}\mathbf{p}_i\cdot\mathbf{A}(x_i)\,(1 + 2\tau_3^{(i)})$$
$$+ \sum_i \{\tfrac{1}{2}\mu_n(1 - 2\tau_3^{(i)}) + \tfrac{1}{2}\mu_p(1 + 2\tau_3^{(i)})\}\,\boldsymbol{\sigma}^{(i)}\cdot\nabla \times \mathbf{A}(x_i)$$

where $\mathbf{p}_i$ is the momentum of the ith nucleon, $\mathbf{A}(x_i)$ the vector potential at its position, $\boldsymbol{\sigma}^{(i)}$ its Pauli spin vector, and $\tau^{(i)}$ its i spin.

From this show that if $\mathbf{T}^2$ is a constant of the motion, the selection rules $\Delta T = 0, \pm 1$ obtains. (*Hint*: The interaction may be divided into a part H_s independent of i spin and a part H_v proportional to T_3.)

14-14 Given that the total cross section for $\pi^+ - p$ reactions at energy E_0 is σ_0, what specific prediction can you make purely on the basis of charge symmetry?

14-15 What would be the ratio between the cross sections of the following reactions; if $f_3 = f_1$ or if $f_3 = 0, f_1 \neq 0$?

$$\pi^+ + p \to \pi^+ + p$$

$$\pi^- + p \to \pi^- + p$$

$$\pi^- + p \to \pi^0 + n$$

14-16 Prove that the phase shift on a pion-nucleon collision at low nergy is proportional to p^{2l+1}, where p is the momentum and the angular nomentum of the colliding particles is $\hbar l$.

14-17 A ω particle (three-pion state) of kinetic energy 100 MeV is enerated in a p-$\bar{p}$ annihilation process. (*a*) How far does it travel before lecomposing into three pions? (Use the resonance width to find the mean ife.) Compare this distance with nuclear dimensions. (*b*) Show that the fact hat only neutral ω particles are known indicates that ω has i spin zero. *c*) What is the maximum momentum in the laboratory for an ω meson enerated in proton-antiproton annihilation at rest? (*d*) What is the maxinum momentum, in the laboratory, of one of its decay pions?

CHAPTER XV

Strange Particles

In 1947 Rochester and Butler obtained cloud-chamber photographs of two cosmic-ray events in which the tracks had the configuration of a V (Fig. 15-1). A careful analysis indicated that the tracks originated from the decay of two new species of particles, now called K and Λ. Subsequently emulsion photographs of other cosmic-ray events showed particles decaying into three pions (Brown, Camerini, Fowler, Muirhead, Powell, and Ritson, 1949) (Fig. 15-2). More new particles appeared in cosmic-ray events during the following few years.

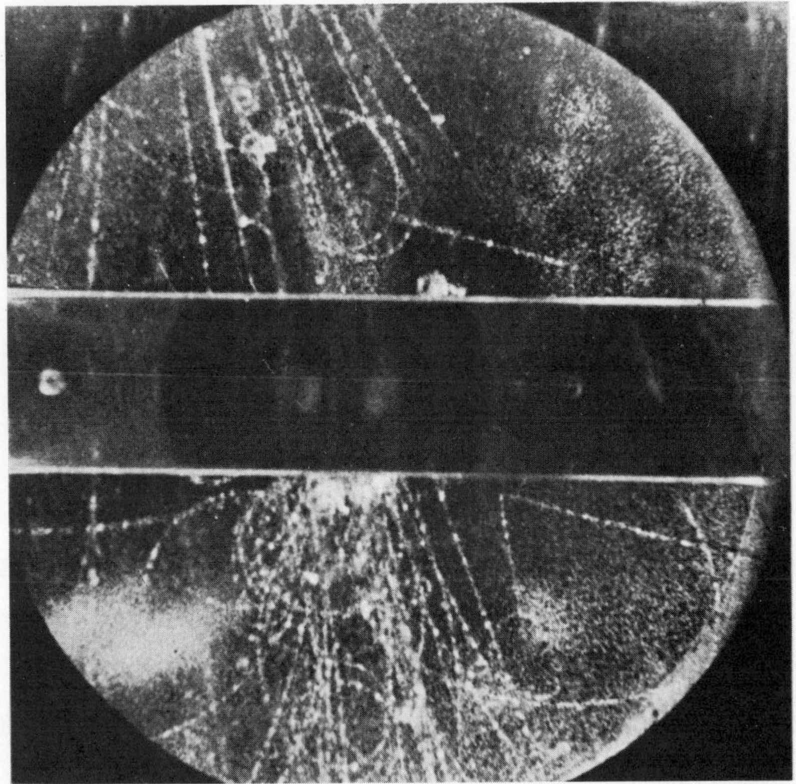

Figure 15-1 First picture showing a neutral particle decaying into a pion and a proton. Such a neutral particle is now called a Λ particle. Originally the authors called them V particles. [From G. D. Rochester and C. C. Butler, *Nature*, **160**, 855 (1947).]

The determination of their masses and modes of decay was one of the major achievements of the early 1950s.

When accelerators reached an energy sufficient for producing these particles in the laboratory, it became apparent that there was a discrepancy between the relatively large cross section for production and the long decay period. This led to the discovery of associated production and to the introduction of the "strangeness" quantum number (Gell-Mann and Nishijima, 1953).

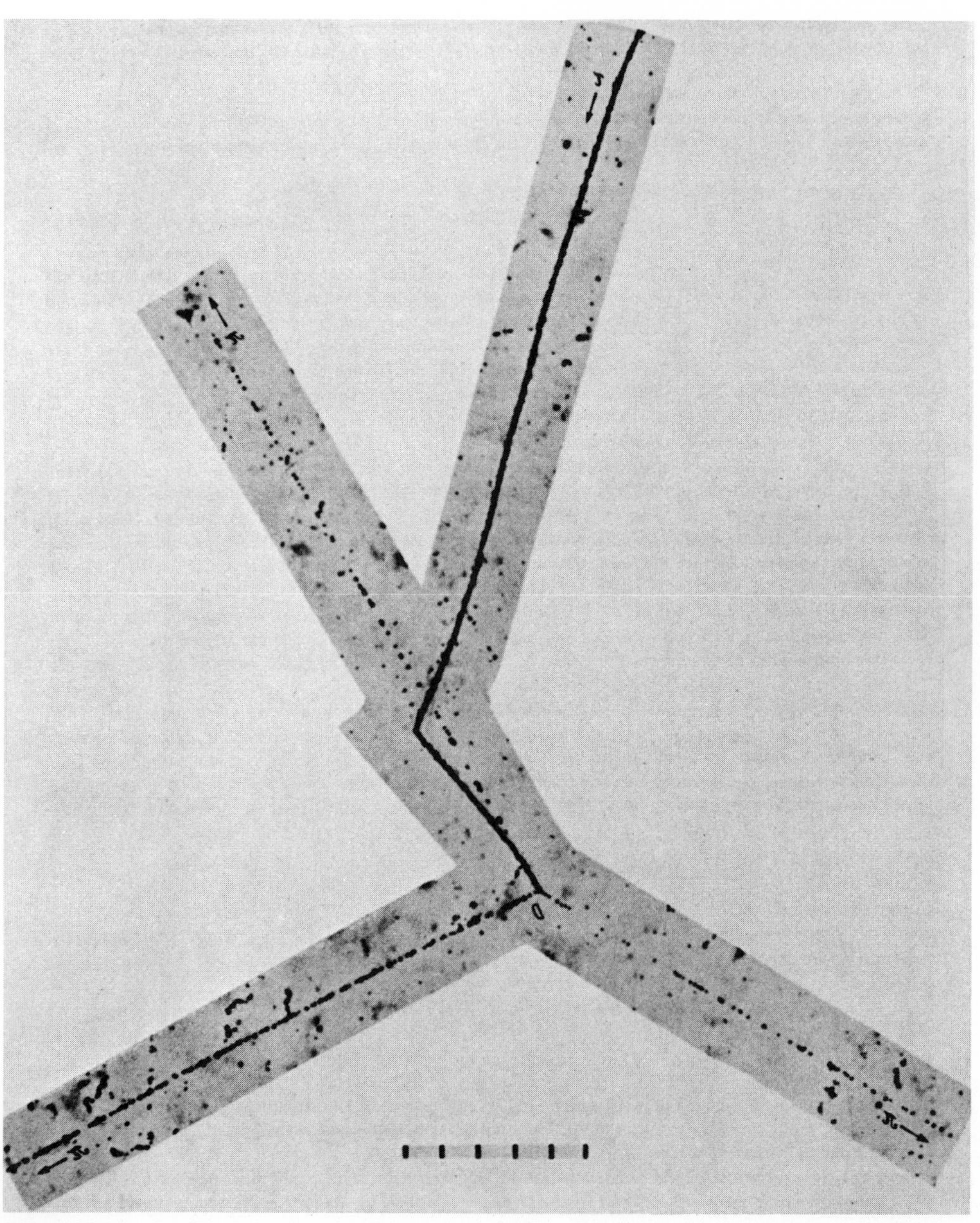

Figure 15-2 Decay of a τ meson into three pions. [Hodgson, 1951, from (PFP 59).]

The particles considered in this chapter are subject to strong interactions and thus *i* spin and intrinsic parity are valid concepts for them. The particles can be divided in groups formed by particles having approximately the same mass, but different charges. This suggests to assign to them an isotopic spin as in the case of the nucleon and the pion, and to group them in *i*-spin multiplets. Particles belonging to the same multiplet have the same T; however, the charge determines T_3. The ordinary spin and the intrinsic parity of particles belonging to the same *i*-spin multiplet is the same. Each particle has an antiparticle.

15-1 Associated Production—Strangeness

If we examine the decay constants of the hyperons (Table 13-1), we find that they are all of order of magnitude 10^{10} sec^{-1}, except for Σ^0, which, however, decays by gamma emission and transforms into another hyperon, the Λ. K mesons have similar or smaller decay constants.

Production cross sections for hyperons and K mesons at about 1.5 BeV are about one tenth the nucleon–pion scattering cross section. On this basis we could try to estimate the decay constant of the hyperons, attributing the decay to an interaction

$$\Lambda \Rightarrow p + \pi \qquad \textbf{(15-1.1)}$$

Its matrix element could be approximately calculated from production if the production reaction were

$$\pi + p \Rightarrow \Lambda + \pi \qquad \textbf{(15-1.2)}$$

(which it is not). This, however, leads to a discrepancy, showing that the decay is very strongly forbidden.

From the production cross section we conclude that the matrix element for Λ production is of the order of $10^{-1/2}$ or one-third that of the Yukawa interaction. If we use this datum to estimate the decay constant of the Λ, we arrive at 10^{22} sec^{-1}, a number 10^{12} larger than the experimental one. A similar contradiction is obtained if we compare the reactions

$$K^0 \Rightarrow 2\pi^0 \qquad \textbf{(15-1.3)}$$

and

$$p + \pi^- \Rightarrow n + K^0 \qquad \textbf{(15-1.4)}$$

In other words, the decay constant is much too small if we assume that the production occurs according to Eq. (15-1.2) or (15-1.4) (which it does not). In Eqs. (15-1.1) to (15-1.4) we have used (for purposes of argument) the strong-interaction symbol $\Rightarrow$. Actually all these reactions are forbidden for strong interactions, as we shall see shortly.

Several hypotheses have been put forward in order to resolve this apparent discrepancy. However, the fact is that the reactions by which Λ and K are formed are not those of Eqs. (15-1.2) and (15-1.4) but

$$\pi^- + p \Rightarrow \Lambda^0 + K^0 \qquad \textbf{(15-1.5)}$$

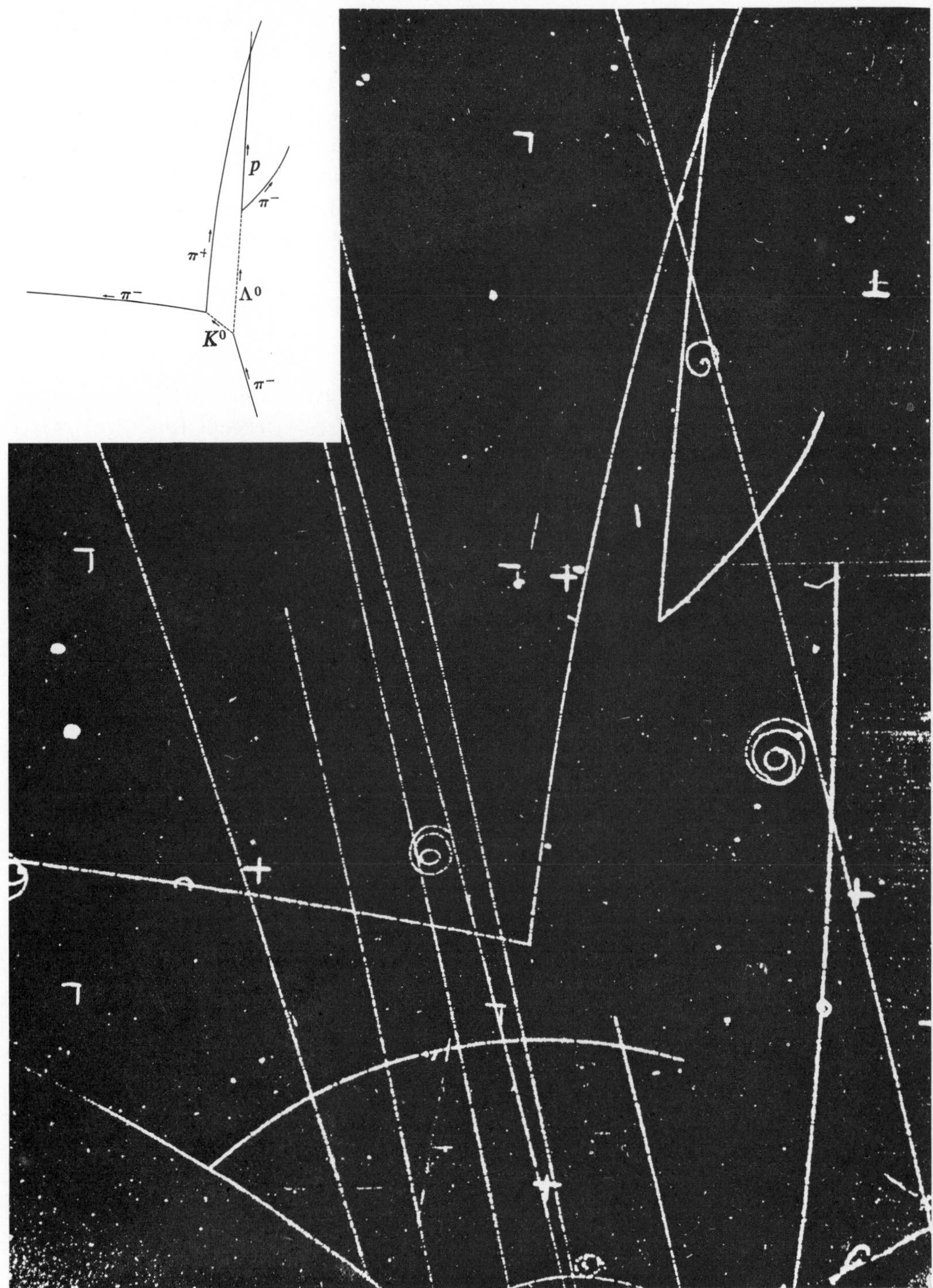

Figure 15-3 Bubble-chamber picture showing the following reactions:

$$\pi^- + p \rightarrow \Lambda^0 + K^0$$

$$\Lambda^0 \rightarrow \pi^- + p$$

$$K^0 \rightarrow \pi^- + \pi^+$$

[Courtesy Lawrence Radiation Laboratory, Berkeley, Calif.]

or similar reactions, in which, starting from pions and nucleons, two particles of the Λ, K, Σ, and Ξ families are formed simultaneously. For instance, the large cross sections for production occur only for "associated production" of a Λ^0 and K^0, starting from $\pi^- + p$ (Figs. 15-3 and 15-4). Which particles are to be associated will be seen shortly.

The decay and production processes thus involve different particles and cannot be simply related (Nambu, Nishijima, Yamaguchi, 1951; Pais, 1952; Fowler, 1954).

This whole subject is systematized by introducing a new additive quantum number called strangeness (S) (Gell-Mann and Nishijima, 1953) and by postulating that, in strong interactions, strangeness must be conserved. At present, these concepts are unrelated to other ideas in physics, and we have no profound "explanation" of their meaning, but shall employ them as very useful semiempirical rules.

The strangeness S of a particle is defined by the relation

$$Q = T_3 + \frac{N}{2} + \frac{S}{2} \tag{15-1.6}$$

where Q is the electric charge in units of $+e$ (proton charge), T_3 is the third component of the *i* spin, and N is the baryon number (the number of nucleons that ultimately appear in the decay or in the final products of a chain of decays of the particle). The quantity $N + S = Y$ is called hypercharge and one may also write Eq. (15-1.6) in the form

$$Q = T_3 + \frac{Y}{2}$$

In order to assign the strangeness to a particle, we must know its T_3. Since particles appear in multiplets—three pions, two K mesons, two nucleons, one Λ, three Σ, etc.—it is possible, from the very multiplicity of these particle multiplets, to assign a T, because $2T + 1$ particles appear in a multiplet, although this criterion is not always sufficient. (Thus, both pions and K mesons appear in three charge states, positive, neutral, and negative, but pions have *i* spin 1, whereas K mesons form two doublets of *i* spin $\frac{1}{2}$.) The strangeness of antiparticles is assigned in a similar manner (considering that one antinucleon is counted as -1 nucleon) and is equal and opposite to the strangeness of the corresponding particle. Strangeness cannot be defined for particles which do not have strong interactions, because *i* spin is not defined for them.

Analysis of the empirical material yields the classification of Fig. 15-5, which illustrates only particles stable against decay by strong interactions. The assignments were made as follows:

1. Λ^0 appears only in one charge state, neutral; hence, it is an *i*-spin singlet; $T = 0 = T_3$. It decays, producing a proton; hence $N = 1$. Equation (15-1.6) then gives $S = -1$.

2. Σ^+, Σ^0, Σ^-. Here $T = 1$ because we have a charge triplet with $T_3 = 1, 0, -1$. Σ particles decay into one nucleon plus bosons; hence, $N = 1$. Equation (15-1.6) then gives $S = -1$.

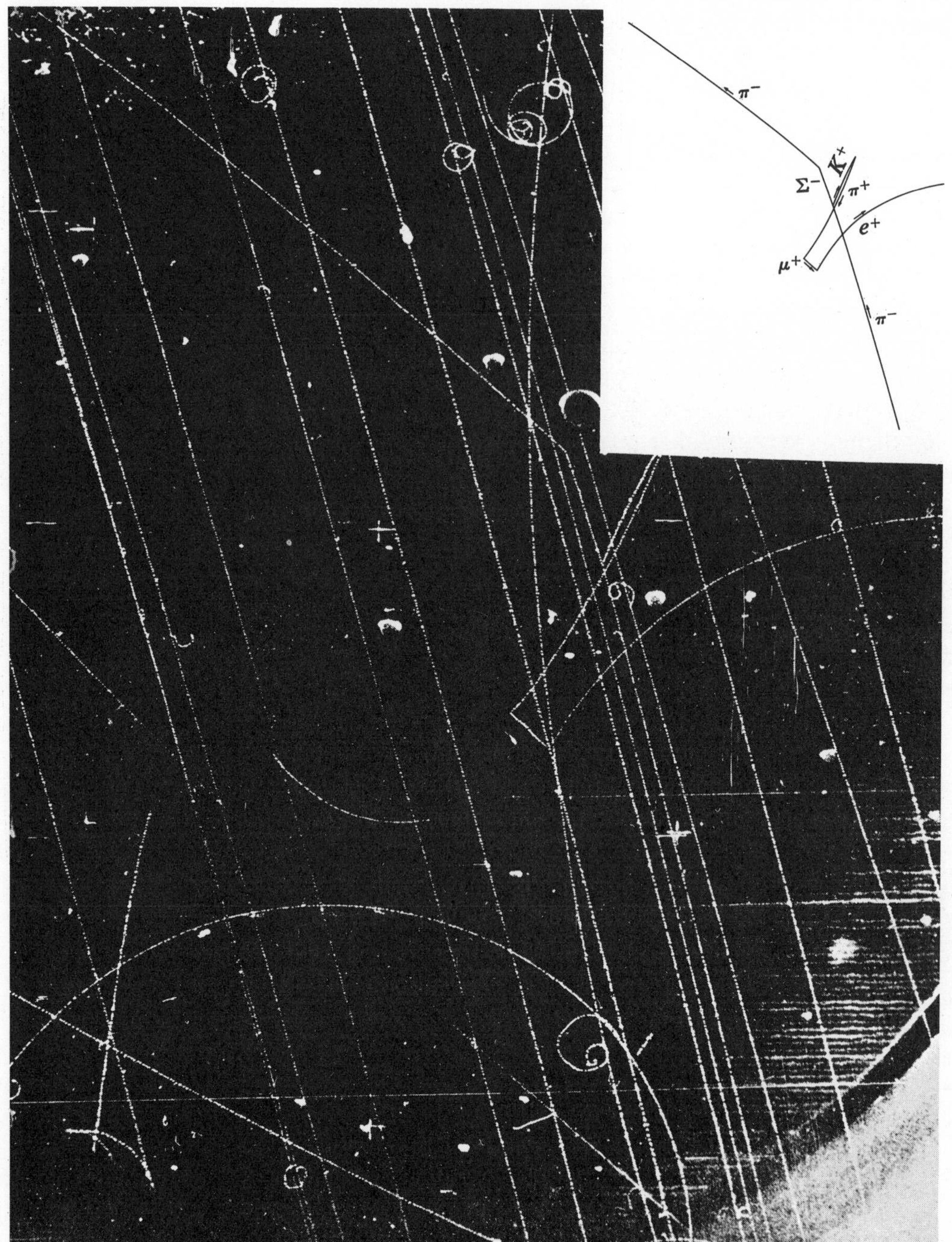

Figure 15-4 Bubble-chamber picture showing the following reactions:

$$\pi^- + p \to \Sigma^- + K^+$$

$$\Sigma^- \to \pi^- + n$$

$$K^+ \to \pi^+ + \pi^0 + \pi^0$$

$$\hookrightarrow \mu^+ + \nu$$

$$\hookrightarrow e^+ + \nu + \bar{\nu}$$

[Courtesy Lawrence Radiation Laboratory, Berkeley, Calif.]

3. Ξ^0 and Ξ^- have been observed, indicating that $T = \frac{1}{2}$, $T_3 = \frac{1}{2}, -\frac{1}{2}$. The decay gives rise to one nucleon, and Eq. (15-1.6) gives $S = -2$. This is confirmed, once the strangeness of the K is assigned, by the observed production reaction (Alvarez, Eberhard, Good, Graziano, Ticho, and Wojcicki, 1959), for example;

$$p + K^- \Rightarrow \Xi^- + K^+$$

4. K mesons. From their decay in pions only, we conclude that $N = 0$.

We know three charged states of K, and we could think that $T = 1$. However, the charged K have different strangeness, as shown by the forbiddenness of $\pi^- + p \Rightarrow K^- + \Sigma^+$, whereas $\pi^- + p \Rightarrow K^+ + \Sigma^-$ is allowed. Furthermore there are two kinds of K^0 (see Sec. 15-6). The K^+, K^-, and the two K^0, respectively, are then interpreted as charge conjugates of each other. We have thus two *i*-spin doublets: K^+ and K^0 with $T = \frac{1}{2}$, $T_3 = \frac{1}{2}, -\frac{1}{2}$ respectively, and hence by Eq. (15-1.6), $S=1$, and their charge conjugates K^- and $\overline{K^0}$ with $T = \frac{1}{2}$, $T_3 = -\frac{1}{2}, +\frac{1}{2}$, respectively, and $S = -1$.

5. Pions with $T = 1$, $N = 0$ have $S = 0$.

6. Nucleons with $T = \frac{1}{2}$, $N = 1$ have $S = 0$.

7. The Ω^- formed by the reaction $K^- + p \Rightarrow \Omega^- + K^+ + K^0$ has strangeness -3, $N = 1$, and hence $T_3 = 0$. It is expected (see Sec. 15–7) to be an *i*-spin singlet. Since leptons do not interact strongly, the concept of strangeness is not applicable to them.

The conservation of strangeness immediately gives selection rules that forbid Eq. (15-1.2) and allow associated production. This was the starting point for the establishment of this quantum number. However, it also gives other selection rules that have been verified experimentally. Thus reactions such as

$$\pi + N \Rightarrow \bar{K} + \Sigma \qquad \text{or} \qquad N + N \Rightarrow \Lambda + \Lambda \tag{15-1.7}$$

do not occur, while reactions such as

$$\pi + N \Rightarrow K + \Sigma \qquad \text{or} \qquad \pi + N \Rightarrow K + \Lambda \tag{15-1.8}$$

are observed. It will be noted that, if strangeness were a multiplicative quantum number, it could not account for the difference between reactions (15-1.7) and (15-1.8).

Besides strangeness, T is also conserved in strong interactions, and this gives relations that are directly verifiable, similar to those mentioned in π-p interactions. For instance, in the reactions

$$K^- + d \Rightarrow \Lambda + n + \pi^0 \tag{15-1.9}$$

$$\Rightarrow \Lambda + p + \pi^- \tag{15-1.10}$$

the i spin on the left is $\frac{1}{2}$. The eigenstate of $T = \frac{1}{2}$, $T_3 = -\frac{1}{2}$, on the right, is

$$+ \sqrt{\tfrac{1}{3}}\,\Lambda n^0 - \sqrt{\tfrac{2}{3}}\,\Lambda p^- \tag{15-1.11}$$

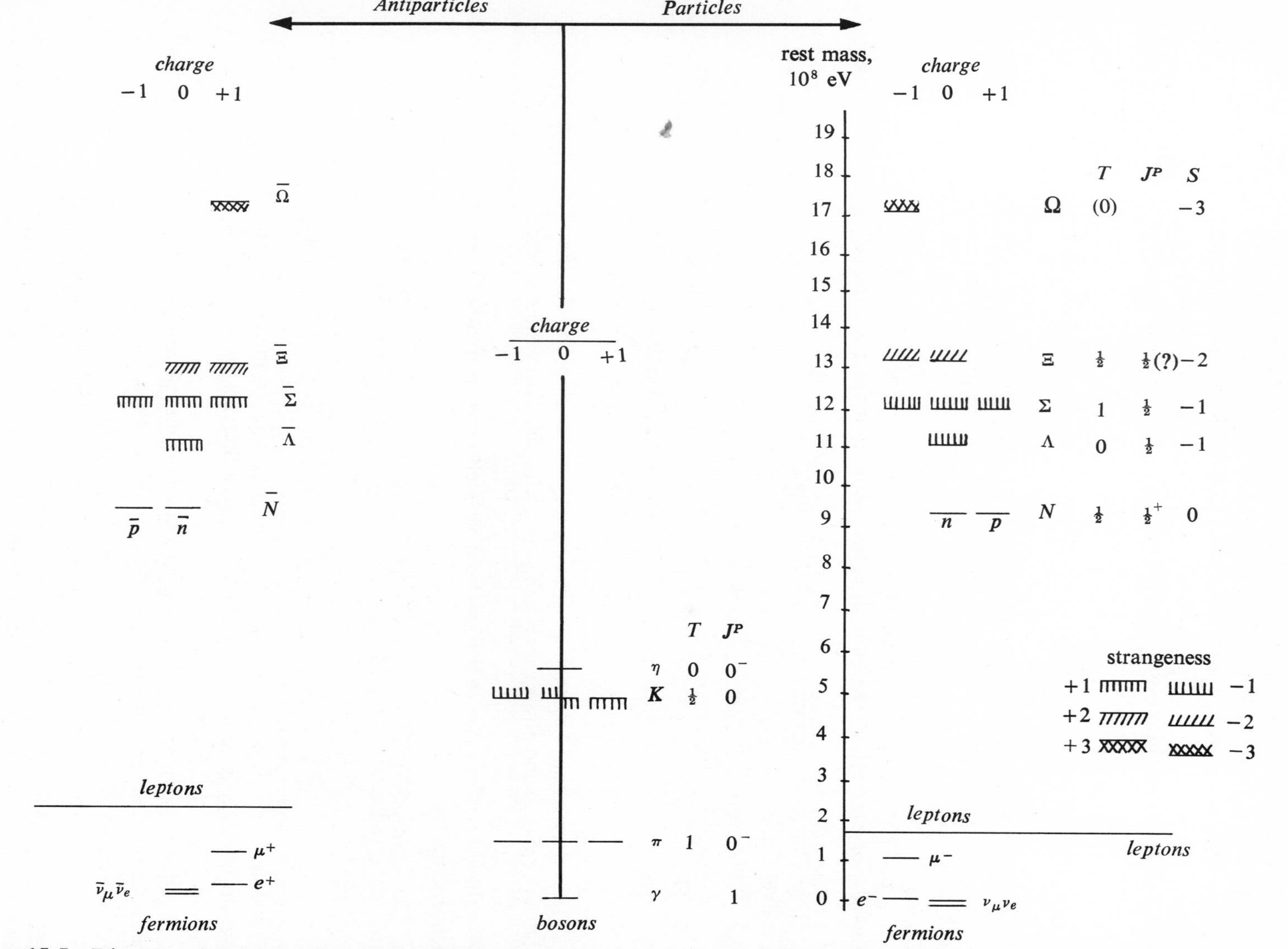

Figure 15-5 Diagram showing properties of particles that cannot decay by strong interactions. [Adapted from A. H. Rosenfeld.]

(compare Table 14-2). Hence, the cross section for the second process [Eq. (15-1.10)] is twice as large as for the first.

Finally we wish to comment briefly on the intrinsic parity of strange particles. Remembering the definition (Sec. 14-4) and the strangeness property, we see that in strong interactions only particles with the same strangeness participate in a reaction such as

$$p + K^- \Rightarrow \Lambda + \pi \tag{15-1.12}$$

Even if we knew all the angular momenta on both sides of the equation, we could conclude, by an argument similar to the one used for pions, only that the Λ and K have the same intrinsic parity or opposite intrinsic parity. In other words, the parity of the (K,Λ) system with respect to the nucleon is defined, but not that of each separate particle. The same is true for the (Σ,K) system and for the (Σ,Λ) system. These three parities, however, are not independent, and two of them determine the third. Thus, if (Σ,K) and (Σ,Λ) have the same parity, (Λ,K) must have parity $+1$.

The case of the Ξ is simpler. Its strangeness, -2, permits reactions such as

$$\Xi^- + p \Rightarrow \Lambda + \Lambda \tag{15-1.13}$$

The intrinsic parity on the right side is obviously positive, and hence the Ξ^- intrinsic parity with respect to the nucleon is in principle measurable. The practical methods for determining intrinsic parities are rather indirect. The results are

(ΛK) system	odd
(ΣK) system	odd
$(\Sigma\Lambda)$ system	even

The Ξ parity is not yet known.

As an example of methods for determining the relative parity, consider the ΛK system. The reaction $K^- + He^4 \Rightarrow {}_{\Lambda}He^4 + \pi^-$ leading to the formation of the ${}_{\Lambda}He^4$ hypernucleus (see Sec. 15-4) has been observed. Now assume that the spin of ${}_{\Lambda}He^4$ is 0. Then since the orbital angular momentum on both sides of the formation equation must be the same, the K^- and Λ have opposite parity. In other words, the $K\Lambda$ system is odd with respect to the nucleon. The weakness of the argument lies in the assumption that ${}_{\Lambda}He^4$ has spin 0 and that it is formed in the ground state. Although both assumptions are very probable, they are not proved.

Particles that are prevented by some selection rule from decaying by a strong interaction can still decay by electromagnetic interaction or by a weak interaction. There are only three electromagnetic decays, including the π°.

$$\begin{aligned} &\pi^0 \rightsquigarrow 2\gamma && \tau = 1.8 \times 10^{-16} \text{ sec} \\ &\left.\begin{aligned} &\Sigma^0 \rightsquigarrow \Lambda + \gamma \\ &\bar{\Sigma}^0 \rightsquigarrow \bar{\Lambda} + \gamma \end{aligned}\right\} && \tau \text{ probably} \sim 10^{-19} \text{ sec} \end{aligned} \tag{15-1.14}$$

The other observed decays of strange particles occur through weak interactions and do not conserve strangeness. Sometimes the decay products comprise neutrinos and other leptons, but at other times they comprise strongly interacting particles only.

15-2 Strong Interactions of Strange Particles

With modern large accelerators it has been possible to generate beams of strange particles. Usually a target of beryllium or platinum, according to whether a light or heavy element is preferred, is bombarded with a primary proton beam. A great variety of nuclear reactions occur in the target, either directly or through the formation of intermediate pions. The target becomes a source of particles of different momenta, mass, and charge. Production of a beam of specific particles requires systems of magnets and electrostatic fields (see Sec. 4-9).

Such beams are used in experiments. If the particles are unstable, they decay in flight and one has spontaneous attenuation in space, with a mean flight distance $\bar{l}$,

$$\bar{l} = \tau c \frac{\beta}{\sqrt{(1 - \beta^2)^{1/2}}} \tag{15-2.1}$$

where τ is the mean life in the rest system.

Neutral particles obviously cannot be deflected electromagnetically. They are sometimes formed at the place of observation by charge-exchange processes. For example, antineutrons are formed by the process (Fig. 15-6)

$$p + \bar{p} \rightarrow n + \bar{n} \tag{15-2.2}$$

and $\Lambda - \bar{\Lambda}$ pairs have been formed by bombarding protons with negative pions (Fig. 15-7).

The particles of the beams are, for the most part, made to interact with protons or deuterons, often in the form of liquid H^2 or D^2. The latter is used to study the interaction with neutrons, since free neutrons are not usable. Observations are made by means of bubble chambers, counter arrays, photographic emulsions, spark chambers, etc. The study of interactions of strange particles is at present progressing rapidly. We shall give only the barest outline of the subject, limiting ourselves to relatively low energies, below the threshold of more complicated processes.

The simplest reactions are those of K with protons and neutrons,

$$\begin{aligned} K^+ + p &\Rightarrow K^+ + p \qquad \text{elastic scattering} \\ K^+ + n &\Rightarrow K^+ + n \qquad \text{elastic scattering} \\ K^+ + n &\Rightarrow K^0 + p \qquad \text{charge exchange} \end{aligned} \tag{15-2.3}$$

This is in agreement with the strangeness of +1 assignment of the K^+. No other particle of strangeness +1 can be formed except K^0.

On the other hand, the K^-, in addition to elastic and charge-exchange

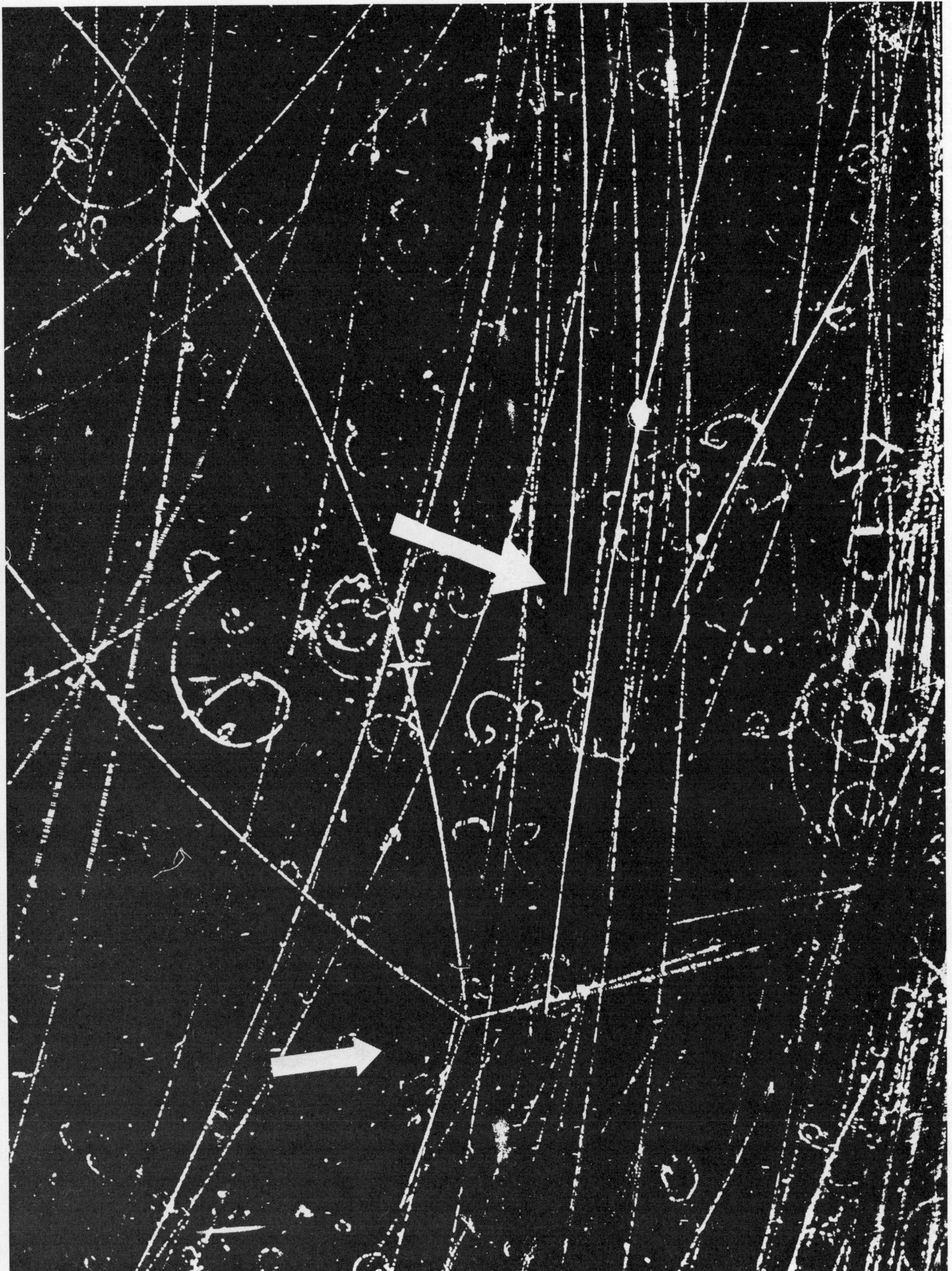

Figure 15-6 Formation of an antineutron (by charge exchange) observed in a propane bubble chamber. The antiproton undergoes charge exchange $p + \bar{p} \Rightarrow n + \bar{n}$ at the spot indicated with an arrow. The annihilation star of the $\bar{n}$ is also indicated. [Courtesy Lawrence Radiation Laboratory, Berkeley, Calif.]

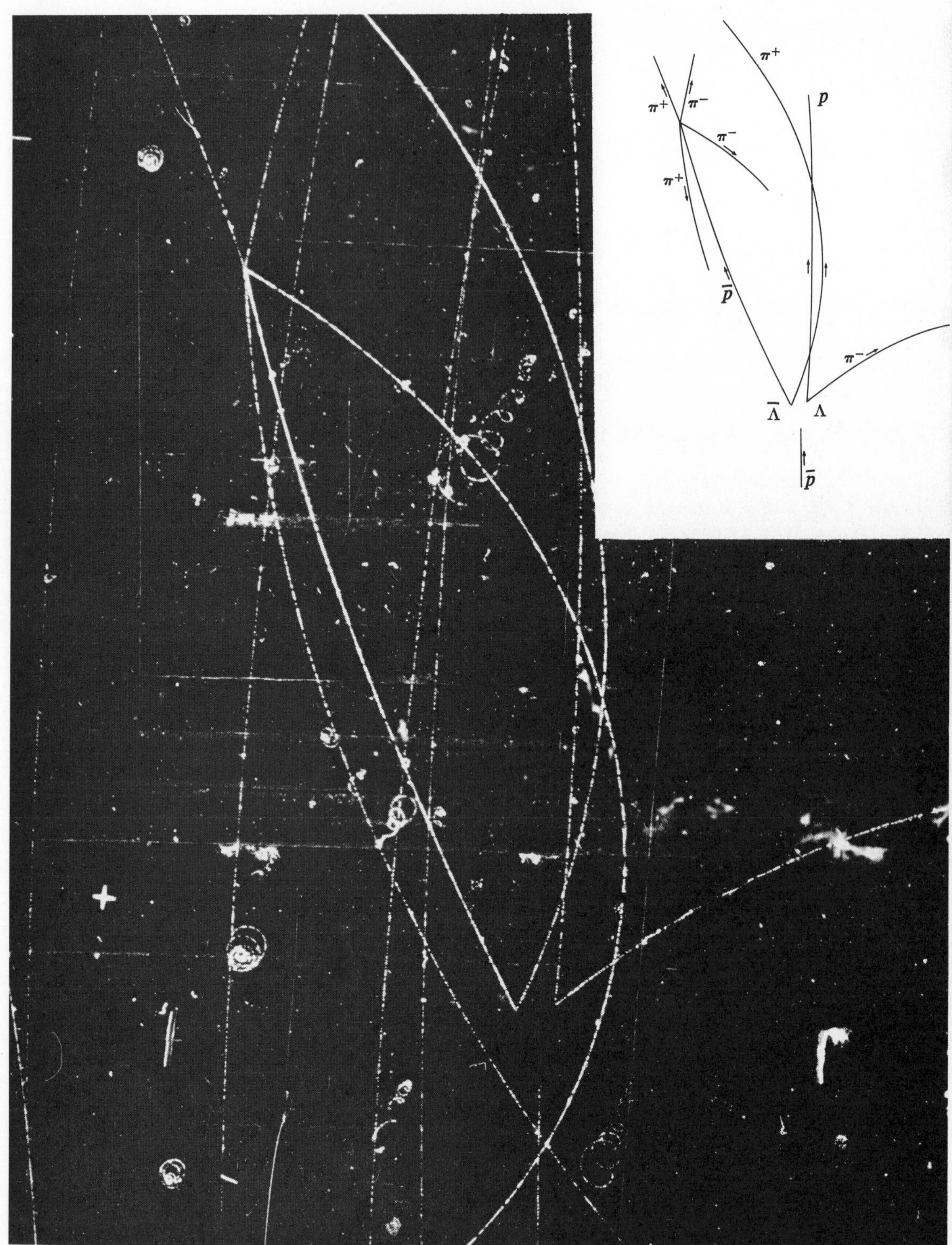

Figure 15-7 Production and decay of neutral lambda and antilambda pair in a hydrogen bubble chamber. The $\bar{\Lambda}$ was produced with a momentum of 720 MeV/c (laboratory). It went backward in the center-of-mass system. The $\bar{p}$ from the decay annihilates forming four charged pions. [Courtesy Lawrence Radiation Laboratory, Berkeley, Calif.]

scattering with formation of $\overline{K^0}$, gives rise to the following exothermic reactions:

$$K^- + p \Rightarrow \begin{cases} \Sigma^+ + \pi^- + 103.1 \text{ MeV} \\ \Sigma^0 + \pi^0 + 105.6 \text{ MeV} \\ \Sigma^- + \pi^+ + 96.6 \text{ MeV} \\ \Lambda^0 + \pi^0 + 181.8 \text{ MeV} \\ \Lambda^0 + \pi^+ + \pi^- + 37.6 \text{ MeV} \\ \Lambda^0 + \pi^0 + \pi^0 + 46.7 \text{ MeV} \end{cases} \tag{15-2.4}$$

With a neutron, the corresponding reactions are

$$K^- + n \Rightarrow \begin{cases} \Sigma^- + \pi^0 + 102.4 \text{ MeV} \\ \Sigma^0 + \pi^- + 102.3 \text{ MeV} \\ \Lambda^0 + \pi^- + 178.5 \text{ MeV} \\ \Lambda^0 + \pi^- + \pi^0 + 43.5 \text{ MeV} \end{cases} \tag{15-2.5}$$

The Λ^0 hyperon gives rise to hyperfragments (Sec. 15-4). No hyperfragments corresponding to the binding of a Σ hyperon are known. On interacting with protons Σ^- gives $\Lambda^0 + n$ or $\Sigma^0 + n$.

The charge-independence assumption applied to the branching ratios of the reactions mentioned above gives results substantiated by experiment.

15-3 Spin Measurements

The determination of spin and intrinsic parity is one of the fundamental tasks in the study of particles. In previous chapters we have described methods that solve this problem for the nucleon, pion, electron, muon, and neutrino. For strange particles there are additional criteria, which we shall describe in this section.

For K mesons the spin is zero. This value appears plausible on the basis of the analogy between the decay

$$K^+ \to \mu^+ + \nu$$

and the decay

$$\pi^+ \to \mu^+ + \nu$$

The polarization of the μ^+ has the same value in both decays. If the spin of K^+ is zero this result is necessary because of the definite helicity of the neutrino and the analogy between the reactions. For a nonzero spin of the K, the result would be a strange accident. However, this argument is clearly not binding, and the existence of two kinds of neutrino further weakens it.

Dalitz in 1953 devised a very ingenious method for obtaining information on the spin and intrinsic parity of a charged particle decaying into three other particles. The method depends on the analysis of spin and parity of the final state and on the conservations laws. If the decay occurs by strong interaction it will give information on both spin and parity. If the decay occurs by weak interaction, the information is limited to the spin.

Consider, for example, a K^+ meson decaying into two positive pions and one negative pion. A statistical study of many such decays in which one measures the energies of the pions and the angles between their trajectories leads to several important conclusions.

Consider the decay in the center-of-mass system of the two equally charged pions, the three momenta of the pions appear as in Fig. 15-8. The pions have negative intrinsic parity and no spin. The system of the two indentical pions, these being bosons, must have an even angular momentum L. Assume that the third (negative) pion has an angular momentum l with respect to the center of mass of the identical pions. The total angular momentum of the system J is limited by

$$L + l \geqslant J \geqslant |L - l|$$

Its intrinsic parity is $(-1)^{l+1}$, because the two identical pions necessarily have positive parity; and the odd pion, with negative intrinsic parity, determines the parity of the system (Fig. 15-8).

If we limit ourselves to the smallest possible values of L and l, we have the possibilities given in Table 15-1 of realizing a given J and parity, with given L and l.

The question now is how to distinguish the different cases experimentally. If one applies golden rule No. 2 to the disintegration, it is possible to derive, from the observed momentum distribution of the products, information on the spin and parity of the decaying particle. To apply golden rule No. 2, we need the density of final states. After some calculation, this factor alone gives for the energy distribution of the negative pion (nonrelativistically)

$$E^{1/2}(E_0 - E)^{1/2}$$

where E is the energy and E_0 is the maximum possible energy of the $\pi^-(E_0 = \frac{2}{3}Q = 50 \text{ MeV})$.

However, we can also say something about the matrix element if the

Table 15-1 Decomposition of the Total Angular Momentum in Three-Body Decay

J^P	L, l
0^+	
0^-	0, 0
1^+	0, 1
1^-	2, 2
2^+	2, 1

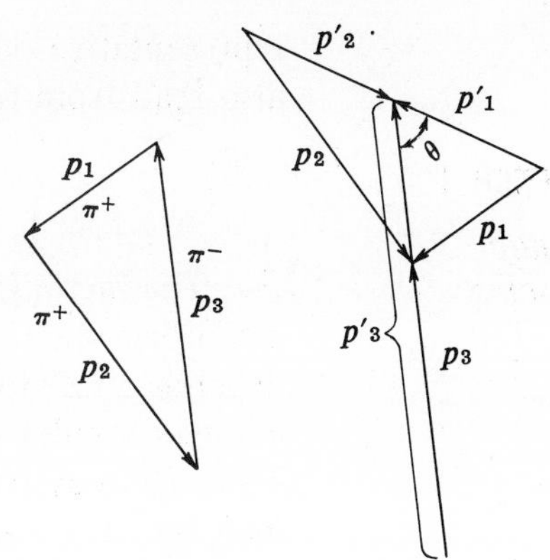

Figure 15-8 Momentum vectors and definitions of l, L. p_1, p_2, p_3 momenta of π^+, π^+, π^- in the laboratory; p_1', p_2', p_3' momenta of π^+, π^+, π^- in system in which center of mass of π^+, π^+ is at rest. p_1', p_2' give angular momentum L; p_3' gives angular momentum l.

linear dimensions of the region in which the interaction takes place are small compared with $\lambda\!\!\!^{-}$ of the escaping pions. Then the eigenfunctions of the latter, near the interaction region, vary as $p_{\pi^+}{}^L$, $p_{\pi^-}{}^l$, where the p_{π^+}, p_{π^-} are the momenta of the pions. The transition probability then contains factors $p_{\pi^-}{}^{2l}$, $p_{\pi^+}{}^{2L}$ from the matrix element. In particular, for a particle having $J = 0$, l and L are zero, the matrix element is constant, and the transition probability depends on E only through the density of final states.

Similarly the angle θ (see Fig. 15-8) may enter into the transition probability w. For $w(E,\theta)$, the calculation yields expressions that depend on the spin and parity of the system (see Table 15-2).

Experimental realization of this analysis is obtained by plotting the kinetic energies of the three pions of a disintegration as distances from three lines in an equilateral triangle (Fig. 15-9). The sum of these distances is constant within the triangle, the height of which is Q. Conservation of momentum restricts the allowed zone to the circle inscribed in the triangle. In view of the identity of the positive pions, we use the convention of plotting the smallest kinetic energy of the positive pions as a distance from the right side of the triangle and the kinetic energy of the negative pion as a distance from the base of the triangle. Consequently, all

Table 15-2 Probability Distribution as a Function of Energy and Angle for Three-Body Decay

Spin parity	$w(E,\theta)$
0^-	$E^{1/2}(E_0 - E)^{1/2}$
1^+	$E^{3/2}(E_0 - E)^{1/2}$
1^-	$E^{5/2}(E_0 - E)^{5/2} \sin^2\theta \cos^2\theta$
2^+	$E^{3/2}(E_0 - E)^{5/2} \sin^2\theta$

representative points are confined to a semicircle. The angle θ may be also read from the figure as

$$\cos\theta = \frac{PN}{NG}$$

The factor $[E(E - E_0)]^{1/2}$, taken from the density of final states, gives a uniform distribution of points in the Dalitz plot. In fact, this factor depends on E alone; furthermore, the area between E and $E + dE$ in the allowed circular zone of the Dalitz diagram is given by $[E(E - E_0)]^{1/2}\,dE$. Thus, for a system having $J = 0$ the representative points are uniformly distributed. For a system 1^+ there is an accumulation in the upper part of the semicircle, as can be seen from Table 15-2.

It is sometimes possible to understand the behavior of a Dalitz plot qualitatively, without having to resort to calculations. For instance, the probability of emission of a pion with vanishing kinetic energy goes to 0 for a system of odd spin–odd parity or even spin–even parity. By this we mean that the matrix element vanishes independently of the phase-space factor. In fact the pion of small momentum must be produced in an s state of odd parity, and then the two other pions must have the same angular momentum but opposite parity than the initial system. For instance, if the initial system is 1^- or 2^+, the two pions should be 1^+ or 2^-, respectively. But these states are not possible for two pions, and hence the transition is forbidden for low energy pions.

As an example Figs. 15-10 and 15-11 give the density of points expected for particles having $J^P = 0^-$ or 1^- and the experimental result based on the observation of the ω meson (see Sec. 14-9) showing that it is a 1^- meson.

In these considerations we have used a nonrelativistic approach for the sake of simplicity. Relativistic corrections are small if the energies involved are small compared with the rest mass of the pions.

There are other ways of plotting the energies of disintegration products of a particle, which are equivalent to the Dalitz plot and yield the same type of information. For example, consider the reaction

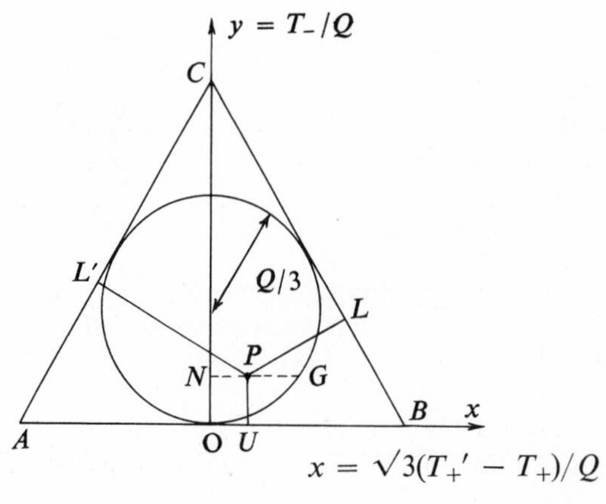

Figure 15-9 Dalitz plot. PL', PL kinetic energies of $\pi^+ = T_+'$, T_+ (T_+ has the lowest energy). PU, kinetic energy of π^-. Circle contains zone permitted by energy-momentum conservation. The coordinates of a representative point referred to the axes marked in the figure are $x = \sqrt{3}(T_+' - T_+)/Q$ and $y = T_-/Q$.

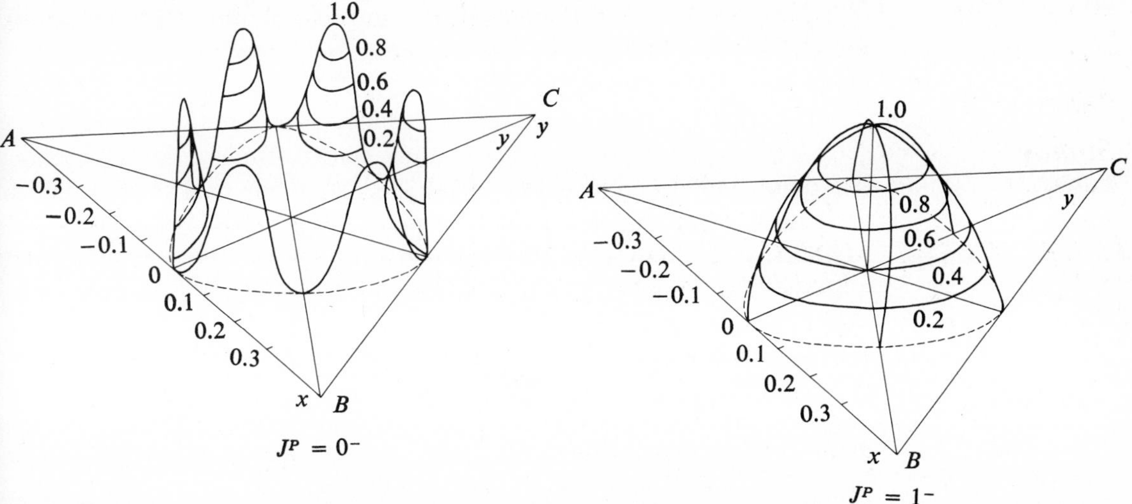

Figure 15-10 Density of points expected in a Dalitz plot for a $J^P = 0^-$ or 1^- system decaying into three pions.

$$K^- + p \rightarrow \overline{K^0} + \pi^- + p \qquad \textbf{(15-3.1)}$$

Call E the total energy and E_1, E_2, E_3 the energies of the three particles formed.

Instead of the triangular plot, one plots (on rectangular coordinates) E_1 against E_2. Lines of constant E_3 are clearly inclined at 45° to the axes because $E_1 + E_2 = E - E_3$. On a line E_1 = constant the particles 2 and 3 are constrained to have, in their own center-of-mass system, a given rest mass and a given momentum p. The only free variable is the angle between p and the direction of flight of the center of mass of particles 2 and 3.

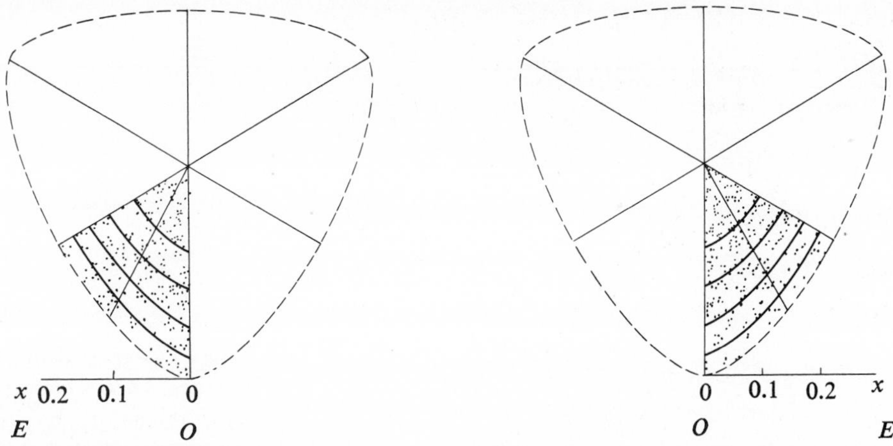

Figure 15-11 Application of the Dalitz plot to the ω meson. At the right only points at the resonant energy have been used, at the left the background. The figures correspond to Fig. 15-10, seen from above. Line OE corresponds to AB.

The region in the E_1E_2 plane containing possible representative points for a given E is limited by a curve. On its boundary the three particles move on the same straight line.

If two of the three particles, for instance 2 and 3, tend to emerge in a state (resonance) of fixed energy in their center of mass, the representative points line up on lines of constant E_1. Often one uses as coordinates the square of the masses (in their center-of-mass system) of couples of particles. For instance, in the example of Eq. (15-3.1) the square of the mass $M^2(\overline{K^0}\pi^-)$ and $M^2(p\pi^-)$ may be used instead of E_p and $E_{\overline{K^0}}$. The two sets of variables are linearly related because, as in our example, one calculates that

$$M^2(p\pi^-) = E^2 + m_{\overline{K^0}}{}^2 - 2EE_{\overline{K^0}} \qquad (c = 1)$$

which for E constant shows the linear relation between $E_{\overline{K^0}}$ and $M^2(p\pi^-)$. Figure 15-21 is an example of this type of plot.

Dalitz plots permit us to assign the spin and parity of the disintegration products. From this data we obtain the spin of the initial particle and if the decay conserves parity (strong interaction), its parity (see Sec. 14-4).

Another method of determining the spin of hyperons, due to Adair (1955) (Fig. 15-12), is the following. Consider the reaction

$$\pi + p \Rightarrow K + \Lambda$$

and assume that the spin of K is 0. For the center-of-mass system consider those cases in which the line of flight of K and Λ is parallel to that of π and p. The component of the angular momentum in this common direction m_J is $\frac{1}{2}$, coming—on the left side of the equation—from the spin of the proton and—on the right side of the equation—from the component of the Λ spin in the direction of the line of flight. Orbital angular momenta are directed perpendicularly to the line of flight and

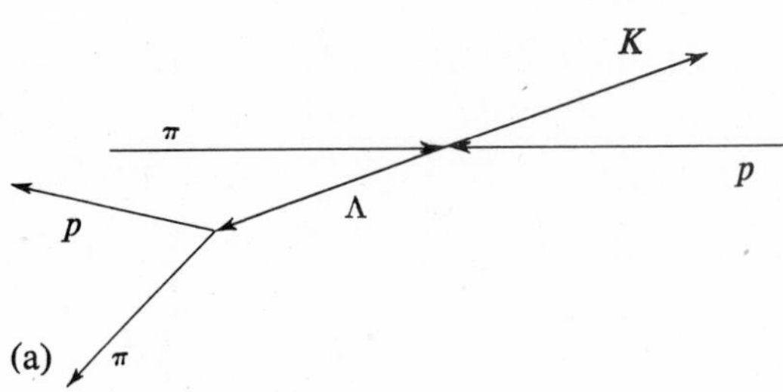

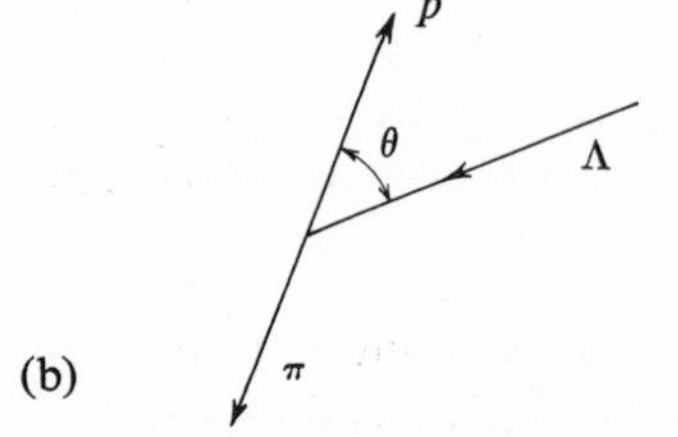

Figure 15-12 Momentum vectors in Adair's model for spin measurement. (a) Center-of-mass-system momenta of reaction $\pi + p \Rightarrow K + \Lambda$. (b) Rest system of Λ. Angle of decay θ.

thus do not contribute to m_J. The Λ decays into a proton and a pion. Designate by θ the angle between the proton and the line of flight of the Λ in the rest system of the Λ. If the Λ has spin $= \frac{1}{2}$, we shall have an isotropic angular distribution of the decay proton. (An anisotropic angular distribution would indicate a spin $> \frac{1}{2}$.) The experiment indicates spin $\frac{1}{2}$. Essentially the method furnishes a sample of aligned (not polarized) Λ and examines their decay. No alignment without polarization is possible if $J = \frac{1}{2}$. In practice, it is necessary to examine Λ escaping at a

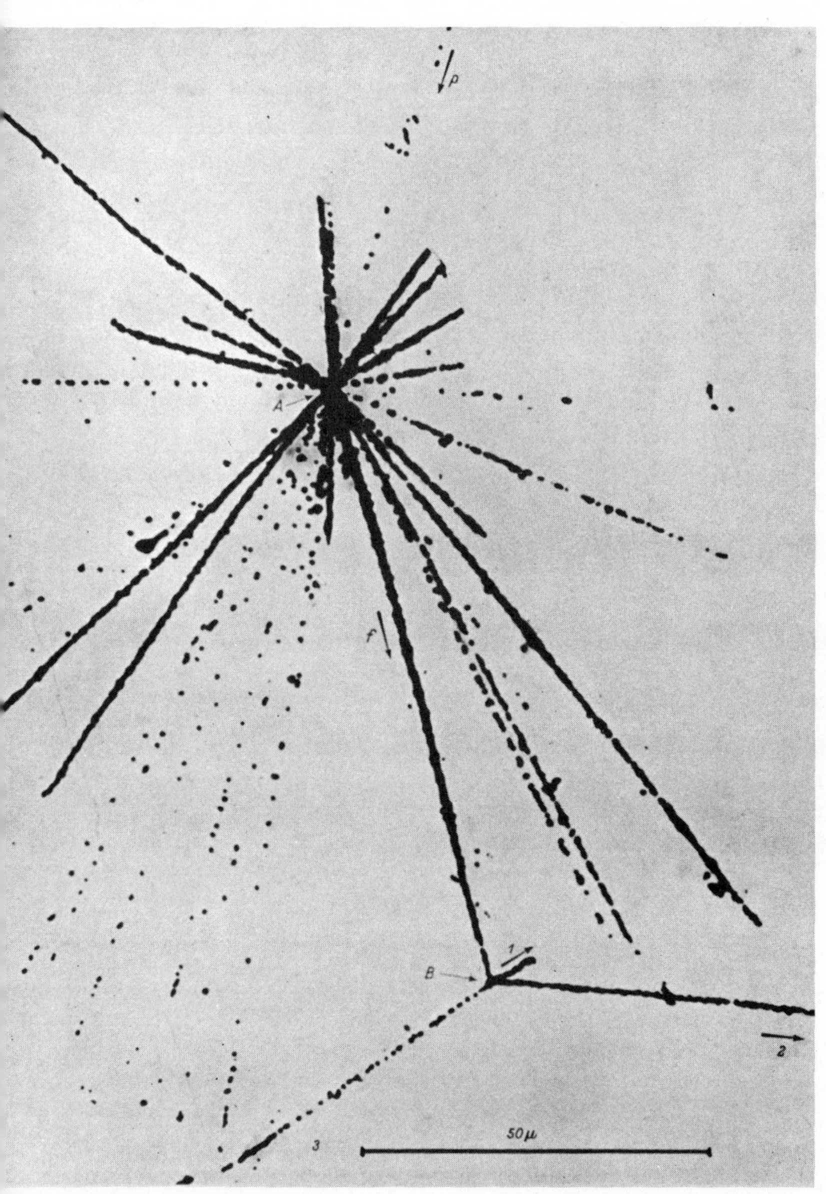

Figure 15-13 First hyperfragment observed by Danysz and Pniewski, 1953. The fragment *f* was produced in star *A* and decayed nonmesonically at point B into three particles: 1, 2, 3.

small angle from the line of flight πp. This introduces a certain probability of observing Λ with $|m_J| \neq \frac{1}{2}$, but it is possible to correct for this effect.

Particles with a spin different from zero may have a magnetic moment. However, the only measurement of magnetic moment attempted up to 1964 has been for the Λ hyperon. There are two results giving one $\mu_\Lambda = -1.5 \pm 0.5$, the other $\mu_\Lambda = 0.0 \pm 0.6$ in nuclear magnetons.

15-4 Hyperfragments

In 1953 Danysz and Pniewski found a fragment, emerging from a high-energy nuclear star formed by cosmic rays, which they interpreted as a nucleus in which a neutron had been replaced by a Λ^0 (Fig. 15-13). Many similar fragments were found later, and the name of hyperfragments or hypernuclei has been adopted for such particles, together with the notation ${}_\Lambda He^4$, etc., indicating a He^4 nucleus in which a neutron has been replaced by a Λ^0. Hyperfragments are formed on capture of strange particles by nuclei. For instance, capture of K^- at rest by He gives rise in a few per cent of the cases to ${}_\Lambda He^4$ or ${}_\Lambda H^4$.

Hyperfragments are unstable and decay, emitting either nucleons and a pion (mesonic decay) (Fig. 15-14) or only nucleons (nonmesonic decay) (Fig. 15-13). The mesonic modes of decay can be thought of as the normal decay of the Λ inside of the nucleus according to the elementary process $\Lambda \rightarrow p + \pi^-$ or $\Lambda \rightarrow n + \pi^0$. The nonmesonic decay corresponds to the elementary processes $\Lambda + p \rightarrow p + n$ or $\Lambda + n \rightarrow n + n$. Examples of mesonic decays are ${}_\Lambda H^4 \rightarrow \pi^- + He^4$; $\pi^- + n + He^3$; $\pi^- + H^2 + H^2$; etc. Examples of nonmesonic decay are ${}_\Lambda Be^8 \rightarrow He^3 + He^4 + n$.

The mean life of hyperfragments has yet to be measured accurately. For ${}_\Lambda H^4$ there is a measurement giving $(1.2 \pm 0.6) \times 10^{-10}$ sec, comparable to the mean life of the free Λ^0; the same order of magnitude is found for other hyperfragments.

The binding energy of the Λ^0 in the nucleus can be measured by suitable energy cycles (Fig. 15-15). For instance, we observe a ${}_\Lambda Be^9$ hyperfragment disintegrating into two He^4, a proton and a π^-, releasing the total kinetic energy of 30.92 ± 0.5 MeV. The energy released by Λ^0 in the $p\pi$ disintegration is 37.56 MeV. Starting from $2He^4$, a proton and a

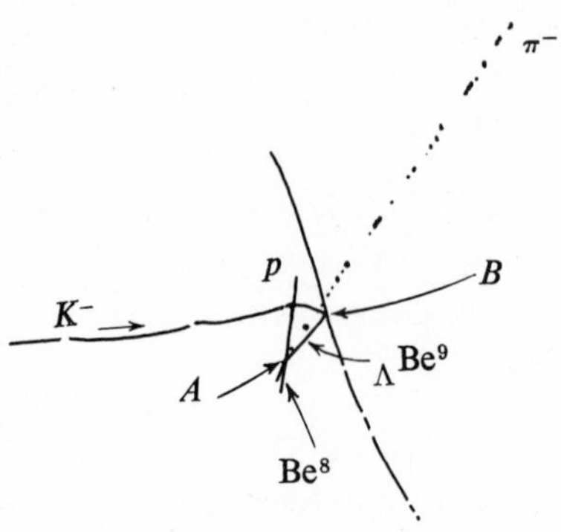

Figure 15-14 A ${}_\Lambda Be^9$ hyperfragment was produced by the nuclear absorption of a negative K-meson from rest. The star produced by the K^- meson absorption is indicated by arrow B. The hyperfragment ${}_\Lambda Be^9$ decayed (at the point indicated by arrow A) into a π^- meson of 26.6 ± 0.6 MeV, a proton, and Be^8. The two alpha tracks of Be^8 begin to separate near their end. [Fry, Schneps, and Swami, *Phys. Rev.* **101**, 1526 (1956)].

negative pion, reassemble the Λ from the proton and π^- spending this energy. We reassemble the two He^4 nuclei to form Be^8, gaining 0.10 MeV. We now have a Λ^0 and Be^8 and have spent, altogether, 37.46 MeV. On binding the Λ^0 to Be^8, we must obtain $37.46 - 30.92 = 6.54$ MeV, which is the binding energy of Λ^0 to Be^8, for form ${}_{\Lambda}Be^9$.

The results of an analysis of the available experimental data are summarized in Fig. 15-16, which gives the binding energy of the Λ^0 in several light nuclei. It is clear that B_Λ is approximately proportional to A. This is in striking contrast to the binding energy of the nucleons, which fluctuates considerably in the case of light nuclei, owing to the exclusion principle. The single Λ^0 is not subject to such special limitations. Thus, for example, whereas ordinary nuclei with $A = 5$ are unbound, there are hyperfragments of mass 5. On the assumption that the Λ^0-nucleon forces are charge-independent, it has been possible to analyze the experimental data, the main conclusions being that the Λ^0-nucleon force is comparable in magnitude to the nucleon-nucleon force and is spin-dependent. The evidence also favors the value of $\frac{1}{2}$ for the Λ^0 spin.

The ratio between mesonic and nonmesonic decay gives another argument for this spin assignment (Cheston and Primakoff, 1953; Ruderman and Karplus, 1956). The mesonic decay of a hyperfragment is considered similar to gamma emission by an excited nucleus. The nonmesonic decay represents an additional channel in the same way that the emission of conversion electrons represents another mode of de-excitation for nuclei. The ratio between mesonic and nonmesonic decays is, then, analogous to the internal conversion coefficient. The calculation indicates a strong dependance of the ratio on the orbital angular momentum l with which the pion is emitted and points to $l = 0$ and to a spin $\frac{1}{2}$ for the Λ^0.

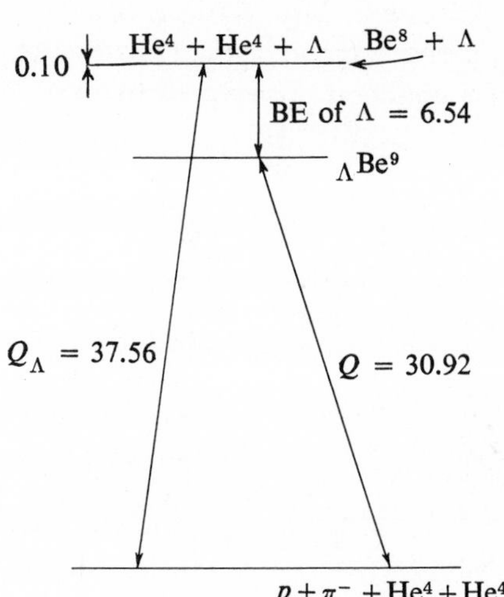

Figure 15-15 Energy balance of the ${}_{\Lambda}Be^9$ hyperfragment disintegration, shown in Fig. 15-14. Energies in MeV.

15-5 Spontaneous Decay of Strange Particles

Strange particles may decay by weak interaction. We shall first consider baryons. Here we have two types of decay: decay into nucleons and pions and decay into nucleons and leptons (leptonic decay). The branching ratio favors the first type of decay overwhelmingly (see Table 15-3).

Consider a typical decay of a strange particle into a nucleon and a meson:

$$\Lambda \to p + \pi^-$$

The cases

$$\Sigma \to N + \pi \qquad \Xi \to \Lambda + \pi$$

with all charge variations, are similar.

In the Λ decay one has observed nonconservation of parity, although all particles involved are strongly interacting. This fact is important because it demonstrates that the violation of parity conservation is not connected exclusively with the neutrino and its single helicity.

Consider Λ particles polarized in the z direction and at rest at the origin of the coordinate system and assume that the spin of the Λ is $\frac{1}{2}$. The decay products $p + \pi$ must be in a state of angular momentum $\frac{1}{2}$, that is, either in a $S_{1/2}$ or $P_{1/2}$ state. Also a combination of the two is permissible if, and only if, parity is not conserved in the decay.

● Call f_s and f_p the complex amplitudes of the s- and p-wave functions in the decay products and call θ and φ the polar angles of escape of the proton. The $S_{1/2}$, $P_{1/2}$ wave functions are, for $J_z = +\frac{1}{2}$,

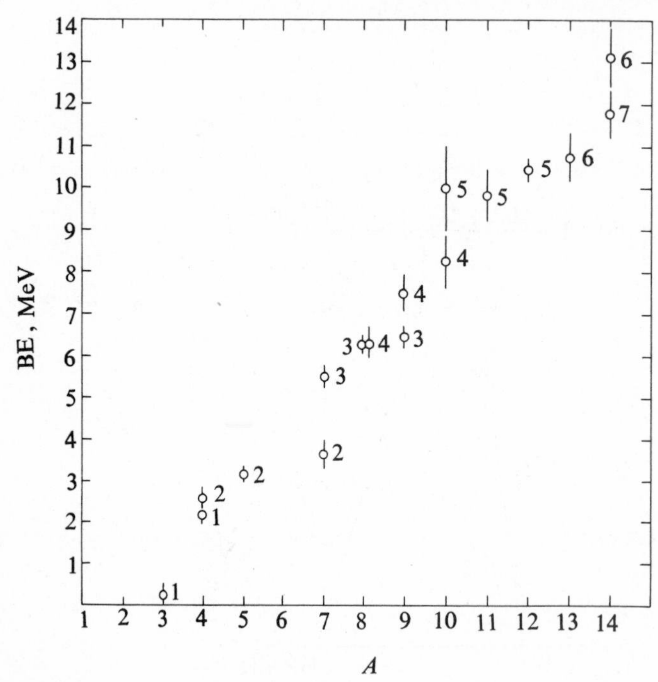

Figure 15-16 Binding energies of Λ in hypernuclei as a function of atomic number A. The points are labeled with the Z of the hyperfragment.

$$Y_0^0 \begin{vmatrix}1\\0\end{vmatrix}$$

and

$$\sqrt{\tfrac{2}{3}}\, Y_1^1 \begin{vmatrix}0\\1\end{vmatrix} - \sqrt{\tfrac{1}{3}}\, Y_1^0 \begin{vmatrix}1\\0\end{vmatrix}$$

and similar expressions for $J_z = -\frac{1}{2}$ (see Appendix I). Since the initial Λ has $J_z = \frac{1}{2}$, the wave function after decay is

$$\psi = f_s Y_0^0 \begin{vmatrix}1\\0\end{vmatrix} + f_p \left[\sqrt{\tfrac{2}{3}}\, Y_1^1 \begin{vmatrix}0\\1\end{vmatrix} - \sqrt{\tfrac{1}{3}}\, Y_1^0 \begin{vmatrix}1\\0\end{vmatrix}\right] \qquad \textbf{(15-5.1)}$$

The complex amplitudes f_s, f_p contain four real numbers; however, one phase is arbitrary. These numbers may be found by measurements on the angular distribution and polarization of the decay proton.

To find the angular distribution of the decay protons, one takes $|\psi|^2$. Taking into consideration the orthogonality relations for spin functions, and introducing the explicit expressions of the spherical harmonics, one obtains

$$\begin{aligned} 4\pi|\psi|^2 &= |f_s - f_p \cos\theta|^2 + |-f_p \sin\theta|^2 \\ &= |f_s|^2 + |f_p|^2 - 2\mathrm{Re}\, f_s^* f_p \cos\theta \end{aligned} \qquad \textbf{(15-5.2)}$$

Given the definition

$$\alpha = \frac{2\mathrm{Re}\, f_s^* f_p}{|f_s|^2 + |f_p|^2} \qquad \textbf{(15-5.3)}$$

the angular distribution is

$$dw(\theta) = \tfrac{1}{2}(1 - \alpha\cos\theta)\, d(\cos\theta) \qquad \textbf{(15-5.4)}$$

It is clear that an asymmetry of the decay occurs only if f_s and f_p are *both* different from 0, which means that parity is not conserved. ●

In practice one does not have polarized Λ at rest. The experiment is then carried out as follows: Λ^0 are produced in the reaction

$$\pi^- + p \rightarrow \Lambda + K^0 \qquad \Lambda \rightarrow \pi^- + p \qquad \textbf{(15-5.5)}$$

The conservation of momentum restricts the trajectories of the incident π, Λ, and K in a single plane; and the Λ may be, and actually is, formed with its spin preferentially oriented perpendicular to this plane. Actually this is the only direction in which the Λ can be polarized by the process of Eq. (15-5.5), because parity is conserved in strong interactions and the argument given in Sec. 10-7 on the direction of the polarization applies here as well. On decay of the Λ the proton produced may escape preferentially up or down with respect to the $K - \Lambda$ plane if, and only if, parity is not conserved in the Λ decay (Fig. 15-17).

Looking from a system in which the Λ^0 is at rest, we find that it is partially polarized and that the direction of emission of the proton is correlated to the direction of polarization, in a way similar to that which

Table 15-3 Dynamics of Strange-Particle Decays[a]

		Q	Momentum p, MeV/c	τ, nsec	Branching ratio
$K^+ \to$ ($M_{K^+} = 493.9$ MeV)	$\pi^+ + \pi^0$	219.3	205.2	12.3	22.4%
	$\mu^+ + \nu$	388.2	235.6		63%
	$\pi^+ + \pi^+ + \pi^-$	75.1	125.5 125.5		5.1%
	$\pi^+ + \pi^0 + \pi^0$	84.3	132.3 133.1		1.8%
	$\pi^0 + \mu^+ + \nu$	253.2	215.2 215.2		3.0%
	$\pi^0 + e^+ + \nu$	358.3	288.5 288.5		4.7%
$K^0 \to$ ($M_{K^0} = 497.8$ MeV)	$\pi^0 + \pi^0$	227.8	209.1	0.09	31% of K_1
	$\pi^+ + \pi^-$	218.6	206.1		69% of K_1
	$\pi^0 + \pi^0 + \pi^0$	92.8	139.3	62	19% of K_2
	$\pi^+ + \pi^- + \pi^0$	83.6	132.9 132.1		11% of K_2
	$\pi^\mp + \mu^\pm + \nu$	252.5	216.1 216.1		31% of K_2
	$\pi + e + \nu$	357.7	229.3 229.3		39% of K_2
$\Lambda^0 \to$ ($M_\Lambda = 1{,}115.45$ MeV)	$p + \pi^-$	37.59	100.23	0.262	64%
	$p + e^- + \bar{\nu}$	176.68	163.12 163.12		<0.04%
	$p + \mu^- + \nu$	71.54	130.77 130.77		0.03%
	$n + \pi^0$	40.89	103.64		36%

$\Sigma^+ \to$ (M_{Σ^+} = 1,189.4 MeV)	$p + \pi^0$	116.1	189.0	0.079	51%
	$n + \pi^+$	110.3	185.1		49%
	$n + \mu^+ + \bar{\nu}$	144.2	202.4 202.4		Partly forbidden? 1 probable event
	$n + e^+ + \bar{\nu}$	249.3	223.6 223.6		1 probable event
	$\Lambda + e^+ + \bar{\nu}$	73.4	71.7 71.7		~0.01%
$\Sigma^0 \to$ (M_{Σ^0} = 1,193.2 MeV)	$\Lambda + \gamma$	77.8	75.2	$\sim 10^{-5}$	~100%
$\Sigma^- \to$ (M_{Σ^-} = 1,197.6 MeV)	$n + \pi^-$	118.5	193.2	0.174	≈100%
	$n + \mu^- + \bar{\nu}$	152.4	209.8 209.8		0.09%
	$n + e^- + \bar{\nu}$	257.5	230.3 230.3		0.2%
	$\Lambda + e^- + \bar{\nu}$	81.6	79.3 79.3		~0.01%
$\Xi^0 \to$ (M_{Ξ^0} = 1,314.4 MeV)	$\Lambda + \pi^0$	63.9	134.8	0.3	≈100%
$\Xi^- \to$ (M_{Ξ^-} = 1,321.2 MeV)	$\Lambda + \pi^-$	66.2	139.2	0.17	≈100%
	$\Lambda + e^- + \bar{\nu}$	205.2	189.7 189.7		~0.3%
	$n + \pi^-$	242.1	303.3		Forbidden? <0.5%
$\Omega^- \to$ (M_{Ω^-} = 1,686 MeV) (1 event)	$\Xi^0 + \pi^-$	232	306		?
	$\Xi^- + \pi^0$	230	302		?
	$\Lambda + K^-$	77	234		?

[a] For three-body decays (e.g., $\mu \to e + \bar{\nu} + \nu$) the quantities tabulated are the maximum momenta attainable by the first two product particles.

occurs in beta decay. The experiment measures the product of the polarization of the Λ and the asymmetry coefficient α. If the Λ has been formed by the reaction in Eq. (15-5.5), escaping at an angle χ (c.m.) from the $\pi - p$ direction, it has a polarization $p(\chi)$. Now let θ designate, as before, the angle between the momentum of the decay proton and the perpendicular to the K-Λ plane in the rest system of the Λ. The probability for the direction of escape is given by

$$w(\chi, \cos\theta)\, d\cos\theta = A[1 - p(\chi)\,\alpha \cos\theta]\, d\cos\theta \qquad \textbf{(15-5.6)}$$

We can interpret $p(\chi)$ as a measure of the polarizing efficiency of the production process and α as a measure of the analyzing efficiency of the decay process. The experiment measures $p\alpha$. In actual experiments it has been found that $|p\alpha| = 0.8$. It is also known that the protons tend to escape parallel to the spin of the Λ ($p\alpha < 0$).

In decays of strange particles by weak interactions into nucleons and pions there seems to be a selection rule

$$\Delta T = \pm \tfrac{1}{2} \qquad \textbf{(15-5.7)}$$

for the isotopic spin. This selection rule applies, naturally, only when the final products all have a well-defined isotopic spin, and it is like all i-spin selection rules, subject to exception due to electromagnetic interactions.

A convenient method of treating the selection rule $\Delta T = \pm \frac{1}{2}$ has been devised by Wentzel (1957). Assume that in the decay of strong-interacting particles a new particle, the "spurion," is emitted, with no spin, momentum, energy, or charge, but with an i spin $\frac{1}{2}$ and $T_3 = \pm \frac{1}{2}$. The statement that in such decay i spin is conserved is then equivalent to the selection rule

$$\Delta T = \tfrac{1}{2} \qquad \textbf{(15-5.8)}$$

As an application of this selection rule, consider the branching ratio in the decay.

$$\begin{aligned} \Lambda^0 &\to p + \pi^- \\ &\to n + \pi^0 \end{aligned} \qquad \textbf{(15-5.9)}$$

The i spin of the Λ^0 is 0. On the right the $p\pi^-$ system and $n\pi^0$ system are described, as in Eq. (14-6.4), by wave functions containing $T = \frac{1}{2}$ and $T = \frac{3}{2}$ components. Only the former counts, for in the latter case $\Delta T = \frac{3}{2}$, and transitions to them are forbidden. The amplitudes of states with $T = \frac{1}{2}$ in $p + \pi^-$ and $n + \pi^0$ are in the ratio $\sqrt{2}:1$. Hence, the branching ratio must be 2:1, in agreement with the experimental result (65 ± 5): (35 ± 5).

The rare leptonic decays of hyperons (Table 15-3) are about an order of magnitude less frequent than one would expect if they are calculated as ordinary beta decays, taking into account the available energy.

K mesons show a great variety of decay modes (Fig. 15-3). These have been observed in photograph emulsions and in cloud or bubble chambers. The decay modes of the charged K so far observed are given in Table 15-3 with their branching ratios.

The decay constant of $K^{\pm}$ is 0.813×10^8 sec^{-1}, corresponding to a mean life of $1.23 \pm 0.008 \times 10^{-8}$ sec. It has been measured in photographic emulsions and with counters. That all modes of decay have the same mean life has been verified, indicating that they are due to the disintegration of the same particle. The magnitude of the decay constant indicates that it is due to weak interactions.

Other conceivable modes of decay, such as

$$K^+ \to \pi^+ + \gamma$$
$$K^+ \to \nu + \bar{\nu} + \pi^+ \quad \textbf{(15-5.10)}$$
$$K^+ \to e^+ + \nu, \text{ etc.}$$

have never been observed. Experiments show that they have branching ratios smaller than about 1 per cent. Their absence is important in order to establish some of the properties of $K^{\pm}$ mesons. For example, the absence of the decay

$$K^+ \to \pi^+ + \gamma \quad \textbf{(15-5.11)}$$

is a strong argument for the assignment of spin 0 to K^+.

The decays of K^- are more difficult to observe than those of K^+, because the K^- interact strongly with nuclei. For K^- the coulomb attraction favors nuclear interactions at the expense of free decay, while the free decay of the K^+ is favored by the Coulomb repulsion, which prevents them from approaching nuclei, furthermore strangeness

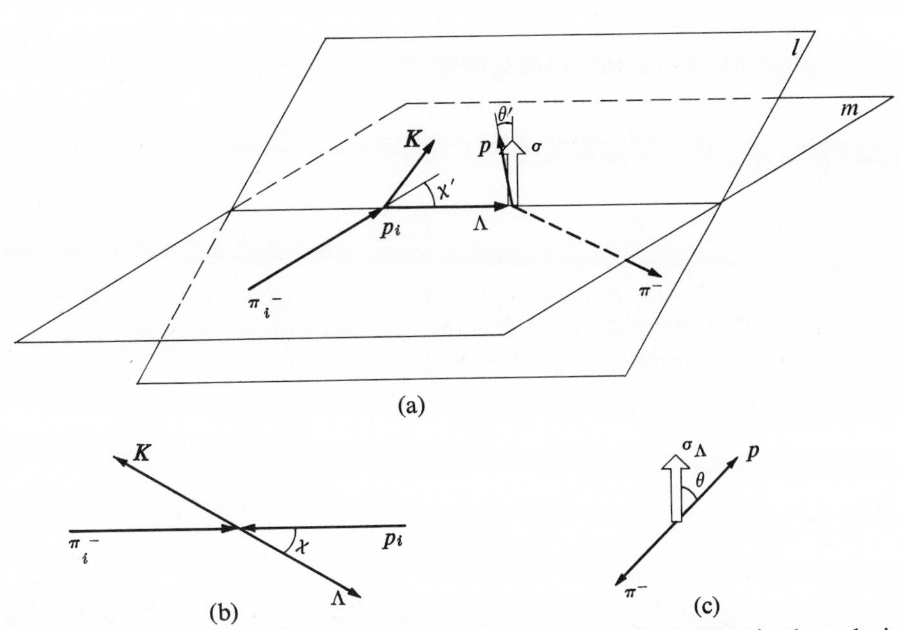

Figure 15-17 Schematic diagram showing the momentum vectors important in the polarization and decay of a Λ. (a) Laboratory system. Note that the momentum of π_i^-, K, and Λ are in plane m (production plane). Spin $\boldsymbol{\sigma}$ is perpendicular to plane m. The momenta of Λ, p, π^- are in plane l (decay plane). (b) The production in the c.m. system of π_i^- and p_i. (c) The Λ decay in a system in which the Λ is at rest. The angles χ, θ correspond to angles χ', θ' in the lab.

conservation prevents many K reactions. However, we must expect that free K^- mesons decay with decay constants identical to those of K^+ in the charge conjugate modes, e.g.,

$$\begin{aligned} K^- &\to \pi^- + \pi^0 \\ &\to \pi^- + \pi^- + \pi^+, \text{ etc.} \end{aligned} \tag{15-5.12}$$

have the same decay constants as

$$\begin{aligned} K^+ &\to \pi^+ + \pi^0 \\ &\to \pi^+ + \pi^+ + \pi^-, \text{ etc.} \end{aligned} \tag{15-5.12a}$$

The case of K^0 is more complicated and will be discussed later.

A close examination of Table 15-3 raises many questions. For instance: Why does Σ^0 decay into $\Lambda^0 + \gamma$, rather than into $n + \pi^0$ or $n + \gamma$ directly? Why do the Ξ hyperons decay into $\Lambda + \pi$, rather than into nucleon plus pion? What prevents K^0 from decaying into 2γ? These and similar questions are left to the reader.

Finally we mention a selection rule that seems at least approximately valid for leptonic decays of strange particles:

$$\Delta S = \Delta Q$$

where ΔS and ΔQ are the change in strangeness and charge *of the strongly interacting particle*.

15-6 The K^0, $\overline{K^0}$ Doublet

We shall assume in what follows that the K^0 mesons are spinless. The K^0, $\overline{K^0}$ particles are generated by strong interactions in which strangeness is conserved, and hence they must have a well-defined strangeness. Typical production reactions are

$$\begin{aligned} K^- + p &\Rightarrow \overline{K^0} + n \qquad S = -1 \\ \pi^- + p &\Rightarrow K^0 + \Lambda^0 \qquad S = 0 \end{aligned} \tag{15-6.1}$$

The strangeness of $\overline{K^0}$ is -1, that of K^0 is $+1$, and because of this they act differently in subsequent strong interactions. For instance, K^0 may interact according to the reaction

$$K^0 + p \Rightarrow K^+ + n \tag{15-6.2}$$

but not according to the reaction

$$K^0 + p \Rightarrow \Sigma^+ + \pi^0 \qquad \text{or} \qquad K^0 + n \Rightarrow K^- + p \tag{15-6.3}$$

whereas $\overline{K^0}$ may react according to

$$\overline{K^0} + p \Rightarrow \Sigma^+ + \pi^0 \qquad \text{or} \qquad \overline{K^0} + n \Rightarrow K^- + p \tag{15-6.4}$$

but not according to

$$\overline{K^0} + p \Rightarrow K^+ + n \tag{15-6.5}$$

We may thus distinguish a K^0 from a $\overline{K^0}$ by a strong interaction (Fig. 15-18).

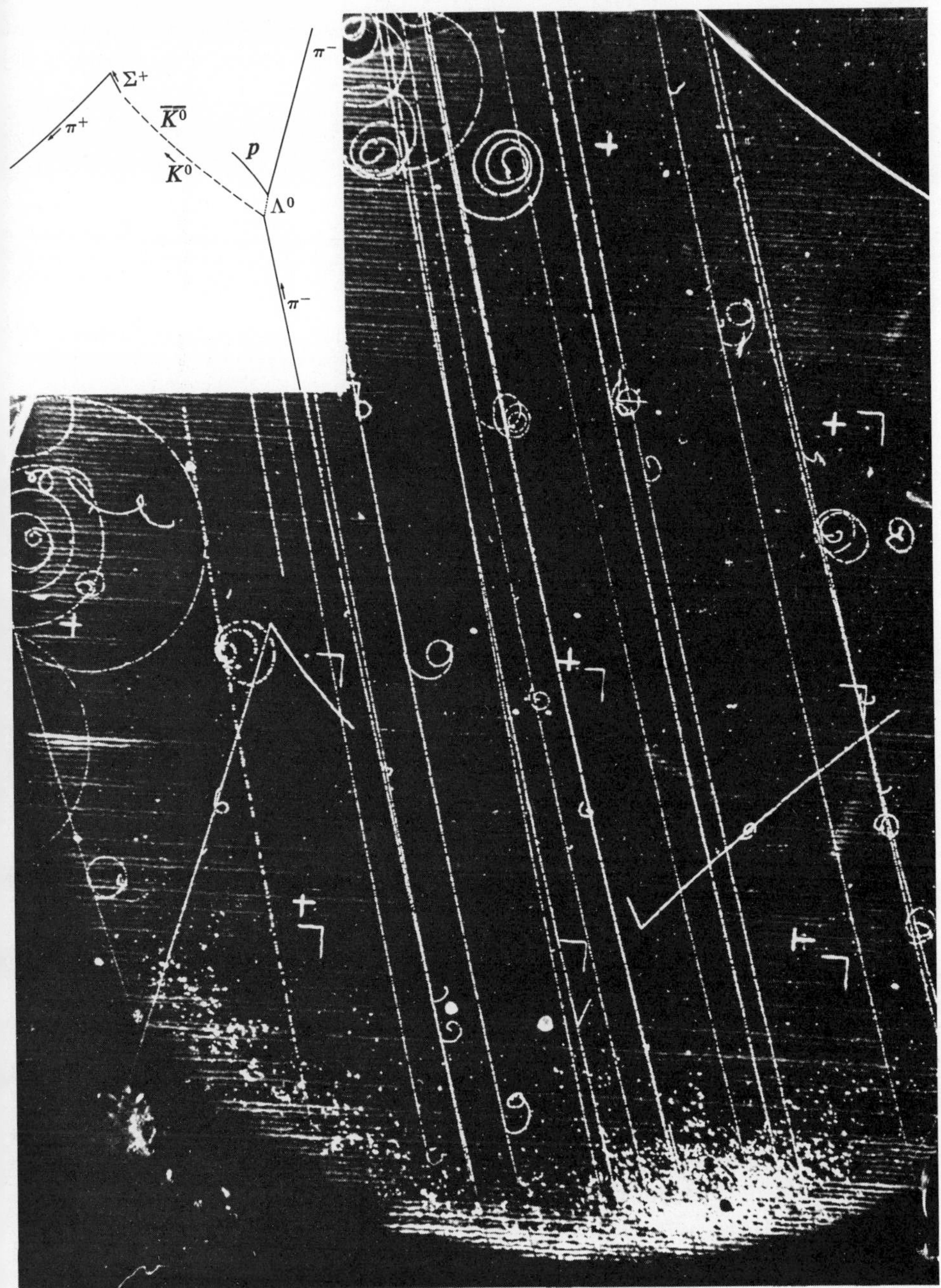

Figure 15-18 Bubble-chamber pictures showing the reactions

$$\pi^- + p \to \Lambda^0 + K^0$$
$$\Lambda^0 \to \pi^- + p$$
$$K^0 \to \overline{K^0}$$
$$\overline{K^0} + p \to \Sigma^+ + \pi^0$$
$$\Sigma^+ \to \pi^+ + n$$

Note the invisible transformation $K^0 \to \overline{K^0}$ evidenced by the subsequent formation of a Σ^+ in a $\overline{K^0}$ collision.

In the decay determined by weak interactions the important conservation law is the *CP* law (charge conjugation times parity transformation). Now the operator C changes $|K^0\rangle$ into $|\overline{K^0}\rangle$, and P leaves it unchanged, except for a possible change of sign. In any case, C^2 and P^2 are identity operators. For convenience we shall use the notation due to Dirac and indicate by $|K\rangle$ the eigenfunction corresponding to a K particle (see Sec. 13-1). We may define the $|\overline{K^0}\rangle$ state as giving

$$CP\,|\,K^0\,\rangle = |\,\overline{K^0}\,\rangle \qquad \text{and we have } CP\,|\,\overline{K^0}\,\rangle = |\,K^0\,\rangle \tag{15-6.6}$$

It is hence clear that K^0 and $\overline{K^0}$ are not eigenstates of *CP*. However, the linear combinations

$$|K_1^0\,\rangle = \frac{1}{\sqrt{2}}(|K^0\,\rangle + |\overline{K^0}\,\rangle)$$
$$|K_2^0\,\rangle = \frac{1}{\sqrt{2}}(|K^0\,\rangle - |\overline{K^0}\,\rangle) \tag{15-6.7}$$

are eigenstates of *CP*, as can be seen by applying Eq. (15-6.6) to them, and precisely

$$CP\,|K_1^0\,\rangle = |K_1^0\,\rangle \qquad CP\,|K_2^0\,\rangle = -|K_2^0\,\rangle \tag{15-6.8}$$

We can also express $|K^0\rangle$ and $|\overline{K^0}\rangle$ through $|K_1^0\rangle$, $|K_2^0\rangle$ as

$$|K^0\,\rangle = \frac{1}{\sqrt{2}}(|K_1^0\,\rangle + |K_2^0\,\rangle)$$
$$|\overline{K^0}\rangle = \frac{1}{\sqrt{2}}(|K_1^0\rangle - |K_2^0\rangle) \tag{15-6.9}$$

We can then say that the production of a K^0 is equivalent to the production of a K_1^0 and a K_2^0 with equal amplitude and a prescribed phase relation (Gell-Mann and Pais, 1955).

The phenomenon is similar to that of the superposition with a given phase relation of light linearly polarized in perpendicular directions. If the phase difference is $\pm\pi/2$, the result for equal amplitudes is circularly polarized light (left or right). Conversely the superposition of left and right circularly polarized light gives rise to linearly polarized light, the direction of the plane of polarization depending on the phase difference of the two rays of equal amplitude. In general the results discussed in this section closely parallel the properties of polarized light, and it is possible to develop optical analogies for these phenomena. An important difference, however, appears in the spontaneous decay of the K^0 mesons, for which there is no analogy in light quanta.

From the fact that K^0, $\overline{K^0}$ are eigenstates of strangeness and K_1^0, K_2^0 are eigenstates of *CP* it follows that we should consider K^0 and $\overline{K^0}$ when we study strong interactions, and K_1^0, K_2^0 when we consider weak interactions. In the decay produced by weak interactions K_1^0 may go only in tates for which the eigenvalue of CP is $+1$ and $K_2{}^0$ only in states for which the eigenvalue of CP is -1. We now apply this to the decay into pions.

The (π^+,π^-) or (π^0,π^0) systems have $CP = +1$. In the latter case this s immediate, because the eigenfunction of two identical bosons is unchanged when the particles are interchanged, an operation which, in the center-of-mass system, is clearly equivalent to P. Moreover, the π^0 is unaffected by charge conjugation, and hence $CP = 1$. For the (π^+,π^-) system the same result obtains. From this it is clear that $K_1{}^0$ can decay nto $\pi^0 + \pi^0$ or $\pi^+ + \pi^-$, but $K_2{}^0$ cannot. The decay constant of $K_1{}^0$ s about 1.08×10^{10} sec^{-1}. The $K_2{}^0$ decays in three pions or by leptonic decays, and its decay constant is about 1.6×10^8 sec^{-1}.

If we form a beam of K^0 by strong interaction [Eq. (15-6.1)], after a few tenths of a nanosecond the $K_1{}^0$ component has disappeared and we are left with a beam of half the initial intensity consisting purely of $K_2{}^0$. This can be proved by verifying that the beam composed of "old" particles can now produce strong interactions characteristic of both $\overline{K^0}$ and K^0, which was impossible for the "young" beam composed only of K^0. Moreover, the beam of $K_2{}^0$ in passing through matter changes the relative amplitudes and phases of its K^0, $\overline{K^0}$ components because K^0 and $\overline{K^0}$ behave differently with respect to strong interactions, and emerges with a $K_1{}^0$ regenerated component, which would appear as a short-lived component decaying into two pions (Pais and Piccioni, 1957; Fig. 15-19).

$K_1{}^0$ and $K_2{}^0$ have very different decay constants. As a consequence we may expect a tiny mass difference between the two particles. The situation is analogous to that of other particles, for example, π^0, $\pi^\pm$; n, p, which differ in their electric charge, and as a consequence in their mass by an amount which can be crudely interpreted as being due to the electromagnetic energy $e^2/r = c^2\,\Delta m$, where r is the "radius" of the particle. In the electromagnetic case $c^2\,\Delta m$ thus appears as a measure of

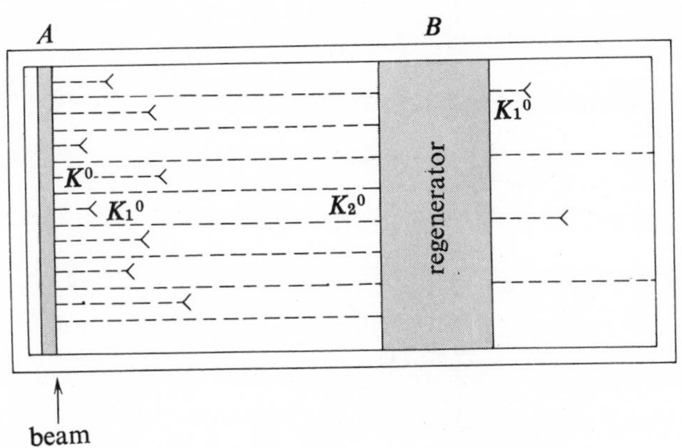

Figure 15-19 Schematic diagram showing the regeneration of $K_1{}^0$ events in a multiplate cloud chamber. The symbol $\langle$ indicates the decay:

$$K_1{}^0 \rightarrow \pi^+ + \pi^-$$

In target A, pions generate K^0. The $K_1{}^0$ component decays fast and only $K_2{}^0$ reach the regenerator B. In crossing it some of them undergo strong interactions and emerge as K^0 having a regenerated $K_1{}^0$ component. [From A. Pais and O. Piccioni, *Phys. Rev.*, **100**, 1487 (1955).]

the electromagnetic energy of the particle. Similarly, for weak interactions we expect a mass difference related to a difference in energy. We may try to guess the order of magnitude of this mass difference by a purely dimensional argument. If the electromagnetic interaction gives a mass difference of the order of 1 MeV, the weak interaction which is 10^{-12} times smaller might give a mass difference of the order of 10^{-6} eV.

We shall now discuss briefly a situation in which the mass difference $m_1 - m_2$ (m_1 = mass of $K_1{}^0$, m_2 = mass of $K_2{}^0$) would be observable (Treiman and Sachs, 1956). Suppose that we generate a beam of K^0 by strong interaction and write the $\psi(t)$ as

$$|\psi(t)\rangle = \frac{1}{\sqrt{2}}|K_1{}^0\rangle \exp -(im_1c^2t/\hbar) \exp -(\Gamma_1 t/2) + \frac{1}{\sqrt{2}}|K_2{}^0\rangle \exp -(im_2c^2t/\hbar) \exp -(\Gamma_2 t/2) \quad \textbf{(15-6.10)}$$

where $\Gamma_{1,2} = 1/\tau_{1,2}$, the reciprocal of the mean life of $K_{1,2}{}^0$. The ψ is such that for $t = 0$ it represents, as it should, K^0. At any time $|\psi(t)\rangle$ can be resolved into a K^0 and a $\overline{K^0}$ component. The former, for example, is

$$\langle K^0|\psi(t)\rangle = \tfrac{1}{2}\{\exp[(-im_1c^2t/\hbar) - \Gamma_1 t/2] + \exp[(-im_2c^2t/\hbar) - \Gamma_2 t/2]\} \quad \textbf{(15-6.11)}$$

and its modulus square

$$\tfrac{1}{4}\{\exp(-\Gamma_1 t) + \exp(-\Gamma_2 t) + 2\exp[-(\Gamma_1 + \Gamma_2)t/2] \cdot \cos[\Delta mc^2t/\hbar]\} \quad \textbf{(15-6.12)}$$

gives the number of K^0 in the beam. The number of $\overline{K^0}$ is given by the same expression, except that the cosine term has a minus sign. If $m_1 = m_2$,

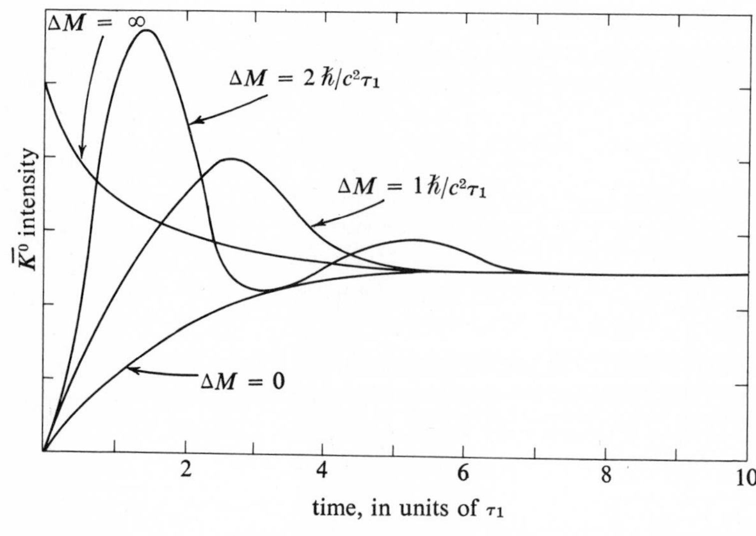

Figure 15-20 The intensity of the $\overline{K^0}$ component is shown as a function of time for three values of the mass difference in units $\hbar/c^2\tau_1$. For $t = 0$ the beam is a pure K^0 beam. [From Camerini et al. (Wisconsin), Birge et al. (Berkeley); *Phys. Rev.*, **128**, 362 (1962).]

Eq. (15-6.12) represents a combination of decreasing exponentials, but if $m_1 \neq m_2$, there are very peculiar oscillations in the number of K^0 or $\overline{K^0}$ in the beam (see Fig. 15-20). The quantitative aspects of the effect depend on the magnitude of the ratio

$$\frac{\Delta mc^2/\hbar}{\Gamma_1} = \frac{\tau_1 c^2 \Delta m}{\hbar} \tag{15-6.13}$$

(we know already that $\Gamma_2 \ll \Gamma_1$) and their experimental investigation is expected to give the mass difference. Equation (15-6.12) does not give a method for finding the sign of $(m_1 - m_2)$; however, there are other experiments that give this sign. The best results available indicate that $(m_2 - m_1)\, c^2 = (0.47 \pm 0.2)\, \hbar/\tau_1 = (3.3 \pm 1.4) \times 10^{-6}$ eV.

15-7 Excited States of Strange Particles and Their Classification

We have seen in Chap. 14 that pion-nucleon collision cross sections show strong fluctuations reminiscent of the resonances occurring in ordinary nuclear reactions. The most prominent example is the $T = \frac{3}{2}$, $J = \frac{3}{2}$ resonance in the pion-nucleon collision. It can be interpreted as the formation of an excited nucleon with the angular momentum $\frac{3}{2}$, and *i* spin $\frac{3}{2}$. The duration of this excited state is, as usual, estimated from the width of the resonance.

Are there similar resonances for other systems involving strange particles? The answer to this question comes from experiments on such reactions as

$$K^- + p \Rightarrow \Lambda + \pi^+ + \pi^- \tag{15-7.1}$$

If one interprets this as a genuine three-body reaction, the kinetic energies of the two pions plotted in a Dalitz plot of T_{π^+} versus T_{π^-} should uniformly occupy the kinematically permissible region. This is equivalent to saying that in golden rule No. 2 the matrix element is constant and the probabilities of the different final states are proportional to the corresponding phase space available. If, however, the reaction proceeds in two steps through the formation of an excited hyperon Y^* of short life,

$$\begin{aligned} K^- + p &\Rightarrow Y^{*\pm} + \pi^{\mp} \\ &\qquad \hookrightarrow \Lambda^\circ + \pi^{\pm} \end{aligned} \tag{15-7.2}$$

The first pion will have a fixed energy in the K^-p center-of-mass system, because it results from a two-body reaction. The second pion will also have a fixed energy in the center of mass of Y^*, and this will give an energy band in the K^-p center-of-mass system. The band width depends on the Q of the Y^* disintegration. The short life of Y^* produces an uncertainty in its total energy. Figure 15-21 gives a plot of the kinetic energies of the two combinations $\Lambda\pi^+$ and $\Lambda\pi^-$ in Eq. (15-7.1) when the K^- have a momentum of 1,220 MeV/c lab. It is apparent from the figure the $(\Lambda\pi^+)$ or $(\Lambda\pi^-)$ system has preferentially the mass $1{,}385 \pm 5$ MeV in its own c.m. system.

We have evidence, therefore, of a resonance in the $\Lambda\pi^{\pm}$ system with a total energy of 1,385 ± 5 MeV. The Y^* of energy 1,385 has been observed not only positively and negatively charged, but also neutral. The next step is to assign quantum numbers to the Y^*. The i spin is 1 because Y^* is clearly an i-spin triplet, as can be seen from the three possible charges. The spin J is shown to be $\geqslant \frac{3}{2}$ by a consideration of the angular distribution of the Y^* production in the K^-p center-of-mass system.

Similar consideration of the reaction

$$K^- + p \Rightarrow \Sigma^\circ + \pi + \pi \qquad \text{(15-7.3)}$$

indicates the existence of an excited hyperon of i spin 0 at mass 1,405 MeV. This subject is being rapidly developed. Table 14-6 summarizes the results.

There have been many attempts to develop a classification of particles on the assumption that some are more "elementary" than others. For instance, as far back as 1949 Fermi and Yang tried to consider the pion

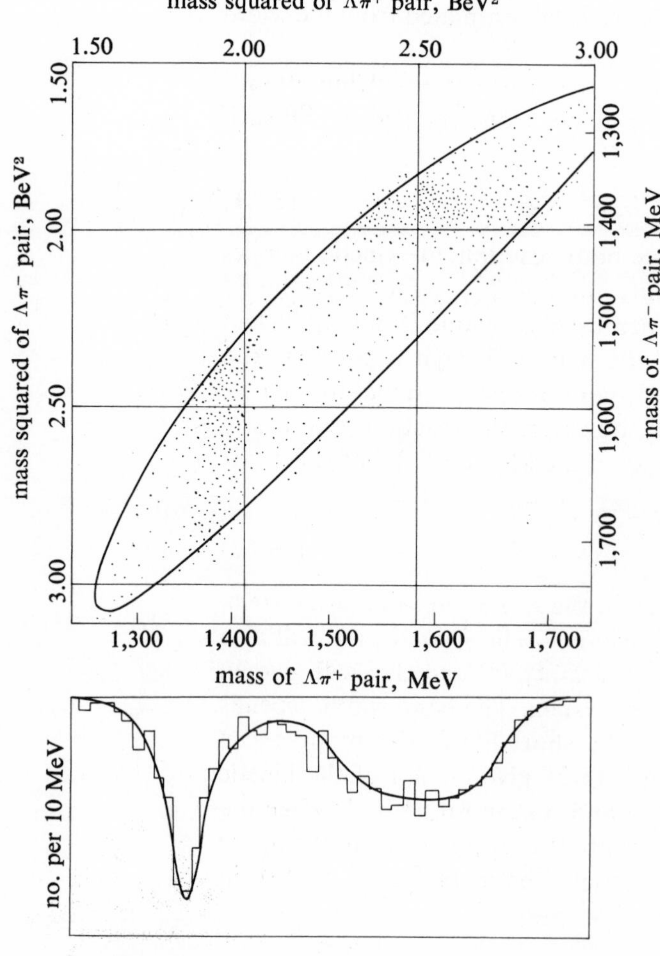

Figure 15-21 Dalitz plot of $\Lambda\pi^+\pi^-$ events from K^-p interactions at 1.22 BeV/c laboratory. The square of $\Lambda\pi^+$ effective mass is plotted against the square of $\Lambda\pi^-$ effective mass. Scales giving the masses in MeV are also shown. If the matrix element for the reaction were constant, the area within the oval would be uniformly populated. Projection of the events onto the $\Lambda\pi^+$ mass axis is displayed to the right of the figure. The curve represents the fitting of Breit-Wigner resonance expressions to the $\Lambda\pi^+$ and $\Lambda\pi^-$ systems. [From Shafer, Murray, and Huwe, *Phys. Rev. Letters*, **10,** 179 (1963).]

as composed of a $N\bar{N}$ pair. More recently Sakata assumed the neutron, proton, and Λ as the fundamental particles and tried to consider all others as formed by these. However, up to now none of these attempts have been successful.

Other attempts have been made to discover symmetries among particles. It has been remarked by S. Sakata, Y. Ne'eman, Gell-Mann, and others that it is possible to collect all presently known particles and resonances in families containing either 1, or 8, or 10, or 27 members.

These numbers form the basis of a classification based on the hypothesis of the invariance of the interaction with respect to two newly introduced quantum numbers, U, V, similar to the known i-spin invariance of the strong interactions. The two new quantum numbers have commutation properties similar to angular momentum vectors and are called U spin and V spin.

The three spins T, U, V are not independent and their interrelation forms the subject of a group theoretical study (unitary symmetry, SU_3 group, eightfold way) beyond the scope of this book.

However, these group theoretical hypotheses bring us to some simple conclusions, some of which have had predictive value and have been strikingly corroborated by experiment. One classifies all particles having the same J and parity and approximately the same mass in a

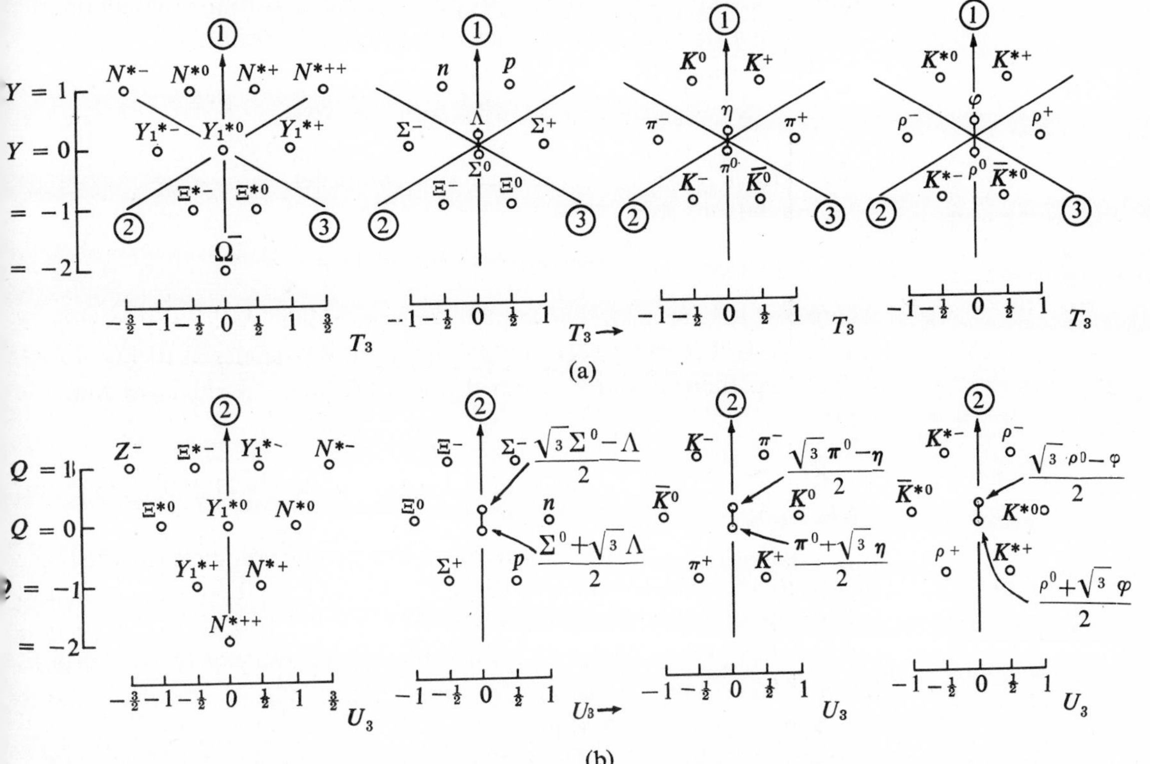

Figure 15-22 Classification of particles and resonances according to the octet and decuplet scheme—abscissa T_3, ordinate Y or S. All particles in a multiplet have the same J^P.

multiplet plotting on the abscissa T_3 and on the ordinate the hypercharge Y. This procedure yields the diagrams of Fig. 15-22. These diagrams are symmetrical with respect to three axes inclined by 120° to each other. Thus, if we turn the figure by 120° we have Fig. 15-22b, in which the abscissa is now U_3, the third component of the U spin, and the ordinate Q, the electric charge.

Note that at the center of the diagrams there is more than one particle and that different linear combinations are to be used in Fig. 15-22a and b.

If U spin were exactly conserved in strong interactions, as i spin is, all particles in the same multiplet, except for electromagnetic effects, would have the same mass. This is not so and one must assume that U-spin invariance of the strong interactions is only approximately valid. An indication of accuracy or inaccuracy of the approximation is given by the relative mass difference of particles in the same multiplet differing in Y.

The interaction that breaks the symmetry has an analogy with the electromagnetic interaction which is not invariant with respect to i-spin rotation (a change in T_3 means a change in charge, even when T is constant). As an hypothesis it has been assumed that this symmetry-breaking interaction bears the same relation to U spin that the electromagnetic interaction bears to i spin. With this assumption it is possible to establish relations between masses of some particles. In particular, Okubo and Gell-Mann have proposed a mass formula based on the hypothesis of U and T invariance of strong interactions.

The formula is, for hyperons,

$$M = M_1 + M_2 Y + M_3 \left[T(T+1) - \frac{Y^2}{4} \right] \qquad \textbf{(15-7.4)}$$

where M_1, M_2, M_3 are constant in one multiplet.

For bosons it is

$$\mu^2 = \mu_0{}^2 + \mu_1{}^2 \left[T(T+1) - \frac{Y^2}{4} \right] \qquad \textbf{(15-7.5)}$$

where $\mu_0{}^2$, $\mu_1{}^2$ are again constant in one multiplet. As an application of Eq. (15-7.4) it is easily seen that, assigning the particles as in Fig. 15-22, or reading their T and Y from Table 14-6, one should have that the masses of

$$N^{-*},\ Y_1{}^{*-},\ \Xi^{*-},\ Z^-$$

are equally spaced. In fact, their masses are 1,238, 1,385, 1,530, and 1,676 MeV.

Furthermore, the hypothesis of SU_3 invariance requires the existence of a particle marked Z^- in Fig. 15-22. It should have $Y = -2, I = 0$, and according to Eq. (15-7.4) mass approximately 1,680 MeV. These predictions have been strikingly fulfilled by the discovery of the Ω^- (Brookhaven, 1964), which is the particle indicated as Z^-.

Similarly Eq. (15-7.4) gives

$$\tfrac{1}{2}(n + \Xi^\circ) = \tfrac{1}{4}(\Sigma^0 + 3\Lambda)$$

where the symbol of the particle stands for the mass of the particle. The agreement with experiment is within a few MeV.

Many other predictions of this hypothesis are accessible to experiment. For instance, there are predictions on the electromagnetic properties, magnetic moments, and electromagnetic mass splittings which agree with the limited amount of experimental material available.

Another set of hypotheses, associated with the name of T. Regge, predicts the "recurrence" of a particle if, all other quantum numbers being unchanged, two units of angular momentum are added. The Regge recurrences have an analogy to the levels of an atomic system, having the same radial quantum number but increasing l. Think of a hydrogen atom (neglecting spin); the energy, assuming as zero the energy of the electron and proton at great distance and at rest, is then given by $-R/(n_r + l)^2$, where R is the Rydberg constant. It is possible for an atomic system to generalize the energy formula and to define the energy as an analytic function of l, considered as a complex variable. However, physical states correspond only to l real and integral. All levels having the same n_r lie on a "Regge trajectory" and are called "recurrences" of the first. A Regge trajectory may contain stable (negative energy) and unstable points. The last ones appear physically as resonances.

In particle physics one has to add two units of angular momentum to obtain a recurrence. This is related to the behavior of exchange forces which change sign for even or odd angular momenta (Sec. 10-7). The recurrences of an octet should then form a new octet.

These ideas on classification of particles are embodied in a nomenclature and symbolism especially suited for them, proposed by Chew, Gell-Mann, and Rosenfeld. Mesons are all indicated by lower-case Greek letters, baryons by upper-case Greek letters. Each letter is given for a combination of the quantum numbers A, Y, T, according to Table 15-4.

To completely characterize a particle, the electric charge, connected to T_3 by

$$Q = T_3 + \frac{Y}{2}$$

the mass in MeV, and the spin and parity are indicated separately thus:

π^0 (137, 0^-) is the ordinary neutral pion

Δ^{++} (1,238, $\frac{3}{2}^+$) is the $\frac{3}{2}$, $\frac{3}{2}$ resonance of the $p\pi^+$ system

With this nomenclature Regge recurrences have the same Greek letter.

Table 15-4 Key to Nomenclature of Particles

Mesons	A	Y	T	Baryons	A	Y	T
η	0	0	0	Λ	1	0	0
π	0	0	1	Σ	1	0	1
κ	0	+1	$\frac{1}{2}$	N	1	+1	$\frac{1}{2}$
$\bar{\kappa}$	0	−1	$\frac{1}{2}$	Ξ	1	−1	$\frac{1}{2}$
				Ω	1	−2	0
				Δ	1	+1	$\frac{3}{2}$

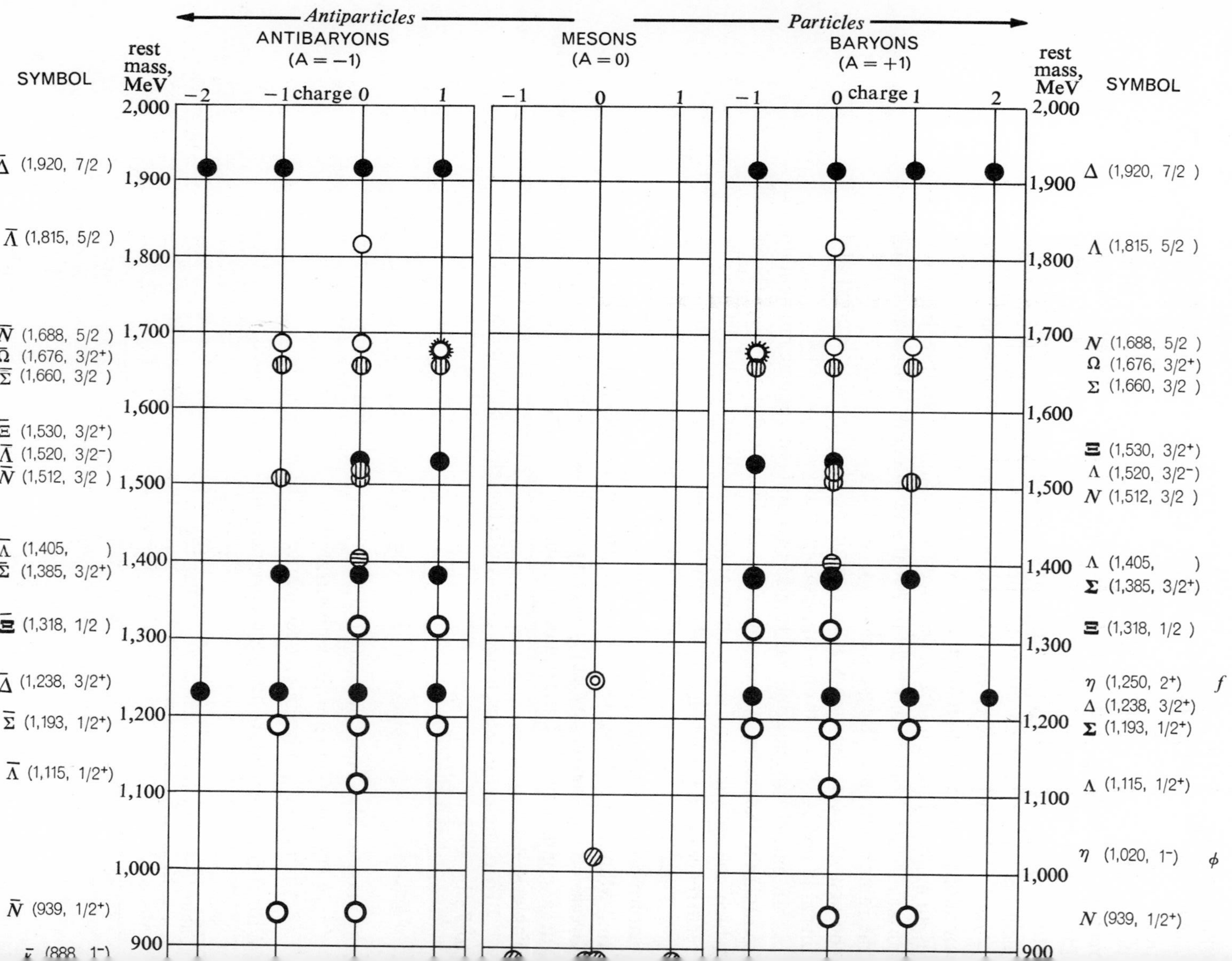
Antiparticles
ANTIBARYONS
(A = −1)
MESONS
(A = 0)
Particles
BARYONS
(A = +1)
SYMBOL
rest mass, MeV
charge
−2 −1 0 1
−1 0 1
−1 0 1 2
2,000
1,900
1,800
1,700
1,600
1,500
1,400
1,300
1,200
1,100
1,000
900
$\bar{\Delta}$ (1,920, 7/2)
$\bar{\Lambda}$ (1,815, 5/2)
$\bar{N}$ (1,688, 5/2)
$\bar{\Omega}$ (1,676, 3/2⁺)
$\bar{\Sigma}$ (1,660, 3/2)
$\bar{\Xi}$ (1,530, 3/2⁺)
$\bar{\Lambda}$ (1,520, 3/2⁻)
$\bar{N}$ (1,512, 3/2)
$\bar{\Lambda}$ (1,405,)
$\bar{\Sigma}$ (1,385, 3/2⁺)
$\bar{\Xi}$ (1,318, 1/2)
$\bar{\Delta}$ (1,238, 3/2⁺)
$\bar{\Sigma}$ (1,193, 1/2⁺)
$\bar{\Lambda}$ (1,115, 1/2⁺)
$\bar{N}$ (939, 1/2⁺)
Δ (1,920, 7/2)
Λ (1,815, 5/2)
N (1,688, 5/2)
Ω (1,676, 3/2⁺)
Σ (1,660, 3/2)
Ξ (1,530, 3/2⁺)
Λ (1,520, 3/2⁻)
N (1,512, 3/2)
Λ (1,405,)
Σ (1,385, 3/2⁺)
Ξ (1,318, 1/2)
η (1,250, 2⁺) f
Δ (1,238, 3/2⁺)
Σ (1,193, 1/2⁺)
Λ (1,115, 1/2⁺)
η (1,020, 1⁻) φ
N (939, 1/2⁺)

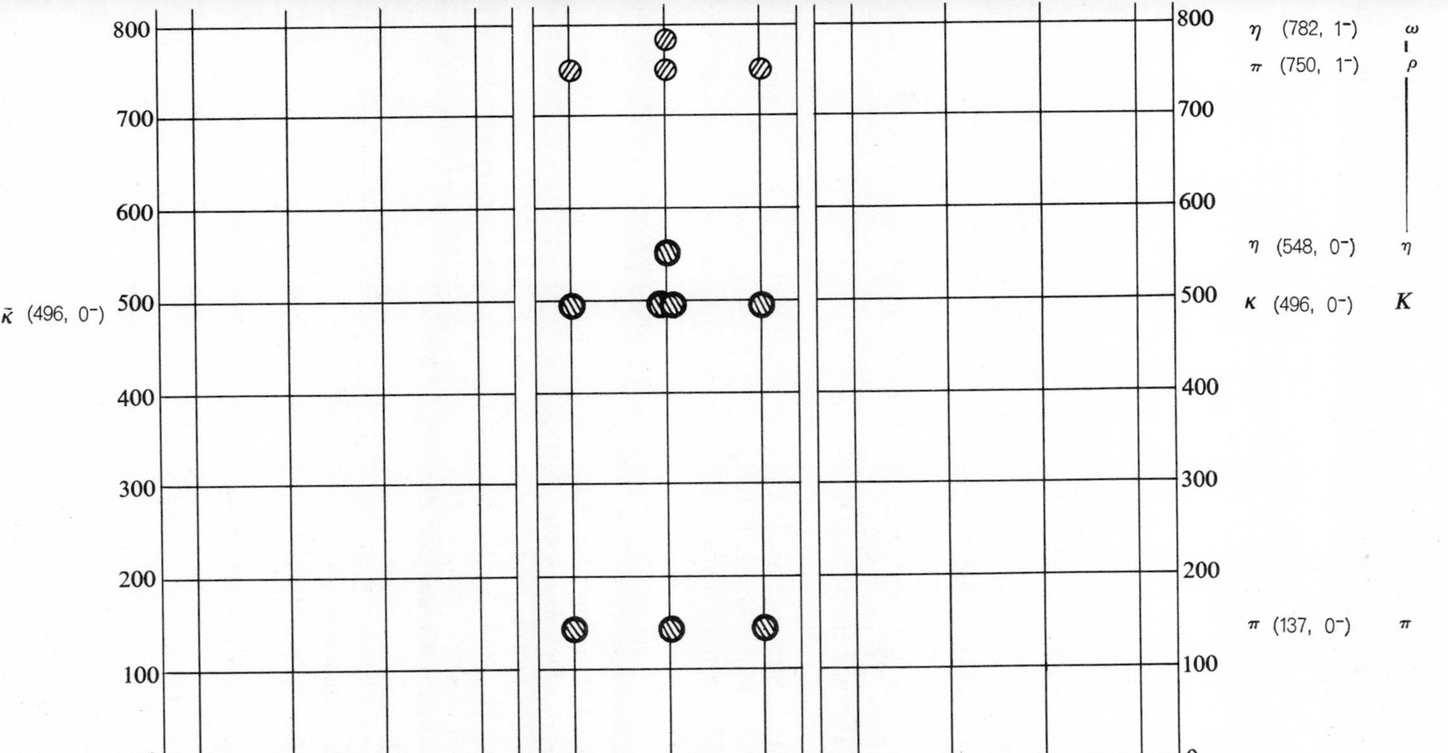

Figure 15-23 Strongly interacting particles are presented with the naming system of Table 15-4. The 82 particles and antiparticles in this chart include only those with a rest mass below 2,000 MeV and with atomic mass number of − 1, 0, or + 1. All the particles shown here are known to exist. Their existence has been predicted by the "eightfold way." The mass assignments are averages for the members of a charge multiplet, or family of states differing only in their electric charge. Multiplets that have the same spin angular momentum (*J*) and parity (*P*) are assigned the same type of shading. The same shading is also assigned to "recurrences" of these particles. Recurrences are particles with 2, 4, 6 (and so on) more units of spin than their "ground" states of lowest mass. (Where parity values have not yet been established they have been left blank, but they have been guessed for purposes of coding.) Stable and metastable particles are heavily circled; unstable particles (also called resonances) are lightly circled. [Adapted from Chew, Gell-Mann, and Rosenfeld, *Sci. Am.*, Feb. 1964.]

Another nomenclature often used (for instance in Table 14-6) gives to baryons of hypercharge 1, 0, −1 the names N_T^*, Y_T^* Ξ_T^*, respectively, and indicates the i spin by the subscript; thus the $\frac{3}{2}$, $\frac{3}{2}$ N-pion resonance would be indicated by $N_{\frac{3}{2}}^*$ (1,238).

Figure 15-23 should leave a fitting last impression to the patient reader of this book.

Bibliography

Adair, R. K., and E. C. Fowler, *Strange Particles*, Wiley-Interscience, New York, 1963.

Alston, M., and M. Ferro-Luzzi, "Pion Hyperon Resonances," *Rev. Mod. Phys.*, **33**, 416 (1961).

Conversi, M. (ed.), *Selected Topics on Elementary Particle Physics* (Varenna Lectures, 1962), Academic Press, New York, 1964.

Crayton, Levi Setti, Raymund, Skjeggestad, Abeledo, Ammar, Roberts, and Shipley, "A Compilation of Hyperfragments Binding Energies," *Rev. Mod. Phys.*, **34**, 186 (1962).

Dalitz, R. H., "On the Strong Interaction of Strange Particles," *Rev. Mod. Phys.*, **33**, 71 (1961).

Dalitz, R. H., "Strange Particle Decay Processes and the Fermi Interaction," *Rev. Mod. Phys.*, **31**, 823 (1959).

Dalitz, R. H., "Strange-Particle Resonant States," *Ann. Rev. Nucl. Sci.*, **13**, 339 (1963).

Dalitz, R. H., *Strong Interaction Physics and the Strange Particles*, Oxford University Press, New York, 1962.

Danysz, M., and J. Pniewski, "Delayed Disintegration of a Heavy Nuclear Fragment," *Phil. Mag.*, **44**, 348 (1953).

Fry, W. F., "Hyperfragments," *Ann. Rev. Nucl. Sci.*, **8**, 105 (1958).

Gell-Mann, M., and A. H. Rosenfeld, "Hyperons and Heavy Mesons (Systematics and Decay)," *Ann. Rev. Nucl. Sci.*, **7**, 407 (1957).

Lipkin, H. J., *Lie Groups for Pedestrians*, Argonne National Laboratory, 1963.

Morpurgo, G., "Strong Interactions and Reactions of Hyperons and Heavy Mesons," *Ann. Rev. Nucl. Sci.*, **11**, 41 (1961).

Nishijima, K., "Charge Independence Theory of V-Particles," *Progr. Theoret. Phys. (Kyoto)*, **13**, 285 (1955).

Nishijima, K., *Fundamental Particles*, Benjamin, New York, 1963.

Pais, A., "Some Remarks on V-Particles," *Phys. Rev.*, **86**, 663 (1952).

Rochester, C. D., and C. C. Butler, "Evidence for the Existence of New Unstable Elementary Particles," *Nature*, **160**, 855 (1947).

Sachs, R. G., "Interference Phenomena of Neutral K Mesons," *Ann. Phys.*, **22**, 239 (1963).

Segrè, E., "Antinucleons," *Ann. Rev. Nucl. Sci.*, **8**, 127 (1958).

Snow, G. A., and M. M. Shapiro, "Mesons and Hyperons," *Rev. Mod. Phys.*, **33**, 231 (1961).

Williams, S. C., *Introduction to Elementary Particles*, Academic Press, New York, 1962.

Problems

15-1 On the basis of phase space and energy considerations alone, calculate the branching ratio of the decay

$$\Sigma^0 = \Lambda^0 + \gamma$$
$$= n + \gamma$$

Compare your results with the experimental data.

15-2 What will be the absolute minimum energy necessary to form K mesons by bombarding hydrogen with protons? Consider separately strong and weak interactions.

15-3 How could one produce a Ξ in the laboratory? Find the threshold.

15-4 Find the threshold for the production of K^0 and $\overline{K^0}$ in π^-–proton collisions.

15-5 What isotopic spin states are involved in the reactions:

$$(a)\ \pi^- + p \to \Lambda^0 + K^0$$
$$(b)\ \pi^+ + p \to \Sigma^+ + K^+$$
$$(c)\ \pi^- + p \to \Sigma^- + K^+$$
$$(d)\ K^- + d \to \Lambda^0 + p + \pi^-$$

15-6 Find methods and threshold energies for the production of K^+ and K^-.

15-7 Suppose that you are studying reactions produced by high-energy protons incident on a hydrogen target. Write a strong reaction which can lead to each of the following products: (*a*) a Λ^0, (*b*) a K^-, (*c*) a Ξ^-, (*d*) an anti-Λ^0.

15-8 Show that the reactions

$$\text{(a)}\ K^- + He^4 \Rightarrow \Sigma^- + He^3$$
$$\text{(b)}\qquad\qquad \Rightarrow \Sigma^0 + H^3$$
$$\text{(a)}\ K^- + He^4 \Rightarrow \Lambda^0 + \pi^- + He^3$$
$$\text{(b)}\qquad\qquad \Rightarrow \Lambda^0 + \pi^\circ + H^3$$

have branching ratios a:b = 2:1.

15-9 Consider the $\Sigma - \pi$ interaction. There are nine possible charge combinations. How many independent interactions may exist under the isospin invariance hypothesis?

15-10 Develop the argument showing that the absence of the decay $K^+ \Rightarrow \pi^+ + \gamma$ indicates a spin zero for K^+.

15-11 Develop the properties of a plot of a three-body reaction (e.g., decay of a τ meson), for which one uses as abscissa and ordinate in cartesian coordinates the kinetic energy of two of the particles.

15-12 Show that in the Dalitz plot in Fig. 15-9, $PN/NG = \cos\theta$.

15-13 Show that for nonrelativistic particles the points describing the decay $K^+ \to 2\pi^+ + \pi^-$ are confined to a circle inscribed in the Dalitz triangle.

15-14 Show that the representative points in a Dalitz plot for extremely relativistic particles are confined to an equilateral triangle inscribed in the Dalitz triangle.

15-15 Show that for two pions the eigenfunction with $T_3 = 0$ are

$$\varphi_{0,0} = \frac{1}{\sqrt{3}}\left[\pi^+(1)\,\pi^-(2) - \pi^0(1)\,\pi^0(2) + \pi^-(1)\,\pi^+(2)\right] \qquad T = 0$$

$$\varphi_{1,0} = \frac{1}{\sqrt{2}}\left[\pi^+(1)\pi^+(2) - \pi^-(1)\pi^+(2)\right] \qquad T = 1$$

$$\varphi_{2,0} = \frac{1}{\sqrt{6}}\left[\pi^+(1)\pi^-(2) + 2\pi^0(1)\pi^0(2) + \pi^-(1)\pi^+(2)\right] \qquad T = 2$$

15-16 Prove that three pions cannot be in a state $J^P = 0^+$.

15-17 Show that the *i*-spin eigenfunction of a system of three pions with $T = 0$ is antisymmetrical with respect to the exchange of the coordinates of any two pions. Show that as a consequence the coordinate eigenfunction must also be antisymmetrical with respect to the exchange of pions.

15-18 From the neutron mean life, $\tau = 1{,}000$ sec, make a rough estimate of the decay rate (in sec^{-1}) you might expect for the decay $\Sigma^- \to \Sigma^0 + e^- + \nu$. ($\Sigma^- - \Sigma^0$ mass difference $= 4.5$ MeV.)

15-19 (*a*) A subject of considerable interest is the beta decay of the Λ^0 particle $\Lambda^0 \to p + e + \bar{\nu}$. Assuming that the matrix element is one, the coupling constant is the same as in neutron decay, and neglecting (as in neutron decay) the Λ^0 recoil energy, calculate the expected beta decay rate of the Λ^0. If the usual Λ^0 decay ($\Lambda^0 \to p + \pi^-$) has mean life 2.5×10^{-10} sec, what is the branching ratio for the beta decay? (*b*) What is the Λ^0 maximum recoil energy? (The mass of $\Lambda^0 = 1{,}115$ MeV.)

15-20 An excited hyperon state Y^* has been found which decays as follows:

$$Y^* \to \Lambda^0 + \pi$$

It has a total energy of 1380 MeV with a full width of half-maximum of about 30 MeV. Calculate (*a*) the mean life of the Y^* and (*b*) its strangeness.

15-21 The π^+ and π^- have precisely the same mass, whereas the Σ^+ and Σ^- do not. Why? Would you expect the K^+ and K^- to have the same mass. If so, why?

APPENDIX A

Time-Dependent Perturbation Theory

We shall give here a summary of the treatment of time-dependent perturbations, which are of great importance in the application of quantum theory to nuclear phenomena.

Given a system with a hamiltonian

$$H = H_0 + \mathscr{H} \tag{A-1}$$

where the operator H_0 is time-independent but $\mathscr{H}$ may contain the time explicitly. We assume the solution of the unperturbed Schrödinger's equation, corresponding to $\mathscr{H} = 0$, to be known:

$$i\hbar\dot{\psi}_0 = H_0\psi_0 \tag{A-2}$$

By separating the time putting

$$\psi_0 = u_0\,(x, y, z) \exp\,(-iE_0t/\hbar)$$

we have

$$\psi_0 = \Sigma_n a_n{}^{(0)} u_n{}^{(0)} \exp\,(-iE_n{}^{(0)}t/\hbar) \tag{A-3}$$

where

$$H_0 u_n{}^{(0)} = E_n{}^{(0)} u_n{}^{(0)} \tag{A-4}$$

with the $u_n{}^{(0)}$ orthonormal and the constants $a_n{}^{(0)}$ independent of time.

We try now to solve the perturbed Schrödinger equation

$$H\psi = ih\dot{\psi} = (H_0 + \mathscr{H})\psi \tag{A-5}$$

by putting

$$\psi = \Sigma\, a_n(t) u_n{}^{(0)} \exp\,(-iE_n{}^{(0)}t/\hbar) \tag{A-6}$$

with the a's now functions of time (method of the variations of constants).

Inserting (A-6) into (A-5), multiplying by $\bar{u}_s{}^{(0)}$ (the bar superscript indicates complex conjugate), and using the orthonormality relations for the $u_n{}^{(0)}$, we obtain

$$\dot{a}_s = -\frac{i}{\hbar}\,\Sigma_n a_n \mathscr{H}_{sn} \exp\,\{i[E_s{}^{(0)} - E_n{}^{(0)}]t/\hbar\} \tag{A-7}$$

where

$$\mathscr{H}_{sn}(t) = \int \bar{u}_s{}^{(0)} \mathscr{H} u_n{}^{(0)}\, d\tau$$

is the matrix element of the perturbation between states s, n. The integral in $d\tau$ is extended to the space variables of which the u are functions. Equation (A-7) is exact. We approximate the solution by substituting on the right side $a_n(0)$ for $a_n(t)$; setting $(E_s^{(0)} - E_n^{(0)})/\hbar = \omega_{sn}$ we then have

$$a_s(t) = a_s(0) - \frac{i}{\hbar} \sum a_n(0) \int_0^t \mathscr{H}_{sn}(t) \exp(i\omega_{sn}t)\, dt \tag{A-8}$$

An important special case arises if the system at time zero is in the state n; then $a_n(0) = 1$ and all other $a_s(0)$ are zero. Equation (A-8) then gives

$$a_s(t) = \frac{-i}{\hbar} \int_0^t \mathscr{H}_{sn}(t) \exp(i\omega_{sn}t)\, dt \tag{A-9}$$

for $s \neq n$.

The perturbation induces transitions from the initial state n to any of the states s; and the probability of finding the system in the state s at time t is $|a_s(t)|^2$.

If $\mathscr{H}$ is time-independent, Eq. (A-9) can be integrated explicitly and we obtain, since $a_s(0) = 0$,

$$-a_s(t) = -\mathscr{H}_{sn} \frac{\exp(i\omega_{sn}t) - 1}{\hbar\omega_{sn}} \tag{A-10}$$

and, correspondingly,

$$|a_s(t)|^2 = 4|\mathscr{H}_{sn}|^2 \frac{\sin^2(\omega_{sn}t/2)}{\hbar^2\omega_{sn}^2} \tag{A-11}$$

This formula as well as the previous one is valid for $|a_s(t)| \ll 1$, that is, for only a short time after the onset of the perturbation.

A very important case is the one in which the levels s form a continuum, such would be the case for the emission of a light quantum under the perturbation caused by a variable electromagnetic field, or the elastic collision of two particles, in which the incident particle can be scattered in any direction. We consider the continuum as the limiting case of many levels very near each other in an energy scale (see Fig. A-1).

The probability of transition to each one of the levels is given by Eq. (A-11). The total transition probability is obtained by summing the probabilities of transition to each level, not their probability amplitudes, because the transitions are incoherent. We call $\rho(E)$ the density

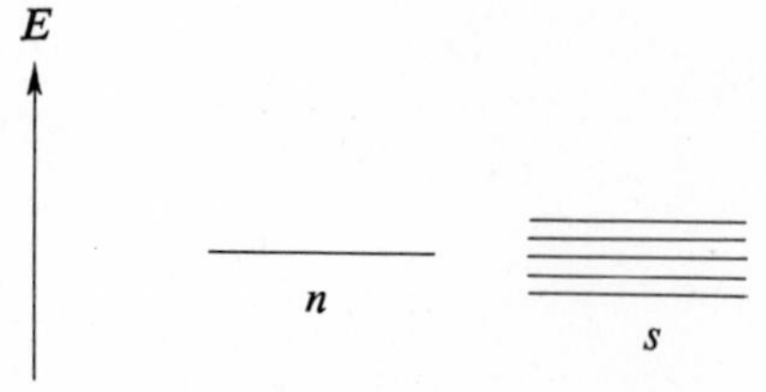

Figure A-1 Energy levels for Eq. (A-9).

of the levels (that is, the number of levels per unit energy interval), and we assume that H_{sn} is the same for all of them. This means that if there are selection rules (e.g., those due conservation of angular momentum), we must count among the final levels only those accessible from the initial one, and that $\rho(E)$ is the density of the accessible final states.

We can then write for the transition probability

$$P(t) = \sum_s |a_s(t)|^2 = 4\langle|\mathscr{H}_{sn}|^2\rangle \Sigma_s \frac{\sin^2 \omega_{sn}t/2}{\hbar^2 \omega_{sn}{}^2} \quad \text{(A-12)}$$

Here we have taken an average value of $|\mathscr{H}_{sn}|^2$.

We transform the sum into an integral. The number of states in energy interval $dE_s = \hbar d\omega_{sn}$ is $\rho(E_s)\, dE_s$, and we have

$$P(t) = 4\langle|\mathscr{H}_{sn}|^2\rangle \int \rho(E_s) \frac{\sin^2 \omega_{sn}t/2}{\hbar^2 \omega_{sn}{}^2}\, d\hbar\omega_{sn} \quad \text{(A-13)}$$

The last integral is extended from $-\infty$ to $+\infty$; however, for large values of t the contributions to the integral come from values of ω_{sn} very near zero, and indeed it can be written, remembering that $\int[(\sin^2 \alpha x)/x^2]dx = \pi\alpha$, as

$$\rho(E_n)\frac{\pi t}{2\hbar} \quad \text{(A-14)}$$

We have then from Eq. (A-13)

$$P(t) = 4\langle|\mathscr{H}_{sn}|^2\rangle \rho(E_n)\frac{\pi t}{2\hbar} \quad \text{(A-15)}$$

or

$$\text{rate of transition} = \frac{2\pi}{\hbar}\langle|\mathscr{H}_{sn}|^2\rangle \rho(E_n) \quad \text{(A-16)}$$

This formula is most important and was called "golden rule No. 2" by Fermi.

Another important application of Eq. (A-9) is obtained when $\mathscr{H}$ has the time dependence $e^{i\omega t}$. For instance, in electromagnetic dipole transition induced by an electric field directed along the x axis, of the form

$$\mathscr{E} = \mathscr{E}_0 \cos \omega t = \frac{\mathscr{E}_0}{2}(e^{i\omega t} + e^{-i\omega t}) \quad \text{(A-17)}$$

we have

$$\mathcal{H}(t) = \tfrac{1}{2}\mathcal{E}_0 xe\,(e^{i\omega t} + e^{-i\omega t})$$

This expression introduced in Eq. (A-9) gives

$$a_s(t) = \frac{i}{\hbar}\,\mathcal{E}_0\tfrac{1}{2}x_{sn}e\int_0^t [e^{i(\omega_{sn}+\omega)t} + e^{i(\omega_{sn}-\omega)t}]\, dt \quad \text{(A-18)}$$

If $\omega_{sn} \neq \omega$ the integral averages out to zero. If $\omega_{sn} \simeq \omega$ one finds

$$|a_s(t)|^2 = \frac{e^2\mathscr{E}_0{}^2}{\hbar^2}|x_{sn}|^2 \frac{\sin^2 (t/2)(\omega - \omega_{sn})}{(\omega - \omega_{sn})^2} \quad \text{(A-19)}$$

Equation (A-19), when treated in the same way as Eqs. (A-11) through (A-15), gives for the transition probability by absorption of radiation having frequencies in an interval containing ω_{sn}

$$\int_{\text{line}} |a_s(t)|^2 \, d\omega = e^2 \mathscr{E}_0^2 |x_{sn}|^2 \frac{\pi}{2\hbar^2} t \tag{A-20}$$

The absorption rate given by Eq. (A-20) can be related to the rate of spontaneous emission from the state s by a famous equation due to Einstein (1917). He proved that the transition rate due to spontaneous emission A_{sn} is related to the transition rate due to absorption $B_{ns}u(\omega)$ in an electromagnetic field having unpolarized and isotropic radiation of energy density, $u(\omega)\, d\omega$ in the frequency interval $d\omega$, by

$$A_{sn} = \frac{\hbar}{\pi^2} \frac{\omega^3}{c^3} B_{ns} \tag{A-21}$$

Now the rate of absorption, according to Eq. (A-20), is

$$\frac{1}{3} \frac{\pi}{2\hbar^2} e^2 \mathscr{E}_0^2 |x_{sn}|^2 = B_{ns} u(\omega) \tag{A-22}$$

where we have introduced a factor $\frac{1}{3}$ because u corresponds to unpolarized radiation and our system absorbs only radiation polarized in the x direction. The energy density is, according to electricity,

$$u = \frac{\mathscr{E}_0^2}{8\pi} \tag{A-23}$$

Hence from Eqs. (A-22) and (A-23)

$$B_{ns} = \frac{4}{3} \frac{\pi^2}{\hbar^2} e^2 |x_{sn}|^2 \tag{A-24}$$

and from Eq. (A-21)

$$A_{sn} = \frac{4}{3} \frac{\omega^3}{\hbar c^3} e^2 |x_{sn}|^2 \tag{A-25}$$

APPENDIX B

Born Collision Formula

An interesting application to collision problems of the method outlined in the previous appendix leads to the famous Born approximation for scattering processes. Let us consider scattering by a fixed center. This center will exert a potential $U(r)$ on the incoming particle of momentum $\mathbf{p} = \hbar\mathbf{k}$. The potential will act as a perturbation and change the direction of the momentum of the particle. The final momentum will then be $\mathbf{p}' = \hbar\mathbf{k}'$, with $|\mathbf{p}| = |\mathbf{p}'|$ because the collision is assumed to be elastic.

To simplify the calculation we shall enclose the system in a box of volume Ω (Ω will disappear from the final formula). The initial state is described by the normalized eigenfunction

$$\frac{1}{\Omega^{1/2}} e^{i\mathbf{k}.\mathbf{r}} \tag{B-1}$$

The final state will have the normalized eigenfunction

$$\frac{1}{\Omega^{1/2}} e^{i\mathbf{k}'.\mathbf{r}} \tag{B-2}$$

The matrix element of the perturbation is, by definition,

$$U_{pp'} = \frac{1}{\Omega} \int e^{i(\mathbf{k}-\mathbf{k}')\cdot\mathbf{r}} U(r)\, d\tau \tag{B-3}$$

which is proportional to the Fourier transform of $U(r)$.

We must now compute the density of the final states. Consider a free particle in a cubic volume of side a. The conditions of quantization give

$$n_x \frac{\pi\hbar}{2p_x} = a \qquad n_y \frac{\pi\hbar}{2p_y} = a \qquad n_z \frac{\pi\hbar}{2p_z} = a \tag{B-4}$$

with n_x, n_y, n_z positive integral numbers.

From Eq. (B-4) we get, immediately,

$$p_x^2 + p_y^2 + p_z^2 = \frac{\pi^2\hbar^2}{4a^2}(n_x^2 + n_y^2 + n_z^2) = p^2 \tag{B-5}$$

Consider a sphere of radius $2ap/\pi\hbar$ in a representative space and the points of integral coordinates within this sphere, lying in the octant where all coordinates are positive. Each point will give a triple of numbers representing a solution of Eq. (B-5) and hence a quantum state of momentum $\leqslant p$. The number of these states is thus numerically equal to the volume of the octant of the sphere of radius $2ap/\pi\hbar$,

$$\mathcal{N}(p) = \frac{4\pi a^3 p^3}{3(2\pi\hbar)^3}$$

and the number of states with momentum between p and $p + dp$ is

$$d\mathcal{N} = \frac{4\pi a^3 p^2\, dp}{(2\pi\hbar)^3} = \frac{4\pi\Omega p^2\, dp}{(2\pi\hbar)^3} \tag{B-6}$$

But the energy of the particle E is related to its momentum by $dE = v\, dp$, which is also true relativistically. From this it follows that

$$\frac{d\mathcal{N}}{dE} = \rho = \frac{4\pi\Omega p^2}{(2\pi\hbar)^3 v} \tag{B-7}$$

or, for the number of final states belonging to scattering into a solid angle $d\omega$,

$$\rho\, d\omega = \frac{\Omega p^2}{(2\pi\hbar)^3 v}\, d\omega \tag{B-8}$$

Now the rate of transition to final states having momentum in the element of solid angle $d\omega$ is also equal to the incident flux v/Ω multiplied by the differential cross section $d\sigma/d\omega$, and we have

$$\frac{1}{\Omega} v \frac{d\sigma}{d\omega}\, d\omega = \frac{2\pi}{\hbar} \left| U_{pp'} \right|^2 \frac{\Omega p^2}{(2\pi\hbar)^3 v}\, d\omega \tag{B-9}$$

From Eq. (B-9) we obtain

$$\frac{d\sigma}{d\omega} = \frac{1}{4\pi^2\hbar^4} \frac{p^2}{v^2} \left|\int e^{i(\mathbf{k}-\mathbf{k}')\cdot\mathbf{r}}\, U(\mathbf{r})\, d\tau\right|^2 \tag{B-10}$$

which is the famous Born formula for the collision cross section. Nonrelativistically $p/v = m$, and we can write

$$\frac{d\sigma}{d\omega} = \frac{m^2}{4\pi^2\hbar^4} \left|\int e^{i(\mathbf{k}-\mathbf{k}')\cdot\mathbf{r}}\, U(\mathbf{r})\, d\tau\right|^2 \tag{B-11}$$

The limits of validity of the approximate formulas (B-10) and (B-11) have been discussed in great detail in quantum mechanics. Here we shall give only the result. If the potential has a finite range L and a depth U, the relation

$$\frac{1}{\hbar} L\left|(p^2 \pm 2mU)^{1/2} - p\right| \ll 1 \tag{B-12}$$

is sufficient for the validity of Born's approximation.

Born's formula gives the right result even for a Coulomb force, a case in which one cannot speak of a range of the potential. In many instances Born's formula gives a simple and rapid means of evaluating scattering cross sections, and it has several applications in the text.

APPENDIX C

Form Factor

Born's formula (Appendix B),

$$\frac{d\sigma}{d\omega} = \left(\frac{m}{2\pi\hbar^2}\right)^2 \left| \int U(r) e^{i(\mathbf{k}-\mathbf{k}')\cdot\mathbf{r}}\, d\tau \right|^2 \tag{C-1}$$

gives the differential scattering cross section as a function of $U(r)$. In the case of a Coulomb field due to a point charge $U = Ze^2/r$ and one obtains the Rutherford formula. For an extended charge distribution we can transform the scattering formula in such a way as to obtain from $d\sigma/d\omega$ the charge density $\rho(r)$ instead of the potential. Moreover the final result [Eq. (C-10)] is expressed in the simple form

$$\frac{d\sigma}{d\omega} = \frac{d\sigma}{d\omega_{\text{Ruth}}} F^2(q) \tag{C-2}$$

where q is the momentum transfer in the collision

$$q = |\mathbf{k} - \mathbf{k}'| = 2k \sin\frac{\theta}{2} \tag{C-3}$$

Starting from Poisson's equation for the electrostatic potential $V(\mathbf{r})$

$$\nabla^2 V = -4\pi\rho \tag{C-4}$$

we transform the integral of Eq. (C-1) by observing that the function

$$e^{i(\mathbf{k}-\mathbf{k}')\cdot\mathbf{r}} = u(\mathbf{r}) \tag{C-5}$$

obeys the equation

$$\nabla^2 u + |\mathbf{k} - \mathbf{k}'|^2 u = 0 \tag{C-6}$$

Applying Green's formula to u and V, we have

$$\int (u\nabla^2 V - V\nabla^2 u)\, d\tau = 0 \tag{C-7}$$

or, using Eqs. (C-4) and (C-5),

$$\int V e^{i(\mathbf{k}-\mathbf{k}')\cdot\mathbf{r}}\, d\tau = 4\pi q^{-2} \int \rho(r) e^{i(\mathbf{k}-\mathbf{k}')\cdot\mathbf{r}}\, d\tau \tag{C-8}$$

In the case of a point charge Ze located at the origin of the coordinates, the integral at the right of Eq. (C-8) is clearly Ze. In this case substituting Eq. (C-8) into Eq. (C-1), taking into account Eq. (C-3), one obtains Rutherford's scattering formula. On the other hand, for an extended charge distribution one will have

$$\frac{d\sigma}{d\omega} = \frac{d\sigma}{d\omega_{\text{Ruth}}} \times \left| \frac{1}{Ze} \int \rho(r)\, e^{i(\mathbf{k}-\mathbf{k}')\cdot\mathbf{r}} d\tau \right|^2 \tag{C-9}$$

The expression

$$F(q) = \frac{1}{Ze} \int \rho(\mathbf{r}) e^{i(\mathbf{k}-\mathbf{k}')\cdot\mathbf{r}}\, d\tau \tag{C-10}$$

is called the form factor. It gives the modification of point scattering caused by the form of the charge distribution.

Expanding the exponential under the integral in Eq. (C-8) we have

$$F(q) = \frac{1}{Ze} \int \rho(\mathbf{r}) \left\{ 1 + i(\mathbf{k} - \mathbf{k}')\cdot\mathbf{r} - \frac{[(\mathbf{k} - \mathbf{k}')\cdot\mathbf{r}]^2}{2!} + \cdots \right\} d\tau \tag{C-11}$$

and for a spherically symmetric nucleus

$$F(q) = 1 - \frac{q^2}{6Ze} \int r^2 \rho(r)\, d\tau + \cdots \tag{C-12}$$

A measurement of $F(q)$ for small q (large de Broglie wavelength) gives in successive approximations the momenta of the charge distribution,

$$\int r^n \rho(r)\, d\tau \tag{C-13}$$

The expression $F(q)$ crudely represents the charge effective in the collision, or the amount of charge in a sphere of radius $\lambda\!\!\!^- = 1/q$.

APPENDIX D

Scattering from a Fixed Center of Force

We assume that the potential U decreases faster than $1/r$ and is central. The scattering center is located at the origin of the coordinates. The Schrödinger equation is

$$\nabla^2\psi + \frac{2m}{\hbar^2}(E - U)\psi = 0 \tag{D-1}$$

We shall try to find a solution of Eq. (D-1) with an asymptotic behavior for ψ given by

$$\psi(\mathbf{r}) = e^{ikz} + f(\theta)\frac{e^{ikr}}{r} \tag{D-2}$$

$$k = \frac{p}{\hbar} \qquad \text{or} \qquad v = \frac{k\hbar}{m} \tag{D-3}$$

Physically Eq. (D-2) represents a plane wave e^{ikz} of amplitude 1 and a spherical outgoing wave of amplitude $f(\theta)$.

The outgoing flux through a large sphere centered at the origin is given by

$$\varphi = \frac{\hbar k}{m}\int |f(\theta)|^2\, d\omega \tag{D-4}$$

as is seen from the expression for current in quantum mechanics. By definition the differential cross section is then

$$|f(\theta)|^2 = \frac{d\sigma}{d\omega} \tag{D-5}$$

We shall now calculate this quantity. We first need an identity

$$e^{ikz} = \frac{\pi\sqrt{2}}{(kr)^{1/2}}\sum_0^\infty i^l(2l + 1)^{1/2}Y_{l,0}(\theta)J_{l+1/2}(kr) \tag{D-6}$$

with the spherical harmonic

$$Y_{l,0}(\theta) = \frac{(2l + 1)^{1/2}}{(4\pi)^{1/2}}P_l(\cos\theta) \tag{D-7}$$

and P_l (cos θ) a Legendre polynomial. The $Y_{l,0}(\theta)$ have the orthonormality property

$$\int Y_{l,0}(\theta)\, Y_{l',0}(\theta)\, d\omega = \delta_{l,l'} \tag{D-8}$$

The $J_{l+1/2}(x)$ are Bessel functions with the asymptotic expressions

$$J_{l+1/2}(x) = \frac{\sqrt{2}}{\sqrt{\pi}} \frac{x^{l+1/2}}{(2l+1)!!} \qquad x \ll 1 \tag{D-9}$$

$$J_{l+1/2}(x) = \left[\left(\frac{2}{\pi x}\right)^{1/2} \sin\left(x - \frac{\pi l}{2}\right)\right] \qquad x \gg 1 \tag{D-10}$$

The identity can be proved by developing e^{ikz} in a series of Legendre polynomials by the usual Fourier method. Figure D-1 shows the first $j_l(x) = (\pi/2x)^{1/2} J_{l+1/2}(x)$.

We now also develop $f(\theta)$ in spherical harmonics,

$$f(\theta) = \sum_l a_l P_l(\cos\theta) = (4\pi)^{1/2} \sum_l \frac{a_l}{(2l+1)^{1/2}} Y_{l,0}(\theta) \tag{D-11}$$

and insert this expression into Eq. (D-2), obtaining asymptotically

$$\psi(r) = \frac{(4\pi)^{1/2}}{kr} \sum_l \frac{Y_{l,0}}{(2l+1)^{1/2}} \left[e^{ikr}\left(-a_l - \frac{i}{2}\frac{2l+1}{k}\right) + e^{-ikr}(-1)^l \frac{i}{2}\frac{2l+1}{k}\right] \tag{D-12}$$

The coefficient of e^{ikr} represents the amplitudes of outgoing waves of

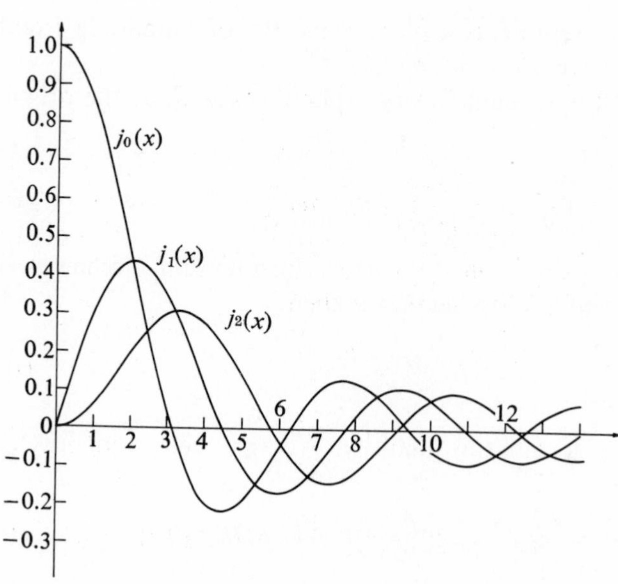

Figure D-1 The functions $(\pi/2x)^{1/2} J_{l+1/2}(x) = j_l(x)$ for $l = 0, 1, 2$. They can be expressed also as

$$j_0(x) = \frac{\sin x}{x};\ j_1(x) = \frac{\sin x}{x^2} - \frac{\cos x}{x};\ j_2(x) = \left(\frac{3}{x^3} - \frac{1}{x}\right)\sin x - \frac{3\cos x}{x^2}$$

different angular momenta l, and similarly the coefficient of e^{-ikr} represents the amplitude of ingoing waves. In a stationary state they must be equal in modulus for each l separately in order to ensure conservation of matter; however, they may have different arguments. We thus have

$$a_l + \frac{i}{2}\frac{2l+1}{k} = e^{2i\delta_l}\left(\frac{i}{2}\frac{2l+1}{k}\right) \tag{D-13}$$

or

$$a_l = \frac{i}{2}\frac{2l+1}{k}(e^{2i\delta_l} - 1) \tag{D-14}$$

The real quantity δ_l is called the phase shift of the lth wave. The δ_l are not determined, by the conservation theorem, but by the asymptotic behavior of $\psi(r)$. The radial part $R(r)$ of $\psi(r)$ can be written $u(r)/r$. Insertion in Eq. (D-1) shows that the asymptotic behavior of $u(r)$ for $r \to \infty$ is

$$u_l(r) = \sin\left(kr - \frac{\pi l}{2} + \delta_l\right) \tag{D-15}$$

if, as assumed, $U(r)$ vanishes rapidly enough. On the other hand, for r small, we have

$$u_l''(r) - \frac{l(l+1)}{r^2}u_l + \frac{2m}{\hbar^2}[E - U(r)]\,u_l = 0 \tag{D-16}$$

Near the origin $u_l(r) = r^{l+1}/(2l+1)!!$, and if we can integrate Eq. (D-16) we find, by joining the solutions for r small and r large, the values of δ_l.

Once the δ_l are known, we find from Eqs. (D-14), (D-11), and (D-5),

$$\frac{d\sigma}{d\omega} = \frac{1}{4k^2}\left|\sum_l (2l+1)P_l(\cos\theta)(e^{2i\delta_l} - 1)\right|^2 \tag{D-17}$$

This can be integrated over the solid angle, and recalling Eq. (D-8), we have

$$\sigma = 4\pi\lambda\!\!\!^{-2}\sum_l (2l+1)\sin^2\delta_l \tag{D-18}$$

We also have the important relation

$$\operatorname{Im} f(0) = \frac{1}{4\pi\lambda\!\!\!^{-}}\sigma \tag{D-19}$$

which is obtained from Eqs. (D-11), (D-14), and (D-18), remembering that $P_l(1) = 1$. Equation (D-19) is sometimes called the "optical theorem."

At low energy δ_0 alone is important; the scattering is spherically symmetric, with a cross section

$$\sigma = 4\pi\lambda\!\!\!^{-2}\sin^2\delta_0 = 4\pi a^2 \tag{D-20}$$

where a, called the scattering length, is susceptible to a simple and important geometrical interpretation (see Sec. 10-2).

When the potential has a range r_0 the phase shifts different from 0 are only those for which $\hbar l < pr_0$. Semiclassically, consider the impact parameter b. For a collision to occur, b must be smaller than r_0; otherwise the particle passes outside the potential well. Now the angular momentum with respect to the center of scattering is $\hbar l = bp$, and this gives

$$\frac{\hbar l}{p} < r_0 \tag{D-21}$$

as a necessary condition for a collision. If

$$\frac{\hbar}{p} = \lambda\!\!\!^{-} \gg r_0 \tag{D-22}$$

only waves with $l = 0$ will be scattered.

APPENDIX E

Effective Range

In Chapter 10 we determined the phase shift of an s wave on being scattered by using a square-well potential. We shall discuss here a more general method, which gives a very good approximation for this phase shift and at the same time does not require a specified form of the potential $V(r)$. Our final result will be Eq. (E-9).

We begin by writing Schrödinger's equation for an s wave and positive energy for the relative motion. Setting $r\psi = u$ as usual, we have

$$\frac{\hbar^2}{M}\frac{d^2u}{dr^2} + (E - V)u = 0 \tag{E-1}$$

or calling $MV/\hbar^2 = U$ and $ME/\hbar^2 = k^2$,

$$\frac{d^2u}{dr^2} + k^2u - U(r)u = 0 \tag{E-2}$$

Taking two different values of the energy E_a, E_b, we have

$$\frac{d^2u_a}{dr^2} + k_a{}^2u_a - U(r)u_a = 0 \tag{E-3}$$

$$\frac{d^2u_b}{dr^2} + k_b{}^2u_b - U(r)u_b = 0 \tag{E-4}$$

Multiplying the first equation [Eq. (E-3)] by u_b and the second by u_a, taking the difference, and integrating, we obtain

$$(u_bu_a' - u_b'u_a)\Big|_0^\infty = (k_b{}^2 - k_a{}^2)\int u_au_b\,dr \tag{E-5}$$

The functions u_a, u_b satisfy the boundary condition

$$u_a(0) = u_b(0) = 0 \tag{E-6}$$

Solutions of Eq. (E-2) for $U(r) = 0$ (free particle) are of the general form

$$v = A\sin(kr + \delta) \tag{E-7}$$

We look for solutions of this type which for large r are identical to u and for $r = 0$ reduce to unity. This last condition determines the constant $A = \sin\delta$. The identity of the asymptotic behavior determines δ.

For the two values of k, k_a and k_b, we then obtain in the same way as for u_a, u_b

$$(v_bv_a' - v_b'v_a)\Big|_0^\infty = (k_b{}^2 - k_a{}^2)\int_0^\infty v_av_b\,dr \tag{E-8}$$

We subtract Eq. (E-5) from Eq. (E-8). The u and v coincide at infinity and thus disappear from the difference; at 0, remembering that $u(0) = 0$ and $v(0) = 1$, we have

$$v_b'(0) - v_a'(0) = k_b \cot \delta_b - k_a \cot \delta_a = (k_b{}^2 - k_a{}^2) \times \int_0^\infty (v_a v_b - u_a u_b)\, dr \tag{E-9}$$

This equation is exact and is the fundamental equation of the effective range theory.

Consider now the case when $k_a = 0$, that is, the case of zero energy. By definition

$$\lim_{k_a \to 0} k_a \cot \delta_a = -\frac{1}{a} \tag{E-10}$$

where a is the Fermi scattering length; substitution in Eq. (E-9) gives

$$k_b \cot \delta_b = -\frac{1}{a} + k_b{}^2 \int_0^\infty (v_a v_0 - u_a u_0)\, dr \tag{E-11}$$

Dropping the suffix b and calling

$$\tfrac{1}{2}\rho(0,E) = \int_0^\infty (v_a v_0 - u_a u_0)\, dr \tag{E-12}$$

we have

$$k \cot \delta = -\frac{1}{a} + \frac{1}{2} k^2 \rho(0,E) \tag{E-13}$$

The integral $\frac{1}{2}\rho(0,E)$ has an integrand that vanishes for r greater than the range of nuclear forces. On the other hand, within this range u_a and u_0 are practically equal because the behavior of the function is dominated by the potential, with little influence from the energy as long as $|k^2| \ll |U|$. If u_a and u_0 are practically the same, v_a and v_0, which are determined by the asymptotic behavior of u_a and u_0, are also the same and we may replace, with good approximation, $\frac{1}{2}\rho(0,E)$ by

$$\tfrac{1}{2}\rho(0,0) = \int_0^\infty (v_0{}^2 - u_0{}^2)\, dr = \tfrac{1}{2} r_0 \tag{E-14}$$

The constant r_0 is called the effective range. Substituting in Eq. (E-13), we have

$$k \cot \delta = -\frac{1}{a} + \frac{1}{2} k^2 r_0 + \cdots \tag{E-15}$$

We have indicated by $\cdots$ the fact that Eq. (E-15) is only approximate.

APPENDIX F

Description of Polarized Beams (Spin 1/2)

A perfectly polarized beam of particles of spin $\frac{1}{2}$ may be represented as superposition with the proper phase relation of two beams having as spin eigenfunctions $\begin{vmatrix} 0 \\ 1 \end{vmatrix}, \begin{vmatrix} 1 \\ 0 \end{vmatrix}$, respectively.

$$\psi = a_1 \begin{vmatrix} 1 \\ 0 \end{vmatrix} + a_2 \begin{vmatrix} 0 \\ 1 \end{vmatrix} \tag{F-1}$$

Here the a's, which can be complex, contain all coordinates except spin. In the case of a free beam of momentum $\hbar\mathbf{k}$, for instance, we can write

$$a_1 = \frac{A_1}{v^{1/2}} e^{i\mathbf{k}\cdot\mathbf{r}} \qquad a_2 = \frac{A_2}{v^{1/2}} e^{i\mathbf{k}\cdot\mathbf{r}}$$

and the intensity of the beam is

$$|a_1|^2 + |a_2|^2 = I \tag{F-2}$$

We define as the degree of polarization in the z direction the difference between the probability of finding the spin parallel or antiparallel to z, that is,

$$P_z = \frac{|a_1|^2 - |a_2|^2}{|a_1|^2 + |a_2|^2} = \frac{|a_1|^2 - |a_2|^2}{I} \tag{F-3}$$

A beam represented by Eq. (F-1) always has, in a suitably chosen direction, the polarization 1, that is, the maximum obtainable value.

In order to treat the partially polarized beam, we introduce a "density matrix"; for the system described by Eq. (F-1) it has the form

$$\rho = \begin{vmatrix} a_1 a_1^* & a_1 a_2^* \\ a_2 a_1^* & a_2 a_2^* \end{vmatrix} \tag{F-4}$$

or

$$\rho_{ij} = a_i a_j^* \tag{F-4a}$$

The density matrix affords the symbolism suitable for treating the case of unpolarized or partially polarized beams. In the first place, remembering that the sum of the diagonal terms of a matrix is called its "trace," we have another way of writing Eq. (F-2), that is,

$$\mathrm{Tr}(\rho) = I \tag{F-5}$$

The degree of polarization P_z of Eq. (F-3) can also be expressed through the density matrix. Remembering that $\sigma_z = \begin{vmatrix} 1 & 0 \\ 0 & -1 \end{vmatrix}$, we have

$$\frac{\text{Tr}(\rho\sigma_z)}{\text{Tr}(\rho)} = P_z \tag{F-6}$$

Thus far the density matrix has represented only a concise way of *writing* formulas. However, if we superimpose several beams *incoherently*, we may define a density matrix for this system by summing the density matrices of the components, which we call $\rho(\alpha)$,

$$\bar{\rho}_{ij} = \sum_{\alpha=1}^{N} \rho_{ij}{}^{(\alpha)} w(\alpha) \tag{F-7}$$

where $w(\alpha)$ is the weight of each state, proportional to the intensity of the beam in the specific case. Note that the density matrix corresponding to the coherent superposition of two beams is Eq. (F-4) and not Eq. (F-7).

The intensity of the resulting beam is again

$$I = \text{Tr}(\bar{\rho}) = \textstyle\sum_\alpha w(\alpha) \tag{F-8}$$

and the expectation value of an operator $\mathcal{O}$ is also given by

$$\langle \mathcal{O} \rangle = \frac{\text{Tr}(\mathcal{O}\bar{\rho})}{\text{Tr}(\bar{\rho})} \tag{F-8a}$$

The 2×2 matrix $\bar{\rho}$ can always be written as

$$\bar{\rho} = a\begin{vmatrix} 1 & 0 \\ 0 & 1 \end{vmatrix} + b_x\begin{vmatrix} 0 & 1 \\ 1 & 0 \end{vmatrix} + b_y\begin{vmatrix} 0 & -i \\ i & 0 \end{vmatrix} + b_z\begin{vmatrix} 1 & 0 \\ 0 & -1 \end{vmatrix} \tag{F-9}$$

if suitable a, b_x, b_y, b_z are chosen. For instance,

$$\bar{\rho}_{11} = a + b_z,\ \bar{\rho}_{12} = b_x - ib_y, \text{ etc.} \tag{F-10}$$

and we can rewrite Eq. (F-9) in a more compact form as

$$\bar{\rho} = a \cdot 1 + \mathbf{b} \cdot \boldsymbol{\sigma} \tag{F-11}$$

where $\boldsymbol{\sigma}$ is the Pauli matrix vector of components $\begin{vmatrix} 0 & 1 \\ 1 & 0 \end{vmatrix} = \sigma_x$, etc. This way of writing has an especially simple physical interpretation.

We have

$$\text{Tr}\ \bar{\rho} = 2a = I \tag{F-12}$$

which gives the physical meaning of a in Eq. (F-11). The direct calculation of $\langle\sigma_x\rangle$, $\langle\sigma_y\rangle$, $\langle\sigma_z\rangle$ according to Eq. (F-8a) gives

$$\langle\sigma_x\rangle = \frac{b_x}{a} \qquad \langle\sigma_y\rangle = \frac{b_y}{a} \qquad \langle\sigma_z\rangle = \frac{b_z}{a} \tag{F-13}$$

The vector $\mathbf{b}$ is thus directed parallel to the expectation value of the spin, and the polarization P is simply

$$\frac{\mathbf{b}}{a} = \mathbf{P} \tag{F-14}$$

Hence the density matrix, is, from Eqs. (F-9), (F-11), and (F-14) related to the directly observable quantities, intensity and polarization of the beam,

$$\bar{\rho} = \tfrac{1}{2} I(\mathbf{1} + \mathbf{P}\cdot\boldsymbol{\sigma}) \tag{F-15}$$

Note that an unpolarized beam has a density matrix multiple of the unit matrix.

How do we describe the effect of scattering on polarization? Suppose that the initial beam is in a pure state ψ_i [Eq. (F-1)], and consider the scattering from a spinless target. The final state will be ψ_f, also a two-row function. Now we define a 2×2 matrix operator S such that

$$S\psi_i = \psi_f \qquad \text{and} \qquad \psi_f^\dagger = \psi_i^\dagger S^\dagger \tag{F-16}$$

The matrix S is a special case of the "scattering matrix," and the dagger means "transposed" and "conjugate." Similar methods are applicable, not only to elastic scattering, but also to nuclear reactions or even to the creation of particles. The scattering matrix allows us to calculate the final density matrix $\rho^{(f)}$ from the initial density matrix $\rho^{(i)}$. By the definition and Eq. (F-16),

$$\rho_{lm}{}^{(i)} = \psi_l{}^{(i)}\psi_m{}^{(i)\dagger} \tag{F-17}$$

and

$$\rho_{lm}{}^{(f)} = \psi_l{}^{(f)}\psi_m{}^{(f)\dagger} \tag{F-18}$$

$$S\psi_l{}^{(i)}\psi_m{}^{(i)\dagger}S^\dagger = S\rho_{lm}{}^{(i)}S^\dagger \tag{F-19}$$

If we normalize $\psi^{(i)}$ in such a way as to represent a beam of unit intensity, the differential scattering cross section $d\sigma/d\omega$ is

$$\frac{\operatorname{Tr}\rho^{(f)}}{\operatorname{Tr}\rho^{(i)}} = \frac{d\sigma}{d\omega} \tag{F-20}$$

The matrix S will depend, for an unpolarized or spinless target, on the scattering angle and energy of the incident beam. Like any 2×2 matrix, S can be written

$$S = g\cdot\mathbf{1} + \mathbf{h}\cdot\boldsymbol{\sigma} \tag{F-21}$$

This way of writing is especially convenient, and we shall see the physical effects of the complex functions g and h. The vector quantity $\mathbf{h}$, which is a function of $\mathbf{k}^{(i)}$, $\mathbf{k}^{(f)}$, the initial and final momentum of the particles, must be an axial vector in order to give a scalar by multiplication with the axial vector $\boldsymbol{\sigma}$. Thus it must be expressed as

$$\mathbf{h} = \frac{\mathbf{k}^{(i)} \times \mathbf{k}^{(f)}}{|\mathbf{k}^{(i)} \times \mathbf{k}^{(f)}|} h(\theta,E) = \mathbf{n}h(\theta) \tag{F-22}$$

where θ is the scattering angle. The unit vector $\mathbf{n}$ perpendicular to the scattering plane will now be assumed as the z axis. We then have

$$S = \begin{vmatrix} g+h & 0 \\ 0 & g-h \end{vmatrix} = g\cdot 1 + h\mathbf{n}\cdot\boldsymbol{\sigma} \tag{F-23}$$

and $g + h$, $g - h$ are the scattering amplitudes for a perfectly polarized beam with spin parallel or antiparallel to z. An unpolarized beam with the density matrix

$$\rho = \tfrac{1}{2} I \begin{vmatrix} 1 & 0 \\ 0 & 1 \end{vmatrix} \tag{F-24}$$

becomes polarized after one scattering,

$$\rho_1 = S\rho_0 S^\dagger = \tfrac{1}{2} \begin{vmatrix} |g + h|^2 & 0 \\ 0 & |g - h|^2 \end{vmatrix} \tag{F-25}$$

and the amount of polarization is given, according to Eq. (F-6), by

$$P = \frac{1}{2} \frac{|g + h|^2 - |g - h|^2}{|g|^2 + |h|^2} = \frac{gh^* + g^*h}{|g|^2 + |h|^2} = \frac{2\mathrm{Re}\,(gh^*)}{|g|^2 + |h|^2} \tag{F-26}$$

On the other hand, if the initial beam is totally polarized perpendicular to the plane of scattering,

$$\rho_0 = I \begin{vmatrix} 1 & 0 \\ 0 & 0 \end{vmatrix} \tag{F-27}$$

On scattering by an angle θ we obtain $\sigma(\theta)$,

$$\sigma(\theta) = \frac{\mathrm{Tr}\,\rho_1}{\mathrm{Tr}\,\rho_0} \tag{F-28}$$

where $\rho_1 = S\rho_0 S^\dagger$ [and S is given by Eq. (F-23)]. If we scatter by an angle $-\theta$, the corresponding S, according to Eq. (F-22), is

$$\begin{vmatrix} g - h & 0 \\ 0 & g + h \end{vmatrix} = S \tag{F-29}$$

The resulting cross sections are

$$\sigma(\pm\,\theta) = (|g|^2 + |h|^2)[1 \pm P(\theta)] \tag{F-30}$$

where P is given by Eq. (F-26). From these cross sections the asymmetry can be immediately calculated.

To characterize completely the scattering of a particle of spin $\frac{1}{2}$ from a spinless center, we need to know the two complex quantities g and h, that is, four real numbers, for instance $|g|$, $|h|$, the phase difference β between g and h and the phase of h, α.

These numbers can be obtained, for instance, by observing

$$\tfrac{1}{2}\,[\sigma(\theta) + \sigma(-\theta)] = |g|^2 + |h|^2 \tag{F-31}$$

Observation of P gives another relation. According to Eqs. (F-26) and (F-30)

$$|g + h| = [\sigma(\theta)(1 + P)]^{1/2} \tag{F-32}$$

$$|g - h| = [\sigma(\theta)(1 - P)]^{1/2} \tag{F-33}$$

The phase factor $e^{i\beta}$ can be determined (possibly with a sign ambiguity) from a triple scattering experiment; for instance, a measurement of R (Fig. 10-16) gives β through the relation

$$R = (1 - P^2)^{1/2} \cos\,(\beta - \theta) \tag{F-34}$$

where θ as usual is the scattering angle. Equations (F-32), (F-33), and (F-34) give thus completely g and h except for the phase α, which is not observable in scattering experiments from one center only.

These results can be extended to more complicated cases, but already the case of two nucleons (spin $\frac{1}{2}$) gives a fairly complicated 4×4 scattering matrix. It is

$$M = \alpha \cdot \mathbf{1} + \beta(\boldsymbol{\sigma}_1 \cdot \mathbf{n})(\boldsymbol{\sigma}_2 \cdot \mathbf{n}) + \gamma(\boldsymbol{\sigma}_1 + \boldsymbol{\sigma}_2) \cdot \mathbf{n} + \delta(\boldsymbol{\sigma}_1 \cdot \mathbf{q})(\boldsymbol{\sigma}_2 \cdot \mathbf{q}) + \epsilon(\boldsymbol{\sigma}_1 \cdot \mathbf{p})(\boldsymbol{\sigma}_2 \cdot \mathbf{p}) \tag{F-35}$$

where $\mathbf{p}$ and $-\mathbf{q}$ are unit vectors in the direction of the momentum of the projectile (1) and of the target (2) after scattering. The $\alpha, \beta, \gamma, \delta, \epsilon$ are complex functions of E and θ.

APPENDIX G

Change of Reference System in Collisions

In this appendix we shall give some formulas frequently used in the study of nuclear collisions and disintegrations. We shall employ energy units for mass, energy, and momentum. This means taking the velocity of light as the unit of velocity. For practical numerical work measure masses in MeV, momenta in MeV/c.

For a single particle we then have

$$\begin{aligned} E &= m\gamma \qquad & T &= m(\gamma - 1) \\ p &= m\beta\gamma \qquad & E &= (m^2 + p^2)^{1/2} \end{aligned} \tag{G-1}$$

where E is the total energy, T the kinetic energy, m the rest mass, and

$$\beta \equiv v \qquad \gamma \equiv (1 - \beta^2)^{-1/2} \tag{G-2}$$

Quantities referred to the center-of-mass system will be asterisked, whereas quantities referred to the laboratory system will not be so marked. Barred quantities $\bar{\beta}$, $\bar{\gamma}$, etc., refer to the velocity of the center of mass with respect to the laboratory.

We shall consider a collision in which a particle of mass m_1 collides with a particle at rest of mass m_2, giving rise to particles m_3, m_4. The conservation of energy and momentum gives

$$\begin{aligned} E_1 + E_2 &= E_3 + E_4 = E \\ \mathbf{p}_1 + \mathbf{p}_2 &= \mathbf{p}_3 + \mathbf{p}_4 = \mathbf{p} \end{aligned} \tag{G-3}$$

The quantity

$$N = (E^2 - p^2)^{1/2} = \frac{E}{\gamma} = E^* \tag{G-4}$$

is the length of the quadrivector energy-momentum and as such is an invariant in any Lorentz reference system. In particular, in the center-of-mass system, where $\mathbf{p}^* = 0$, by definition $N = E^*$. We have also

$$\begin{aligned} \bar{\beta} &= \frac{\mathbf{p}}{E} \\ \bar{\gamma} &= \frac{E}{E^*} \end{aligned} \tag{G-5}$$

The collision problem may be solved graphically, according to Blaton (1950), as follows: Given m_1, m_2, T_1, first obtain

$$\begin{aligned} E^* &= [(m_1 + m_2)^2 + 2T_1 m_2]^{1/2} \\ \bar{\gamma} &= \frac{E}{E^*} = \frac{m_1 + m_2 + T_1}{E^*} \\ \bar{\beta} &= \frac{p_1}{m_1 + m_2 + T_1} \\ \bar{\eta} &= \bar{\beta}\bar{\gamma} = \frac{p_1}{E^*} \end{aligned} \tag{G-6}$$

In the center-of-mass system we have

$$\begin{aligned} E^* &= E_3^* + E_4^* \\ |p_3^*| = |p_4^*| &= (E_3^{*2} - m_3^2)^{1/2} = (E_4^{*2} - m_4^2)^{1/2} \end{aligned} \tag{G-7}$$

Eliminating E_4^* and p_4^*, we obtain

$$E_3^* = \frac{E^{*2} + m_3^2 - m_4^2}{2E^*} \tag{G-8}$$

In the nonrelativistic case the vector $\mathbf{p}_3^*$ starting from the origin with the center-of-mass angle θ^* is transformed to the laboratory system by adding to the component parallel to the direction of $\mathbf{p}_1$, a vector of magnitude $m_3\bar{\beta}$ (Fig. G-1). In the relativistic case the corresponding construction is more complicated. We must draw an ellipse of semiaxes $\bar{\gamma}p_3^*$ and p_3^* concentric with the circle of radius p_3^*. We then mark on the major axis of the ellipse the points of abscissas $-\bar{\eta}E_3^* \equiv N_3$ and $+\bar{\eta}E_4^* \equiv N_4$. The vector $\mathbf{p}_3$ (laboratory) is obtained by joining point N_3 with point Q, where Q is the intercept of the ellipse with the parallel to its major axis passing through the end of $\mathbf{p}_3^*$; $\mathbf{p}_4$ is obtained by joining Q with N_4 (Fig. G-2). This construction is proved by the transformation rules of the energy-momentum four-vector.

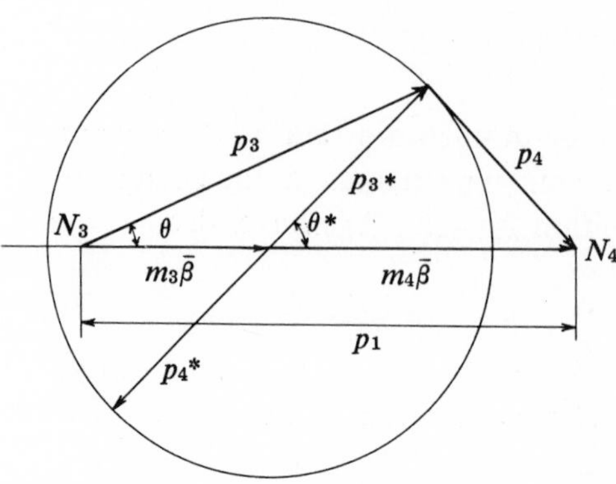

Figure G-1 Transformation from laboratory to center-of-mass reference system in a binary collision. Nonrelativistic case.

Analytically the ellipse construction gives the relation between θ_i and θ_i^*,

$$\tan \theta_i = \frac{1}{\bar{\gamma}} \frac{\sin \theta_i^*}{\bar{\beta}(E_i^*/p_i^*) + \cos \theta_i^*} \tag{G-9}$$

From this we can derive the important transformation between differential scattering cross sections. We have first

$$\sigma_i(\theta_i,\varphi_i)\, d \cos \theta_i = \sigma^*(\theta_i^*,\varphi_i^*)\, d \cos \theta_i^* \tag{G-10}$$

where $\sigma(\theta,\varphi)$ are differential scattering cross sections. It is then possible to find the relation between $d \cos \theta_i^*$ and $d \cos \theta_i$ through Eq. (G-9). We note also that

$$\frac{1}{p} \frac{d^2\sigma}{dE\, d\Omega}$$

is a relativistic invariant.

We add here for convenience the transformation formula for four-vectors such as

$$(x_1, x_2, x_3, ict) \qquad \left(p_1, p_2, p_3, i\frac{E}{c}\right) \tag{G-11}$$

from a system moving with velocity β with respect to the given system,

$$\begin{vmatrix} \gamma & 0 & 0 & i\beta\gamma \\ 0 & 1 & 0 & 0 \\ 0 & 0 & 1 & 0 \\ -i\beta\gamma & 0 & 1 & \gamma \end{vmatrix} \begin{vmatrix} x_1 \\ x_2 \\ x_3 \\ ict \end{vmatrix} = \begin{vmatrix} x_1' \\ x_2' \\ x_3' \\ ict' \end{vmatrix} \tag{G-12}$$

This formula is the Lorentz transformation written in matrix form.

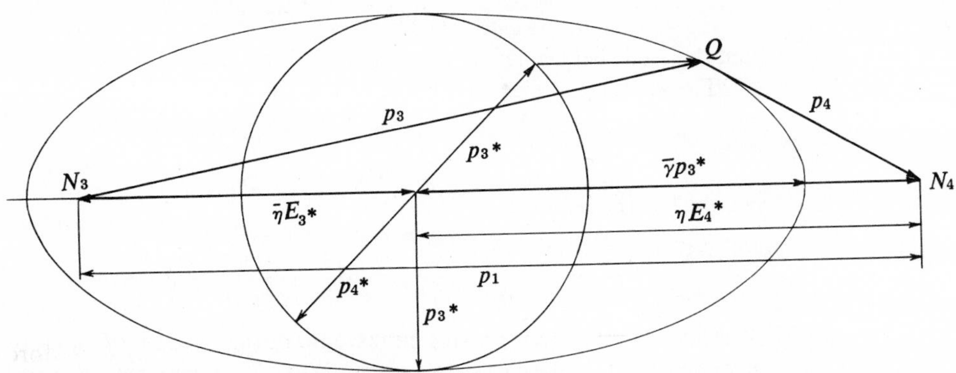

Figure G-2 Transformation from laboratory to center-of-mass system in a binary collision. Relativistic case.

Bibliography

Blaton, J., "On a Geometrical Interpretation of Energy and Momentum Conservation in Atomic Collisions and Disintegration Processes," *Kgl. Danske Vidensk. Selskab, Mat-fys. Medd.*, **24,** No. 20 (1950).

Dedrick, K. G., "Kinematics of High Energy Particles," *Rev. Mod. Phys.*, **34,** 429 (1962); **35,** 414 (1963).

Hagedorn, R., *Relativistic Kinematics*, Benjamin, New York, 1963.

Problems

G-1 Show that the laboratory threshold energy for producing new particles of mass $m_3 + m_4 + \cdots = M$ by colliding a particle of mass m_1 on a particle of mass m_2 at rest is

$$T_1 = \frac{M}{m_2}\left(m_1 + m_2 + \frac{M}{2}\right)$$

G-2 In a nucleon (M_1), nucleus (M_2) elastic collision, one has the (non-relativistic) formulas

$$\tan\theta_1 = \frac{M_2 \sin\theta_1^*}{M_1 + M_2\cos\theta_1^*}$$

$$E_1^* = \frac{M_2 \; E_1}{M_1 + M_2}$$

$$d\Omega^* = \frac{[M_1\cos\theta_1 + (M_2^2 - M_1^2\sin^2\theta_1)^{1/2}]^2}{M_2\,(M_2^2 - M_1^2\sin^2\theta_1)^{1/2}}$$

G-3 In a nucleon-nucleon elastic collision, one has the following relativistic formulas (m_2 at rest)

$$T_1 = 2m(\bar{\gamma} - 1)$$

$$\tan\theta_1 = \frac{1}{\bar{\gamma}}\tan\frac{\theta_1^*}{2}$$

$$\tan\theta_2 = \frac{1}{\bar{\gamma}}\tan\frac{\theta_1^*}{2}$$

$$\theta_1^* = \pi - \theta_2^*$$

Find the angle between p_1, p_2 after the collision.

The kinetic energies after the collision are

$$T_1\ \cos^2\ \theta_{1,2}\left(1 + \frac{T_2\sin^2\theta_{1,2}}{2m}\right)^{-1}$$

and one has the relation

$$\frac{d\cos\theta_2}{d\cos\theta_1^*} = \frac{\overline{\gamma^2}}{4}\left(\frac{1 - \overline{\beta^2}\cos^2\theta_2}{\cos\theta_2}\right)^2$$

G-4 Justify the following mnemonic device given by Crawford to write an approximate relativistic (R) formula if one remembers a nonrelativistic one (NR). Write the NR formula and add to the rest energy of each moving particle $\frac{1}{2}$ of the total kinetic energy in the center-of-mass system, $T/2$.

Examples:

a. A particle m_1 incident on m_2 at rest has in the center-of-mass the NR kinetic energy

$$T_1^* = T_1\left(\frac{m_2}{m_1 + m_2}\right)^2$$

Relativistically,

$$T_1^* = T_1\left(\frac{m_2}{m_2 + m_1 + T/2}\right)^2$$

b. A particle at rest disintegrates into two with total kinetic energy T:

$$T = T_1 + T_2$$

NR:

$$T_1 = \frac{Tm_2}{m_2 + m_1}$$

R:

$$T_1 = \frac{T(m_2 + T/2)}{m_1 + T/2 + M_2 + T/2} = \frac{T(m_2 + T/2)}{m_1 + m_2 + T}$$

G-5 Find the threshold (laboratory kinetic energy) for forming anti-protons in proton-proton collisions.

G-6 A particle has a mean life τ. A beam of these particles of speed β is formed in the laboratory. How does the intensity vary along the beam?

APPENDIX H

Motion of Ions in Electromagnetic Fields

We give here some results from electricity and mechanics which are helpful in charged-particle orbit problems.

Maxwell's equation in vacuum,

$$\nabla \times \mathbf{B} = \frac{1}{c}\frac{\partial \mathbf{E}}{\partial t} \tag{H-1}$$

$$\nabla \times \mathbf{E} = -\frac{1}{c}\frac{\partial \mathbf{B}}{\partial t} \tag{H-2}$$

$$\nabla \cdot \mathbf{B} = 0 \tag{H-3}$$

$$\nabla \cdot \mathbf{E} = 0 \tag{H-4}$$

as is well known, can be solved by introducing a vector potential **A** and a scalar potential V such that

$$\mathbf{B} = \nabla \times \mathbf{A} \tag{H-5}$$

$$\mathbf{E} = -\nabla V - \frac{1}{c}\frac{\partial \mathbf{A}}{\partial t} \tag{H-6}$$

Many accelerating machines have cylindrical symmetry and also symmetry with respect to a plane. It is thus convenient to introduce cylindrical coordinates r, θ, z, where $z = 0$ defines the plane of symmetry perpendicular to the axis of symmetry. Expressing Maxwell's equation in these coordinates for a field with cylindrical symmetry, we have $\mathbf{A} = A_\theta(r,z,t)$,

$$B_r = -\frac{\partial A_\theta}{\partial z} \tag{H-7}$$

$$B_\theta = 0 \tag{H-8}$$

$$B_z = \frac{1}{r}\frac{\partial (rA_\theta)}{\partial r} \tag{H-9}$$

$$E_\theta = -\frac{1}{c}\frac{\partial A_\theta}{\partial t} - \frac{1}{r}\frac{\partial V}{\partial \theta} \tag{H-10}$$

In order to study the motion of a point of rest mass m_0, relativistic mass m, and charge e in such a field, we write the relativistic equation, corresponding to the classical equation

$$\mathbf{F} = m_0\mathbf{a} = e\left(\mathbf{E} + \frac{\mathbf{v}}{c} \times \mathbf{B}\right) \tag{H-11}$$

$$\frac{d(m\mathbf{v})}{dt} = e\left(\mathbf{E} + \frac{\mathbf{v}}{c} \times \mathbf{B}\right) \tag{H-12}$$

It is convenient to write this equation in the more sophisticated hamiltonian form. The relativistic hamiltonian is

$$\mathscr{H} = eV + c\left[m_0^2c^2 + \left(\mathbf{p} - \frac{e}{c}\mathbf{A}\right)^2\right]^{1/2} \tag{H-13}$$

where the *canonical* momentum and the coordinates p_x, p_y, p_z, x, y, z are independent variables and $\mathbf{A}(x,y,z,t)$, $V(x,y,z,t)$ are the vector and scalar potentials.

That this is the correct hamiltonian may be seen from the following. We write Hamilton's equations,

$$\frac{\partial \mathscr{H}}{\partial p_x} = \dot{x} \qquad -\frac{\partial \mathscr{H}}{\partial x} = \dot{p}_x \tag{H-14}$$

From Eqs. (H-13) and (H-14) we have

$$\dot{x} = \frac{c\left(p_x - \dfrac{e}{c}A_x\right)}{\left[m_0^2c^2 + \left(\mathbf{p} - \dfrac{e}{c}A^2\right)^2\right]^{1/2}} = \frac{c^2\left(p_x - \dfrac{e}{c}A_x\right)}{\mathscr{H} - eV} \tag{H-15}$$

or, in vector form,

$$\frac{\mathbf{v}}{c} = \frac{c[\mathbf{p} - (e/c)\,\mathbf{A}]}{\mathscr{H} - eV} \tag{H-15a}$$

from which, using Eq. (H-13), we get

$$1 - \left(\frac{v}{c}\right)^2 = \left(\frac{m_0c^2}{\mathscr{H} - eV}\right)^2 \tag{H-16}$$

Upon introducing

$$m = \frac{m_0}{[1 - (v^2/c^2)]^{1/2}} = \frac{\mathscr{H} - eV}{c^2} \tag{H-17}$$

Eq. (H-15a) gives

$$\mathbf{p} - \frac{e}{c}\mathbf{A} = m\mathbf{v} \tag{H-18}$$

Hence

$$\mathbf{p} = m\mathbf{v} + \frac{e}{c}\mathbf{A} \tag{H-18a}$$

which defines canonical momentum $\mathbf{p}$ in the presence of a vector potential.

The equations of motion are

$$\dot{p}_x = -\frac{\partial \mathscr{H}}{\partial x}$$

$$= e\left\{\frac{\left(p_x - \frac{e}{c}A_x\right)\frac{\partial A_x}{\partial x} + \left(p_y - \frac{e}{c}A_y\right)\frac{\partial A_y}{\partial x} + \left(p_z - \frac{e}{c}A_z\right)\frac{\partial A_z}{\partial x}}{\left[m_0{}^2c^2 + \left(p - \frac{e}{c}A\right)^2\right]^{1/2}}\right\}$$

$$- e\frac{\partial V}{\partial x}$$

$$= \frac{e}{c}\left(\dot{x}\frac{\partial A_x}{\partial x} + \dot{y}\frac{\partial A_y}{\partial x} + \dot{z}\frac{\partial A_z}{\partial x}\right) - e\frac{\partial V}{\partial x} \qquad \textbf{(H-19)}$$

and similarly for $\dot{p}_y$, $\dot{p}_z$. We want to show that they are the same as Eq. (H-12).

From Eq. (H-18) we have

$$\frac{d}{dt}(m\dot{x}) = \dot{p}_x - \frac{e}{c}\dot{A}_x$$

$$= \dot{p}_x - \frac{e}{c}\left(\frac{\partial A_x}{\partial x}\dot{x} + \frac{\partial A_x}{\partial y}\dot{y} + \frac{\partial A_x}{\partial z}\dot{z} + \frac{\partial A_x}{\partial t}\right) \qquad \textbf{(H-20)}$$

Using Eq. (H-19),

$$\frac{d}{dt}(m\dot{x}) = \frac{e}{c}\left[\left(\frac{\partial A_y}{\partial x} - \frac{\partial A_x}{\partial y}\right)\dot{y} - \left(\frac{\partial A_x}{\partial z} - \frac{\partial A_z}{\partial x}\right)\dot{z}\right] - \frac{e}{c}\frac{\partial A_x}{\partial t} - e\frac{\partial V}{\partial x} \qquad \textbf{(H-21)}$$

From Eqs. (H-5) and (H-6) this is seen to be the x component of Eq. (H-12).

The equation in the hamiltonian form can now be expressed in cylindrical coordinates for a field having the symmetry indicated above, with r, θ, and z used as variables and

$$p_r = m\dot{r} \qquad p_\theta = r\left(mr\dot{\theta} + \frac{e}{c}A_\theta\right) \qquad p_z = m\dot{z} \qquad \textbf{(H-22)}$$

used as canonical momenta. The hamiltonian for $V = 0$ is

$$\mathscr{H} = c\left[m_0{}^2c^2 + p_r{}^2 + \left(\frac{p_\theta}{r} - \frac{e}{c}A_\theta\right)^2 + p_z{}^2\right]^{1/2} \qquad \textbf{(H-23)}$$

and Hamilton's equations give, after some calculation

$$\dot{p}_r = \frac{1}{m}\left(\frac{p_\theta}{r^2} + \frac{e}{c}\frac{\partial A_\theta}{\partial r}\right)\left(\frac{p_\theta}{r} - \frac{e}{c}\frac{A_\theta}{r}\right) \qquad \textbf{(H-24)}$$

$$\dot{p}_\theta = 0 \qquad \text{or} \qquad p_\theta = \text{constant} \qquad \textbf{(H-25)}$$

and

$$\dot{p}_z = \frac{1}{m}\left(\frac{p_\theta}{r} - \frac{e}{c}A_\theta\right)\left(\frac{e}{c}\frac{\partial A_\theta}{\partial z}\right) \qquad \textbf{(H-26)}$$

These are the equations of motion. They can also be written, by using Eq. (H-22),

$$\frac{d}{dt}(m\dot{r}) = mr\dot{\theta}^2 + \frac{e}{c}r\dot{\theta}B_z \qquad \textbf{(H-27)}$$

and

$$\frac{d}{dt}\left(mr^2\dot{\theta} + \frac{e}{c}rA_\theta\right) = Q_\theta \qquad \textbf{(H-28)}$$

$$\frac{d}{dt}(m\dot{z}) = \frac{e}{c}r\dot{\theta}B_r \qquad \textbf{(H-29)}$$

Here Q_θ is a possible external torque, usually due to applied electric fields. If $Q_\theta = 0$ the equations have the generalized angular momentum integral

$$mr^2\dot{\theta} + \frac{e}{c}rA_\theta = \text{constant} \qquad \textbf{(H-30)}$$

If A_θ depends on time explicitly, we have a change in the mechanical angular momentum $mr^2\dot{\theta}$ of the particle, as shown by Eq. (H-30).

The total energy of the particle may be obtained by multiplying Eqs. (H-24) through (H-26) by $\dot{r}$, $\dot{\theta}$, and $\dot{z}$, respectively, and summing them up. We obtain

$$\frac{d}{dt}(mc^2) = -\frac{e}{c}r\dot{\theta}\frac{\partial A_\theta}{\partial t} + \dot{\theta}Q_\theta \qquad \textbf{(H-31)}$$

The integral p_θ = constant is particularly interesting in many applications, including cosmic rays and plasma physics. In the absence of V and if **A** is directed tangentially,

$$\mathbf{A} = A_\theta\mathbf{e}_\theta \qquad \textbf{(H-32)}$$

where ($\mathbf{e}_\theta$ is a unit vector in the tangential direction); remembering that the electric field is

$$\mathscr{E} = -\frac{1}{c}\frac{\partial\mathbf{A}}{\partial t} \qquad \textbf{(H-33)}$$

we have

$$\frac{d}{dt}mc^2 = -\frac{e}{c}r\dot{\theta}\mathscr{E} + \dot{\theta}Q_\theta \quad \text{or} \quad \frac{d}{dt}(mc^2) = e\mathbf{v}\cdot\mathscr{E} + \dot{\theta}Q_\theta \qquad \textbf{(H-34)}$$

which expresses the conservation of energy, $\dot{\theta}Q_\theta\,dt$ being the work performed by the external torque.

APPENDIX I

Composition of Angular Momenta

We give here, without proofs, a summary of the rules for obtaining the eigenfunctions of a system composed of two parts having angular momentum properties. These rules are the quantum-mechanical translation of the vector-model rules of composition of angular momenta. The components have eigenfunctions labeled according to their value of the total angular momentum j_1 and j_2 and of the z components of j_1 and j_2: m_1 and m_2. The compound system has eigenfunctions labeled according to the value of the total angular momentum of the compound system J and of its z component M. The eigenfunctions of the compound system are linear combinations of products of the component eigenfunctions. The coefficients of these linear combinations are called Clebsch–Gordan coefficients.

For the components one has the possible values of m_1, m_2:

$$m_1 = j_1, \quad j_1 - 1, \quad j_1 - 2 \cdots, -j_1$$

$$m_2 = j_2, \quad j_2 - 1, \quad j_2 - 2 \cdots, -j_2$$

and j_1, j_2 are positive integral or half-integral numbers. For the resultant system one has

$$j_1 + j_2 \geqslant J \geqslant |j_1 - j_2| \qquad M = J, J-1, \cdots - J$$

All this is well known from the vector model and from quantum mechanics.

Now call $|j_1 m_1\rangle$ and $|j_2 m_2\rangle$ the eigenfunctions of the components corresponding to definite values of j_1, m_1 and j_2, m_2. The resultant eigenfunctions labeled according to J and M have the form[1]

$$|JM\rangle = \sum_{m_1+m_2=M} \langle j_1 j_2 m_1 m_2 | JM \rangle |j_1 m_1\rangle |j_2 m_2\rangle$$

The coefficients $\langle j_1 j_2 m_1 m_2 | JM\rangle$ (Clebsch–Gordan coefficients) are given for some of the simplest cases in Table I-1, where each rectangle is labeled $j_1 \times j_2$. As an example we see that if $j_1 = 1, j_2 = \frac{1}{2}$ we use the

[1] The sum must be extended over all values of m_1, m_2, such that $m_1 + m_2 = M$.

rectangle labeled $1 \times \frac{1}{2}$. J can have the values $\frac{1}{2}$ or $\frac{3}{2}$. For $J = \frac{3}{2}$, M can take the values $\frac{3}{2}, \frac{1}{2}, -\frac{1}{2}, -\frac{3}{2}$. The corresponding eigenfunctions are[1]

$$|\tfrac{3}{2}\,\tfrac{3}{2}\rangle = |1\;1\rangle|\tfrac{1}{2}\,\tfrac{1}{2}\rangle$$

$$|\tfrac{3}{2}\,\tfrac{1}{2}\rangle = \sqrt{\tfrac{2}{3}}|1\;0\rangle|\tfrac{1}{2}\,\tfrac{1}{2}\rangle + \sqrt{\tfrac{1}{3}}|1\;1\rangle|\tfrac{1}{2}\,-\tfrac{1}{2}\rangle$$

$$|\tfrac{3}{2}\,-\tfrac{1}{2}\rangle = \sqrt{\tfrac{2}{3}}|1\;0\rangle|\tfrac{1}{2}\,-\tfrac{1}{2}\rangle + \sqrt{\tfrac{1}{3}}|1\,-1\rangle|\tfrac{1}{2}\,\tfrac{1}{2}\rangle$$

$$|\tfrac{3}{2}\,-\tfrac{3}{2}\rangle = |1\,-1\rangle|\tfrac{1}{2}\,-\tfrac{1}{2}\rangle$$

These mathematical formulas apply to any other set of operators (to *i* spin, for instance), obeying the same commutation relations as the angular momentum.

We give here also, for reference, the first spherical harmonics that are (as well known) explicit forms of eigenfunctions of angular momentum labeled according to j and m for j integral number (Table I-2).

[1] These, except for notation, are the same as given in Table 14-2.

Table I-1 Clebsch–Gordan Coefficients

$1/2 \times 1/2$

m_1	m_2	J 1, M +1	J 1, M 0	J 0, M 0	J 1, M −1
+1/2	+1/2	1			
+1/2	−1/2		$\sqrt{1/2}$	$\sqrt{1/2}$	
−1/2	+1/2		$\sqrt{1/2}$	$-\sqrt{1/2}$	
−1/2	−1/2				1

$1 \times 1/2$

m_1	m_2	J 3/2, M +3/2	J 3/2, M +1/2	J 1/2, M +1/2	J 3/2, M −1/2	J 1/2, M −1/2	J 3/2, M −3/2
+1	+1/2	1					
+1	−1/2		$\sqrt{1/3}$	$\sqrt{2/3}$			
0	+1/2		$\sqrt{2/3}$	$-\sqrt{1/3}$			
0	−1/2				$\sqrt{2/3}$	$\sqrt{1/3}$	
−1	+1/2				$\sqrt{1/3}$	$-\sqrt{2/3}$	
−1	−1/2						1

$3/2 \times 1/2$

m_1	m_2	J 2, M +2	J 2, M +1	J 1, M +1	J 2, M 0	J 1, M 0	J 2, M −1	J 1, M −1	J 2, M −2
+3/2	+1/2	1							
+3/2	−1/2		$\sqrt{1/4}$	$\sqrt{3/4}$					
+1/2	+1/2		$\sqrt{3/4}$	$-\sqrt{1/4}$					
+1/2	−1/2				$\sqrt{1/2}$	$\sqrt{1/2}$			
−1/2	+1/2				$\sqrt{1/2}$	$-\sqrt{1/2}$			
−1/2	−1/2						$\sqrt{3/4}$	$\sqrt{1/4}$	
−3/2	+1/2						$\sqrt{1/4}$	$-\sqrt{3/4}$	
−3/2	−1/2								1

$2 \times 1/2$

m_1	m_2	J 5/2, M +5/2	J 5/2, M 3/2	J 3/2, M +3/2	J 5/2, M +1/2	J 3/2, M +1/2	J 5/2, M −1/2	J 3/2, M −1/2	J 5/2, M −3/2	J 3/2, M −3/2	J 5/2, M −5/2
+2	1/2	1									
+2	−1/2		$\sqrt{1/5}$	$\sqrt{4/5}$							
+1	+1/2		$\sqrt{4/5}$	$-\sqrt{1/5}$							
+1	−1/2				$\sqrt{2/5}$	$\sqrt{3/5}$					
0	+1/2				$\sqrt{3/5}$	$-\sqrt{2/5}$					
0	−1/2						$\sqrt{3/5}$	$\sqrt{2/5}$			
−1	+1/2						$\sqrt{2/5}$	$-\sqrt{3/5}$			
−1	−1/2								$\sqrt{4/5}$	$\sqrt{1/5}$	
−2	+1/2								$\sqrt{1/5}$	$-\sqrt{4/5}$	
−2	−1/2										1

1×1

m_1	m_2	J 2, M +2	J 2, M +1	J 1, M +1	J 2, M 0	J 1, M 0	J 0, M 0	J 2, M −1	J 1, M −1	J 2, M −2
+1	+1	1								
+1	0		$\sqrt{1/2}$	$\sqrt{1/2}$						
0	+1		$\sqrt{1/2}$	$-\sqrt{1/2}$						
+1	−1				$\sqrt{1/6}$	$\sqrt{1/2}$	$\sqrt{1/3}$			
0	0				$\sqrt{2/3}$	0	$-\sqrt{1/3}$			
−1	+1				$\sqrt{1/6}$	$-\sqrt{1/2}$	$\sqrt{1/3}$			
0	−1							$\sqrt{1/2}$	$\sqrt{1/2}$	
−1	0							$\sqrt{1/2}$	$-\sqrt{1/2}$	
−1	−1									1

Table I-1 *(continued)*

$3/2 \times 1$

m_1	m_2	$J=5/2$, $M=+5/2$	$5/2$, $+3/2$	$3/2$, $+3/2$	$5/2$, $+1/2$	$3/2$, $+1/2$	$1/2$, $+1/2$	$5/2$, $-1/2$	$3/2$, $-1/2$	$1/2$, $-1/2$	$5/2$, $-3/2$	$3/2$, $-3/2$	$5/2$, $-5/2$
$+3/2$	$+1$	1											
$+3/2$	0		$\sqrt{2/5}$	$\sqrt{3/5}$									
$+1/2$	$+1$		$\sqrt{3/5}$	$-\sqrt{2/5}$									
$+3/2$	-1				$\sqrt{1/10}$	$\sqrt{2/5}$	$\sqrt{1/2}$						
$+1/2$	0				$\sqrt{3/5}$	$\sqrt{1/15}$	$-\sqrt{1/3}$						
$-1/2$	$+1$				$\sqrt{3/10}$	$-\sqrt{8/15}$	$\sqrt{1/6}$						
$+1/2$	-1							$\sqrt{3/10}$	$\sqrt{8/15}$	$\sqrt{1/6}$			
$-1/2$	0							$\sqrt{3/5}$	$-\sqrt{1/15}$	$-\sqrt{1/3}$			
$-3/2$	$+1$							$\sqrt{1/10}$	$-\sqrt{2/5}$	$\sqrt{1/2}$			
$-1/2$	-1										$\sqrt{3/5}$	$\sqrt{2/5}$	
$-3/2$	$+0$										$\sqrt{2/5}$	$-\sqrt{3/5}$	
$-3/2$	-1												1

2×1

m_1	m_2	$J=3$, $M=+3$	3, $+2$	2, $+2$	3, $+1$	2, $+1$	1, $+1$	3, 0	2, 0	1, 0	3, -1	2, -1	1, -1	3, -2	2, -2	3, -3
$+2$	$+1$	1														
$+2$	0		$\sqrt{1/3}$	$\sqrt{2/3}$												
$+1$	$+1$		$\sqrt{2/3}$	$-\sqrt{1/3}$												
$+2$	-1				$\sqrt{1/15}$	$\sqrt{1/3}$	$\sqrt{3/5}$									
$+1$	0				$\sqrt{8/15}$	$\sqrt{1/6}$	$-\sqrt{3/10}$									
0	$+1$				$\sqrt{6/15}$	$-\sqrt{1/2}$	$\sqrt{1/10}$									
$+1$	-1							$\sqrt{1/5}$	$\sqrt{1/2}$	$\sqrt{3/10}$						
0	0							$\sqrt{3/5}$	0	$-\sqrt{2/5}$						
-1	$+1$							$\sqrt{1/5}$	$-\sqrt{1/2}$	$\sqrt{3/10}$						
0	-1										$\sqrt{6/15}$	$\sqrt{1/2}$	$\sqrt{1/10}$			
-1	0										$\sqrt{8/15}$	$-\sqrt{1/6}$	$-\sqrt{3/10}$			
-2	$+1$										$\sqrt{1/15}$	$-\sqrt{1/3}$	$\sqrt{3/5}$			
-1	-1													$\sqrt{2/3}$	$\sqrt{1/3}$	
-2	0													$\sqrt{1/3}$	$-\sqrt{2/3}$	
-2	-1															1

Note: When calculating terms which are linear in the above coefficients (e.g., interference, polarization), the sign convention becomes important. This table follows the one in Blatt and Weisskopf, Edmonds, Rose, Condon and Shortley, etc. Other authors (e.g., Schiff, Bethe, and de Hoffmann) use different conventions.

Table I-2 The First Spherical Harmonics

$$Y_0^0 = \sqrt{\frac{1}{4\pi}}$$

$$Y_1^0 = \sqrt{\frac{3}{4\pi}}\cos\theta; \qquad Y_1^1 = -\sqrt{\frac{3}{8\pi}}\sin\theta\, e^{i\phi}$$

$$Y_2^0 = \sqrt{\frac{5}{4\pi}}\left(\frac{3}{2}\cos^2\theta - \frac{1}{2}\right); \qquad Y_2^1 = -\sqrt{\frac{15}{8\pi}}\sin\theta\cos\theta\, e^{i\phi}$$

$$Y_2^2 = \frac{1}{4}\sqrt{\frac{15}{2\pi}}\sin^2\theta\, e^{2i\phi}$$

$$Y_3^0 = \sqrt{\frac{7}{4\pi}}\left(\frac{5}{2}\cos^3\theta - \frac{3}{2}\cos\theta\right); \qquad Y_3^1 = -\frac{1}{4}\sqrt{\frac{21}{4\pi}}\sin\theta\,(5\cos^2\theta - 1)\, e^{i\phi}$$

$$Y_3^2 = \frac{1}{4}\sqrt{\frac{105}{2\pi}}\sin^2\theta\cos\theta\, e^{2i\phi}; \qquad Y_3^3 = -\frac{1}{4}\sqrt{\frac{35}{4\pi}}\sin^3\theta\, e^{3i\phi}$$

$$(Y_l^m)^* = (-1)^m\, Y_l^{-m}$$

Name Index

Subject Index